THERMODYNAMICS

A MACROSCOPIC-MICROSCOPIC TREATMENT

Joachim E. Lay

Professor of Mechanical Engineering
Michigan State University

CHARLES E. MERRILL BOOKS, INC., COLUMBUS, OHIO

Second printing with corrections

First Printing......................June, 1963
Second Printing...............August, 1964

Preface

The appearance of another book on engineering thermodynamics when there is already a lengthy and distinguished list of such books calls for a certain amount of explanation if not, perhaps, an outright apology. Thermodynamics is an important subject in the engineering curriculum; it is taught in one form or another to practically all students of engineering. Throughout the years the structure and treatment of classical thermodynamics has been well solidified, and in fact has not changed much from the time of Clausius, whether concepts be introduced by means of heat engine cycles or by means of a list of axioms or theorems.

In the recent upheaval and modernization of engineering curriculum, however, the idea of teaching thermodynamics from a statistical or microscopic viewpoint has been proposed, with all the advantages (and disadvantages) pertaining thereto. But a presentation of engineering thermodynamics (at the undergraduate level) starting from probability theory and based entirely on the statistical viewpoint is neither pedagogically sound nor actually feasible; and a combination of the best of both approaches, classical and statistical, must of necessity be used. The present textbook takes cognizance of this fact and has sought to complement, if not integrate, the classical treatment with the statistical treatment. The first chapters represent essentially a classical treatment. This is followed by several chapters on statistical mechanics and kinetic theory of matter, and, in turn, by representative applications, both macroscopic and microscopic. Topics covered in the latter portion of the book make use of classical and statistical results without much discrimination. Altogether, there is sufficient material for a course up to a year in length for more than one curriculum, and at a level and rigor such that it can be used either as a terminal course or as an introduction to graduate study.

It is worthwhile to point out that while the text is ostensibly written for mechanical engineering students, its outlook is not sectarian but rather universal in that it regards thermodynamics as a science whose principles and disciplines apply to all fields of engineering. Mathematical tools such as partial differential calculus, homogeneous functions, Lagrangian multipliers, etc., are developed and used with good effect. Definitions, axioms, and important results are clearly delineated; and a large number of worked-out example problems are distributed throughout the text. Problems at the end of chapters are both of the drill type and of the analytical type so as to stimulate and challenge the student's thinking. Because of the large selection of material available, it should not be difficult for an individual instructor to construct any kind of course to meet the particular needs of his classes. For example, for those who prefer to teach essentially a classical thermodynamics course, the following is a suggestion for such a plan: Chapters 1 through 11, Sections 12.4 through 12.7, 14.1 to 14.7, Chapter 15, Sections 16.1 to 16.9, Chapters 17, 18, Sections 19.1 to 19.28, 19.34 to 19.36, and 21.1 to 21.10. On the other hand, for those who like the statistical treatment, Chapters 12, 13, and 14 may be directly combined with Chapters 2, 3, 4, 7, 9 and 21 to form a course which gives insight to the molecular structure of thermodynamics.

Although much of the material has been class tested, and the presentation is based on the author's teaching throughout the years, no particular claim is laid to the originality of the topics contained in the book. The author has drawn heavily on his own studies, on the many excellent textbooks published in this country and abroad, and on a number of technical papers published in journals. It is with pleasure that he acknowledges indebtedness to all these sources; and while it is not possible to single out individual references here, he has endeavored to give appropriate credit at specific places in the text. Last but not least, the author wishes to express his thanks to the students and teachers who have used his notes in recent years and who have had to endure the delays and corrections associated with the preparation of such notes. Their support and encouragement contributed in no small measure to the completion of the project. To every reader, student or teacher, the author wishes a pleasant and profitable journey through the book.

East Lansing, Michigan   JOACHIM E. LAY
January, 1963

Table of Contents

PART I CLASSICAL THERMODYNAMICS

PART II STATISTICAL MECHANICS AND KINETIC THEORY

PART III REPRESENTATIVE APPLICATIONS

APPENDICES

PART I

CLASSICAL
THERMODYNAMICS

CHAPTER 1

Definitions, Concepts, and Mathematical Preparation

1.1 Introduction

Thermodynamics is the science dealing with the relations among heat, work, and the properties of systems which are in equilibrium.* It is a subject of great generality, applicable to all types of systems: mechanical, chemical, or electrical. As a science, its development is based on a number of empirical laws or premises from which all predictions concerning the physical behavior of systems may be logically deduced.

---

 * *Classical* thermodynamics is limited to the study of systems in equilibrium. A more correct name for such a study would be "thermostatics." However, through usage, the word "thermodynamics" has prevailed.

Historically, the origin of thermodynamics is traced to the publication in 1824 by the French engineer, N. L. S. Carnot, of his early studies on the performance of steam engines. Since then, its scope has been broadened to cover refrigerating machines as well as other types of heat engines. From the middle of the nineteenth century, thermodynamics has grown so greatly that today an understanding of it is essential for much of the work of the engineer, the physicist, and the chemist.

It is the purpose of this text to present the principles of thermodynamics in a rigorous and understandable manner* and, by means of mathematics, develop relations which are useful in the science of engineering. The treatment starts with the so-called _classical_ approach; i.e., matter is regarded as continuous, and the behavior of systems is described in terms of measurable properties, without resort to a description of the behavior of individual molecules. This is distinguished from the approach based on _statistical mechanics_, wherein the laws of mechanics are applied to the individual molecules. For a first course in thermodynamics, the classical approach offers results of sufficient validity and accuracy, and it is pedagogically better suited to the student. Consequently, it is the approach followed in the first part of the text. Later, however, _statistical mechanics_ and _information theory_ are introduced to give greater understanding, unity and elegance to the structure of thermodynamics.

1.2   Thermodynamics System

The term _system_, in thermodynamics, refers to _a definite quantity of matter bounded by some closed surface_. The surface may be a real one, like that of a tank enclosing a certain amount of liquid, or it may be imaginary, like the boundary of a certain mass of liquid as it flows along a pipe. The boundary surface need not be constant in shape or volume. Thus, when a gas expands against a moving piston (for example), the volume enclosed by the surface changes. _The combination of matter and space_ external to _a system_ is called its _surroundings_. Figure 1.1 illustrates the concept of a system; in this case, attention is focused on the gas (the working medium). The boundary of the system is shown by the dotted line.

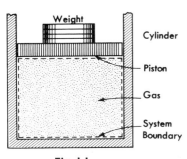

Fig. 1.1
Example of Thermodynamic System.

---

* The objective of this book is to make thermodynamics understandable _to the student_. For this reason, a large number of illustrative examples has been included in the development of each topic.

Thermodynamics is concerned with the interactions of a system and its surroundings, or one system and another. Strictly speaking, no material crosses the boundary of a given system. Sometimes, however, a system is defined as *a region of space within a prescribed boundary. If mass is allowed to cross the boundary*, the system is called an *open system*; *if no mass crosses the boundary*, the system is called a *closed system*.* A closed system can only exchange energy with the surroundings or with other systems; *if it does not exchange energy*, it is called an *isolated system*. A system which is *thermally insulated from its surroundings* is called an *adiabatic system*. It can, however, exchange work with its surroundings. If it does not, it becomes an isolated system.

1.3 Macroscopic and Microscopic Point of View

The description of a system using a few of its measurable properties constitutes a point of view (of matter) called *macroscopic.* This point of view is illustrated in the following example. Select as a system the contents of an automobile engine cylinder. At any moment, the system occupies a certain volume, depending on the position of the piston. This volume is readily measurable by determining the position of the piston. Another quantity useful in the description of the system is the pressure of the gases in the cylinder. To this end, a pressure gauge may be used to measure pressure changes as the engine operates. Other measurable quantities are the temperature and the chemical composition. The system may be described by means of the above quantities, which are, in essence, large-scale characteristics or properties of the system. They are called *macroscopic coordinates,* and provide a macroscopic description of the system. Different systems may require different macroscopic coordinates for their description, but all macroscopic coordinates have the following characteristics in common: (1) they involve no special assumptions concerning the structure of matter, (2) they are readily measurable, and (3) only a few of them are needed to describe a system adequately.

A *microscopic* point of view, on the other hand, assumes that the gas in the cylinder consists of a large number of particles, all having the same mass and each moving with an independent velocity. The description of any one particle is prescribed by its three cartesian coordinates x, y, and z, and by the three components u, v, and w of its velocity. Thus, six numbers are required to fix the position and velocity of a particle. For a system

---

* The terms "open" and "closed" system will not be used extensively in this text because of their inherent contradication. In such applications as fluid flow, where it is convenient to draw attention to a fixed region in space rather than to a fixed mass of fluid, the concept of a *control volume* is preferred. A control volume is *any volume of fixed position and shape through which matter flows.*

composed of N mass-points, a microscopic description would then require the knowledge of $6N$ variables. Such a dynamic definition of the state of a system is too complicated to be used. Therefore, the assumption is made that even when discussing very small portions of a system, these portions are large, compared to the size of the particles. In the first part of this book, this assumption will hold true, and it will not be necessary to describe the behavior of individual particles.

1.4 Mathematical Preparation

Thermodynamics is a discipline in logic applied to the study of energy transformations. Its entire structure is erected upon fundamental axioms such as the zeroth, first, and second laws of thermodynamics, and the fact that *the state of a homogeneous system is fixed when two independent properties are fixed.* The relations governing the transformation of energy through heat and work not only derive from these basic postulates, but are best expressed in the language of mathematics. Thus, it is necessary for students who are studying thermodynamics to have a good working knowledge of calculus and partial differentiation. To achieve this, the following sections are presented at this stage.*

Consider a simple thermodynamic system with definite values for its pressure p, temperature T, and volume V. Any one of these properties will be seen to be related in a definite way to the other two. The relationship is usually expressible in the form of a mathematical equation, and the property (e.g., pressure) then becomes a function of the other two (volume and temperature). The variables p, V, and T are often used to describe the state of a substance. They are connected by the functional relationship

$$F(p, V, T) = 0 \tag{1.1}$$

commonly called the *equation of state.* Equation (1.1) may always, in theory, be solved for any one of the variables: $p = p(V, T)$; $V = V(p, T)$; $T = T(p, V)$, so that fixing any two variables automatically fixes the third. It is an experimental fact that, except in special cases (such as a change of phase), any two variables uniquely determine any other variable, and thereby the state of the system. The two variables (e.g., V, T) (which may vary independently of each other) are called independent variables, whereas the variable (in this case p), whose value is fixed for each pair of values of V and T, is called the dependent variable.

Example 1.1. A certain gas obeys the equation of state $pv = RT$, where p is the absolute pressure, v the specific volume, R the gas constant, and T the absolute

---

* Those already familiar with partial differentiation may skip the next few sections and refer to them only as the need arises. A fresh knowledge of mathematical manipulations, however, will add much to the orderly and efficient study of thermodynamics.

temperature. (a) Write this in explicit forms for p, v, and T respectively. (b) Show that $dp/p + dv/v = dT/T$.

Solution. (a) The explicit forms for p, v, and T are

$$p = \frac{RT}{v}; \quad v = \frac{RT}{p}; \quad T = \frac{pv}{R}$$

(b) Taking the logarithm of the equation of state ($pv = RT$) gives $\ln p + \ln v = \ln R + \ln T$, and differentiation of this gives

$$\frac{dp}{p} + \frac{dv}{v} = \frac{dT}{T}$$

The same result may also be obtained by differentiating both sides of the equation of state and dividing through by $pv(= RT)$. This is left as an exercise to the student.*

$$\frac{p\,dv + v\,dp}{pv} = \frac{R\,dT}{RT} \Rightarrow \frac{dv}{v} + \frac{dp}{p} = \frac{dT}{T}$$

1.5 Differentiation in Two Variables

Let the volume V of a gas depend on the absolute temperature T and on the absolute pressure p. Let each of the variables T and p be independent of the other. The change in volume resulting from a simultaneous change in both temperature and pressure is then given by the fundamental theorem of partial differentiation

$$dV = \left(\frac{\partial V}{\partial T}\right)_p dT + \left(\frac{\partial V}{\partial p}\right)_T dp \tag{1.2}$$

In the above example, dV is known as a total differential, whereas $(\partial V/\partial T)_p$ $(\partial V/\partial p)_T$ are known as partial derivatives. They denote, respectively, the rate of volume change with respect to temperature, with pressure kept constant, and the rate of volume change with respect to pressure, with temperature kept constant.

Relations of the form of Eq. (1.2) occur throughout thermodynamics. It is essential that the student develop an understanding of their manipulation. For example, Eq. (1.2) may be changed from the differential notation to the derivative notation by dividing through by dt

$$\frac{dV}{dt} = \left(\frac{\partial V}{\partial T}\right)_p \frac{dT}{dt} + \left(\frac{\partial V}{\partial p}\right)_T \frac{dp}{dt} \tag{1.3}$$

Still another form may be taken by Eq. (1.2) if the independent variables

---

* The formal discussion of equations of state will be undertaken later in the text. The relation $pv = RT$ is known as the *ideal-gas equation*.

T and p are in turn expressed as functions of two new variables say, x and y. Thus,

$$dT = \left(\frac{\partial T}{\partial x}\right)_y dx + \left(\frac{\partial T}{\partial y}\right)_x dy$$

and

$$dp = \left(\frac{\partial p}{\partial x}\right)_y dx + \left(\frac{\partial p}{\partial y}\right)_x dy$$

whereupon Eq. (1.2) becomes

$$dV = \left(\frac{\partial V}{\partial T}\right)_p \left[\left(\frac{\partial T}{\partial x}\right)_y dx + \left(\frac{\partial T}{\partial y}\right)_x dy\right] + \left(\frac{\partial V}{\partial p}\right)_T \left[\left(\frac{\partial p}{\partial x}\right)_y dx + \left(\frac{\partial p}{\partial y}\right)_x dy\right]$$

or

$$dV = \left[\left(\frac{\partial V}{\partial T}\right)_p \left(\frac{\partial T}{\partial x}\right)_y + \left(\frac{\partial V}{\partial p}\right)_T \left(\frac{\partial p}{\partial x}\right)_y\right] dx +$$

$$+ \left[\left(\frac{\partial V}{\partial T}\right)_p \left(\frac{\partial T}{\partial y}\right)_x + \left(\frac{\partial V}{\partial p}\right)_T \left(\frac{\partial p}{\partial y}\right)_x\right] dy$$

From this it may be concluded that

$$\left(\frac{\partial V}{\partial x}\right)_y = \left(\frac{\partial V}{\partial T}\right)_p \left(\frac{\partial T}{\partial x}\right)_y + \left(\frac{\partial V}{\partial p}\right)_T \left(\frac{\partial p}{\partial x}\right)_y \qquad (1.4)$$

and

$$\left(\frac{\partial V}{\partial y}\right)_x = \left(\frac{\partial V}{\partial T}\right)_p \left(\frac{\partial T}{\partial y}\right)_x + \left(\frac{\partial V}{\partial p}\right)_T \left(\frac{\partial p}{\partial y}\right)_x \qquad (1.5)$$

Equations (1.4) and (1.5) are the fundamental relations for the transformation of partial derivatives. Various useful expressions are obtained by letting x and y respectively be a particular variable. For example, letting $y = p$, Eqs. (1.4) and (1.5) reduce to

$$\left(\frac{\partial V}{\partial x}\right)_p = \left(\frac{\partial V}{\partial T}\right)_p \left(\frac{\partial T}{\partial x}\right)_p \qquad (1.6)$$

$$\left(\frac{\partial V}{\partial p}\right)_x = \left(\frac{\partial V}{\partial T}\right)_p \left(\frac{\partial T}{\partial p}\right)_x + \left(\frac{\partial V}{\partial p}\right)_T \qquad (1.7)$$

since $(\partial p/\partial x)_p = 0$, and $(\partial p/\partial p)_x = 1$. Equation (1.6) is recognized as the ordinary *chain rule* of partial differentiation; it holds true for any number of transformations as long as the same variable is held constant throughout. Equation (1.7) will find application in later chapters of this text.

As another example, let $x = V$ and $y = T$ in Eqs. (1.4) and (1.5), so that no new variables are introduced. Then,

$$\left(\frac{\partial V}{\partial p}\right)_T \left(\frac{\partial p}{\partial V}\right)_T = 1 \tag{1.8}$$

$$\left(\frac{\partial V}{\partial T}\right)_p + \left(\frac{\partial V}{\partial p}\right)_T \left(\frac{\partial p}{\partial T}\right)_V = 0 \tag{1.9}$$

since $(\partial V/\partial V)_T = 1$, $(\partial T/\partial V)_T = 0$, $(\partial V/\partial T)_V = 0$, $(\partial T/\partial T)_V = 1$. Equation (1.8) may be written as

$$\left(\frac{\partial V}{\partial p}\right)_T = \frac{1}{(\partial p/\partial V)_T} \tag{1.10}$$

which is an important reciprocal relation in partial differentiation. Equation (1.9) can, by multiplying throughout by $(\partial T/\partial V)_p$, be transformed into

$$\left(\frac{\partial V}{\partial T}\right)_p \left(\frac{\partial T}{\partial V}\right)_p + \left(\frac{\partial V}{\partial p}\right)_T \left(\frac{\partial p}{\partial T}\right)_V \left(\frac{\partial T}{\partial V}\right)_p = 0$$

Since $(\partial V/\partial T)_p (\partial T/\partial V)_p = 1$, this becomes

$$\left(\frac{\partial V}{\partial p}\right)_T \left(\frac{\partial p}{\partial T}\right)_V \left(\frac{\partial T}{\partial V}\right)_p = -1 \tag{1.11}$$

$$\text{or} \quad \left(\frac{\partial V}{\partial p}\right)_T = \frac{-\left(\frac{\partial T}{\partial p}\right)_V}{\left(\frac{\partial V}{\partial T}\right)_p}$$

Equation (1.11) is the cyclic relation involving the partial derivatives of the three variables p, V, and T. It is of fundamental importance in thermodynamic analysis, and should be remembered by the student.

For a simple system involving only three variables, classical thermodynamics gives physical meaning to some of the partial derivatives. For example

$$\beta = \frac{1}{V}\left(\frac{\partial V}{\partial T}\right)_p \tag{1.12}$$

is the coefficient of volume expansion. It is the volume change under temperature, per unit volume.

The expression

$$\kappa = -\frac{1}{V}\left(\frac{\partial V}{\partial p}\right)_T \tag{1.13}$$

is the isothermal compressibility. This is the change in volume accompanying change in pressure, with the temperature held constant.

Yet another expression,

$$B = -V\left(\frac{\partial p}{\partial V}\right)_T \tag{1.14}$$

is called the *isothermal bulk modulus*. This is the *pressure change per volume change*. The minus sign is inserted in Eqs. (1.13) and (1.14) because the volume of a substance decreases as the pressure is increased.

Example 1.2. Given three gases: (a) a perfect gas, obeying the equation of state $pv = RT$, (b) a Clausius gas, obeying $p(v-b) = RT$, and (c) a van der Waals' gas, obeying $(p+a/v^2)(v-b) = RT$, find β and κ for each case.

Solution. (a). For a perfect gas, $pv = RT$, so that

$$\beta = \frac{1}{v}\left(\frac{\partial v}{\partial T}\right)_p = \frac{1}{v}\left[\frac{\partial}{\partial T}\left(\frac{RT}{p}\right)_p\right] = \frac{1}{v}\left(\frac{R}{p}\right) = \frac{1}{T}$$

and

$$\kappa = -\frac{1}{v}\left(\frac{\partial v}{\partial p}\right)_T = -\frac{1}{v}\left[\frac{\partial}{\partial p}\left(\frac{RT}{p}\right)\right]_T = -\frac{1}{v}\left(-\frac{RT}{p^2}\right) = \frac{1}{p}$$

(b). Calculations for a Clausius gas, similar to the above, are left to the student.

(c). For a van der Waals' gas, $(p+a/v^2)(v-b) = RT$. Here, it is not convenient to calculate $(\partial v/\partial T)_p$ or $(\partial v/\partial p)_T$ directly, because van der Waals' equation is cubic in v. It is better to make use of the cyclic relation

$$\left(\frac{\partial v}{\partial T}\right)_p\left(\frac{\partial T}{\partial p}\right)_v\left(\frac{\partial p}{\partial v}\right)_T = -1$$

and write

$$\left(\frac{\partial v}{\partial T}\right)_p = -\frac{(\partial p/\partial T)_v}{(\partial p/\partial v)_T}$$

Van der Waals' equation can be solved explicitly for p to give

$$p = \frac{RT}{v-b} - \frac{a}{v^2}$$

so that

$$\left(\frac{\partial p}{\partial T}\right)_v = \frac{R}{v-b}; \quad \left(\frac{\partial p}{\partial v}\right)_T = -\frac{RT}{(v-b)^2} + \frac{2a}{v^3}$$

Thus,

$$\beta = \frac{1}{v}\left(\frac{\partial v}{\partial T}\right)_p = \frac{1}{v}\left[\frac{R/(v-b)}{-RT/(v-b)^2 + 2a/v^3}\right] = \frac{Rv^2(v-b)}{RTv^3 - 2a(v-b)^2}$$

Similarly, there is obtained

$$\kappa = -\frac{1}{v}\left(\frac{\partial v}{\partial p}\right)_T = \frac{v^2(v-b)^2}{RTv^3 - 2a(v-b)^2}$$

Example 1.3. The coefficient of volume expansion for mercury, as given in standard tables, is 0.1819×10^{-3} increase in volume per unit volume per degree Centigrade. The compressibility, also given in standard tables, is 3.92×10^{-6} contraction in unit volume per atmosphere. Compute the pressure that would develop if liquid mercury at 1 atm is heated at constant volume from 0 °C to 1 °C.

Solution. By definition,

$$\beta = \frac{1}{V}\left(\frac{\partial V}{\partial T}\right)_p = 0.1819 \times 10^{-3}$$

$$\kappa = -\frac{1}{V}\left(\frac{\partial V}{\partial p}\right)_T = 3.92 \times 10^{-6}$$

From Eq. (1.11):

$$\left(\frac{\partial p}{\partial T}\right)_V = -\frac{(\partial V/\partial T)_p}{(\partial V/\partial p)_T} = \frac{0.1819 \times 10^{-3}}{3.92 \times 10^{-6}} = 46.4$$

Thus, if mercury at 1 atm and 0 °C were to be heated at constant volume to 1 °C, the pressure would become $1 + 46.4 = 47.4$ atm.

Example 1.4. Find $\partial u/\partial s$ and $\partial u/\partial t$ if $ux = y$, $x = 2s + 4t$, and $y = 2s - 4t$.

Solution. Consider u as a function of x and y. Then

$$du = \left(\frac{\partial u}{\partial x}\right)dx + \left(\frac{\partial u}{\partial y}\right)dy$$

Next, consider x and y as functions of s and t:

$$dx = \left(\frac{\partial x}{\partial s}\right)ds + \left(\frac{\partial x}{\partial t}\right)dt$$

$$dy = \left(\frac{\partial y}{\partial s}\right)ds + \left(\frac{\partial y}{\partial t}\right)dt$$

Replacing in the expression for du gives

$$du = \left[\left(\frac{\partial u}{\partial x}\right)\left(\frac{\partial x}{\partial s}\right) + \left(\frac{\partial u}{\partial y}\right)\left(\frac{\partial y}{\partial s}\right)\right]ds + \left[\left(\frac{\partial u}{\partial x}\right)\left(\frac{\partial x}{\partial t}\right) + \left(\frac{\partial u}{\partial y}\right)\left(\frac{\partial y}{\partial t}\right)\right]dt$$

Thus,

$$\left(\frac{\partial u}{\partial s}\right) = \left(\frac{\partial u}{\partial x}\right)\left(\frac{\partial x}{\partial s}\right) + \left(\frac{\partial u}{\partial y}\right)\left(\frac{\partial y}{\partial s}\right)$$

$$\left(\frac{\partial u}{\partial t}\right) = \left(\frac{\partial u}{\partial x}\right)\left(\frac{\partial x}{\partial t}\right) + \left(\frac{\partial u}{\partial y}\right)\left(\frac{\partial y}{\partial t}\right)$$

In the present problem,

$$\frac{\partial u}{\partial x} = -\frac{y}{x^2}; \quad \frac{\partial u}{\partial y} = \frac{1}{x}; \quad \frac{\partial x}{\partial s} = 2; \quad \frac{\partial x}{\partial t} = 4; \quad \frac{\partial y}{\partial s} = 2; \quad \frac{\partial y}{\partial t} = -4$$

so that, upon substitution,

$$\frac{\partial u}{\partial s} = -\frac{2y}{x^2} + \frac{2}{x} = \frac{4t}{(s+2t)^2}$$

$$\frac{\partial u}{\partial t} = -\frac{4y}{x^2} - \frac{4}{x} = -\frac{4s}{(s+2t)^2}$$

1.6   Integration in Two Variables

There occur, in thermodynamics as well as in physics, expressions of the form

$$M(x, y)dx + N(x, y)dy \tag{1.15}$$

where $M(x, y)$ and $N(x, y)$ are given functions of x and y. Let this be integrated between two points, (x_1, y_1) and (x_2, y_2) in the x–y plane.

$$\int_{x_1, y_1}^{x_1, y_2} [M(x, y)dx + N(x, y)dy] = \int_{x_1}^{x_2} M(x, y)dx + \int_{y_1}^{y_2} N(x, y)dy \tag{1.16}$$

To carry out the integration, the relation between x and y must be known or given. In other words, a relation $y = f(x)$ (specifying the path in the x–y plane along which the integration is to be performed) must be given. For this reason, integrals of the above form are called _line integrals,_ and functions obtained from such integrations are called _line or path functions,_ because their values, in general, depend on the path chosen for the integration.

There is, however, a particular case which is of special interest in thermodynamics: When a function $z(x, y)$ exists, whose differential form is given by Eq. (1.15) and whose change between two points $[(x_1, y_1)$ and $(x_2, y_2)]$ depends _only_ on the coordinates of the points. The integral of Eq. (1.15) has then the same value, regardless of the path of integration, and is simply

$$\int_{x_1, y_1}^{x_2, y_2} [M(x, y)dx + N(x, y)dy] = z(x_2, y_2) - z(x_1, y_1) \tag{1.17}$$

The function $z(x, y)$ is then said to be a _point function,_ and the differential dz is said to be an _exact_ or _perfect differential._

To inquire into the conditions for exactness of an expression such as Eq. (1.15), let there be an exact differential dz such that

$$dz = \left(\frac{\partial z}{\partial x}\right)dx + \left(\frac{\partial x}{dy}\right)dy = M(x, y)dx + N(x, y)dy$$

Then

$$\left(\frac{\partial z}{\partial x}\right) = M(x, y); \quad \left(\frac{\partial z}{\partial y}\right) = N(x, y)$$

Since the order of differentiation

$$\left(\frac{\partial^2 z}{\partial x \partial y} = \frac{\partial^2 z}{\partial y \partial x}\right)$$

is immaterial,* it follows that

$$\frac{\partial M(x, y)}{\partial y} = \frac{\partial N(x, y)}{\partial x} \qquad (1.18)$$

Equation (1.18) is a most important relation in thermodynamics. It is the *necessary* condition for an expression such as $M(x, y)\, dx + N(x, y)\, dy$ to be exact. That it is also a *sufficient* condition may be seen by starting with

$$\frac{\partial M}{\partial y} = \frac{\partial N}{\partial x}$$

and showing that $M\, dx + N\, dy$ is an exact differential. Consider the expression:

$$\Phi(x, y) = N - \frac{\partial}{\partial y} \int M\, dx \qquad (1.19)$$

Then

$$\frac{\partial \Phi}{\partial x} = \frac{\partial N}{\partial x} - \frac{\partial}{\partial x}\left(\frac{\partial}{\partial y} \int M\, dx\right)$$

$$= \frac{\partial N}{\partial x} - \frac{\partial}{\partial y}\left(\frac{\partial}{\partial x} \int M\, dx\right)$$

$$= \frac{\partial N}{\partial x} - \frac{\partial M}{\partial y} = 0$$

Thus, $\Phi(x, y)$ is a function of y alone, i.e. $\Phi(x, y) = \phi(y)$.

Now, let

$$f(x, y) = \int M(x, y)\, dx + \int \phi(y)\, dy \qquad (1.20)$$

Then

$$\frac{\partial f}{\partial x} = \frac{\partial}{\partial x} \int M(x, y)\, dx = M$$

---

* This is true whenever z and its first and second derivatives are continuous and single-valued in some region of the x–y plane.

and

$$\frac{\partial f}{\partial y} = \frac{\partial}{\partial y} \int M(x,y)\ dx + \phi(y)$$

$$= \frac{\partial}{\partial y} \int M\ dx + \left(N - \frac{\partial}{\partial y} \int M\ dx\right)$$

$$= N$$

Hence,

$$df = \left(\frac{\partial f}{\partial x}\right)dx + \left(\frac{\partial f}{\partial y}\right)dy$$

$$= M\ dx + N\ dy$$

The relation $\partial M/\partial y = \partial N/\partial x$ is therefore a *necessary* as well as *sufficient* condition for $M\ dx + N\ dy$ to be exact.

Example 1.5. Determine whether $(x^2 + y^2)dx + 2xydy$ is exact or not. If exact, find the function of $f(x, y)$ such that $df = (x^2 + y^2)dx + 2xydy$.

Solution. Here, $M = x^2 + y^2$, $N = 2xy$, and

$$\frac{\partial M}{\partial y} = 2y = \frac{\partial N}{\partial x}$$

The expression $(x^2 + y^2)dx + 2xydy$ is thus an exact differential, and it is possible to seek a function $f(x, y)$ such that

$$\frac{\partial f}{\partial x} = x^2 + y^2; \quad \frac{\partial f}{\partial y} = 2xy$$

Integrating the first with respect to x while holding y constant gives

$$f(x, y) = \frac{x^3}{3} + y^2x + \phi(y)$$

Differentiating this with respect to y while holding x constant, and setting the result equal to $2xy$, gives

$$2xy + \frac{d\phi}{dy} = 2xy$$

or

$$\frac{d\phi}{dy} = 0$$

so that

$$\phi(y) = C$$

Thus

$$f(x, y) = \frac{x^3}{3} + xy^2 + C$$

Example 1.6. Evaluate the integral

$$\int_{(0,0)}^{(1,3)} [(x^2+y^2)dx+2xydy]$$

and verify, by choosing two different paths of integration, that its value depends only on the end points (0, 0) and (1, 3).

Solution. The preceding example showed that $(x^2+y^2)dx+2xydy$ is the exact differential of the function $x^3/3+xy^2+C$. To evaluate the integral along any path from (0, 0) to (1, 3), simply write

$$\int_{(0,0)}^{(1,3)} [(x^2+y^2)dx+2xydy] = \int_{(0,0)}^{(1,3)} d\left(\frac{x^3}{3} + xy^2 + C\right) = \left[\frac{x^3}{3} + xy^2 + C\right]_{(0,0)}^{(1,3)} = \frac{28}{3}$$

To verify that this answer is independent of the integration path, choose a straight line between (0, 0) and (1, 3), and a path composed of (0, 0), to (1, 0), followed by (1, 0) to (1, 3), (see Fig. 1.2). The value of the integral along the first path $(y = 3x)$ is

$$\int_{(0,0)}^{(1,3)} [(x^2+y^2)dx+2xydy] = \int_0^1 (x^2+9x^2)dx + \int_0^3 \frac{2y^2}{3}dy = \frac{28}{3}$$

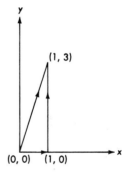

Fig. 1.2

The value of the integral along the second path is obtained by letting $y = 0$,

$dy = 0$ from (0, 0) to (1, 0), and $x = 1$, $dx = 0$ from (1, 0) to (1, 3):

$$\int_{(0,0)}^{(1,3)} (x^2+y^2)dx+2xydy = \int_0^1 x^2dx + \int_0^3 2ydy = \frac{28}{3}$$

Thus, the same answer is obtained along different paths of integration.

Note that the value of the cyclic integral

$$\oint [(x^2+y^2)dx+2xydy]$$

i.e., the integration around a closed path, is exactly zero. Why? Is this always the case for any integral? These facts will be of importance in later chapters.

Example 1.7. Evaluate the integral

$$\int_{(1,0)}^{(-1,0)} (x^3-y^3)dy$$

along the semi-circle $y = \sqrt{1-x^2}$ and along the path $(1, 0)-(1, 1)-(-1, 1)-(-1, 0)$, as shown in Fig. 1.3.

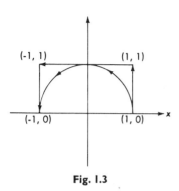

Fig. 1.3

Solution. Here, $M = 0$, $N = x^3 - y^3$, so that $\partial M/\partial y \neq \partial N/\partial x$. Consequently, a different value of the integral will be obtained according to which path is chosen. To evaluate the integral along $y = \sqrt{1-x^2}$, it is possible to use y as a parameter, and this gives

$$\int_{(1,0)}^{(-1,0)} (x^3 - y^3) dy =$$

$$\int_0^1 [(1-y^2)^{3/2} - y^3] dy + \int_1^0 [-(1-y^2)^{3/2} - y^3] dy$$

where $x = \sqrt{1-y^2}$ has been used on the first part, and $x = -\sqrt{1-y^2}$ has been used on the second part.

It is also possible to use x as a parameter, in which case the integral becomes

$$\int_{(1,0)}^{(-1,0)} (x^2 - y^3) dy = \int_1^{-1} [x^3 - (1-x^2)^{3/2}] \frac{-x dx}{\sqrt{1-x^2}}$$

In either case, the integration is awkward to carry out, and it is better to represent the semi-circle parametrically as

$$x = \cos t, \quad y = \sin t, \quad 0 \leqslant t \leqslant \pi$$

The line integral along the semi-circle then becomes

$$\int_{(1,0)}^{(-1,0)} (x^3 - y^3) dy = \int_0^{\pi} (\cos^3 t - \sin^3 t) \cos t \, dt = \frac{3\pi}{8}$$

The evaluation of the integral along the path $(1, 0)-(1, 1)-(-1, 1)-(-1, 0)$ is left to the student. The answer, however, will not be equal to $3\pi/8$. In other words, a different answer is obtained for each different path of integration.

Let the student also verify (by choosing any closed path) that the cyclic integral

$$\oint (x^3 - y^3) dy$$

is *not* zero. This is because $(x^3 - y^3) dy$ is *not* an exact differential.

1.7   Integration Around Closed Path

The preceding examples have set the stage for introducing the notion of *cyclic integration*. This is *the integration around a path which closes on itself.* Cyclic integration plays an important part in thermodynamics, because it will be seen that work and heat are often computed as areas enclosed by certain closed curves plotted against appropriate coordinates. Essentially, thermodynamics is the study of relations between heat, work, and properties of systems. Properties* serve to establish the state of a system; they are state functions, and the integral of their differentials around a closed path is zero, because the system returns to its original state after one cycle.

Whenever the integral of a given differential $Mdx + Ndy$ around an arbitrary closed path is zero, it can be concluded that the differential is exact. Referring to Fig. 1.4, let the integral from 1 to 2 be performed along two different paths A and B as shown. When the limits on one of the integrals is reversed, the two paths constitute a closed curve around which the integral has been postulated to be zero. Thus

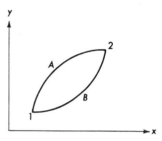

$$\oint_A \int_1^2 (Mdx + Ndy) + \oint_B \int_2^1 (Mdx + Ndy) = 0$$

$$(1.21)$$

where $\oint_A$ denotes integration along curve A, and $\oint_B$ denotes integration along curve B. Equation (1.21) gives

Fig. 1.4

$$\oint_A \int_1^2 (Mdx + Ndy) - \oint_B \int_1^2 (Mdx + Ndy) = 0$$

or

$$\oint_A \int_1^2 (Mdx + Ndy) = \oint_B \int_1^2 (Mdx + Ndy) \qquad (1.22)$$

i.e., the respective integrals along paths A and B have the same value. Since the two paths can be chosen arbitrarily, the integration depends only on the end states 1 and 2, and the differential $Mdx + Ndy$ is, therefore, exact.

Example 1.8. When a system at a pressure p undergoes an expansion dV, the work[†] done is $dW = pdV$. If the expansion is from 1 to 2 along the path $1 - A - 2$

---

* A *property* is a characteristic, such as pressure, temperature, etc., which is used to identify the state of a system. It must have a unique numerical value whenever the system is in a given particular state.

† *Work* may be defined as the product of a force and the distance moved in the direction of the force. For a system undergoing an expansion, this becomes the product of a pressure and a volume change. A more thorough discussion of work is given in Chap. 2.

of Fig. 1.5(a), the total amount of work done is

$$\int_1^2 dW = \int_1^2 p\,dV = \text{area under } 1\text{–}A\text{–}2$$

It is clear that this is *dependent* on the path chosen in going from 1 to 2, since a different path such as 1–*B*–2 would give a different area. The differential dW is therefore *inexact*, and for this reason is written with a bar through it.

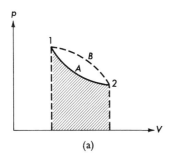
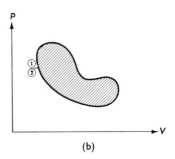

(a)   (b)

Fig. 1.5

Now, consider a cyclic operation as shown in Fig. 1.5(b), in which a quantity of work $\oint dW$ appears or disappears each time around the cycle. Experiment shows that an equivalent amount of heat* $\oint dQ$ appears or disappears also, so that

$$\oint(dQ - dW) = 0$$

This last equation states that the cyclic integral of the quantity $dQ - dW$ is zero. Therefore, $dQ - dW$ must be the exact differential of a quantity E such that

$$dE = dQ - dW \qquad (1.23)$$

The quantity E is called the *energy* of the system. Its existence, as defined by Eq. (1.23), constitutes the first law of thermodynamics.†

---

* *Heat,* denoted by the the symbol Q, is a form of energy transfer associated with temperature difference. It will be introduced in Chaps. 3 and 4.

† This example is not meant to be an exposition of the first law of thermodynamics at this stage. It merely illustrates the power and elegance of mathematics in connection with the study of thermodynamics.

1.8   Thermodynamic Variables

For a system consisting of a given mass of pure substance, the following variables are most often encountered in thermodynamics:

Pressure · · · ·	p
Volume · · · · ·	V
Absolute Temperature ·	T
Internal Energy · · ·	U
Enthalpy · · · ·	H
Entropy · · · · ·	S
Helmholtz Function · ·	A
Gibbs Function · · ·	G

Each will be defined in its proper place in the text. It is an experimental fact that the state of a homogeneous system is fixed when two properties are fixed. Thus, with the exception of cases of change of phase, any two variables may be chosen as independent, leaving the other six dependent. The existence of a functional dependence is one of the postulates of thermodynamics. The particular function for a particular substance must, of course, be determined by experiment. In theoretical analysis, however, it is always possible (for example) to write $V(p, T)$ to indicate that the volume is to be considered as a function of pressure and temperature. The choice of independent variables is purely a matter of convenience, and transformation to other independent variables is often done.

Because of the ease in measuring them, pressure and temperature are frequently chosen as independent variables, so that experimental data may lead to tables or empirical expressions for such concepts as volume, internal energy, entropy, as functions of pressure and temperature. In other words, if the functions $V(p, T)$, $U(p, T)$, $S(p, T)$, are considered known, and if it is desired to compute (for example) the function $U(S, V)$, then the mathematical procedure is to solve the two simultaneous equations

$$\begin{cases} S = S(p, T) \\ V = V(p, T) \end{cases} \tag{1.24}$$

and obtain p and T in terms of S and V. These values of p and T are then substituted into the given expression $U(p, T)$ to give $U(S, V)$ as required. Clearly, the importance of mathematics in the study of thermodynamics cannot be overstressed.

1.9 Property

In thermodynamics, a *property* is *any measurement or quantity which serves to describe a system.* Thus, besides chemically identifying the substance of which a system is composed, the state of the system must be specified by such characteristics as pressure, specific volume, temperature, modulus of elasticity, etc. The state* of a given system is its condition or position relative to other systems or to the surroundings. At any instant, the state of a system may be determined by giving the values of its properties at that instant. The sort of characteristic to be used in describing the state of any system is found by experience, and will of course depend upon the nature of the system. For example, observable characteristics such as shape and color are often irrelevant in a thermodynamic system not involving surface tension effects. On the other hand, shape is an important characteristic in a system involving surface effects. Similarly, properties involving a relationship between a system and its surroundings, such as position or velocity, may be omitted from consideration in many problems. The essential feature of a property is that it has a definite numerical value when the system is in a particular state, and that this value can be determined by measurements or examination *without* recourse to the past or future history of the system. Pressure, temperature, and specific volume are among the examples which fulfil this requirement. Since the value of a property is independent of the process through which the system has passed in reaching a particular state, it follows that a change in the value of a property depends only on the *initial* and *final* states of the system. Mathematically, this is stated as follows: *If ψ is a quantity which represents a property of a system, then $d\psi$ is an exact differential, and the total change between states 1 and 2 of the system can be written as*

$$\int_1^2 d\psi = \psi_2 - \psi_1 \qquad (1.25)$$

The state of a system at any instant depends upon the values of the properties at that instant. In other words, it is fixed by fixing the values of the properties. Since there are numerous relationships among the properties of particular systems, only a limited number of properties need be given to establish the state of a system, because the remaining properties may always be calculated from the given ones. The number of properties required to determine the state of a system depends upon the complexity of the system, but for a single-phase homogeneous system, the state is fixed when any *two* independent properties are fixed. This is the type of system (often called simple system) to which attention is restricted in the first part of the text.

* The term "state" is not to be confused with the solid, liquid, or vapor form of a substance. These forms are commonly referred to as "phases."

Example 1.9. If $pv = RT$, (where $p = $ pressure, $v = $ specific volume, $R = $ a constant and $T = $ temperature) determine whether the following quantities

$$\int \left(\frac{dT}{T} - \frac{vdp}{T} \right) \qquad \text{and} \qquad \int \left(\frac{dT}{T} + \frac{pdv}{v} \right)$$

can be used as properties.

Solution. The problem resolves to determining whether the differentials

$$\left(\frac{dT}{T} - \frac{vdp}{T} \right) \quad \text{and} \quad \left(\frac{dT}{T} + \frac{pdv}{v} \right)$$

are exact or not. Since each differential is of the form $Mdx + Ndy$, the test for exactness (see Sec. 1.6), namely,

$$\left(\frac{\partial M}{\partial y} \right)_x = \left(\frac{\partial N}{\partial x} \right)_y$$

can be applied. Thus, for the first differential:

$$\left[\frac{\partial(1/T)}{\partial p} \right]_T \stackrel{?}{=} \left[\frac{\partial(-v/T)}{\partial T} \right]_p = \left[\frac{\partial(-R/p)}{\partial T} \right]_p$$

or

$$0 \stackrel{?}{=} 0$$

Consequently, $dT/T - vdp/T$ is exact and may be written as

$$\frac{dT}{T} - \frac{vdp}{T} = ds \quad \checkmark$$

where s is a quantity whose physical significance will become apparent later in the text. At present, all that need be said about it is that it is a property. In other words,

$$\int \left(\frac{dT}{T} - \frac{vdp}{T} \right) = \int ds \quad \checkmark$$

is a point function.

As for the second differential, $(dT/T + dpv/v)$, the test for exactness gives

$$\left[\frac{\partial(1/T)}{\partial v} \right]_T \stackrel{?}{=} \left[\frac{\partial(p/v)}{\partial T} \right]_v = \frac{R}{v^2}$$

or

$$0 \stackrel{?}{=} \frac{R}{v^2}$$

The differential is not exact, and therefore

$$\int \left(\frac{dT}{T} + \frac{pdv}{v} \right)$$

is not a point function. It cannot be used as a property.

1.10 Intensive and Extensive Properties

An *intensive property* is one whose value is independent of the mass of the system. Such properties as temperature, pressure, density, and specific volume are intensive properties, for they are the same for the entire system and thus are independent of the mass of the system.

An *extensive property*, on the other hand, is proportional to the mass of the system. Volume is an example of extensive property. Other examples are length, area, charge, and magnetization.

The ratio of an extensive property to the mass is called the *specific value* of that property. Thus, if the total volume of a system is denoted by V, and the mass by m, then specific volume (or volume per unit mass) is

$$v = \frac{V}{m} \tag{1.26}$$

In general, capital letters will be used in the text to represent extensive variables, and small letters will be used to represent intensive variables. The only exception to this convention is the use of m for mass.*

1.11 Thermodynamic Equilibrium

An important assumption is implicit when talking about properties of a system. It is evident, when referring to *the* temperature or *the* pressure of a system, that the temperature or pressure should be the same at all points in the system. For example, in an isolated system, though the temperature and pressure as measured at various points throughout the system may initially vary with time, the rates of change become smaller and smaller until eventually no further change occurs. The system then attains a state of equilibrium, whereupon the thermodynamic coordinates are the same at all points of the homogeneous system. In other words, a system is said to be in equilibrium if no further changes occur within it when it is isolated from its surroundings. The properties, such as pressure and temperature, must then be uniform throughout the system. For, if the pressure is not uniform (because of turbulence, for example), internal changes (diffusion) will occur in the isolated system until the turbulence has died away and the pressure has become uniform. Similarly, if the temperature is not uniform throughout the isolated system, a spontaneous redistribution of temperature will occur until all parts of the system are at the same temperature. Thus, only under *equilibrium* conditions can single values be ascribed to the

---

* The capital letter M is usually reserved for the *molecular weight*. This is the mass of a *mole* of substance. For example, a pound-mole of oxygen has a mass of 32 pounds; a gram-mole of oxygen has a mass of 32 grams. Unless otherwise stated, a mole is understood to be a pound-mole.

properties of a system. More precisely, a system is in equilibrium when mechanical equilibrium (no unbalance of forces), thermal equilibrium (no temperature gradients), and chemical equilibrium (no reaction) simultaneously exist.

In essence, equilibrium is a concept associated with the absence of tendency for spontaneous changes when the system is isolated. For example: A metal bar conducting heat is not in thermodynamic equilibrium because, if the heat flow is stopped, the temperature gradient in the bar will spontaneously level out. A combustible mixture of oxygen and hydrogen at room temperature is not in thermodynamic equilibrium, since a reaction occurs if the mixture is ignited. However, a gas in a cylinder being compressed by a slowly moving piston is in equilibrium because, if the system is isolated (by stopping the piston), no further change in state takes place. The major part of thermodynamics is concerned with systems which are in equilibrium, or idealized to be in equilibrium. This is what is meant by the previous statement that a more proper name for thermodynamics would be *thermostatics*. The study of non-equilibrium states is commonly referred to as *irreversible thermodynamics*.

1.12 Process

When a system changes from one equilibrium state to another, it does so by means of a *process*. This is a change in the state and therefore in the coordinates of the system. Thus, if a system passes through a continuous series of equilibrium states during a process, these states can be located on a diagram of appropriate coordinates, and a line representing the path of the process can be drawn through all the points. Such a process is called a *reversible* process (see Fig. 1.6(a)). It is analogous to the frictionless process referred to in ordinary mechanics.

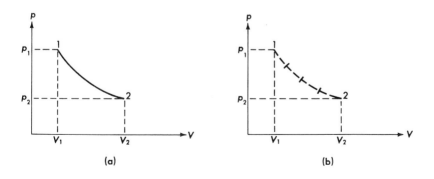

(a)   (b)

Fig. 1.6   Representation of Reversible and Irreversible Process.

On the other hand, if a system passes through a series of non-equilibrium states during a process, these states cannot be located on any coordinate diagram because each property does not have a unique value. This process is said to be *irreversible* it can always be assumed, however, that a system is in a state of equilibrium at the beginning and end of a process, so that irreversible processes may be represented on a diagram by a dotted line joining the initial and final state points. This indicates that the intermediate states are indeterminate.* Fig. 1.6(b) illustrates an irreversible process.

In actual practice, no thermodynamic process is entirely reversible (just as no mechanical process is entirely frictionless), because they more often must take place with finite differences of pressure or of temperature between a system and its surroundings. The notion of a reversible process however, is an indispensable tool in thermodynamic analysis. The full significance of these ideas will be illustrated later in the text.

1.13   Engineering Units

In order to arrive at correct answers for numerical problems involving thermodynamics, it is essential to understand the units of force, mass, weight and density in the engineering system of units. For this reason, the following review is included to enable students to perform calculations in more than one system of units.

Force. The basic unit of force in the British system is the pound force (lbf). It is defined as the force exerted on a "standard pound body" (a certain mass of platinum preserved at the Standards Office in Westminster, London) at a locality of standard gravitational acceleration of 32.174 ft/sec².

Mass. This is a quantity of matter; its magnitude is independent of the force acting on it. The symbol used for it is lbm. As stated above, the standard pound mass is kept in London. A pound mass (lbm) is an *absolute* quantity of matter. This means that one pound mass is one pound of matter regardless of where it is located—be it at sea level or in outer space.

The relation between force, mass, length, and time is given by Newton's second law of motion, which states that force is proportional to the product of mass and acceleration: $F \sim ma$. If this is to be written as an equality, a constant of proportionality must be introduced. This constant will have magnitude and dimensions depending on the units chosen for force, mass, length, and time. Let the constant be $1/g_c$, so that $F \sim ma$ becomes

---

* Strictly speaking, *classical thermodynamics* is restricted to the study of systems in equilibrium, and therefore to reversible processes. It can, however, be applied to processes which involve non-equilibrium states, provided that the initial and final states of the process are equilibrium states.

$$F = \frac{ma}{g_c} \qquad (1.27)$$

If the unit of force is chosen to be the pound force (lbf), the unit of mass the pound mass (lbm), and the standard gravitational acceleration to be 32.174 ft/sec², then Eq. (1.27) becomes

$$1 \text{ lbf} = \frac{(1 \text{ lbm})(32.174 \text{ ft/sec}^2)}{g_c} \qquad (1.28)$$

and, for this to hold, it is required that

$$g_c = 32.174 \frac{\text{lbm ft}}{\text{lbf sec}^2} \qquad (1.29)$$

Note that g_c is simply a conversion factor which depends only on the units involved. It is not an acceleration, and does not change with location. The acceleration is a, and this changes according to location.

Example 1.10. Find the force of gravity acting on a pound mass at a location where the acceleration of gravity is $g = 30.8$ ft/sec².

Solution.

$$F = \frac{ma}{g_c} = \frac{mg}{g_c} = \frac{(1 \text{ lbm})(30.8 \text{ ft/sec}^2)}{(32.174 \text{ lbm ft/lbf sec}^2)} = 0.956 \text{ lbf}$$

Weight. The weight of a body is the force exerted on its given mass by the local gravitational field of the earth. Its relation to mass is given by Newton's equation $w = mg/g_c$. Thus, in the example above, at a locality where g is 30.8 ft/sec², the body has a weight of 0.956 pounds (force). It still has a mass of one pound. Frequently, in engineering literature, both mass and weight are simply expressed as pounds. This leads to confusion, and it is then necessary to determine from the context which of the two quantities is actually meant. While no numerical error may result from such usage as long as the acceleration due to gravity is approximately 32.2 ft/sec², it should nevertheless be borne in mind that the units of pound mass and pound force are *not* dimensionally equal.

Density and Specific Volume. The density of a substance is the mass per unit volume. Its usual symbol is ρ, and its definition for a continuum is given by the equation

$$\rho = \frac{1}{v} = \lim_{\Delta V \to \Delta V'} \frac{\Delta m}{\Delta V} \qquad (1.30)$$

where $\Delta V'$ is the smallest volume for which the substance can be considered a continuum. The specific volume (v) is the volume per unit-mass; it is the reciprocal of the density. The common units for density and specific volume used in this text are lbm/ft³ and ft³/lbm respectively.

Since classical thermodynamics is based on the existence of continuum properties, it is of interest at this stage to define and discuss the concept of a continuum. For illustrative purposes, consider the density of a fluid at a point P. To do this, surround point P by a volume ΔV, and measure

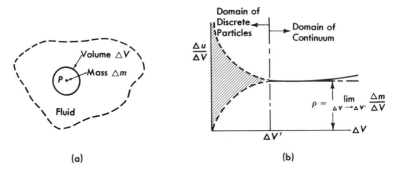

Fig. 1.7 Definition of Density.

the mass Δm within the volume. This is shown in Fig. 1.7(a). Let the ratio $\Delta m/\Delta V$ be taken and plotted against ΔV. It is seen in Fig. 1.7(b) that as ΔV is shrunk about point P, the ratio $\Delta m/\Delta V$ departs from is asymptotic value at $\Delta V'$ and takes values either infinitely small or infinitely large. This is because when ΔV becomes extremely small, it contains so few particles that the ratio $\Delta m/\Delta V$ fluctuates substantially as particles pass into and out of the volume. Equation (1.30) defines the density at a point with this restriction in mind.

For most engineering applications, $\Delta V'$, the smallest volume for which the fluid can be considered a continuum, is far smaller than any significant dimension of the engineering installation. There are situations, however, where this is not true. In the field of high-speed, high-altitude flight (involving such objects as long-range ballistic missiles, sounding rockets, and earth satellites) consideration must be given to the fact that at 300,000 feet, the mean free molecular path* is about one inch, and can easily be of the same order as the boundary layer thickness of the vehicle. At 500,000 feet, the mean free path increases to 10 feet, and becomes of the same order as the dimension of the vehicle itself! Under these conditions, the fluid no longer can be treated as a continuum, and aerodynamic and thermodynamic analyses must take into account the kinetic theory concept wherein the fluid is considered as an assembly of discrete particles. The continuum (wherein the mean free path does not exceed a significant dimension of the vehicle) simply does not exist under these conditions.

---

* The mean free path is the average distance a molecule travels between collisions with similar particles It is an important quantity in the kinetic theory of gases.

1.14   Other Systems of Units

The system of units just described is the so-called *Engineering-English* system. There are, however, other systems of units. They are not used extensively in this text, but they are encountered in the literature, and, for this reason, they are mentioned briefly here.

The *British Absolute* system is based on three fundamental units: (1) the foot as the unit of length, (2) the pound as the unit of mass, and (3) the second as the unit of time. The remaining unit of force, named the *poundal*, is derived from these three fundamental units. In this system, the *poundal is defined as the force required to accelerate a mass of one pound at the rate of* 1 *ft/sec²*. Thus

$$F = \frac{ma}{g_c} \quad \text{or} \quad 1 \text{ poundal} = \frac{(1 \text{ lbm})(1 \text{ ft/sec}^2)}{g_c} \tag{1.31}$$

and

$$g_c = 1\frac{\text{lbm ft}}{\text{poundal sec}^2} \tag{1.32}$$

Note that the constant of proportionality $1/g_c$ now has the magnitude of unity.

The *Metric Absolute* system is based on the three fundamental units of (1) centimeter for the unit of length, (2) gram for the unit of mass, and (3) second for the unit of time. The unit of force is derived from these three units, and is called the *dyne*. *A dyne is the force required to accelerate a mass of one gram at the rate of* 1 *cm/sec²*. Thus

$$F = \frac{ma}{g_c} \quad \text{or} \quad 1 \text{ dyne} = \frac{(1 \text{ gm})(1 \text{ cm/sec}^2)}{g_c} \tag{1.33}$$

and

$$g_c = 1\frac{\text{gm cm}}{\text{dyne sec}^2} \tag{1.34}$$

Again, the magnitude of $1/g_c$ is unity.

The *British Gravitational* system differs from the British absolute system in that force is chosen as a fundamental unit instead of mass. The fundamental units are: the foot as the unit of length, the pound as the unit of force, and the second as the unit of time. The *unit of mass* becomes a derived unit, and is called the *slug*. The slug is defined as *the mass which will be accelerated at the rate of* 1 *ft/sec² when acted upon by force of one pound*. Thus

$$F = \frac{ma}{g_c} \quad \text{or} \quad 1 \text{ lbf} = \frac{(1 \text{ slug})(1 \text{ ft/sec}^2)}{g_c} \tag{1.35}$$

and

$$g_c = 1 \frac{\text{slug ft}}{\text{lbf sec}^2} \qquad (1.36)$$

Note again that g_c is unity. Corresponding to the British gravitational system there is the *Metric Gravitational* system, which is based on the centimeter, gram, and second, as the units of length, force, and time respectively; the remaining unit of mass is derived from these. Finally, there is the much advocated *mks* system, wherein the meter, kilogram, and second are chosen as fundamental units of length, mass, and time respectively, and the force is a derived unit called the *newton*.

Although the engineering system is the one used in this text, it is of interest to know that

$$1 \text{ ft} = 0.3048 \text{ meter}$$

$$1 \text{ lbf} = 32.174 \text{ poundals} = 4.448 \times 10^3 \text{ dynes}$$

$$1 \text{ lbm} = \frac{1}{32.174} \text{ slugs} = 0.453 \text{ kgm.}$$

The above discussion on units may be conveniently summarized in the following table:

TABLE 1.1

SUMMARY OF UNITS

Mass	Force	Length	Time	g_c
lbm	lbf	ft	sec	$32.174 \dfrac{\text{lbm-ft}}{\text{lbf-sec}^2}$
lbm	poundal	ft	sec	$1 \dfrac{\text{lbm-ft}}{\text{poundal-sec}^2}$
gm	dyne	cm	sec	$1 \dfrac{\text{gm-cm}}{\text{dyne-sec}^2}$
slug	lbf	ft	sec	$1 \dfrac{\text{slug-ft}}{\text{lbf-sec}^2}$
kgm	newton	meter	sec	$1 \dfrac{\text{kgm-meter}}{\text{newton-sec}^2}$

1.15 Pressure

The definition of pressure for a continuous medium is

$$p = \lim_{\Delta A \to \Delta A'} \frac{\Delta F_n}{\Delta A} \qquad (1.37)$$

where ΔF_n is the component of force normal to ΔA, and $\Delta A'$ is the smallest area over which the medium can be considered a continuum. The unit of pressure which is consistent with the units used in this text is pounds of force per square foot (lb/ft²). However, it is common practice to give pressure in pounds per square inch (lb/in²). Therefore, the student should introduce, in numerical calculations, the factor of 144 in² = 1 ft² whenever necessary.

Thermodynamic relations are for the most part concerned with *absolute pressure*. ⟨This is the pressure exerted by a system on its boundaries.⟩ The word absolute is used to differentiate it from the gage pressure, because, in practice, most pressure and vacuum gages read only the difference between the absolute pressure and the atmospheric pressure. To obtain the absolute pressure, the atmospheric pressure must be added to the gage pressure. In other words

$$P_{\text{absolute}} = P_{\text{gage}} + P_{\text{atmospheric}} \qquad (1.38)$$
$$(\text{SURROUNDINGS})$$

Equation (1.38) is to be used for pressures above atmospheric. For pressures below atmospheric, the gage pressure would be negative, and it is common practice to apply the term "vacuum" to the magnitude of the gage pressure. Thus, a gage pressure of −5 psi is spoken of as a vacuum of 5 psi. The relationship between absolute pressure, gauge pressure, atmospheric pressure, and vacuum is shown graphically in Fig. 1.8. In engineering practice, pressures are generally measured by means of Bourdon gages or manometers (the student should at this stage familiarize himself with these instruments from the laboratory). Since pressures are directly proportional to manometric fluid heights, they are often expressed in units of: inches of mercury, inches of water, or millimeters of mercury. The relation between absolute pressure and vacuum reading is therefore

Inches absolute = Inches barometric − Inches vacuum   (1.39)

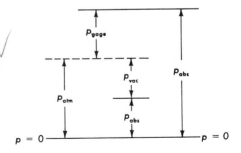

Fig. 1.8. Relation between Absolute, Gage, and Vacuum Pressures.

It is useful to note that a column of mercury one inch high and one square inch in cross section weighs 0.491 pounds, and, therefore, exerts a pressure of 0.491 psi. A column of water of similar dimensions weighs 0.0361 pounds and therefore exerts a pressure of 0.0361 psi. The density of water being 62.4 pounds per cubic foot (corresponding to ordinary room temperature), a column of water one foot high would exert a pressure of 62.4 psf = 0.434 psi. In some applications, pressure readings are also referred to as "feet" or "head" of fluid. For equal pressures, the relation between heights of fluids is given by

$$\frac{g\rho_1 h_1}{g_c} = \frac{g\rho_2 h_2}{g_c} \tag{1.40}$$

or, numerically,

$$\rho_1 h_1 = \rho_2 h_2 \tag{1.41}$$

where ρ and h are the density and height of fluid respectively.

For a fluid in static equilibrium, the relationship between pressure and elevation is given by the basic equation of fluid statics,

$$dp = -\rho \frac{g}{g_c} dz = -\gamma dz \tag{1.42}$$

where γ is the specific weight of the fluid, and z is the elevation measured positively upward. The minus sign stems from the fact that as z increases, p decreases. The derivation of Eq. (1.42) is listed as a problem at the end of the chapter. For liquids which are only slightly compressible, the specific weight can be assumed constant, so that Eq. (1.42) is readily integrated.

Example 1.11. In measuring the pressure in an air chamber, a liquid of specific gravity 0.8 shows a height of 17 inches. To what pressure is this equivalent in inches of water?

Solution. Recalling that the specific gravity of a fluid is the ratio of its density to that of water, Eq. (1.41) gives

$$(0.8)(17) = (1)(h_2)$$

hence

$$h_2 = 13.6 \text{ inches of water}$$

Example 1.12. The "standard atmosphere" is defined as the pressure exerted by a column of mercury 760 millimeters in height and having a specific gravity of 13.59 when located in a region where the acceleration of gravity is standard. Compute the pressure in psia produced by the column of mercury.

Solution. Since water has a specific weight of 62.4 pounds/ft³, the specific weight of mercury is 13.59 (62.4) = 848 pounds/ft³ or 0.491 pounds/in³. Recalling that 2.54 cm = 1 in., the height of the mercury column is $z = 76/2.54 = 29.9$ in. Equation (1.42) is then integrated between the limits of ($p = p$, $z = 0$) and ($p = 0$, $z = 29.9$) to give

$$\int_p^0 dp = -0.491 \int_0^{29.9} dz$$

or

$$p = 0.491(29.9) = 14.7 \text{ psia}$$

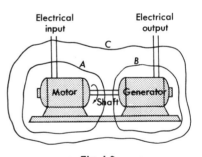

PROBLEMS

1.1. Consider the motor-generator set as shown. The thermodynamic boundaries are arbitrarily chosen. Consider the three systems defined by boundaries *A*, *B*, and *C*. Associate the proper system with the following energy effects:

(a) mechanical energy input, electrical energy output
(b) electrical energy input, electrical energy output
(c) electrical energy input, mechanical energy output.

1.2. Examples of systems encountered in thermodynamic analysis range from small portions of apparatus to complex power plants. State and discuss the most logical choice of a system in the following cases:

(a) flow of a gas through a pipe
(b) compression of a gas
(c) operation of an automobile engine
(d) turning of an output shaft against a resisting torque.

Fig. l.9

Use of Thermodynamic Boundaries.

1.3. Two states are identical if all possible physical measurements on a macroscopic level are equal. Does this mean that every molecule comprising the system has the same location and velocity in the two states?

1.4. Find the differentials of the following functions:

(a) $u = x/y$
(b) $u = x^2 + y^2$
(c) $u = \arctan y/x$
(d) $u = xy/z$

1.5. Evaluate $\partial u/\partial x$ and $\partial u/\partial y$ for the following:

(a) $u = \dfrac{x}{x^2+y^2}$

(b) $u = x \sin xy$

(c) $x^3+xy^2-x^2u+u^3-2 = 0$

1.6. Show that the equation of state of a substance may be written in the differential form of

$$\frac{dv}{v} = -\kappa dp + \beta dT$$

Hint: Consider v as a function of p and T.

1.7. In fluid mechanics, there are two commonly accepted ways of studying the flow. One way (called the Eulerian point of view) consists of watching the fluid pass through a fixed region of space. Another way (called the Lagrangian point of view) consists of following the fluid as it flows along. Let the temperature T of a system be a function of space and time: $T = T(x, y, z, t)$. Find and interpret the expression for dT/dt along the path $x = x(t)$, $y = y(t)$, $z = z(t)$. Is this the Eulerian or Langragian point of view?

1.8. Show that if $y = f(x)$, and $x = e^t$, then

$$\frac{d^2y}{dt^2} = \frac{d^2y}{dx^2}e^{2t} + \frac{dy}{dx}e^t$$

1.9. (a) Show that an infinitesimal change in pressure at constant volume may be expressed as $dp = B\beta dT$ which, for small temperature changes in a solid, may be integrated by assuming B and β to be constant: $p_2-p_1 = B\beta(T_2-T_1)$.

(b) A block of metal has a volume expansivity and an isothermal bulk modulus of 5×10^{-5} degrees Centigrade and 1.5×10^{12} dynes/cm², respectively. It is initially at 1 atm and a temperature of 20 °C. If the temperature is raised at constant volume to 32 °C, what will be the final pressure in atmospheres? Note: $1.01 \times \times 10^6$ dynes/cm = 1 atm.

1.10. Verify the truth of the proposition that $\partial^2 u/\partial x \partial y = \partial^2 u/\partial y \partial x$ in the following examples:

(a) $u = x^3 \sin y$

(b) $u = x/(x^2+y^2)$

(c) $u = x \sin xy$

1.11 Show that

$$\left(\frac{\partial \beta}{\partial p}\right)_T = -\left(\frac{d\kappa}{\partial T}\right)_p$$

Hint: Make use of the fact that

$$\frac{\partial^2 V}{\partial T \partial p} = \frac{\partial^2 V}{\partial p \partial T}$$

1.12. A substance has the following volume expansivity and isothermal compressibility: $\beta = 1/T$; $\kappa = 1/p$.   Find the equation of state.

1.13. Find the total differential of the function $u = (x+y)^3$. Show that the differential coefficients satisfy the condition for exactness, and integrate du to obtain the original expression for u plus a constant.

1.14. In each of the following cases, determine whether or not the expression is an exact differential. If the expression is the differential of a function $f(x, y)$ find f.

(a) $2x(x^3+y^3)dx+3y^2(x^2+y^2)dy$

(b) $e^y dx+x(e^y+1)dy$

(c) $(1+e^x)dy+e^x(y-x)dx$

(d) $(e^{x+y}+e^{x-y})(dx-dy)$

1.15. Evaluate the following integrals along the straight line connecting the end points:

(a) $\int_{(1,1)}^{(3,4)} y\,dx$

(b) $\int_{(0,0)}^{(2,2)} y^2\,dx$

(c) $\int_{(1,1)}^{(4,2)} x\,dy$

1.16. Test the expression

$$du = (2x+y)dx+(2x+y)dy$$

for exactness, and integrate it clockwise around a square whose vertices are $(1, 1), (-1, 1), (-1, -1), (1, -1)$.

1.17. Determine whether the following quantities can be used as properties:

(a) $y\,dx$

(b) $x\,dy$

(c) $(x\,dy+y\,dx)$

(d) $p\,dv$

(e) $(p\,dv+v\,dp)$

1.18. State whether the following properties of a system are intensive or extensive, dependent or independent: mass, specific weight, volume, specific volume, density, strain, molecular weight, concentration, pressure, temperature, surface area, elevation, velocity.

1.19. In order to be in equilibrium, a system must be homogeneous or must consist of homogeneous parts. Is the condition of homogeneity sufficient? Select a system comprised of iron, water vapor, and air at room temperature; this system consists of a number of homogeneous parts in contact. How does the possibility of oxidation of the iron affect equilibrium?

1.20. A layer of gas between two metal plates which are at different temperatures is suddenly isolated with reference to transfer of mass and energy. Is this system in thermodynamic equilibrium? Discuss.

1.21. A supercooled liquid is a liquid very carefully cooled to a temperature below that at which it ordinarily solidifies. Is this system in thermodynamics equilibrium? Discuss.

1.22. (a) Determine the force necessary to accelerate a mass of 10 pounds at the rate of 11 ft/sec².

(b) Determine the weight of a mass of 10 pounds at a location where the acceleration of gravity is 30.6 ft/sec².

1.23. (a) A pound mass is weighed at a location where $g = 30.00$ ft/sec² on a spring scale originally calibrated in a region where $g = 32.17$ ft/sec². What will be the reading?

(b) The same mass is weighed on a beam balance. What will be the reading?

(c) A cubic foot of water at 70 °F weighs 62.4 pounds at a location where $g = 32.17$ ft/sec². What is its specific weight and its density (in lbm/ft³ and in slugs/ft³) at the location where $g = 30.00$ ft/sec²?

1.24. The acceleration of gravity is given as function of elevation above sea level by the relation $g = a - bh$ where $a = 32.16$ ft/sec², and $b = 3.32 \times 10^{-6}$ for h in feet.

(a) What is the gravity force acting upon an airplane at 30,000 ft. elevation when its weight at sea level is 10,000 pounds?

(b) If the airplane is travelling at 500 mph, how much kinetic and potential energy does it have relative to sea level?

1.25. Why is it wrong to write the potential energy and the kinetic energy as mz and $\frac{1}{2} m \mathcal{V}^2$ respectively? Will these expressions give numerically correct results at a location where $g = 32.147$ ft/sec²?

1.26. For laminar flow conditions, the coefficient of viscosity or dynamic viscosity of a fluid is defined as

$$\mu = \frac{\text{shear stress}}{\text{shear rate}}$$

Show that, in force units,

$$\mu = \frac{\text{force} \times \text{time}}{(\text{length})^2}$$

and, in mass units,

$$\mu = \frac{\text{mass}}{\text{length} \times \text{time}}$$

1.27. The attractive force between two masses m_1 and m_2 having dimensions that are small compared with their mutual separation distance r is given by Newton's third law:

$$F = k \frac{m_1 m_2}{r^2}$$

where $k = 6.67 \times 10^{-11}$ newtons m^2/kg^2. What is the total gravitational force which the sun ($1.97 \times 10^{30}\, kg$) and the earth ($5.95 \times 10^{24}\, kg$) exert on the moon ($7.37 \times 10^{22}\, kg$) at an instant when the earth–moon–sun cycle is $90°$? The earth–moon and sun–moon distances are $380 \times 10^3\, km$ and $150 \times 10^3\, km$ respectively.

1.28. (a) It is an experimental fact that the mass which entered into Newton's third law of gravitation is the same as the mass defined by Newton's second law of motion. Show that if g is the gravitational intensity (force per unit mass on the surface of the earth), then

$$g = \frac{km_e}{r^2}$$

where m_e is the mass of the earth (kg), r is its radius (m), and k is a constant whose value is 6.67×10^{-11} newtons m^2/kg^2.
(b) The radius of the earth is 6370 km. What is its mass if the acceleration of gravity is 9.8 m/sec^2?

1.29. (a) A satellite is to circle the earth at 950 km above the surface with only the attraction of the earth acting on it. Determine the speed at which the satellite must travel. Hint: the acceleration of a body moving with velocity $\mathscr{V}$ in a circular path of radius r is $r\mathscr{V}^2$ in the radial direction; this must be equal to the gravitational intensity at an altitude of 950 km.
(b) The first artificial earth satellite was reported to have circled the earth at 18,000 mph and its maximum height above the earth's surface was given as 560 miles. Assuming the orbit to be circular and taking the mean diameter of the earth to be 7920 miles, determine the gravitational acceleration at this height.

1.30. (a) A local barometer reads 30.05 inches of mercury at 95 °F. What is the pressure in inches of mercury at 32 °F if the deduction for temperature correction is $p(t-32)/10,000$ where p is in inches of mercury and t is in degrees Fahrenheit?
(b) A manometer contains a fluid having a density of 56.5 lbm/ft³. The difference in level of the two columns is 14 inches. What is the pressure difference in lbf/in²?

1.31. A large chamber is separated into two compartments as shown. The two compartments are kept at different pressures. Pressure gage A reads 42 psig and pressure gage B reads 15 psig. If the local barometer is 30.10 inches mercury, determine the absolute pressures existing in the compartments, and the reading of gage C.

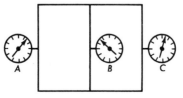

Fig. 1.10

1.32. A bell jar 10 inches in diameter is evacuated until a vacuum gage connected to it reads 27.5 inches of mercury. The local barometer is 29.8 inches of mercury. Find the absolute pressure inside the jar in pounds per square inch, and determine the force required to lift the jar off the plate on which it rests.

1.33. Calculate the height of the atmosphere necessary to produce a pressure $p_0 = 14.7$ psia and a specific volume $v_0 = 13.5$ cu ft/lbm at the earth's surface. Consider the atmosphere to be a column of fluid, and the relation between pressure

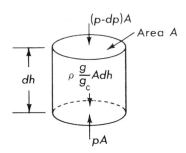

Fig. 1.11   Force Balance on an Element of Atmosphere.

and specific volume to be pv^n = constant, where $n = 1.4$. Assume the acceleration of gravity to be constant and equal to 32.17 ft/sec². Hint: consider a balance of forces on an elemental portion of the atmosphere.

CHAPTER 2

Work Transfer

2.1 Work

Historically, thermodynamics originated with man's endeavour to convert heat into mechanical work in the most efficient manner. As previously stated, thermodynamics is the science dealing with relations between properties of a system and the quantities *work and heat* which cause a change in the state of the system. Because *work, heat* and *temperature* are such important thermodynamic concepts, a precise definition of each of these quantities is necessary.

In mechanics, work is defined as *the product of a force and the distance moved in the direction of the force.* Consider first the work transfer associated with a system undergoing a reversible process. This is shown in

Fig. 2.1 where part of the boundary is allowed to move under such conditions that the external resistance is
only infinitesimally smaller than that
produced by the pressure within the
system. If A is the area of the piston,
the infinitesimal work dW, corresponding to an infinitesimal displacement dL
of the piston, is

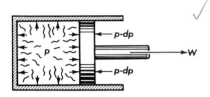

Fig. 2.1 Example of Work.

$$dW = p\,A\,dL = p\,dV \qquad (2.1)$$

where dV is the infinitesimal change in volume. If expansion occurs from
p_1 to p_2 in such a way that the restraining external force is changed continuously so that it is only infinitesimally different from pA at all times,
the work done during the process is

$$W = \int_1^2 p\,dV \qquad (2.2)$$

To integrate Eq. (2.2), we must know the relationship between p and V,
that is, the path of the process must be well defined. Thus, work is a path
function, and for this reason its differential is written as dW. For the same
reason, its magnitude during a process will be written as

$$W = \int_1^2 dW = W_{1-2} \qquad (2.3)$$

and never as

$$\int_1^2 dW = W_2 - W_1$$

The restrictions under which the expression $dW = p\,dV$ holds are:
(1) the system is closed, (2) there are no viscous effects within the system,
(3) the pressure (as well as other properties) has the same value on all
boundaries of the system, and (4) there are no gravity, electric, or magnetic
effects. Conditions (2) and (3) simply mean that throughout the system
all properties are uniform and single-valued at all times. In other words,
these are precisely the conditions for the process to be reversible, namely,
that the system should pass through a series of equilibrium states. This
process may be represented by a full line on a diagram of appropriate
coordinates (in this case p and V) as discussed in Sec. 1.12. The area under
the curve then represents the work done during the process. Condition (4)
requires some explanation. Take, for example, the case of gravity. The
statement that it be ruled out simply means that the effect of gravity is
negligible in comparison with other effects. If, for instance, the pressure

of 80 °F air stored in a 5 ft diameter spherical tank is given as 45 psia, it
is of no concern where in the system the pressure is 45 psia, because the
difference in air pressure between the highest point and the lowest point
in the tank is extremely small.

The reason for using the word _reversible_ can now be fully understood.
Since the external restraining force is never materially different from pA,
the expansion process may be stoppped at any point and reversed by an
infinitesimal change in the external force. The system will then return
through the same series of states, and the same quantity of work will be
done on the system by the surroundings as was done on the surroundings
by the system.

The standard unit of work in the Engineering-English system is the
ft lbf. Other units of work may also be used: the dyne cm, for example,
which is called an erg, or the joule, which is 10^7 ergs. _Power is the rate at
which work is done_, for example, ft lbf/sec. It is often measured in terms of
horsepower (1 hp = 33,000 ft lbf/min = 550 ft lbf/sec).

By thermodynamic convention, work is taken to be _positive_ when it is
done _by_ a system on its surroundings, and _negative_ when it is done _on_ the
system by the surroundings. Diagramatically, positive work is represented
by an arrow directed outward from a system, and negative work by an
arrow directed into the system.

Example 2.1. A mass of gas in a cylinder fitted with a movable piston expands
isothermally (constant temperature) and reversibly from a state (p_1, V_1) to a state
(p_2, V_2) according to the process $pV = C$, where C is a constant. If p_1 = 30 psia,
V_1 = 1.5 cu ft, and V_2 = 4 cu ft, what is the work done?

Solution. The work done during the process is

$$W = \int_{V_1}^{V_2} p\,dV = C\int_{V_1}^{V_2} \frac{dV}{V} = p_1 V_1 \ln \frac{V_2}{V_1}$$

$$= \left(30\frac{\text{lbf}}{\text{in}^2}\right)\left(144\frac{\text{in}^2}{\text{ft}^2}\right)(1.5 \text{ ft}^3) \ln \frac{4}{1.5}$$

$$= 6350 \text{ ft lbf}$$

Notice that under the condition of reversibility of the problem, equilibrium
pressure exists throughout the system, and integration is possible by means of
the pressure-volume relation pV = constant. The assumption of reversibility is
justified in view of the fact that the average velocity of gas molecules at ordinary
temperatures is around 1600 fps. Since piston speeds seldom exceed 60 fps, the
piston is fairly stationary relative to the gas molecules, and acceleration forces
are negligible. This makes the pressure uniform throughout the system at all
times. This situation, known as _fully-resisted expansion_ (or _compression_), arises
when all the effort of the fluid goes into moving the piston and not into moving
itself. Actual processes are not reversible, but if they proceed slowly and do not
depart infinitesimally from ideal equilibrium conditions, they are called _quasi-static_ processes and can be treated as reversible processes.

2.2 Thermodynamic Definition of Work

Because thermodynamics is concerned with interactions between a system and its surroundings, and these interactions are of two kinds, namely, work and heat, it is desirable to use a definition for work which has somewhat greater scope than the definition used in ordinary mechanics. Thus, in thermodynamics *work is said to be done by a system during a given process if the sole effect external to the system could be reduced to the rise of a weight.*

The above definition is actually motivated by the need to distinguish between work and heat as required by the second law of thermodynamics (Chap. 7). At this stage, however, it is possible to explain the definition and to show that it covers the usual kind of work treated in mechanics.

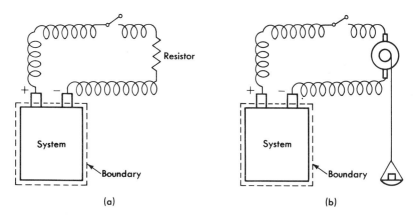

Fig. 2.2 Illustration of Thermodynamic Definition of Work.

First, to show that the thermodynamic definition covers a wide field, consider the system shown in Fig. 2.2(a) which illustrates an electrical storage battery. External to the system, the terminals are connected to a resistance by means of a switch. Let the switch be closed for a period of time during which current flows through the battery and the resistance, which becomes warmer as a result. Clearly the system (battery) has interacted with the surroundings, but can this interaction be classified as work? According to the definition in mechanics, the answer would be "No," for no force has moved through a distance. Yet, according to the thermodynamic definition, the answer is "Yes," because the resistance can be replaced by an electric motor which winds up a string on which a weight is suspended. This is shown in Fig. 2.2(b). Let the current flow be the same as in case (a). The situation, as far as the battery (system) is concerned, is no different than in (a). Yet this time, the sole effect external to the system has been the rise of a weight (assuming friction in the motor bearings to be eliminated). Thus, the system has done work.

To show that the thermodynamic definition also covers the case of the mechanics definition, consider the system shown in Fig. 2.3(a), and let the

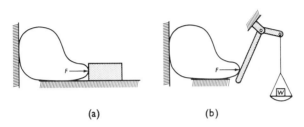

(a)   (b)

Fig. 2.3   Relation between Mechanics and Thermodynamic Definition of Work.

system exert a force on the surroundings at a location on its boundary. The surroundings are a block which is being pushed along a rough surface. Let the boundary be displaced, thereby displacing the block on the rough surface. Work is done, according to the mechanics definition, but no weight has been raised in the surroundings. However, the same process, when carried out in changed surroundings as shown in Fig. 2.3(b), could have raised a weight, and this could have been the sole external effect. Thus, the definition of work in mechanics fits into the definition of work in thermodynamics.

It is appropriate to discuss some of the words used in the thermodynamic definition for *work*: The words *sole effect* imply that there is another kind of interaction between a system and its surroundings, namely, heat (to be defined later), which can have the rise of a weight as part of its effect. For example, a system consisting of a hot body placed in contact with water could cause the water to boil. The steam produced can then drive a steam engine which, in turn, can raise a weight. It will later be shown, however, that there are always other effects: either the steam does not return to its original state after passing through the engine, or the surroundings become warmer. In other words, the weight raising is not the sole effect, and, consequently, heat is not the same as work. The distinction between the two will be given by the second law of thermodynamics.

The use of the word *external* in the definition emphasizes the fact that work is defined only with reference to a system boundary, i.e., work is an interaction *across* the boundary. If, for example, the boundary of the system were drawn to also enclose the block and rough surface in Fig. 2.3, the work would be zero, since there would be no external effects relative to this new system. It may also be noted that work is, by nature, *transient*. It is present during an interaction between a system and its surroundings (or between a system and another), but it does not exist before or after the interaction. *It is not a characteristic or property of a system.*

2.3   Case of $W \neq \int p dV$

The student should always keep in mind that the equality between work and $\int p dV$ holds only when a system passes through a series of equilibrium states. That $\int p dV$ is not equal to the work in an irreversible process may be easily shown by means of the free expansion process illustrated in Fig. 2.4.

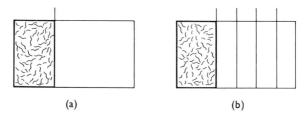

(a)   (b)

Fig. 2.4   Free Expansion.

Let a container be divided into two compartments by a sliding partition. Let one compartment contain a mass of gas, the system at pressure p_1 and volume V_1, and the other compartment be evacuated. When the partition is withdrawn or punctured, the gas undergoes an expansion which is not restrained by an equal and opposing force at the moving boundary. When the system has settled down to an end state of equilibrium at pressure p_2 and volume V_2, the two states, 1 and 2, can be located on a p–V diagram, but the intermediate states are indeterminate, because no single values of p and V can be ascribed to the system. Some intermediate states could be plotted if the process were to be carried out in a number of steps, as in Fig. 2.4(b): let a number of partitions be interposed; after each partition is withdrawn and the gas has settled down to an equilibrium state, let the pressure and volume be measured and the corresponding state point be plotted on a p–V diagram. If a dotted curve is drawn through all such points, the curve may be used to represent the irreversible process as in Sec. 1.12, and the area under the curve could be found by computing $\int_1^2 p dV$. But this area would *not* represent work, because no work was done by the system (since no external force has been moved through a distance). The example just cited may be an extreme case; in general, there is some

restraining force at the moving boundary of a system, and some work will
be done by the fluid during the expansion. But, unless the process is
reversible, the work done will always be less than $\int p\,dV$. Similarly, if compression work is to be done on a system, the work required will always
be greater than $\int p\,dV$ unless the compression is reversible, in which case the
work done equals $\int p\,dV$. The requirement for reversibility, namely, that
the external force in the surroundings should differ only infinitesimally
from the internal force due to the pressure of the system, means that there
is no excess force available for accelerating the system or the boundary.
This implies that a reversible expansion (or compression) is an infinitely
slow process. Since any real process must occur with finite time, it is clear
that a reversible process represents an ideal which can be approached
but never attained in practice.

Example 2.2. Consider the process illustrated in Fig. 2.5. A gas (the system)
expands from a volume of 1.5 cu ft to 2.0 cu ft while receiving 4000 ft lbf of work
from a paddle wheel. The pressure remains constant at 100 psia. Determine
the net amount of work done by the system.

Solution. Assuming the pressure at
the piston face to be uniform at each
stage of the process, the work done on
the piston is given by $\int p\,dV$. For the
case of a constant pressure, this becomes

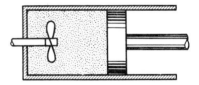

Fig. 2.5 Expanding Gas
under Action of Piston and Paddle Wheel.

$$p\int_{1,5}^{2,0}dV = 100(144)(2.0-1.5)$$

$$= 7200 \text{ ft lbf}$$

However, this is not the net work done by the system. The latter receives 4000 ft lbf
of work from the paddle wheel, and, according to the usual sign convention, this
work is -4000. Thus, the net work done by the system is

$$W_{\text{net}} = 7200-4000 = 3200 \text{ ft lbf}$$

2.4 Work of a Cycle; Indicator Diagram

When a system, in passing through a series of processes, returns to its
initial state, it is said to have undergone a *cycle*. The net work of the
cycle is therefore

$$W_{\text{cycle}} = \oint p\,dV \qquad (2.4)$$

where the symbol $\oint$ denotes integration along a closed path.
The net work done upon the piston of a reciprocating engine or compres-

sor may be determined from an indicator diagram. This is simply a plot of pressure vs. piston position obtained by a device called an indicator (the

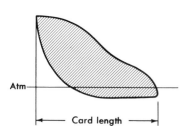

student should, at this stage, acquaint himself with the indicators available in the laboratory). The work done upon the piston during a cycle is

$$W_{\text{cycle}} = \oint p A dL \qquad (2.5)$$

where A is the area of the piston, and L is the distance travelled by the piston.

Fig. 2.6 Indicator Diagram.

Equation (2.5) may be written in terms of the *mean effective pressure* (p_m) as

$$W_{\text{cycle}} = p_m A L \qquad (2.6)$$

where L is the length of the piston stroke. The mean effective pressure is equal to the average height of the indicator diagram multiplied by the indicator spring constant; the average height is usually obtained by measuring the indicator diagram with a planimeter and dividing the area by the length of the diagram.

Example 2.3. A single-cylinder, single-acting, 2-stroke cycle diesel engine has a bore and stroke of 12 by 15 inches. An indicator diagram taken in connection with a test of this engine has an area of 0.26 sq in. and a length of 2.75 in. The spring constant is 400 psi per in. Determine: (a) the mean effective pressure, (b) the indicated horsepower if the engine is running at 300 rpm.

Solution. (a) The mean effective pressure is

$$p_m = \frac{0.26}{2.75}(400) = 37.8 \text{ psi}$$

(b) The piston area is $A = \pi(12)^2/4 = 113$ sq in.; the piston travel is $L = 15/12 = 1.25$ ft. The indicated horsepower is

$$ihp = \frac{p_m L A N}{33000}$$

where N is the number of cycles per minute. A 2-stroke cycle, single-acting engine completes one cycle for every revolution of the crankshaft. Thus,

$$ihp = \frac{(37.8)(1.25)(113)(300)}{(33000)} = 48.6$$

2.5 Other Types of Work

So far, and for most of engineering thermodynamics, attention is confined to systems whose equilibrium states are describable in terms of the coordinates p, V, and T. For such systems (known as chemical systems) the work during an infinitesimal process is given by $dW = pdV$. In other words, p is the intensive coordinate; V is the extensive coordinate; and p is said to be the force conjugate to the displacement dV. There are occasions, however, when an engineer is called upon to apply thermodynamics to other systems. Generalized, the concept of work may be stated as follows: *Work, $F_k dX_k$, is done by a system if, during a displacement of the coordinate X_k the product $F_k dX_k$ can be reflected solely in the rise of a weight.* Here are the expressions for the work associated with various systems other than chemical.

Elastic Bar. For an elastic bar in tension or compression, the intensive and extensive coordinates are stress (σ) and strain (ϵ), and the elemental work done per unit volume is

$$dW = -\sigma d\epsilon \tag{2.7}$$

where the minus sign is present due to the fact that a positive value of $d\epsilon$ means an extension of the bar, for which work must be done *on* the system. To integrate Eq. (2.7), we must know the relation between stress and strain for the particular process. In general, it is convenient to stick to a constant-temperature process, in which case the relation between stress and strain is given by Young's isothermal modulus,

$$E_T = \frac{\sigma}{\epsilon} \tag{2.8}$$

Stretched Wire. Let a wire be under tension $\mathscr{T}$. The infinitesimal work done, corresponding to a change in length dL, is

$$dW = -\mathscr{T} dL \tag{2.9}$$

This can be integrated if the relation between $\mathscr{T}$ and L for a given process is known.

Surface Film. Consider a liquid film having a surface tension $\mathscr{S}$. For an infinitesimal change in area dA the work done by the system is

$$dW = -\mathscr{S} dA \tag{2.10}$$

Reversible Cell. Consider a reversible cell of emf $\mathscr{E}$ to be connected to

a potentiometer, as shown in Fig. 2.7. The balancing potential at the point
of zero current (equilibrium) is equal, by definition, to the emf $\mathscr{E}$ of the
chemical reaction. Let the external potential difference be made infinitesi-

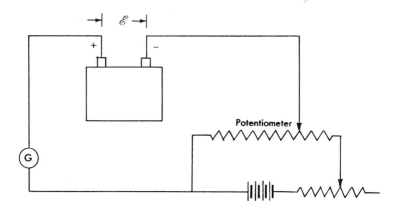

Fig. 2.7   Reversible Transfer of Electricity.

mally smaller than $\mathscr{E}$, and let a quantity of positive electrical charge,
dQ_e, be transported through the external circuit in a direction from the
positive to the negative electrode.* The work done by the cell is

$$dW = - \mathscr{E}dQ_e \qquad (2.11)$$

where the minus sign is present due to the fact that when the cell is discharging through the external circuit, dQ_e is a negative quantity, i.e., the
state of charge of the cell decreases by dQ_e. If the external potential
difference is made slightly larger than $\mathscr{E}$, electricity is transported in the
opposite direction, and charging the cell involves an increase in Q_e or a
positive dQ_e. In either case, the work done is given correctly by Eq. (2.11).

Since the current (i) equals dQ_e/dt, where t is time, Eq. (2.11) can also
be written as

$$dW = - \mathscr{E}idt$$

or

$$\frac{dW}{dt} = - \mathscr{E}i \qquad (2.12)$$

Equation (2.12) is the basis for the definition of a unit of power, the *watt*.

---

* This is the conventional description of an electrical current. Note, however, that
this is opposite to the direction of election drift.

This is the power developed by a current of 1 ampere flowing through a potential of 1 volt.

Dielectric Polarization. Let an insulator be placed between two oppositely charged parallel plates as shown in Fig. 2.8. The molecules will orient themselves because of the applied electrical field. In the interior of the material there will be no net charge, but, due to the rotation of the molecules there will be a net negative charge on the left surface and a net positive charge on the right surface. If the charges on the two plates per unit area are Q_e/A and $-Q_e/A$, the electric field intensity between the plates, before the insulator is inserted, is $\mathscr{E} = Q_e/\epsilon_0 A$, where ϵ_0 is the permittivity of free space. Because of the net charge per unit area Q'_e/A on the surface of the insulator, the field intensity in the insulator, after insertion, is $\mathscr{E} = (Q_e - Q'_e)/\epsilon_0 A$. Thus, for points inside the insulator it appears as though there were a net charge per unit area of

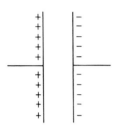

Fig. 2.8 Plate Capacitor.

$$\frac{(Q_e - Q'_e)}{A} \quad \text{and} \quad -\frac{(Q_e - Q'_e)}{A}$$

on the two plates. The size of Q'_e depends upon the material, but it can never be equal or larger than Q_e; otherwise the electric field would drop to zero. It is an experimental fact that the induced charge Q'_e is directly proportional to the inducing charge Q_e. For this reason the field intensity is written as

$$\mathscr{E} = \frac{Q_e}{\epsilon A} \tag{2.13}$$

where $\epsilon = Q_e/(Q_e - Q'_e)\epsilon_0$ is a constant characteristic of the material called the *permittivity*. The ratio ϵ/ϵ_0 is called the *dielectric constant*. The potential difference between the plates is

$$V = \mathscr{E}d = \frac{Q_e}{\epsilon A}d \tag{2.14}$$

where d is the distance between the plates.

When working with electricity, it is often desirable to store a quantity of charge. Since charge can only be placed on one body by transferring it from another body, two conducting bodies related to each other in some kind of geometric arrangement are required. Electrons can then be taken from one body, leaving it positive, and transferred to the other, making it negative. The two bodies are known as a condenser. The ratio of the potential difference between the two bodies to the charge transferred from one to the other is a measure of the ability of the pair of bodies to store charge. This ratio is called *capacitance*:

$$C = \frac{Q_e}{V} \tag{2.15}$$

Since energy is required to carry a charge from one body to another, a capacitor or condenser stores energy at the same time that it stores charge. The work dW done in moving a charge dQ_e through a potential difference V is

$$dW = VdQ_e \tag{2.16}$$

Since $V = Q_e/C$, and C is a constant dependent only on geometric factors, Eq. (2.16) can be integrated to give the work done in charging a capacitor:

$$W = \int VdQ_e = \frac{1}{C}\int_0^{Q_e} Q_e dQ_e = \frac{Q_e^2}{2C} = \frac{VQ_e}{2} \tag{2.17}$$

Magnetization. As a final example of a system in which work other than pdV is done, consider a substance in a magnetic field. Let a thin toroidal ring of material be covered with a winding, as shown in Fig. 2.9. Let A be the cross sectional area of the substance, L the mean circumference, N the number of windings, and i the current. The magnetic field is described by the field intensity, $\mathscr{H}$. In a toroidal winding, $\mathscr{H} = Ni/L$. The action of a magnetic field on a substance produces a magnetization or magnetic moment, $\mathscr{M}$, so that the total effect of the current in the winding consists of the establishment of the field, and the magnetization of matter within the field. This total effect is termed the magnetic induction, $\mathscr{B}$, and is written

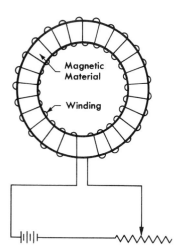

Fig. 2.9 Magnetic System.

$$\mathscr{B} = \mu_0(\mathscr{H} + \mathscr{M}) \tag{2.18}$$

where $\mathscr{M}$ is the magnetization per unit volume and μ_0 is the permeability of free space. This action can be described qualitatively by saying that B is made up of two parts: one arising directly from the "external" current in the winding, and the other arising from the "internal" currents associated with oriented spin and orbital motions of the electrons in the material. The ratio of the magnetic induction to the field strength, termed the *permeability* of the material, is $\mathscr{B}/\mathscr{H} = \mu$.

Let the current and, in time dt, the magnetic induction be changed by the amount $d\mathscr{B}$. Then, by Faraday's law of electromagnetic induction, there is induced in the winding a back emf, $\mathscr{E} = -NA(d\mathscr{B}/dt)$. During the time internal dt, a quantity of electricity, dQ_e, is transferred in the circuit, so that the work done is

$$dW = \mathscr{E}\,dQ_e = -NA\frac{d\mathscr{B}}{dt}\,dQ_e$$

$$= -NA\frac{dQ_e}{dt}\,d\mathscr{B} = -NAi\,d\mathscr{B} \tag{2.19}$$

where $dQ_e/dt = i$, the electric current. Since the magnetic field intensity is $\mathscr{H} = Ni/L$, Eq. (2.19) becomes

$$dW = -AL\mathscr{H}\,d\mathscr{B} = -V\mathscr{H}\,d\mathscr{B} \tag{2.20}$$

where $V = AL$ is the volume. Since $\mathscr{B} = \mu_0(\mathscr{H} + \mathscr{M})$, Eq. (2.20) may also be written

$$dW = -\mu_0 V\mathscr{H}\,d\mathscr{H} - \mu_0 V\mathscr{H}\,d\mathscr{M} \tag{2.21}$$

The first term on the right hand side of Eq. (2.21) represents the work done in increasing the magnetic field in a volume V of empty space; the second term represents the work done in increasing the magnetization of the material by the amount $d\mathscr{M}$. Omitting the first term, the work done by the system is thus

$$dW = -\mu_0 V\mathscr{H}\,d\mathscr{M} \tag{2.22}$$

where the minus sign indicates that work input is required to increase the magnetization of a substance (in which case $d\mathscr{M}$ is positive).

The preceding development has shown that in each case it is possible to write the expression for the work done in the form of

$$dW = F_k\,dX_k \tag{2.23}$$

where F_k is a generalized force, and dX_k is a generalized displacement. Although the pdV type of work is the most frequently encountered, it is well to keep in mind that there are other ways in which work can be done. The following table summarizes the discussion by giving the conjugate pairs F_k and dX_k for each type of system.

TABLE 2.1

Generalized Work

System	Generalized force	Generalized displacement	Work done
Chemical	Pressure, p	Volume, dV	$p\,dV$
Elastic bar	Stress, σ	Strain, $d\epsilon$	$-\sigma\,d\epsilon$
Stretched wire	Tension, $\mathscr{T}$	Extension, dL	$-\mathscr{T}\,dL$
Reversible cell	Emf, $\mathscr{E}$	Charge, dQ_e	$-\mathscr{E}\,dQ_e$
Condenser	Voltage, V	Charge, dQ_e	$-V\,dQ_e$
Magnetic	Magnetic field, $\mathscr{H}$	Magnetization, $d\mathscr{M}$	$-\mathscr{H}\,d\mathscr{M}$

Example 2.4. The capacitance of a parallel-plate condenser formed by two aluminium sheets separated by a layer of air is 0.0885 μf. What is the charge on either plate and the energy stored when the potential difference between plates is 100 volts?

Solution. From Eq. (2.15),

$$Q_e = CV$$

In the mks system of units Q_e, C, and V are in coulombs, farads, and volts respectively, Thus,

$$Q_e = (0.0885 \times 10^{-6})(100) = 8.85 \times 10^{-6} \text{ coulombs}$$

The energy stored, expressed in joules, is

$$W = \frac{VQ_e}{2} = \frac{(100)(8.85 \times 10^{-6})}{2} = 442.5 \times 10^{-6} \text{ joules}$$

Example 2.5. Experimentally, we find that, for many paramagnetic substances, the magnetization is directly proportional to the magnetic intensity and inversely proportional to the Kelvin temperature, i.e.

$$\mathscr{M} = C\frac{\mathscr{H}}{T}$$

where C is a constant known as Curie's constant. Show that, if Curie's law is obeyed, the work done during a constant-temperature reversible process from state 1 to state 2 is

$$W = \frac{\mu_0 VT}{2C}(\mathscr{M}_1^2 - \mathscr{M}_2^2)$$

Solution. From Eq. (2.22),

$$dW = -\mu_0 V\mathscr{H}\,d\mathscr{M}$$

Using Curie's law, this becomes

$$dW = -\frac{\mu_0 VT\mathscr{M}}{C}\,d\mathscr{M}$$

Integration between states 1 and 2 gives

$$W = \frac{\mu_0 VT}{2C} (\mathcal{M}_1{}^2 - \mathcal{M}_2{}^2)$$

PROBLEMS

2.1. Discuss the use of absolute pressure and gage pressure when evaluating the work of a system by $\int p\,dV$.

2.2. During an expansion process, the volume of a gas changes from 4 cu ft to 6 cu ft while the pressure changes according to the relation

$$p = 30V + 100$$

where p = psia and V = cu ft. Determine the work done by the gas. Give the answer in foot-pounds force and in kilowatt-hours.

2.3. A gas in a cylinder is compressed frictionlessly, from 15 psia and 1 cu ft to 100 psia, in such a manner that pV = constant. Determine the work done. Also, sketch the process on p–V coordinates.

2.4. A gas undergoes a process according to the relation pV^n = constant. Show that the work done between states 1 and 2 is

$$W = \frac{p_2 V_2 - p_1 V_1}{1 - n}$$

2.5. A balloon, initially collapsed, is slowly filled with helium, forming a sphere 25 ft in diameter. The helium comes from a pressure tank, and the filling process is so slow that the gas temperature and pressure remain equal to atmospheric values (60 °F and 14.7 psia). Determine the work done by the tank-balloon system.

2.6. Find the work done by a pound of gas during a reversible constant-temperature expansion from an initial specific volume v_1 to a final specific volume v_2 if the equation state of the gas is $p(v - b) = RT$ where b and R are constants.

2.7. Show that, for a van der Waals gas which has the equation of state

$$\left(p + \frac{a}{v^2}\right)(v - b) = RT$$

the work done at constant temperature per unit mass of gas is

$$RT \ln \frac{v_2 - b}{v_1 - b} - a\left(\frac{1}{v_1} - \frac{1}{v_2}\right)$$

where v_1 and v_2 denote the initial and final specific volumes respectively. Hint: Solve for p in van der Waals' equation, then make use of $\int p\,dv$.

2.8. A gas having the equation of state

$$pv = RT + b(T)p$$

is expanded isothermally and reversibly from an initial specific volume v_1 to a final specific volume v_2. Show that the work done per unit mass of gas is

$$RT \ln \frac{v_2 - b(T)}{v_1 - b(T)}$$

2.9. Work is done by a system on its surroundings if the sole effect could be reduced to the lifting of a weight. Discuss the meaning of *sole effect* in the thermodynamic definition for work. For example, water can be caused to boil and the steam used to drive an engine which raises a weight. Is the boiling of water classified as work, or are there other effects between the system and the surroundings?

2.10. (a) Show that, when the pressure on a solid is increased reversibly and isothermally, the work is given by

$$W = -\int_{p_1}^{p_2} \frac{V}{B} p \, dp$$

where $B = -V(\partial p/\partial V)_T$ is the isothermal bulk modulus. If V and B are taken to be constants, this may be integrated to give

$$W = -\frac{V}{2B} (p_2{}^2 - p_1{}^2)$$

where p_1 and p_2 are the initial and final pressures respectively. (b) Determine the work required to compress isothermally 1 lbm of copper at 70 °F from 1 atm to 1000 atm. For copper, $1/B = 5.9$ times $10^{-8}(\text{lbf/in}^2)^{-1}$, and the specific volume at 60° and 1 atm is 1.82 times 10^{-3} ft^3/lbm.

2.11. Mechanical work is the result of action of a force on a moving boundary of a system, and its magnitude is given by pdV. Give an example where $dV = 0$, yet $W \neq 0$.

2.12. A 6-cylinder, 4-stroke gasoline engine is run at a speed of 2500 rev/min. The indicator card of a cylinder has an area of 3.60 sq. in and a length of 2.42 in. The spring constant is 80 psi/in. The cylinder bore is 6 in., and the piston stroke is 6.5 in. Determine: (a) the mean effective pressure and, (b) the indicated horsepower of the engine.

2.13. A spring whose natural length is 16 in. requires a force of 20 lbf to extend its length 1 in. What is the work done when its length is extended from 15 to 18 in., assuming the spring to be stressed reversibly and isothermally? Represent the work on rectangular coordinates, using force as the ordinate, and distance as the abscissa.

2.14. Gas, initially at 50 psia, is contained in a cylinder fitted with a frictionless movable piston, as shown in Fig. 2.10. The piston is forced against the gas by a

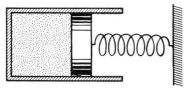

Fig. 2.10

spring which exerts a force directly proportional to the volume of the gas. In addition, atmospheric pressure of 14.7 psia acts on the spring side of the piston. Determine the work done by the gas when it expands from 0.5 cu ft to 2.5 cu ft.

2.15. The equation of state of an elastic bar is

$$\mathcal{T} = K \left(\frac{L}{L_0} - \frac{L_0^2}{L^2} \right) T$$

where $\mathcal{T}$ is the tension, L is the length, T is the temperature, K is a constant, and L_0 is the length at zero tension. Determine the work required to compress the bar isothermally to one-half its length.

2.16. A double soap film with liquid in between is stretched across a U-shaped wire, as shown in Fig. 2.11. If the surface tension is $\mathcal{S}$, and one side of the film

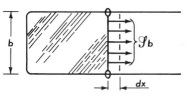

Fig. 2.11

is movable by means of a wire of length b, show that the work done during an infinitesimal displacement of the wire is $dW = -\mathcal{S}dA$, where $\mathcal{S}$ is the surface tension (force/area), and A the surface area of the film ($dA = 2bdx$).

2.17. An electrical battery, thermally insulated, is being discharged at constant pressure (atmospheric) and constant volume. During a 1-hr test, it is found that while a current of 50 amps at 2 volts flows, the temperature increases from 68 °F to 90 °F. Determine the change in internal energy of the cell during the period of operation. The work done during a discharge is

$$W = \int_{Q_{e_1}}^{Q_{e_2}} \mathcal{E}dQ_e = -\int_1^2 \mathcal{E}idt$$

where $\mathcal{E}$ = emf, Q_e = quantity of electricity, i = current, and t = time.

2.18. The potential difference between a pair of parallel conducting plates of area A separated by a distance d is

$$V = \frac{Q_e}{\epsilon A} d$$

where Q_e is the charge and ϵ is the permittivity of the insulating medium between the plates. What is the capacitance of the plates, and what effect does a larger value of ϵ have on the ability of the plates to store charge?

2.19. The equation of state for a paramagnetic substance may be written

$$\mathscr{M} = C \frac{\mathscr{H}}{T}$$

where C is a constant known as Curie's constant. Determine the work done in changing the magnetic intensity isothermally from $\mathscr{H}_1$ to $\mathscr{H}_2$.

2.20. What is the capacity of two concentric cylindrical electrodes in a vacuum tube if the potential difference between concentric cylinders is

$$V = \frac{Q_e}{2\pi\epsilon_0 l} \ln \frac{r_2}{r_1}$$

where l is the length, and r_1 and r_2 are the inner and outer radii? The electrodes are 0.10 m long and 0.01 m and 0.02 m in diameter respectively. Use the mks system of units, with a value of $\epsilon_0 = 8.85$ times 10^{-12} farads/meter for the permittivity of a vacuum.

CHAPTER 3

Zeroth Law of Thermodynamics

3.1 Temperature

Although temperature is a familiar property of systems, it is difficult to define, because the definition must be arrived at in an indirect way (through the notion of equality of temperature).

Let two bodies, one hot and one cold, be placed in contact with each other, while isolated from all other bodies. In time, the hot body becomes colder, or the cold body becomes hotter, or both bodies undergo a change. Finally, all changes in the properties of the bodies cease and the bodies are said to be in thermal equilibrium with each other. The definition of temperature equality may be stated as follows: Two systems have *equal* temperatures if there are no changes in their properties when they are brought into contact. Otherwise stated: Two systems which are in thermal equilibrium have a property in common; this property is called *temperature*. Note that what has been defined is really equality of temperature, and that it is the invariance of properties which implies the equality of temperature. The definition must not be reversed; it does *not* imply that when two systems are equal in temperature, no further changes result from their communication. For example, water and sulphuric acid, initially at the same temperature, will rise in temperature when mixed.

3.2   Zeroth Law of Thermodynamics

Let the concept of temperature equality be applied to three systems: A, B, and C as shown in Fig. 3.1. For example, system A may consist of a mass

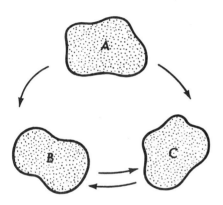

Fig. 3.1   Illustration for Zeroth Law.

of gas enclosed in a rigid vessel fitted with a pressure gage. If there is no change of pressure when this system is brought into contact with system B, a block of copper, then the two systems are equal in temperature (of course, systems A and B are assumed not to react with each other chemically or electrically). Experiment shows that if system A is brought into contact with a third system, C, again with no change of properties, then systems B and C will show no change in their properties when brought into contact (provided they do not react with each other chemically or electrically). Therefore, B and C must be equal in temperature. This leads to the following postulate, known as the *Zeroth law* of thermodynamics: *If two systems are each equal in temperature to a third, they are equal in temperature to each other.* Although the axiom seems obvious, it is *not* derivable from other observations of nature; for this reason it is given the status of a law. The student will realize that this law is really the basis of all temperature measurement.

3.3   Mathematical Establishment of Temperature

The preceding sections have established the notion of temperature by focusing attention on its equality (or inequality) rather than by any direct definition. This is because a concise definition of temperature is difficult to express, and, for pedagogical reasons, it is advisable to introduce temperature by means of working examples. There is, however, a more elegant (but also more abstract) way of defining temperature. It is based on mathematical argument, and is arrived at in the following manner.

Consider two isolated bodies, A and B, each in an equilibrium state, and assume, for simplicity, that they consist of two masses of gas m_A and m_B. Let the two bodies have volumes V_A, V_B, and pressures p_A, p_B, respectively. It is quite clear that V_A alone will not determine p_A, for if V_A is fixed, p_A may take on different values. Similarly, p_B is not determined by V_B alone. Let the two bodies be brought into thermal contact. In general, changes will take place in both until, eventually, the composite system attains a new state of equilibrium. For example, if V_A and V_B are fixed, p_A and p_B will generally change until they finally reach an equilibrium value in such a way that if one is known the other is always found to be of a related value. In other words, the equilibrium values of p_A, p_B, V_A, and V_B cannot be varied independently but are related by the functional relationship

$$F_{AB}(p_A, p_B, V_A, V_B) = 0 \qquad (3.1)$$

Consider now a third body C, and let it be in thermal equilibrium with A. The conditions under which A and C are in equilibrium are then expressed by the relation

$$F_{AC}(p_A, p_C, V_A, V_C) = 0 \qquad (3.2)$$

Eqs. (3.1) and (3.2) may each be solved for p_A:

$$p_A = f_{AB}(p_B, V_A, V_B) \qquad (3.3)$$

$$p_A = f_{AC}(p_C, V_A, V_C) \qquad (3.4)$$

so that equating the two expressions for p_A gives

$$f_{AB}(p_B, V_A, V_B) = f_{AC}(p_C, V_A, V_C) \qquad (3.5)$$

In the foregoing, the two bodies B and C are separately in equilibrium with the body A. According to the Zeroth law of thermodynamics, they must be in equilibrium with one another, so that Eq. (3.5) must be equivalent to the relation

$$F_{BC}(p_B, p_C, V_B, V_C) = 0 \qquad (3.6)$$

It is seen that, although Eq. (3.5) contains the variable V_A, Eq. (3.6) does not. If the two equations are to be equivalent, it can only mean that the functions f_{AB} and f_{AC} contain V_A in such a way that it cancels out on both sides of Eq. (3.5). In other words, f_{AB} and f_{AC} must be of the form

$$f_{AB} = \phi(V_A)\theta_2(p_B, V_B) + \eta(V_A) \qquad (3.7)$$

$$f_{AC} = \phi(V_A)\theta_3(p_C, V_C) + \eta(V_A) \tag{3.8}$$

so that Eq. (3.5) becomes, after cancellation,

$$\theta_2(p_B, V_B) = \theta_3(p_C, V_C) \tag{3.9}$$

Now, Eqs. (3.4) and (3.8) may be combined to give

$$p_A = f_{AC}(p_C, V_A, V_C)$$
$$= \phi(V_A)\theta_3(p_C, V_C) + \eta(V_A)$$

or

$$\theta_3(p_C, V_C) = \frac{p_A}{\phi(V_A)} - \frac{\eta(V_A)}{\phi(V_A)} = \theta_1(p_A, V_A) \tag{3.10}$$

Finally, Eqs. (3.9) and (3.10) give

$$\theta_1(p_A, V_A) = \theta_2(p_B, V_B) = \theta_3(p_C, V_C) \tag{3.11}$$

Equation (3.11) states that, for any substance, it is possible to find a function $\theta(p, V)$ which has the same value for all systems in thermal equilibrium with one another. Stated otherwise, each function $\theta(p, V)$ is equal to a common parameter t:

$$\theta_1(p_A, V_A) = \theta_2(p_B, V_B) = \theta_3(p_C, V_C) = t \tag{3.12}$$

The quantity t is called *empirical temperature*. It is defined by Eq. (3.12), though not numerically since a quantity $t' = g(t)$ where g is any single-valued function that would do equally well. What has been established, however, is the fact that, by means of the Zeroth law, *there exists a function of the state of a substance which takes on the same value for all substances in thermal equilibrium with one another. This function is called the temperature.*

3.4   Temperature Scale

The temperatures of a group of bodies may be compared by bringing a particular body A (henceforth called a thermometer) into contact with each in turn. Such a body should possess an easily observable characteristic (termed a thermometric property) such as the length of a mercury column in a capillary tube, the pressure of a gas in a closed vessel, or the resistance of a platinum wire.

The first step in establishing a temperature scale is to assign numerical values to certain easily reproducible temperatures. The reproducible temperatures selected as reference points are usually (1) the *ice point*, which is the equilibrium temperature of ice and air-saturated water under a pressure of 14.696 psia, and (2) the *steam point*, which is the equilibrium temperature of pure liquid water in contact with its vapor at 14.696 psia.

They are chosen as reference temperatures because they can be accurately reproduced in the laboratory. There are two common scales in use: the Fahrenheit and the Centigrade (or Celsius). On the Fahrenheit scale the ice-point and the steam point are assigned the numbers 32 and 212 respectively, with 180 sub-divisions in between. On the Centigrade scale the ice-point and the steam point are assigned the numbers 0 and 100 respectively, with 100 sub-divisions in between. It is easily seen that the relationship between Fahrenheit and Centigrade temperatures, t_F and t_C is

$$t_F = \frac{9}{5} t_C + 32 \qquad (3.13)$$

$$t_C = \frac{5}{9} (t_F - 32) \qquad (3.14)$$

The fraction 9/5 comes of course, from the ratio of the sub-divisions 180/100.

So far, only temperatures between the ice-point and the steam-point have been defined. But the temperature range can be extended beyond the fixed points by extrapolation; the uniform graduation of the glass tube can obviously be continued above and below the fixed points. In practice, the extrapolation is limited by the fact that mercury freezes at $-38\ °F$, and glass becomes unsuitable as casing material at high temperature. These difficulties are met by adopting different fluids and casing materials, or by using a thermometric property other than thermal expansion.

It should be remarked further that prior to 1954 each of the above scales was based on two fixed points, but that the Tenth Conference on Weights and Measures in 1954 redefined the Centigrade scale in terms of a single fixed point and the magnitude of the degree. The single fixed point is the triple-point of water, which is assigned the value 0.01 °C. (The triple-point of a substance is that state in which solid, liquid, and vapor can exist in equilibrium.) For most purposes, however, there is essential agreement between the old and the new temperature scales.

3.5 Ideal Gas Scale

Since not all materials expand linearly with temperature, different thermometers made of different substances indicate somewhat different temperatures, except at the ice and steam points. It is therefore desirable to conceive of a temperature scale which is independent of the properties of a particular substance. It will be seen in Chap. 7 that this can be done on the basis of the second law of thermodynamics; the temperature scale so arrived at is called the thermodynamic scale. It is possible at this stage, however, to define a temperature scale, identical with the thermodynamic scale, yet not based on the second law of thermodynamics. There exists a group of substances (all gases) such as hydrogen, helium, oxygen and nitrogen, which exhibit excellent agreement among themselves when used as a thermometric substance. The standard centigrade scale is defined on this basis.

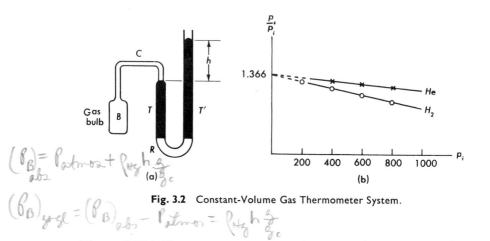

Fig. 3.2 Constant-Volume Gas Thermometer System.

Figure 3.2(a) illustrates a constant volume gas thermometer. The gas bulb B connects through a glass capillary C to a U-tube arrangement T–T' by means of a flexible hose R at the bottom. The gas in B is kept at constant volume by keeping the mercury level in tube T at the tip of the capillary. This is done by raising or lowering tube T'. The difference in height between the two mercury columns is then the gage pressure.

Let an initial quantity of gas be contained in the gas bulb, such that when the bulb is at the ice point the pressure p_i is equivalent to 1000 mm Hg abs. Let the bulb be brought to the steam point and p_s be measured. Let the ratio p_s/p_i be determined and labeled $(p_s/p_i)_{1000}$. Now, withdraw some gas from the gas bulb, such that at the ice point the pressure is equivalent to 900 mm Hg abs. Bring the bulb to the steam point, record the pressure at the steam point, and determine the ratio $(p_s/p_i)_{900}$. Let this procedure be repeated with more and more gas withdrawn from the bulb and p_i decreasing steadily. If the values of $(p_s/p_i)_{1000}$, $(p_s/p_i)_{900}$, $(p_s/p_i)_{800}$ . . . are plotted against p_i, they form a straight line which when extrapolated, gives a value of $(p_s/p_i) = 1.366$ at $p_i = 0$. Moreover, if the experiment is repeated with a different gas, another straight line is obtained, and this straight line, when extrapolated, will give the same value of $p_s/p_i = 1.366$ at $p_i = 0$. Figure 3.2(b) shows the plot of the data for two different gases, hydrogen and helium. Note that the extrapolation of the data yields a common intercept. A temperature scale independent of the properties of any individual substance may thus be defined by writing

$$\left\{ \frac{T_s}{T_i} = \lim_{p_i \to 0} \frac{p_s}{p_i} = 1.366 \right. \tag{3.15}$$

$$\left. T_s - T_i = 180 \right. \tag{3.16}$$

The above defines the commonly known _Rankine_ or _Absolute Fahrenheit_ scale. The solution of the set of equations is

$$\left\{ T_s = 671.7\,^\circ\text{R} \right. \tag{3.17}$$

$$\left. T_i = 491.7\,^\circ\text{R} \right. \tag{3.18}$$

Similarly, if the interval between steam and ice points is assigned a value 100, then

$$\left\{ \frac{T_s}{T_i} = \lim_{p_i \to 0} \frac{p_s}{p_i} = 1.366 \right. \tag{3.19}$$

$$\left. T_s - T_i = 100 \right. \tag{3.20}$$

Equations (3.19) and (3.20) define the _Kelvin_ or _Absolute Centigrade_ scale; their solution gives

$$\left\{ T_s = 373.2\,^\circ\text{K} \right. \tag{3.21}$$

$$\left. T_i = 273.2\,^\circ\text{K} \right. \tag{3.22}$$

The relation between absolute and ordinary temperature is

$$\text{Degrees Rankine} = \text{Degrees Fahrenheit} + 459.7 \tag{3.23}$$

$$\text{Degrees Kelvin} = \text{Degrees Centigrade} + 273.2 \tag{3.24}$$

In both the Rankine and Kelvin scales, a temperature T, other than those of the steam and ice points, is found by making a series of measurements of pressure p and setting

$$\frac{T}{T_i} = \lim_{p_i \to 0} \frac{p}{p_i} \tag{3.25}$$

Equation (3.25) establishes T uniquely, since T_i is already known.

3.6 Heat

Heat is a form of energy defined in terms of temperature. Experience shows that when two bodies originally at different temperatures are brought into contact, they come to equilibrium and reach a common temperature. It can be said that the two bodies have influenced each other; in other words _heat is the interaction between systems which occurs by virtue of their temperature difference._ Heat is transferred across a boundary from a system at higher temperature to a system at lower temperature, and can be measured by the mass of a prescribed material which is raised in temperature from one level to another.

The definition implies the important fact that heat, like work, is a *transient* quantity which can be identified *only as it crosses the boundary* of a system which is interacting with the surroundings or with other systems. Heat is not a property possessed by a system, and its differential is, therefore, not exact. For this reason, if Q denotes heat, its differential will be written as dQ in this text, and the total heat transferred during a process in which a system passes from state 1 to state 2 will be written as

$$Q = \int_1^2 dQ = Q_{1-2} \qquad (3.26)$$

and never as

$$Q = \int_1^2 dQ = Q_2 - Q_1$$

To elaborate, consider a hot block of copper as one system and cold water in a beaker as another system. It is recognized that originally neither system contains any heat, since there are no changes taking place within each (isolated) system. Let the copper block be placed in the water: the two systems are then in thermal communication, and heat is transferred from the copper block to the water. However, when equilibrium temperature is established, heat transfer no longer exists, and neither of the systems contain any heat at the conclusion of the process (just as neither of them contained any heat prior to the process). In other words, heat can never be said to be in a system *before* or *after* a change of its state. It only exists as something which crosses the boundary of a system while a change is taking place within the system as the result of a temperature difference between the system and its surroundings.

By convention, if, in a heat interaction, a system receives heat, Q is positive. If the system surrenders heat, Q is negative. Positive Q is represented by an arrow directed into the system; negative Q by an arrow directed outward from the system. Figure 3.3 illustrates a positive Q. If, during a process, a system is separated from its surroundings or from other systems by an insulator that renders the heat transfer negligible, the process is termed *adiabatic*. The distinguishing feature of an adiabatic process is the formula $Q = 0$.

The unit of heat in the Engineering-English system is the Btu (British thermal

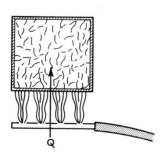

Fig. 3.3 Positive Heat Transfer.

unit). It was originally defined as *the heat required to raise one pound of water by one degree Fahrenheit.* Similarly, the unit of heat in the metric system is the calorie. This is *the amount of heat required to raise one gram of water by one degree Centigrade.* Because a slightly different quantity of heat is necessary at different points of the temperature scale to raise the temperature of a unit mass of water by one degree, it should be noted that the unit used most often is the 60-degree Btu, for which the temperature rise must be from 60 °F to 61 °F. A newer and more accurate definition of the unit of heat, however, is in terms of electrical energy: *1 I.T. calorie = 4.1867 absolute joules.* This is accomplished by means of the *equivalence of heat and mechanical work,* known as the first law of thermodynamics and discussed in the next chapter.

A few comments are appropriate at the conclusion of the present chapter. It was previously stated that thermodynamics is essentially the science dealing with the relations between properties of a system and the quantities *heat* and *work.* These quantities have certain similarities in that neither work nor heat are properties of a system, but both are transient quantities, appearing only as boundary interactions during changes of state within the system. They are spoken of as energy *in transition* and cannot be used to describe the state of a system, though they serve to describe the process undergone by the system. Their essential difference, however, is established by their definitions: *Heat is an interaction caused by a temperature difference between a system and its surroundings; work is done by a system during a process if the sole effect of the system on its surroundings can be reduced to the lifting of a weight.* This will be made clearer by the second law of thermodynamics (Chapter 7).

PROBLEMS

3.1. In the mathematical establishment of temperature, it was shown that

$$\theta_1(p_A, v_A) = \theta_2(p_B, v_B) = \ldots = t$$

defines a parameter t having the property of being constant for all bodies in thermal equilibrium. This means that for a given value of t, p and v cannot both vary arbitrarily, since $t = \theta(p, v)$. In general, it is customary to fix either p or v and let the variation of the other be a measure of t. For example, if v is fixed, p could be used as a measure of the temperature by writing

$$t = ap+b$$

where a and b are constants. On the other hand, if p is held constant, v could be used as a measure of temperature by writing

$$t = cv+d$$

Discuss the constant volume and constant pressure gas thermometers in light of the above statements, and how a temperature scale may be established, i.e., how the constants a, b, c, and d may be determined.

3.2. To establish a temperature scale, a system (Fig. 3.4) with coordinates x and y is chosen as a thermometer, and a set of rules is adopted for assigning a numerical value to the temperature associated with each isotherm. The simplest procedure is to keep one coordinate (y) constant and let the other (x) vary. The temperature associated with each isotherm then becomes a function of x which is called the *thermometric property*. Given the following list of thermometric properties, name the thermometer associated with each, and discuss the merits of each thermometer: pressure, volume, electric resistance, thermal emf, and length.

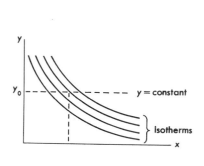

Fig. 3.4

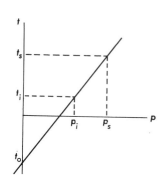

Fig. 3.5

3.3. Referring to Fig. 3.5 temperatures are measured on the constant-volume gas thermometer scale by using a linear relationship between temperature and pressure.

(a) Show that

$$t - t_0 = \left(\frac{t_s - t_i}{p_s - p_i}\right)p = \frac{t_s - t_i}{p_s / p_i}\left(\frac{p}{p_i}\right)$$

where the subscripts i, s, and o denote respectively conditions at the ice-point, and at the steam-point, and the temperature at which the gas pressure is zero.

(b) If $p_s / p_i = 1.3661$, and $t = 32$ for $p = p_i$, what is the value of t_0 on the Fahrenheit scale?

3.4. The following problem is based on Lord Kelvin's suggestion of a logarithmic scale. The pressure of an ideal gas kept at constant volume is given by the relation

$$p = KT$$

where T is the Kelvin temperature and K is a constant. Define a temperature scale t in terms of the ideal gas temperature such that $t_i = 0$, $t_s = 100$, and $t \to -\infty$ when $T \to 0$.

3.5. (a) A certain temperature scale has the ice point at zero and the steam point at 80. What is the temperature of absolute zero?

(b) A temperature scale of the form

$$t = ae^x + b$$

is chosen between 0 °C and 100 °C, where a and b are constants. Determine, on this scale, the temperatures corresponding to 50 °C and -50 °C of a linear scale.

3.6. The length of the mercury column in a certain mercury-in-glass thermo-meter is 5 cm when the thermometer is at the ice-point, and 25 cm when the thermometer is at the steam point. Consider this length as the property x and a scale t', to be defined by the quadratic equation

$$t' = ax^2 + b$$

where $t' = 0°$ at the ice-point and $t' = 100°$ at the steam point. Compare the t' scale with the centigrade scale t, where t is linearly defined in terms of x (with the same values as t' at the ice and steam points). Make the comparison by plotting t' versus t (4 to 5 points are sufficient).

3.7. (a). Convert 110 °F to °C, -40 °C to °F, 100 °F to °R, 60 °C to °K, 1600 °R to °K, and 370 °K to °F. (b). At what temperature will a system have the same numerical value on the Centigrade and Fahrenheit scales? on the Rankin and Kelvin scales?

3.8. Two mercury-in-glass thermometers are accurately calibrated at 32 °F and 212 °F. One has a tube of constant diameter; the other has a tube of conical bore. Both thermometers have the length between 32 °F and 212 °F uniformly divided. At what temperature on the conical bore thermometer will the reading deviate the most from that of the constant diameter thermometer?

3.9. Suppose that instead of defining temperature t as a linear function of some thermometric property X, a temperature t' is defined according to the relation

$$t' = a + bX + cX^2$$

where $a = 1$, $b = 0.1$, and $c = 0.05$. Let the value of X be 1.0 at the ice point, and 1.2 at the steam point. Let the value of t' be 32° at the ice point, and 212° at the steam point. If equal increments in temperature correspond to equal incre-ments in the thermometric property, what is the temperature when $X = 1.1$?

3.10. The emf $\mathscr{E}$ of a thermocouple having one junction kept at the ice point and the other junction at a temperature t measured by a Centigrade mercury-in-glass thermometer is

$$\mathscr{E} = 0.20t - 5 \times 10^{-4}t^2$$

where $\mathscr{E}$ is in millivolts.

(a) Sketch the graph of $\mathscr{E}$ versus t by computing the emf at $t = -100$ °C, 0 °C, 100 °C, etc.

(b) Let the emf $\mathscr{E}$ be taken as a thermometric property, and a temperature scale t' be defined by the relation

$$t' = a \,\mathscr{E} + b$$

such that $t' = 0°$ at the ice point and $t' = 100°$ at the steam point. Sketch the graph of $\mathscr{E}$ versus t' by finding the numerical values of a and b.

(c) Sketch the graph of t' versus t by finding the value of t' at $t = -100$ °C, 0 °C, 100 °C, etc. What kind of a scale is the t' scale?

3.11. A temperature scale is to be established by assuming that the change in volume of a gas is proportional to both the volume at a fixed standard temperature and the temperature change:

$$\Delta V = \beta V_0 \, \Delta t$$

If $V_0 = V_i$, the volume at the ice point, $t_0 = t_i = 0$ at the ice point, and $\beta = 1/273$, show that the lowest temperature on such a scale is $t = -273$.

3.12. A mercury-in-glass thermometer was originally calibrated at 32 °F and 212 °F by full immersion. It is dipped into a liquid to the 50 °F mark. The temperature shown by the thermometer is 175 °F, while the stem temperature is 68 °F. What is the true temperature of the liquid? The coefficient of thermal expansion of mercury is 96×10^{-6} cu ft/cu ft °F, and that of glass is 1.8×10^{-6} ft/ft °F.

3.13. A certain thermometer, using pressure as the thermometric property, gives values to p of 1.86 and 6.81 at the ice-point and the steam-point respectively. The temperatures of the ice-point and the steam-point are assigned the numbers 32 and 212 respectively. Determine the temperature corresponding to $p = 2.5$, if the temperature t is defined in terms of p by the relation

$$t = a \ln p + b$$

where a and b are constants.

3.14. Illustrate and discuss, by means of a concrete example, the following statements: (a) heat does not inevitably cause a temperature rise, (b) heat is not always present when a temperature rise occurs. Is it correct to speak of the heat contained in a body?

3.15. What is meant by an adiabatic wall? A diathermic wall? Give several examples of the use of each type of wall in engineering application.

3.16. Is $\int dQ$ dependent or independent of path? Discuss this in relation with the heating of a body from an initial temperature to a final temperature, first, at a constant pressure, then at a constant volume. Should an elemental heat flow be written as dQ or $\not dQ$?

3.17. (a) Which of the following forms of energy may properly be called heat? (1) the energy in the hot exhaust gases of an automobile engine, (2) the energy received by the earth from the sun, (3) the energy in a warm radiator, (4) the energy which passes from the hot gases to the water in the cylinder jacket of an automobile engine. (b) In each of the following cases, indicate with +, −, or 0 whether work or heat is present, or is non-existent for the system in question: (1) an air compressor, (2) a pressure cooker, (3) an automobile engine, (4) a storage battery.

CHAPTER 4

First Law of Thermodynamics

The field of thermodynamics is governed entirely by three so-called laws: the *first*, *second*, and *third* laws of thermodynamics. These three laws, along with the *zeroth* law, constitute the foundation upon which the science of thermodynamics is built. They are not theorems, in the sense that they can be proven, but are really postulates based on experimental fact; their chief claim to acceptance is that they have never been disproved by experience. The zeroth law, presented in the last chapter, is the basis of temperature measurement. The first law, to be introduced in this chapter, is concerned with the definition and conservation of energy as applied to systems which undergo changes of state resulting from transfers of heat and work across their boundaries.

4.1 Cycle

A system is said to undergo a cyclic change or cycle if, in passing through a series of states, it returns to its initial state. Consider, for example, a quantity of water placed in a vessel as in Fig. 4.1(a). Let the water be stirred by a paddle-wheel actuated by a falling weight. Choosing the water

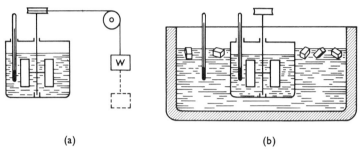

(a)   (b)

Fig. 4.1 Joule's Experiment.

as the thermodynamic system, we see that work is added to the system and that the temperature of the system rises. The amount of work can be measured by the distance through which the weight falls, and, since work is done on the system, this work will be negative.

After the water is allowed to come to rest, let the vessel containing the water be brought into contact with a bath. In this way, the system is restored to its initial state, thus completing a cycle. While in contact with the bath, the heat flow to the bath may be measured by the amount of ice meltage. Since heat has crossed the boundary of the system into the surroundings (bath), the heat will be negative. From this experiment, it is seen that when a system is taken through a complete cycle, the summation of either work or heat quantities has a value different from zero. Thus, expressed mathematically,

$$\oint dW \neq 0, \quad \oint dQ \neq 0.$$

4.2 First Law of Thermodynamics

Experiments similar to the above were carried out by Joule (1843) with various systems and various sorts of work. He found that, in each case, the net quantity of heat (Btu) to be removed from the system was directly proportional to the net quantity of work (ft lbf) done on the system during the cycle. In equation form, this is expressed as

$$-\oint dQ \propto -\oint dW$$

or

$$-\oint dQ = -\frac{1}{J}\oint dW \tag{4.1}$$

where J is a constant (known as the mechanical equivalent of heat) whose value depends only on the units selected for Q and W.

The first law of thermodynamics is a generalization of this result that covers all cyclic changes, including those during which a net amount of heat is supplied to the system and a net amount of work is done by the system.* Many cyclic experiments have been carried out by workers since Joule, and, although the number of systems and processes which have been investigated has obviously not been exhausted, the uniformity of the outcome has led Eq. (4.1) to be regarded as universally true. The latter, when written as

$$\oint dW = J\oint dQ \tag{4.2}$$

then becomes the statement for the first law of thermodynamics: *Whenever a system undergoes a cyclic change, the algebraic sum of the work transfers is proportional to the algebraic sum of the heat transfers.*

The first law, adopted as an axiom, is one of the foundation stones upon which the structure of classical thermodynamics is built. Joule's experiments, and those of others who came after him all lend support to this law. They *do not*, however, constitute a proof, for a proof can only be formulated if the first law is shown to be a consequence of some broader and more general proposition about nature. Since no instance of contradiction has ever been found, Eq. (4.2) has been accepted as fact. This is what is meant by the statement in Chap. 1 that classical thermodynamics is an *axiomatic* science built on a number of premises.

4.3 Mechanical Equivalence of Heat

Joule's constant, J, expresses the number of work units (ft lbf for example) equivalent to one heat unit (Btu for example). It enables heat quantities

---

* For example, a gas within a cylinder fitted with a movable piston may have a source of heat applied to it. The gas expands, pushing the piston and thereby doing work. The gas may be returned to its original state by having a heat sink, i.e. a body at lower temperature applied to it.

to be expressed in work units and work quantities to be expressed in heat units. While this does not imply that heat and work are the same thing, it does establish the exchange rate between the two. Therefore, once the first law of thermodynamics has been established, the need for *separate* units disappears. In other words, there is no longer justification for two sets of absolute standards, e.g. the primary standards of mass, length, and time, to which the unit of work may be referred, and a standard thermometer and mass of water, to which the unit of heat may be referred. To elaborate: The unit of heat (such as the Btu or the calorie) was originally defined without reference to the unit of work. For example, the Btu was defined as the amount of heat required to raise the temperature of one pound of water from 60 °F to 61 °F under a pressure of 1 atmosphere. The first law of thermodynamics, which relates heat and work directly, makes it possible to define the unit of heat in terms of the unit of work and vice versa. Thus, in 1929 the First International Steam Table Conference defined a heat unit (the calorie) in terms of a work unit (the watt-hour). The latest standardization, laid down in 1948 by the Ninth General Conference on Weights and Measures, defines a heat unit in terms of the absolute joule, so that a heat unit now depends *only* on the primary standards of mass, length, and time. In terms of the Engineering-English system of units, the net result is that 1 Btu = 778.16 ft lbf. This gives

$$J = 778.16 \text{ ft lbf/Btu} \qquad (4.3)$$

However, throughout this text, the more convenient value of $J = 778$ ft lbf/Btu will be used.

Since no fundamental distinction now exists between the unit of heat and the unit of work, the J can be dropped from Eq. (4.2), and the first law of thermodynamics may be written, using any set of *consistent* units, as

$$\oint dW = \oint dQ \qquad (4.4)$$

or

$$\oint (dQ - dW) = 0. \qquad (4.5)$$

Example 4.1. During a cycle, composed of 4 processes, the heat transfers were +23 Btu, −4 Btu, −10 Btu, and +2 Btu. Determine the net work for the cycle.

Solution. The net heat transfer for the cycle is

$$\oint dQ = 23 - 4 - 10 + 2 = 11 \text{ Btu}$$

The net work transfer is thus

$$\oint dW = J\oint dQ$$

$$= 778\,(11) = 8558\ \text{ft lbf}$$

4.4 Energy

The first law of thermodynamics, in the form of Eq. (4.5), has a number of important consequences which are stated in the form of corollaries. These are propositions (3 in number) which are deduced from the first law and are often proved by "contradiction."

Corollary 1: There exists a property of a system, called energy, *E, such that a change in its value is equal to the difference between the heat supplied and the work done during any change in state.* In other words, *There exists a point function such that*

$$dE = dQ - dW \qquad (4.6)$$

Proof: Assume that the converse of the proposition is true. In other words, let

$$\oint (dQ - dW)$$

depend upon the process as well as upon the end states. In Fig. 4.2, let *A* and *B* be any two processes by which a system changes from state 1 to state 2. The assumption is that

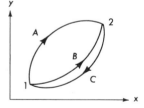

$$\oint_A^2 (dQ - dW) \ne \oint_B^2 (dQ - dW) \quad (4.7)$$

where $\oint_{A\,1}^{2}$ denotes integration from 1 to 2 along path *A*, and $\oint_{B\,1}^{2}$ denotes integration from 1 to 2 along path *B*.

Let the system return to its original state by a third process, *C*. For each of the cycles, 1–A–2–C–1 and 1–B–2–C–1, the following may be written:

Fig. 4.2 Arbitrary Processes between Common End Points.

$$\oint_{(1-A-2-C-1)} (dQ - dW) = \oint_A^2 (dQ - dW) + \oint_2^2 (dQ - dW)$$

$$\oint_{(1-B-2-C-1)} (dQ - dW) = \oint_B^2 (dQ - dW) + \oint_2^1 (dQ - dW)$$

If the two equations be subtracted one from the other, it follows from the assumption of Eq. (4.7) that

$$\oint_{(1-A-2-C-1)}(dQ - dW) \neq \oint_{(1-B-2-C-1)}(dQ - dW) \tag{4.8}$$

but this contradicts the first law, as expressed by Eq. (4.5), which says that these quantities must be equal since they are both zero. Therefore, the proposition stated in the corollary must be true.

The property E, an extensive property, is called the *energy* of the system and, for a system of unit mass, is given the lower-case symbol e. The existence of E has a very natural explanation: Interactions occurring *at the boundary* of a system occur solely in the forms of heat transfer and work transfer; consequently, interactions *within a* system must be given another name, energy. Physically, the quantity E includes many kinds of energy, some of them already familiar from a knowledge of ordinary mechanics. Newton's laws of motion show that relative to a fixed frame of reference in a gravitational field a body may have kinetic energy

$$KE = \frac{m\mathscr{V}^2}{2g_c} \tag{4.9}$$

and potential energy

$$PE = \frac{mg}{g_c} \tag{4.10}$$

where $\mathscr{V}$ is the velocity, z the elevation, and the other symbols as previously defined. E must, therefore, include these types of energy. Similarly, from Coulomb's law, an electric energy may be defined, and this energy must be contained in E. The same is true for magnetic energy if the system comprises magnetic poles or loop currents.

There is, however, a type of energy included in E which is peculiar to thermodynamics. Consider, as in the case of Joule's experiment, a simple system, ignoring motion, gravity, and other effects. According to the results of the experiment, the quantity E has increased, but this increase is not in kinetic energy, potential energy, or any of the above-mentioned energies. In other words, even in the absence of all other effects, a difference in the stored energy of a system can be discerned by measurements of heat and work. This form of energy, which is independent of motion, gravity, electricity, magnetism, and surface tension, is called *internal energy*. It is represented by the symbol U. Physically, and in the example just mentioned, an increase in U is associated with a rise in temperature of the system, although this correspondence does not always exist. Like E, U is an extensive property, and, for a system of unit mass, it is represented by the lower-case symbol u.

On the basis of the foregoing discussion, E can then be written as

$$E = U + KE + PE + \ldots \qquad (4.11)$$

or

$$E = U + \frac{m\mathcal{V}^2}{2g_c} + \frac{mg}{g_c}z + \ldots \qquad (4.12)$$

and, per unit mass of substance,

$$e = u + \frac{\mathcal{V}^2}{2g_c} + \frac{g}{g_c}z + \ldots \qquad (4.13)$$

Note that just as the thermodynamic definition of work is more general than the definition of work in mechanics, so the thermodynamic definition of energy is more general than the definition of energy in mechanics. Note also that thermodynamics provides no information as to absolute values of internal energy. Conveniently, the internal energy of a substance is assigned a zero value at some arbitrary reference state, just as the potential energy of a body is assigned a zero value at some arbitrary datum plane.

Equation (4.6) is an alternative statement of the first law of thermodynamics. In fact, it is used more often than Eq. (4.5) because it applies to a process rather than to a cycle. When integrated between two states 1 and 2, it is written

$$\Delta E = Q - W \qquad (4.14)$$

where $\Delta E = E_1 - E_2$ represents the change in the stored energy of the system.* In the absence of motion, gravity, and other effects, this simplifies to

$$\Delta U = Q - W \qquad (4.15)$$

where ΔU is the change in internal energy (a form of stored energy which is independent of motion, gravity, electricity, magnetism, and surface tension).

Example 4.2. A quantity of gas is compressed in such a manner that it requires 2320 ft lbf of work while its internal energy increases by 1.4 Btu. Determine the heat transferred during the process.

Solution. Although a system may move, it is customary to assume (unless otherwise prohibited in the statement of the problem) that it is stationary as

---

* As previously stated, heat and work are not properties of a system, but are often spoken of as energy in transition. Strictly speaking, the term energy refers to the stored energy of a system.

a whole. Thus, effects of motion and gravity are negligible, and the first law in the form of Eq. (4.15) gives

$$Q = \Delta U + W$$

Here, $\Delta U = 1.4$ Btu, $W = -2320$ ft lbf $= -2.98$ Btu (note the sign convention for work done on a system), and

$$Q = 1.4 - 2.98 = -1.58 \text{ Btu}$$

The minus sign indicates that heat is abstracted from the gas during the compression.

4.5 Conservation of Energy

A second consequence of the first law of thermodynamics is the following statement.

Corollary 2: In an isolated system, the energy of the system remains constant.

Proof: By definition of an isolated system, $Q = W = 0$. Therefore, $E_2 - E_1 = \Delta E = 0$.

Corollary 2 is commonly known as the Law of Conservation of Energy.* All that can happen in an isolated system is a spontaneous redistribution of energy between its parts until a state of equilibrium is reached. The energy of the system as a whole, however, remains unchanged. Figure 4.3(a) illustrates an isolated system. It consists of two bodies at different

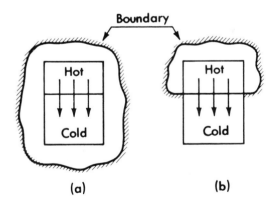

(a)   **(b)**

Fig. 4.3 Selection of System based on Boundary.

---

* More precisely, what is conserved in an isolated system is energy *and* mass, since the two are related by Einstein's equation, $E = \frac{m}{g_c} C^2$, where C is the velocity of light. However, the change in mass accompanying a chemical reaction is so small that it is ignored in thermodynamics. This, of course, would not be the case in nuclear reactions.

temperatures, the boundary of the system being imagined to be an insulating wall isolating both bodies from the surroundings. The system is in a non-equilibrium state, since at least one property, temperature, is not uniform throughout the system. There will be a spontaneous redistribution of energy between the two parts of the system until the temperatures become equal, in which case the system is in equilibrium and any property will have the same value throughout the system. Motion and gravity effects are absent so that E is simply U, and the first law shows that $\Delta U = 0$. In other words, the internal energy of the system remains constant.

Note that the term *heat* has no meaning in Fig. 4.3(a), since no energy crosses the boundary. On the other hand, if one body had been considered to be the system and the other to be a part of the surroundings, as in Fig. 4.3(b), then heat is said to be transferred to the surroundings, and Q will be negative instead of zero. The selection of the system (by drawing a boundary) is all-important in thermodynamic analysis. In fact, it is the first step in the solution of any problem.

4.6   Perpetual Motion Machine of First Kind

A third and final consequence of the first law is:

Corollary 3: *A perpetual motion machine of the first kind is impossible.*

Proof: A perpetual motion machine is a device which produces a continuous supply of work *without* requiring any interaction from surroundings or other systems. Such a device would, in effect, create energy. Equation (4.5) states that, if a net amount of heat is not supplied during a cycle, no net amount of work can be obtained. The existence of a perpetual motion machine would therefore violate the first law of thermodynamics (which cannot be proved). It is an experimental fact that no such machine has ever been created, despite attempts to invent one.*

Example 4.3. A system undergoes a cycle composed of 4 processes. The heat and work transfer in each process are shown by the accompanying tabulation:

Process	Q (Btu)	W (ft lbf)
1–2	443	99,400
2–3	−412	0
3–4	−222	−49,700
4–1	255	0

---

* It is always possible to devise a machine to deliver a limited amount of work without requiring interaction from the surroundings. For example, a compressed gas will expand and do work at the expense of the internal energy of the gas. However, the device cannot produce work continuously.

Show that the data is consistent with the first law, and determine the ratio of positive work (work done by the system) to heat supplied.

Solution. The summation of heat transfers for the cycle is

$$\oint dQ = 443 - 412 - 222 + 225 = 64 \text{ Btu}$$

The summation of work transfers is

$$\oint dW = 99,400 - 49,700 = 49,700 \text{ ft lbf} = 64 \text{ Btu}$$

Thus, $\oint dQ = \oint dW$, which is in accordance with the first law. The ratio of positive work to heat supplied, commonly known as *thermal efficiency*, is

$$\eta = \frac{64}{443 + 255} = 0.0915 \text{ or } 9.15 \text{ per cent}$$

Example 4.4. A system, consisting of a pound of water, is moving at a velocity of 80 fps at an elevation of 1500 ft above sea level. The value of its internal energy, as found from steam tables,* is 180.02 Btu/lbm. What is the energy of the system?

Solution. The energy here is

$$E = U + \frac{1}{2} \frac{m}{g_c} \mathcal{V}^2 + \frac{mg}{g_c} z$$

or, per unit mass

$$e = u + \frac{\mathcal{V}^2}{2g_c} + \frac{g}{g_c} z$$

$$= (180.02 \times 778) + \frac{(80)^2}{2 \times 32.2} + 1500$$

$$= 140,000 + 99.4 + 1500 = 141,599 \text{ ft lbf}$$

Note that the potential and kinetic energies are very small by comparison with the internal energy. In many applications this is the case, and, consequently, these energy quantities are neglected.

PROBLEMS

4.1. A system consists of air enclosed in a cylinder. The air undergoes a complete cycle in the following manner: in the compression stroke the piston exerts 11,500 ft lbf of work on the air and the water jacket removes 105 Btu. In the expansion stroke the air exerts 21,000 ft lbf of work on the piston. Find the amount of heat added to the air.

---

* The subject of steam tables will be formally introduced later in the text.

4.2. A system undergoes a process between the temperatures 100 °F and 200 °F. The heat transferred per degree rise in temperature, at each temperature attained during the process, is given by the relation

$$\frac{dQ}{dT} = 0.45 \frac{\text{Btu}}{°\text{R}}$$

The work done by the system per degree rise in temperature, at each temperature attained, is given by the relation

$$\frac{dW}{dT} = (1 - 0.02R) \frac{\text{Btu}}{°T}$$

Determine the increase in internal energy of the system during the process.

4.3. From the familiar definition of power: 1 hp = 33,000 ft lbf/min = 0.746 kw, verify the following relations pertaining to work: 1 hp hr = 2545 Btu, 1 kw hr = 3413 Btu.

4.4. A steady electric current flows through a resistor which is immersed in running water. Considering the resistor as the system, state whether the heat flow, work flow, and energy change is respectively +, −, or 0.

4.5. A rigid vessel having adiabatic walls is divided into two compartments by means of a partition. One compartment contains a gas at temperature T_1 and pressure p_1; the other contains a similar gas at temperature T_2 and pressure p_2. The partition is removed. What conclusion may be drawn from the first law?

4.6. Assume that when coal is burned in a home furnace the heat supplied to the home is 8200 Btu/lbm of coal. If the same home could be heated electrically with perfect conversion of electrical work into heat, and if the cost of electricity is 1.8 cents per kw-hr, to what price can coal rise per ton before its cost equals that of electricity?

4.7. A sealed bomb is immersed in a bath of water which is kept at uniform temperature by stirring. The bomb contains a crucible holding 1 gram mass of fuel oil and an atmosphere of oxygen at a pressure of 20 atm. The oil is ignited electrically from the outside, and 45 seconds after ignition no detectable temperature rise occurs in the water bath. Thereafter, the bath temperature rises until it becomes steady at 4.9 °F above its original reading. If the mass of the water bath is 7.5 lbm, by how much has the energy of the bomb and its contents increased, (a) 45 seconds after ignition, and (b) when the temperature reading has become steady? In part (a), can it be said that an increase in internal energy is being compensated by a decrease in chemical energy?

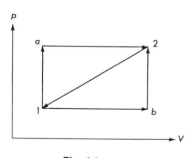

Fig. 4.4

4.8. A system (Fig. 4.4) is taken from state 1 to state 2 along the path 1–a–2. During this process, 75 Btu of heat flows into the system which, in turn, does 28 Btu of work. How much heat flows into the system along path 1–b–2 if the work done is 11 Btu? If, in returning the system from 2 to 1, the work required is 19 Btu, how much heat is absorbed or rejected by the system?

4.9. An auditorium containing 950 people has a temporary failure in its air-conditioning system. Assuming the average heat transfer from a person (at rest) to the surroundings to be 400 Btu/hr, what is the increase in internal energy of the air in the auditorium during the first 20 minutes? Considering the auditorium and all its contents as the system, how much does the energy change?

4.10. An electrical battery, thermally insulated, is being discharged at constant pressure (atmospheric) and constant volume. During a one hour test, it is found that a current of 50 amps at 2 volts flows, while the temperature increases from 68 °F to 90.5 °F. Determine the change in internal energy of the cell during the period of operation.

4.11. In an experimental determination of J, the mechanical equivalent of heat, an electric current is maintained in a coil of wire surrounded by a mass m of water, and the rise in temperature of the water is noted. If the potential difference across the coil is V, the current is i, and the time necessary for a temperature rise of one degree is t, what is the value of J in terms of V, i, t, and m?

4.12. A pound of water at 32 °F is converted to steam at 500 °F in a constant pressure process at 200 psia. The volume of the water is 0.016 cu ft, and that of the steam is 2.728 cu ft. If 1268.3 Btu are furnished during the process, what percentage goes to changing the internal energy, and what percentage goes to expansion?

4.13. A pound of water is heated from 100 °F to 200 °F under a pressure of 1 atmosphere. How could the heat effect be quantitively measured, if it is assumed that the Btu is defined as that amount of heat required to increase the temperature of one pound of water from 61.5 °F to 62.5 °F?

4.14. A system undergoes a cycle composed of four process: 1–2, 2–3, 3–4, and 4–1. During the cycle, energy transfers are measured as follows:

Process	$Q(Btu/min)$	$W(ft\ lbf/min)$	$\Delta E(Btu/min)$
1–2	100	30,000	—
2–3	50	—	75
3–4	−50	—	—
4–1	0	15,000	—

(a) Complete the table and, (b) determine the rate of work done in horsepower.

4.15. A missile of mass m traveling at a velocity of 2100 fps hits the ground and comes to rest. Assuming that no heat has been transferred to the ground upon impact, find (a) the change in the energies E and U of the missile and,

(b) the temperature increase of the missile if its internal energy is expressed by the relation

$$dU = mc\,dT$$

where $c = 0.26$ Btu/lbm °R.

4.16. Two balls of putty, weighing two pounds apiece and moving toward each other on a horizontal plane, collide and cohere. Before collision each ball has a velocity of 600 fps; after collision the velocity is zero. For the system consisting of the two balls, find the change in the energies E and U.

4.17. In each of the following cases, state whether heat has been transferred, work done, and E and U changed: (a) A mixture of fuel and oxygen is burned in a constant volume "bomb" immersed in a water bath. After the process, the temperature of the water is observed to rise. (b) A viscous liquid is stirred in an insulated container, thereby undergoing a temperature rise. (c) A mixture of hydrogen and oxygen enclosed in a rigid and thermally insulating container is exploded by a spark. There is a considerable increase in temperature and pressure.

4.18. A system consists of a 10 lbm of copper initially 30 ft above the floor. The copper and the floor are at the same temperature. The copper block is allowed to fall. Determine ΔE_u, ΔE_k, ΔE_p, and ΔE corresponding to the following conditions: (a) At the instant the block is about to hit the floor; (b) just after the block has come to rest on the floor; (c) after enough heat has been transferred so that the block and the floor are essentially at the same temperature they were initially. The subscripts u, k, and p refer to the internal energy, kinetic energy, and potential energy respectively.

4.19. An insulated vessel is divided into two compartments by a membrane. One compartment contains water, the other holds a fairly strong sulfuric acid. The vessel, initially at a temperature T_1, is sealed. (a) If the membrane is broken and the temperature rises to T_2, what is the change in the energy of the vessel and its contents? (b) What is the change in energy if, after the membrane is broken the vessel is allowed to cool down to T_1 by withdrawing heat from it?

4.20. A storage battery, having a terminal potential of 12 volts, delivers a current of 10 amperes for 2 hours. What is the heat transfer if the stored energy of the battery decreases by 1200 Btu?

4.21. A d-c motor operating at 800 rpm draws a current of 50 amperes at 24 volts. The torque applied to its shaft is 95 lbf-in. What is the rate of heat flow?

4.22. The gravitational acceleration g varies with altitude h above the earth's surface according to the relationship

$$g = a(b+h)^{-2}$$

where a and b are constants. What is the potential energy of a body of mass m at an elevation h relative to the earth's surface?

4.23. A tank 10 ft long, 6 ft wide, and 8 ft deep is filled with water. How much work is required to raise all the water over the top edge of the tank?

4.24. The first law of thermodynamics is sometimes stated in the following manner: When a system changes from an initial state to a final state by adiabatic means only, the work done is the same for *all* adiabatic processes connecting the two states. Discuss this proposition, and conclude from it that there exists a property of the system whose final value, minus its initial value, equals the work done. What is the function called?

4.25. For an infinitesimal quasi-static process of a chemical system, the first law is written as

$$dQ = dU + pdV$$

where p, V, and T are the thermodynamic coordinates, any two of which may be chosen as independent. Write the equation of the first law for the systems whose respective coordinates are the following: (a) σ, ϵ. T, (b) $\mathscr{P}$, A, T, (c) $\mathscr{E}$, Q_e, T, (d) $\mathscr{H}$, $\mathscr{M}$, T. Identify these systems.

CHAPTER 5

First Law Analysis of Closed System

5.1 Introduction

The objectives of this chapter are to apply the first law of thermodynamics to a system undergoing various kinds of processes from one state to another, and to develop relations which are of general validity and usefulness.

The basic statement of the first law, as given in the preceding chapter, applies to a system which is defined as a collection of matter within prescribed boundaries. Although the boundaries need not be constant in shape or volume (as in the case of a mass of gas being expanded or compressed), the mass of the system is, by definition, constant. Strictly speaking, no material crosses the boundaries of a given system. Practice, however, has condoned the use of the terms "closed system" and "open system."

A closed system is one having no mass transfer across its boundaries. An open system has mass transfer across its boundaries; therefore, its mass is not necessarily constant. Since all systems are really closed systems, it is better to use the term "stationary system" or "non-flow system" to describe a closed system, and the term "control volume" or "flow system" to describe an open system. In the present chapter the discussion is restricted to stationary systems. The application of the first law to flow systems will be discussed in the next chapter.

5.2 Pure Substance

In order to apply thermodynamic analysis to engineering systems, a knowledge of the physical properties of various substances is required. For this reason, the concept of a pure substance is now introduced. A *pure substance* is a substance which is chemically homogeneous and which remains invariant in chemical composition. In other words, it is a one-constituent system of one or more phases. Thus, a system consisting of oxygen, existing as a vapor, a liquid, a solid, or a combination of these, is a pure substance. The same may be said about water: water alone, ice alone, steam alone, a mixture of ice and water, or a mixture of liquid water and steam are all pure substances, for every phase has the same chemical composition. Air, though it is a mixture of several gases, is considered a pure substance as long as it is all vapor or all liquid. However, if it is part liquid and part vapor the mixture is no longer classified as a pure substance, for the liquid phase will be richer in nitrogen than the gaseous phase. A mixture of carbon monoxide and oxygen is a pure substance as long as it remains invariant in chemical composition. However, if a reaction occurs and some of the CO combines with some of the O_2 to form CO_2, the system is no longer considered as a pure substance, because the chemical composition has changed.

Thermodynamically, the importance of the concept of a pure substance lies in the experimental fact that, in the absence of motion, gravity, capillarity, electricity, and magnetism, the state of a pure substance is fully established if *two* independent properties are known. Thus, a given mass of gas or liquid of specified chemical composition will, at a given temperature and pressure, occupy a fixed volume. In other words, the pressure (p), the specific volume (v), and the temperature (T) of a gas or liquid are linked by a functional relationship of the form

$$F(p, v, T) = 0 \qquad (5.1)$$

This relationship which may be expressed either by a mathematical formula or by experimentally determined numerical tables, is called the *equation of state* of the substance. The three variables, p, v, and T, are called para-meters of state; if any two of them are known, the third one can be deter-mined by using Eq. (5.1). This equation can, at least in theory, be solved with respect to any one of the variables, so that the functional relationship between the variables can always be written down in three equivalent forms:

$$p = p(v, T); v = v(p, T); T = T(p, v) \qquad (5.2)$$

From among the familiar properties, such as pressure, temperature, specific volume, internal energy, viscosity, or electrical resistivity, any two intensive properties may be selected, procided they are independent of each other. When their values are fixed, the values of all other properties can be found through equations such as Eq. (5.2). *Properties are indepen-dent of each other if they are not defined in terms of each other.* Thus, specific volume and density are properties which are not independent of each other. The same holds for electrical resistivity and electrical conductivity. Pressure and temperature, on the other hand, are independent of each other, allowing a pure substance to form in the vapor phase or the liquid phase, but not in a mixture of these phases, such as in vaporiza-tion or condensation. Because pressure, volume, and temperature are properties which are directly measurable, they are called *primary properties*, and are commonly used in describing the state of a pure substance.

Equation (5.1) in its various forms and involving two independent properties is the equation of state for gases, liquids, and solids. It is essentially an empirical relation, because it must be obtained by experimen-tation rather than by thermodynamic reasoning alone. It is also quite complicated for most substances and is usually presented in the form of tables or charts.* There is, however, one substance whose equation of state is very simple. This is the *ideal* or *perfect gas*, which is defined as follows:

(1) An ideal or perfect gas obeys the equation of state $pv = RT$.

(2) Its internal energy is a function of temperature alone, i.e., $(\partial u / \partial p)_T = 0$.

The constant R is called the *gas constant.* Its units are ft lbf/lbm-°R or Btu/lbm-°R. Although an ideal gas represents a hypothetical substance defined by the relations $pv = RT$ and $(\partial u / \partial p)_T = 0$, real gases at low pressure and high temperature do exhibit very nearly ideal-gas behavior. Thus, many of the processes discussed in this chapter will be illustrated by use of this simple equation of state. The analysis, however, is perfectly general, and is applicable to all types of systems, with the sole stipulation that they be pure substances.

---

* The subject of property tables and charts will be formally presented in later chapters.

5.3 Constant-Volume Process

A constant-volume process is characterized by the fact that W must be zero or negative in the first law equation

$$Q = W + (U_2 - U_1) \tag{5.3}$$

Figure 5.1(a) illustrates a constant-volume process. A mass of fluid in a rigid container is being churned while heat is being added from the surroundings. Figure 5.1(b) shows the process on a p-V diagram.

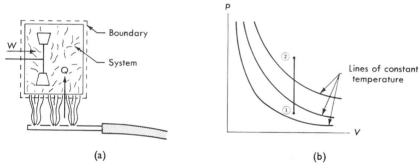

(a)　　　　　　　　　　　　　　(b)

Fig. 5.1 Constant-Volume Process.

Paddle-wheel work (stirring) may be present, but displacement work is excluded by the rigidity of the container. The fluid within the container may be any pure substance. Provided that the process involves a continuous succession of equilibrium states (which is possible when the stirring rate is low), the process may be represented on a property-diagram by a line marked V = constant.

Increasing the internal energy of a system by using the viscous effect inherent in the movement of a fluid is, however, to be avoided. In general, whenever reference is made to a constant volume process, the assumption is that work done is zero, unless otherwise stated. Thus, Eq. (5.3) becomes

$$Q = U_2 - U_1$$

or, in differential form,

$$dQ = dU \tag{5.4}$$

stated in words: For a constant volume process, the heat transfer is equal to the change in internal energy of the system.

5.4   Constant-Pressure Process

Many processes take place while the system is under constant hydro-static pressure. Figure 5.2 illustrates such a case: a fluid is enclosed in a

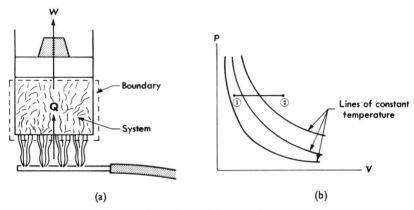

Fig. 5.2   Constant-Pressure Process.

cylinder by a piston on which rests a constant weight. If heat is supplied, such as the case here, the fluid expands, and work is done by the system against the constant restraining force. If heat is extracted, the fluid contracts, and work is done on the system by the constant force.

Assuming friction and turbulence to be negligible, the process is reversible and may be represented by a continuous line marked p = constant, as in Fig. 5.2(b). Since the elemental work dW for a reversible process is equal to pdV, the first law gives

$$dQ - dW = dQ - pdV = dU$$

or

$$dQ = dU + pdV$$

Since p is constant, this may be written as

$$dQ = dU + d(pV)$$
$$= d(U + pV) = dH \qquad (5.5)$$

where $H = U + pV$ is called the *enthalpy*. Its meaning is discussed in the next section

5.5   Enthalpy

In thermodynamic analysis, the combination $U + pV$ occurs so frequently that it has been given the name enthalpy and the symbol H. Thus, by definition,

$$H = U+pV \tag{5.6a}$$

or, per unit mass,

$$h = u+pv \tag{5.6b}$$

Note that, since each of the quantities on the right-hand side of Eq. (5.6) is a property, enthalpy is a property. Note also that, in order to add the internal energy and the pressure-volume product, the units for both must be the same. In this text, the units for internal energy and enthalpy are Btu/lbm. Thus when pressure is in lbf/ft^2 and specific volume in ft^3/lbm, the factor $J = 778$ ft lbf/Btu must be introduced in the denominator of the pv term. In other words,

$$h = u+ \frac{pv}{J} \tag{5.6c}$$

However, modern tendency is to omit the factor J, because it is unnecessary so long as consistent units are used throughout the equation.

Although enthalpy is both a property and has the units of energy, it may or may not be treated as an energy quantity. This is because the pv term sometimes does not represent energy. Only in the case of a fluid entering or leaving a control volume does pv represent energy. For example, neither the product pv nor torque are energy quantities, even though both have units of energy. Finally, note that, since absolute values of internal energy cannot be obtained, there can be no absolute values for enthalpy. This is no drawback, however; only *changes* in internal energy and enthalpy are of any concern in thermodynamics analysis.

Example 5.1. A pound of air is initially at a pressure of 100 psia and a volume of 1.5 cu ft. Heat is transferred to it, and it expands at constant pressure to a volume of 3 cu ft. During this process its internal energy has increased by 70 Btu. (a) Considering the process to be reversible, find the amount of heat transferred. (b) If the heat transferred is actually measured to be 90 Btu, how much work has been dissipated?

Solution. (a) Since the process is considered reversible, the work done is

$$W = \int_1^2 pdV = p(V_2-V_1)$$

$$= (100)(144)(3-1.5) = 21{,}600 \text{ ft lbf} = 27.8 \text{ Btu}$$

The heat transferred is then

$$Q = (U_2-U_1)+p(V_2-V_1) = 70+27.8 = 97.8 \text{ Btu}$$

(b) The system changes between the same end states according to the pressure-volume relationship in part (a). Therefore, ΔU and $\int p \, dV$ are the same, but the heat transfer is less (90 Btu instead of 97.8 Btu). The difference lies in the fact that friction is present in part (b); thus $p \, dV$ no longer equals the work done. A dissipative term (negative work in the nature of paddle-wheel work) is therefore included in the writing of the first law for the process:

$$Q = (U_2 - U_1) + \int_1^2 p \, dV - W_{\text{dissipated}}$$

Here,

$$90 = 70 + 27.8 - W_{\text{dissipated}}$$

which gives

$$W_{\text{dissipated}} = 7.8 \text{ Btu} = 6060 \text{ ft lbf}$$

Example 5.2. Show that, for a constant pressure process,

$$dQ = \left[\left(\frac{\partial U}{\partial T} \right)_p + p \left(\frac{\partial V}{\partial T} \right)_p \right] dT$$

Solution. Since $dW = p \, dV$ for a quasi-static process the first law may be written

$$dQ = dU + p \, dV$$

Choosing T and p as independent variables, this becomes

$$dQ = \left(\frac{\partial U}{\partial T} \right)_p dT + \left(\frac{\partial U}{\partial p} \right)_T dp + p \left[\left(\frac{\partial V}{\partial T} \right)_p dT + \left(\frac{\partial V}{\partial p} \right)_T dp \right]$$

$$= \left[\left(\frac{\partial U}{\partial T} \right)_p + p \left(\frac{\partial V}{\partial T} \right)_p \right] dT + \left[\left(\frac{\partial U}{\partial p} \right)_T + p \left(\frac{\partial V}{\partial p} \right)_T \right] dp$$

and, at constant pressure, this simplifies to

$$dQ = \left[\left(\frac{\partial U}{\partial T} \right)_p + p \left(\frac{\partial V}{\partial T} \right)_p \right] dT$$

5.6   Specific Heat

The processes discussed in the last two sections afford an opportunity to introduce yet another property: *specific heat* or *heat capacity*. Originally, this was defined as the amount of heat required to change, under certain conditions, the temperature of a unit mass of substance by one degree. Mathematically, this is expressed as

$$c_n = \frac{1}{m} \lim_{\substack{T_2 \to T_1 \\ Q \to 0}} \frac{Q}{T_2 - T_1} = \frac{1}{m} \frac{dQ}{dT} \tag{5.7}$$

or

$$dQ = m c_n \, dT \tag{5.8a}$$

and, for a system of unit mass,

$$dq = c_n \, dT \tag{5.8b}$$

where c_n denotes the specific heat, and the subscript n denotes the particular process under which the heat transfer takes place.

The total quantity of heat transferred to or from a system when its temperature changes from T_1 to T_2 is given by

$$Q = \int_{T_1}^{T_2} mc_n dT \tag{5.9}$$

Integration of Eq. (5.9), however, requires knowledge of the process by which the temperature of the system changes from T_1 to T_2. For example, if the system is under constant external hydrostatic pressure, its volume will generally increase as its temperature increases. On the other hand, if the system is maintained at constant volume, its pressure will increase as the temperature increases. Thus, there is a variety of ways of going from one to the other between two isothermal (constant temperature) lines. This is illustrated in Fig. (5.3).

Here, two isotherms of a system, T and $T+\Delta T$, are shown on a p-V plane. Starting from an initial state A on the isotherm T, we see that there are any number of ways of reaching the isotherm $T+\Delta T$. The specific heat may thus have any value, depending on the process undergone by the system. Most measurements of specific heat capacity, however, are made with the system subjected to either *constant volume or constant pressure* conditions. Under these circumstances, two new properties may be defined: the specific heat at constant volume, and the specific heat at constant pressure. In other words,

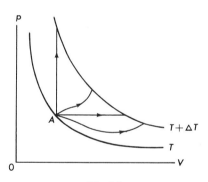

Fig. 5.3

Dependence of Heat Transfer upon Path.

$$c_v = \frac{(dq)_v}{(dT)_v} \tag{5.10}$$

$$c_p = \frac{(dq)_p}{(dT)_p} \tag{5.11}$$

where the subscripts v and p denote that the heat transfer and the temperature change are subject to the respective restrictions of $v = $ constant and $p = $ constant. Now $(dq)_v = (du)_v$ in a constant volume process, and

$(dq)_p = (dh)_p$ in a constant pressure process. Thus, Eqs. (5.10) and (5.11) become

$$c_v = \frac{(du)_v}{(dT)_v} = \left(\frac{\partial u}{\partial T}\right)_v \tag{5.12}$$

$$c_p = \frac{(dh)_p}{(dT)_p} = \left(\frac{\partial h}{\partial T}\right)_p \tag{5.13}$$

Equations (5.12) and (5.13) define respectively the *specific heat at constant volume* and the *specific heat at constant pressure*. Both are properties of a system, since they are defined in terms of u, h, and T, which are all properties.

5.7   Reversible Transfer of Heat

In connection with work and reversibility, it was pointed out in Secs. (1.12) and (2.3) that a process caused by a finite unbalanced force is irreversible, and cannot be described by means of thermodynamic coordinates that refer to the system as a whole. Similarly, if a heat transfer occurs from one system to another at a finite lower temperature, the process is irreversible, since the energy cannot be made to flow back from the colder to the warmer system. If, however, the temperature difference between the two systems is infinitesimal, the rate of heat transfer will be infinitely slow, and an infinitesimal change in the temperature of either system will cause heat to flow in the opposite direction. Theoretically, a heat transfer process becomes *reversible* when the two systems are at the same temperature. In practice, this condition is never attained, but a *quasi-static* process is conceivable, wherein the difference between temperatures is negligible for all practical purposes. In such a case, the heat transfer may easily be calculated in terms of macroscopic coordinates. One way of carrying out a quasi-static process is to have a system come in thermal contact with a *heat reservoir*. A heat reservoir is a body of such large mass that a finite amount of heat flow will *not* bring about an appreciable change in its temperature. For example, the ocean and the ambient air are heat reservoirs, because no ordinary amount of heat added to the ocean or to the air would produce a temperature rise in these bodies. Thus, no change occurs in the thermodynamic coordinates of a heat reservoir when heat flows in or out of it. From this it is seen that the quasi-static process of a system in contact with a heat reservoir is an isothermal one.

To have a reversible flow of heat involving temperature change, that is to equate q with $\int c_n dT$, the following scheme is conceived. Imagine the system to be in contact *successively* with a series of reservoirs, ranging in temperature from T_1 to T_2, in such a way that the difference in temperature between the system and each reservoir is *infinitesimal*. This can be done by having a large number of reservoirs. Under these conditions, the process is reversible, and the heat transfer obtained by integration is

$$q = \int_{T_1}^{T_2} c_n dT \qquad (5.14)$$

where n is an index corresponding to the particular process under study (for example, $c_n = c_v$ for a constant-volume process, and $c_n = c_p$ for a constant-pressure process).

Example 5.3. The specific heat of a certain substance at constant pressure is

$$c_p = a + bT^2 \qquad (5.15)$$

where a and b are constants. Determine the heat transferred to change m mass of the substance from T_1 to T_2 at constant pressure.

Solution. Equation (5.14) becomes, with the restriction of constant pressure kept in mind:

$$Q = m \int_{T_1}^{T_2} c_p dT = m \int_{T_1}^{T_2} (a + bT^2) dT$$

$$= ma(T_2 - T_1) + m\left(\frac{b}{3}\right)(T_2^3 - T_1^3)$$

As a numerical example, let the specific heat for methane gas at constant pressure be

$$c_p = 0.282 + 0.46 \times 10^{-4} T$$

where T is in degrees Rankine. The heat required to raise 3 pounds of methane from 80 °F to 640 °F is then

$$Q = 3 \int_{540}^{1100} (0.282 + 4.6 \times 10^{-4} T) \, dT = 1113 \text{ Btu.}$$

5.8 Constant-Temperature Process

Let the system be put in contact with a constant-temperature bath, as shown in Fig. 5.4(a), and let the heat and work quantities be so proportioned that the temperature of the system remains the same. The process then becomes a constant-temperature or isothermal process, which is reversible (since temperature gradients are excluded by definition). It is represented on a diagram of appropriate coordinates in Fig. 5.4(b). Note that the force on the piston must be reduced as expansion proceeds, so that the temperature of the system remains constant while it receives heat. Conversely, if the system undergoes a compression, the force on the piston must be increased as heat is transferred at constant temperature out of the system. The first law relation for an isothermal reversible process is simply

$$dQ = dU + dW = dU + pdV \qquad (5.16)$$

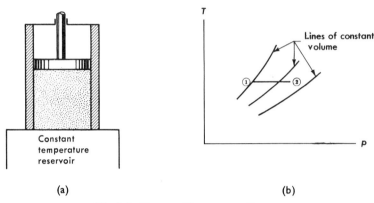

(a)   (b)

Fig. 5.4   Constant-Temperature Process.

5.9   Reversible-Adiabatic Process

A process which involves no heat exchange between a system and its surroundings is termed adiabatic $(dQ = 0)$. This is a process undergone by a system which is thermally insulated from the surroundings. For such a process the first law gives

$$dW = -dU \qquad (5.17)$$

that is, work done by the system comes from a lowering of the internal energy of the system, and, conversely, work done on the system results in an increase of the internal energy of the system. Furthermore, if the adiabatic process consists of a relatively slow expansion or compression of a fluid behind a frictionless piston, it approaches a reversible process, and pdV may be substituted for dW to give

$$pdV = -dU \qquad (5.18)$$

If an algebraic equation $U = U(p, V)$, relating p, V, and U, is known,

Eq. (5.18) becomes

$$pdV = -dU(p, V)$$

which may be integrated to give a relation between p and V, enabling the process to be represented as in Fig. 5.5.

Example 5.4. The relation between u, p, and v for many gases is of the form

$$u = a + bpv$$

where a and b are constants. Show that for a reversible adiabatic process

$$pv^\gamma = \text{constant}$$

where $\gamma = (b + 1)/b$.

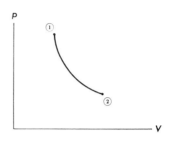

Fig. 5.5
Reversible-Adiabatic Process.

Solution. From Eq. (5.18), the slope of a reversible adiabatic is $du/dv = -p$. Here,

$$\frac{du}{dv} = \frac{d(a+bpv)}{dv} = bv\frac{dp}{dv} + bp$$

$$= b\left(p + v\frac{dp}{dv}\right)$$

Setting this equal to $-p$ gives

$$b\left(p + v\frac{dp}{dv}\right) = -p$$

Dividing both sides by bp and rearranging gives

$$\frac{dp}{p} + \left(\frac{b+1}{b}\right)\frac{dv}{v} = 0$$

or

$$d\ln p + \left(\frac{b+1}{b}\right)d\ln v = 0$$

Letting $(b+1)/b = \gamma$, this becomes

$$d\ln p + \gamma\, d\ln v = 0$$

and, upon integration,

$$pv^\gamma = \text{constant}$$

Example 5.5. (a) Show that the slope of a reversible-adiabatic on $p\text{-}v$ coordinates is

$$\frac{dp}{dv} = -\frac{1}{\kappa v}\frac{c_p}{c_v}$$

where

$$\kappa = -\frac{1}{v}\left(\frac{\partial v}{\partial p}\right)_T$$

(b) Show that, for a perfect gas having an equation of state $pv = RT$ and constant specific heats c_p and c_v, the equation for a reversible-adiabatic process is

$$pv^\gamma = \text{constant}$$

where $\gamma = c_p/c_v$.

Solution. (a) Consider p and v as independent variables. Then Eq. (5.18) becomes

$$p\,dv = -\left[\left(\frac{\partial u}{\partial p}\right)_v dp + \left(\frac{\partial u}{\partial v}\right)_p dv\right]$$

or

$$\left[p + \left(\frac{\partial u}{\partial v}\right)_p\right] dv = -\left(\frac{\partial u}{\partial p}\right)_v dp$$

Solving for dp/dv gives

$$\frac{dp}{dv} = -\frac{1}{(\partial u/\partial p)_v}\left[p + \left(\frac{\partial u}{\partial v}\right)_p\right] \tag{5.19}$$

To get this in "standard" form, i.e., in terms solely of the specific heats, the state coordinates (p, v, T), and their partial derivatives, $(\partial u/\partial p)_v$ and $(\partial u/\partial v)_p$ will now be eliminated. From the chain rule $(\partial u/\partial p)_v = (\partial u/\partial T)_v(\partial T/\partial p)_v$ and the definition $(\partial u/\partial T)_v = c_v$, the student can easily verify that

$$\left(\frac{\partial u}{\partial p}\right)_v = \frac{\kappa}{\beta}c_v \tag{5.20}$$

where $\beta = 1/v(\partial v/\partial T)_p$, and $K = -1/v(\partial v/\partial p)_T$.
Similarly, to eliminate $(\partial u/\partial v)_p$, the reader can write $h = u + pv$, whereupon partial differentiation gives

$$\left(\frac{\partial h}{\partial v}\right)_p = \left(\frac{\partial u}{\partial v}\right)_p + p \tag{5.21}$$

The first term is easily rewritten as

$$\left(\frac{\partial h}{\partial v}\right)_p = \left(\frac{\partial h}{\partial T}\right)_p\left(\frac{\partial T}{\partial v}\right)_p = \frac{c_p}{v\beta}$$

so that

$$\left(\frac{\partial u}{\partial v}\right)_p = \frac{c_p}{v\beta} - p \tag{5.22}$$

Equations (5.20) and (5.22) enable Eq. (5.19) to be written as

$$\frac{dp}{dv} = -\frac{\beta}{\kappa c_v}\left[p + \frac{c_p}{v\beta} - p\right]$$

$$= -\frac{1}{\kappa v}\frac{c_p}{c_v} \tag{5.23}$$

which is the desired result.

(b) Apply Eq. (5.23) to a perfect gas. Also, $\kappa = 1/p$ for a perfect gas (the reader can check this), so that

$$\frac{dp}{dv} = - \left(\frac{p}{v}\right)\left(\frac{c_p}{c_v}\right)$$

or

$$\frac{dp}{p} = - \left(\frac{c_p}{c_v}\right)\frac{dv}{v}$$

This integrates into

$$pv^\gamma = \text{constant}$$

where

$$\gamma = \frac{c_p}{c_v}$$

5.10 Reversible-Polytropic Process

The formula for a reversible-adiabatic process, obtained in the preceding examples, is of such convenience in engineering calculations that it has been extended to other processes. Consider the family of processes that have the pressure-volume relation

$$pV^n = \text{constant} \tag{5.24}$$

where n is any number. In many processes it is found that the states during an expansion or compression can be adequately described by a relation of the form of Eq. (5.24). These processes are termed *polytropic*, and n is termed the "index" of the expansion or compression. It can readily be seen that when $n = 0$, the relation reduces to $p = \text{constant}$, and that when $n = \infty$, it reduces to $V = \text{constant}$.

For a reversible-polytropic process, the initial, final, and any intermediate state are related by

$$p_1 V_1{}^n = p_2 V_2{}^n = pV^n$$

while the elemental work is given by $dW = pdV$. The total work, corresponding to a change from state 1 to state 2, may then be found by integration:

$$W = \int_1^2 pdV = p_1 V_1{}^n \int_1^2 \frac{dV}{V^n} = \frac{p_1 V_1{}^n (V_2{}^{1-n} - V_1{}^{1-n})}{1-n}$$

$$= \frac{p_2 V_2{}^n V_2{}^{1-n} - p_1 V_1{}^n V_1{}^{1-n}}{1-n} = \frac{p_2 V_2 - p_1 V_1}{1-n} \tag{5.25}$$

The heat transfer, work done, and change in internal energy are related, as usual, by the first law: $dQ = dU + pdV$. This is integrated into

$$Q = U_2 - U_1 + \int_1^2 pdV = U_2 - U_1 + \frac{p_2 V_2 - p_1 V_1}{1-n} \qquad (5.26)$$

Figure 5.6 shows a number of common reversible-polytropic processes on the p-V diagram. Starting from the same initial state represented by

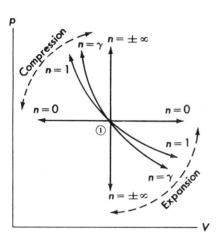

point ① the lower-right quadrant contains expansion processes, while the upper-left quadrant contains compression processes. The area under each curve represents the work done in that particular process. Note that, clockwise, the value of n increases from either zero to infinity or from minus infinity to zero. The value of n is usually positive, but it is possible to have processes fall into the two quadrants where n is negative. Such processes, however, do not occur often, for it would mean that the pressure and volume increase or decrease simultaneously.*

Fig. 5.6 Reversible Polytropic Processes.

Example 5.6. Calculate the work done and the heat transferred between states 1 and 2 in a polytropic process for one pound of perfect gas ($pv = RT$) with constant specific heats.

Solution. Since $p_1 v_1^n = p_2 v_2^n = pv^n$, the work done is

$$w = \int_1^2 pdv = p_1 v_1^n \int_1^2 \frac{dv}{v^n}$$

$$= \frac{p_2 v_2 - p_1 v_1}{1-n}$$

$$= \frac{R(T_2 - T_1)}{1-n}$$

The heat transferred is

$$q = (u_2 - u_1) + \int_1^2 pdv$$

---

* This happens if energy is transferred to an expansion process at such a rate that the pressure rises instead of falls, or if energy is transferred to a compression process at such a rate that the pressure falls even though the volume decreases.

Now, $(u_2 - u_1)$ may be expressed in terms of the specific heat at constant volume and the temperature change. For, by definition,

$$c_v = \left(\frac{\partial u}{\partial T}\right)_v$$

Since u depends only on temperature for a perfect gas, the partial derivative notation becomes

$$c_v = \frac{du}{dT}$$

This integrates to

$$u_2 - u_1 = c_v(T_2 - T_1)$$

Thus, the heat transferred is

$$q = c_v(T_2 - T_1) + \int_1^2 p\,dv$$

$$= c_v(T_2 - T_1) + \frac{R(T_2 - T_1)}{1 - n}$$

$$= \left(c_v + \frac{R}{1 - n}\right)(T_2 - T_1)$$

It is convenient to simplify the quantity $[c_v + R/(1 - n)]$. To do this, use is made of the definition for enthalpy:

$$h = u + pv$$
$$= u + RT$$

Since, for a perfect gas, u is a function only of T, h also turns out to be a function only of T. Therefore, in the definition

$$c_p = \left(\frac{\partial h}{\partial T}\right)_p$$

the partial derivative becomes a total derivative, and

$$c_p = \frac{dh}{dT} = \frac{d(u + RT)}{dT}$$

$$= \frac{du}{dT} + R$$

$$= c_v + R$$

Replacing R by $(c_p - c_v)$, the expression for the heat transferred thus becomes

$$q = \frac{c_p - nc_v}{1 - n}(T_2 - T_1) = c_n(T_2 - T_1)$$

where the quantity

$$c_n = \frac{c_p - nc_v}{1 - n}$$

is often referred to as the *polytropic specific heat*.

TABLE 5.1
PROCESS–RELATIONS FOR PERFECT GAS

Process	Constant pressure	Constant volume	Constant temperature	Reversible adiabatic	General or polytropic
Exponent in $pv^n = C$	$n = 0$	$n = \infty$	$n = 1$	$n = \gamma$	$n = n$
p, v, T relations	$\dfrac{T_2}{T_1}=\dfrac{v_2}{v_1}$	$\dfrac{T_2}{T_1}=\dfrac{p_2}{p_1}$	$p_1v_1=p_2v_2$	$p_1v_1{}^\gamma = p_2v_2{}^\gamma$ $\dfrac{T_2}{T_1}=\left(\dfrac{v_1}{v_2}\right)^{\gamma-1}$ $=\left(\dfrac{p_2}{p_1}\right)^{(\gamma-1)/\gamma}$	$p_1v_1{}^n = p_2v_2{}^n$ $\dfrac{T_2}{T_1}=\left(\dfrac{v_1}{v_2}\right)^{n-1}$ $=\left(\dfrac{p_2}{p_1}\right)^{(n-1)/n}$
Heat added (Btu)	$mc_p(T_2-T_1)$	$mc_v(T_2-T_1)$	$\dfrac{p_1v_1}{J}\ln\dfrac{v_2}{v_1}$	0	$mc_n(T_2-T_1)$ $= mc_v\left(\dfrac{\gamma-n}{1-n}\right)(T_2-T_1)$
$\displaystyle\int_1^2 pdv$	$p_1(v_2-v_1)$	0	$p_1v_1\ln\dfrac{v_2}{v_1}$	$\dfrac{p_2v_2-p_1v_1}{1-\gamma}$	$\dfrac{p_2v_2-p_1v_1}{1-n}$
$-\displaystyle\int_1^2 vdp$	0	$v(p_1-p_2)$	$p_1v_1\ln\dfrac{v_2}{v_1}$	$\dfrac{\gamma(p_2v_2-p_1v_1)}{1-\gamma}$	$\dfrac{n(p_2v_2-p_1v_1)}{1-n}$
Specific heat c:	c_p	c_v	∞	0	$c_n = c_v\left(\dfrac{\gamma-n}{1-n}\right)$

Example 5.7. As a summary for the study of processes, verify Table 5.1, using a perfect gas $(pv = RT)$ with constant specific heats as the thermodynamic medium.

Solution. Most of the results have already been derived in preceding examples. The integral $-\int_1^2 vdp$, however, merits some discussion. This is the work done in the case of a flow system (see Chap. 6) and is equal to the area to the left of the curve, representing the process, rather than to the area under the curve, as in the case of a non-flow system. The integral is included here to make the table complete. The rest of the derivation is left to the student.

5.11 Constant-Internal-Energy Process

It is possible to conceive of a reversible process in which the heat transfer and the work done exactly balance each other. In such a case, the process would be one of constant internal energy and would be represented by a line labeled $u = $ constant as in Fig. (5.7). The first law would then give

$$dQ = dW = pdV \qquad (5.27)$$

The most important practical example of a constant-internal-energy process, however, happens to be irreversible. This is the diaphragm-bursting process already introduced in Sec. 2.3. Consider a perfectly insulated $(dQ = 0)$ rigid container divided into two compartments, as shown in Fig. 5.8(a). One compartment is filled with gas; the other compartment is evacuated.

When the diaphragm is punctured (or removed), the gas will expand freely into that part of the container originally evacuated. The specific volume of the gas will increase; its pressure will decrease; and its temperature will probably decrease. This change of state, however, takes place *without* the displacement of a boundary against an external resistance, so that the work done is zero $(dW = 0)$. The first part of Eq. (5.27) is still satisfied, since $dq = dW = 0$, but not the second part, since $dW \neq pdV$. The

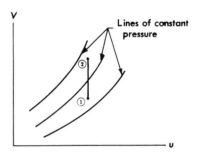

Fig. 5.7
Constant Internal Energy Process.

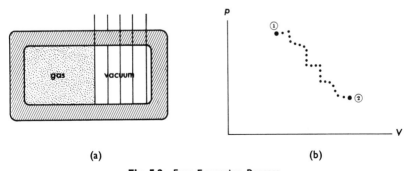

(a)   (b)

Fig. 5.8 Free Expansion Process.

process, however, is still one of constant internal energy, since

$$dU = dQ - dW = 0 \qquad (5.28)$$

but it is an *irreversible* process because, apart from the initial and final states, the remaining states are not equilibrium states. The pressure, for example, at any intermediate stage in the process is not uniform throughout the system. Thus, no points can be located on a diagram to represent the intermediate states, and, consequently, no smooth curve may be drawn to represent the process.

If something approaching a continuous line is desired, the technique introduced in Sec. 2.3 may be used to modify the process between the initial and final states. By providing a large number of partitions in the exhausted space, a number of intermediate states may be plotted and these will trace out a line of constant internal energy as in Fig. 5.8(b). The noteworthy item, however, is that it is not possible for the gas to return to one portion of the container and leave a vacuum in the other portion when the partitions are put back in place. A free expansion process cannot be reversed exactly along the original path of change without introducing the work of heat quantities which played no part in the original process.

Example 5.8. Two insulated vessels are connected by means of a valve. One vessel contains 15 pounds of nitrogen at 220 psia and 115 °F; the other vessel contains 2 pounds of nitrogen at 90 psia and 60 °F. The valve separating the two vessels is opened, and the gases mix. Find the temperature and the pressure after equilibrium has been reached. Consider nitrogen to be a perfect gas, obeying the equation of state $pv = RT$ (where $p = psfa$, $v =$ cu ft/lbm, $T = $ °R, $R = 55.1$ ft lbf/lbm °R) and having internal energy $u = c_v T$.

Solution. Considering both vessels to be the system, the process is one of constant internal energy. This is because neither energy nor mass cross its boundaries. Since $dQ = dW = 0$, dU must also equal zero. A system with these characteristics is called an *isolated* system. The process, however, is irreversible. Let T_m be the equilibrium temperature after mixture has occurred. Since internal energy is conserved, the gain in internal energy of one gas must equal the loss in internal energy of the other. This fact may be expressed by writing

$$(15)(c_v)(575 - T_m) = (2)(c_v)(T_m - 520)$$

Solving for T_m gives

$$T_m = 568 \text{ °R} = 108 \text{ °F}$$

The pressure of the mixture may be obtained by applying the equation of state

$$pV = (17)(RT)$$

to the mixture. Here, V is the volume, corresponding to 17 pounds of nitrogen. The remainder of the solution is left to the student.

5.12   Irreversible Processes

With the exception of free expansion, all the processes discussed in the preceding sections are reversible (or idealized to be so). This is because only reversible processes can be represented in all intermediate states either by an equation or by a continuous curve on a diagram of properties. In practice, however, most processes are usually irreversible, due to friction, turbulence, temperature gradients, and so on. While they are not easy to analyze, it is nevertheless of interest to show how some of them may be treated.* The situation is not entirely hopeless as long as the initial and final states of a process are equilibrium states. For example, in cases where friction and turbulence are present $\int p\,dV$ no longer represents work, and, therefore, a dissipative term (in the nature of paddle-wheel work) must be included in writing the first law for the process:

$$Q = (U_2 - U_1) + \int_1^2 p\,dV - W_{\text{dissipated}} \qquad (5.29)$$

Note that, if the irreversible process is an expansion, work is done by the system, but this work is less than the value of $\int_1 p\,dV$. Similarly, if the irreversible process is a compression, work is done on the system, and this work is greater than $\int_1^2 p\,dV$.

Example 5.9. A certain gas has a relation between p, v, and u given by

$$u = 35 + 0.5\,pv$$

where u = Btu/lbm, p = psia, and v = cu ft/lbm. Three pounds of this gas expand from a pressure of 100 psia and a specific volume of 2 cu ft/lbm to a pressure of 15 psia, according the the process $pv^{1.2}$ = constant. Determine Q, ΔU, and W if (a) the process is reversible, and (b) 10 Btu of work are lost due to internal friction.

Solution. (a) Since the process is reversible,

$$W = \int_1^2 p\,dV = \frac{p_2 V_1 - p_1 V_1}{1 - n}$$

$$= \frac{(15)(144)(V_2) - (100)(144)(6)}{1 - 1.2}$$

V_2 is determined from $p_1 V_1^{1.2} = p_2 V_2^{1.2}$, or

$$V_2 = V_1 \left(\frac{p_1}{p_2}\right)^{1/1.2} = 6\left(\frac{100}{15}\right)^{0.833} = 29.1 \text{ cu ft}$$

---

* A more complete discussion of irreversible processes will be presented later in the text.

Replacing this in the expression for the work gives

$$W = 118{,}000 \text{ ft lbf} = 152 \text{ Btu}$$

The change in internal energy is given by

$$\Delta U = m(u_1 - u_2)$$
$$= 3(35 + 0.5 p_2 v_2 - 35 - 0.5 p_1 v_1)$$
$$= -82 \text{ Btu}$$

The heat transferred is

$$Q = W + \Delta U = 152 - 82 = 70 \text{ Btu}$$

(b) The system changes between the same end states and along a dotted path similar to the one introduced above. Hence $\Delta U = -82$ Btu (since U is a property), and $\int_1^2 p\,dV = 152$, but the work is now

$$W = \int_1^2 p\,dV - W_{\text{dissipated}}$$
$$= 152 - 10 = 142 \text{ Btu}$$

and the heat transferred is

$$Q = \Delta U + \int_1^2 p\,dV - W_{\text{dissipated}}$$
$$= -82 + 152 - 10 = 60 \text{ Btu}$$

The above example illustrates the fact that work is not always equal to $\int p\,dV$. Other instances in which $\int p\,dV$ does not represent work are in the free expansion of a gas ($\int p\,dV \neq 0$, $W = 0$), and in the dissipation of paddle-wheel work in a system of fixed boundary ($\int p\,dV = 0$, $W \neq 0$). The reader should bear in mind that the only case in which work may become equal to $\int p\,dV$ is a quasi-static process involving a displacement of the boundary of the system.

5.13   Energy Relation for Simple System

This chapter now closes with the development of the energy equation, a relation which expresses the internal energy of a simple homogeneous system as a function of any pair of the thermodynamic coordinates, p, v, and T, the specific heats and the partial derivatives of the coordinates. Such an equation is useful, because, with the equation of state, it completely determines all the properties of a system.

The energy equation cannot be derived from the equation of state alone, but must depend upon additional experimental data, such as specific heats. From this information, the partial derivatives of u, with respect to the state variables, may be calculated, and the energy equation may then be obtained through integration.

The objective, therefore, is to obtain an equation for du in terms of specific heats and any pair of state variables and their partial derivatives. This is done by considering systematically each pair of the three variables,

p, v, and T, as independent. The following is an outline of the procedure, with some of the intermediate steps being left to the student.

p and v independent. When p and v are selected as independent variables, the change of u may be written as

$$du = \left(\frac{\partial u}{\partial p}\right)_v dp + \left(\frac{\partial u}{\partial v}\right)_p dv \qquad (5.30)$$

The coefficients $(\partial u/\partial p)_v$ and $(\partial u/\partial v)_p$ must be expressed in terms of c_p, c_v, and the partial derivatives of the state variables. To do this for the first coefficient, write the chain rule of partial differentiation $(\partial u/\partial p)_v = (\partial u/\partial T)_v(\partial T/\partial p)_v$ and make use of the definition $(\partial u/\partial T)_v = c_v$, as well as of the relation $(\partial T/\partial p)_v = \kappa/\beta$ (which the student can easily verify). The result is

$$\left(\frac{\partial u}{\partial p}\right)_v = \frac{\kappa}{\beta} c_v \qquad (5.31)$$

Similarly, to eliminate $(\partial u/\partial v)_p$, write $h = u + pv$, and get

$$\left(\frac{\partial u}{\partial v}\right)_p = \left(\frac{\partial h}{\partial v}\right)_p - p$$

But $(\partial h/\partial v)_p = (\partial h/\partial T)_p(\partial T/\partial v)_p = c_p/v\beta$ (as the student will check). Thus

$$\left(\frac{\partial u}{\partial v}\right)_p = \frac{c_p}{v\beta} - p \qquad (5.32)$$

Substitution of Eqs. (5.31) and (5.32) into Eq. (5.30) gives the equation for du in *standard form:*

$$du = \left(\frac{\kappa}{\beta} c_v\right) dp + \left(\frac{c_p}{v\beta} - p\right) dv \qquad (5.33)$$

v and T independent. When v and T are selected as independent variables, the differential of u becomes

$$du = \left(\frac{\partial u}{\partial v}\right)_T dv + \left(\frac{\partial u}{\partial T}\right)_v dT \qquad (5.34)$$

The coefficient $(\partial u/\partial T)_v$ is, by definition, c_v. The coefficient $(\partial u/\partial v)_T$, however, must be altered to a function of the specific heats and the state variables. From Prob. (5.27) at the end of the chapter, the student can establish that

$$c_p - c_v = \left[p + \left(\frac{\partial u}{\partial v}\right)_T\right]\left(\frac{\partial v}{\partial T}\right)_p = pv\beta + v\beta\left(\frac{\partial u}{\partial v}\right)_T \qquad (5.35)$$

Thus

$$\left(\frac{\partial u}{\partial v}\right)_T = \frac{c_p - c_v}{v\beta} - p \tag{5.36}$$

and Eq. (5.34) becomes

$$du = \left[\frac{c_p - c_v}{v\beta} - p\right]dv + c_v dT \tag{5.37}$$

T and p independent. If T and p are chosen independent, then

$$du = \left(\frac{\partial u}{\partial T}\right)_p dT + \left(\frac{\partial u}{\partial p}\right)_T dp \tag{5.38}$$

To eliminate the coefficient $(\partial u/\partial T)_p$, use the result obtainable in Prob. (5.26), along with the definition of β to get

$$\left(\frac{\partial u}{\partial T}\right)_p = c_p - pv\beta \tag{5.39}$$

To eliminate the coefficient $(\partial u/\partial p)_T$, write the first law relation $dq = du + p\,dv$ and consider T and p as independent variables:

$$dq = \left(\frac{\partial u}{\partial T}\right)_p dT + \left(\frac{\partial u}{\partial p}\right)_T dp + p\left[\left(\frac{\partial v}{\partial T}\right)_p dT + \left(\frac{\partial v}{\partial p}\right)_T dp\right]$$

$$= \left[\left(\frac{\partial u}{\partial T}\right)_p + p\left(\frac{\partial v}{\partial T}\right)_p\right]dT + \left[\left(\frac{\partial u}{\partial p}\right)_T + p\left(\frac{\partial v}{\partial p}\right)_T\right]dp$$

But $(\partial u/\partial T)_p + p(\partial v/\partial T)_p = c_p$, as previously mentioned. Thus,

$$dq = c_p dT + \left[\left(\frac{\partial u}{\partial p}\right)_T + p\left(\frac{\partial v}{\partial p}\right)_T\right]dp \tag{5.40}$$

Letting $v = $ constant, this becomes

$$(dq)_v = c_v(dT)_v = c_p(dT)_v + \left[\left(\frac{\partial u}{\partial p}\right)_T + p\left(\frac{\partial v}{\partial p}\right)_T\right](dp)_v$$

whence

$$c_v = c_p + \left[\left(\frac{\partial u}{\partial p}\right)_T + p\left(\frac{\partial v}{\partial p}\right)_T\right]\left(\frac{\partial p}{\partial T}\right)_v \tag{5.41}$$

Now, after checking, the student will find that

$$\left(\frac{\partial p}{\partial T}\right)_v = -(v\beta)\left(\frac{-B}{v}\right) = B\beta \tag{5.42}$$

Replacing $(\partial v/\partial p)_T$ and $(\partial p/\partial T)_v$ *by* $-v\kappa$ and $B\beta$, Eq. (5.42) becomes

$$c_v = c_p + \left[\left(\frac{\partial u}{\partial p}\right)_T - pv\kappa\right]\ (B\beta)$$

which gives

$$\left(\frac{\partial u}{\partial p}\right)_T = pv\kappa - \frac{c_p - c_v}{B\beta} \qquad (5.43)$$

Finally, Eqs. (5.39) and (5.43) enable Eq. (5.38), to be written as

$$du = (c_p - pv\beta)dT + \left(pv\kappa - \frac{c_p - c_v}{B\beta}\right)dp \qquad (5.44)$$

Eqs. (5.33), (5.37), and (5.44) are useful because they enable the internal energy of a substance to be calculated from the equation of state and from the specific heat data of the substance.

Example 5.10. A perfect gas is defined by the relations

$$\begin{cases} pv = RT \\ \left(\dfrac{\partial u}{\partial v}\right)_T = 0 \end{cases}$$

A van der Waals gas,† on the other hand, is defined by the relations

$$\begin{cases} \left(p + \dfrac{a}{v^2}\right)(v - b) = RT \\ \left(\dfrac{\partial u}{\partial v}\right)_T = \dfrac{a}{v^2} \end{cases}$$

Calculate the internal energy for a perfect gas and for a van der Waals' gas respectively.

Solution. Of the three *du* relations, Eq. (5.37) is the most convenient to use. With it,

$$du = c_v dT + \left(\frac{c_p - c_v}{v\beta} - p\right)dv$$

From the definition of a perfect gas, why must the coefficient of *dv* be zero in the above relation? For a perfect gas

$$du = c_v dT$$

This integrates into

$$u = u_0 + \int_{T_0}^{T} c_v dT$$

As for van der Waals' gas, its definition enables Eq. (5.37) to be written as

$$du = c_v dT + \frac{a}{v^2}dv$$

---

† The subject of perfect gases and real gases will be formally discussed in Chap. 14.

Integration then gives

$$u = u_0 + \int_{T_0}^{T} c_v dT + a\left(\frac{1}{v_0} - \frac{1}{v}\right)$$

PROBLEMS

5.1. Three pounds of nitrogen are heated in a reversible, non-flow, constant volume process from a temperature of 100 °F until the pressure is doubled. Determine (a) the final temperature, (b) the change in internal energy, (c) the change in enthalpy, and (d) the heat transfer. Consider nitrogen to be an ideal gas with $R = 55.1$ ft lbf/lbm-°R, $c_v = 0.1776$ Btu/lbm-°R.

5.2. A system receives 170 Btu of heat at constant volume. It then rejects 180 Btu of heat, while it has 40 Btu of work done on it at constant pressure. If an adiabatic process which will restore the system to its initial state can be found, how much work will be done during that process? If the value of the internal energy in the initial state is arbitrarily taken to be zero, what are the values of internal energy at the other two states?

5.3. During a constant-pressure reversible non-flow process, heat is added to 5 pounds of air at 70 °F and 14.7 psia until the volume is 220 cu ft. Determine (a) the work done, (b) the change in internal energy, (c) the change in enthalpy, and (d) the heat transfer. Consider air to be a perfect gas with $R = 53.3$ ft lbf/lbm-°R, $c_p = 0.24$ Btu/lbm-°R.

5.4. A pound of air is expanded between two states as it does 21,600 ft lb. of work and receives 22.5 Btu of heat. A second expansion, which requires a heat input of only 20 Btu, is to be found between the same initial states. Determine the change of internal energy in the first expansion and the work done by the air in the second.

5.5. Air is contained in an insulated cylinder closed by a piston. A paddle-wheel, rotated by means of a shaft extending through the cylinder wall, causes the fluid to undergo a fully-resisted, constant-pressure process as the piston moves outwards. Show that the stirring work, in this case, is equal to the increase in the enthalpy of the fluid.

5.6. Water at 32 °F has a density of 62.42 lbm/cu ft, while ice at the same temperature has a density of 57.2 lbm/cu ft. Find the work done by a system comprising 1 lbm of ice at atmospheric pressure and 32 °F as it melts to water at constant temperature and pressure. If the internal energy of a pound of ice increases by 144 Btu as it melts, how much heat is actually transferred to the ice during the melting process?

5.7. An ideal gas, occupying a volume of 4 cu ft at 230 psia, expands in a reversible, non-flow, isothermal process until the volume is 13 cu ft. Determine (a) the final pressure, (b) the work done, and (c) the heat transfer.

5.8. A system composed of 0.75 lbm of air is at a pressure of 45 psia and a temperature of 260 °F. What are the temperature and pressure if it receives

450 Btu of heat at constant volume? If the air expands adiabatically while doing 385,000 ft lbf of work, what is the change in internal energy during the expansion? Is the value of this property lower or higher than before the heating process?

5.9. Air at 80 °F and 15 psia is compressed reversible and polytropically from 10 cu ft to 2 cu ft. Determine the final pressure, temperature, work done, and heat transferred when the index of compression is respectively 1, 1.4, and 0.9.

5.10. A cylinder of 3 inch internal diameter is fitted with a spring-loaded piston. The spring has a stiffness of 80 lbf/in of compression. Air, initially at a volume of 0.016 cu ft, a temperature of 65 °F, and a pressure of 40 psia, is in the cylinder. Assuming the spring pressure to be the only external force acting on the piston, what amount of heat must be supplied for the piston to move a distance of 1.5 inches?

5.11. A quantity of gas initially at a volume of 5 cu ft, a pressure of 55 psia, and a temperature of 300 °F is allowed to expand reversibly and adiabatically to 15 psia. By heating at constant pressure the enthalpy of the gas is then raised by 26 Btu. What is the total work done?

If the operation is replaced by a single reversible poly-tropic expansion which results in the same final state, what index of expansion is required?

5.12. Consider an elemental portion of the atmosphere to be as shown in Fig. 5.9. A balance of forces shows that

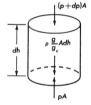

Fig. 5.9

$$dp = -\rho \frac{g}{g_c} dh$$

$$= -\frac{p}{RT} \frac{g}{g_c} dh$$

This may be solved to find the values of p and ρ at different heights. (a) Assuming isothermal conditions, integrate between p_0 and p, and 0 and h to obtain

$$\rho = \rho_0 \exp\left(-\frac{g}{g_c} \frac{h}{RT}\right)$$

(b) Assuming adiabatic conditions ($pv^\gamma = p_0 v_0{}^\gamma$), integrate between the same limits and obtain

$$\rho = \rho_0\left[1 - \left(\frac{\gamma-1}{\gamma}\right)\frac{g}{g_c}\frac{h}{p_0 v_0}\right]^{1/(\gamma-1)}$$

5.13. A system consisting of a pure substance undergoes a process in which its internal energy decreases by 11 Btu, while 6 Btu of heat is added to it. (a) Determine the magnitude and direction of the work done. (b) If, in undergoing a different process between the same end-states the work done had been zero, what would have been the magnitude and sign of the heat transfer?

5.14. The specific heat of dry air at constant pressure is

$$c_p = 0.3263 - \frac{0.1135 \times 10^3}{T} + \frac{0.03695 \times 10^6}{T^2}$$

where $T = {}^\circ R$. What percentage of error is introduced in calculating the amount of heat necessary to raise the temperature of 1 lbm of dry air from 100 °F to 2000 °F if the arithmetic mean of the specific heats at 100 °F and 2000 °F is used?

5.15. The specific heat at constant pressure of a gas is expressed by the relation

$$c_p = a + bT + cT^2$$

where a, b, and c are constants, and T is the instantaneous absolute temperature. If $a = 0.216$, $b = 0$, what is the value of c when 1287 Btu per lbm are required to raise the temperature of a certain gas from 100 °F to 2000 °F?

5.16. (a) Three pounds of ice at 18 °F are placed in an insulated vessel containing 25 pounds of water at 100 °F. The specific heat of ice is 0.5 Btu/lbm-°F; that of water is 1 Btu/lbm-°F. The latent heat of fusion of ice is 144 Btu/lbm. Determine the final temperature of the mixture. (b) The specific heat of wrought iron is 0.113 Btu/lbm-°F; that of water is 1.0 Btu/lbm-°F. A 9 lbm piece of iron at a temperature of 1100 °F is immersed in 3 cu ft of water (density: 62.4 lbm/cu ft). What must be the initial temperature of the water if the resultant temperature is 50 °F?

5.17. A certain gas has the equation of state

$$pv = 0.4 \, (t + 460)$$

and the relation for internal energy

$$u = u_o + 0.2t$$

where p = psia, v = cu ft/lbm, $t = {}^\circ F$, and u = Btu/lbm. A cylinder fitted with a piston contains 0.9 cu ft of the gas at a pressure of 50 psia and a temperature of 180 °F. The gas is allowed to expand to a lower pressure so that the work done by the gas is 2100 ft lbf and the heat transfer from the gas is 1.8 Btu. (a) Find the temperature of the gas after expansion. (b) If the gas undergoes a different process between the same end states in which the heat transfer is zero, what is the work done by the gas?

5.18. A system undergoes a constant-volume, non-flow process 1–2, during which is receives 160 Btu of heat. Next, if undergoes a constant-pressure, non-flow process 2–3, during which 175 Btu of heat are transferred out of it while 40 Btu of work are done on it. (a) Determine the work transfer if a non-flow, reversible adiabatic process 3–1 restores the system to its initial state. (b) Find the internal energy of the system at states 2 and 3 if an arbitrary zero value is assigned to the internal energy at state 1.

5.19. Five pounds of air are initially at 250 psia and 80 °F (point 1). Point 2 is at 100 psia and 80 °F. Find the heat transferred, the work done, and the change in internal energy for each of the processes 1–a–2, 1–b–2, and 1–c–2. Consider air to be a perfect gas having an equation of state $pv = RT$ and an internal energy $u = c_v T$.

5.20. A certain gas obeys the Clausius equation of state $p(v - b) = RT$ and has its internal energy given by $u = c_v T$. Show that the equation for a reversible adiabatic process is

$$p(v - b)^\gamma = \text{constant}$$

where $\gamma = c_p / c_v$.

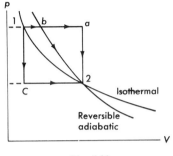

Fig. 5.10

5.21. Show that, for a perfect gas undergoing a reversible adiabatic process, (a) $pv^\gamma = \text{constant}$, (b) $Tv^{\gamma-1} = \text{constant}$, (c) $Tp^{(1-\gamma)/\gamma} = \text{constant}$.

5.22. It is often desirable to determine the value of n in the relation $pV^n = \text{constant}$. Show that if $pV^n = \text{constant}$ is plotted on logarithmic coordinate paper, the slope may be directly measured as shown in Fig. 5.11.

5.23. (a) Two curves, one representing a reversible-adiabatic process undergone by a perfect gas and the other an isothermal process by the same gas, intersect at some point on the p-v diagram. Show that the ratio of the slope of the adiabatic curve to the slope of the isothermal curve is equal to γ. (b) Determine the ratio of the work done during a reversible-adiabatic process to the work done during an isothermal process for a gas having a value of γ equal to 1.6. Both processes have a pressure ratio of 5.

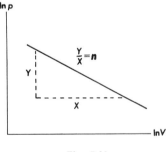

Fig. 5.11

5.24. (a) If the heat capacity of water is 1 Btu/lbm-°F at 65 °F, what is the heat capacity for water at 35 °C in cal/gm-°C? Give the relation between Btu/lbm-°F and cal/gm-°C. (b) Can the units Btu/lbm-°F and Btu/lbm-°R be used interchangeably? Explain.

5.25. The heat capacity at constant magnetic field of a paramagnetic solid may be expressed as

$$C_{\mathcal{H}} = \frac{a + b\mathcal{H}^2}{T^2} + CT^3$$

where a, b, and c are constants. What is the heat transferred during a process in which $\mathscr{H}$ remains constant while the temperature changes from T_1 to T_2?

5.26. A great number of relations pertaining to specific heats may be obtained by making use of the fact that a simple system is completely described by any two independent thermodynamic coordinates. Starting with the definition

$$c_n = \frac{dq}{dT} = \frac{du+pdv}{dT}$$

select p and T as independent variables; then, put in the restriction of p = constant to obtain

$$c_p = \left(\frac{\partial u}{\partial T}\right)_p + p\left(\frac{\partial v}{\partial T}\right)_p$$

or

$$\left(\frac{\partial u}{\partial T}\right)_p = c_p - p\left(\frac{\partial v}{\partial T}\right)_p$$
$$= c_p - pv\beta$$

5.27. (a) Considering u as a function of T and v, then holding p constant, show that

$$\left(\frac{\partial u}{\partial T}\right)_p = \left(\frac{\partial u}{\partial T}\right)_v + \left(\frac{\partial u}{\partial v}\right)_T\left(\frac{\partial v}{\partial T}\right)_p$$

(b) Substitute this into the result of Prob. 5.26 and obtain

$$c_p - c_v = \left[p + \left(\frac{\partial u}{\partial v}\right)_T\right]\left(\frac{\partial v}{\partial T}\right)_p$$

5.28. Show that for a perfect gas, the difference in specific heats is

$$c_p - c_v = \frac{R}{J}$$

5.29. The equation of state of a solid is

$$v = v_0 + aT - bp$$

and its internal energy equation is

$$u = cT - apT$$

where a, b, c, and v_0 are constants. Determine (a) the specific enthalpy, and (b) the heat capacities c_p and c_v.

5.30. A perfect gas is defined by the relations

$$\begin{cases} pv = RT \\ \left(\frac{\partial u}{\partial p}\right)_T = 0 \end{cases}$$

Show that the 6 partial derivatives of the internal energy become

$$\left(\frac{\partial u}{\partial v}\right)_T = 0 \qquad\qquad \left(\frac{\partial u}{\partial p}\right)_T = 0$$

$$\left(\frac{\partial u}{\partial T}\right)_v = c_v \qquad\qquad \left(\frac{\partial u}{\partial p}\right)_v = -\frac{v}{R}c_v$$

$$\left(\frac{\partial u}{\partial T}\right)_p = c_v \qquad\qquad \left(\frac{\partial u}{\partial v}\right)_p = \frac{p}{R}c_v$$

5.31. Considering each pair of the three variables p, v, and T as independent, derive expressions for the enthalpy in terms of the specific heats, the state variables and their partial derivatives. For instance, in the case of p and v independent, obtain

$$dh = \left(v + \frac{\kappa}{\beta}c_v\right)dp + \frac{c_p}{\beta}\frac{dv}{v}$$

In the case of T and p independent, obtain

$$dh = c_p dT + \left[v - \frac{(c_p - c_v)\kappa}{\beta}\right]dp$$

Hint: Start with the differential of the internal energy, which, according to the first law, is a function of state, and may be written as

$$du = \left(\frac{\partial u}{\partial p}\right)_v dp + \left(\frac{\partial u}{\partial v}\right)_p dv$$

Eliminate $(\partial u/\partial p)_v$ and $(\partial u/\partial v)_p$ in favor of the specific heats, the state variables and their partial derivatives, then make use of the definition for enthalpy: $dh = du + pdv + vdp$.

CHAPTER 6

First Law Analysis of Steady-Flow

6.1 Flow Process and Control Volume

While discussing processes in the preceding chapter, attention was focused on a fixed mass of material (the thermodynamic system) and heat and work transfers at the system boundary were related to changes of energy within the boundary. Processes which are analyzed in this fashion are commonly known as *non-flow processes*

In many engineering installations, however, the natural focus of attention is of a piece of equipment through which material flows continuously in and out. An example of this is shown in Fig. 6.1. High-pressure and high-temperature fluid enters a turbine casing, passes between alternate rows of fixed and moving blades, and emerges with less internal energy

but with greater velocity than at its entry. Here, it would be too difficult
and impractical to follow the history of each element of fluid (the system)
in order to compute its energy changes and the heat and work interactions across its boundary. Instead, by a judicious selection of the
boundary, the average change of state of the fluid as it flows through the
turbine may be related to the shaft work delivered by the turbine and to
the heat transfer from the turbine. A process viewed in this fashion is
commonly known as a *flow process*.

In analyzing flow processes, a new
concept is introduced: the *control
volume*; a very useful concept whenever fluid flow is involved. Consider
again the example of Fig. 6.1. The
first and most important step is to
draw an imaginary envelope (in
dotted line) around the turbine.
This envelope cuts the entry and exhaust pipes at sections, marked 1
and 2, which are located sufficiently
upstream and downstream to damp
out fluctuations within the turbine.
Under these conditions, the flow
may be taken as steady, that is, invariant with time. The space bounded
by the imaginary envelope is called
the *control volume*; the envelope itself
is called the *control surface*. Thus, a
control volume is any volume that is
of fixed shape and position, relative
to an observer. In addition to matter which flows across the boundary,
external work (such as shaft work) and heat transfer are present. The
external work is indicated by an arrow and marked W; the heat transfer
is indicated by an arrow marked Q. The sign convention is the same as the
one adopted for systems in Sects. 2.1 and 3.6; namely, positive W is directed
out of the control volume, while positive Q is directed *into* the control
volume.

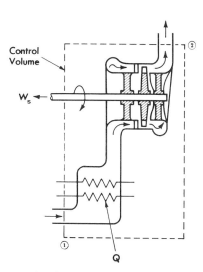

Fig. 6.1 Flow through Heating Chamber
and Turbine.

Note that the *control volume* and the *system* concepts have the common
feature of being defined by a boundary. The system-boundary may, and
usually does, change shape, position, and orientation relative to an observer.
The control-volume boundary does not. By definition, matter flows
across the control-volume boundary, but not across the system-boundary.
Because of these characteristics the control volume is sometimes labelled
an *open* system. This designation, however, is not recommended in this text

because of its inherent inconsistency (since by definition, a system is always *closed* as long as the principle of conservation of matter holds).

6.2 First Law of Thermodynamics for Control Volume

Consider the control volume in Fig. 6.2, with its contents shaded for convenience. Let m_1 denote a quantity of matter entering the control volume at point 1 and m_2 denote a quantity of matter leaving the control volume at point 2. Within the control volume, heat and work are exchanged

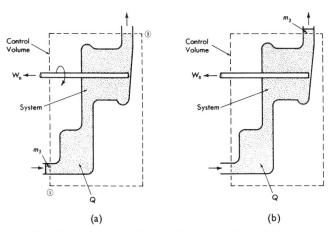

Fig. 6.2   Comparison Between System and Control Volume.

between the fluid and the surroundings. In order to make use of the first law which applies to a collection of matter, a system must first be chosen. Let the boundary of the system include the fluid contained in the control volume at any instant, plus the portion m_1 of the fluid about to enter the control volume. The system then undergoes a configuration change, from Fig. 6.2(a) to Fig. 6.2(b). In other words, starting at time $t = t_0$, the system is in the configuration of Fig. 6.2(a). At $t_0 + dt$, the system assumes the configuration of Fig. 6.2(b). Continuous flow may be regarded as a succession of these non-flow processes carried out for every element of fluid entering the control volume.

At any given point in the flow, an element of fluid has a relevant mechanical and thermodynamic state given by the mechanical and thermodynamic properties of the element as it flows through the control volume. Thus, if the element m_1 is moving with velocity $\mathscr{V}_1$ at a height z_1 above a reference level and is assumed small enough for the properties to be uniform throughout its extent, it possesses kinetic energy and potential energy in amount of $\dfrac{m_1}{2g_c}\mathscr{V}_1^2$ and $\dfrac{m_1 g}{g_c}z_1$ respectively. If $u_1 m_1$ is the internal energy of the element m_1, then the total energy of the element is given by

$$\left(u_1 + \frac{\mathscr{V}_1^2}{2g_c} + \frac{g}{g_c}z_1\right)m_1$$

The total energy of the system (m_1 + the mass in the control volume) at time $t = t_0$ is

$$E_1 = \left(u_1 + \frac{\mathscr{V}_1^2}{2g_c} + \frac{g}{g_c}z_1\right)m_1 + \left[\int_V e\rho dV\right]_{t_0} \tag{6.1}$$

where dV is an element of volume, and the integration over the control volume is taken over at time $t = t_0$.

At a later time $(t_0 + dt)$, the system has moved partly through the control volume. Its boundary is then as shown in Fig. 6.2(b), and its energy is

$$E_2 = \left(u_2 + \frac{\mathscr{V}_2^2}{2g_c} + \frac{g}{g_c}z_2\right)m_2 + \left[\int_V e\rho dV\right]_{t_0 + dt} \tag{6.2}$$

where the integration over the control volume is taken at time $t = t_0 + dt$. Subtracting Eq. (6.1) from Eq. (6.2) and dividing by dt gives the rate of energy change of the system:

$$\dot{E}_2 - \dot{E}_1 = \left(u_2 + \frac{\mathscr{V}_2^2}{2g_c} + \frac{g}{g_c}z_2\right)\dot{m}_2 - \left(u_1 + \frac{\mathscr{V}_1^2}{2g_c} + \frac{g}{g_c}z_1\right)\dot{m}_1 + \frac{\partial}{\partial t}\int_V e\rho dV \tag{6.3}$$

where the dot indicates time rate.

Now, according to the first law of thermodynamics,

$$Q = (E_2 - E_1) + W$$

or, in terms of time rates

$$\dot{Q} = (\dot{E}_2 - \dot{E}_1) + \dot{W} \tag{6.4}$$

The next step in the analysis is to apply Eq. (6.4). However, before doing this, the composition of the term W must first be discussed. Referring to Fig. 6.2, it is seen that total work is the sum of (1) the shaft work W_s, and (2) the displacement work done by the movement of the system boundary at sections 1 and 2. This displacement work is evaluated as follows: For the element m_1 to enter the control volume, the system must be compressed, decreasing its volume by $m_1 v_1$. This is accompanied by a force $p_1 A_1$ moving through a distance $m_1 v_1 / A_1$, where A_1 is the cross-sectional area of the control volume at point 1. The work done by the surroundings on the system is therefore $m_1 p_1 v_1$, and this is a minus quantity (according to the convention previously adopted). Similarly, for the element m_2 to leave the control volume at point 2, work of the amount $m_2 p_2 v_2$ must be done by the system, and this would be a plus quantity. The total work is thus

$$W = W_s + m_2 p_2 v_2 - m_1 p_1 v_1$$

or, dividing through by dt to obtain the rate:

$$\dot{W} = \dot{W}_s + \dot{m}_2 p_2 v_2 - \dot{m}_1 p_1 v_1 \tag{6.5}$$

Equations (6.3) and (6.5) allow the first law of thermodynamics, namely Eq. (6.4), to be written as

$$\dot{Q} = \left(u_2 + \frac{\mathscr{V}_2^2}{2g_c} + \frac{g}{g_c}z_2\right)\dot{m}_2 - \left(u_1 + \frac{\mathscr{V}_1^2}{2g_c} + \frac{g}{g_c}z_1\right)\dot{m}_1$$

$$+ \frac{\partial}{\partial t}\int_V e\rho\,dV + \dot{W}_s + p_2 v_2 \dot{m}_2 - p_1 v_1 \dot{m}_1$$

or

$$\left(u_1 + p_1 v_1 + \frac{\mathscr{V}_1^2}{2g_c} + \frac{g}{g_c}z_1\right)\dot{m}_1 + \dot{Q} =$$

$$= \left(u_2 + p_2 v_2 + \frac{\mathscr{V}_2^2}{2g_c} + \frac{g}{g_c}z_2\right)\dot{m}_2 + \dot{W} + \frac{\partial}{\partial t}\int_V e\rho\,dV \tag{6.6}$$

where the subscript s has been dropped from $\dot{W}$, if it is understood that W represents shaft work. (It is customary to leave out the subscript unless it is absolutely needed. Here, there is no possibility of confusion, since the flow work has been denoted by pv.)

Equation (6.6) is the *general energy equation* for flow systems in the absence of capillarity, electricity, and magnetism. An important equation in engineering science, it is applicable whether the flow rates and properties vary with time or not. For the special case which follows it is, however, used in a somewhat simpler form.

6.3   Steady-Flow Energy Equation

The general relation developed in the preceding section may be simplified if *steady-flow* conditions are assumed. These conditions are: (1) *that the mass rate of flow into and out of the control volume are equal and constant with respect to time, i.e.,*

$$\dot{m}_1 = \dot{m}_2 = \dot{m}$$

(2) *that the state of the fluid at any given location does not vary with time,*

i.e., all terms involving $\partial/\partial t$ *are zero:*

$$\frac{\partial}{\partial t}\int_V e\rho dV = 0$$

and (3) *that the rates of heat and work transfer are constant.* Under these conditions, Eq. (6.6) becomes

$$\dot{m}\left(u_1+p_1v_1+\frac{\mathscr{V}_1^2}{2g_c}+\frac{g}{g_c}z_1\right)+\dot{Q} = \dot{m}\left(u_2+p_2v_2+\frac{\mathscr{V}_2^2}{2g_c}+\frac{g}{g_c}z_2\right)+\dot{W} \qquad (6.7)$$

or, with $h = u+pv$,

$$\dot{m}\left(h_1+\frac{\mathscr{V}_1^2}{2g_c}+\frac{g}{g_c}z_1\right)+\dot{Q} = \dot{m}\left(h_2+\frac{\mathscr{V}_2^2}{2g_c}+\frac{g}{g_c}z_2\right)+\dot{W} \qquad (6.8)$$

Equation (6.8) is known as the *steady-flow energy equation*. It is written for any set of consistent units.

Example 6.1. A turbine, operating under steady-flow conditions, receives 10,000 pounds of steam per hour. The steam enters the turbine at a velocity of 8000 ft/min, an elevation of 13 ft, and a specific enthalpy of 1196 Btu/lbm. It leaves the turbine at a velocity of 18,000 ft/min, an elevation of 3 ft, and a specific enthalpy of 971 Btu/lbm. Heat losses from the turbine to the surroundings amount to 16,000 Btu/hr. Determine the horse-power output of the turbine.

Solution. This is a steady-flow system, so that Eq. (6.8) applies:

$$\dot{m}\left(h_1+\frac{\mathscr{V}_1^2}{2g_c}+\frac{g}{g_c}z_1\right)+\dot{Q} = \dot{m}\left(h_2+\frac{\mathscr{V}_2^2}{2g_c}+\frac{g}{g_c}z_2\right)+\dot{W}$$

Choosing Btu/hr as the consistent set of units:

$$10,000\left[1196+\frac{(8000/60)^2}{(2)(32.2)(778)}+\frac{(32.2)(13)}{(32.2)(778)}\right]-16,000 =$$

$$= 10,000\left[971+\frac{(18,000/60)^2}{(2)(32.2)(778)}+\frac{(32.2)(3)}{(32.2)(778)}\right]+\dot{W}$$

Notice that the kinetic and potential energies are quite small in comparison with the other terms. Consequently, they can be dropped without appreciable error:

$$(10,000)(1196)-16,000 = (10,000)(971)+\dot{W}$$
$$\dot{W} = 2,234,000 \text{ Btu/hr}$$

Since 2,545 Btu/hr = 1 hp, the rate of work done is

$$W = \frac{2,234,000}{2,545} = 878 \text{ hp}$$

Notice also that in steady-flow, the mass, heat, and work transfer rates are constant with respect to time, so the dots may be omitted in Eq. (6.8). An alternate for the steady-flow energy equation is thus

$$m\left(h_1 + \frac{\mathscr{V}_1^2}{2g_c} + \frac{g}{g_c}z_1\right) + Q = m\left(h_2 + \frac{\mathscr{V}_2^2}{2g_c} + \frac{g}{g_c}z_2\right) + W$$

or, on a per unit mass basis, is

$$h_1 + \frac{\mathscr{V}_1^2}{2g_c} + \frac{g}{g_c}z_1 + q = h_2 + \frac{\mathscr{V}_2^2}{2g_c} + \frac{g}{g_c}z_2 + w \tag{6.9}$$

Equation (6.9) is a form of the first law popular in engineering applications involving the flow of fluids. If the ft lbf is chosen as the unit of energy, if Eq. (6.9) is multiplied throughout by g_c/g, where g_c = lbm ft/lbf sec², and if g is the local acceleration of gravity, each term will be in units of *feet*. For example, the dimension of the first term will be

$$\left(\frac{\text{Btu}}{\text{lbm}}\right)\left(\frac{778 \text{ ft lbf}}{\text{Btu}}\right)\left(\frac{\text{lbm ft/lbf sec}^2}{\text{ft/sec}^2}\right) = \text{ft}$$

The dimension of the second term is,

$$\frac{(\text{ft/sec})^2}{\text{lbm ft/lbf sec}^2} \cdot \frac{\text{lbm ft/lbf sec}^2}{\text{ft/sec}^2} = \text{ft}$$

and likewise for the other terms. Hydraulic engineers often refer to these terms as *heads,* or more specifically as "enthalpy head," "velocity head," or "potential head." In each case, the feet referred to are the *feet of fluid* flowing through the control volume.

6.4 Continuity Equation in Steady-Flow

In the solution of flow problems it is often necessary to make use of the relationship between velocity, area, and specific volume. This relationship, known as the equation of continuity, will now be derived for the case of one-dimensional steady-flow.

Consider a stream-tube* segment, as shown in Fig. 6.3. If the flow is steady, the mass of fluid passing through a given section must equal the mass passing through all other sections, i.e.,

$$\rho_1 \mathscr{V}_1 A_1 = \rho_2 \mathscr{V}_2 A_2 = \rho_3 \mathscr{V}_3 A_3 = \text{- - -}$$

---

* A stream-tube is an imaginary pipe enclosing the flow which is of sufficiently small cross-section for the velocity to be taken as uniform across the cross-section. Fluid passes through the ends of the tube, but not through the sides.

where ρ denotes density, $\mathscr{V}$ velocity, and A area. An equivalent statement is

$$\rho \mathscr{V} A = \text{constant} \quad (6.10)$$

Equation (6.10) is known as the *continuity equation* for steady, one-dimensional flow. By using logarithmic differentiation, or by taking the differential and dividing by the original equation, it is often written in the form

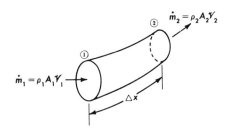

$$\frac{d\rho}{\rho} + \frac{d\mathscr{V}}{\mathscr{V}} + \frac{dA}{A} = 0 \quad (6.11)$$

Fig. 6.3 Flow through Tube Segment.

The continuity equation is the mathematical statement of the principle of conservation of mass. It often provides a second equation, in addition to the first law, which is of great help in the solution of engineering problems.

Example 6.2. The density of a certain gas flowing in a pipe is 0.075 lbm/cu ft; at some section downstream, the density is 0.055 lbm/cu ft. If the velocity upstream is 20 fps, what is the velocity downstream?

Solution. Let subscripts 1 and 2 denote upstream and downstream conditions. Then, from continuity,

$$\rho_1 \mathscr{V}_1 A_1 = \rho_2 \mathscr{V}_2 A_2$$

and, since $A_1 = A_2$,

$$\frac{\mathscr{V}_2}{\mathscr{V}_1} = \frac{\rho_1}{\rho_2}$$

or

$$\mathscr{V}_2 = (20)\frac{0.075}{(0.055)} = 27.3 \text{ fps}$$

6.5 Relations for Flow Processes

Having developed the steady-flow energy equation, what remains to be done is to apply it to the various processes encountered in engineering. In other words, the same thing that was done for non-flow processes should now be done for flow processes. This repetition, however, is unnecessary because the previous results hold, with the exception of the expression for work. It is only necessary to remember that the fundamental difference between non-flow processes and flow processes is that in the latter case flow work pv must be included as an energy quantity.

For convenience, let a flow system of unit mass be considered. The energy equation for steady-flow is

$$h_1 + \frac{\mathscr{V}_1^2}{2g_c} + \frac{g}{g_c}z_1 + q = h_2 + \frac{\mathscr{V}_2^2}{2g_c} + \frac{g}{g_c}z_2 + w$$

This may be written in differential form as

$$dh + d\left(\frac{\mathscr{V}^2}{2g_c}\right) + d\left(\frac{g}{g_c}z\right) = dq - dw$$

Since $h = u + pv$, dh may be replaced by $du + pdv + vdp$, so that

$$du + pdv + vdp + d\left(\frac{\mathscr{V}^2}{2g_c}\right) + z\left(\frac{g}{g_c}z\right) = dq - dw \qquad (6.12)$$

Now, insofar as the fluid is concerned, i.e., to an observer travelling with the fluid, $du + pdv = dq$, so that Eq. (6.12) becomes

$$vdp + d\left(\frac{\mathscr{V}^2}{2g_c}\right) + d\left(\frac{g}{g_c}z\right) = -dw$$

or

$$w = -\int_{p_1}^{p_2} vdp - \frac{\mathscr{V}_2^2 - \mathscr{V}_1^2}{2g_c} - \frac{g}{g_c}(z_2 - z_1) \qquad (6.13)$$

which, in the case of negligible kinetic and potential energy changes, becomes

$$w = -\int_1^2 vdp \qquad (6.14)$$

Equation (6.14) is notwworthy. It not only gives the work for a steady-flow process but also points out the fundamental difference in the work term for a flow process and a non-flow process. Recall that, in the case of a non-flow process, the work was equal to

$$\int_1^2 pdv$$

Equation (6.14), however, states that the work in the case of a flow process, where kinetic and potential energy changes are negligible, is

$$-\int_1^2 vdp$$

The comparison of the two cases is shown by the shaded areas in Fig. 6.4.

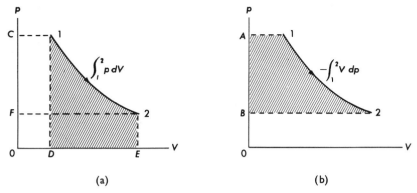

(a) (b)

Fig. 6.4 Work for Non-Flow and Flow Processes.

The result could have been anticipated by noting that the area
A–1–2–B in Fig. 6.4(b) is given by $- \int_1^2 v\,dp$ (the minus sign gives a positive
number for the integral in the case of an expansion process such as the
one shown). This area can be obtained from Fig. 6.4(a) by writing

$$p_1 v_1 + \int_1^2 p\,dv - p_2 v_2 = \text{area C–1–2–F} \tag{6.15}$$

The term $p_1 v_1$ represented by the area 0–C–1–D is the flow work brought
into the control volume by virtue of the incoming fluid. The term $\int_1^2 p\,dv$
(represented by the area D–1–2–E) is the work within the control volume.
The term $-p_2 v_2$ (represented by the area E–2–F–0) is the flow work leaving
the control volume by virtue of the outgoing fluid. The sum of the terms
on the left hand side of Eq. (6.15) represents the work in a steady-flow
process, and since the area C–1–2–F in Fig. 6.4(a) equals the area A–1–2–B
in Fig. 6.4(b), Eq. (6.15) becomes

$$w = p_1 v_1 + \int_1^2 p\,dv - p_2 v_2 = \text{area A–1–2–B} = - \int_1^2 v\,dp$$

which is the same as Eq. (6.14).

Example 6.3. A pump receives water at 15 psia and delivers it at 100 psia.
Neglecting volume, elevation, and velocity changes of the water, find the required work per pound of water. The specific volume of water is 0.016 cu ft/lbm.

Solution. This is a steady-flow system; consequently

$$w_s = - \int_{p_1}^{p_2} v\,dp = v(p_1 - p_2) =$$
$$= 0.016(144)(15 - 100) = -196 \frac{\text{ft lbf}}{\text{lbm}} = -0.252 \frac{\text{Btu}}{\text{lbm}}$$

Note that pdv of non-flow is precisely zero. The flow work constitutes the whole answer in this case.

6.6 Throttling Process

A process of considerable importance which has not yet been mentioned is the throttling process, based on the Joule-Thomson* experiment as

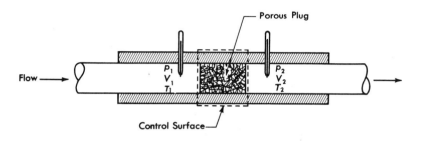

Fig. 6.5 Joule-Thomson Experiment.

shown in Fig. 6.5. A continuous stream of gas at a pressure p_1 and temperature T_1 flows through a porous plug in a tube and emerges at a lower pressure p_2. The entire installation is thermally insulated. The process can be analyzed by the usual technique of following the system as it flows through the plug. However, as a variation, the following analysis is used instead:

$$\begin{bmatrix} \text{Energy entering} \\ \text{control volume} \end{bmatrix} - \begin{bmatrix} \text{Energy leaving} \\ \text{control volume} \end{bmatrix} = \begin{bmatrix} \text{Energy stored in} \\ \text{control volume} \end{bmatrix}$$

Under steady-state conditions there is no change in energy stored in the control volume, and the first law reduces to

$$\begin{bmatrix} \text{Energy entering} \\ \text{control volume} \end{bmatrix} = \begin{bmatrix} \text{Energy leaving} \\ \text{control volume} \end{bmatrix}$$

Applying this to the problem at hand, it is seen that the energy entering the control volume is

$$m_1\left(u_1 + \frac{\mathscr{V}_1^2}{2g_c} + p_1 v_1 + \frac{g}{g_c} z_1\right)$$

---

* Also known as Joule-Kelvin experiment (Thomson was knighted Lord Kelvin).

while the energy leaving the control volume is

$$m_2\left(u_2 + \frac{\mathscr{V}_2^2}{2g_c} + p_2 v_2 + \frac{g}{g_c} z_2\right)$$

Equating the energy entering to the energy leaving (and noting that $m_1 = m_2$) given

$$u + \frac{\mathscr{V}_1^2}{2g_c} + p_1 v_1 + \frac{g}{g_c} z_1 = u_2 + \frac{\mathscr{V}_2^2}{2g_c} + p_2 v_2 + \frac{g}{g_c} z_2$$

If changes in kinetic and potential energies are neglected, this becomes

$$u_1 + p_1 v_1 = u_2 + p_2 v_2$$

or

$$h_1 = h_2 \qquad (6.16)$$

Equation (6.16), which states that the initial and final enthalpies are equal, is characteristic of a process which occurs whenever a fluid expands from a region of high pressure to a region of lower pressure, exchanges no heat with its surroundings, does no work, and whose kinetic and potential energies do not change. Such a process is usually referred to as *throttling*. This situation is encountered in pipe flow whenever a valve, friction, or other restrictive device is present. Figure 6.6. illustrates the throttling of a fluid by means of a partially opened valve in a pipe line. Throttling is essentially an irreversible process: it degrades energy that could have been converted into work and dissipates it in the form of aimless turbulence. The ratio of the temperature change to the pressure change in a throttling process is

$$\mu_J = \left(\frac{\partial T}{\partial p}\right)_h \qquad (6.17)$$

This is called the *Joule-Thomson coefficient*. A positive μ_J means that the temperature of the gas drops during throttling; a negative μ_J means that the temperature rises during throttling. A more detailed discussion of this coefficient will be given later in the text.

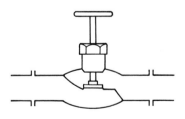

Fig. 6.6
Throttling Process in a Pipe Line.

6.7 Comparison of Steady-Flow Energy Equation with Euler and Bernoulli Equations

By now it should be clear that the thermodynamics and mechanics of flow processes are intimately related. In this section, a short discussion is devoted to clarifying the distinction between the steady-flow energy equation and two equations which are of importance in the science of fluid mechanics: the Euler equation and the Bernoulli equation. This is in order because the steady-flow energy equation is often confused with one or the other of these equations.

Consider a fluid element of cross-section dA flowing along a stream-tube, as shown in Fig. 6.7. Let z be the height measured vertically above

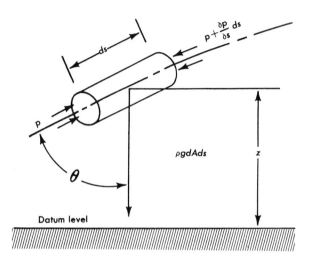

Fig. 6.7 Steady-Flow in Stream-Tube.

a fixed datum level, s be the distance measured along the axis of the stream-tube, θ be the angle the streamline makes with the vertical direction, and ρ be the density (lbm per unit volume). Newton's second law of motion (mass times acceleration = summation of forces) gives

$$\frac{\rho}{g_c} dA\, ds\, \frac{d\mathcal{V}}{dt} = p\, dA - \left(p + \frac{\partial p}{\partial s} ds\right) dA - \rho \frac{g}{g_c} dA\, ds \cos\theta$$

$$= -\frac{\partial p}{\partial s} ds\, dA - \rho \frac{g}{g_c} dA\, ds \cos\theta$$

or

$$\frac{\rho}{g_c} \frac{d\mathcal{V}}{dt} = -\frac{\partial p}{\partial s} - \rho \frac{g}{g_c} \cos\theta \qquad (6.18)$$

Now, $d\mathscr{V}$ can be written as

$$d\,\mathscr{V} = \frac{\partial \mathscr{V}}{\partial s}\,ds + \frac{\partial \mathscr{V}}{\partial t}\,dt$$

Substituting this in Eq. (6.18) gives

$$\left(\frac{\partial \mathscr{V}}{\partial s}\frac{ds}{dt} + \frac{\partial \mathscr{V}}{\partial t}\right) = -\frac{\partial p}{\partial s} - \rho\frac{g}{g_c}\cos\theta \qquad (6.19)$$

Under steady-flow conditions $\partial/\partial t = 0$, $\partial/\partial s = d/ds$, so that Eq. (6.19) becomes

$$\frac{\rho}{g_c}\frac{\partial \mathscr{V}}{ds}\frac{ds}{dt} = -\frac{dp}{ds} - \rho\frac{g}{g_c}\cos\theta \qquad (6.20)$$

But $ds/dt = \mathscr{V}$ and $\cos\theta = dz/ds$. Thus, Eq. (6.20) may be written as

$$\frac{\rho}{g_c}\mathscr{V}\frac{d\mathscr{V}}{ds} = -\frac{dp}{ds} - \rho\frac{g}{g_c}\frac{dz}{ds}$$

or

$$\frac{dp}{\rho} + \frac{\mathscr{V}d\mathscr{V}}{g_c} + \frac{g}{g_c}dz = 0 \qquad (6.21)$$

Equation (6.21) is the *Euler equation*. Notice that it has been derived from considerations of momentum. Its restrictions are the following: (1) steady-flow, (2) absence of friction (since no shear stresses were included in the summation of forces),* and (3) absence of shaft or stirring work, and (4) absence of capillary, electric, and magnetic effects.

To integrate Eq. (6.21), the relation between p and ρ must be known. In the case of an incompressible fluid (ρ = constant), and Eq. (6.21) becomes

$$\frac{1}{\rho}(p_2 - p_1) + \frac{\mathscr{V}_2^{\,2} - \mathscr{V}_1^{\,2}}{2g_c} + \frac{g}{g_c}(z_2 - z_1) = 0$$

or

$$\frac{p_1}{\rho} + \frac{\mathscr{V}_1^{\,2}}{2g_c} + \frac{g}{g_c}z_1 = \frac{p_2}{\rho} + \frac{\mathscr{V}_2^{\,2}}{2g_c} + \frac{g}{g_c}z_2 \qquad (6.22)$$

Equation (6.22) is the *Bernoulli equation*. Its conditions of validity are the same as those for the Euler equation. Note that the dimensions are energy per unit mass (ft lbf/lbm). If Eq. (6.21) is multiplied throughout by g_c/g, each term will be in units of *feet*. Bernoulli's equation expressed verbally is: *In the absence of viscosity or turbulence, the total head (ft)*

---

* A *Euler equation* may be derived by including frictional forces, but it is seldom used as such.

representing the sum of the pressure head, the velocity head, and the static head is constant along a streamline.

Equation (6.21) is often referred to as an energy equation, because it proves to be a restricted form of the steady-flow energy equation. To show the connection between the two, let Eq. (6.9), (the steady-flow energy equation per unit mass) be applied to two sections which are an infinitesimal distance apart along the streamline. This is shown in Fig. 6.8. Then,

$$dh + d\left(\frac{\mathscr{V}^2}{2g_c}\right) + d\left(\frac{g}{g_c}z\right) - dq + dw = 0$$

Moreover, if the shaft work is zero,

$$dh + d\left(\frac{\mathscr{V}^2}{2g_c}\right) + d\left(\frac{g}{g_c}z\right) - dq = 0$$

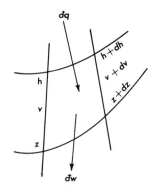

Fig. 6.8 Derivation of Euler Equation from First-Law Considerations.

or, upon replacing dh by $du + pdv + vdp$,

$$du + pdv + vdp + d\left(\frac{\mathscr{V}^2}{2g_c}\right) + d\left(\frac{g}{g_c}z\right) - dq = 0 \tag{6.23}$$

For an observer who is traveling *with* the system (fluid), the first law states that

$$du + pdv - dq = 0$$

and consequently Eq. (6.23) becomes

$$vdp + d\left(\frac{\mathscr{V}^2}{2g_c}\right) + d\left(\frac{g}{g_c}z\right) = 0 \tag{6.24}$$

Equation (6.24) is the same as Eq. (6.21) which was derived from Newton's laws of motion long before the first law of thermodynamics was enunciated. This has led to the belief that the steady-flow energy equation is merely an extended form of the Euler equation. This is not so; Euler's equation is based only on Newton's second law of motion, whereas the steady-flow energy equation is based on Newton's second law of motion *and* on the first law of thermodynamics. The latter is valid whether friction is present or not. In other words, the steady-flow energy equation is general; the Euler and Bernoulli equations are not.

Example 6.4. Water (of density 62.4 lbm/cu ft) flows through a pump at the rate of 965 gallons per minute. It enters the pump at a pressure of 10 psig, a velocity of 128 ft/min, and an elevation 4 ft below the center line of the pump. It leaves the pump at a pressure of 50 psig, a velocity of 170 ft/min, and an elevation 2 ft below the center line of the pump. Determine (a) the ft of total head, and (b) the hydraulic horsepower.

Solution. (a) Since 1 gallon of water weighs 8.33 pounds, 965 gpm = 8000 lbm/min. Equation (6.23), when integrated, has a constant on the right-hand side. If this constant is to be in units of feet, the equation must be multiplied by g_c/g. However, g can be considered as numerically equal to g_c in most cases, so that the total head is simply,

$$h_t = \frac{1}{62.4}[(50)(144) - (10)(144)] + \left[\frac{(170/60)^2}{(2)(32.2)} - \frac{(128/60)^2}{(2)(32.2)}\right]$$

$$+[(-2)-(-4)] = 92.5 + 0.1 + 2 = 94.6 \text{ ft}$$

Notice the small value of the velocity head as compared to the pressure and potential heads. This is often the case with hydraulic systems.

(b) The hydraulic horsepower is the power necessary to lift 8000 pounds of water per minute to a height of 94.6 ft:

$$\text{Hydraulic hp} = \frac{(m)(g/g_c)(h_t)}{(33,000 \text{ ft lbf/hp})}$$

$$= \frac{(8000 \text{ lbm/min})\left(\dfrac{32.2 \text{ ft/sec}^2}{32.2 \text{ lbm ft/lbf sec}^2}\right)(94.6 \text{ ft})}{(33,000 \text{ ft lbf/hp min})}$$

$$= 23 \text{ hp}$$

6.8 Flow Measurement

A topic of considerable importance in engineering is the measurement of flow. This is especially evident when it is realized that a knowledge of velocities and flow rates is essential in the solution of many problems. The development of the continuity equation and the Euler equation affords a good opportunity to discuss flow measurement. The following devices for measuring flow are all based on the equations developed in the preceding sections.

Pitot Tube. This is an important instrument which measures the actual velocity of flow at a local point. It is illustrated in Fig. 6.9. Suppose a body of fluid passes point 1 with certain conditions of pressure, velocity, specific volume, and temperature. A pitot tube is a small tube inserted in a stream of flowing fluid with the open end facing upstream. The fluid enters the tube, and is brought to rest, thus developing a stagnation or total pressure. Manometers connected to measure the difference between total pressure and static pressure enable the velocity of the fluid to be calculated.

Neglecting heat transfer, shaft work, and elevation change, the energy balance between points 1 and 2 is given by Eq. (6.9);

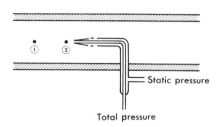

Fig. 6.9 Pitot-Static Tube.

$$h_1 + \frac{\mathscr{V}_1^2}{2g_c} = h_2$$

or

$$\mathscr{V}_1 = \sqrt{2g_c(h_2 - h_1)}$$

For a compressible fluid obeying the perfect gas relations of $pv = RT$ and $h = c_p T$, this becomes

$$\mathscr{V}_1 = \sqrt{2g_c c_p (T_2 - T_1)} = \sqrt{2g_c c_p T_1[(T_2/T_1) - 1]}$$

$$= \sqrt{2g_c c_p T_1[(p_2/p_1)^{(\gamma-1)/\gamma} - 1]} \qquad (6.25)$$

Here, p_2 is the stagnation or total pressure, p_1 is the static pressure, and $\gamma \ (= c_p/c_v)$ is the exponent of the path of compression, $pv^\gamma = $ constant.

For an incompressible fluid, $h = u + pv$, and $u_2 = u_1$ so that Eq. (6.9) gives

$$\mathscr{V}_1 = \sqrt{2g_c(p_2 v_2 - p_1 v_1)} = \sqrt{2g_c v_1(p_2 - p_2)} \qquad (6.26)$$

since $v_2 = v_1$ for an incompressible fluid. Eq. (6.26) may be used to approximate compressible-flow if the velocity is small (relative to the speed of sound in the flowing medium).

Venturi. A venturi-meter is shown diagramatically in Fig. 6.10. It

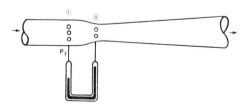

Fig. 6.10 Venturi-Meter.

operates by restricting the area of flow. If A_1 and A_2 are the cross-sectional areas corresponding to the pressure tappings, and if the fluid is considered incompressible, Bernoulli's equation

$$\frac{p_1}{\rho} + \frac{\mathscr{V}_1^{\,2}}{2g_c} = \frac{p_2}{\rho} + \frac{\mathscr{V}_2^{\,2}}{2g_c}$$

and the continuity equation

$$A_1\mathscr{V}_1 = A_2\mathscr{V}_2$$

combine to give

$$\mathscr{V}_1 = \sqrt{\frac{2g_c(p_1-p_2)}{\rho[(A_1^{\,2}/A_2^{\,2})-1]}}$$

and, therefore, a theoretical discharge of

$$Q = A_1\mathscr{V}_1 = A_1\sqrt{\frac{2g_c(p_1-p_2)}{\rho[(A_1^{\,2}/A_2^{\,2})-1]}} \tag{6.27}$$

Because of non-uniformity of the velocity distribution and frictional effects, the actual discharge will be less than the theoretical value given by Eq. (6.27). The theoretical discharge is, therefore, multiplied by a discharge coefficient C to give the actual discharge:

$$Q_{\text{actual}} = CA_1\sqrt{\frac{2g_c(p_1-p_2)}{\rho[(A_1^{\,2}/A_2^{\,2})-1]}} \tag{6.28}$$

For a well designed venturi-meter, the value of C is between 0.95 and 0.98.

Orifice-plate. The orifice-plate works on the same principle as a Venturi-meter, and the resulting equations are the same; namely,

$$Q = A_1\sqrt{\frac{2g_c(p_1-p_2)}{\rho[(A_1^{\,2}/A_2^{\,2})-1]}}$$

and

$$Q_{\text{actual}} = CA_1\sqrt{\frac{2g_c(p_1-p_2)}{\rho[(A_1^{\,2}/A_2^{\,2})-1]}}$$

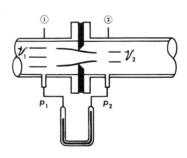

A_1 is the cross-sectional area of the pipe, and A_2 is the area of the orifice. The numerical value of C, the discharge coefficient, is around 0.62.

Fig. 6.11 Orifice-Meter.

Rotameter. The preceding devices depend on the measurement of a variable pressure difference. A rotameter, on the other hand, depends on the measurement of a variable flow area by means of the location of a float inside a tapered glass tube. This is shown in Fig. 6.12. The annular passage between the float and the tapered tube may be regarded as an orifice. Thus, the equation for an orifice applies:

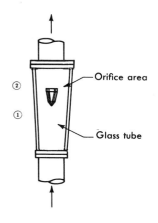

Orifice area

②

①

Glass tube

$$Q_{\text{actual}} = CA_1 \sqrt{\frac{2g_c(p_1 - p_2)}{\rho[(A_1{}^2/A_2{}^2) - 1]}} \quad (6.29)$$

The pressure difference $(p_1 - p_2)$, practically constant, is fixed by the weight of the float, and A_1 and A_1/A_2 are determined by the geometry of the instrument and the position of the float. In practice, the instrument is simply calibrated to provide a scale of volume flow against height of float.

Fig. 6.12 Rotameter

Example 6.5. The stagnation or total pressure measured from a Pitot tube in a flow of air is 16 psia, while the static pressure is 14 psia. The stagnation temperature is 85 °F (this is the temperature measured by a thermometer or a thermocouple inserted into the flow: it records the temperature of the fluid brought to a stop, and not of the fluid in motion). Determine the actual fluid temperature and the flow velocity. Consider air as a perfect gas $(pv = RT)$ having a specific heat at constant pressure of $c_p = 0.24$ Btu/lbm-°R, a ratio of specific heats $\gamma = 1.4$, and a gas constant $R = 53.3$ ft lbf/lbm-°R.

Solution. From $p_1 v_1{}^\gamma = p_2 v_2{}^\gamma$ the following may be written

$$p_1{}^{1/\gamma} v_1 = p_2{}^{1/\gamma} v_2$$

Replacing v_1 by RT_1/p_1 and v_2 by RT_2/p_2, this becomes

$$p_1{}^{1/\gamma}\left(\frac{T_1}{p_1}\right) = p_2{}^{1/\gamma}\left(\frac{T_2}{p_2}\right)$$

or

$$\frac{T_2}{T_1} = \left(\frac{p_2}{p_1}\right)^{(\gamma-1)/\gamma}$$

Here, $T_2 = 85\ °F = 545\ °R$ $p_2 = 16$ psia, and $p_1 = 14$ psia. Thus,

$$\frac{545}{T_1} = \left(\frac{16}{14}\right)^{(1.4-1)/1.4} = 1.039$$

whence

$$T_1 = 525 \,°R = 65 \,°F$$

The flow velocity is obtained from Eq. (6.25),

$$\mathscr{V}_2 = \sqrt{2g_c c_p T_1 \left[\left(\frac{p_2}{p_1}\right)^{(\gamma-1)/\gamma} - 1\right]}$$

Before substituting into this equation, the student should note that the quantity under the radical has units of

$$\left(\frac{\text{lbm ft}}{\text{lbf sec}^2}\right)\left(\frac{\text{Btu}}{\text{lbm-}°R}\right)(°R) = \frac{\text{ft Btu}}{\text{lbf sec}^2}$$

Therefore, it is necessary to multiply by 778 ft lbf/Btu in order to obtain ft^2/sec^2. Performing this gives

$$\mathscr{V}_1 = \sqrt{(2)(32.2)(0.24)(525)[1.039 - 1](778)}$$

$$= 495 \text{ ft/sec}$$

It is of interest to know what the answer would have been if the simpler formula for incompressible flow, namely Eq. (6.26), had been used instead:

$$\mathscr{V}_1 = \sqrt{2g_c v_1 (p_2 - p_1)}$$

Here,

$$v_1 = \frac{RT_1}{p_1} = \frac{(53.3)(525)}{(14)(144)} = 13.9 \text{ ft}^3/\text{lbm}$$

Thus,

$$\mathscr{V}_1 = \sqrt{2(32.2)(13.9)(16-14)(144)} = 509 \text{ ft/sec}$$

6.9 Engineering Applications of Steady-Flow Energy Equation

While it is not the intent to list here all of the possible applications of the steady-flow energy equation, it is desirable that a number of examples be given to illustrate the wide use of this equation in engineering problems. The following are typical examples of steady-flow installations. It is well to keep in mind that is is not necessary to carry along all the terms listed in the steady-flow energy equation but that practice will establish which terms to cancel out or to neglect. The accompanying results, while important, should not be memorized. They are included merely to show how the analysis is performed.

Insulated Duct. Consider the adiabatic flow of a fluid in an insulated pipe or duct, as shown in Fig. 6.13. Leaving out irrelevant terms such as heat transfer, potential energy, and shaft work, the steady-flow energy equation yields

$$h_1 + \frac{\mathscr{V}_1^2}{2g_c} = h_2 + \frac{\mathscr{V}_2^2}{2g_c} \qquad (6.30)$$

Fig. 6.13 Insulated Duct.

Equation (6.30) holds true whether friction at the wall is appreciable or not, for it states, in effect, that energy is conserved. It is often convenient to unite h and $(\mathscr{V}^2/2g_c)$ in a single term. Thus, the *stagnation enthalpy*, h_0, is defined as

$$h_0 = h + \frac{\mathscr{V}^2}{2g_c} \qquad (6.31)$$

Note that h_0 is the value that h would take if the fluid is made stagnant, that is if it is brought to rest reversibly and adiabatically. Equation (6.30) states that, in adiabatic steady-flow, with no shaft work and no potential energy change, the stagnation enthalpy remains the same.

Nozzle and Diffuser. A nozzle is a device in which the kinetic energy of a flowing fluid is increased as a result of a drop in pressure. Fig. 6.14(a) shows a subsonic nozzle. The energy equation for a nozzle is

$$h_1 + \frac{\mathscr{V}_1^2}{2g_c} = h_2 + \frac{\mathscr{V}_2^2}{2g_c}$$

or

$$\mathscr{V}_2^2 - \mathscr{V}_1^2 = 2g_c(h_1 - h_2)$$

Now, $\mathscr{V}_1$ and $\mathscr{V}_2$ are related by the continuity equation

$$A_1 \mathscr{V}_1 / v_1 = A_2 \mathscr{V}_2 / v_2 \text{ should be;}$$

$$\mathscr{V}_1^2 = \mathscr{V}_2^2 (A_2 v_1 / A_1 v_2)^2$$

Hence

$$\mathscr{V}_2^2 \left[1 - \left(\frac{A_2 v_1}{A_1 v_2} \right)^2 \right] = 2g_c(h_1 - h_2)$$

or

$$\mathscr{V}_2 = \left[\frac{1}{1 - (A_2 v_1 / A_1 v_2)^2} \right]^{1/2} \sqrt{2g_c(h_1 - h_2)} \qquad (6.32)$$

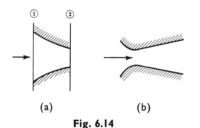

(a)   (b)

Fig. 6.14

Subsonic Nozzle and Diffuser

The quantity within brackets is a correction for initial velocity; its value is usually unity, and consequently

$$\mathscr{V}_2 = \sqrt{2g_c(h_1 - h_2)} \qquad (6.33)$$

For a compressible fluid, obeying the perfect gas relations of $pv = RT$ and $h = c_p T$, Eq. (6.33) becomes

$$2 = \sqrt{2g_c c_p (T_1 - T_2)} = \sqrt{2g_c c_p T_1 (1 - T_2/T_1)}$$

$$= \sqrt{2g_c c_p T_1 [1 - (p_2/p_1)^{(\gamma-1)/\gamma}]} \qquad (6.34)$$

Where $\gamma = c_p/c_v$ is the exponent for the path of expansion, $pv^\gamma = $ constant.

Reversing the process in a nozzle results in a compression of the fluid at the expense of its kinetic energy. A device in which this occurs is called a *diffuser*; it is shown in Fig. 6.14(b). The shape of a diffuser differs somewhat from that of a nozzle because of the difficulty in having the fluid fill a diverging passage. The same equations apply to a diffuser as to a nozzle.

Boiler. Boilers, condensers, and evaporators have as their main function the transfer of heat to or from a steady-flowing medium. A boiler may be analyzed as a steady-flow system by selecting a control volume, as shown in Fig. 6.15. The velocities of flow, in and out, are rather equal; the difference in height, between inlet and outlet, is often neglected; and there is no shaft work. The steady-flow energy equation then gives

$$u_1 + p_1 v_1 + q = u_2 + p_2 v_2$$

or

$$q = h_2 - h_1 \qquad (6.35)$$

here, q may be thought of as occurring at the expense of the "chemical energy" of the fuel used in the boiler.

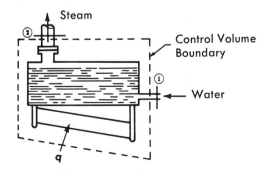

Fig. 6.15 Boiler.

Condenser. As in the case of a boiler, the primary objective of a condenser is to transfer heat. Figure 6.16 illustrates a surface condenser.

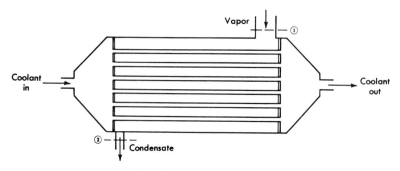

Fig. 6.16   Surface Condenser.

Vapor, passing over a bank of tubes, is condensed as it comes into contact with the surface of the tubes; the tubes being maintained at a lower temperature than the vapor by the flow of cooling water. Let m_A denote the mass rate of fluid A (vapor) and m_B denote the mass of fluid B (coolant). Neglecting changes in elevation and velocity, the steady-flow energy equation gives

$$m_A h_{A_{in}} + m_B h_{B_{in}} = m_A h_{A_{out}} + m_B h_{B_{out}}$$

or

$$m_A(h_{A_{in}} - h_{A_{out}}) = m_B(h_{B_{out}} - h_{B_{in}}) \qquad (6.36)$$

Evaporator. Figure 6.17 shows the evaporator of a refrigerating installation. Freon enters a coil (in contact with the air in a refrigerator cabinet)

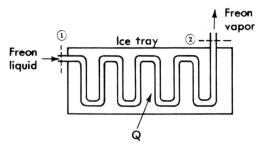

Fig. 6.17   Evaporator.

as a liquid and leaves as vapor. Notice that this is the reverse of the process occurring in a condenser. Inlet and outlet velocities are small; there is no shaft work and no elevation changes. The steady-flow energy equation becomes simply

$$q = h_2 - h_1 \tag{6.37}$$

When the specific enthalpy of the Freon at inlet and at exit is known, the refrigeration capacity can be determined by using Eq. (6.37).

Combustion Chamber. Imagine the combustion chamber of a gas turbine or the furnace of a steam power plant to be as shown in Fig. 6.18.

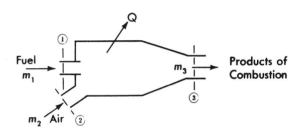

Fig. 6.18 Combustion Chamber.

Fuel enters at section 1 at a rate m_1, air enters at section 2 at a rate m_2, and combustion products leave at section 3 at a rate m_3. The material balance is

$$m_1 + m_2 = m_3 \tag{6.38}$$

Neglecting velocity changes, the energy balance is

$$m_1 h_1 + m_2 h_2 + m_1 Q_f = m_3 h_3 + Q \tag{6.39}$$

where q_f is the chemical energy or heat released by the combustion of a unit mass of fuel. Eqs. (6.38) and (6.39) are to be solved simultaneously.

Turbine and Compressor. A turbine is a device for extracting work from a flowing fluid expanding from a high pressure to a low pressure. Fig. 6.19 illustrates a turbine; the expanding fluid is accelerated in a set of fixed nozzles, and the resulting high-speed jet is directed toward a row of curved blades attached to a

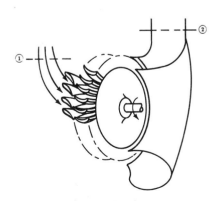

Fig. 6.19 Turbine.

rotor. The fluid changes direction as it passes over the blades; thus, a force is exerted on the blades equal to the fluid's rate of momentum change. The absolute velocities of the fluid at the inlet and the outlet of the turbine are approximately equal. Neglecting heat losses to surroundings, the work done per unit mass of fluid is

$$w = h_1 - h_2 \qquad (6.40)$$

Equation (6.40) enables the power to be calculated if the mass flow rate is known.

A *rotary compressor* may be regarded as a reversed turbine, doing work on a fluid to *raise* its pressure. The bladed rotor, driven from an external source, increases the velocity of the fluid. The fluid then flows through a set of diffusers which reduce its velocity to a value approximately equal to that at the inlet to the compressor. Equation (6.40) applies, but w will be negative because h_2 is greater than h_1.

A steady-state may be assumed for a *reciprocating compressor*, such as that shown in Fig. 6.20, if a receiver of big enough capacity is inserted in the discharge line to damp out the pulsations. Some heat transfer, however, does occur in a reciprocating compressor because of (1) the relatively low speed of flow and (2) the large cylinder wall area. The steady flow energy equation for a reciprocating compressor is

$$w = q + (h_1 - h_2) \qquad (6.41)$$

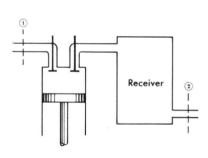

Fig. 6.20

Reciprocating Compressor with Receiver.

Example 6.6. An air and water mixture having an enthalpy of 54 Btu/lbm enters a dehumidifier (Fig. 6.21) at the rate of 700 lbm/hr. Water with an enthalpy of 18 Btu/lbm drains out of the dehumidifier at the rate of 15 lbm/hr. The air and water vapor mixture leaves the dehumidifier with an enthalpy of 20 Btu/lbm. Write the steady-flow energy balance for the flow system, and determine the heat removed in Btu/hr.

Solution. Without the effects of shaft work or changes in kinetic and potential energy, the energy balance in Fig. 6.21 is

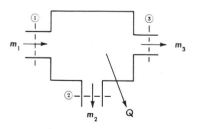

Fig. 6.21 Dehumidifier.

$$m_1 h_1 = m_2 h_2 + m_3 h_3 + Q$$

or

$$700(54) = 15(18) + m_3(20) + Q$$

where Q is the heat removed. The mass balance is

$$m_3 = m_1 - m_2 = 700 - 15 = 685 \text{ lbm/hr}$$

Thus,

$$Q = 700(54) - 15(18) - 685(20)$$
$$= 23,830 \text{ Btu/hr}$$

6.10   Variable-Flow Processes

So far, the discussion has been concerned mainly with steady-flow, which involves the assumption that properties at each point along the flow are constant with respect to time. A control volume, however, may have mass crossing its boundaries under conditions other than steady-flow. The properties of the flowing fluid may vary with time, or the quantity of material entering the control volume may not equal the quantity leaving it. In other words, the rates of mass and energy transfer into and out of the control volume are not the same in the case of variable or transient-flow processes as they are in steady-flow. Examples of variable or transient flow processes are: the flow in and out of a tank, the initial flow of water through the cooling jacket of an automobile engine (before it reaches steady-state operating temperature), and the energy-storage rise (paralleling the temperature rise) in the metal of a steam turbine just after steam is admitted to it, even though the mass rate of steam entering and leaving the turbine may be the same. Since the analysis of variable-flow processes, in general cases, is complicated, their treatment is illustrated by means of the two specific examples below.

Tank Filling. Consider the charging of a vessel from a supply main, as shown in Fig. 6.22. The problem can be solved either by use of system analysis or control volume analysis. Let m_i be the mass of fluid in the tank at the start, and p_i, v_i, and T_i be the initial conditions in the tank. Let m_f be the final mass in the tank, and p_f, v_f, and T_f be the final conditions in the tank.

In *system analysis*, the collection of matter which makes up the system must be kept distinct from its surroundings during the whole process. Accordingly, a boundary surface is selected, such

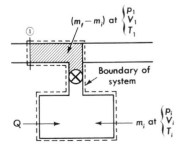

Fig. 6.22   System Analysis for Tank Filling Process.

that the total amount of matter is contained within it at all times. During the process, the envelope, always containing the same mass of gas, collapses until it becomes identical with the shape of the vessel. The initial energy of the system is composed of the internal energy in the tank, $m_i u_i$, and the energy in the line, $(m_f - m_i)(u_1 + \mathcal{V}_1^2/2g_c)$:

$$E_i = m_i u_i + (m_f - m_i)\left(u_1 + \frac{\mathcal{V}_1^2}{2g_c}\right)$$

The energy of the system at the end of the process is the internal energy in the tank:

$$E_f = m_f u_f$$

The work done during the process includes the collapse of that portion of the envelope outside the tank from a volume of $(m_f - m_i)v_i$ to a zero volume. This portion of the envelope, being always within the pipe, is subject at all times to the pressure p_1. The work is thus

$$W = p_1[0 - (m_f - m_i)v_1] = -(m_f - m_i)p_1 v_1$$

Application of the first law, $Q = (E_f - E_i) + W$, gives

$$Q = m_f u_f - m_i u_i - (m_f - m_i)\left(u_1 + \frac{\mathcal{V}_1^2}{2g_c}\right) - (m_f - m_i)p_1 v_1$$

which may be written, with $u + pv = h$, as

$$Q = m_f u_f - m_i u_i - (m_f - m_i)\left(h_1 + \frac{\mathcal{V}_1^2}{2g_c}\right) \tag{6.42}$$

Equation (6.42) is the energy relation for a tank-filling process.

The same result may be obtained by use of *control volume analysis* by selecting the tank as the control volume. Initially, the tank contains m_i amount of fluid at p_i, v_i, and T_i. At the end of the process, the tank contains m_f amount of fluid at p_f, v_f, and T_f. The initial energy in the tank is $m_i u_i$, and the final energy is $m_f u_f$. The amount of fluid entering the tank is $(m_f - m_i)$, and the energy associated with this is

$$(m_f - m_i)(u_1 + p_1 v_1 + \mathcal{V}_1^2/2g_c) = (m_f - m_i)(h_1 + \mathcal{V}_1^2/2g_c)$$

Note that when control volume analysis is used, the flow work pv must be included in the energy term. Now, according to control volume analysis, the energy added to the control volume equals the increase in stored energy of the control volume. Therefore,

$$(m_f - m_i)\left(h_1 + \frac{\mathcal{V}_1^2}{2g_c}\right) + Q = m_f u_f - m_i u_i \tag{6.43}$$

Equation (6.43) is the energy relation for a tank filling process, as obtained by use of control volume analysis. It is the same as Eq. (6.42), which was arrived at by system analysis.

In the particular case of the filling of insulated empty tanks, $Q = 0$, $m_i = 0$, and the previous result simplifies to

$$\left(h_1 + \frac{\mathscr{V}_1^2}{2g_c} \right) = u_f \qquad (6.44)$$

Furthermore, if the kinetic energy in the pipe line is negligible, then

$$h_1 = u_f \qquad (6.45)$$

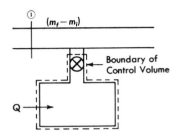

Fig. 6.23 Control Volume Analysis for Tank Filling.

that is, the specific internal energy in the charged tank equals the specific enthalpy in the line.

Tank Discharge. Consider a tank discharging into surroundings that have constant properties, such as a pipe or the atmosphere. In Fig. 6.24, let m_i be the initial mass in the tank (at conditions p_i, v_i, T_i), and let m_f be the remaining mass in the tank (at conditions p_f, v_f, T_f). Using *system analysis*, let a boundary containing mass m_i be selected. Initially, the energy in the system is $E_i = m_i u_i$. At the end of the process, a quantity of gas $(m_i - m_f)$ has left the tank (but not the system), and the energy of the system is that of the tank, plus that in the surroundings:

$$E_f = m_f u_f + (m_i - m_f)\left(u_2 + \frac{\mathscr{V}_2^2}{2g_c} \right)$$

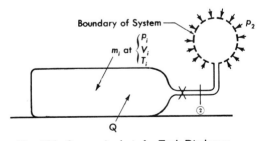

Fig. 6.24 System Analysis for Tank Discharge.

To find the work done, attention is directed to the fluid which leaves the tank. The sole volume change during the process is: the portion of the system outside the tank increases in volume from zero to a volume corresponding to surrounding conditions. The work is thus

$$W = p_2[(m_i - m_f)v_2 - 0] = (m_i - m_f)p_2 v_2$$

The first law, $Q = (E_f - E_i) + W$, then gives

$$Q = m_f u_f + (m_i - m_f)\left(u_2 + \frac{\mathscr{V}_2^2}{2g_c}\right) - m_i u_i + (m_i - m_f)p_2 v_2$$

or

$$Q = m_f u_f - m_i u_i + (m_i - m_f)\left(h_2 + \frac{\mathscr{V}_2^2}{2g_c}\right) \qquad (6.46)$$

Equation (6.46) is the energy relation for a tank discharge process.

The same result can, of course, be obtained by means of *control volume* analysis. Let the tank be chosen as the control volume. The initial energy stored in the tank is

$$E_i = m_i u_i$$

The energy stored in the tank after discharge is

$$E_f = m_f u_f$$

The energy leaving the tank is

$$(m_i - m_f)\left(h_2 + \frac{\mathscr{V}_2^2}{2g_c}\right)$$

The energy entering the tank is Q. Now, according to control volume analysis, the energy leaving the tank minus the energy entering the tank must equal the decrease in the stored energy of the tank. Hence,

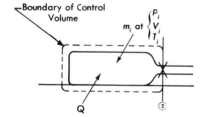

Fig. 6.25 Control Volume Analysis for Tank Discharge.

$$(m_i - m_f)\left(h_1 + \frac{\mathscr{V}_2^2}{2g_c}\right) - Q = m_i u_i - m_f u_f$$

or

$$Q = m_f u_f - m_i u_i + (m_i - m_f)\left(h_2 + \frac{\mathscr{V}_2^2}{2g_c}\right) \qquad (6.47)$$

which is the same as Eq. (6.46). In many respects, control volume analysis is both shorter and easier to apply than system analysis.

Example 6.7. A 50 cu ft tank is filled with air at a pressure of 100 psia and a temperature of 250 °F. The air is discharged to the atmosphere through a valve.

Neglecting heat transfers, find the amount of work obtainable from the kinetic energy. Consider air to be a perfect gas ($pv = RT$; $R = 53.3$ ft lbf/lbm-°R; $c_p = 0.24$ Btu/lbm-°R; $c_v = 0.17$ Btu/lbm-°R).

Solution. The perfect gas relation applied to m_i pounds of gas (initially in the tank) is $p_i m_i v_i = m_i R T_i$, or $(100)(144)(50) = (m_i)(53.3)(710)$, from which

$$m_i = \frac{(100)(144)(50)}{(53.3)(710)} = 19 \text{ lbm}$$

The final temperature of the air in the tank is obtained from the expression (developed in Chap. 5)

$$\frac{T_i}{T_f} = \left(\frac{p_i}{p_f}\right)^{(\gamma-1)/\gamma}$$

or

$$\frac{710}{T_f} = \left(\frac{100}{14.7}\right)^{(1.4-1)/1.4}$$

This gives

$$T_f = T_2 = 410 \text{ °R} = -50 \text{ °F}$$

The amount of air left in the tank is given by $p_f m_f v_f = m_f R T_f$, or $(14.7)(144)(50) = (m_f)(53.3)(410)$. Thus,

$$m_f = \frac{(14.7)(144)(50)}{(53.3)(410)} = 4.84 \text{ lbm}$$

From Eq. (6.47), with $Q = 0$, the kinetic energy is,

$$(m_i - m_f)\frac{\mathcal{V}_2^2}{2g_c} = m_i u_i - m_f u_f - (m_i - m_f)h_2$$
$$= m_i c_v T_i - m_f c_v T_f - (m_i - m_f)c_p T_2$$
$$= 19(0.17)(710) - 4.84(0.17)(410) - 13.54(0.24)(410)$$
$$= 2293 - 1730 = 563 \text{ Btu}$$

This is the amount of energy that could be converted into work by a frictionless turbine, for example.

Example 6.8. An insulated tank contains carbon dioxide at 190 °F and 600 psia. A valve on the side of the tank is opened, and gas escapes until the pressure reaches 100 psia. Show that the gas *in* the tank undergoes a reversible adiabatic process, and calculate the temperature of the CO_2 remaining in the tank. Assume carbon dioxide to be a perfect gas with a specific heat ratio $\gamma = 1.29$.

Solution. Consider any small portion of the total mass of gas within the tank, and choose a system, such that none of the gas in the system escapes from the tank during the discharge process. Imagine the boundary surface of the system to be a membrane which is perfectly free to expand or conduct heat. At any instant during the process, both the temperature and the pressure in the tank are substantially uniform, and the system therefore undergoes a reversible adiabatic expansion.

The final temperature of the CO_2 in the tank is obtained from the relation:

$$\frac{T_1}{T_2} = \left(\frac{p_1}{p_2}\right)^{(\gamma-1)/\gamma}$$

or

$$\frac{650}{T_2} = \left(\frac{600}{100}\right)^{(1.29-1)/1.29}$$

whence

$$T_2 = 435\,°R = -25\,°F$$

PROBLEMS

6.1. A system consisting of 2.5 lbm of a pure substance and having a specific internal energy of 7.5 Btu/lbm is moving with a velocity of 500 fps at an elevation 4000 ft above sea level. The system undergoes a process which results in a final specific internal energy of 9.2 Btu/lbm, a final velocity of 750 fps, and a final elevation of 5600 ft. During the process, the total work done on the system is 2600 ft lbf. Determine the magnitude and direction of the heat transfer.

6.2. Liquid water flows steadily downward through a vertical conveying duct. The enthalpy at a point 600 ft above a reference level is 90 Btu/lbm; at a point 100 ft above the same reference it is 89 Btu/lbm. Neglecting heat losses, determine the velocity of the water stream at the lower level if the velocity at the upper level is 35 fps.

6.3. In fluid mechanics, it is common practice to speak of the Eulerian and Lagrangian points of view. The Eulerian observer is stationed at a fixed position in space and watches the fluid go by. The Lagrangian observer travels along with the fluid. (a) Discuss and associate these points of view with the thermodynamic concepts of "system" and "control volume." (b) In which of these cases do the terms pv and h represent energy?

6.4. A gas flows steadily through a machine and expands frictionlessly from 100 psia to 15 psia according to the relation

$$pv^{1.25} = 32,500$$

where p is in psfa and v is in ft³/lbm. What is the heat transferred in Btu/lbm if the enthalpy of the gas decreases 33 Btu/lbm? Neglect changes in potential and kinetic energy.

6.5. (a) Give the conditions of validity for the following expression of the work done:

$$w = vdp - KE - PE$$

(b) Discuss this in connection with the flow of an incompressible fluid through a horizontal pipe of constant cross-sectional area. $PE = 0$, $KE = 0$, $w = 0$, but $vdp \neq 0$ because of pressure drop due to friction.

6.6. The temperature change in a throttling process may be calculated by considering a reversible process that has the same end points. From the definition of the Joule-Thomson coefficient, $\mu_J = (\partial T/\partial p)_h$, show that

$$dh = c(dT - \mu_J dp)$$

Hint: Use the cyclic relation $(\partial T/\partial p)_h \, (\partial p/\partial h)_T \, (\partial h/\partial T)_p = -1$.

6.7. For a homogeneous system of mass m, show that the relation between the Joule-Thomson coefficient μ_J and the quantity $(\partial H/\partial p)_T$ is

$$\mu_J = -\frac{1}{mc_p}\left(\frac{\partial H}{\partial p}\right)_T$$

and consequently, for a perfect gas, $\mu_J = 0$. Hint: consider H as a function of T and p, and write $dH = (\partial H/\partial T)_p \, dT + (\partial H/\partial p)_T \, dp$.

6.8. The steady-flow energy equation may be written

$$dq - dw = du + pdv + vdp + \frac{V dV}{g_c} + \frac{g}{g_c}dz$$

where w is the shaft work. If the last three terms of the above equation are taken to be zero by Euler's equation, and if the shaft work is non-existent, what does the steady-flow energy equation reduce to? Is the result a particular form of the first law for a pure substance, in the absence of gravity, motion, electricity, magnetism, and capillarity, with only displacement work present?

6.9. Air at 25 psia and 70 °F stagnation temperature, is flowing in a 12″. ID circular cross-section duct. A pitot-tube traverse of the duct shows a mean velocity head of 0.36 inches H₂O. The room temperature is 80 °F and the barometer is 29.9 inches Hg. Determine how many cfm of air flow in the duct.

6.10. A 3 by 2 venturi is used to meter air. The air enters the venturi at 22 psig and 160 °F, and the pressure drop is 7.5 inches H₂O. The surroundings are at 29.5 inches Hg and 85 °F. Find the equivalent cfm of free air flowing, if the discharge coefficient is 0.95.

6.11. A long, well-insulated pipe-line carries steam. At the point where the steam enters the pipe, the inside diameter is 3 in., the pressure of the steam is 500 psia, the specific volume is 1.13 ft³/lbm, and the specific enthalpy is 1286.2 Btu/lbm. At a certain point downstream, the diameter is 2 in., the pressure is 450 psia, the specific volume is 1.16 ft³/lbm, and the specific enthalpy is 1252.3 Btu/lbm. Determine the velocity at the point downstream and the mass flow rate of the steam.

6.12. The coefficient of a sharp-edged orifice is determined by means of an accurately calibrated gasometer. The diameter of the orifice is 0.75 inches, and that of the pipe is 2 inches. The upstream pressure is 30 psia, and the drop across the orifice is 3.2 inches of mercury. The temperature of the air upon entry to the orifice is 80 °F. The mass flow rate measured by the gasometer is 5.3 lbm/min. Find the coefficient of discharge of the orifice.

6.13. Air expands reversibly and adiabatically through a nozzle from inlet stagnation conditions of 100 psia and 500 °F to an exit pressure of 15 psia. Determine the exit velocity and the mass flow rate if the exit is 1.2 in². Assume a specific heat ratio of $\gamma = 1.4$.

6.14. An ideal gas enters a nozzle with a velocity $\mathscr{V}_1$. Following reversible adiabatic expansion, it leaves with a velocity $\mathscr{V}_2$. Assuming a constant specific heat ratio, show that the exit velocity is

$$\mathscr{V}_2 = \sqrt{\mathscr{V}_1^2 + \frac{2\gamma g_c R T_1}{\gamma - 1}\left[1 - \left(\frac{p_2}{p_1}\right)^{(\gamma-1)/\gamma}\right]}$$

6.15. A nozzle delivers a jet of water in a vertical direction with a velocity of 95 ft/sec. Resistance due to air friction is such that 90 per cent of the kinetic energy is converted to potential energy on the ascent, and 90 per cent of the potential energy is converted to kinetic energy on the descent. From energy considerations, find: (a) the peak elevation, (b) the velocity at the time of return to the earth's surface.

6.16. A certain diffuser reduces the velocity of an air stream from 840 fps to 100 fps. The inlet pressure is 14.7 psia and the inlet temperature is 600 °F. The diffuser efficiency is 92 per cent. Determine (a) the outlet pressure, and (b) the outlet area for a mass flow of 19 lbm/sec.

6.17. From the differential form of the Euler equation and of the continuity equation, derive the following relation for the reversible adiabatic flow of a gas through a nozzle:

$$\frac{dA}{A} = -\left(1 - \frac{\mathscr{V}^2}{g_c dp/d\rho}\right)\frac{d\mathscr{V}}{\mathscr{V}}$$

where A = area, $\mathscr{V}$ = velocity, p = pressure, and ρ = density. Discuss the variation of nozzle area in relation to the quantity $c^2 = dp/d\rho$.

6.18. A jet plane travels through the air at a speed of 650 mph at an altitude of 20,000 ft, where the pressure is 6.75 psia and the temperature is 10.5 °F. Air passes through the diffuser of the engine and leaves with a velocity of 300 fps. Assuming the flow to be adiabatic and reversible, what is the pressure and temperature at the outlet of the diffuser?

6.19. Water at 65 °F flows from the bottom of a large tank through a nozzle to the atmosphere. The water level is kept constant at 10 ft above the nozzle, and the nozzle diameter is 1.5 inches. (a) Determine the discharge velocity and flow rate in gpm if heat transfer and frictional effects are neglected. (b). In a real nozzle, there is always some friction so that the velocity of discharge will be less than that calculated in (a). If the measured velocity is 95 per cent of the ideal velocity, what is the change in internal energy of the water while passing through the nozzle? Assume adiabatic flow.

6.20. In the steady-flow of an ideal gas with constant specific heats, the relation between stagnation and static conditions is given by

$$h + \frac{\mathscr{V}^2}{2g_c} = h_t$$

$$\frac{T_t}{T} = \left(\frac{p_t}{p}\right)^{(\gamma-1)/\gamma} = \left(\frac{v}{v_t}\right)^{\gamma-1}$$

where the subscript t denotes stagnation conditions. From a Pitot tube, the stagnation pressure in a flow of air is found to be 20 lbf/in²; the static pressure

15 lbf/in²; and the stagnation temperature 90 °F. What is the air stream temperature and velocity?

6.21. Steam flows through a turbine nozzle from a steam line in which the steam has a specific enthalpy of 1250 Btu/lbm. After expansion it leaves the nozzle with an enthalpy of 970 Btu/lbm. For steady-flow conditions, and considering the flow to be adiabatic, determine the exit velocity if the initial velocity is 12,000 fpm.

6.22. In the test of a steam turbine, the following data were recorded: enthalpy at inlet = 1250 Btu/lbm; inlet velocity = 100 fps; elevation at inlet = 15 ft above a reference plane; enthalpy at exit = 950 Btu/lbm; exit velocity = 200 fps; elevation at exit = 9 ft above reference plane; work output = 220,000 ft lbf/lbm of steam. For steady-flow conditions, determine the heat per lbm of steam transferred to surroundings.

6.23. A heat exchanger consisting of a bundle of metal tubes submerged in a stream of water is used to heat oil from 65 °F to 150 °F. The oil flows through the tubes and has an enthalpy given by $h = 0.4t + 0.00025t^2$, where h = Btu/lbm, and t = °F. The water enters at 190 °F and leaves at 110 °F; its specific enthalpy is given by $h = t - 32$. Neglecting velocity and elevation changes, find the water flow rate (lbm/hr) required to heat 10,000 lbm/hr of oil.

6.24. Steam flows steadily into a condenser at the rate of 9,600 lbm/hr. The specific enthalpy at entry is 981 Btu/lbm and the specific volume is 295 ft³/lbm. The condensate leaves with a specific enthalpy of 80 Btu/lbm and negligible velocity. What is the heat transfer to the cooling water per pound of steam if the heat loss from the condensing steam to the surroundings is 3000 Btu/min?

6.25. Air is steadily supplied to the combustion chamber of a gas turbine at the rate of 28 lbm/sec. The temperature of the air is 375 °F, its velocity is 280 fps, and its specific enthalpy is 76.2 Btu/lbm. Liquid fuel at a temperature of 60 °F flows into the combustion chamber at the rate of 1560 lbm/hr. Products of combustion leave the chamber at 1380 °F, a velocity of 660 fps, and a specific enthalpy of 337.5 Btu/lbm. Selecting 60 °F as datum temperature for the enthalpy of the fuel, determine the specific enthalpy of the entering fuel stream. Neglect fuel stream velocity and heat transfer to the atmosphere.

6.26. A water-jacket air compressor compresses 100 cu ft/min of air having an initial specific volume of 13 cu ft/lbm. During the operation, the enthalpy of the air is increased by 35 Btu/lbm, and heat is transferred to the cooling water and the surroundings at the rate of 155 Btu/min. Neglecting changes in kinetic and potential energy, determine the horsepower required to drive the compressor.

6.27. An ammonia compressor with a water jacket discharges 2 lbm/min of refrigerant with a specific enthalpy of 700 Btu/lbm. The specific enthalpy of the ammonia in the suction line is 650 Btu/lbm. Power supplied to drive the compressor is 9.5 hp. Neglecting changes in velocity and elevation, determine the rate of heat transfer to the jacket water.

6.28. An aircraft refrigerating installation uses a small turbine in the following manner: Air at a pressure of 43 psia and a temperature of 135 °F flows steadily into the turbine at a velocity of 150 fps. The air leaves the turbine at a pressure of 16.8 psia, a temperature of 35 °F, and a velocity of 480 fps. If the shaft work delivered by the turbine is 18,000 ft lbf/lbm of air, what is the magnitude and sign of the heat transfer per pound of air flowing?

6.31. An evacuated tank is fitted with a valve through which atmospheric air slowly fills it to atmospheric pressure. Assuming atmospheric air to be at 29.92 in. Hg and 70 °F, what will be the temperature of the air in the tank? Consider the internal energy of the air to be given by $u = u_0 + 0.17t$ where u = Btu/lbm, u_0 = value of u at 0 °F, and t = °F. The equation of state for air is $pv = 53.3 \ (t + 460)$, where p = psfa, v = cu ft/lbm, and t = °F.

6.32. A 10 cu ft tank contains oxygen at 75 °F and 400 psia. If the safety valve is opened, the oxygen will rush out until the pressure in the tank reaches atmospheric pressure (14.7 psia). Assuming that the gas which remains in the tank has undergone a reversible adiabatic expansion, determine: (a) the amount of gas in the tank when the pressure equals atmospheric pressure, (b) the temperature of the gas remaining in the tank, (c) the work done in forcing gas out of the tank. Consider the oxygen to be described by $pv = 48.3 \ (t + 460)$; $u = 0.157t$; where p = psfa, v = cu ft/lbm, t = °F, and u = Btu/lbm.

6.33. (a) What is the maximum amount of work that can be performed by a gas stored in a 10 cu ft tank at 78 °F and 100 psia if the gas is maintained at constant temperature by heat conduction from surroundings? The pressure of the surroundings is 15 psia, and the gas obeys the relations $pv = 53.3 \ (t + 460°)$; $u = u_0 + 0.172t$, where p = psfa, v = ft³/lbm, t = °F, u = Btu/lbm, and u_0 = value of u at 0 °F. (b) What is the rate of heat transfer if, at a given instant, work is performed at the rate of 4.5 hp?

6.34. A compressed air bottle is used to drive a small turbine as an emergency starter for an engine. The bottle contains air at 500 psia and 60 °F. The turbine, exhausting to atmosphere, produces an average output of 4.8 hp for a period of 31 seconds. The pressure in the bottle falls to 50 psia during the process. Assuming reversible adiabatic expansion, determine the necessary capacity of the bottle.

CHAPTER 7

Second Law of Thermodynamics

7.1 Limitations of First Law

The first law of thermodynamics establishes a fixed rate of exchange between heat and work, and stipulates that, in carrying out a process, a balance of energy must hold. It is, so to speak, a law of conservation of energy, but it does not specify the *direction* of the process under consideration. Until now, it has been tacitly assumed that every change of thermodynamic state can proceed in either direction. For example, a gas in a cylinder can be expanded or compressed. Kinetic energy and potential energy may be transformed from one to the other with equal facility (as in the action of a pendulum). Disallowing the factor of friction, this principle applies to phenomena studied in mechanics.

The interchange of work and heat, however, differs in a fundamental way from the interchange of different forms of work. For example, when a flywheel is stopped by a friction brake, the brake gets hot, and the internal energy of the brake increases by an amount equal to the decrease in kinetic energy of the flywheel. Now, the first law would be equally well satisfied if the hot brake were to cool off and give back its internal energy to the flywheel, causing the latter to resume its rotation. This, however, is *never seen* to happen. The action of the brake in stopping the flywheel by friction is an *irreversible* process.

As another example, consider a tank of water in which a paddle wheel is revolved by means of a falling weight. Let the water constitute the system, and let this system undergo a cycle in which work is first done on the system by the lowering of the weight, with the decrease of potential energy equal to the increase of internal energy of the water. The cycle is then completed by transferring heat from the system to the surroundings so that the water regains its initial state. Energy is conserved, with work being converted entirely into internal energy of the water, then into heat transfer to the surroundings. Experience, however, shows that the cycle cannot be reversed, that is, heat cannot be transferred back from the surroundings to the water to cause the weight to rise, even though such an occurrence would not violate the principle of conservation of energy.

As a third example, consider two bodies at different temperatures in thermal contact in an insulated box. Energy is transferred from the higher-temperature body to the lower-temperature body; the amount of energy lost by the former is equal to the amount of energy gained by the latter. This accords with the first law. But it would still be in accordance with the first law if the reverse process were to occur, namely, that energy (in the same amount) be transferred from the lower-temperature body to the higher-temperature body. However, this does not occur.

The striking fact in all these examples is that, even though the conversion of work into heat in a cyclic process may always be complete, the conversion of heat into work may only be partial. For example, part of the heat supplied to a heat engine may be converted into work, but part of it must also be rejected to a heat sink. This, of course, is no violation of the first law, but the question comes to mind as to whether or not the complete conversion of heat into work is possible, even in a perfect, frictionless engine. All the evidence points out that there exists a *directional* law which imposes a limitation on energy transformations other than that imposed by the first law. This law is the second law of thermodynamics. It is discussed in this chapter.

7.2 Heat Engine

Before introducing the second law, it is necessary to define the term, *heat engine*. A heat engine is a *cyclically* operating system across whose boundaries flow only *heat* and *work*. This definition includes any device (operating cyclically) which has as its primary purpose the conversion of heat into work. In a heat engine, the working fluid, while undergoing a series of processes, periodically returns to its initial state. An example of heat engine is the power plant shown in Fig. 7.1. The working fluid, H_2O,

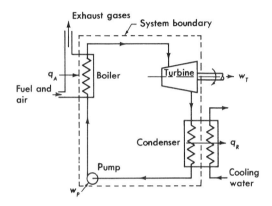

Fig. 7.1 Steam Power Plant.

flows steadily through the boiler, turbine, condenser, and feed pump, executing a cycle. Entering the boiler as water, it is vaporized and passed into the turbine. Emerging from the turbine (still steam but at a lower temperature and pressure), it enters the condenser. There, it becomes water again. To complete the cycle, it is returned by means of the feed pump to the boiler.

If a system boundary is drawn as shown by the dotted line, in Fig. 7.1, four interactions cross it. These are, on the basis of a unit mass of working fluid (H_2O): q_A, the heat transfer from the combustion products to the steam in the boiler; w_T, the work done by the turbine; q_R, the heat transfer from the condensing steam to the cooling water, and w_P, the work consumed by the feed pump. For convenience, let q_A, q_R, w_T and w_P stand for absolute numerical values. The first law for a cyclic process,

$$\oint dq = \oint dw$$

then gives

$$q_A - q_R = w_T - w_P \tag{7.1}$$

Now, the efficiency of any device is the ratio of the output to the input. Here, the output sought is work: $w_T - w_P$; the input is the amount of heat required to manufacture steam: q_A. Thus, the *thermal efficiency* of the *closed* cycle* is

$$\eta = \frac{w_T - w_P}{q_A} = \frac{q_A - q_R}{q_A} \qquad (7.2)$$

Experience reveals that the heat rejected, q_R, amounts to more than two-thirds the magnitude of the heat added, q_A. Thus, the efficiency of a heat engine is usually less than one-third of that which the first law would allow if the entire heat input, q_A, were to be converted into work. Why must this always be? The answer is given by the second law of thermodynamics. For the time being, it can be seen that, if steam is to be condensed after it leaves the turbine, heat must be transferred from it. On the other hand, if the exhaust steam were not condensed, the pump would have to do much more work than when pumping liquid back to the boiler. Thus, heat must be rejected at some part of the cycle.

Another example of a heat engine is represented by a cylinder fitted with a piston and enclosing a quantity of gas. Heat is supplied at high temperature, the gas expands, and work is done on the piston. The latter, through a connecting rod, rotates a crankshaft. The gas is allowed to expand further, under adiabatic conditions, to a temperature significantly lower than that at which heat is supplied. Next, it is compressed while heat is removed, and finally, it is further compressed adiabatically to its original state (its state at the start of the cycle).

A third example of a heat engine is the *thermocouple*. Although it is used primarily as a temperature-measuring device, it operates in the manner of a heat engine. Two wires of dissimilar metals are joined at their ends to form a loop. One junction is placed in a cold bath (usually a mixture of ice and water); the other is at the temperature to be measured. An electro-motive force develops between the junctions. Heat is added at the hot junction and rejected at the cold junction. The resultant electromotive force causes a flow of electric current which can be converted to mechanical work.

The common feature in all of these devices is that heat is received by the system at a high temperature (source temperature), heat is rejected by the system at a lower temperature (sink temperature), and work is performed on the surroundings. This is shown schematically in Fig. 7.2(a). Here, the objective is to convert heat into work, and to deliver this work to the surroundings.

---

* In a *closed* cycle, the working fluid is circulated over and over again. In an *open* cycle, the working fluid is rejected at the end of each cycle. Strictly speaking, only those devices operating under a closed cycle can be classified as heat engines.

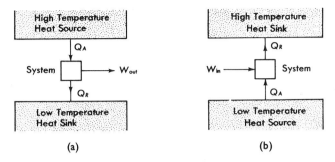

Fig. 7.2 Heat Engine and Heat Pump.

If the objective is to cause flow of heat from a lower-temperature body to a higher-temperature body, as in Fig. 7.2(b), the device is called a *heat pump* or *refrigerator*.

Considering the working fluid in any one of these devices as operating cyclically, the first law (for a system of arbitrary mass) gives

$$\oint dQ = \oint dW \qquad (7.3)$$

For the heat engine shown in Fig. 7.2(a),

$$\oint dW = \oint dQ = Q_A - Q_R,$$

and the efficiency is

$$\eta = \frac{\oint dW}{Q_A} = \frac{Q_A - Q_R}{Q_A}$$

$$= 1 - \frac{Q_R}{Q_A} \qquad (7.4)$$

Equation (7.4) defines the *thermal efficiency* of a heat engine. For the installation depicted in Fig. 7.2(b),

$$\oint dQ = Q_R - Q_A,$$

but the efficiency varies according to the objective in mind. If the purpose is to transfer an amount Q_R of heat to a higher-temperature body (such as in the case of heating a house in winter time), the device is a heat pump, and the efficiency (called coefficient of performance) is

$$COP_{\text{heat pump}} = \frac{\text{energy effect sought}}{\text{energy input required}}$$

$$= \frac{Q_R}{Q_R - Q_A} = \frac{1}{1 - Q_A/Q_R} \qquad (7.5)$$

Equation (7.5) defines the *coefficient of performance* for a *heat pump*. If the purpose is to refrigerate a body by abstracting an amount Q_A of heat from it, the device is known as a *refrigerator,* and the efficiency becomes

$$\text{COP}_{\text{refrigerator}} = \frac{\text{energy effect sought}}{\text{energy input required}}$$

$$= \frac{Q_A}{Q_R - Q_A} = \frac{1}{Q_R/Q_A - 1} \tag{7.6}$$

Equation (7.6) defines the *coefficient of performance* for a *refrigerating machine*. Note that, for convenience, both Q_A and Q_R are assumed to represent absolute values of heat transfers in this and the next chapter.

Example 7.1. (a) Heat is supplied to a heat engine at the rate of 1150 Btu/min, and the engine output is 10 hp. What is the thermal efficiency of the engine and the rate of heat rejection?

(b) A building having a heat requirement of 100,000 Btu/hr. is to be heated by a heat pump that absorbs heat from the cold outside air and delivers heat to the building. To operate the pump, 14,800 Btu/hr of work is required. What amount of heat is absorbed from the outside air, and what is the coefficient of performance?

Solution. (a) Q_A = 1150 Btu/min.; $\oint dW$ = 10(42.42) = 424.2 Btu/min., thus,

$$\eta = \frac{\oint dw}{Q_A} = \frac{424.2}{1150}$$

$$= 0.368 \text{ or } 36.8 \text{ per cent}$$

The rate of heat rejection is

$$Q_R = 1150 - 424.2 = 725.8 \text{ Btu/min.}$$

(b) The amount of heat rejected by the heat pump to the building is Q_R = 100,000 Btu/hr. The work input to the pump is

$$Q_R - Q_A = 14,800 \text{ Btu/hr.}$$

Thus,

$$Q_A = 85,200 \text{ Btu/hr.}$$

The coefficient of performance is

$$\text{COP}_{\text{heat pump}} = \frac{Q_R}{Q_R - Q_A} = \frac{100,000}{14,800} = 6.75$$

Note: As a matter of practical concern, it should be pointed out that the heat-pump method of heating buildings is usually not economically competitive with other methods of heating unless outside temperatures are above 35 °F.

7.3   Second Law of Thermodynamics: Kelvin–Planck Statement

The preceding sections should not lead to the premature conclusion that heat can never be converted into work (in any particular process). Consider the system shown in Fig. 7.3. A cylinder fitted with a frictionless piston contains a certain amount of liquid and its vapor. The piston weight exactly balances the pressure of the vapor, and the whole system is immersed in a constant-temperature bath. Let an infinitesimal weight be added to the piston. As the piston moves downward, the vapor condenses to a liquid at constant temperature. Eventually, when the piston rests upon the liquid surface, an amount of heat equal to the heat of condensation of the vapor will have been transferred from the system to the surroundings. In this process, work has been entirely converted into heat.

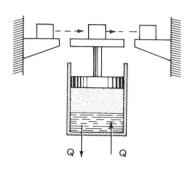

Fig. 7.3   Reversible Evaporation and Condensation.

Now, let an infinitesimal weight be removed from the piston so that the equivalent pressure is slightly less than the vapor pressure of the liquid. The liquid will vaporize, and the piston will be raised to its initial position. During this process, an amount of heat equal to that originally withdrawn will have been added to the system. Also, heat will have been entirely converted into work. Thus, under certain conditions, heat may be entirely converted into work.

However, the above example brings out a most important point, namely that the work done *on* the system during the first part of the cycle exactly equals the work done *by* the system during the second part of the cycle. The two processes put together form a *cycle*, and the *net* work of the cycle operating off a *single* heat reservoir is *zero*. In other words, no net work can be obtained from a *cyclically* operating system exchanging heat with its surroundings at a single temperature. This is a universal experience, and leads to the following statement of the *second law of thermodynamics*:

It is impossible to construct an engine which, operating in a cycle, will produce no other effect than the extraction of heat from a single heat reservoir and the performance of an equivalent amount of work.

This statement, elegant as it is concise, is commonly known as the

Kelvin*-Planck† statement of the second law. It is one of several classical statements on the subject.

7.4 Perpetual Motion Machine of the Second Kind

In the discussion of the first law, the concept of a perpetual motion machine of the first kind was introduced. Such a machine, shown in Fig. 7.4(a), would create energy out of nothing, violating the first law. There is, however, nothing implicit in the first law to the effect that some portion of the heat supplied to a heat engine must be rejected and that consequently the thermal efficiency cannot be unity. The second law expresses the fact that some heat must *always* be rejected during a cycle and that the efficiency of the cycle must be *less* than unity. In other words, at some point in the cycle, the working fluid (system) must be in contact with a high-temperature reservoir to receive heat, and at some other point it must be in contact with a low-temperature reservoir to reject heat. The minimum number of reservoirs required is thus two.

Without violating the first law, it is possible to conceive of a machine that would receive heat continuously from a single source, and convert this heat into work. Such a machine is shown schematically in Fig. 7.4(b).

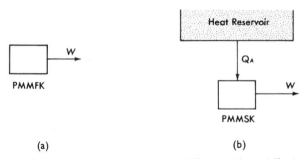

(a)   (b)

Fig. 7.4 Perpetual Motion Machines of First and Second Kind.

The machine receives heat from a single heat reservoir and converts all of the heat into work. It does not create energy, but, as a heat engine, it would convert heat entirely into work and would have an efficiency of

---

* William Thomson (1824–1907), knighted Lord Kelvin for his scientific contributions, was professor of natural philosophy at the University of Glasgow. He helped establish the first and second laws of thermodynamics.

† Max Planck (1858–1947) was professor of physics at the University of Berlin. He wrote a treatise on thermodynamics, but is best known for his work on radiation and quantum theory. He was awarded the Nobel prize in 1918.

unity. Such a machine could drive a ship using the ocean as the sole source of heat, or it could derive work from the energy of the atmosphere at no cost. It would, however, violate the second law of thermodynamics; therefore, it is called a *perpetual motion machine of the second kind*. It has *never* been successfully created, despite the fact that many machines have been devised and claimed by their inventors to operate in violation of the second law. All, however, have been proved not to do so. The second law thus rests upon experimental foundation, just like the first law. It is, however, *not* a deduction from the first law, but stands by itself as a separate and independent axiom of nature. Like the first law, its validity rests upon the fact that it has never been disproved by experience.

Example 7.2. Consider the following occurrences: (a) A dry-cell produces work in the form of an electric current while exchanging heat solely with a constant-temperature atmosphere, (b) An isothermal reversible expansion of a perfect gas absorbs heat from a single heat reservoir, and converts it completely to work, (c) a household refrigerator with the door closed is in thermal contact solely with the constant-temperature atmosphere of a room; it receives work from the electrical lines, and operates in a cycle. Do these occurrences represent a violation of the second law?

Solution. The question is answered for case (b). There is no violation here since this is *not* a cycle. If the gas were recompressed isothermally and reversibly to its original state, the work for the complete cycle would be zero. Discussion of the other two cases is left to the student.

7.5 Clausius' Statement of Second Law

The second law, like the first law, has its corollaries. The first of these (known as the *Clausius* * *statement*) has often been used as an alternate statement for the second law. *Corollary 1: Heat cannot pass spontaneously from a lower-temperature body to a higher-temperature body.* The term "spontaneously" means that, except for the bodies taking part in the exchange of heat, there is no other change taking place in the surroundings. In other words, it is impossible to have a system operating in a cycle which transfers heat from a cooler to a hotter body without work being done on the system by the surroundings.

Proof: The proof is by contradiction. Furthermore, in what follows, it will be shown that the Kelvin-Planck statement and the Clausius statement of the second law are completely equivalent to each other. Assume, con-

---

* Rudolph Julius Emmanuel Clausius (1822–1888) was a German physicist. He helped develop the second law and was instrumental in introducing the property called entropy (see Chap. 9).

trary to the corollary, that a system can be constructed which will operate in a cycle and will transfer heat from a lower-temperature reservoir to a higher-temperature reservoir without receiving work from the surroundings. This is shown schematically in Fig. 7.5(a) where 10 Btu are transferred

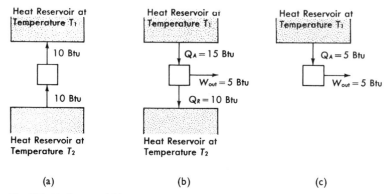

Heat Reservoir at
Temperature T_1

10 Btu

10 Btu

Heat Reservoir at
Temperature T_2

Heat Reservoir at
Temperature T_1

$Q_A = 15$ Btu

$W_{out} = 5$ Btu

$Q_R = 10$ Btu

Heat Reservoir at
Temperature T_2

Heat Reservoir at
Temperature T_1

$Q_A = 5$ Btu

$W_{out} = 5$ Btu

(a)   (b)   (c)

Fig. 7.5   Violation of Clausius Statement Leading to Violation of Kelvin-Planck
Statement.

spontaneously from the lower-temperature reservoir to the higher-temperature reservoir.

Construct a heat engine which operates between the two reservoirs, and takes in 15 Btu from the high-temperature reservoir, delivers 5 Btu of work to the surroundings, and rejects 10 Btu to the lower-temperature reservoir. This is shown in Fig. 7.5(b). The heat engine is legitimate, and violates no law. Now, assume that the heat pump and the heat engine are coupled together. The 10 Btu transferred into and out of the lower-temperature reservoir cancel each other, and there is no net heat transfer at T_2. The heat engine, the heat pump, and the higher-temperature reservoir together constitute a device which now operates continuously from the single heat reservoir at T_1, and which converts heat completely into work. The result is shown in Fig. 7.5(c), but this is a violation of the second law (in the form of the Kelvin-Planck statement). The assumption of spontaneous heat flow from lower-temperature to higher-temperature cannot hold, and the proposition stated in the corollary must therefore be true.

The preceding development has shown that a violation of the Clausius statement of the second law is a violation of the Kelvin-Planck statement of the second law. To proceed further, it is now shown that a violation of the

Kelvin-Planck statement is also a violation of the Clausius statement. Assume, contrary to Kelvin-Planck's statement, that it is possible to have an engine which operates from a single heat reservoir and completely converts the heat it receives into work. This is shown in Fig. 7.6(a), where

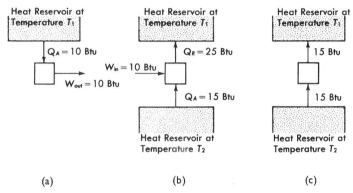

(a)   (b)   (c)

Fig. 7.6 Violation of Kelvin-Planck Statement Leading to Violation of Clausius Statement.

a heat engine takes in 10 Btu from the heat reservoir at temperature T_1, and converts this into 10 Btu of work.

Construct a heat pump which operates between the heat reservoir at temperature T_1 and a heat reservoir at a lower temperature T_2. This is shown in Fig. 7.6(b). Let this heat pump draw 15 Btu from the heat reservoir at T_2, and by means of 10 Btu of work, discharge 25 Btu to the heat reservoir at T_1. The heat pump is perfectly legitimate, and violates no law. Now, let the heat engine in (a) be coupled with the heat pump in (b) by having the output work of the engine drive the heat pump. The 10 Btu transferred out of the heat reservoir at T_1 along with the 25 Btu transferred into the same reservoir leave 15 Btu transferred into the reservoir, and the net effect will be a transfer of 15 Btu from the reservoir at T_2 to the reservoir at T_1. This is shown in Fig. 7.6(c), where 15 Btu of heat flows spontaneously from the heat reservoir at the lower temperature T_2 to the heat reservoir at the higher temperature T_1. This constitutes a violation of the Clausius statement of the second law.

It is seen that a violation of the Kelvin-Planck statement leads to a violation of the Clausius statement, and a violation of the Clausius statement leads to a violation of the Kelvin-Planck statement. The two statements are therefore completely equivalent.

7.6   Importance of Second Law

The preceding sections have shown that, although the second law may be stated in many different forms, these are all equivalent, even if they appear at first to bear no relation to each other. Thus, if any one of the statements of the second law is accepted as a postulate, all the other statements can be derived from this initial axiom.

A query as to why the second law is so valuable may be asked at this stage. It may be recalled that the zeroth law is basic to the measurement of temperature, and that the first law provides the energy balance which is the start of almost every engineering problem. The second law, even in its somewhat abstract form, is no less useful. It will eventually be seen that it provides the answer to a variety of problems such as (a) determining the maximum possible efficiency of a heat engine, or the maximum coefficient of performance of a refrigerating machine, (b) determining whether a particular process is possible or not, (c) predicting the direction and extent of a chemical reaction, (d) establishing a temperature scale which is independent of the physical properties of any substance, and (e) defining a very useful property called entropy. However, before taking up these problems and discussing other corollaries of the second law, the concepts of reversibility and irreversibility (which were first introduced in Chaps. 1 and 2) must be developed more fully.

7.7   Reversibility and Irreversibility

It should be obvious by now that some processes are only theoretical. The second law renders certain processes impossible. The processes that are possible fall into two categories: *reversible* processes which bring about changes in a system and its surroundings that can be completely erased; *irreversible* processes which involve changes in the system and its surroundings that are permanent. These processes are defined as follows:

A process is reversible with respect to a system and its surroundings if the system and the surroundings can be completely restored to their respective initial states by reversing the direction of the process. A process is irreversible if it does not fulfil these conditions.

The notion of reversibility is a keystone of classical thermodynamics; a system can, of course, always be returned to its original state, but this fact alone does not guarantee reversibility. The surroundings and other systems *must also* be restored to their exact original state. To clarify matters, the definition of reversibility is illustrated in the light of three factors which commonly affect engineering processes:

Friction. Consider a gas confined in an insulated cylinder fitted with a piston. Let the system (gas) undergo an adiabatic expansion from an initial state to a final state, and assume that there is friction between the piston and the cylinder walls. Work is done by the system. When the system is re-compressed to its original volume, the work required, however, is larger than that delivered during expansion, since, in both cases, friction works against motion. To restore the system to its initial state, more work must be done on it, and also some heat may have to be transferred from it in order to re-establish the original temperature. Thus, the reversal of the process cannot proceed in such a way as to have the same amounts of work and heat transfer which existed in the original process, thereby leaving the surroundings unchanged. A process with friction present is, therefore, *not* reversible.

Finite Temperature Difference. As an illustrative example, consider the expansion of a gas taking place at constant temperature in a cylinder fitted with a frictionless piston. During the expansion, let the cylinder be brought into contact with a heat reservoir whose temperature is above that of the system. Heat then flows from the reservoir to the system. When the system is recompressed, heat must leave the system, and this can be done only by bringing the system in contact with a different reservoir whose temperature is lower than that of the system. In the return process, the compression work equals the expansion work (since there is no friction), and the heat transferred out of the system equals the heat transferred into the system during the initial expansion process. The surroundings (which include the two heat reservoirs) are *not*, however, returned to their original state. The heat that was transferred out of the higher-temperature reservoir has not been transferred back to it, but has been transferred to a different reservoir instead. The process, though reversible with respect to the system, is not reversible with respect to the surroundings. For this reason, processes occurring without friction, but with external heat transfers through finite temperature differences, are often called *internally reversible.* They are, however, externally irreversible. Processes that are reversible with respect to both the system and the surroundings are often called *externally rever-sible.* Figure 7.7 illustrates this distinction. The system consists of a liquid

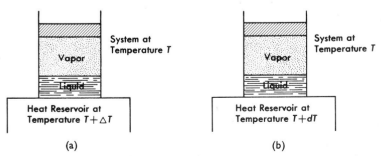

Fig. 7.7 Internally and Externally Reversible Process.

in equilibrium with its vapor at a temperature T. A frictionless movable piston maintains a constant pressure during evaporation. As far as the system itself is concerned, the process of evaporation is reversible, since condensation may occur by the addition of an infinitesimal weight on the piston, and the transferring of some heat out of the system. In other words, the system behaves just as though heat were being transferred to or from it across an infinitesimal temperature difference, so that Figs. 7.7(a) and 7.7(b) both represent internally reversible processes. Externally, however, only Fig. 7.7(b) represents a reversible process, since heat transfer across a finite temperature difference ΔT as in Fig. 7.7(a) would not return the heat to the same reservoir when the process is reversed.

Only when heat is transferred from a reservoir whose temperature essentially equals that of the system (in which case the temperature difference becomes an infinitesimal dT) is the process externally reversible. Only then can heat taken from the reservoir during the expansion be transferred back to it during recompression. Under no circumstance can heat transfers occur at large or finite temperature difference between reservoir and system if reversibility is to be obtained.

The foregoing has discussed what constitutes reversibility for an isothermal process. For a system undergoing a non-isothermal process, heat may be transferred reversibly at a varying temperature by using a *large number* of reservoirs of different temperatures, so that, at any one time, the difference in temperature between reservoir and system is *infinitesimally small*. This is shown in Fig. 7.8. Consider a system at a temperature T_1. Let a heat reservoir at temperature $T_1 + dT$ be brought into contact with it. The heat transfer operation is reversible, since there is but an infinitesimal temperature difference between system and reservoir. As the temperature of the system changes, successive heat reservoirs are brought into contact with it; each time, the temperature difference between system and reservoir is infinitesimal. Meanwhile, the pressure and volume may vary according to any relation, subject only to the restriction that there be no friction and no unbalance of forces. A heat flow under these conditions is then said to be quasi-static or reversible.

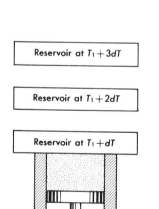

Fig. 7.8
Reversible Heat Transfer
at Varying Temperature.

Finite Pressure Difference. Consider the system formed by a gas under pressure in a cylinder fitted with a piston. Let the piston be held in place by a pin as shown in Fig.7.9(a). When the pin is removed, the piston is forced

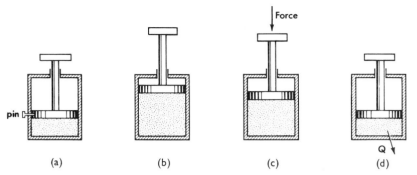

Fig. 7.9 Irreversible Expansion Through Finite Pressure Difference.

abruptly against the cylinder top. This is shown in Fig. 7.9(b). The discussion of previous chapters makes it fairly evident that this expansion process is not reversible, since the pressure of the system (the gas) does not equal external pressure. That the process is not reversible can be shown in light of the definition for reversibility just given. Let the direction of the process be reversed by exerting a force on the piston and compressing the gas until the pin can be reinserted in the piston. Notice that the work done on the gas during compression is greater than the work done by the gas during expansion, because a force has to be applied to the piston in order to compress the gas. To restore the system to its initial state, an amount of heat must then be transferred out of the gas. However, this leaves the surroundings changed by (1) the amount of excess work required for compression, and (2) the amount of heat transferred to the surroundings. The abrupt expansion of a gas is therefore *not* reversible with respect to the system and the surroundings.

To show how the expansion process may be made reversible, let the piston be loaded with a number of small weights so that when the pin is removed, the piston and weights just balance the pressure of the gas. The process then becomes a quasi-static process, shown in Fig. 7.10(a).

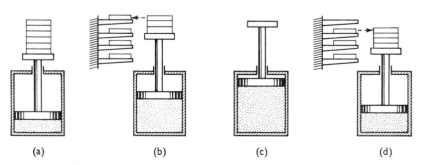

Fig. 7.10 Reversible Expansion Through Infinitesimal Pressure Difference.

As the gas expands, and the piston is raised, let the weights be slid off one at a time, allowing the pressure of the system to be always equal to the external pressure. This is shown in Fig. 7.10(b). When the piston has reached the top of the cylinder, as in Fig. 7.10(c), all the weights would have been taken off, and the work done by the system is then given by

$$W_{1-2} = \int_{V_1}^{V_2} p\,dV \tag{7.7}$$

To reverse the process, let the piston start from its raised position, and let the weights be put back on it one at a time. This is shown in Fig. 7.10(d). At all times, the external pressure equals the internal pressure, and the work done on the system when the piston has been lowered to its initial position is

$$W_{2-1} = \int_{V_2}^{V_1} p\,dV \tag{7.8}$$

By making the weights small, and the number of weights large, Eqs. (7.7) and (7.8) become equal, except for sign, so that both the system and the surroundings are back in exactly the same state they started from. The process of restrained expansion is therefore reversible.

7.8   Examples of Irreversible Processes

Engineers are interested in reversible as well as irreversible processes. They want to use reversible processes in devices such as engines and turbines because these processes yield the greatest work output under given conditions. Similarly, refrigerators, compressors, fans, and pumps require less work input when reversible processes are used. On the other hand, engineers are interested in irreversible processes, mainly so they can avoid them, or in some cases, to use them for a specific purpose. In what follows, a number of reversible and irreversible processes are listed and discussed.

First of all, it should be mentioned that reversible processes are neither easily found nor easily proven to be reversible. Irreversible processes, however, are relatively easy to recognize, so that once certain elements of irreversibility are established, reversible processes are identified simply by the absence of these irreversibilities. For these reasons, examples of irreversible processes will be discussed first. They will be proven irreversible by means of the following criterion based on the second law: *A process is irreversible if a perpetual motion machine of the second kind results from its being assumed reversible.* Below are a number of irreversible processes commonly encountered in engineering:

Relative Motion with Friction. Consider first the case of friction between solids in relative motion as illustrated in Fig. 7.11. In this process a block slides down a rough inclined plane. There is considerable friction, and both block and plane increase in temperature during the process. Is the process reversible, i.e., can the block and plane cool, and the block slide up the plane to its initial position? The answer is "no." To prove this by means of the criterion stated above, let the process be assumed to be reversible, as in Fig. 7.12(a), i.e., the block can slide up the plane to its initial position

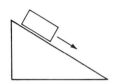

Fig. 7.11 Example of Solid Friction.

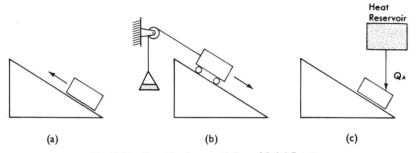

(a)   (b)   (c)

Fig. 7.12 Proof for Irreversibility of Solid Friction.

while both the plane and the block decrease in temperature. Now, let the block be placed on rollers, and by means of a rope and pulley arrangement, raise a weight as it rolls down the incline [Fig. 7.12(b)]. Next, let heat be transferred from a reservoir [Fig. 7.12(c)], raising the temperature of the block and plane to that which would have been reached if the block had slid down with friction present. The result of the sequence of events is this: the system (block and plane) has undergone a cycle, and the net effect has been that a weight has been raised and a corresponding amount of heat transferred from a single heat reservoir. This constitutes a perpetual motion machine of the second kind, and the assumption of reversibility for the friction motion of the block down the incline is therefore incorrect.

Consider now the case of fluid friction; an example of this is shown in Fig. 7.13 where steam flows in a long thermally insulated pipe. Because of

Fig. 7.13 Example of Fluid Friction.

friction and turbulence, there is a pressure drop from point 1 to point 2, even though the enthalpy remains constant. Is the process reversible? Intuitively, the answer is "no." However, to prove this formally, let the contrary assumption be made, i.e., let steam flow from point 2 to point 1, at the same time regaining its initial pressure. This is shown in Fig. 7.14(a).

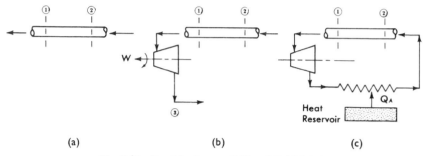

(a)   (b)   (c)

Fig. 7.14 Proof for Irreversibility of Fluid Friction.

Now, let the steam expand to a pressure $P_3 = P_2$ through an adiabatic turbine [Fig. 7.14(b)], performing shaft work. Its enthalpy decreases, but its pressure and velocity are respectively the same as those existing at point 2. Finally, let the steam be heated through communication with a heat reservoir to an enthalpy equal to that at point 2 [Fig. 7.14(c)]. The result of the sequence of events is again the production of work during a cycle while heat is being exchanged with a single reservoir. This is a violation of the second law, and the assumption of reversibility for the frictional flow of a fluid is thus false.

Free Expansion. Consider the free or unrestrained expansion of a gas as shown in Fig. 7.15. An insulated tank is separated into two compartments

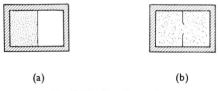

(a)   (b)

Fig. 7.15 Free Expansion.

by a partition. One compartment holds a gas, the other compartment is evacuated. The partition is punctured, and the gas expands to fill the entire tank. There is no work done, and since $Q = 0$, it follows that $\Delta U = 0$. Is the process reversible, i.e. can the gas (now occupying the entire tank) return through the partition to occupy only one side of the partition as it initially did? To show that the process is irreversible, assume it to be reversible, and see what would happen. The sequence of events is shown in Fig. 7.16.

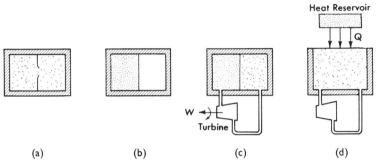

(a)   (b)   (c)   (d)

Fig. 7.16   Proof of Irreversibility for Free Expression.

Starting with Fig. 7.16(a) let the gas be passed through the partition to only one side, against the increasing pressure of the gas, and without any interaction with the surroundings. The result is Fig. 7.16(b). Now, connect a turbine or engine to the gas, and let it expand, until the pressure is the same on both sides of the partition [Fig. 7.16(c)]. Work is done, and the internal energy of the gas decreases. Next, remove part of the tank insulation and add heat to the gas until its internal energy is restored to its initial value [Fig. 7.17(d)]. The result of this cycle of events is that work has been produced while heat has been exchanged with only a single reservoir. This is a violation of the second law, and the assumption of reversibility for the free expansion process is invalid.

Combustion. All spontaneous changes in chemical composition are irreversible. As an illustration, consider the process of combustion. Let a stream of hydrogen and a stream of oxygen at atmospheric pressure enter a combustion chamber as shown in Fig. 7.17. Combustion occurs, and

Fig. 7.17   Combustion Chamber.

assuming no excess hydrogen or oxygen, a stream of steam (combustion product) leaves the chamber at high temperature (but still atmospheric pressure). Is the process reversible? To answer this, assume the process to be reversible and see whether the consequence violates the second law or not. Thus, in Fig. 7.18(a) the hot product of combustion is assumed to

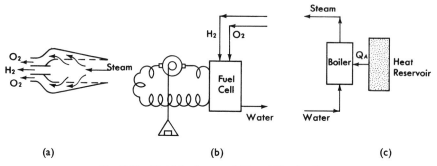

(a)   (b)   (c)

Fig. 7.18   Proof for Irreversibility of Combustion.

dissociate (without transfer of heat or work) into cold hydrogen and oxygen streams. Let the streams of hydrogen and oxygen be supplied to a fuel cell [Fig. 7.18(b)]. This is a device which produces electricity by combining hydrogen and oxygen. The electricity is used to raise a weight, and the water leaving the fuel cell is passed through a boiler [Fig. 7.18(c)], emerging as high temperature steam at atmospheric pressure. The result of these events is a cycle wherein a weight is raised and heat is exchanged with a single reservoir. This constitutes a perpetual motion machine of the second kind, invalidating the assumption of reversibility for the combustion process.

Diffusion.   The last case of irreversible process to be discussed in detail is diffusion. This is the mixing of two unlike fluids. Consider, for example, two ideal gases A and B at first separated into partial volumes V_A and V_B [Fig. 7.19(a)]. Both gases are at the same temperature T and pressure p.

(a)   (b)

Fig. 7.19   Adiabatic Mixing of Two Gases.

When the partition is removed, the gases mix, each gas undergoing a free-expansion, constant-temperature process to fill the tank [Fig. 7.19(b)].

Is the process reversible? To answer this question, assume that it is. In other words, the mixture [Fig. 7.20(a)] is assumed to separate spontaneously into two parts [Fig. 7.20(b)].

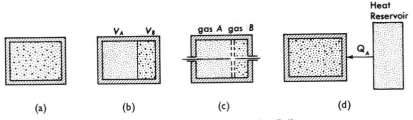

(a) (b) (c) (d)

Fig. 7.20 Proof of Irreversibility for Gas Diffusion.

Let V_A and V_B be, respectively, the partial volumes of gas A and gas B. Now, imagine the diffusion to be accomplished with the aid of semi-permeable membranes [Fig. 7.20(c)]. A semi-permeable membrane is a membrane that can be crossed by one gas, but not the other (such membranes exist for pairs of fluids). In Fig. 7.20(c), the piston to the left is permeable to gas A only, and the piston to the right is permeable to gas B only. Thus as gas A expands, it exerts no pressure on the left piston (since it can pass through it freely), but exerts pressure on the right piston, pushing it back until the volume of gas A becomes the total volume V. Similarly, gas B exerts pressure on the left piston, but not on the right piston. In other words, during the process of diffusion by means of semi-permeable membranes, works is done by each gas, so that heat must be supplied from the surroundings if the expansion of each gas is to be kept isothermal. During the isothermal expansion from their respective initial volumes V_A and V_B to the total volume V, the pressure of each gas decreases from p to $(V_A/V)p$ and $(V_B/V)p$ respectively. Making use of results previously developed (see Chapt. 5, Ex. 5.7), the isothermal work done by each gas is

$$W_A = \left(\frac{V_A}{V}p\right)(V)\ln\frac{V}{V_A} = pV_A \ln\frac{V}{V_A} \tag{7.9}$$

$$W_B = \left(\frac{V_B}{V}p\right)(V)\ln\frac{V}{V_B} = pV_B \ln\frac{V}{V_B} \tag{7.10}$$

The total work is thus

$$W = W_A + W_B = pV_A \ln\frac{V}{V_A} + pV_B \ln\frac{V}{V_B}$$

$$= pV\left[\left(\frac{V_A}{V}\right)\ln\left(\frac{V}{V_A}\right) + \left(\frac{V_B}{V}\right)\ln\left(\frac{V}{V_B}\right)\right] \tag{7.11}$$

and this is also the quantity of heat which must be supplied by the reservoir [Fig. 7.20(d)] to return the system to the original state [Fig. 7.20(a)]. Thus, after one cycle of events, work has been done, and heat has been supplied by a single reservoir. This, of course, is a violation of the second law, and the supposition of reversibility for a mixing process between two different gases cannot hold.

The examples discussed above are but a few of the many irreversible processes that are encountered in engineering. The following are some additional irreversible processes which have not been mentioned before: plastic deformation, flow of electricity through a resistance, sudden changes of phase, shock wave in gas flow, and hydraulic jump in water flow. Each of these cases may be proved irreversible in the manner shown above.

7.9 Examples of Reversible Processes

As mentioned earlier, reversible processes cannot be proven reversible in the same formal manner that was employed for irreversible processes. Rather, a process is recognized as reversible if it contains none of the elements of irreversibility that have been listed above. To be specific, the following are a number of processes which are important in engineering and which may be regarded as reversible. It will be noted that, in each case, means can be found to restore the system and the surroundings to their respective initial states.

Relative Motion Without Friction. Let a block accelerate down a smooth inclined plane under the influence of a gravitational force. If friction is entirely absent, the process is reversible because the block can then be led along a smooth runway and up another inclined plane. It would eventually come to rest, reverse direction, and return to its original state. The surroundings would not have been affected (since no heat would have been generated and transferred to it through friction), and the process is therefore reversible.

Extension and Compression of a Spring. A spring may be extended or compressed by an appropriately varying force. If a small amount of tension is slowly applied, the spring will elongate a short distance. By infinitesimally relaxing the force, the spring may be restored to its original length, and the work done by the spring will essentially equal the work done on the spring while stretching it. The extension or compression of a spring is therefore reversible if an infinitesimally varying force is applied.

Frictionless Adiabatic Expansion or Compression. Let a gas in a cylinder expand without heat transfer against a frictionless piston which is acted upon by a restrained external force. The flywheel and connecting linkages are not shown in Fig. 7.21, but they are also assumed to be frictionless. The inertia of the flywheel is assumed to be great enough that the piston movement is relatively slow in response to pressure changes within the system. Because of the slow movement of the piston relative to the speed of gas molecules, equilibrium exists, and the resistance offered by the external surroundings (piston and flywheel) is but infinitesimally less than the pressure of the gas against the boundaries. The process is reversible, since an infinitesimal increase in pressure from the surroundings would reverse the process; its path can thus be plotted on p-V coordinates. When the piston reaches the crank-end dead center, the flywheel has its greatest store of kinetic energy. As the piston is moved back towards head-end dead center as the expense of the stored energy of the flywheel, the force exerted by the surroundings is infinitesimally greater than the resistance offered by the gas, and compression proceeds over the original expansion, except for algebraic sign.

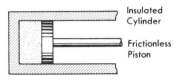

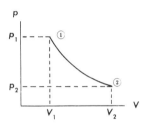

Fig. 7.21 Reversible Adiabatic Expansion-Compression.

Isothermal Expansion or Compression. Consider a gas in a cylinder fitted with a frictionless piston. A heat reservoir of temperature only infinitesimally higher than that of the system is brought into contact with the system [Fig. 7.22]. As the gas receives heat, it expands and does work. If the temperature of the reservoir is reduced slightly below that of the gas, heat will flow from the gas to the reservoir, and work of equal amount will be done on the gas. The expansion (and compression) of the gas is therefore a reversible process, if the temperature difference between the system and the surroundings is made infinitesimally small.

Polytropic Expansion or Compression. A polytropic process usually requires that both heat and work cross the boundaries of the system. The heat transfer, although no longer at a con-

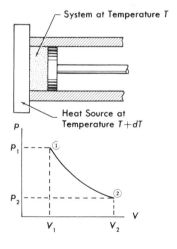

Fig. 7.22 Reversible Isothermal Expansion-Compression.

stant temperature, can be made to occur across an infinitesimal temperature difference by using a large number of heat reservoirs (as previously stated). Under these conditions, and assuming no friction and no unbalance of forces, the process becomes a reversible polytropic process.

Electrolysis. Consider the electrolysis of water as shown in Fig. 7.23. A potential difference exists between the plates of a cell containing water which is rendered electrically conducting by the dissolution of potassium hydroxide. When a small current is passed through, bubbles of hydrogen and oxygen appear, respectively, at the negative and positive electrodes. The process is reversible because it is possible, by suitable means, to have hydrogen and oxygen recombine and produce an electrical current. Such a process is the basis of a device known as the *fuel cell.*

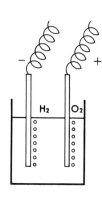

Fig. 7.23
Electrolysis of Water.

The study of reversible and irreversible processes such as those described in the preceding sections leads to the following concluding remarks: (1) If, in any process, work is used to accomplish the same effect that could be accomplished by heat, then the process is irreversible. The stirring of a fluid by means of a paddle wheel to increase its internal energy is a prime example of this statement. (2) Although reversible processes do not actually occur in practice, they nevertheless play an important role in thermodynamics. Just as point masses, frictionless pulleys, and weightless chords serve as useful idealizations in the study of mechanics, so reversible processes serve to simplify thermodynamic analysis immeasurably.

PROBLEMS

7.1 (a) Does the Clausius statement prohibit the transfer of heat from a lower temperature body to a higher temperature body? (b) A refrigerator does not operate unless it receives an energy input (usually in the form of work) from some source other than the two bodies between which it is causing heat to flow. How does this fit in with Clausius' statement?

7.2. Perpetual motion machines are generally of three kinds. The first kind produces energy from nothing, the second kind operates cyclically from a single heat reservoir while producing work, and the third kind is a device which, once set in motion, continues in motion for an infinitely long time. Give an example of each type of machine, and discuss their usefulness. Does a perpetual motion machine of the third kind produce work?

7.3. (a) A dry cell produces work in the form of an electric current while exchanging heat solely with a single reservoir (the constant temperature atmosphere). Is this a violation of the second law? (b) A storage battery which exchanges heat solely with a constant temperature atmosphere undergoes a cycle consisting of the following processes: 1–2, 2700 watt-hours of electrical energy flow into the battery, while 680 Btu of heat flow out to the atmosphere; 2–1, 2350 watt-hours of electrical energy flow out from the battery   Find the magnitude and direction of the heat transferred in process 2–1.

7.4. Discuss each of the following occurrences in terms of their reversibility. If they are not reversible, identify the source of their irreversibility. (a) Water is evaporated at a constant temperature by the addition of heat. (b) Water is evaporated at a constant temperature by the addition of work. (c) Air is compressed slowly by a frictionless piston in an insulated cylinder. (d) Air is heated at a constant volume from T_1 to T_2 by the addition of heat. (e) Two liquids at different temperatures mix in an insulated container. (f) Two gases at the same temperature mix in an insulated container.

7.5. In each of the following cases, state how reversible conditions may be approximated: (a) dropping a weight from a table top to the floor, (b) stopping a rotating flywheel, (c) emptying a reservoir full of water by letting the water fall into a pond below, (d) allowing a weight to slide down an inclined plane.

7.6. (a) It is often useful to distinguish between mechanical irreversibility, thermal irreversibility, and chemical irreversibility. Give an example of each, and discuss how each could be minimized. (b) Experience shows that in charging a storage battery, heat is liberated to the atmosphere. Does this make the storage battery irreversible?

7.7. (a) A small steel ball is dropped from a certain height on a hard steel plate and rebounds almost to its original elevation. Would the process be classified as reversible in the limit? (b) A lead ball is dropped from a certain height on a hard steel plate. Prove, as was done in Sec. 7.8, that the process is irreversible.

7.8. A process occurs in which a system receives 5 Btu of heat from a reservoir and delivers 10 Btu of work. Can the initial state of the system be reached by an adiabatic process? Hint: The processes together form a cycle.

7.9. An engine with 28 per cent thermal efficiency is used to drive a refrigerator having a coefficient of performance of 5. Determine the heat supplied to the engine for each Btu of heat removed from the cold body by the refrigerator.

7.10. (a) Devise a perpetual motion machine of the second kind using the atmosphere or the ocean as a single heat reservoir. (b) What would be the thermal efficiency of such a machine?

7.11. Show that two reversible-adiabatic lines cannot intersect. Hint: The proof is by contradiction. Assume that the reversible adiabatics do intersect, and complete the cycle with an isothermal. The net effect of the cycle is to produce work from a single heat reservoir.

7.12. Show, by means of the second law and Ohm's law of electric conduction, that a finite flow of electricity in a conductor of resistance R is irreversible.

7.13. During an irreversible mixing of gases, no work is done and no heat is transferred. Show that for the case of mixing in equal parts (by volume) of two gases, the lost work (i.e., work that could have been obtained) is

$$0.693 \, pV$$

where p is the total pressure, and V is the volume of the gaseous mixture.

7.14. Consider the steady adiabatic flow of a fluid through a nozzle-diffuser arrangement as shown in Fig. 7.24. Can the process be made reversible? State

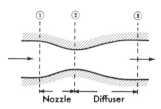

Fig. 7.24

the variation of kinetic energy and enthalpy between each section. Why is it that the diffuser portion is longer than the nozzle portion? Does flow separation have anything to do with it?

7.15. A statement, known as the Carathéodory statement of the second law is the following: In the vicinity of any given state of a substance, there are states which cannot be reached by means of adiabatic processes alone. Show that this follows from the Clausius statement on the Kelvin-Planck statement of the second law.

CHAPTER 8

Corollaries of the Second Law

8.1 Reversible Cycle; Carnot Cycle

Chapters 8 and 9 deal with further consequences of the second law. The reversible processes discussed in the preceding chapter are now put together to form a cycle. Such a cycle is called a *reversible cycle*. When the cycle is reversed, all the heat and work quantities are reversed in direction without their magnitude being affected. The cycle may consist of reversible non-flow processes, or it may be an open or closed cycle consisting of reversible steady-flow processes. The idea of a reversible cycle was first introduced by Carnot,* and its importance will shortly become evident

---

* Nicholas Leonard Sadi Carnot (1792–1832), French engineer and army officer. He originated the ideal of cycles in the study of heat engines and laid the foundations for the second law. His only paper, *Reflections on the Motive Power of Heat,* is one of the milestones of thermodynamics.

For the present, it is sufficient to assume that for best performance, a heat engine should operate on a cycle which consists solely of processes that are perfect in the thermodynamic sense. That this is indeed the case will be proved in the next section. The cycle proposed by Carnot has the working medium receiving heat at one temperature and rejecting heat at another temperature. Thus, two heat reservoirs are required, which of course, is the minimum specified by the second law. This means that the cycle will consist of *two isothermals* and *two reversible adiabatics*. Referring to Fig. 8.1, the Carnot engine works in the manner described below.

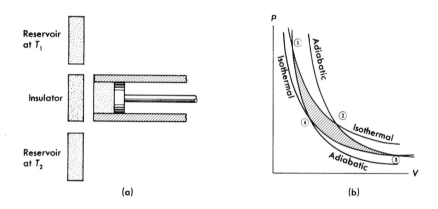

Fig. 8.1 Carnot Engine and Carnot Cycle.

A cylinder fitted with a frictionless piston contains a quantity of working substance (the system). The cylinder walls and the piston are perfect heat insulators, while the cylinder head is a perfect heat conductor. Two reservoirs at temperatures T_1 and T_2 are provided, together with a heat insulator. Let the cycle be started with the gas at temperature T_1 corresponding to point 1 on the pressure-volume diagram. The heat reservoir of temperature T_1 is placed in contact with the cylinder head, and the gas is allowed to expand isothermally from state 1 to state 2 on the pressure-volume diagram. In this process, work is delivered by the system to the surroundings, and a quantity of heat Q_A is absorbed by the system from the reservoir at T_1. The insulator is next brought into contact with the cylinder head, so that the system becomes insulated; the gas is then allowed to expand quasi-statically to a temperature T_3. This is shown by line 2–3 on the p-V diagram. The heat reservoir of temperature T_3 is now placed in thermal contact with the cylinder head, and the gas is isothermally compressed from state 3 to state 4. In this process, work is done on the system by the surroundings, and an amount of heat Q_R is rejected to the reservoir at T_3. Finally, the insulator is brought into contact with the cylinder head, and the gas is compressed adiabatically and reversibly to state 1. This completes the cycle.

Since the system is carried through a cycle, there is no change in its internal energy, i.e., $\Delta U = 0$, and the first law gives

$$\oint dW = \oint dQ = Q_A - Q_R \qquad (8.1)$$

where $\oint dW$ is the net work, and Q_A and Q_R are, respectively, the heat added to, and rejected from the system. The net work is positive, for it is seen from the pressure-volume diagram that the work done *by* the system in the two expansion stages 1 to 2 and 2 to 3 is greater than the work done *on* the system in the two compression stages 3 to 4 and 4 to 1. The thermal efficiency, which is the ratio of the work delivered to the heat added at the high-temperature, is

$$\eta = \frac{\oint dW}{Q_A} = \frac{Q_A - Q_R}{Q_A} \qquad (8.2)$$

It will be shown in Sect. 8.3 that this efficiency depends *only* on the temperatures of the heat reservoirs.

The chief characteristic of the Carnot cycle is its reversibility, since it is composed entirely of reversible processes of the type described in Sec. 7.9. It therefore represents a standard of perfection against which other engines may be compared. Analytically, it has the advantage of being simple to calculate. Although it would be impractical to construct (because the resultant engine would be extremely large for the power it would produce, and the maximum pressure would be much in excess of the average pressure), Carnot's hypothetical engine has, among all engines operating between two given heat reservoirs, the *maximum* efficiency. This will also be proved in the next section.

One last remark: There are other reversible cycles besides the Carnot, although the latter is certainly the most well known. Many reversible cycles will suggest themselves to the student; some of these are listed as problems at the end of the chapter. All that is necessary is to evolve a combination of individually reversible processes which will return the system to its original state.

Example 8.1. Derive an expression for the thermal efficiency of a Carnot engine using an ideal gas as the working fluid in terms of the reservoir temperatures. Also, show that, for such a cycle, $\oint (dQ/T) = 0$.

Solution. An ideal gas is defined by the relations $pv = RT$ and $du = c_v dT$. Referring to Fig. 8.1 and selecting a unit mass of fluid as the basis for calculations, the heat transferred and the work done in each successive process are calculated as follows:

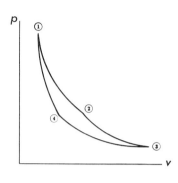

Process 1–2: isothermal, pv = constant

$$\Delta u = 0, \ w = \int_1^2 p\,dv = p_1 v_1 \ln (v_2/v_1) =$$

$$p_1 v_1 \ln (p_1/p_2)$$

$$q = w = p_1 v_1 \ln (p_1/p_2) = R T_1 \ln (p_1/p_2)$$

Process 2–3: reversible adiabatic, pv^γ = constant

Fig. 8.2 Carnot Cycle (repeated)

$$q = 0, \ w = -\Delta u = -c_v(T_3 - T_2)$$

Process 3–4: isothermal, pv = constant

$$\Delta u = 0, \ w = \int_3^4 p\,dv = -p_3 v_3 \ln (v_3/v_4) = -p_3 v_3 \ln (p_4/p_3)$$

$$q = w = -p_3 v_3 \ln (v_3/v_4) = -p_3 v_3 \ln (p_4 p_3) = -R T_3 \ln (p_4/p_3)$$

Process 4–1: reversible adiabatic, pv^γ = constant

$$q = 0, \ w = -\Delta u = -c_v(T_1 - T_4) = c_v(T_4 - T_1)$$

The net work for the cycle is

$$\oint dW = \oint dq = q_{1-2} + q_{3-4}$$

$$= R T_1 \ln (p_1/p_2) - R T_3 \ln (p_4/p_3) \tag{8.3}$$

Since processes 2–3 and 4–1 are reversible adiabatics,

$$\frac{p_2}{p_3} = \left(\frac{T_2}{T_3}\right)^{\gamma/(\gamma-1)}; \frac{p_1}{p_4} = \left(\frac{T_1}{T_4}\right)^{\gamma/(\gamma-1)}$$

But $T_2 = T_1$, and $T_3 = T_4$ so that the above relations become

$$\frac{p_2}{p_3} = \frac{p_1}{p_4}$$

or

$$\frac{p_1}{p_2} = \frac{p_4}{p_3}$$

This result makes it possible to write Eq. (8.3) as

$$\oint dw = R T_1 \ln (p_1/p_2) - R T_3 \ln (p_4/p_3)$$

$$= R(T_1 - T_3) \ln (p_1/p_2)$$

The efficiency of the cycle is the net work divided by the heat added, or

$$\eta = \frac{\oint dw}{q_{1-2}} = \frac{R(T_1 - T_3)\ln(p_1/p_2)}{RT_1\ln(p_1/p_2)}$$

$$= \frac{T_1 - T_3}{T_1} \tag{8.4}$$

Equation (8.4) shows that the efficiency of the Carnot cycle employing a perfect gas depends *only* on the temperatures T_1 and T_3 of the heat reservoirs, and is *independent* of the characteristics of the working substance. (A more general proof of this statement will be given in Sec. 8.3.) The results of the computations are summarized below:

Process	Heat Transferred	Work Done	dq/T
1–2	$RT_1\ln(p_1/p_2)$	$RT_1\ln(p_1/p_2)$	$R\ln(p_1/p_2)$
2–3	0	$-c_v(T_3-T_2)$	0
3–4	$-RT_3\ln(p_4/p_3)$	$-RT_3\ln(p_4/p_3)$	$-R\ln(p_4/p_3)$
4–1	0	$-c_v(T_4-T_1)$	0

Notice that

$$\oint \frac{dQ}{T} = R\ln\frac{p_1}{p_2} - R\ln\frac{p_4}{p_3} = 0 \tag{8.5}$$

since $p_1/p_2 = p_4/p_3$. This is an important result, and is kept in mind for future reference.

From this problem, two important points should be noted: First, the thermal efficiency of a Carnot cycle is independent of the substance used; this will be shown to apply to any *reversible* cycle between two given reservoirs. Even if an actual gas (which might deviate considerably from perfect gas behavior) were used, and the energy effects for the individual processes might be difficult to calculate, the thermal efficiency of a reversible cycle would still be the same, and for temperature limits T_1 and T_3, would be given by Eq. (8.4). Second, the cyclic integral of dq/T is zero for a reversible cycle. The reason for these results will become evident in the next section.

Example 8.2. A given thermocouple consists of a strip of copper wire and a strip of constantan wire fused together end to end to form a loop. An electric motor is placed in the loop, half-way between the junctions. One junction is placed into a beaker filled with ice and water; the other junction is kept at a temperature of 250 °F. The system absorbs heat at the high-temperature junction, and rejects heat at the low-temperature junction. Neglecting electrical resistance, heat conduction, and mechanical friction, what maximum amount of work can be developed from the absorption of 120 calories of heat at the hot junction?

Solution. Under reversible conditions of operation, the efficiency would be that of a Carnot engine, namely

$$\eta = \frac{710 - 492}{710} = 0.307 \text{ or } 30.7 \text{ per cent}$$

The work produced would then be

$$W = (120)(0.307) = 36.8 \text{ calories} = 0.147 \text{ Btu}$$

8.2   Carnot Refrigerator and Heat Pump

If a Carnot cycle is operated in reverse, it no longer produces work; it becomes a refrigerator or heat pump requiring work input. This refrigerator or heat pump absorbs heat Q_A from a low-temperature source and rejects heat Q_R to a high-temperature sink. The net work required to operate the cycle is

$$\oint dW = Q_R - Q_A \tag{8.6}$$

The coefficient of performance of the reverse Carnot cycle employed as refrigerator is

$$\text{COP} = \frac{Q_A}{\oint dW} = \frac{Q_A}{Q_R - Q_A} = \frac{T_L}{T_H - T_L} \tag{8.7}$$

where the subscripts L and H refer to the low-temperature source and high-temperature sink respectively.

On the other hand, if the reverse Carnot cycle is used as heat pump, then the coefficient of performance is

$$\text{COP} = \frac{Q_R}{\oint dW} = \frac{Q_R}{Q_R - Q_A} = \frac{T_H}{T_H - T_L} \tag{8.8}$$

where the subscripts on the temperatures have the same meaning as before. Note that the purpose of a refrigerator is to remove heat from a body, whereas the purpose of a heat pump is to supply heat to a building. This explains the difference in the expressions for the COP of a refrigerator and of a heat pump.

8.3   Carnot Theorems

Having discussed the reversible cycles, it is now possible to resume the presentation of additional corollaries of the second law. The Clausius statement given in Chapter 7 is corollary 1. The following corollaries (numbers 2, 3 and 4) are commonly known as *Carnot theorems*.

Corollary 2: No engine operating between two heat reservoirs, each having a fixed temperature, can be more efficient than a reversible engine operating between the same reservoirs.

The proof of this is by contradiction: Suppose that an irreversible engine I is more efficient than a reversible engine R operating between the same two reservoirs. This is illustrated in Fig. 8.3(a), where W_I, the work output of engine I is shown to be greater than the work output W_R of engine R for the same amount of heat Q_1 supplied to the two engines.

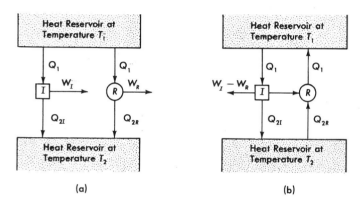

(a)   (b)

Fig. 8.3   Proof for Carnot Theorems.

Let engine R be reversed and driven by engine I. Since engine R operates on a reversible cycle, its heat and work quantities remain unchanged, except for direction. This means that when I is driving R, there will be some work left over, namely $W_{net} = W_I - W_R$. This is shown in Fig. 8.3(b). Now, Q_{2R} is greater than Q_{2I} since engine R is less efficient than engine I; therefore, engine I, engine R, and heat reservoir at T_1 form a combination which draws an amount of heat $Q_{2R} - Q_{2I}$ from a single reservoir, and produces a net amount of work $W_I - W_R$. This is a perpetual motion machine of the second kind, and a violation of the second law. Thus, the assumption that Engine I is more efficient than Engine R is false, and the corollary is proved. Other corollaries pertaining to heat engines are listed below.

Corollary 3: All reversible engines operating between two heat reservoirs, each having its own fixed temperature, have the same efficiency.

This is proved very simply by letting R_1 and R_2 be any two reversible engines. Then, by the Corollary 2, the efficiency of R_1 cannot be greater than the efficiency of R_2 and vice-versa. Consequently, the efficiencies of R_1 and R_2 must be equal.

Corollary 4: The efficiency of any reversible engine operating between two reservoirs is independent of the nature of the working fluid and depends only on the temperature of the reservoirs.

This may be proved in the following manner: Let a Carnot engine drive a Carnot heat pump operating between the same heat reservoirs as shown in Fig. 8.4(a). The engine receives heat Q_1 from the reservoir at T_1 and rejects

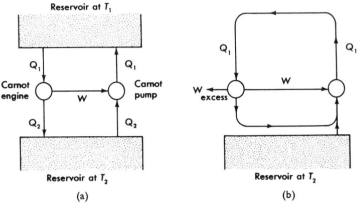

Fig. 8.4 Combination Carnot Engine and Heat Pump.

heat Q_2 to the reservoir at T_2. The pump absorbs heat Q_2 from the reservoir at T_2 and rejects heat Q_1 to the reservoir at T_1. The net output of the combination engine-pump must be zero, since each heat or work quantity for the engine is canceled by that for the pump. Now, let it be assumed that some factor other than temperature could make the engine more efficient. This factor may be the working substance. Then more work will be delivered by the engine than the work required by the heat pump, and the installation shown in Fig. 8.4(b) would result. The reservoir at T_1 would not be needed, and the combination engine-pump would deliver work from the single reservoir at T_2. This cannot be, and the assumption that the efficiency of a reversible engine depends on some factor other than the temperatures of the reservoirs is thus false.

8.4   Thermodynamic Temperature Scale

It was pointed out in Chap. 3 that a temperature scale defined in terms of the physical properties of a substance has definite shortcomings. In other words, except at the ice point and the steam point, which are calibration points, different thermometers tend to read different temperatures. This is so because different materials have different temperature-volume or temperature-pressure relations, so that a temperature scale based upon the volume change or pressure change of one material will not agree at all points with a scale base upon these same characteristics of another material. The developments in this chapter, however, allow the following statement (in the form of yet another corollary) to be made:

Corollary 5: *A temperature scale can be defined in a manner independent of the nature of the thermometric substance.*

In proving this, it will first be shown that, for any reversible engine, the ratio of the heat absorbed Q_1 to the heat rejected Q_2 is *independent* of the nature of the working substance. The same statement is *not* true of the temperature ratio *if* temperatures are measured by thermometers using various thermometric substances. Write the defining expression for thermal efficiency as

$$\eta_{12} = \frac{Q_1 - Q_2}{Q_1} = 1 - \frac{Q_2}{Q_1} \tag{8.9}$$

where η_{12} denotes the efficiency of an engine operating between heat reservoirs 1 and 2. Let the temperatures of these reservoirs be θ_1 and θ_2. Here, θ_1 (rather than the usual T) is employed to designate temperature since the temperature scale has yet to be defined. Since, for a reversible engine, η_{12} is function only of temperatures θ_1 and θ_2, it follows from Eq. 8.9 that

$$1 - \frac{Q_2}{Q_1} = f(\theta_1, \theta_2) \tag{8.10}$$

where f denotes some functional relationship. In terms of a new function ϕ, Eq. 8.10 may be written as

$$\frac{Q_1}{Q_2} = \phi(\theta_1, \theta_2) \tag{8.11}$$

Now, consider three reversible engines R_1, R_2 and R_3 operating as shown in Fig. (8.5). Engine R_1 operates between reservoirs at θ_1 and θ_2 by receiving

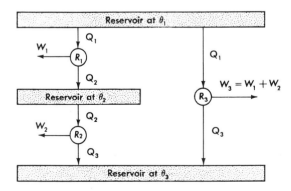

Fig. 8.5 Establishment of Absolute Temperature Scale by means of Reversible Engines.

heat Q_1 at θ_1 and rejecting heat Q_2 at θ_2. Engine R_2 receives heat Q_2 at temperature θ_2 and rejects heat Q_3 at temperature θ_3. Engine R_3 operates between θ_1 and θ_3. It receives the same amount of heat Q_1 at θ_1 and, since it has the same efficiency as the combination of engines R_1 and R_2 in series, its work W_3 must be equal to $W_1 + W_2$, and its heat rejection at θ_3 must be equal to Q_3. Just as Eq. (8.11) was written for engine R_1, so can the following equations be written for engines R_2 and R_3 respectively:

$$\frac{Q_2}{Q_3} = \phi(\theta_2, \theta_3) \tag{8.12}$$

$$\frac{Q_1}{Q_3} = \phi(\theta_1, \theta_3) \tag{8.13}$$

Since

$$\frac{Q_1}{Q_2} = \frac{Q_1/Q_3}{Q_2/Q_3}$$

Eqs. (8.11), (8.12), and (8.13) combine to give

$$\phi(\theta_1, \theta_2) = \frac{\phi(\theta_1, \theta_3)}{\phi(\theta_2, \theta_3)} \tag{8.14}$$

To find the function ϕ which satisfies Eq. (8.14), note that, since θ_3 does not appear on the left-hand side of the equation, the function ϕ must necessarily be of the form

$$\phi(\theta_1, \theta_3) = \frac{\psi(\theta_1)}{\psi(\theta_3)}$$

$$\phi(\theta_2, \theta_3) = \frac{\psi(\theta_2)}{\psi(\theta_3)}$$

so that, upon substitution into Eq. (8.14),

$$\phi(\theta_1, \theta_2) = \frac{\psi(\theta_1)/\psi(\theta_3)}{\psi(\theta_2)/\psi(\theta_3)} = \frac{\psi(\theta_1)}{\psi(\theta_2)} \tag{8.15}$$

Eqs. (8.11) and (8.15) then give

$$\frac{Q_1}{Q_2} = \frac{\psi(\theta_1)}{\psi(\theta_2)} \tag{8.16}$$

where ψ is a function whose choice defines the temperature scale. Now, there is infinite choice of possible forms for $\psi(\theta)$, but obviously, the simplest choice is to set $\psi(\theta) = \theta$, whereupon Eq. (8.16) becomes

$$\frac{Q_1}{Q_2} = \frac{\theta_1}{\theta_2}$$

or, using the more common symbol T to denote temperature,

$$\frac{Q_1}{Q_2} = \frac{T_1}{T_2} \tag{8.17}$$

Eq. (8.17) defines the *absolute* or *thermodynamic scale*. This scale is entirely *independent* of the thermometric substance, since its establishment is based only on the efficiency of reversible engines, and this efficiency is independent of any working substance. If a positive number T_0 is assigned to some reservoir in an easily reproducible reference state (as for example, a pure substance melting at atmospheric pressure), the temperature T of any other reservoir may be uniquely determined by means of Eq. (8.17) in the form of

$$T = T_0 \frac{Q}{Q_0} \tag{8.18}$$

Eq. (8.18) introduces the concept of absolute zero, i.e., $T = 0$ when $Q = 0$. It is for this reason that the thermodynamic scale is also called the absolute scale.

8.5 Absolute Fahrenheit and Centigrade Scales

To construct an absolute temperature scale, consider a string of reversible engines as shown in Fig. 8.6. Starting with a heat reservoir at temperature T_1, engine R_1 absorbs heat Q_1 from the reservoir and rejects heat Q_2 at temperature T_2 to engine R_2, which in turn rejects heat Q_3 at T_3 to engine R_3 and so on. The temperatures are so chosen that the work output of each engine is the same, i.e.,

$$W = Q_1 - Q_2 = Q_2 - Q_3 = Q_3 - Q_4 \tag{8.19}$$

Furthermore, from the definition of the absolute scale,

$$\frac{Q_1}{T_1} = \frac{Q_2}{T_2} = \frac{Q_3}{T_3} = \frac{Q_4}{T_4} \tag{8.20}$$

Equations (8.19) and (8.20) combine to give

$$T_1 - T_2 = T_2 - T_3 = T_3 - T_4 = \ldots \tag{8.21}$$

In other words, the string of reversible engines, each producing equal work, leads

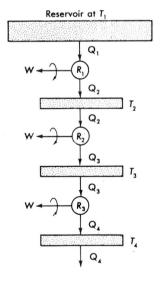

Fig. 8.6 Construction of Temperature Scale by means of Reversible Engines.

to equal increments of temperature ΔT. The size of ΔT can be fixed by choosing W and Q_1. However, it is more usual to choose the steam-point and the ice-point as temperature references and to assign the difference between these points the value of 180 degrees. Thus,

$$T_s - T_i = 180 \tag{8.22}$$

Next, a reversible engine is operated between the two temperatures, and the heat transfers measured. The results (experimental) show that

$$\frac{Q_s}{Q_i} = 1.366,$$

and consequently,

$$\frac{T_s}{T_i} = 1.366 \tag{8.23}$$

Eqs. (8.22) and (8.23) are solved simultaneously to give

$$T_s = 672$$
$$T_i = 492$$

The above defines the Rankine or absolute Fahrenheit scale. It is seen that the relation between degrees Rankine and degrees Fahrenheit is

$$^\circ R = ^\circ F + 460 \tag{8.24}$$

Similarly, if the difference in temperature between the steam point and the ice point is 100 degrees, then the solution of the set of equations

$$\left\{ \begin{array}{ll} T_s - T_i = 100 & (8.25) \\ \dfrac{T_s}{T_i} = 1.366 & (8.26) \end{array} \right.$$

gives

$$T_s = 373$$
$$T_i = 273$$

Eqs. (8.25) and (8.26) define the Kelvin or absolute centigrade scale. The relationship between degrees Kelvin and degrees centigrade is

$$^\circ K = ^\circ C + 273 \tag{8.27}$$

The above discussion shows how a temperature scale may be obtained by taking measurements of heat and work, without having to depend on the physical properties of any particular thermometric substance. For most practical purposes, however, the thermodynamic or absolute temperature scale agrees closely with the ideal gas temperature scale defined in Sec. 3–5. This is formally shown in the next section.

Example 8.3. An absolute temperature scale is to be constructed, using the melting point of sulfur as the temperature of a reservoir, and putting together a string of reversible engines as shown in Fig. 8.7. The first engine receives 1300 Btu from the reservoir at the melting point of sulfur, delivers 1 Btu of work and rejects 1299 Btu to the second engine. Subsequent engines receive the exact amount of heat rejected from the previous engine and deliver exactly 1 Btu of work. If the temperature difference between successive reservoirs is set equal to one degree, what is the absolute temperature of melting sulfur on this scale?

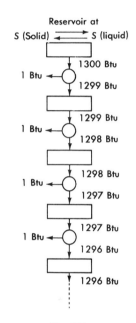

Solution. The answer of 1300° may be seen right away, because the data for the problem has been somewhat conveniently arranged. However, the student may check this by writing $Q_1 = 1300$, $T_1 - T_2 = 1$, $Q_1 - Q_2 = 1$, $Q_1/T_1 = Q_2/T_2$, and solving for $T_1 = 1300°$.

8.6   Ideal-Gas Temperature Scale and Absolute Temperature Scale

Fig. 8.7
Reversible Engines in Series.

Referring to Fig. 8.8, let θ_1 and θ_2 be the temperatures of two heat reservoirs on a scale of temperature using an ideal gas as thermometric substance. It was shown in Ex. 8.1 that for a Carnot cycle using such a gas as the working substance, the heat transferred during the isothermal process 1–2 at the temperature θ_1 is

$$q_1 = R\theta_1 \ln (p_1/p_2)$$

Similarly, the heat transferred during the isothermal process 3–4 at the temperature θ_3 is

$$q_3 = R\theta_3 \ln (p_4/p_3)$$

where q_3 has been expressed as a positive number for convenience, since it is understood that heat is rejected at temperature θ_3. Thus,

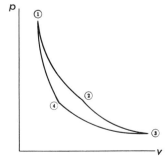

Fig. 8.8 Carnot Cycle (repeated).

$$\frac{q_1}{q_3} = \frac{\theta_1 \ln(p_1/p_2)}{\theta_3 \ln(p_4/p_3)} \tag{8.28}$$

Now, Ex. 8.1 also showed that $p_1/p_2 = p_4/p_3$; so that Eq. (8.28) becomes

$$\frac{q_1}{q_3} = \frac{\theta_1}{\theta_3} \tag{8.29}$$

Comparison of Eqs. (8.29) and (8.17) reveals that the ideal-gas temperature scale and the absolute temperature scale are defined by exactly the same relation. In other words, the absolute temperature and the ideal-gas temperature scale are numerically equal to each other, and both temperatures, Rankine and Kelvin, may be designated by T and measured with a gas thermometer.

Example 6.6. A Carnot engine uses, as a working substance, a gas whose equation of state is $p(v - b) = R\theta$, and whose internal energy is a function of θ only. Show that the thermometric temperature θ is equal to the absolute temperature T.

Solution. For a gas whose internal energy is a function of θ only, the first law may be written as

$$dq = du + p\,dv = c_v\,d\theta + p\,dv$$

Referring to Fig. 8.9, an infinitesimal heat transfer during the isothermal process 1–2 is then

$$dq = p\,dv$$

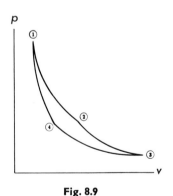

Fig. 8.9
Carnot Cycle (repeated).

$$= p\left[\left(\frac{\partial v}{\partial p}\right)_\theta dp + \left(\frac{\partial v}{\partial \theta}\right)_p d\theta\right] = p\left(\frac{\partial v}{\partial p}\right)_\theta dp$$

where p and θ have been chosen as independent variables. The quantity $(\partial v/\partial p)_\theta$ is now calculated for the particular gas. From the equation of state $p(v - b) = R\theta$, partial differentiation gives

$$p\left(\frac{\partial v}{\partial p}\right)_\theta + v - b = 0$$

or

$$\left(\frac{\partial v}{\partial p}\right)_\theta = \frac{b - v}{p}$$

Replacing this in the expression for dq gives

$$dq = p\left(\frac{\partial v}{\partial p}\right)_\theta dp = p\left(\frac{b - v}{p}\right)dp$$

$$= (b - v)dp = -\frac{R\theta}{p}dp$$

The heat transferred during the isothermal process 1–2 at temperature θ, is thus

$$q_1 = - R\theta_1 \int_1^2 \frac{dp}{p} = - R\theta_1 \ln\frac{p_2}{p_1} = R\theta_1 \ln\frac{p_1}{p_2}$$

Also, the heat transferred during the isothermal process 3–4 at temperature θ_3 is

$$q_3 = R\theta_3 \ln\frac{p_4}{p_3}$$

The ratio of the amounts of heat transfers at θ, and θ_3 is thus

$$\frac{q_1}{q_3} = \frac{R\theta_1 \ln(p_1/p_2)}{R\theta_3 \ln(p_4/p_3)} \tag{8.30}$$

Now, $p_1/p_2 = p_4/p_3$. This can be shown by considering the reversible adiabatic process 2–3 from temperature θ_2 to temperature θ_3: the first law gives

$$dq = 0 = c_v d\theta + p dv$$

which can be written with the aid of the equation of state $p(v-b) = R\theta$, as

$$- c_v d\theta = p dv = \frac{R\theta}{v-b} dv$$

Integrating between states 2 and 3, this becomes

$$- \frac{l}{R} \int_{\theta_2}^{\theta_3} c_v \frac{d\theta}{\theta} = \ln\frac{v_3-b}{v_2-b} = \ln\frac{R\theta_3/P_3}{R\theta_2/P_2} \tag{8.31}$$

Similarly, for the reversible adiabatic process 4–1 from temperature θ_4 to temperature θ_1.

$$- \frac{1}{R} \int_{\theta_4}^{\theta_1} c_v \frac{d\theta}{\theta} = \int_{v_4}^{v_1} \frac{dv}{v-b} = \ln\frac{v_1-b}{v_4-b} = \ln\frac{R\theta_1/P_1}{R\theta_4/P_4}$$

or

$$- \frac{1}{R} \int_{\theta_1}^{\theta_4} c_v \frac{d\theta}{\theta} = \ln\frac{R\theta_4/P_4}{R\theta_1/P_1} \tag{8.32}$$

Since $\theta_1 = \theta_2$ and $\theta_3 = \theta_4$, Eqs. (8.31) and (8.32) show that

$$\ln\frac{R\theta_3/P_3}{R\theta_2/P_2} = \ln\frac{R\theta_4/P_4}{R\theta_1/P_1}$$

which simplifies to

$$\frac{p_1}{p_2} = \frac{p_4}{p_3} \tag{8.33}$$

Eq. (8.33) enables Eq. (8.30) to be written as

$$\frac{q_1}{q_3} = \frac{\theta_1}{\theta_3} \tag{8.34}$$

In other words, the ratio of the heat added to the heat rejected is equal to the ratio of the reservoir temperatures. But this is precisely the same relation as Eq. (8.17), which defines the absolute temperature. Therefore $\theta = T$.

8.7 International Temperature Scale

The International Temperature Scale is a commonly agreed upon scale which is defined by specifying a number of fixed points, together with a method of interpolating between them. It was adopted by 31 nations in 1927 and later modified slightly in 1948 at the Ninth General Conference on Weights and Measures. Table 8.1 gives the six fixed points, including the two fundamental points for melting ice and boiling water upon which it is based The values assigned to these points are as close to the thermodynamic scale as measurements with gas thermometers permit.

At states other than those listed, the temperature is computed by means of the following interpolation formulas:

From −190 *to* 0 °C: The temperature t is defined by the relation

$$R_t = R_0[1 + At + Bt^2 + C(t - 100)t^3]$$

where R_t = resistance at temperature t of a platinum resistance thermometer; R_0 = resistance at 0 °C; and A, B, C = constants determined by measurements of R_t at the steam, sulfur, and oxygen points respectively.

From 0 *to* 660 °C: The temperature t is defined by the relation

$$R_t = R_0(1 + At + Bt^2)$$

where R_t, R_0, A and B are as defined in the range of −190 to 0 °C.

TABLE 8.1

FIXED POINTS FOR THE INTERNATIONAL TEMPERATURE SCALE

Fixed points	Standard system at 1 atm pressure	Temperature °C
Oxygen-point	Oxygen boiling	−182.97
Ice-point	Ice melting	0.000
Steam-point	Water boiling	100.000
Sulfur-point	Sulfur boiling	444.6
Silver-point	Silver melting	960.8
Gold-point	Gold melting	1063.0

From 660 *to* 1063 °C: The temperature t is defined by the relation

$$\mathscr{E}(t) = a + bt + ct^2$$

where $\mathscr{E}(t)$ = emf of a thermocouple of platinum and platinum-rhodium thermocouple, with one junction at 0 °C and the other at temperature t; a, b, c = constants calculated from measured values of $\mathscr{E}$ at the freezing point of antimony (660 °C), the silver point, and the gold point respectively.

Above Gold Point (1063 °C): Temperatures above the gold point are defined by Planck's radiation law, which relates the intensity of radiation of a given wavelength from a black body to its absolute temperature. The intensity of radiation of a selected wavelength from an unknown source is measured and compared to the intensity of radiation of the same wavelength emitted by a black body at the gold point. Substitution of the intensity ratio in Planck's equation enables calculation of the absolute temperature of the unknown source.

8.8 Absolute Zero

From the definition of the absolute temperature $(T/T_i = Q/Q_i)$, it follows that the value of a temperature T on the Kelvin scale is given by

$$T = (273.16)\frac{Q}{Q_i} \tag{8.35}$$

Eq. (8.35) shows that zero is the smallest value that T can have, since this corresponds to the minimum of $Q = 0$. Negative temperatures have no physical meaning on the absolute or thermodynamic scale. This is evident from the consideration of a Carnot engine. Let the engine take in heat Q_1 from a reservoir at temperature T_1, and reject heat Q_2 to a reservoir at temperature T_2. The question is: How low can T_2 get? The work done by the engine is $Q_1 - Q_2$, and the thermal efficiency is thus

$$\eta = \frac{Q_1 - Q_2}{Q_1} = 1 - \frac{Q_2}{Q_1} \tag{8.36}$$

From the definition of absolute temperatures, Q_2/Q_1 may be replaced by T_2/T_1, so that Eq. (8.36) becomes

$$\eta = 1 - \frac{T_2}{T_1} \tag{8.37}$$

Since no engine can have an efficiency greater than unity (otherwise it would violate the second law by converting heat completely into work), it is seen that the smallest value T_2 can have is zero. In fact, it is impossible, in the absence of a perfect insulator, to bring a system to absolute zero of temperature. This may be proved by referring to Fig. 8.10, which shows a system A in the process of being reduced to a temperature of absolute zero by means of a reversible heat pump. In the absence of a perfect insulator,

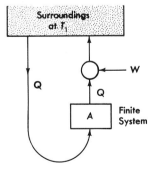

Fig. 8.10 Unattainability of Absolute Zero.

a certain amount of heat Q is bound to leak into A. Let T_1 denote the absolute temperature of the surroundings, and T denote the absolute temperature of the system. The work required by the heat pump is then (see Sec. 7.2):

$$\oint dw = \frac{Q(T_1 - T)}{T}$$

Now, as T becomes zero, the work required becomes

$$\oint dW = \frac{QT_1}{0} = \infty$$

This means that an infinite supply of work is required to operate the heat pump. Thus, absolute zero is a conceptual limit rather than a temperature that can actually be achieved.

PROBLEMS

8.1. An inventor claims to have developed an engine which takes in 90,000 Btu at a temperature of 265 °F, delivers 15.5 kw-hr of work, and rejects the rest at -90 °F. Discuss the validity of the claim.

8.2. A certain engine has a fuel rate of 0.41 lbm hp-hr. If 18,400 Btu can be produced by the combustion of 1 lbm of fuel, what is the thermal efficiency of the engine?

8.3. A reversible engine (Carnot) is to deliver work in the amount of 95 ft lbf per cycle. The heat supplied per cycle is 0.32 Btu at 500 °F. Find: (a) the temperature at which heat is rejected, (b) the thermal efficiency of the engine.

8.4. A refrigerator operating on the reversed Carnot cycle removes 40 Btu/min of heat from a reservoir at 35 °F and rejects heat to a reservoir at 100 °F. Determine: (a) the horsepower required, (b) the heat rejected to the hot reservoir, (c) the coefficient of performance.

8.5. A heat pump operating on the reversed Carnot cycle abstracts heat from a cold reservoir at 45 °F and rejects heat to a hot reservoir at 75 °F. Find: (a) the heat rejected for each kw-hr, (b) the coefficient of performance, (c) the cost of operation for a heat rejection of 80,000 Btu/hr if the cost of electricity is 2 cents per kw-hr.

8.6. On a summer day at 90 °F, there is available an artesian well of 55 °F. Consider the thermodynamic engine operating between these reservoirs for the purpose of raising water from the well. If 45 lbm of water is to be raised 25 ft, how much heat must be transferred into the well?

8.7. Claude, a French engineer, designed and built a heat engine cycle on the coast of Cuba, using the warm surface water of the Gulf Stream as the high-temperature source, and the deep water as the low-temperature sink. If the surface water is at 86 °F, and the deep water at 40 °F, determine the maximum efficiency of an engine seeking to convert the energy of the warm water into work.

8.8. The Carnot cycle is not the only reversible cycle. Another example of a reversible cycle is the Ericcson cycle (Fig. 8.11), which consists of two isothermals and two isobarics. The feature of the cycle is the inclusion of a regenerator. This makes it possible to supply heat and reject heat isothermally. Discuss the practicability of such a cycle. Would the efficiency of a gas turbine cycle be improved by the addition of a regenerator? What is the efficiency of an Ericcson cycle compared to that of a Carnot cycle operating between the same temperature limits?

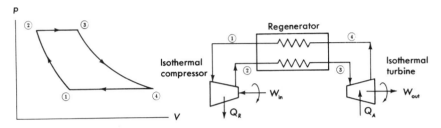

Fig. 8.11 Ericcson Cycle.

8.9. A power cycle is to exchange heat with only two reservoirs, each at a fixed temperature. If the cycle is to be reversible, heat can be transferred between the system and the reservoirs only during isothermal processes. During non-isothermal processes, heat can be transferred from one part of the cycle to another part of the cycle by means of a regenerator. The Stirling cycle (Fig. 8.12) is an example of reversible cycle which uses regenera-tion. During process 1–2, heat is added iso-thermally to the working fluid from the high - temperature reservoir. During the constant-volume process 2–3, heat is trans-ferred from the fluid to a regenerator. During process 3–4, heat is rejected isothermally to the low-temperature reservoir. During the constant-volume process 4–1, heat is trans-ferred to the fluid from the regenerator. Sketch a possible arrangement for a Stirling engine and discuss the merits of the cycle.

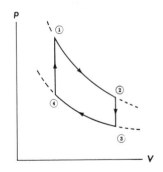

Fig. 8.12 Stirling Cycle.

8.10. One pound of air ($pv = RT$; $c_v = 0.17$) undergoes the cycle shown on the p-v diagram in Fig. 8.13. The maximum pressure of the cycle is 500 psia, the maximum volume is 4 cu ft, and the initial volume is 1.5 cu ft. The process 2–3 is reversible adiabatic. Determine the efficiency of the cycle and compare it with the efficiency of a reversible engine operating between the extremes of temperature of the cycle.

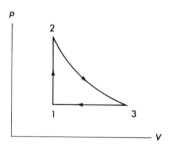

Fig. 8.13

8.11. There are two ways of increasing the efficiency of a Carnot engine: (a) to increase the temperature of the source, keeping the temperature of the sink constant, (b) to decrease the temperature of the sink, keeping the temperature of the source constant. Which is the more effective way?

8.12. Discuss the practicability of a Carnot engine. How would the size of the engine compare with the amount of power developed? Would it be better to carry out the functions of heating and cooling in separate devices, such as boiler and condenser?

8.13. Two reversible engines are connected in series. The first one receives heat at T degrees Rankine and rejects heat at 1800 °F. The second one receives the heat rejected by the first and in turn rejects heat at 600 °F. Determine the temperature T for: (a) equal efficiencies of the two engines, (b) for equal work delivery of the two engines.

8.14. A certain heat engine is designed and built with great care so as to approach reversible conditions. When supplied with 985 Btu of heat from a reservoir at 800 °F, the engine delivers 560 Btu of work and rejects 425 Btu of heat to a reservoir at 75 °F. Assuming that an increment of 1 °F equals an increment of 1 °θ, what does the experiment indicate the value of Fahrenheit temperature to be when it is zero on the thermodynamic temperature scale θ?

8.15. It was shown in Sec. 8.4 that a temperature scale is defined by the general relation

$$\frac{Q}{Q_0} = \frac{\psi(\theta)}{\psi(\theta_0)}$$

where ψ is any chosen function. Kelvin first proposed a temperature scale defined by

$$\theta = \theta_0 \ln \frac{Q}{Q_0}$$

Discuss the merits of such a scale. What would its range be?

8.16. The lowest temperatures that have been reached are of the order of 0.001 °K. Estimate the minimum cost of extracting 1 calorie of heat from a system at 0.001 °K if the cost of work is 2.6 cents/kw-hr. Consider the heat sink to be the ambient atmosphere at 70 °F.

CHAPTER 9

Entropy

9.1 Introduction

Just as the first law of thermodynamics leads to the definition of energy as a property of a system, so the second law, in the form of Clausius' inequality, leads to the definition of a new property of fundamental importance. This property is *entropy*.

The Clausius inequality is a relation between the heat transfers of a system with an arbitrary number of heat reservoirs and the absolute temperatures of these reservoirs when the system undergoes a cycle. In the discussion of the Carnot cycle, it was established that, for any reversible cycle operating between two reservoirs,

$$\frac{Q_1}{T_1} = \frac{Q_2}{T_2} \tag{9.1}$$

where Q_1 and Q_2 are the heat transfers (for convenience considered as positive, absolute numbers) and T_1 and T_2 are the absolute temperatures of the reservoirs. Eq. (9.1) may be written as

$$\frac{Q_1}{T_1} - \frac{Q_2}{T_2} = 0 \qquad (9.2)$$

Now, if the sign convention of $+$ for heat added, and $-$ for heat rejected is adhered to, this becomes

$$\frac{Q_1}{T_1} + \frac{Q_2}{T_2} = 0 \qquad (9.3)$$

i.e., the summation of the ratios of heat transfers to absolute temperatures for a Carnot cycle equals zero. Eq. (9.3) is applicable to any reversible cycle (such as the Carnot cycle) operating between two reservoirs. This result can be extended (in the form of a cyclic integral) to a system operating between any number of heat reservoirs. But first, as a preliminary step, it will be shown that any reversible process may be approximated by a series of reversible adiabatic and isothermal processes.

Consider the reversible process $A–B$ shown in Fig. 9.1. From A, draw a reversible adiabatic curve $A–A'$; likewise from B, draw the reversible adiabatic curve $B–B'$. Next, draw an isothermal curve $A'–B'$ such that the area under the zig-zag curve $A–A'–B'–B$ is equal to the area under the original curve $A–B$. Thus,

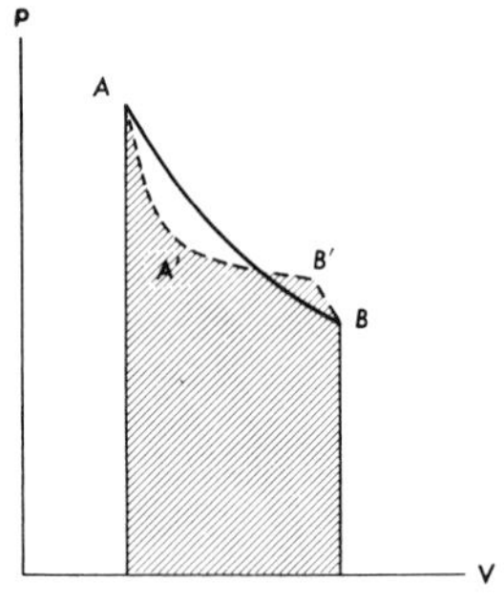

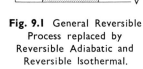

$$W_{A-B} = W_{A-A'-B'-B}$$

Now, the first law states that

$$Q_{A-B} = (U_B - U_A) + W_{A-B} \qquad (9.4)$$

Fig. 9.1 General Reversible Process replaced by Reversible Adiabatic and Reversible Isothermal.

and

$$Q_{A-A'-B'-B} = (U_B - U_A) + W_{A-A'-B'-B} \qquad (9.5)$$

Since W_{A-B} and $W_{A-A'-B'-B}$ are equal, Eqs. (9.4) and (9.5) give

$$Q_{A-B} = Q_{A-A'-B'-B}$$

In other words, the heat transfer during the reversible process $A–B$ is the same as the heat transfer during the process $A–A'–B'–B$. Since there is no heat transfer in the two reversible adiabatics $A–A'$ and $B–B'$, this means that

$$Q_{A-B} = Q_{A'-B'}$$

This is a significant result, because it makes it possible to replace any reversible process in which the temperature may change in any manner by a series of reversible adiabatic and isothermal processes so that the heat transferred, the work done, and the internal energy change are the same.

9.2 Clausius' Inequality

Consider the general case of a reversible cycle involving any number of heat reservoirs at different temperatures. This is shown by the continuous curve *A–B–C–D–A* of Fig. 9–2. Let the cycle be broken down into a

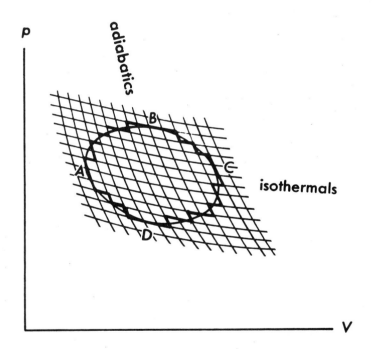

Fig. 9.2 General Cycle Approximated by Large Number of Carnot Cycles.

number of small Carnot cycles by drawing the crosshatched set of isothermal and adiabatic lines. The outside boundaries of the small Carnot cycles form a zigzag curve which follows closely the path of the original cycle. The inside boundaries of the Carnot cycles cancel out, since each section is traversed once in a forward direction and once in a reverse direction. Application of Eq. (9.3) to all the Carnot cycles gives

$$\sum \frac{Q}{T} = 0 \qquad (9.6)$$

Now, as the number of Carnot cycles becomes larger and larger (by making each cycle smaller and smaller), the zigzag curve approximates more and more closely the original cycle, so that in the limit, for differential Carnot cycles, Eq. (9.6) becomes, upon replacement of the summation of finite terms by a cyclic integral,

$$\oint \frac{dQ}{T} = 0 \qquad (9.7)$$

Equation (9.7) is for a reversible cycle. For a cycle which is not reversible, the cyclic integral is less than zero. This may be seen by noting that the thermal efficiency of a Carnot cycle is

$$\frac{Q_1 - Q_2}{Q_1} = \frac{T_1 - T_2}{T_1} \qquad (9.8)$$

For an irreversible cycle, however, the thermal efficiency is less, so that

$$\frac{Q_1 - Q_2}{Q_1} < \frac{T_1 - T_2}{T_1} \qquad (9.9)$$

Equation (9.9) gives

$$\frac{Q_1}{T_1} - \frac{Q_2}{T_2} < 0 \qquad (9.10)$$

and therefore

$$\oint \frac{dQ}{T} < 0 \qquad (9.11)$$

for any irreversible cycle. Equations (9.7) and (9.11) allow the following corollary, known as the Clausius inequality, to be stated as:

Corollary 6: Whenever a system undergoes a cycle, the integral around the cycle of dQ/T is less than zero for an irreversible cycle, and equal to zero for a reversible cycle, i.e.

$$\oint \frac{dQ}{T} \leqslant 0 \qquad (9.12)$$

Example 9.1. A steam power plant operates between a constant-temperature boiler at 328 °F and a constant-temperature condenser at 126 °F as shown in

Fig. 9.3. Water enters the boiler as saturated liquid, and steam leaves the boiler as saturated vapor. The specific enthalpies of the working medium at various points are as shown in the figure. Verify the Clausius inequality for this cycle.

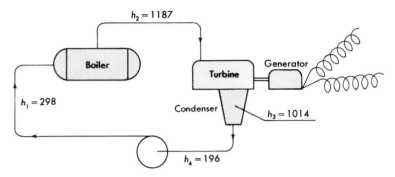

Fig. 9.3 Steam Power Plant.

Solution. Consider the working medium (steam or water) as the system. Heat transfer occurs at two places: the boiler and the condenser. The heat transferred in the boiler is

$$q_{\text{boiler}} = h_2 - h_1 = 1187 - 298$$
$$= 889 \text{ Btu/lbm}$$

Similarly, the heat transferred in the condenser is

$$q_{\text{condenser}} = h_4 - h_3 = 196 - 1014$$
$$= -818 \text{ Btu/lbm}$$

The cyclic integral of dq/T is thus

$$\oint \frac{dq}{T} = \frac{q_{\text{boiler}}}{T_{\text{boiler}}} + \frac{q_{\text{condenser}}}{T_{\text{condenser}}}$$

$$= \frac{889}{788} - \frac{818}{586} = -0.26 \text{ Btu/lbm } ^\circ\text{R}$$

which satisfies the *Clausius inequality.*

It is interesting to compute the cyclic integral of dq/T for a Carnot cycle operating between the same temperature limits of 328 °F and 126 °F. As a numerical example, assume that the Carnot engine takes in 1000 Btu per pound of working medium at the high-temperature heat reservoir. Since the efficiency of the Carnot cycle in this case is

$$\eta = \frac{788 - 586}{788} = 0.256 \text{ or } 25.6 \text{ per cent}$$

the heat rejected to the low-temperature reservoir is

$$q_R = (1 - 0.256)(1000) = 744 \text{ Btu/lbm}$$

The cyclic integral of dq/T is thus

$$\oint \frac{dq}{T} = \frac{q_A}{T_A} - \frac{q_R}{T_R} = \frac{1000}{788} - \frac{744}{586} = 0$$

Here, the equality sign holds, since the Carnot cycle is a reversible cycle.

Example 9.2. Heat is transferred by conduction from a reservoir at 800 °F to a reservoir at 200 °F. For a transfer of 3000 Btu per hour, determine $\oint(dQ/T)$.

Solution. The system is the medium through which heat is conducted. $T_1 = 1260$ °R, $T_2 = 660$ °R, $Q_1 = +3000$ Btu/hr (heat enters the system from the high-temperature reservoir), $Q_2 = -3000$ Btu/hr (heat leaves the system to enter the low-temperature reservoir). Thus,

$$\oint \frac{dQ}{T} = \frac{Q_1}{T_1} + \frac{Q_2}{T_2} = \frac{3000}{1260} - \frac{3000}{660}$$

$$= -2.17 \text{ Btu/hr °R}$$

The answer checks with the Clausius inequality; heat transfer between reservoirs of *different* temperatures is basically an *irreversible* process; therefore, $\oint dQ/T$ should turn out to be negative. Note also that, since it has received 3000 Btu and given up 3000 Btu, the system has undergone a cycle, thus returning to its initial temperature.

9.3 Entropy

The distinguishing feature of a reversible cycle, namely Eq. (9.7), enables the definition of a new energy quantity just as the statement of the first law enabled the definition of energy:

Corollary 7: There exists a property (denoted by S) of a system such that a change in its value is equal to

$$S_2 - S_1 = \int_1^2 \frac{dQ}{T} \tag{9.13}$$

for any reversible process undergone by the system between states 1 and 2. This property is called entropy.

The *proof* is very simple, especially if the mathematical background presented in Secs. 1.6 and 1.7 has been mastered. From the fact that

$$\oint \left(\frac{dQ}{T}\right)_{\text{rev}} = 0 \tag{9.14}$$

it follows that

$$\left(\frac{dQ}{T}\right)_{\text{rev}} = dS \tag{9.15}$$

where dS is an exact differential and the subscript "rev" is a reminder that Eqs. (9.14) and (9.15) hold true only for a reversible cycle and a reversible process respectively. It may, however, be worthwhile to repeat here the demonstration that $(dQ/T)_{rev} = 0$ means that $\int(dQ/T)_{rev}$ depends only on the given end states and not on the path followed in going from one state to another.

The proof is by contradiction: Assume that the converse is true, i.e. that $\int_1^2 (dQ/T)_{rev}$ depends upon a particular reversible process as well as upon the end states. In Fig. 9.4, let A and B denote any two reversible processes by which a system can change from state 1 to state 2. The assumption is that

$$\oint_{1\,A}^{2} \frac{dQ}{T} \neq \oint_{1\,B}^{2} \frac{dQ}{T} \qquad (9.16)$$

Now, let states 1 and 2 be connected by a third reversible process C. Together, processes A and C, and B and C form reversible cycles. For each of the reversible cycles,

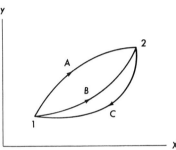

Fig. 9.4

$$\oint_{1-A-2-C-1} \left(\frac{dQ}{T}\right) = \oint_{1\,A}^{2} \frac{dQ}{T} + \oint_{1\,C}^{2} \frac{dQ}{T} \qquad (9.17)$$

$$\oint_{1-B-2-C-1} \left(\frac{dQ}{T}\right) = \oint_{1\,B}^{2} \frac{dQ}{T} + \oint_{2\,C}^{1} \frac{dQ}{T} \qquad (9.18)$$

Subtracting Eqs. (9.17) and (9.18) from each other and taking into account Eq. (9.16) gives

$$\oint_{1-A-2-C-1} \left(\frac{dQ}{T}\right) \neq \oint_{1-B-2-C-1} \left(\frac{dQ}{T}\right)$$

In other words, the cyclic integral along the reversible cycles $1-A-2-C-1$ and $1-B-2-C-1$ are different from each other. But this violates corollary 6, which stipulated that these integrals must be equal (since they are both zero). Consequently, the assumption stated by Eq. (9.16) cannot be true, and corollary 7 is proved. Thus,

$$\int_1^2 \left(\frac{dQ}{T}\right)_{rev} = S_2 - S_1 \qquad (9.19)$$

or, in differential form,

$$\left(\frac{dQ}{T}\right)_{rev} = dS \tag{9.20}$$

keeping in mind the fact that Eqs. (9.19) and (9.20) hold only for a reversible process. The property S is called the entropy (a name first introduced by Clausius). Equation (9.20) indicates that when the inexact differential dQ is multiplied by $1/T$, it becomes, during a reversible process, an exact differential. The fact that $1/T$ is an integrating factor is sometimes taken as an alternate statement* of the second law of thermodynamics.

9.4   Calculation of Entropy Change

The preceding section pointed out that the entropy of a system has a definite value corresponding to each state of the system, and that the entropy change between two given states is independent of the process, reversible or not, connecting the two states. The actual calculation of the entropy change, however, must be done by imagining a reversible path between the two states, for

$$\int_{1}^{2} \frac{dQ}{T} = \Delta S$$

holds only for a reversible process. Since entropy is a point function, it does not matter what the particular reversible path is, so long as it is reversible. The situation is somewhat analogous to that of the more familiar case of computing the change of potential energy of a given mass in a gravitational field. This change is determined by computing the ideal work required to move the mass from one elevation to the other; the ideal work is that required in the absence of friction. The actual work done in moving the mass along a certain path from one elevation to another will, in general, be higher than the ideal work, but the computation for the change of potential energy is not based on it.

The technique of computing entropy changes thus begins with the choice of any reversible path (usually the one most convenient for calculation purposes) between the same given end states of the system. For a simple homogeneous system undergoing a reversible change, the first law and the second law combine to give

---

* The concepts of absolute temperature and entropy can also be derived without recourse to heat engine cycles by the method of Carathéodory (1903), who showed that $(dQ)_{rev}$ has an integrating factor, $1/T$. The proof, however, is rather complicated, and is based on the knowledge of Pfaffian equations. (For a discussion of Carathéodory's statement of the second law, see Prob. 7.15.)

$$\Delta S = \int \left(\frac{dQ}{T}\right)_{\text{rev}} = \int \left(\frac{dU + dW}{T}\right)_{\text{rev}} \qquad (9.21)$$

In the absence of motion, gravity, electricity, magnetization, and capillarity, the only kind of work permitted in a reversible process is that done by normal forces (as distinguished from shearing forces) on slowly moving boundaries of the system. Consequently, $(dW)_{\text{rev}} = pdV$, and Eq. 9.21 becomes

$$TdS = dU + pdV \qquad (9.22)$$

or, alternatively (upon elimination of dU by use of the definition for enthalpy: $H = U + pV$)

$$TdS = dH - Vdp \qquad (9.23)$$

Equations (9.22) and (9.23) are of fundamental importance in thermodynamics, for they are relations in terms of properties only. They enable the entropy change between any two states of a system to be calculated without measuring heat and work, once the relationship between p, V, T, and U or H is known for the system.

Note that although each of the equations $dW = pdV$, $dQ = dU + pdV$, and $dQ = TdS$ is true only for reversible processes, Eqs. (9.22) and (9.23) are not restricted to reversible processes, because S, T, U, H, p, and V are all properties of a system, and they change by the same amount in all processes (reversible or not) between any given pair of equilibrium states. Note also that just as the first law defined only a change in energy, so the second law defines only a change in entropy. For, if in Eq. (9.21), state 1 is chosen as a reference state 0, then the entropy at any other state x is given by

$$S - S_0 = \int_0^x \left(\frac{dQ}{T}\right)_{\text{rev}} \qquad (9.21)$$

or, alternatively, using Eqs. (9.22) and (9.23)

$$S_x - S_0 = \int_0^x \frac{dU}{T} + \int_0^x \frac{p}{T} dV$$

$$S_x - S_0 = \int_0^x \frac{dH}{T} - \int_0^x \frac{V}{T} dp$$

The entropy is thus defined, except for an additive constant (the constant of integration). As far as the first law and second law of thermodynamics are concerned this indeterminacy cannot be removed by any further theoretical reasoning. However, in most engineering problems, only entropy *differences* are dealt with, so that the additive constant plays no role whatever.* The units of entropy in this text are either Btu/lbm-°R or Btu/°R (although calorie/gm-°K or calorie/°K are occasionally encountered), depending on whether or not the system referred to has unit mass. This is because entropy is an extensive property, for, if the mass of a system is increased, the heat quantities necessary to bring about the same changes in the state of the system must also be increased. The small letter s will be used to denote entropy per unit mass (specific entropy), while the capital letter S will be used to represent the entropy of a system of any size.

Example 9.3. Find the entropy change for three pounds of a perfect gas whose specific heat c_v is $(4.5+0.007T)$ Btu/lbm-°R during a constant-volume process from 175 °F to 200 °F.

Solution. For a perfect gas, $pv = RT$, $du = c_v dT$. Thus, Eq. (9.22) gives

$$Tds = du+pdv = c_v dT+pdv$$

or

$$ds = c_v \frac{dT}{T} + \frac{p}{T}dv = c_v \frac{dT}{T} + R\frac{dv}{v}$$

and, upon integration,

$$s-s_0 = \int_{T_0}^{T} c_v \frac{dT}{T} + R \ln \frac{v}{v_0}$$

where s_0 is a constant of integration. This is a general expression for the entropy change of a perfect gas. In the present case of a constant-volume process, $dv = 0$, and the entropy change is simply

$$ds = c_v \frac{dT}{T}$$

This may be integrated in the manner of

$$\Delta s = (s_2-s_0)-(s_1-s_0)$$

$$= \int_{T_0}^{T_2} c_v \frac{dT}{T} - \int_{T_0}^{T_1} c_v \frac{dT}{T} = \int_{T_1}^{T_2} c_v \frac{dT}{T}$$

$$= \int_{635}^{660} (4.5+0.007T) \frac{dT}{T}$$

$$= 4.5 \ln \frac{660}{635} +0.007(660-635)$$

$$= 0.349 \text{ Btu/lbm-°R}$$

* In those problems where the additive constant must be taken into account, it is usually postulated that the value of entropy at absolute zero for all chemical elements is equal to zero. In other words, $S = 0$ at $T = 0$. This is known as the third law of thermodynamics, and is discussed in a later chapter.

and, for three pounds,

$$\Delta S = 3(0.349) = 1.047 \text{ Btu/°R}$$

Example 9.4. One pound of air ($R = 53.3$ ft lbf/lbm-°R, $c_p = 0.24$ Btu/lbm-°R, $c_v = 0.17$ Btu/lbm-°R) expands from 30 psia and 800 °R to 15 psia and 700 °R. Calculate the entropy change and verify that it is the same along different paths of integration.

Solution. In Fig. 9.5, the end states (represented by points 1 and 2) are given, so that the entropy change will be the same, regardless of whether the process

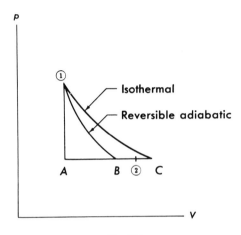

Fig. 9.5

connecting the states is reversible or irreversible, flow or non-flow. To calculate the entropy change, however, a reversible path must be chosen. One possible path is 1–*A*–2, consisting of a reversible constant-volume process 1–*A* followed by the constant-pressure process *A*–2. The entropy change associated with this path is

$$\Delta s = \int_1^A \frac{dq}{T} + \int_A^2 \frac{dq}{T} = \int_1^A c_v \frac{dT}{T} + \int_A^2 c_p \frac{dT}{T}$$

$$= c_v \ln\frac{T_A}{T_1} + c_p \ln\frac{T_2}{T_A} \tag{9.24}$$

Now, T_A is determined to be 400 °R (from a constant-volume process starting at T_1, p_1, and ending at p_2), so that Eq. (9.24) becomes

$$\Delta s = 0.17 \ln\frac{400}{800} + 0.24 \ln\frac{700}{400}$$

$$= 0.016 \text{ Btu/lbm-°R}$$

Another possible path for computing the entropy change is 1–B–2, consisting of a reversible adiabatic process 1–B followed by a constant-pressure process B–2. Corresponding to this,

$$\Delta s = \int_1^B \frac{dq}{T} + \int_B^2 \frac{dq}{T} \tag{9.25}$$

But

$$\int_1^B \frac{dq}{T} = 0,$$

since $dq = 0$ for process 1–B, and Eq. (9.25) gives

$$\Delta s = \int_B^2 \frac{dq}{T} = \int_B^2 c_p \frac{dT}{T} = c_p \ln \frac{T_2}{T_B}$$

T_B is determined to be 656 °R (from reversible adiabatic expansion from T_1, p_1 to $p_B = p_2$). Thus,

$$\Delta s = 0.24 \ln \frac{700}{650} = 0.016 \text{ Btu/lbm-°R}$$

It is seen that Δs is the same along either reversible path. The student may easily verify that, along a third reversible path, say 1–C–2, the result will also be $\Delta s = 0.16$ Btu/lbm-°R.

9.5 Temperature—Entropy Diagram

The preceding developments show that the heat transferred in a reversible process may be evaluated from the equation

$$Q_{1-2} = \int_{S_1}^{S_2} T dS \tag{9.26}$$

This integral can be interpreted graphically as the area under a *reversible* path, when this path is traced as a curve on a diagram in which temperature and entropy are chosen as coordinates. This is similar to the representation of work on a pressure-volume diagram. In Fig. 9.6, the

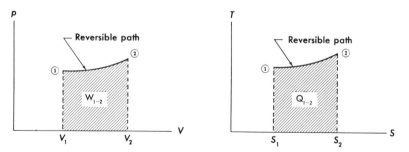

Fig. 9.6 Representation of Heat and Work for Reversible Process.

p–V and T–S diagrams indicate the variation of p with respect to V, and T with respect to S for a system undergoing a particular reversible process between states 1 and 2.

From the respective definitions of work and heat, it follows that, for a reversible process,

$$W_{1-2} = \int_1^2 p\,dV; \quad Q_{1-2} = \int_1^2 T\,dS$$

Note, however, that only under the imposed condition of reversibility, do these areas have any significance as concerning work and heat. To emphasize this point, a convention is often adopted that if a path is drawn between two end states as a full curve, the process connecting these points is understood to be reversible. If a path is represented by a dashed line as in Fig. 9–7, then it is understood that the process between the end states is

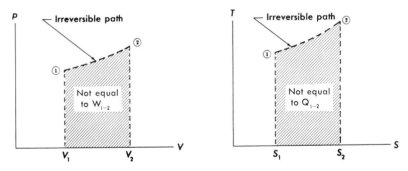

Fig. 9.7 Approximate Representation for Irreversible Process.

irreversible. In such a case, the areas under the curve have *no* significance as to work and heat. The reason for this distinction is that the system, in going from state 1 to state 2 irreversibly, may pass through some equilibrium states which are disconnected, in contrast to a reversible path wherein *all* of its points are equilibrium points, differing, say, in pressure and temperature, only infinitesimally from the surroundings.

The graphical representation for a cyclic transformation is shown in Fig. 9.8. On the p–V diagram, positive work is represented by an area to the right of the curve (looking in the direction of the process, such as from 1 to 2). Thus, in the series of expansion processes A–1, 1–2, and 2–B, work is positive, because it is done *by* the system; in the series of compression processes B–3, 3–4, and 4–A work is negative, because it is done *on* the system. Similarly, on the T–S diagram, Q is positive (i.e., heat is added to the system) if it is represented by an area to the right of the curve looking in

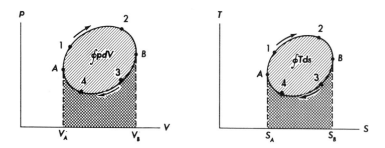

Fig. 9.8 Work and Heat in a Cyclic Transformation.

the direction of the process. All this, of course, is subject to the stipulation that the processes be reversible. For a cyclic transformation the first law gives $\oint dW = \oint dQ$. Under reversible conditions, this becomes

$$\oint p\,dV = \oint T\,dS \qquad (9.27)$$

Equation (9.27) states that the area within the closed curve on the p–V diagram equals that within the corresponding closed curve on the T–S diagram when both areas are measured in the *same* units.

As a specific example, let the Carnot cycle be represented on both the p–V and T–S diagrams. Heretofore, it has been represented only on the p–V diagram. The isothermal processes 1–2 and 3–4 are, of course, represented by horizontal lines on the T–S diagram. As for the reversible adiabatics, $dQ = 0 = T\,dS$, and, since $T \neq 0$, $dS = 0$. Thus, reversible adiabatic processes are also *isentropic* (constant entropy) processes. Figure 9.9 depicts the Carnot cycle on both the p–V and T–S diagrams.

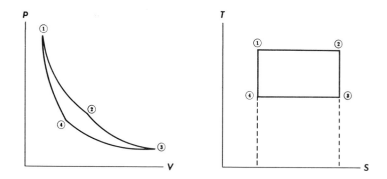

Fig. 9.9 Carnot Cycle on p–V and T–S Coordinates.

The efficiency of the Carnot cycle is most easily obtained from the T–S diagram: the area enclosed within 1–2–3–4 is the net work, whereas the area under 1–2 is the heat added to the engine. Thus,

$$\eta = \frac{\oint dW}{Q_A} = \frac{(T_1 - T_4)(S_2 - S_1)}{T_1(S_2 - S_1)} = \frac{T_1 - T_4}{T_1} = \frac{T_H - T_L}{T_H}$$

where the subscripts H and L refer to the high-temperature and low-temperature heat reservoirs respectively. This equation checks with the results previously obtained in Chap. 8.

9.6 Tds Equations

In Sec. 9.4. the following relation was developed:

$$Tds = du + pdv \qquad (9.28)$$

This relation is often labeled the *fundamental equation of thermodynamics*, because it combines the *first law* (in the form of $dq = du + pdv$) and the *second law* (in the form of $dq = Tds$) into a single equation.

Equation (9.28), being a relation between properties, is valid for any process of a pure substance, although it was obtained by using statements of the first and second laws, which are restricted to reversible processes. Despite its importance, however, Eq. (9.28) is too general to be of much use in its present form; it is therefore desirable to develop alternate relations which are more valuable in specific cases. As an illustration of this point, recall that, in Sec. 5.12, relations were developed for the internal energy as a function of any pair of the thermodynamic coordinates p, v and T. The same will now be done for the entropy. The reason for this is seen in the following example: Suppose that an expression is to be obtained for the entropy of a perfect gas and of a van der Waals gas respectively. In the case of a perfect gas (defined by the relations $pv = RT$ and $du = c_v dT$), no difficulty is encountered in applying the fundamental equation of thermodynamics ($Tds = du + pdv$). The entropy is simply

$$ds = \frac{du}{T} + \frac{p}{T}dv = \frac{c_v}{T}dT + R\frac{dv}{v}$$

Integration then gives

$$s - s_0 = \int_{T_0}^{T} \frac{c_v}{T}dT + R\ln\frac{v}{v_0}$$

and, if c_v is constant,

$$s = c_v \ln\frac{T}{T_0} + R\ln\frac{v}{v_0} + s_0 \qquad (9.29)$$

In the case of a van der Waals gas, however, the procedure is more complex. The equation of a van der Waals gas is

$$\left(p+\frac{a}{v^2}\right)(v-b) = RT$$

Here, the fundamental equation of thermodynamics is no longer easy to apply directly, and alternate relations must be employed. These relations, known as *Tds* equations, are obtained by considering T and v, T and p, and p and v as successive pairs of independent variables:

T and v independent. If T and v are chosen as independent variables, then du may be expressed as

$$du = \left(\frac{\partial u}{\partial T}\right)_v dT+\left(\frac{\partial u}{\partial v}\right)_T dv$$

Replacing this in $Tds = du+pdv$ gives

$$ds = \frac{1}{T}\left[\left(\frac{\partial u}{\partial T}\right)_v dT+\left(\frac{\partial u}{\partial v}\right)_T dv\right] + \frac{p}{T}dv$$

$$= \frac{1}{T}\left(\frac{\partial u}{\partial T}\right)_v dT+\frac{1}{T}\left[p+\left(\frac{\partial u}{\partial v}\right)_T\right]dv \qquad (9.30)$$

But ds can also be written

$$ds = \left(\frac{\partial s}{\partial T}\right)_v dT+\left(\frac{\partial s}{\partial v}\right)_T dv \qquad (9.31)$$

Comparing Eqs. (9.30) and (9.31) with each other, and noting that dT and dv are independent, it is seen that

$$\left(\frac{\partial s}{\partial T}\right)_v = \frac{1}{T}\left(\frac{\partial u}{\partial T}\right)_v \qquad (9.32a)$$

$$\left(\frac{\partial s}{\partial v}\right)_T = \frac{1}{T}\left[p+\left(\frac{\partial u}{\partial v}\right)_T\right] \qquad (9.32b)$$

Now the objective in these manipulations is to express every partial derivative in *standard form*, i.e., in terms of the coefficient of volume expansion

$$\beta = \frac{1}{v}\left(\frac{\partial v}{\partial T}\right)_p,$$

the compressibility

$$\kappa = -\frac{1}{v}\left(\frac{\partial v}{\partial p}\right)_T,$$

the specific heats, and the state variables p, v, and T. The partial derivative $(\partial s/\partial T)_v$ is easily put into standard form when it is recalled that

$$c_v = \left(\frac{\partial u}{\partial T}\right)_v.$$

Then Eq. (9.32a) becomes

$$\left(\frac{\partial s}{\partial T}\right)_v = \frac{c_v}{T} \tag{9.33}$$

To express the partial derivative $(\partial s/\partial v)_T$ in standard form, further manipulation is required. Applying the useful fact that the second derivative of s with respect to T and v is independent of the order of differentiation, Eqs. (9.32a) and (9.32b) give (upon partial differentiation of the first with respect to v, and of the second with respect to T):

$$\frac{\partial^2 s}{\partial v \partial T} = \frac{1}{T}\frac{\partial^2 u}{\partial v d T} \tag{9.34}$$

$$\frac{\partial^2 s}{\partial T \partial v} = -\frac{1}{T^2}\left[p+\left(\frac{\partial u}{\partial v}\right)_T\right]+\frac{1}{T}\left[\left(\frac{\partial p}{\partial T}\right)_v + \frac{\partial^2 u}{\partial T \partial v}\right] \tag{9.35}$$

Setting the right-hand sides of Eqs. (9.34) and (9.35) equal to each other gives

$$\left[p+\left(\frac{\partial u}{\partial v}\right)_T\right] = T\left(\frac{\partial p}{d T}\right)_v = \frac{T\beta}{\kappa} \tag{9.36}$$

With this result, Eq. (9.32b) becomes

$$\left(\frac{\partial s}{\partial v}\right)_T = \frac{\beta}{\kappa} \tag{9.37}$$

which is in standard form. Equations (9.31), (9.33), and (9.37) then enable the entropy change to be expressed as

$$ds = \frac{c_v}{T}dT+\frac{\beta}{\kappa}dv$$

or

$$Tds = c_v dT+\frac{T\beta}{\kappa}dv \tag{9.38}$$

Equation (9.38) is the first of three *Tds equations* that are of fundamental importance in thermodynamics. Its usefulness is immediately shown by applying it to the van der Waals gas which is defined by the equation of state

$$\left(p + \frac{a}{v^2}\right)(v - b) = RT$$

Since this is a cubic equation in v, the coefficient

$$\beta = \frac{1}{v}\left(\frac{\partial v}{\partial T}\right)_p$$

is best calculated by use of the cyclic relation

$$\left(\frac{\partial v}{\partial T}\right)_p \left(\frac{\partial T}{\partial p}\right)_v \left(\frac{\partial p}{\partial v}\right)_T = -1,$$

giving

$$\beta = -\frac{1}{v}\left(\frac{\partial v}{\partial T}\right)_p = -\frac{1}{v}\frac{(\partial p/\partial T)_v}{(\partial p/\partial v)_T}$$

$$= -\frac{1}{v}\left[\frac{R/(v-b)}{(2a/v^3) - RT/(v-b)^2}\right]$$

$$= \frac{Rv^2(v-b)}{RTv^3 - 2a(v-b)^2} \tag{9.39}$$

Similarly, the coefficient

$$\kappa = -\frac{1}{v}\left(\frac{\partial v}{\partial p}\right)_T$$

is calculated to be

$$\kappa = \frac{v^2(v-b)^2}{RTv^3 - 2a(v-b)^2} \tag{9.40}$$

Equation (9.38) then gives

$$ds = c_v \frac{dT}{T} + \frac{\beta}{\kappa} dv$$

$$= c_v \frac{dT}{T} + \frac{Rv^2(v-b)}{v^2(v-b)^2} dv$$

$$= c_v \frac{dT}{T} + \frac{Rdv}{v-b} \tag{9.41}$$

so that the entropy change is

$$s - s_0 = \int_{T_0}^{T} \frac{c_v}{T} dT + R \ln \frac{v - b}{v_0 - b} \qquad (9.42)$$

and, if c_v is constant,

$$s - s_0 = c_v \ln \frac{T}{T_0} + R \ln \frac{v - b}{v_0 - b} \qquad (9.43)$$

Note that Eq. (9.43) is the same as the corresponding equation for an ideal gas, Eq. (9.29), but with the volume reduced from v to $(v-b)$.

T and p independent. To obtain a second Tds equation, consider T and p as independent variables. Starting from the fundamental equation $Tds = du + pdv$, du and dv are first expressed in terms of T and p as

$$du = \left(\frac{\partial u}{\partial T}\right)_p dT + \left(\frac{\partial u}{\partial p}\right)_T dp \qquad (9.44)$$

$$dv = \left(\frac{\partial v}{\partial T}\right)_p dT + \left(\frac{\partial v}{\partial p}\right)_T dp \qquad (9.45)$$

In Sec. 5.12, it was shown that Eq. (9.44) can be transformed into

$$du = (c_p - pv\beta)dT + \left(pv\kappa - \frac{c_p - c_v}{B\beta}\right)dp \qquad (9.46)$$

and that

$$c_p - c_v = \left[p + \left(\frac{\partial u}{\partial v}\right)_T\right]\left(\frac{\partial v}{\partial T}\right)_p$$

This may be written, with the aid of Eq. (9.36) as

$$c_p - c_v = \frac{T\beta}{\kappa}\left(\frac{\partial v}{\partial T}\right)_p$$

But $(\partial v / \partial T)_p = v\beta$, so that

$$c_p - c_v = \frac{v T \beta^2}{\kappa} \qquad (9.47)$$

Equation (9.47) enables Eq. (9.46) to be written as

$$du = (c_p - pv\beta)dT + (pv\kappa - vT\beta)dp \qquad (9.48)$$

As for Eq. (9.45), it can easily be seen from the definitions of β and κ that it is

$$dv = v\beta dT - v\kappa dp \qquad (9.49)$$

Replacing du and dv by their values from Eqs. (9.48) and (9.49), the fundamental equation $Tds = du + pdv$ becomes

$$Tds = (c_p - pv\beta)dT + (pv\kappa - vT\beta)dp + p(v\beta dT - v\kappa dp)$$

which simplifies to

$$Tds = c_p dT - vT\beta dp \qquad (9.50)$$

Equation (9.50) is the second of the famous Tds equations.

p and v independent. To get the third Tds equation, the same procedure is followed, except that p and v are now considered independent variables. Then

$$du = \left(\frac{\partial u}{\partial p}\right)_v dp + \left(\frac{\partial u}{\partial v}\right)_p dv$$

Recall again, from Sec. 5.12, that this equation may be transformed into

$$du = \frac{\kappa c_v}{\beta} dp + \left(\frac{c_p}{v\beta} - p\right) dv \qquad (9.51)$$

Thus, $Tds = du + pdv$ becomes

$$Tds = \frac{\kappa c_v}{\beta} dp + \left(\frac{c_p}{v\beta} - p\right) dv + p\, dv$$

or

$$Tds = \frac{\kappa c_v}{\beta} dp + \frac{c_p}{v\beta}\, dv \qquad (9.52)$$

which is the third Tds equation. Equations (9.38), (9.50), and (9.52) are three equations of fundamental importance in thermodynamics. A physical meaning to the three equations may be obtained by reference to Fig. (9.10). Points (p_0, v_0, T_0) and (p, v, T) are the two end states for which the entropy difference is to be calculated. The three evaluations of the entropy change $s - s_0$ as given by Eqs. (9.38), (9.50), and (9.52) are equivalent to integrating the entropy change along the paths $A-C-B$, $A-D-B$, and $A-E-B$ respectively. For example, if Eq. (9.38) is solved for ds and integrated, the first term on the right-hand side would be integrated along the path $A-C$, at constant volume, while the second term would be integrated along the path $C-B$

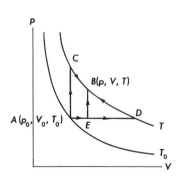

Fig. 9.10

at constant temperature. A similar illustration holds for Eqs. (9.50) and (9.52). The net entropy change along all three paths is the same, since entropy is a point function.

Example 9.5. Show that a reversible adiabatic process is also an isentropic process and develop relations for p and v, T and p, and T and v for a perfect gas undergoing an isentropic process.

Solution. Since the process is reversible, $dw = pdv$, and $dq = Tds$. The process being also adiabatic, $dq = 0 = Tds$. Since T cannot be zero, ds must be equal to zero. Thus, a reversible adiabatic process is also an isentropic process.

To develop isentropic relations between p and v, T and p, and T and v for a perfect gas, write

$$Tds = du + pdv = 0$$

or

$$du = -pdv \qquad (9.53)$$

Now, for a perfect gas, $du = c_v\, dT$, and $dT = (p/R)dv + (v/R)dp$ (obtained from differentiation of the equation of state $pv = RT$). Substitution of these into Eq. (9.53) gives

$$\frac{c_v}{R}(pdv + vdp) + pdv = 0 \qquad (9.54)$$

Making use of $R = c_p - c_v$, Eq. (9.54) becomes

$$\frac{c_v}{c_p - c_v}(pdv + vdp) + pdv = 0$$

and, upon simplification and rearrangement,

$$\frac{dp}{p} + \frac{c_p}{c_v}\frac{dv}{v} = 0 \qquad (9.55)$$

Equation (9.55) integrates into

$$pv^\gamma = \text{constant} \qquad (9.56)$$

where

$$\gamma = \frac{c_p}{c_v} \qquad (9.57)$$

Equation 9.56 is the relation between p and v for the isentropic process of an ideal gas. The corresponding relations between p and T, and between T and v are found by combining Eq. (9.56) with the equation of state ($pv = RT$). The result (which the student should verify) is

$$Tp^{(1-\gamma)/\gamma} = \text{constant} \qquad (9.58)$$
$$Tv^{(\gamma-1)} = \text{constant} \qquad (9.59)$$

The plot of an isentropic on p–v coordinates is shown in Fig. 9.11. For purposes of comparison, an isothermal ($pv = $ constant), an isobaric ($p = $ constant), and an isometric ($v = $ constant) have also been included. Similar plots may be done using any pair of independent variables.

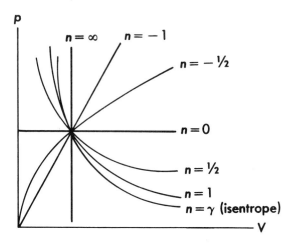

Fig. 9.11 Polytropes of a Perfect Gas.

Example 9.6. What is the increase in temperature of a solid or liquid when it is compressed reversibly and adiabatically? Assume reversible conditions. For a small range in temperature, show that the temperature rise corresponding to a volume change is

$$T_2 - T_1 = -\frac{\beta T_1}{\kappa c_v}(v_2 - v_1)$$

Solution. From the *Tds* equation (9.35),

$$Tds = 0 = c_v dT + \frac{T\beta}{\kappa}dv$$

or

$$\frac{dT}{T} = -\frac{\beta}{\kappa c_v}dv$$

Let T_1 be the initial temperature, and ΔT a small rise in temperature when the system is compressed from v_1 to v_2. Then

$$\int_{T_1}^{T_1 + \Delta T} \frac{dT}{T} = -\frac{\beta}{\kappa c_v} \int_{v_1}^{v_2} dv$$

or

$$\ln\frac{T_1 + \Delta T}{T_1} = \ln\left(1 + \frac{\Delta T}{T_1}\right) = -\frac{\beta}{\kappa c_v}(v_2 - v_1)$$

Using a series expansion for the left side of the equation, this can be written as

$$\frac{\Delta T}{T_1} - \frac{1}{2}\left(\frac{\Delta T}{T_1}\right)^2 + \frac{1}{3}\left(\frac{\Delta T}{T_1}\right)^3 - \frac{1}{4}\left(\frac{\Delta T}{T_1}\right)^4 + \ldots = -\frac{\beta}{\kappa c_v}(v_2 - v_1)$$

and, neglecting terms of higher-order,

$$\frac{\Delta T}{T_1} = -\frac{\beta}{\kappa c_v}(v_2 - v_1)$$

or

$$T_2 - T_1 = -\frac{\beta T_1}{\kappa c_v}(v_2 - v_1) \qquad (9.60)$$

Equation (9.60) is the expression for the temperature rise of a solid or liquid during adiabatic compression. If β is positive, $T_2 > T_1$ when $v_2 < v_1$. This is the case with most solids and liquids, i.e., the temperature increases when the volume is decreased adiabatically. If β is negative, then $T_2 < T_1$ when $v_2 < v_1$. This is the case for water between 0 °C and 4 °C. In other words, within that range, the temperature of water decreases during a reversible adiabatic compression.

9.7 Principle of Entropy Increase

The preceding sections have shown that the entropy change for a reversible process is given by $dS = dQ/T$. The question of entropy change for an irreversible process is now introduced. In Fig. (9.12), let a system change from state 1 to state 2 by a reversible process 1–A–2 and return to state 1 by either the reversible process 2–B–1 or the irreversible process 2–C–1. Since the cycle 1–A–2–B–1 is reversible, the Clausius inequality becomes

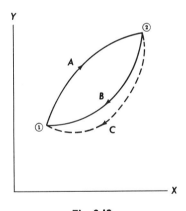

$$\oint_{1}^{2}{}_A \frac{dQ}{T} + \oint_{2}^{1}{}_B \frac{dQ}{T} = 0$$

Processes 1–A–2 and 2–C–1 together, however, form an irreversible cycle, so that the Clausius inequality gives

$$\oint_{1}^{2}{}_A \frac{dQ}{T} + \oint_{2}^{1}{}_C \frac{dQ}{T} \leqslant 0$$

Fig. 9.12

Subtracting the first equation from the second gives

$$\oint_{2}^{1}{}_C \frac{dQ}{T} - \oint_{2}^{1}{}_B \frac{dQ}{T} \leqslant 0$$

Reversing limits and transposing, this becomes

$$\oint_{1}^{2}{}_B \frac{dQ}{T} \geqslant \oint_{1}^{2}{}_C \frac{dQ}{T} \qquad (9.61)$$

Since process 1–*B*–2 is reversible, dQ/T may be replaced by dS, in the first integral, and Eq. (9.61) becomes

$$\int_1^2 dS \geqslant \oint_{1}^{2} {}_C \frac{dQ}{T}$$ (9.62)

or, in differential form,

$$dS \geqslant \frac{dQ}{T}$$ (9.63)

Equation (9.63) states that, for an irreversible process, the entropy change no longer equals dQ/T, but is *greater* than dQ/T. For an irreversible cycle, Eq. (9.63) becomes

$$\oint dS \geqslant \oint \frac{dQ}{T}$$ (9.64)

Equations (9.63) and (9.64) are important: they state that the effect of irreversibility is always to *increase* the entropy of a system (as compared with the absence of irreversibility, in which case $dS = dQ/T$).

Next, consider an *isolated* system. This is a system which exchanges no heat and no work with the surroundings. Thus, $Q = 0 = W$, and, in accordance with the first law, the system can only assume those states for which the total internal energy remains constant. The second law, however, requires that the system assume only those states for which the entropy increases or remains constant. Equation (9.63) becomes, with $dQ = 0$,

$$(dS)_{\text{isolated}} \geqslant 0$$ (9.65)

Equation (9.65) is the celebrated *Principle of Entropy Increase*. It is stated here in the form of a corollary to the second law (number 8, and last in the series):

Corollary 8: *The entropy of an isolated system either increases or in the limit remains constant.**

As illustration of the foregoing developments, let two bodies at different temperatures be brought adiabatically into contact, and allowed to attain thermal equilibrium. The total internal energy remains the same, for the two bodies together can be taken to constitute an isolated system. Since no heat is absorbed or given up by this isolated system, $dQ/T = 0$, and this may lead to the premature conclusion that the entropy change is also zero. However, such is *not* the case: The entropy change is not zero, because the

---

* Since all naturally occurring processes are irreversible, any spontaneous change in nature is accompanied by a net increase in entropy. This led Clausius to state that "the energy of the universe is a constant; the entropy of the universe tends towards a maximum." By universe, Clausius meant the combination of a system and its surroundings.

entropy change as given by $\int(dQ/T)$ holds only for a *reversible* process. Here, there is a transfer of heat through a finite temperature difference, and the process is an irreversible one. To be specific, consider the process of mixing one pound of water at 150 °F with one pound of water at 50 °F. The result is two pounds of water at 100 °F. In order to find the difference in entropy between the initial and final states, imagine a reversible path between these states. It does not matter what the particular reversible path is, so long as it is reversible, for the result of the calculation will be the same for any reversible path, as shown in Sec. 9.4. Consequently, let a *reversible* process between the same end states be devised. Imagine an infinite series of heat reservoirs at temperatures ranging from 50 °F to 150 °F. Let the water originally at 50 °F be heated reversibly to 100 °F by using the series of reservoirs between 50 °F and 100 °F. Let the water originally at 150 °F be cooled reversibly to 100 °F by using the series of reservoirs between 150 °F and 100 °F. The result is two pounds of water at 100 °F, with the entire process being reversible.

The entropy change of one pound of water being heated reversibly from 50 °F to 100 °F is then

$$\Delta s = \int \frac{dq}{T} = \int_{510}^{560} \frac{c_p dT}{T}$$

$$= \ln \frac{560}{510} = 0.095 \text{ Btu/°R}$$

since c_p for water is 1 Btu/lbm-°R.

The entropy change of one pound of water being cooled reversibly from 150 °F to 100 °F is

$$\Delta s = \int \frac{dq}{T} = \int_{610}^{560} \frac{c_p dT}{T}$$

$$= \ln \frac{560}{610} = -0.086 \text{ Btu/°R}$$

The net entropy change is thus $0.095 - 0.086 = 0.009$ Btu/°R, an increase.

Example 9.7. Air expands through a device from 75 psia and 400 °F to 15 psia and 85 °F in a steady-flow process while rejecting 15 Btu/lbm of heat to surroundings at 80 °F. Is the process reversible, and if not, what is the increase in entropy of the universe?

Solution. The entropy change for the air is easily calculated, since the end states are known. T_1, p_1, T_2, and p_2 being given, it is convenient to work with an equation having T and p as independent variables. Thus, Eq. 9.23 may be used to give

$$\Delta s_{\text{air}} = \int_1^2 \frac{dh}{T} - \int_1^2 \frac{v}{T}\,dp = \int_1^2 c_v \frac{dT}{T} - \int_1^2 R\frac{dp}{p}$$

$$= 0.24 \ln \frac{545}{860} - \frac{53.3}{778} \ln \frac{15}{75} = 0.00$$

The entropy change for the air turns out to be zero. However, this should not lead to the conclusion that the process is reversible, because heat has been *abstracted* from the air, so that if the process had been reversible, Δs would have been negative (because Δs for a reversible process is equal to $\int dq/T$, and dq is negative).

Now, the system (i.e. the air flowing through the device) together with the surroundings form the universe (which now becomes an isolated system). Since heat is being added to the surroundings in the amount of 15 Btu/lbm of air, the entropy change of the surroundings is

$$\Delta s_{\text{surr}} = \frac{15}{540} = 0.0278 \text{ Btu/lbm-}^\circ R$$

The entropy change of the universe is thus

$$\Delta s_{\text{air}} + \Delta s_{\text{surr}} = 0.00 + 0.0278 = 0.0278 \text{ Btu/lbm-}^\circ R$$

For a flow rate of 10,000 lbm/hr (which is not unusual in engineering applications), this represents an entropy increase of 278 Btu/hr of the universe.

Example 9.8. Develop an expression for the entropy change in the mixing of two ideal gases at constant temperature and pressure.

Solution. Consider two ideal gases A and B, at first separated as in Fig. 9.13(a). When the partition is removed, the gases mix, and the temperature

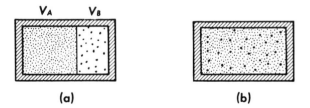

V_A V_B

(a)   **(b)**

Fig. 9.13   Adiabatic Mixing of Ideal Gases.

remains the same [Fig. 9.13(b)]. In Sec. 7.8, it was shown that the isothermal mixing of gases is an irreversible process, so an entropy increase is to be expected. In order to determine the entropy change, a reversible path must be devised to transform the initial state of unmixed gases into the final state of a mixture of gases. This is accomplished by use of semi-permeable membranes, and it was found in Sec. 7.8 that, during the reversible process, heat equal to

$$Q = pV_A \ln \frac{V}{V_A} + pV_B \ln \frac{V}{V_B} = N_A \bar{R} T \ln \frac{V}{V_A} + N_B \bar{R} T \ln \frac{V}{V_B} \tag{9.66}$$

must be supplied, where $\bar{R}$ is the *universal gas constant* (1545 ft-lbf/mole-°R). The entropy change is therefore

$$\Delta S = \frac{Q}{T} = N_A \bar{R} \ln \frac{V}{V_A} + N_B \bar{R} \ln \frac{V}{V_B} \tag{9.67}$$

Equation (9.67) shows that the entropy change is positive, since $V(= V_A + V_B)$ is greater than either V_A or V_B. For the case of equal volumes of each gas at the start, Eq. (9.67) reduces to

$$\Delta S = (N_A + N_B)\bar{R} \ln 2 = N\bar{R} \ln 2 \tag{9.68}$$

where N is the total number of moles of gases A and B.

9.8 Entropy and Reversibility

As a further elaboration of the principle of entropy increase let the entropy change be used as a criterion of reversibility.

Consider the process of heat conduction between two bodies A and B at temperatures T_A and T_B respectively, with $T_A > T_B$. This is shown schematically in Fig. 9.14. If a boundary (dotted line) be drawn around both bodies, the result is a system which does not exchange heat or work with its surroundings. In other words, the system is an isolated system, and the principle of entropy increase may be readily applied to it. For a transfer of heat dQ from body A to body B, the entropy change is $-dQ/T_A$ for body A, and $+dQ/T_B$ for body B. The entropy change for the combined system of bodies A and B is then

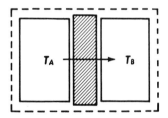

Fig. 9.14 Heat Transfer Through Finite Temperature Difference.

$$dS = dS_A + dS_B$$

$$= \frac{dQ}{T_A} + \frac{dQ}{T_B} = dQ\left(\frac{1}{T_B} - \frac{1}{T_A}\right)$$

$$= dQ\left(\frac{T_A - T_B}{T_A T_B}\right) \tag{9.69}$$

and this is seen to be positive. Thus, heat transfer between systems at different temperatures is an irreversible process; the irreversibility, as seen from Eq. (9.69), is due to the difference $T_A - T_B$.

---

* The relation between $\bar{R}$, the gas constant per mole, and R, the gas constant per pound, is $\bar{R} = MR$ where M is the molecular weight.

Another consequence of the principle of entropy increase, this time in relation to steady-flow processes, is seen in the following case: Consider the adiabatic flow of a fluid through a control volume as shown in Fig. 9.15.

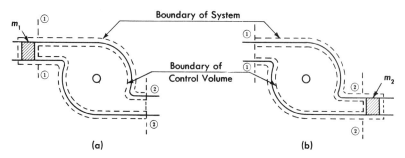

Fig. 9.15 Entropy Change in Adiabatic Flow.

Choosing the fluid as the system, the entropy of the system in its initial configuration [Fig. 9.1(a)] consists of the entropy of mass m_1 plus the entropy of the material within the control volume:

$$s_i = m_1 s_1 + \left[\int_V \rho s dV \right]_{t=t_0} \tag{9.70}$$

where the subscript 1 refers to conditions at the entrance of the control volume and the integration is over the control volume at time $t = t_0$. At a later time ($t = t_0 + dt$), the configuration of the system is as shown in Fig. 9.15(b), and the entropy of the system is that of mass m_2 plus the entropy of the material within the control volume:

$$s_f = m_2 s_2 + \left[\int_V \rho s dV \right]_{t=t_0+dt}$$

where the integration over the control volume is taken at time $t_0 + dt$.

Since the process is adiabatic, the final entropy must be either greater than or equal to the initial entropy (by virtue of the principle of entropy increase). Thus,

$$m_2 s_2 + \left[\int_V \rho s dV \right]_{t=t_0+dt} \geqslant m_1 s_1 + \left[\int_V \rho s dV \right]_{t=t_0}$$

or

$$m_2 s_2 - m_1 s_1 + \frac{\partial}{\partial t} \int_V \rho s dV \geqslant 0 \tag{9.72}$$

Now, for steady-flow, $m_1 = m_2$, and $\partial/\partial t = 0$ (since the properties at all points within the control volume do not change with time). Thus, Eq. (9.72) becomes

$$s_2 - s_1 \geqslant 0 \qquad (9.73)$$

In other words, the specific entropy of the fluid at exit must be greater than, or equal to, the specific entropy at entrance. Only for reversible (frictionless) adiabatic flow can the entropy at exit be equal to the entropy at entrance. For this reason, the reversible adiabatic flow is often called isentropic flow. The principle of entropy increase thus provides valuable information as to the direction of a process.

9.9 Criterion for Equilibrium

The preceding sections show that, when irreversible processes are compared with reversible processes, the following feature emerges. The former processes result in an increase in the entropy of the universe, but in the latter, no net change in the entropy of the universe occurs. In other words, entropy is *not* conserved, except in reversible processes. This is unlike classical mechanics, where such concepts as energy, momentum, and angular momentum obey the conservation principle.

When a beaker of hot water is mixed with a beaker of cold water, the heat lost by the hot water is equal to the heat gained by the cold water, and energy is conserved. On the other hand, while the entropy of the hot water decreases in the mixing process, this decrease does not equal the increase in entropy of the cold water, and the total entropy of the system is greater at the end of the mixing process than it was at the beginning of the process. Nor can this increase of entropy acquired in the irreversible process ever be wiped out, even if the system were made to go back to its initial state. The first law says: energy can neither be created nor destroyed. The second law says: entropy cannot be destroyed, but it can be created.

The principle of entropy increase occurs in *all* natural process, for all natural processes take place at finite rate, with finite differences of pressure and temperature between parts of a system, or between a system and its surroundings. Let an isolated system ($dQ = dW = 0$) be at a certain initial energy. As a result of the first law, the system can subsequently assume only those states which have the same internal energy as initially. However, the principle of entropy increase places a further restriction on the possible subsequent states. Of all the states of equal internal energy, only those of *higher* entropy than the initial state can be assumed by the system. The succession of states proceeds to that state at which the system has the highest value of entropy consistent with its initial internal energy: the state of stable equilibrium.

This is illustrated schematically in Fig. 9.16. The fundamental equation for a simple system, $TdS = dU + pdV$, can be considered as defining a

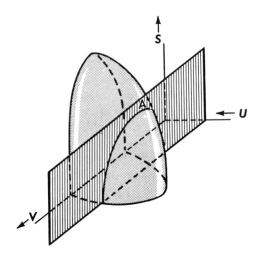

Fig. 9.16 Illustration of Principle of Maximum Entropy.

surface in a "thermodynamic" space. The coordinates in this space are U, V and S. The relation $S = S(U, V)$ then describes the surface shown. States of constant internal energy lie on the intersection curve of the surface and the plane $U = U_1$. The principle of maximum entropy characterizes an equilibrium state as that state which maximizes the entropy along the curve (point A). This is often expressed in the form of the following theorem, called the

Criterion of Equilibrium: The necessary and sufficient condition for stability of an isolated system is that, in all possible variations* of the state of the system which do not alter its total internal energy, the variation of the entropy shall be negative. In other words

$$(dS)_U < 0 \qquad (9.74)$$

where the subscript U denotes that the total internal energy is to be constant. The criterion makes it possible to decide whether a system in any particular thermodynamic state is in stable equilibrium or not. Note that Eq. (9.74) is simply another expression for the condition of maximum entropy. This is evident from Fig. 9.16.

---

* A possible variation is an imagined physically possible state change. For example, a marble at the bottom of a bowl may be imagined to move in any way, but it cannot go through the wall of the bowl.

Example 9.9. Two solid bodies of unit mass having respective specific heats c_1 and c_2 are respectively at temperature T_1 and T_2, with $T_1 > T_2$. They are brought into thermal contact, and allowed to come to equilibrium temperature. Show that the entropy change is

$$(c_1+c_2)\left[\ln\frac{c_1T_1+c_2T_2}{c_1+c_2} - \ln\left(T_1{}^{c_1}T_2{}^{c_2}\right)^{1/(c_1+c_2)}\right]$$

and that it is always positive.

Solution. The equilibrium temperature is first determined. From conservation of energy:

$$c_1(T_1-T_3) = c_2(T_3-T_2)$$

or

$$T_3 = \frac{c_1T_1+c_2T_2}{c_1+c_2}$$

where T_3 is the equilibrium temperature.

Since entropy is a property, its change is the same as that which would take place if bodies 1 and 2 were brought to T_3 by a reversible process. The total change in entropy is thus

$$\Delta S = \int_{T_1}^{T_3}\frac{c_1 dT}{T} + \int_{T_2}^{T_3}\frac{c_2 dT}{T} = c_1\ln\frac{T_3}{T_1} + c_2\ln\frac{T_3}{T_2}$$

and, upon replacing T_3 by its value in terms of T_1 and T_2,

$$\Delta S = c_1\ln\frac{c_1T_1+c_2T_2}{(c_1+c_2)T_1} + c_2\ln\frac{c_1T_1+c_2T_2}{(c_1+c_2)T_2}$$

$$= c_1\ln\frac{c_1T_1+c_2T_2}{c_1+c_2} - c_1\ln T_1 + c_2\ln\frac{c_1T_1+c_2T_2}{c_1+c_2} - c_2\ln T_2$$

$$= (c_1+c_2)\ln\frac{c_1T_1+c_2T_2}{c_1+c_2} - \ln T_1{}^{c_1} - \ln T_2{}^{c_2}$$

$$= (c_1+c_2)\ln\frac{c_1T_1+c_2T_2}{c_1+c_2} - \ln T_1{}^{c_1}T_2{}^{c_2}$$

$$= (c_1+c_2)\left[\ln\frac{c_1T_1+c_2T_2}{c_1+c_2} - \frac{1}{c_1+c_2}\ln T_1{}^{c_1}T_2{}^{c_2}\right]$$

$$= (c_1+c_2)\left[\ln\frac{c_1T_1+c_2T_2}{c_1+c_2} - \ln\left(T^{c_1}{}_2 T^{c_2}\right)^{1/(c_1+c_2)}\right]$$

This is always greater than zero, for the weighted arithmetic mean

$$\frac{c_1T_1+c_2T_2}{c_1+c_2}$$

is always greater than the weighted geometric mean

$$(T_1{}^{c_1}T_2{}^{c_2})^{1/(c_1+c_2)}$$

when c_1, c_2, T_1, and T_2 are positive quantities.†

---

† This is a theorem in algebra. It is also proved in Prob. 9.18 at the end of the chapter.

Example 9.9. Show that a system with parts at different temperatures cannot be in stable equilibrium.

Solution. The proof consists in finding a possible variation at constant energy for which the entropy of the system increases. Consider the system to be comprised of two parts in contact, but at different temperatures T_1 and T_2. Let the hotter part at T_1 undergo a small decrease dU in energy, and the colder part T_2 undergo an equal increase in energy. The change in entropy of the hotter part is then $-dU/T_1$ and that of the colder part is $+dU/T_2$. The change in entropy of the system is thus

$$(dS)_U = -\frac{dU}{T_1} + \frac{dU}{T_2} = \left(\frac{1}{T_2} - \frac{1}{T_1}\right)dU$$

and, since $T_1 > T_2$,

$$(dS)_U > 0$$

The system, therefore, cannot be in stable equilibrium.

Thermodynamics has often been described as a science of energy and entropy. The truth of that statement becomes more and more evident when it is observed that the essence of the second law consists in the existence of entropy and in the impossibility of its decreasing under certain defined conditions. In the behavior of any natural processes, the principle of entropy increase occupies the managing position, for it dictates the manner of the transformation; the principle of energy conservation simply does the bookkeeping.

PROBLEMS

9.1. One pound of air undergoes a cycle composed of the following three reversible processes: a constant-pressure expansion from 15 psia, 50 °F to 150 °F; a constant-volume cooling to 50 °F; an isothermal compression back to 15 psia. Sketch the p–v and T–s diagram of the cycle, and determine: (a) $\oint dq$, $\oint dw$, $\oint ds$; (b) the change in entropy for each process.

9.2. A heat engine receives 500 Btu of heat per cycle from a reservoir at 540 °F and rejects heat to a reservoir at 40 °F in the hypothetical amounts of (a) 375 Btu per cycle, (b) 250 Btu per cycle, and (c) 125 Btu per cycle. Which of these respective cases represent a reversible cycle, an irreversible cycle, and an impossible cycle?

9.3. Heat is transferred by conduction from a reservoir at 400 °F to a reservoir at 80 °F at the rate of 200 Btu/hr. Determine $\oint dQ/T$. What would $\oint dQ/T$ and Δ_S be if a reversible engine had been used to transfer heat from these two reservoirs? How much horsepower would such an engine have developed?

9.4. A reversible heat engine absorbs 1000 Btu of heat at 500 °F, produces 417 Btu of work, and discards the rest at 100 °F. Determine the change in entropy of (a) the heat source, (b) the heat sink, (c) the universe as a whole.

9.5. The latent heat of fusion of ice at 32 °F is 143 Btu/lbm. Find the entropy increase of a pound of ice as it changes to liquid in each of the following ways: (a) heat is supplied reversibly to a mixture of ice and water at 32 °F, (b) the mixture of ice and water is stirred by means of a paddle wheel.

9.6. Determine the entropy change of a pound of perfect gas which is initially at 130 °F, 9 atm, and is expanded *irreversibly* to 1 atm, 70 °F. The process is not characterized by constant temperature, constant pressure, or constant volume, and is not adiabatic. Hint: the solution will be a perfectly general one for the entropy change of a perfect gas. As entropy is a state function, any path that is *reversible* will be satisfactory for determining Δs. Let the gas be first expanded isothermally to 1 atm and then cooled at constant pressure to the final temperature of 70 °F, both steps being reversible.

9.7. Sketch the T–s, p–v, T–v, p–h, and h–s diagrams for a Carnot cycle employing a perfect gas as the working medium. Do the same for the cycle described in Prob. 9.1.

9.8. The units of c_p and c_v may be either Btu/lbm-°F or Btu/lbm-°R. Can the units of entropy in expressions such as

$$\Delta s = \int_1^2 c_p \frac{dT}{T}$$

and

$$\Delta s = \int_1^2 c_v \frac{dT}{T}$$

be Btu/lbm-°F or Btu/lbm-°R?

9.9. Derive the following equation for the entropy of a perfect gas:

$$s = c_v \ln \frac{T}{T_0} + R \ln \frac{v}{v_0} + s_0$$

$$s = c_p \ln \frac{T}{T_0} - R \ln \frac{p}{p_0} + s_0$$

$$s = c_p \ln \frac{v}{v_0} + c_v \ln \frac{p}{p_0} + s_0$$

9.10. A certain gas having an equation of state

$$(p+1)(v-1) = RT$$

undergoes a reversible adiabatic process between (p_1, T_1) and (p_2, T_2). Derive an expression for the temperature T_2 in terms of T_1, p_1, p_2, R, and c_p. Hint: Make use of the Tds equation with p and T as independent variables.

9.11. Derive the following relations for a van der Waals gas undergoing a reversible adiabatic process.

$$T(v-b)^{R/c_v} = \text{constant}$$

$$\left(p + \frac{a}{v^2}\right)(v-b)^{(R+c_v)/c_v} = \text{constant}$$

9.12. Can the entropy of a system be decreased by an irreversible process? Hint: Take a gas which is compressed irreversibly and isothermally; compare the entropy change of the gas with that of the surroundings.

9.13. A 3 cu ft vessel of air at a pressure of 15 psia and a temperature of 70 °F is stirred by a paddle wheel until the pressure becomes 30 psia. The walls of the vessel are adiabatic, and the paddle wheel is actuated by an electric motor. Considering air to be a perfect gas with a value of $c_p = 0.24$ Btu/lbm-°R, and a value of R $= 53.3$ ft lb/lbm-°R, determine the work and the change in entropy. Hint: The work is obtained from the first law (with $Q = 0$):

$$W = -\Delta U = -mc_v\Delta T$$

The temperature change ΔT is not given; by means of the perfect gas law ($pV = mRT$) it is replaced by Δp to give

$$W = -mc_v\left(\frac{V}{mR}\Delta p\right) = -\frac{Vc_v}{R}\Delta p$$

The entropy change is very simply obtained by use of the Tds equation with v and p as independent variables.

9.14. Show that, for a liquid or solid, the entropy may be given by the approximate relation

$$s = c_p \ln T - v_0\beta p + v_0\beta p_0 - c_p \ln T_0 + s_0$$

Hint: From the Tds equation, with T and p as independent variables, obtain

$$s = \int_{T_0}^{T} c_p \frac{dT}{T} - \int_{p_0}^{p} v\beta dp + s_0$$

where the first integral is evaluated at the pressure p_0 and the second at the temperature T. Neglect the variation of c_p with T_1 and set $v = v_0$.

9.15. A vessel is divided into two equal compartments by a membrane. One compartment contains 1 mole of nitrogen at 70 °F and 1 atm pressure, the other compartment contains 1 mole of oxygen at the same conditions. The membrane is punctured, and the gases are allowed to mix. Determine the entropy change of the contents of the vessel. Consider nitrogen and oxygen to be perfect gases having a universal gas constant of $\bar{R} = 1545$ ft lb/lbf mole°-R $= 1.986$ Btu/lb mole-°R̄.

9.16. Show that the adiabatic bulk modulus is γ times the isothermal bulk modulus for all fluids:

$$\left(\frac{\partial p}{\partial v}\right)_s = \gamma\left(\frac{\partial p}{\partial v}\right)_T$$

Verify this result for a perfect gas ($pv = RT$, $du = c_v dT$). Hint: First establish from $dq = Tds$, that

$$c_v = T\left(\frac{\partial s}{\partial T}\right)_v$$

and

$$c_p = T\left(\frac{\partial s}{\partial T}\right)_p.$$

Then use cyclic relation to write

$$\frac{(\partial p/\partial v)_s}{(\partial p/\partial v)_T} = \frac{(\partial s/\partial v)_p(\partial p/\partial s)_v}{(\partial T/\partial v)_p(\partial p/\partial T)_v} = \frac{(\partial s/\partial T)_p}{(\partial s/\partial T)_v} = \gamma$$

9.17. Give the restrictions, if any, under which the following relations are true: (1) $dQ = dU + p dV$, (2) $dQ = dU + dW$, (3) $T dS = dU + dW$, (4) $T ds = dU + p dV$, (5) $dU + dW = 0$, (6) $T dS = 0$, (7) $dU + p dV = 0$.

9.18. In Ex. 9.9, it was claimed that

$$\frac{c_1 T_1 + c_2 T_2}{c_1 + c_2} > \left(T_1^{c_1} T_2^{c_2} \right)^{1/(c_1 + c_2)}$$

where c_1, c_2, T_1, and T_2 are positive quantities. Prove this. Hint: Let

$$\alpha_1 = \frac{c_1}{c_1 + c_2}; \quad \alpha_2 = \frac{c_2}{c_1 + c_2}$$

then the problem becomes

$$\alpha_1 T_1 + \alpha_2 T_2 \overset{?}{\geqslant} T^{\alpha_1} T_2^{\alpha_2}$$

or, since $\alpha_2 = 1 - \alpha_1$,

$$\alpha_1 \left(\frac{T_1}{T_2} \right) + (1 - \alpha_1) \overset{?}{\geqslant} \left(\frac{T_1}{T_2} \right)^{\alpha_1}$$

Let $x = T_1/T_2$, take the derivative with respect to x and set it to zero. Solve the resulting equation for x.

9.19. A heat exchanger uses 10,000 lbm/hr of water to cool a hydrocarbon oil from 280 °F to 150 °F. The oil, flowing at the rate of 5000 lbm/hr, has an average specific heat of 0.6 Btu/lbm-°F. The water enters the exchanger at 70 °F. Determine: (a) the total change of entropy as a result of the heat-exchange process, (b) the amount of work that could have been obtained had the process of cooling the oil been carried out by using the heat to operate a Carnot engine with a sink temperature of 80 °F.

9.20. Show that, for an ideal gas, the slope of a constant-pressure line and of a constant-volume line on T–s coordinates is T/c_p and T/c_v respectively. How does the slope of a constant-pressure line compare with that of a constant-volume line at the same temperature?

9.21. The principle of maximum entropy may also be stated in the form of a principle of minimum energy. The latter principle characterizes the equilibrium state as one having minimum energy for a given total entropy. Verify this in Fig. 9.17 by passing a plane $s = s_0$ which intersects the surface representing the fundamental equation $T ds = du + p dv$. Show that point A fulfills the requirements for equilibrium.

9.22. A steel casting weighing 70 pounds and having a temperature of 800 °F is quenched in 300 pounds of 70 °F oil having a specific heat of 0.6

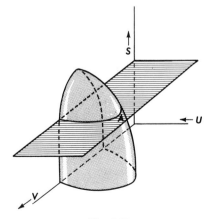

Fig. 9.17

Btu/lbm-°F. The specific heat of the steel is 0.12 Btu/lbm-°F. Neglecting heat transfer to surroundings, find the change in entropy of (a) the casting, (b) the oil, (c) the universe. Hint: First find the equilibrium temperature of the oil and the steel casting by writing an energy balance.

9.23. A constant-temperature source at 1600 °R transfers 3000 Btu of heat to a system which is at the constant temperature of 750 °R. The surroundings are at 60 °F. Determine: (a) the entropy change of the source, (b) the entropy change of the system, (c) the entropy production accompanying the heat transfer, (d) the change in available and unavailable energy referred to surroundings at 65 °F. Sketch the proceedings on T–S coordinates and label pertinent areas.

9.24. Two identical bodies of mass m and constant specific heat c are at temperatures T_1 and T_2. They are used as source and sink for a heat engine. Show that the maximum work obtainable is given by

$$mc(\sqrt{T_1} - \sqrt{T_2})^2$$

Hint: Maximum work is obtained when the engine operates along a reversible cycle. In that case, the entropy change of the composite system formed by the two bodies is zero.

9.25. A mass m of liquid at temperature T_1 is mixed with an equal mass of the same liquid at temperature T_2. (a) Show that the resultant entropy change of the universe is

$$2mc \ln \frac{(\sqrt{T_1} + \sqrt{T_2})/2}{\sqrt{T_1 T_2}}$$

(b) Prove that this is necessarily positive. Hint: Draw a semicircle of diameter $T_1 + T_2$.

9.26. Two bodies of the same mass and same specific heats are at temperatures T_1 and T_2 respectively. The temperature of surroundings is T_0. Assume that $T_1 > T_2 > T_0$. On the basis that each body can supply the amount of heat Q to a reversible engine, determine the maximum work obtainable when (a) the two bodies operate independently, (b) the two bodies are brought together without doing work to a common temperature and used as a single reservoir to supply heat to a reversible engine.

9.27. A mole of oxygen at 35 psia and 65 °F is in an insulated container which is connected through a valve to a second container (also insulated) filled with 2 moles of nitrogen at 15 psia and 85 °F. The valve is opened, and adiabatic mixing takes place. Calculate the entropy change for the mixing process. Consider both gases to be ideal. For oxygen, $R = 48.29$ ft lbf/lbm-°R, $c_p = 0.219$ Btu/lbm-°R, $c_v = 0.157$ Btu/lbm-°R. For nitrogen, $R = 55.15$ ft lbf/lbm-°R, $c_p = 0.248$ Btu/lbm-°R, $c_v = 0.177$ Btu/lbm-°R. Hint: Together, the two containers form an isolated system. Thus, $\Delta U = 0$. From this, find the equilibrium temperature. The entropy change of each gas is then

$$\Delta S = C_v \ln \frac{T_2}{T_1} + R \ln \frac{V_2}{V_1}$$

where the subscripts 1 and 2 denote conditions "before" and "after" adiabatic mixing. The entropy change for the process is

$$\Delta S_{\text{oxygen}} + \Delta S_{\text{nitrogen}}$$

9.28. Consider the mixing of two ideal gases at constant temperature and pressure. Show that, if the volumes of each gas are equal at the start, the entropy change per mole of mixture is

$$s = \bar{R} \ln 2$$

Discuss what happens when the gases change from being different to being the same. (This problem is sometimes known as Gibbs' paradox.)

9.29. A reversible process is characterized by the fact that its path at any desired number of points lies entirely on the thermodynamic surface (Fig. 9.16). How would an irreversible process between identical end-states be represented on the thermodynamic surface?

9.30. Two bodies, each of equal mass m and heat capacity c, are at temperatures T_1 and T_2 respectively ($T_1 > T_2$). If the first body is used as the source of heat for a reversible engine and the second as the sink, show that the maximum work obtainable from such an arrangement is

$$mc(T_1 + T_2 - 2\sqrt{T_1 T_2})$$

Hint: Apply Clausius' equality to the reversible engine and obtain the common temperature reached by the two bodies as

$$T_3 = \sqrt{T_1 T_2}.$$

9.31. Consider a bar of length l having a linear temperature distribution as shown in Fig. 9.18. For a bar having density ρ and specific heat c, what is the work

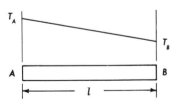

Fig. 9.18

that can be obtained by using opposite portions as source and sink for a reversible engine? Hint: Obtain an expression for the entropy change of each element of the bar as function of distance. Express the fact that the total entropy change is zero, and solve for the equilibrium temperature of the bar.

CHAPTER 10

Potential Functions, Maximum Work, Availability and Irreversibility

10.1 Maximum Work

The study of the second law of thermodynamics in the preceding chapter forms a convenient starting point for the study of a number of topics which are of interest to the engineer. First among these is the concept of the maximum work that can be done by a system in any given state.

Consider a system in an essentially infinite atmosphere (the surroundings) as shown in Fig. 10.1. For almost all thermodynamic systems, the surroundings consist of an atmosphere of uniform pressure and temperature. This atmosphere is large by comparison with the system, so that its pressure and temperature are not materially changed by any process undergone by the system. What is the maximum work which can result from the inter-action of the system (in a given initial state) with its surroundings? In other words, assuming heat exchange to occur between system and sur-roundings only, what is the total work (including the work done in pushing back the atmosphere) which can be obtained?

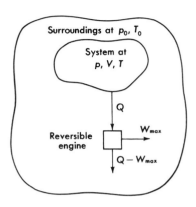

Fig. 10.1
System Within Its Environment.

A qualitative answer is first given by stating that the maximum work is the work which is delivered when the change is *reversible*. The proof of this is by contradiction: suppose that there is a process by which the change of state can occur which yields more work than that obtained in a reversible process. Let the sys-tem execute a cycle comprising the assumed process and the reverse of the reversible process. In the latter process, the system receives an amount of work equal to that de-livered by the reversible process (but less than that delivered by the as-sumed process). Thus, a net amount of work is delivered elsewhere than to the system and surroundings, and since the system can exchange heat with the surroundings only, this arrangement constitutes a machine which continuously delivers work from a single heat reservoir. According to the second law of thermodynamics, this is impossible, and the assumption cannot hold that there is a process which delivers more work than a reversible process. Thus, no process between two given states can deliver more work than a reversible process. By the same token all reversible processes between same end states will deliver the same amount of work.

10.2 Available and Unavailable Energy

The maximum work in relation to a cycle will be discussed first. When a system undergoes a power cycle and eventually returns to its initial state, the net work is equal to the net heat transfer. Even under ideal conditions, however, not all the heat supplied can be converted into work, and there-fore heat can be said to have available and unavailable parts.

Consider a reservoir at temperature T_1 from which a quantity of heat Q is extracted. If a colder reservoir (say, the surroundings at temperature

T_0) is at hand, a Carnot engine [Fig. 10.2(a)] may be used to convert some of this heat into work. The amount of work obtained is

$$W = Q\left(\frac{T_1 - T_0}{T_1}\right) = Q\left(1 - \frac{T_0}{T_1}\right) = Q - T_0 \Delta S \qquad (10.1)$$

since $Q/T_1 = \Delta S$. In Fig. 10.2(a) the area A–1–2–B represents the heat supplied, and the area 1–2–3–4 represents the work delivered.

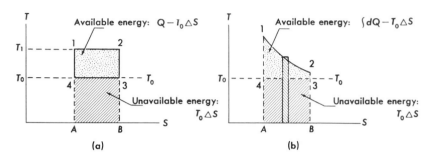

Fig. 10.2   Available and Unavailable Energy.

Equation (10.1) gives the maximum work obtainable in a cycle operating between two constant-temperature limits T_1 and T_0. Because of this, the area 1–2–3–4 is often referred to as the *available energy*. It is that portion of the heat supplied which is convertible into work. Similarly, the area A–4–3–B, equal to $T_0 \Delta S$ and representing the heat which must be rejected to the sink (surroundings at temperature T_0), is called the *unavailable energy*. In other words, available energy is that part of the heat supplied to or taken from a system which can be converted into work by means of an externally reversible engine.

The same result holds for the case of a finite reservoir which supplies heat at a varying temperature [Fig. 10.2(b)]. The process can always be broken up into a series of infinitesimal Carnot cycles, which supply dQ amount of heat at a temperature T (no longer constant) and discard heat at the sink temperature T_0 (constant). The work done is

$$W = \int\left(1 - \frac{T_0}{T}\right)dQ = \int dQ - \int T_0 \frac{dQ}{T}$$

$$= \int dQ - T_0 \int \frac{dQ}{T} = \int dQ - T_0 \Delta S \qquad (10.2)$$

and this may be interpreted in the same manner as in case (a).

The above concepts may be further illustrated by means of another example. Suppose that an amount of heat Q is conducted along a copper bar from a region of temperature T_1 to a region of appreciably lower temperature T_2 as in Fig. 10.3. This is an irreversible process, because after the occurrence, there has been a loss in the possibility of converting into work, some of the heat Q extracted at the high-temperature T_1. This loss would not have occurred had a reversible engine been installed between the two reservoirs. In other words, after conduction has taken place, Q is at the temperature T_2 instead of T_1, and the fraction of it convertible into work (referred to surroundings at T_0) is $Q(1 - T_0/T_2)$ instead of $Q(1 - T_0/T_1)$ had it stayed at the higher temperature and conduction not taken place. The amount of energy which has become unavailable for work is thus

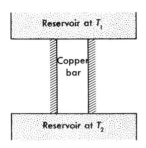

Fig. 10.3
Heat Conduction.

$$Q\left(1 - \frac{T_0}{T_1}\right) - Q\left(1 - \frac{T_0}{T_2}\right) = T_0\left(\frac{Q}{T_2} - \frac{Q}{T_1}\right) = T_0 \Delta S \qquad (10.3)$$

The above further illustrates the fact that, whenever an irreversible process takes place, the effect on the universe is a decrease of energy from the available to the unavailable. The amount of this decrease, as seen from Eqs. (10.1), (10.2) and (10.3) is the temperature T_0 of the surroundings times the entropy change.

Example 10.1. A heat source at 1140 °F transfers heat at the rate of 3000 Btu/min to a system remaining at 540 °F. There is available a heat sink at 80 °F. Assuming that these temperatures remain constant, find: (a) the change in entropy of the source, (b) the entropy production accompanying the heat transfer, (c) the original available energy, and (d) the available energy after heat transfer.

Solution. (a) The entropy change of the source is

$$\Delta S_{\text{source}} = \int \frac{dQ}{T} = \frac{Q}{T} = \frac{-3000}{1600} = -1.87 \text{ Btu/°R-min}$$

a decrease, since heat is flowing out of the source. This is shown as length A–B in Fig. 10.4; the area under 1–2 being equal to −3000 Btu.

(b) The entropy change of the system receiving the heat at a constant temperature of 540 °F (= 1000 °R) is

$$\Delta S_{\text{system}} = \int \frac{dQ}{T} = \frac{Q}{T} = \frac{3000}{1000} = 3 \text{ Btu/°R-min}$$

This is shown as length B–C. The entropy production accompanying the heat transfer is

$$\Delta S_{\text{net}} = \Delta S_{\text{source}} + \Delta S_{\text{system}} = -1.87 + 3 = 1.13 \text{ Btu/°R min}$$

It is represented by length $A–C$. Note that a rather large entropy production is to be expected whenever heat is transferred irreversibly from one temperature to an appreciably lower temperature as is the case here.

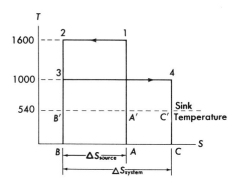

Fig. 10.4 Irreversible Heat Transfer: Constant Temperatures.

(c) The original available energy is

$$Q - T_0 \Delta S = 3000 - 540(1.87) = 1990 \text{ Btu}$$

This is the available energy corresponding to the 3000 Btu of heat at 1600 °R, just *prior* to its transmission to the system. Note that both Q and ΔS have been taken as absolute quantities, i.e. positive, since heat transfer has not yet occurred, and it is therefore meaningless to consider direction.

(d) The available energy after heat transfer has taken place is

$$Q - T_0 \Delta S = 3000 - 540(3) = 1380 \text{ Btu}$$

This is the available energy possessed by 3000 Btu of heat at 1000 °R, and is represented by the area $3–4–C'–B'$. The original available energy is represented by the area $1–2–B'–A'$. Note that the respective areas under 1–2 and 3–4 are of the same magnitude (3000 Btu), but that a decrease of energy has occurred, since the final available energy area $3–4–C'–B'$ is clearly smaller than the original available energy area $1–2–B'–A'$. The results of this example emphasize the desirability of always transferring heat with as small a temperature difference as possible, because whenever heat is transferred through a finite temperature difference, there is a decrease in work capacity of the energy so transferred.

Example 10.2. For another illustration of irreversible heat transfer, consider the common method of power production in which fuel is burned under a boiler and the steam generated is used to drive an engine or a turbine. In this case, the chemical energy of the fuel is used to produce mechanical work. Let the hot gases, which transfer heat to the boiler, be cooled from 1900 °F to 1000 °F, while the water evaporates at a constant temperature of 410 °F. Let the specific heat of the gases be 0.24 Btu/lbm-°R, and the latent heat of the water be 816.3 Btu/lbm. Assuming all the heat transferred from the gases goes to the water, determine:

(a) the total entropy increase of the combined system of gas and water as a result of irreversible heat transfer, and (b) the increase in unavailable energy referred to a surrounding temperature of 80 °F. Perform the calculations on the basis of one pound of water evaporated.

Solution. (a) The entropy change of the combined system is the sum of the entropy changes of the gas and water. In each case, the entropy change can be found by considering a reversible process between the end states. The entropy change per pound of water is 816.3/870 = 0.938; the entropy change of the gas is

$$\Delta S_{gas} = \int \frac{dQ}{T} = \int_{2360}^{1460} \frac{mc_p dT}{T} = mc_p(\ln 1460 - \ln 2360)$$

Now, per pound of water, $mc_p(1900 - 1000) = 816.3$, so that $mc_p = 816.3/900$, and the entropy change of the gas is

$$\Delta S_{gas} = \frac{816.3}{900} (\ln 1460 - \ln 2360) = -0.435 \text{ Btu/°R}$$

the total change of entropy is thus

$$\Delta S_{net} = \Delta S_{water} + \Delta S_{gas} = 0.938 - 0.435 = 0.503 \text{ Btu/°R}$$

an increase, due to the irreversible heat transfer.

(b) Since there is an increase in entropy, an increase in unavailable energy is to be expected. Referring to Fig. 10.5, the original unavailable energy is represented by the area A–B–B'–A', whose magnitude is

$$540(0.435) = 230 \text{ Btu}$$

After transfer of heat from the hot gases to the steam, the unavailable energy is represented by the area C–B–B'–C', whose magnitude is

$$540(0.938) = 506 \text{ Btu}$$

The increase in unavailable energy is therefore

$$506 - 230 = 276 \text{ Btu}$$

and this is represented by the area A–A'–C'–C whose magnitude: $T_0 \Delta S = 540(0.503) = 272$ Btu, serves as a check to the answer.

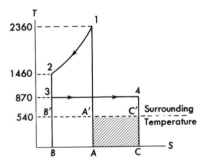

Fig. 10.5 Irreversible Heat Transfer: Variable Temperatures.

10.3 Thermodynamic Potential Functions

Before proceeding with the general quantitative answer to the question posed in Sec. 10.1, namely, the maximum useful work obtainable in a process from a system and its surroundings, the concept of *thermodynamic potential function* will first be introduced.

Up to this point, the properties of a system that have been studied and used fall into two broad classifications: (1) Quantities such as pressure p, absolute temperature T, and specific volume v. These items are measurable in the laboratory, and, together with the heat capacity c_p, make up practically all the experimental data upon which classical thermodynamics relies. (2) Quantities such as internal energy u, enthalpy h, and entropy s, which cannot usually be measured directly, except in a few instances such as in the measurement of Δu by evaluation of $\int c_v \, dT$ for a system at constant volume. In both classes, the quantities are point functions, and their differentials are exact.

There are, however, other thermodynamic quantities of importance, which can be arrived at by mathematical manipulation. For example, the combination of the first and second laws gives single relation

$$Tds = du + pdv$$

which may be written as

$$du = Tds - pdv \tag{10.4}$$

In Eq. (10.4), the two extensive quantities, s and v are the independent variables, whereas the two intensive quantities, T and $-p$, are conjugate to them. The internal energy, u, is regarded as a function of the variables s and v. The selection of independent variables, however, is largely a matter of choice. Of the variables p, v, T, and s, there are four possibilities of combining one mechanical and one thermal variable into a pair: s and v, s and p, T and v, and T and p. This leads to the following situation: it is often desirable to replace in an equation, such as $du = Tds - pdv$, one of the independent variables, say, v, in terms of its conjugate $-p$. To this end, it is necessary to subtract, from the dependent variable (u), the product of the two conjugate variables ($-pv$). This gives

$$d(u + pv) = du + pdv + vdp = Tds + vdp \tag{10.5}$$

so that the independent variables are now s and p instead of s and v. Similarly, in order to change the independent variable from s to T in Eq. (10.4), it is necessary to subtract from u the product Ts:

$$d(u - Ts) = du - Tds - sdT = -pdv - sdT \tag{10.6}$$

and to change the independent variables from s to T and v to p, it is necessary to subtract the products Ts and $-pv$:

$$d(u - Ts + pv) = d(h - Ts) = du - Tds - sdT + pdv + vdp$$
$$= -sdT + vdp \tag{10.7}$$

The manipulations illustrated above are examples of *Legendre transformations* (of great importance in the advanced study of mechanics and thermodynamics). They enable an equation to be expressed in terms of a set of independent variables chosen to be particularly convenient in a given situation. In Eq. (10.5), the quantity in parenthesis, $(u+pv)$, is already familiar. It has been given the symbol h, and the name enthalpy. Similarly, in Eqs. (10.6) and (10.7), the quantities in parentheses, $(u-Ts)$ and $(h-Ts)$ are given respectively, the symbols a and g, and the names Helmholtz function and Gibbs' function:

$$u - Ts \equiv a = \text{Helmholtz function} \qquad (10.8)$$

$$h - Ts \equiv g = \text{Gibbs' function} \qquad (10.9)$$

Substitution of these symbols into Eqs. (10.5), (10.6), and (10.7) yields

$$dh = Tds + vdp \qquad (10.10)$$

$$da = -pdv - sdT \qquad (10.11)$$

$$dg = -sdT + vdp \qquad (10.12)$$

Equations (10.10), (10.11), and (10.12) show that the differentials dh, da, and dg have the same simple form when expressed in terms of the independent variables associated with them as du has when it is expressed in terms of s and v in Eq. (10.4). The quantities $u(s, v)$, $h(s, p)$, $a(v, T)$, and $g(T, p)$ are known as *thermodynamic potentials*. They are all extensive properties of a system and have the dimensions of energy.

10.4 Helmholtz Function

The foregoing development is not just an exercise in mathematics. It has application in both physical chemistry and engineering.

Consider a system and its surroundings as shown in Fig. 10.6.* By definition, a system is any region in space within prescribed boundaries, with the surroundings being everything outside the system boundaries. If the gas is chosen as the system, then the atmosphere, the heat reservoir, and the piston and its rod form the surroundings. For most applications, the atmosphere is so large in comparison with the system that its pressure and temperature are not

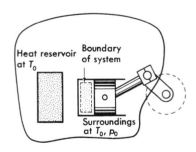

Fig. 10.6 Combination of System and Surroundings.

---

* The boundary of the surroundings is drawn in the present manner to show that part of the work consists in merely pushing back the atmosphere. That part of the work which can be delivered to things other than the system and the surroundings is called *useful work*. It will be discussed in Sec. 10–6.

changed by any process undergone by the system. Let p_0, T_0 denote the pressure and temperature of the atmosphere. What is the maximum amount of work (including the work done in pushing back the atmos- phere) which can be done by the system when it goes from one specified state to another while exchanging heat only with the atmosphere?

Consider first the case of a non-flow process: the work done during an infinitesimal change of the system between two equilibrium states is given by the first law:

$$dW = -dU + dQ \qquad (10.13)$$

Equation (10.13) states that the work done on the piston and rod is pro- vided in part by the system, whose internal energy decreases by $-dU$, and in part by the heat reservoir, which supplies the quantity of heat dQ. Let the system absorb heat from the reservoir at T_0; the principle of entropy increase states that, in any process, the entropy of the system and sur- roundings can only increase, or in the limit, for reversible processes, stay constant. If dS denotes the entropy change of the system and dS_0 that of the reservoir (which is part of the surroundings), then, for the combination of system and surroundings,

$$dS + dS_0 \geqslant 0$$

But $dS_0 = -dQ/T_0$, where dQ is the amount of heat leaving the reservoir. Thus,

$$dS - \frac{dQ}{T_0} \geqslant 0$$

or

$$dQ \leqslant T_0 dS$$

Replacing dQ by this value, Eq. (10.13) gives

$$dW \leqslant -dU + T_0 dS \qquad (10.14)$$

which, for a finite process between equilibrium states 1 and 2, is integrated into

$$W \leqslant (U_1 - U_2) - T_0(S_1 - S_2) \qquad (10.15^*)$$

For the case in which the initial and final temperatures of the system and the temperature of the reservoir are all equal, Eq. (10.15) may be written as

$$(W)_T \leqslant [(U_1 - T_1 S_1) - (U_2 - T_2 S_2)]_T \leqslant (A_1 - A_2)_T \qquad (10.16)$$

---

* Note that this equation is of general validity. For, if the system surrenders an amount of heat dQ to the reservoir, the entropy change of the reservoir is $dS_0 = +dQ/T_0$. But then the first law becomes $dW = -dU - dQ$, and this, with the principle of entropy increase, $dS + dS_0 \geqslant 0$, still gives the same result.

where the property $U - TS \equiv A$ is the *Helmholtz function*, and the subscript T is a reminder that the temperature remains constant. Equation (10.16) states that the upper limit for the work done in any non-flow process during which a system has initial and final temperatures equal to that of the surroundings, T_0, and exchanges heat only with the surroundings at the temperature, T_0, is equal to the decrease of its Helmholtz function: $A_1 - A_2$. The maximum work is done when the process is reversible, in which case the equality sign in Eq. (10.16) holds; whereas, if the process is irreversible, the work done is less than this maximum. Because its decrease represents the maximum amount of work obtainable, the quantity A is sometimes called *free energy* by physicists. The latter designation however, is subject to confusion, for it is used by chemists to denote the Gibbs function $(H - TS)$. In this text, the quantity $A \equiv U - TS$ will mostly be referred to as the *Helmholtz function*, and the term free energy will not be used.

Depending on whether a process in question produces work or requires work, the actual work produced or consumed between given end states will be respectively less than and more than the reversible work between the same states. Thus, if work is done by the system during a constant temperature change of state from 1 to 2, ΔA is negative, and the actual work obtained, though positive, cannot be numerically greater than ΔA. On the other hand, if work is done on the system during an isothermal process, ΔA is positive, and the actual work required is numerically greater than ΔA.

Example 10.3. From the following data on steam:

p	t	h	s	v
1000 psia	800 °F	1389 Btu	$1.567 \frac{\text{Btu}}{°\text{R}}$	0.688
14.7	800 °F	1432 Btu	$2.058 \frac{\text{Btu}}{°\text{R}}$	51

determine the maximum work that can be obtained from 5 pounds of steam undergoing a non-flow isothermal process between the end states (1000 psia, 800 °F) and (14.7 psia, 800 °F).

Solution. From Eq. (10.16) the maximum work is equal to $(A_1 - A_2)$. This conclusion may also be arrived at as follows: From the definition of the Helmholtz function $(A \equiv U - TS)$,

$$dA = dU - TdS - SdT$$
$$= pdV - SdT$$

For a reversible non-flow isothermal process, this becomes

$$W = \int_1^2 p\,dV = -(A_2 - A_1)$$

At the conditions given in the problem, steam cannot be considered a perfect gas, and the evaluation of the work done by integration of the expression $\int p\,dV$ is not convenient because no simple relation between p and V exists. Helmholtz's function, however, can be used to advantage, since it is a point function, and its value between two states is easily obtainable. The maximum work is thus

$$W_{max} = (A_1 - A_2)_T = [(U_1 - T_1 S_1) - (U_2 - T_2 S_2)]_T$$

Since no data on internal energy is given in the problem, the calculation of Helmholtz functions will have to be done in terms of the enthalpy. Thus,

$$A_1 = ma_1 = 5(u_1 - T_1 s_1) = 5(h_1 - p_1 v_1 - T_1 s_1)$$

and

$$A_2 = m_2 a_2 = 5(u_2 - T_2 s_2) = 5(h_2 - p_2 v_2 - T_2 s_2)$$

Replacing this in the expression for the maximum work and noting that $T_1 = T_2$ gives

$$W_{max} = [5(h_1 - p_1 v_1 - T_1 s_1) - 5(h_2 - p_2 v_2 - T_2 s_2)]_{T=1260}$$

$$= 5[(h_1 - h_2) + (p_2 v_2 - p_1 v_1) + T_1(s_2 - s_1)]_{T=1260}$$

$$= 5\left[(1389 - 1432) + \frac{144}{778}(14.7 \times 51 - 1000 \times 0.688) + (1260)(2.058 - 1.567)\right]$$

$$= 5780 \text{ Btu}$$

The Helmholtz function is of primary usefulness in problems involving chemical and electrochemical processes which proceed essentially at constant temperature and volume. It is also important in statistical mechanics, where it is possible, by statistical methods, to calculate the Helmholtz function of a substance as function of T and v. The equation of state and the entropy of the substance may then be obtained from relations such as $p = -(\partial a/\partial v)_T$; $s = -(\partial a/\partial T)_v$. These relations are derived in problems at the end of the chapter.

Example 10.4. Show that for an ideal gas, the specific Helmholtz function is

$$a = \int_{T_0}^{T'} c_v dT - T \int_{T_0}^{T} c_v \frac{dT}{T} - RT \ln\frac{v}{v_0} + u_0 - T s_0$$

where u_0 and s_0 are respectively the specific internal energy and entropy at the reference state p_0, v_0, T_0.

Solution. The easiest way to do this is to recall that for an ideal gas,

$$u = u_0 + \int_{T_0}^{T} c_v dT; \quad s = s_0 + \int_{T_0}^{T} c_v \frac{dT}{T} + R \ln\frac{v}{v_0}$$

Therefore,

$$a = u - Ts = u_0 + \int_{T_0}^{T} c_v dT - T s_0 - T \int_{T_0}^{T} c_v \frac{dT}{T} - RT \ln\frac{v}{v_0}$$

or

$$a = \int_{T_0}^{T} c_v dT - T \int_{T_0}^{T} c_v \frac{dT}{T} - RT \ln \frac{v}{v_0} + u_0 - Ts_0$$

For the case of a perfect gas with constant c_v,

$$a = c_v(T - T_0) - c_v T \ln \frac{T}{T_0} - RT \ln \frac{v}{v_0} + u_0 - Ts_0$$

10.5 Gibbs' Function

The preceding section showed that the maximum work obtainable in a non-flow isothermal process during which a system exchanges heat solely with the surroundings is equal to the decrease in the Helmholtz function of the system. Consider now the case of a steady-flow isothermal process during which the system exchanges heat only with the ambient atmosphere.

In any flow process, work that relates to the surroundings, such as flow work at entry and flow work at exit, must be included in the expression for the total work. Keeping in mind that, at the entrance point, flow work $mp_1 v_1$ is supplied from the surroundings to the system, whereas at the exit point, flow work $mp_2 v_2$ is supplied by the system to the surroundings, it is seen that the quantity $(mp_2 v_2 - mp_1 v_1) = (p_2 V_2 - p_1 V_1)$ must be subtracted from the right-hand side of Eq. (10.15):

$$W \leqslant (U_1 - U_2) - T_0(S_1 - S_2) - (p_2 V_2 - p_1 V_1)$$

$$\leqslant (U_1 + p_1 V_1 - T_0 S_1) - (U_2 + p_2 V_2 - T_0 S_2)$$

and, upon replacement of T_0 by T_1 or T_2 (since the process is at the temperature of the surroundings),

$$(W)_T \leqslant [(U_1 + p_1 V_1 - T_1 S_1) - (U_2 + p_2 V_2 - T_2 S_2)]_T$$

$$\leqslant (G_1 - G_2)_T \tag{10.17}$$

where the property $U + pV - TS \equiv G$ is the *Gibbs function*, and the subscript T is a reminder that the temperature remains constant.

Equation (10.17) states that the upper limit for the work done in a steady-flow isothermal process during which a system exchanges heat only with the surroundings is equal to the decrease of its Gibbs function: $G_1 - G_2$. The maximum work is obtained when the process is reversible, in which case the equality sign in Eq. (10.17) holds; whereas, if the process is irreversible, the work done is less than this maximum.

Note that if the process is of the kind that produces work, the actual work obtained will be less than or equal to $(G_1 - G_2)$. On the other hand, if the process is one which requires work, the actual work input will be greater than or equal to $(G_1 - G_2)$. This is what is meant by Eq. (10.17).

Example 10.5. Determine the minimum work required for the compression of 5 pounds of carbon dioxide from 120 °F and 80 psia, to 120 °F and 800 psia in a steady-flow process. The following is an abstract of properties for CO_2:

p	t	h	s
80 psia	120 °F	177 Btu	0.44 Btu/°R
800 psia	120 °F	153 Btu	0.30 Btu/°R

Solution. From Eq. (10.17), the minimum work required is $(G_1 - G_2)$. However, this result may also be obtained as follows: From the definition of the Gibbs function, $G \equiv H - TS$,

$$dG = dH - Tds - SdT = Vdp - SdT$$

For a reversible, steady-flow, isothermal process, this becomes

$$W = -\int_1^2 Vdp = G_1 - G_2$$

Thus,

$$(W_{\min})_T = (G_1 - G_2)_T = 5[(h_1 - T_1 s_1) - (h_2 - T_2 s_2)]_{T=580}$$

$$= 5[(177 - 580 \times 0.44) - (153 - 580 \times 0.30)]$$

$$= -285 \text{ Btu}$$

Of course, the answer could, in theory, be obtained by taking the integral,

$$-5\int_1^2 vdp$$

However, the integral cannot be accurately or easily evaluated, since no simple relation between volume and pressure exists for CO_2.

Example 10.6. Show that, for an ideal gas, the specific Gibbs function becomes

$$g = \int_{T_0}^{T} c_v dT - T\int_{T_0}^{T} c_v \frac{dT}{T} - RT \ln\frac{v}{v_0} + u_0 - Ts_0 + pv$$

Solution. This rather formidable looking expression is easily obtained by simply adding to the Helmholtz function a, the term pv. For, by definition:

$$g = h - Ts = u + pv - Ts$$

$$= a + pv$$

and using the result of Example 10.4,

$$g = \int_{T_0}^{T} c_v dT - T\int_{T_0}^{T} c_v \frac{dT}{T} - RT \ln\frac{v}{v_0} + u_0 - Ts_0 + pv$$

10.6 Useful Work

The preceding sections have shown how to calculate the maximum work obtainable from a system which is at the temperature of the atmosphere both initially and finally, and which exchanges heat only with the atmosphere. Part of the work, however, may consist of pushing back the atmosphere and may not be deliverable beyond the boundaries of the surroundings (atmosphere). This part of the work is $p_0(V_2 - V_1)$, where p_0 is the atmospheric pressure and V_1 and V_2 are the initial and final volumes of the system. That part of the work which is deliverable to things other than the system and surroundings is called the *useful work*.

As a specific example, suppose that it is required to calculate the maximum useful work obtainable when a system passes between two states, each of which is at the pressure and temperature of the atmosphere. This is the case in many industrial plants, for raw materials, fuel, and cooling water enter at the temperature and pressure of the surroundings, and products and waste leave in approximately this same condition. For the purpose of simplicity, let a non-flow process be considered. Under these circumstances, the work term may be divided into two parts: (1) Work done on the surroundings as the result of expansion of the system, which, in such cases as chemical reactions, cannot be delivered to things other than the system and the surroundings. This is equal to $p_0 dV$, where p_0 is the pressure of the surroundings and dV is the volume change, reversible or irreversible, of the system. (2) Useful work, such as shaft work, electrical work, or magnetic work. Then, for a process at constant pressure and temperature, this useful work may be obtained as follows: Equation (10.15) gives the total work for a system which exchanges heat only with a single reservoir at temperature T_0:

$$W \leqslant (U_1 - U_2) - T_0(S_1 - S_2)$$

Subtracting $p_0(V_2 - V_1)$ from the right-hand side of this equation gives the useful work in a constant-pressure, constant-temperature process:

$$(W_{\text{useful}})_{p,T} \leqslant (U_1 - U_2) - T_0(S_1 - S_2) - p_0(V_2 - V_1)$$

$$\leqslant (U_1 + p_0 V_1 - T_0 S_1) - (U_2 + p_0 V_2 - T_0 S_2)$$

or, since $p_1 = p_2 = p_0$, and $T_1 = T_2 = T_0$,

$$(W_{\text{useful}})_{p,T} \leqslant (U_1 + p_1 V_1 - T_1 S_1) - (U_2 + p_2 V_2 - T_2 S_2)_{p,T}$$

$$\leqslant (G_1 - G_2)_{p,T} \tag{10.18}$$

Equation (10.18) is an important result. It sets an upper limit for the useful work obtainable from a system undergoing a non-flow, constant-temperature, constant-pressure process. (A system undergoing a chemical reaction in an open vessel fulfils these conditions.) The maximum work is obtainable when the process is reversible, in which case the equality sign holds. For any actual or irreversible process, the work done is less than this maximum. Because its decrease equals the maximum useful work, the quantity G is often called *free energy* by chemists. However, the term *Gibbs function* is preferable, and consequently it is used almost exclusively in this text.

Note the similarity between Eqs. (10.17) and (10.18). In each, the decrease in the Gibbs function is involved in some manner. Equation (10.17), however, is less restrictive, because, it can be used for isothermal flow processes even when the terminal states are not at the same pressure. The same statement can be made about Eq. (10.16), which is also applicable to isothermal constant volume processes.

10.7 Availability

As pointed out earlier, the attention of the engineer is directed largely toward the control of processes to produce the maximum amount of work (or to consume the minimum amount of it). So far, the discussion has been restricted to processes between end states which are at the same temperature. There are cases, however, where the terminal temperatures differ so widely that analysis on the basis of isothermal work is not justified. Consider a system S shown in Fig. 10.7, and its surroundings (atmosphere) within which it resides, and with which it can exchange heat and work.

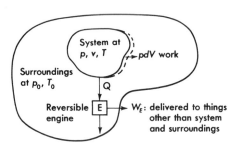

Fig. 10.7   System Within Its Environment.

Boundary A separates the system (at pressure p and temperature T) from the surroundings (at pressure p_0 and temperature T_0). This boundary can be deformed so that the pressure p of the system can be brought to p_0, the environment pressure. Boundary B is of such extent that it may be considered a constant-volume enclosure. Let any transfer of heat between system and surroundings be through the intermediary of a reversible engine E between T and T_0. The source of temperature T will then be decreasing continuously until T_0 is reached by the system. This is the ideal manner of transferring heat. In practice, high-temperature heat may be rejected directly to the surroundings, but this would be an irreversible operation, since work that could have been obtained from the use of a reversible engine would be wasted. The work done by the system against surroundings is the pdV work; the work done by the reversible engine is W_E.

By definition, the *availability* of a given system is the maximum useful work (total work minus pdV work) which can be obtained in a process during which the system comes to equilibrium with its surroundings. Equilibrium means that the system is at the same pressure and temperature as its surroundings and at rest (relative to its surroundings), so that there is no possibility of obtaining work by interaction between the system and the surroundings. This state of the system within the surroundings is called the *dead state*. Should the system be in any state other than the dead state, it will spontaneously change its condition toward the dead state without the aid of any work from a source external to the system and surroundings. For any change in the state of the system to the dead state, the maximum useful work (which can be delivered to things other than the system and surroundings) is the *availability*, and this *availability* depends not only on the condition of the system, but also on the condition of the surroundings.

10.8 Availability in Non-Flow

To make use of potential functions in finding maximum work, consider first a non-flow process. Let U_1, V_1, and S_1 be the initial values of internal energy, volume, and entropy of the system, and U_0, V_0, and S_0 their final values (when the system has attained equilibrium with the surroundings). Subject to the usual restriction that, during the process (which may be reversible or irreversible), the system exchanges heat only with the surroundings at T_0, the useful work is obtained from Eq. (10.15) by subtracting from the right-hand side the pdV work. Thus,

$$W_{\text{useful}} \leqslant (U_1 - U_0) - T_0(S_1 - S_0) - p_0(V_0 - V_1) \qquad (10.19)$$

where subscripts 1 and 0 have replaced the subscripts 1 and 2 (since the process is from a given initial state to the dead state). Equation (10.19) may be written as

$$W_{\text{useful}} \leqslant (U_1 + p_0 V_1 - T_0 S_1) - (U_0 + p_0 V_0 - T_0 S_0)$$

$$\leqslant \Phi_1 - \Phi_0 \qquad (10.20)$$

where the quantity

$$\Phi = U + p_0 V - T_0 S \qquad (10.21)$$

is defined as the *availability function.*

Equation (10.20) states that the useful work obtainable when a system changes, reversibly or irreversibly, from any state to the dead state is equal to or less than the decrease in the availability function. The quantity Φ is a property, for U, V, and S are properties of the system and p_0 and T_0 are the pressure and temperature of the surroundings. It is, however, a *composite* property, for it depends on both the state of the system and that of the surroundings or environment. Equation (10.20) sets an upper value for the useful work that can be obtained when a system undergoes a transformation to the dead state temperature and pressure (T_0, p_0) of the environment (usually the earth's atmosphere). This upper limit is the decrease in the availability function. In the limit, for a reversible process, the maximum useful work (the availability) is obtained. Thus,

$$W_{\text{max. useful}} \equiv \text{Availability} = \Phi_1 - \Phi_0 \qquad (10.22)$$

For the general case of a system which undergoes a change from a state 1 (in which its availability is $\Phi_1 - \Phi_0$), to state 2 (in which its availability is $\Phi_2 - \Phi_0$), the maximum useful work or availability change of the process is

$$W_{\text{max. useful}} = (\Phi_1 - \Phi_0) - (\Phi_2 - \Phi_0) = \Phi_1 - \Phi_2 \qquad (10.23)$$

Note that, in the latter case, all restrictions of constant temperature and constant pressure have been lifted.

Example 10.6. In a certain process, steam at a pressure of 120 psia and a temperature of 1200 °F is taken to a pressure of 50 psia and a temperature of 600 °F. Determine the maximum useful work per pound of steam that can be obtained in this transformation. The following is an abtract of properties for steam:

$p(psia)$	$T(°F)$	v(cu ft/lbm)	h(Btu/lbm)	s(Btu/lbm-°R)
120	1200	8.212	1635.3	1.9664
50	600	12.532	1332.5	1.8368

Consider the ambient atmosphere to be at a pressure of 14.7 psia and a temperature of 60 °F.

Solution. The maximum useful work per pound of steam is the difference in the specific availability functions corresponding to the two end states:

Maximum work $= \phi_1 - \phi_2$

$$= (u_1 + p_0 v_1 - T_0 s_1) - (u_2 + p_0 v_2 - T_0 s_2)$$

Since internal energies are not given in the table of steam properties, they are calculated from the enthalpy data by recalling that $u = h - pv$. Thus,

$$u_1 = h_1 - p_1 v_1 = 1635.3 - \frac{(120)(144)(8.212)}{778}$$

$$= 1452.8 \text{ Btu/lbm}$$

$$u_2 = h_2 - p_2 v_2 = 1332.5 - \frac{(50)(144)(12.532)}{778}$$

$$= 1332.5 - 116 = 1216.5 \text{ Btu/lbm}$$

The availability or maximum useful work for the process is thus

$$W_{\text{max. useful}} = (u_1 + p_0 v_1 - T_0 s_1) - (u_2 + p_0 v_2 - T_0 s_2)$$

$$= \left[1452.8 + \frac{(14.7)(144)(8.211)}{778} - (520)(1.9664) \right] -$$

$$- \left[1216.5 + \frac{(14.7)(144)(12.532)}{778} - (520)(11.8368) \right]$$

$$= 157.2 \text{ Btu/lbm}$$

This is the useful work theoretically obtainable in a reversible change between the given end states. The actual useful work (corresponding to an irreversible process) would, of course, be less than this amount.

10.9 Availability in Steady-Flow

The preceding section discussed the concept of availability for a non-flow process. The same idea holds for a steady-flow process, except that the expression for the availability function becomes slightly different.

In the case of a flow process, the availability of each unit mass of fluid at a specified state with respect to an environment at pressure p_0 and temperature T_0 is augmented by the amount of work that can be delivered by virtue of the flow, namely, $(p_1 v_1 - p_0 v_1)$, where the subscript 1 denotes a given initial state. For a steady-flow of mass m, the increase in availability becomes $m(p_1 v_1 - p_0 v_1) = (p_1 V_1 - p_0 V_1)$. Adding this to the right-hand side of Eq. (10.19) gives

$$W_{\text{useful}} \leqslant (U_1 - U_0) - T_0(S_1 - S_0) - p_0(V_0 - V_1) + (p_1 V_1 - p_0 V_1) \qquad (10.24)$$

which, upon collection of terms, becomes

$$W_{\text{useful}} \leqslant (U_1 + p_1 V_1 - T_0 S_1) - (U_0 + p_0 V_0 - T_0 S_0) \leqslant B_1 - B_0 \qquad (10.25)$$

where the quantity

$$B \equiv U + pV - T_0 S = H - T_0 S \qquad (10.26)$$

is defined as the *availability function for steady-flow*, commonly known as the *Darrieus function*.

Equation (10.25) states that the useful work obtainable in a flow process to the dead state is equal to or less than the decrease in the function B. This function, like the function Φ of the preceding section, is a *composite* property of the system and its surroundings. In the limit, for a reversible steady-flow process to the dead state, the maximum work obtainable is equal to the decrease in the Darrieus function:

$$W_{\text{max. useful}} \equiv \text{Availability} = B_1 - B_0 \qquad (10.27)$$

For the general case of a flow system undergoing a change from a state 1 to a state 2 (not necessarily dead state), the useful work is given by

$$W_{\text{useful}} \leqslant (B_1 - B_0) - (B_2 - B_0) \leqslant B_1 - B_2 \qquad (10.28)$$

and the maximum useful work or availability change is

$$W_{\text{max. useful}} = B_1 - B_2 \qquad (10.29)$$

Note again that, in Eq. (10.29), all restrictions of constant temperature and constant pressure have been lifted.

Example 10.7. Air at 100 psia and 160 °F flows through a turbine with a velocity of 300 fps. It leaves the turbine at 15 psia, 50 °F, and with a velocity of 180 fps. Determine the maximum useful work obtainable per pound of air, and compare this with the actual work done. Consider air to be a perfect gas having a specific heat $c_p = 0.24$ Btu/lbm-°R, and the surroundings to be at 77 °F and 14.7 psia.

Solution. The maximum useful work obtainable for the change of state which occurs in the turbine is given by Eq. (10.29), with a term added to the right-hand side to take care of the kinetic energy:

$$w_{\text{max. useful}} = b_1 - b_2 + \frac{\mathscr{V}_1^2 - \mathscr{V}_2^2}{2g_c}$$

$$= (h_1 - T_0 s_1) - (h_2 - T_0 s_2) + \frac{\mathscr{V}_1^2 - \mathscr{V}_2^2}{2g_c}$$

Now, $h = c_p T$ for a perfect gas, so that

$$w_{\text{max. useful}} = c_p(T_1 - T_2) - T_0(s_1 - s_2) + \frac{\mathscr{V}_1^2 - \mathscr{V}_2^2}{2g_c}$$

Furthermore, the entropy change of a perfect gas is given by

$$s_1 - s_2 = c_p \ln\frac{T_1}{T_2} - R \ln\frac{p_1}{p_2}$$

Therefore,

$$w_{\text{max. useful}} = c_p(T_1 - T_2) - T_0\left(c_p \ln\frac{T_1}{T_2} - R \ln\frac{p_1}{p_2}\right) + \frac{\mathcal{V}_1^2 - \mathcal{V}_2^2}{2g_c}$$

$$= 0.24(620 - 210) - 537\left(0.24 \ln\frac{620}{510} - \frac{53.3}{778} \ln\frac{100}{15}\right) + \frac{\overline{300}^2 - \overline{180}^2}{(2)(32.16)(778)}$$

$$= 61.5 \text{ Btu/lbm}$$

The actual work is found in the manner of Chap. 6 from the steady-flow energy equation,

$$w = (h_1 - h_2) + \frac{\mathcal{V}_1^2 - \mathcal{V}_2^2}{2g_c} = c_p(T_1 + T_2) + \frac{\mathcal{V}_1^2 - \mathcal{V}_2^2}{2g_c}$$

$$= 0.24(620 - 510) - \frac{\overline{300}^2 - \overline{180}^2}{(2)(32.16)(778)} = 27.6 \text{ Btu/lbm}$$

Example 10.8. Consider the parallel-flow heat exchanger shown in Fig. 10.8: Two fluids A and B enter at the same end. A is the hotter fluid, and B is the colder fluid. As they proceed along the heat exchanger, they approach equilibrium temperature. Excluding phase changes, the temperature of the hot fluid decreases from T_{A_1} to T_{A_2}, while that of the cold fluid increases from T_{B_1} to T_{B_2}. Assuming the mass flow rates to be equal, and the specific heats to be constant and equal for both fluids, what is the loss in availability?

Solution. The entropy change for fluid A is

$$\Delta S_A = mc_p \ln\frac{T_{A_2}}{T_{A_1}}$$

and for fluid B is

$$\Delta S_B = mc_p \ln\frac{T_{B_2}}{T_{B_1}}$$

The change in availability for fluid A is

$$B_{A_2} - B_{A_1} = (H_{A_2} - T_0 S_{A_2}) - (H_{A_1} - T_0 S_{A_1})$$

or

$$\Delta B_A = \Delta H - T_0 \Delta S_A$$

$$= mc_p(T_{A_2} - T_{A_1}) - mT_0 c_p \ln\frac{T_{A_2}}{T_{A_1}}$$

Similarly, for fluid B,

$$\Delta B_B = \Delta H_B - T_0 \Delta S_B$$

$$= mc_p(T_{B_2} - T_{B_1}) - mT_0 c_p \ln\frac{T_{B_2}}{T_{B_1}}$$

where T_0 is the temperature of the environment.

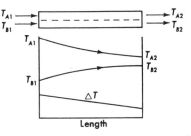

Fig. 10.8 Temperature Distribution in Parallel Heat Exchanger.

The total change in availability is

$$\Delta B_A + \Delta B_B = mc_p[(T_{A_2} - T_{A_1}) + (T_{B_2} - T_{B_1})] - mT_0c_p\left[\ln\frac{T_{A_2}}{T_{A_1}} + \ln\frac{T_{B_2}}{T_{B_1}}\right]$$

But $mc_p[T_{A_2} - T_{A_1}) + (T_{B_2} - T_{B_1})] = 0$, since the heat lost by the hot fluid equals that gained by the cold fluid. Thus,

$$\Delta B_A + \Delta B_B = -mT_0c_p\left[\ln\frac{T_{A_2}}{T_{A_1}} + \ln\frac{T_{B_2}}{T_{B_1}}\right] = -mT_0c_p\ln\left[\frac{T_{A_2}}{T_{A_1}}\cdot\frac{T_{B_2}}{T_{B_1}}\right]$$

$$= mT_0c_p\ln\left[\frac{T_{A_1}}{T_{A_2}}\cdot\frac{T_{B_1}}{T_{B_2}}\right]$$

The result shows that there is a loss in availability. For, as seen from the temperature plot in Fig. 10.8, the ratio $T_{A_1}/T_{A_2}\cdot T_{B_1}/T_{B_2}$ can only be less than unity. One way of minimizing the loss of availability to zero is to have T_{A_1} equal T_{B_2}, and T_{A_2} equal T_{B_1}. This means cooling the hot fluid to the lowest temperature of the cold fluid, and heating the cold fluid to the highest temperature of the hot fluid. This is precisely what is sought in a counter-flow heat exchanger, wherein, by making the two fluids enter at opposite ends of the exchanger, the temperature difference between the two fluids can be kept quite small. This is shown in Fig. 10.9. In a parallel-flow heat exchanger, it is not possible to cool the hot fluid to the lowest temperature of the cold fluid and heat the cold fluid to the highest temperature of the hot fluid. Examination of the temperature plot in Fig. 10.8 will bear this out. Hence, parallel-flow heat exchange is a highly irreversible process, when compared to counter-flow heat exchange.

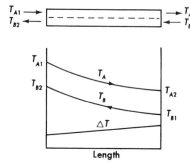

Fig. 10.9 Temperature Distribution in Counterflow Heat Exchanger.

10.10 Irreversibility

Because actual processes are far from being reversible, the actual work W for a given change of state (in which the only heat transfer is with surroundings) is always less than the reversible work $W_{\max}$. The irreversibility I of a process is, by definition, the difference between the maximum work obtainable and the actual work obtained, i.e.

$$I = W_{\max} - W \tag{10.30}$$

or, equivalently,

$$I = W_{\max\ useful} - W_{useful} = -\Delta\Phi - W \tag{10.31}$$

Equation (10.31) may be more conveniently rewritten in terms of the entropy. To do this, Φ is first replaced by its definition, $U + p_0 V - T_0 S$, to give

$$I = -\Delta U - p_0 \Delta V + T_0 \Delta S - W \tag{10.32}$$

Next, consider the combination of system and surroundings (atmosphere) and note that such a combination exchanges no heat with outside things. The work for this composite system is then, according to the first law,

$$W = -\Delta U - \Delta U_{\text{surr}} \tag{10.33}$$

where ΔU and $U\Delta_{\text{surr}}$ refer to the internal energy changes of the system and surroundings respectively. Substitution of Eq. (10.33) into Eq. (10.32) gives

$$I = \Delta U_{\text{surr}} - p_0 \Delta V + T_0 \Delta S \tag{10.34}$$

Now, the atmosphere being a large medium whose outer boundary may be considered unchanged, the volume displacements of the system and its surroundings are related by

$$\Delta V + \Delta V_{\text{surr}} = 0 \tag{10.35}$$

Applying the fundamental relation $TdS = dU + pdV$ to the surroundings gives

$$T_0 \Delta S_{\text{surr}} = \Delta U_{\text{surr}} + p_0 \Delta V_{\text{surr}} \tag{10.36}$$

Equations (10.35) and (10.36) enable Eq. (10.34) to be written as

$$
\begin{aligned}
I &= \Delta U_{\text{surr}} - p_0 \Delta V + T_0 \Delta S \\
&= \Delta U_{\text{surr}} + p_0 \Delta V_{\text{surr}} + T_0 \Delta S \\
&= T_0 \Delta S_{\text{surr}} + T_0 \Delta S \\
&= T_0 \Delta (S_a + S) \tag{10.37}
\end{aligned}
$$

Thus, the irreversibility is equal to the temperature of the atmosphere multiplied by the increase in entropy of everything involved in the process. From the principle of entropy increase, it is seen that $I \geqslant 0$.

When speaking of actual processes, the term effectiveness is sometimes used. By definition, the effectiveness, $\mathscr{E}$, of a process, is the ratio of the actual useful work obtained to the maximum useful work obtainable, i.e.

$$\mathscr{E} = \frac{W_{\text{useful}}}{W_{\text{max. useful}}} = \frac{W_{\text{useful}}}{W_{\text{useful}} + I}$$

From the thermodynamic standpoint, all reversible processes between given end states are equally effective in producing useful work, so that the effectiveness of any reversible process is unity. The effectiveness of an actual process, however, is always less than unity.

Example 10.9. In a certain flow process, the fluid is taken in from 100 psia and 1000 °F to 10 psia and 500 °F, while 150 Btu/lbm of useful work is produced. The properties of the fluid are as follows:

p	t	h	s
100 psia	100 °F	1531 Btu/lbm	1.919 Btu/lbm-°R
40 psia	500 °F	1785 Btu/lbm	1.814 Btu/lbm-°R

Considering the ambient atmosphere to be at 14.7 psia and 60 °F, find the degree of effectiveness and the irreversibility of the process.

Solution. The maximum useful work of the process is obtained by taking the difference in the specific availability functions corresponding to the given end states:

$$w_{\text{max. useful}} = b_1 - b_2 = (h_1 - T_0 s_1) - (h_2 - T_0 s_2)$$
$$= [1531 - 520(1.919)] - [1285 - 520(1.814)]$$
$$= 191 \text{ Btu/lbm}$$

The effectiveness of the process is

$$\mathscr{E} = \frac{w_{\text{useful}}}{w_{\text{max useful}}} = \frac{150}{191} = 0.785 \text{ or } 78.5 \text{ per cent}$$

The irreversibility per unit mass of fluid is

$$i = w_{\text{max useful}} - w_{\text{useful}} = 191 - 150 = 41 \text{ Btu/lbm}$$

PROBLEMS

10.1. Steam at 118 psia and 340 °F undergoes a non-flow isothermal expansion to 75 psia. During the process, it receives heat isothermally, and its entropy increases from 1.5891 Btu/lbm-°R to 1.6489 Btu/lbm-°R. How much of the heat added per round of steam is available energy if the surroundings temperature is 80 °F?

10.2. In a certain Carnot cycle heat is supplied at 400 °F and rejected at 90 °F. The working fluid is water, which, while receiving heat, evaporates from liquid at 400 °F to vapor at the same temperature. The entropy change for this process is 0.9608 Btu/lbm-°R. Assuming the cycle to operate on a stationary unit mass of water, determine: (a) the heat supplied, (b) the available energy, (c) the unavailable energy, (d) the change in available energy when the sink temperature is lowered to 65 °F.

10.3. In a certain process a vapor, while condensing at 850 °F, transfers heat to water evaporating at 650 °F, the resulting heat to be used in a power cycle which rejects heat at 80 °F. Determine the fraction of available energy in the heat transferred from the process vapor at 850 °F which is lost due to irreversible heat transfer to the water at 600 °F.

10.4. Three pounds of water are contained in an insulated tank. Work in the amount of 2000 ft lbf is performed on the water by means of a paddle wheel. If the initial temperature of the water is 100 °F, and the temperature of the surroundings is 60 °F, determine the entropy change.

10.5. What is the maximum quantity of work that could be obtained from stack gases at 450 °F and 1 atm pressure if the lowest surroundings temperature is 80 °F? Perform calculations on a pound basis, and consider the gases to have a specific heat c_p of 0.25 Btu/lbm-°F.

10.6. The creation of a heat source for a power cycle (see Fig. 10.10) usually accomplished in the following manner: Fuel and air at atmospheric temperature

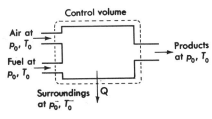

Fig. 10.10

and pressure enter a control volume and irreversible mixing takes place. A spark or a flame sets off an irreversible chemical reaction with attainment of high temperature. As heat is transferred out, the temperature of the hot gases falls back to that of the atmosphere. State and discuss the maximum work obtainable.

10.7. Two identical blocks of metal have a mass of 5 lbm and a specific heat of 0.11 Btu/lbm-°R. One is at an initial temperature of 1200 °R and the other is at an initial temperature of 600 °R. The two blocks are placed in thermal communication and allowed to come to temperature equilibrium. Determine the loss of available energy if the surroundings are at a temperature of 540 °R.

10.8. Consider the irreversible process 1–2 in Fig. 10.11, during which heat is added to a system. How much of this heat can be converted into work if the surroundings are at T_0? Hint: Let the system be returned to its initial state 1, thus completing a cycle. The maximum work output will be obtained

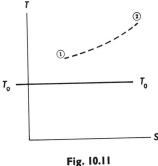

Fig. 10.11

if the heat rejected by the system while being restored to state 1 is a minimum.

10.9. From the definition of the Helmholtz function $a = u - Ts$, show that

$$p = -\left(\frac{\partial a}{\partial v}\right)_T; \qquad s = -\left(\frac{\partial a}{\partial T}\right)_v$$

and hence

$$u = a - T\left(\frac{\partial a}{\partial T}\right)_v$$

10.10. From the definition of the Gibbs function, $g = h - Ts$, show that

$$v = \left(\frac{\partial g}{\partial p}\right)_T; \qquad s = -\left(\frac{\partial g}{\partial T}\right)_p$$

and hence

$$u = g - T\left(\frac{\partial g}{\partial T}\right)_p - p\left(\frac{\partial g}{\partial p}\right)_T$$

10.11. Derive and discuss the meaning of the following expressions:

$$\int_1^2 p\,dv = a_1 - a_2$$

$$-\int_1^2 v\,dp = g_1 - g_2$$

Give the restrictions associated with each expression.

10.12. Derive the following Gibbs-Helmholtz equations for a constant-volume process and a constant-pressure process respectively:

$$\left(\frac{\partial a}{\partial T}\right)_v = \frac{a - u}{T}$$

$$\left(\frac{\partial g}{\partial T}\right)_p = \frac{g - h}{T}$$

Hint: The first result follows directly from Problem 10.9. To obtain the second result, make use of $s = -(\partial g/\partial T)_p$ and the definition for g.

10.13. Show that the specific Gibbs function for an ideal gas is

$$g = \int_{T_0}^T c_p\,dT - T\int_{T_0}^T c_p\frac{dT}{T} + RT\ln\frac{p}{p_0} - Ts_0 + RT_0 + u_0$$

10.14. The following data is abstracted from steam tables at 200 °F. If a is arbitrarily assumed to be zero for liquid water at 200 °F, what is the value of a at 200 °F and 1 psia? Hint: First calculate the internal energy u, then apply $\Delta a = \Delta u - T\Delta s$.

	p	v	h	s
liquid	11.53	0.0166	168	0.294
vapour	1.0	392.6	1150.4	2.051

10.15. For the isothermal expansion of an ideal gas, show that the increase in the specific Gibbs function is

$$g_2 - g_1 = RT \ln\frac{p_2}{p_1}$$

10.16. Show that the Gibbs-Helmholtz relation

$$g = h + T\left(\frac{\partial g}{\partial T}\right)_p$$

may be written in the following alternate forms:

$$\left[\frac{\partial(g/T)}{\partial T}\right]_p = -\frac{h}{T^2}$$

$$\left[\frac{\partial(g/T)}{\partial(1/T)}\right]_p = h$$

10.17. (a) The latent heat of evaporation for water at 300 °F and 67 psia is 910 Btu/lbm. The specific volumes for water and steam are respectively 0.0175 cu ft/lbm and 6.47 cu ft/lbm. Find Δu, Δs, Δh, and Δg, when one pound of water is converted into steam. (b) What is the specific Gibbs function for superheated steam at 500 psia, 800 °F, which has a specific enthalpy of 1412 Btu/lbm and a specific entropy of 1.657 Btu/lbm-°R?

10.18. A cylinder fitted with a piston contains one pound of air at 18 psia and 90 °F. What is the minimum shaft work required to bring the air to 80 psia and 200 °F? Consider air to be a perfect gas having constant specific heats of $c_p = 0.24$ Btu/lbm-°R and $c_v = 0.17$ Btu/lbm-°F. Hint: The minimum shaft work required is $\phi_2 - \phi_1$.

10.19. The mixing of pure materials or the separation of a mixture into components is an extremely important operation in chemical industry. Such mixing or separation can be accomplished reversibly by using semipermeable membranes. Each membrane is assumed permeable to only one material; the material flowing through at its partial pressure in the mixture. (a) Devise an apparatus to reversibly and isothermally separate air (79 per cent N_2, 21 per cent O_2) initially at 68 °F and 1 atm into its pure components, each under a total pressure of 1 atm. (b) Determine the value of ΔG and ΔS for each pound-mole of air separated. Hint: Consider an apparatus as shown in Fig. 10.12. The description and

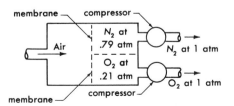

Fig. 10.12

sequence of operation is left to the reader. $-\Delta G$ is equal to the sum of the reversible isothermal compression work of each gas from its partial pressure to atmospheric pressure. Thus

$$-\Delta G = (0.79)(1544)(528) \ln \frac{0.79}{1}$$

$$+(0.21)(1544)(528) \ln \frac{0.21}{1}$$

Consider the gases to be ideal, and $\Delta H = 0$ for the isothermal separation. Thus

$$\Delta G = \Delta H - T\Delta S = -T\Delta S$$

or

$$\Delta S = -\frac{\Delta G}{T}$$

10.20. The system in Fig. 10.13 consists of a unit mass of steam within a cylinder fitted with a piston. Let the steam be initially at a state (p_1, T_1). Let the final state be (p_2, T_2). Let p_0 be the surroundings pressure (atmospheric). Consider the following sequence of processes:

1–a: isentropic expansion to state a.

a–b: isothermal-isobaric compression to state b such that $s_b = s_2$.

b–2: isentropic compression to state 2. Show that for the process 1–2, the useful work a is given by

$$\phi_1 - \phi_2$$

Hint: The first law applied to the entire sequence of processes is $q = (u_2 - u_1) + w$, where w is the sum of the useful work and the work done on surroundings is $p_0(v_2 - v_1)$. In each process, consider (1) the work done on or by surroundings, and (2) the heat transferred.

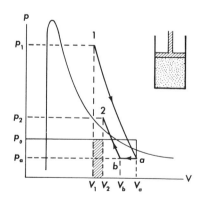

Fig. 10.13

10.21. Show that the respective specific availability functions for a non-flow and a flow system may be written as

$$\phi = h + (p_0 - p)v - T_0 s$$

and

$$b = h - T_0 s + \frac{V^2}{2g_c} + \frac{g}{g_c}z$$

10.22. The steam turbine in Fig. 10.14 receives 100,000 pounds of steam per hour. This steam has a specific enthalpy $h_1 = 1307$ Btu/lbm and a specific entropy $s_1 = 1.5894$ Btu/lbm-°R. At point 2 in the turbine, steam is bled off (for processing use) at the rate of 20,000 pounds per hour. The specific enthalpy of the second steam rate is $h_2 = 1179$ Btu/lbm, and the specific entropy is

$$s_2 = 1.6650 \text{ Btu/lbm-°R}$$

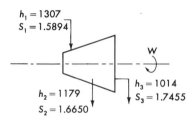

Fig. 10.14

The balance of the steam leaves the turbine at point 3, with a specific enthalpy $h_3 = 1014$ Btu/lbm, and a specific entropy $s_3 = 1.7455$ Btu/lbm °R. The surroundings are at a pressure and temperature of 14.7 psia and 77 °F, with a corresponding specific enthalpy of water $h_0 = 45$ Btu/lbm and a specific entropy of water $s_0 = 0.0876$ Btu/lbm-°R. Neglecting changes in kinetic and potential energies, determine the availability of the steam entering and leaving the turbine and the maximum work per hour. Hint: The availability of the steam entering the turbine is

$$10,000[(h_1 - h_0) - T_0(s_1 - s_0)]$$

The availability of the steam leaving the turbine is

$$20,000[(h_2 - h_0) - T_0(s_2 - s_0)] + 80,000[(h_3 - h_0) - T_0(s_3 - s_0)]$$

10.23. Water at 50°F is available in large quantities to be converted into ice at 0 °F by means of a refrigeration device. The enthalpy of the water is 18.07 Btu/lbm; that of the ice is -158.9 Btu/lbm. What is the minimum work required of the refrigeration device if the surroundings temperature is 50 °F? Consider the operation to be a steady-flow process. Assume specific heats for water and ice to be 1 Btu/lbm-°F and 0.5 Btu/lbm-°F respectively.

10.24. Make up a list of important relations in this chapter and give the restrictive conditions pertaining to each relation. Discuss the availability of heat and the availability of a system (more precisely, of a system-surroundings combination).

10.25. (a) Show that the specific irreversibility of an adiabatic steady-flow process is given by

$$i = T_0(s_2 - s_1)$$

where T_0 is the surroundings temperature. (b) Air at a temperature of 1540 °F and 90 psia flows across a restriction in a pipe and the pressure drops to 15 psia. What is the specific irreversibility referred to a surroundings temperature of 60 °F?

10.26. Air enters a compressor at 15 psia and 65 °F with a velocity of 350 fps. It leaves the compressor at 70 psia and 400 °F with a velocity of 200 fps. What is the maximum work and the irreversibility if the process is adiabatic?

10.27. A pressure vessel having a volume of 35 cu ft contains air at 150 psia and 300 °F. The air is cooled to 70 °F by heat transfer with the surroundings only. Assuming the surroundings to be at 70 °F, calculate the change in availability, the maximum work and irreversibility of the process.

CHAPTER 11

General Thermodynamic Relations

11.1 Introduction

The laws of thermodynamics, along with the methods of differential calculus, make it possible to deduce a number of very useful general relations among thermodynamic properties. These relations, to be derived in the present chapter, are valid for all systems that, in equilibrium, (a) change state only when heat and mechanical work cross their boundaries, and (b) require only two independent properties to determine their thermodynamic state. These conditions are satisfied by single-component systems (in the absence of gravitational, electric, magnetic, and surface effects). They are also satisfied by systems consisting of a mixture of substances, provided no chemical reaction is taking place.

The purpose here is to derive some of the more important property relations, chiefly those which are useful when tables of properties are to be made from experimental data. Of the eight properties which may be used to describe the thermodynamic state of a system (p, v, T, u, h, s, a, and g) only p, v, and T are directly measurable. Therefore, it is convenient to introduce other combinations of properties, relatively easy to measure, that, together with measurements of p, v, and T, make it possible to determine the remaining properties. These combinations are all defined as *the rate of change of one property with respect to another while the remaining properties are held constant.* Thus, the methods of partial differentiation play an important part in thermodynamics, as witnessed by the large number of mathematical manipulations that have been included in this text.

11.2 Maxwell's Equations

It was previously pointed out that the first and second laws of thermodynamics combine to give the fundamental relation

$$Tds = du + pdv$$

or

$$du = Tds - pdv \tag{11.1}$$

Equation (11.1) is valid for any process, reversible or irreversible, because it is concerned only with properties. It also contains only perfect differentials; therefore, a large number of thermodynamic relations may be derived from it with ease. This also applies to the following functions:

Enthalpy: $h = u + pv$

Helmholtz function: $a = u - Ts$

Gibbs function; $g = h - Ts$

whose differentials are

$$dh = du + pdv + vdp$$
$$= Tds + vdp \tag{11.2}$$
$$da = du - Tds - sdT$$
$$= -pdv - sdT \tag{11.3}$$
$$dg = dh - Tds - sdT = d(u + pv) - Tds - sdT$$
$$= du + pdv + vdp - Tds - sdT$$
$$= Tds - pdv + pdv + vdp - Tds - sdT$$
$$= vdp - sdT \tag{11.4}$$

Equations (11.1), (11.2), (11.3), and (11.4) give the differential of u, h, a, and g with respect to any two independent properties. Since du, dh, da, and dg are exact differentials, it follows that

$$\left(\frac{\partial T}{\partial v}\right)_s = -\left(\frac{\partial p}{\partial s}\right)_v \qquad (11.5)$$

$$\left(\frac{\partial T}{\partial p}\right)_s = \left(\frac{\partial v}{\partial s}\right)_p \qquad (11.6)$$

$$\left(\frac{\partial p}{\partial T}\right)_v = \left(\frac{\partial s}{\partial v}\right)_T \qquad (11.7)$$

$$\left(\frac{\partial v}{\partial T}\right)_p = -\left(\frac{\partial s}{\partial p}\right)_T \qquad (11.8)$$

Equations (11.5), (11.6), (11.7), and (11.8) are known as *Maxwell's equations* in thermodynamics; they relate the properties p, v, T, and s for any homogeneous system in a state of equilibrium.

Example 11.1. Show that for a system obeying the perfect gas relation $pv = RT$ it follows from Maxwell's equations that $(\partial u/\partial v)_T = 0$, and hence the internal energy is a function of temperature only.

Solution. From Eq. (11.1),

$$du = Tds - pdv$$

Dividing through by dv and inserting the restriction of constant temperature gives

$$\left(\frac{\partial u}{\partial v}\right)_T = T\left(\frac{\partial s}{\partial v}\right)_T - p$$

Substituting Maxwell's equation (11.7) gives

$$\left(\frac{\partial u}{\partial v}\right)_T = T\left(\frac{\partial p}{\partial T}\right)_v - p$$

But $(\partial p/\partial T)_v = R/v$ from the equation of state, so that

$$\left(\frac{\partial u}{\partial v}\right)_T = \frac{RT}{v} - p = 0$$

i.e. the internal energy for a perfect gas is independent of volume.

That the internal energy for a perfect gas is also independent of pressure may be shown by writing the chain relation

$$\left(\frac{\partial u}{\partial v}\right)_T = \left(\frac{\partial u}{\partial p}\right)_T \left(\frac{\partial p}{\partial v}\right)_T$$

or

$$0 = \left(\frac{\partial u}{\partial p}\right)_T \left(\frac{\partial p}{\partial v}\right)_T$$

Since $(\partial p/\partial v)_T = -RT/v^2$ and therefore is not zero, $(\partial u/\partial p)_T$ must be equal to zero, and the internal energy for a perfect gas is *independent* of pressure.

11.3 Quantities Derivable from p, v, T Measurements

It was previously pointed out that, of the many thermodynamic properties, only p, v, and T are directly measurable; specific heat data may be determined experimentally, although not without difficulty. From such information, it is possible to analyze and predict the behavior of many systems as they undergo various processes. It is of interest at this point to examine the information that can be deduced directly from p, v, T measurements:

Equation of State. If a series of experiments in which the volume of a substance is measured against the temperature while the pressure is maintained constant, a family of constant pressure lines on a $v-T$ diagram is obtained. This is illustrated in Fig. 11.1. An equation can usually be found to express the relationship between the three variables p, v, and T, at least over a limited range of values. Of course, no single equation is good for all phases of a substance, and sometimes more than one equation is required for a given phase; however such equations are useful. Equations relating p, v, and T are known as *equations of state.* A typical form is

$$pv = A + \frac{B}{v} + \frac{C}{v^2} + \cdots \quad (11.9)$$

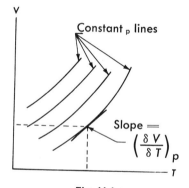

Fig. 11.1

Isobars on v — T Coordinates.

where the coefficients A, B, C, ... are functions of temperature and are different for different substances. Note that the characteristic equation for a perfect gas ($pv = RT$) is a particularly simple example of the above representation. Also note that an equation of state is by nature an empirical result, and cannot be deduced from the laws of thermodynamics, although the general form of the equation may be predicted by considerations based on kinetic theory of gases and statistical mechanics.

Coefficient of Expansion and Compressibility. The slope of a constant pressure line at a point on a $v-T$ diagram as in Fig. 11.1 is $(\partial v/\partial T)_p$. If this is divided by the volume at the point, the property called *coefficient of volume expansion* (β) is obtained:

$$\beta = \frac{1}{v}\left(\frac{\partial v}{\partial T}\right)_p \qquad (11.10)$$

Values of β can be obtained and tabulated for a range of pressures and temperatures. In tables of physical properties, β is usually given as an average over a small range of temperature, at atmospheric pressure:

$$\bar{\beta} = \frac{v_2 - v_1}{v_1(T_2 - T_1)} \qquad (11.11)$$

Similarly, if the p, v, T data is plotted as a family of constant-temperature lines on a p–v diagram, the slope of a curve at a given point is $(\partial v/\partial p)_T$. Dividing this by the volume at the point gives the property known as *isothermal compressibility* (κ) of the substance:

$$\kappa = -\frac{1}{v}\left(\frac{\partial v}{\partial p}\right)_T \qquad (11.12)$$

Tables of properties, however, usually give κ as an average over a small range of pressure at atmospheric temperature, i.e.

$$\bar{\kappa} = -\frac{v_2 - v_1}{v_1(p_2 - p_1)} \qquad (11.13)$$

The cyclic property of partial differentials:

$$\left(\frac{\partial p}{\partial T}\right)_v \left(\frac{\partial T}{\partial v}\right)_p \left(\frac{\partial v}{\partial p}\right)_T = -1$$

makes it possible to relate β and κ as follows:

$$\left(\frac{\partial p}{\partial T}\right)_v \left(\frac{1}{v\beta}\right)(-v\kappa) = -1$$

or

$$\left(\frac{\partial p}{\partial T}\right)_v = \frac{\beta}{\kappa} \qquad (11.14)$$

Both β and κ are constants for solids and liquids. For a perfect gas, $\beta = 1/T$ and $\kappa = 1/p$.

11.4 Specific Heat Relations

Because data concerning the relationship between p, v, and T is not sufficient to enable all of the other properties to be determined, other measurable quantities must be introduced. These are the specific heats c_v and c_p, and the Joule-Thomson coefficient μ. Relations for the first two quantities are developed below; the Joule-Thomson coefficient will be treated in Sec. 11.5.

During a process at constant volume, the first law states that the increase of internal energy must equal the heat transferred. Thus, if a calorimetric experiment is conducted with a known mass of substance at constant volume, the quantity of heat required to raise the temperature of a unit mass by ΔT may be measured, and the quantity $(\Delta u/\Delta T)_v$ obtained in this way is the mean specific but at constant volume over the temperature range ΔT. As the temperature range is reduced, the value approaches that of $(\partial u/\partial T)_v$, so that, in the limit, the specific heat at constant volume becomes

$$c_v = \left(\frac{\partial u}{\partial T}\right)_v \qquad (11.15)$$

Similarly, the first law states that the increase of enthalpy during a constant pressure process equals the heat supplied. If a calorimetric experiment is carried out with a substance at constant pressure, the heat required to raise the temperature of a unit mass by ΔT yields the quantity $(\Delta h/\Delta T)_p$ which is the mean specific heat at constant pressure. In the limit, for a temperature range made infinitesimally small, the specific heat at constant pressure becomes

$$c_p = \left(\frac{\partial h}{\partial T}\right)_p \qquad (11.16)$$

Although discussion of experimental methods for determining c_p and c_v is outside the scope of this text, a number of relations involving specific heats will be derived beginning with the relation between c_p, c_v, β, and κ. Recall that, in Sec. 9.6, the following Tds equations were obtained:

$$Tds = c_v dT + T\left(\frac{\partial p}{\partial T}\right)_v dv$$

$$Tds = c_p dT - T\left(\frac{\partial v}{\partial T}\right)_p dp$$

Equating these two expressions and solving for dT gives

$$dT = \frac{T(\partial p/\partial T)v}{c_p - c_v}dv + \frac{T(\partial v/\partial T)_p}{c_p - c_v}dp$$

Comparing this with

$$dT = \left(\frac{\partial T}{\partial v}\right)_p dv + \left(\frac{\partial T}{\partial p}\right)_v dp$$

it is seen that

$$\left(\frac{\partial T}{\partial v}\right)_p = \frac{T(\partial p/\partial T)_v}{c_p - c_v} \qquad (11.17)$$

$$\left(\frac{\partial T}{\partial p}\right)_v = \frac{T(\partial v/\partial T)_p}{c_p - c_v} \qquad (11.18)$$

Equations (11.17) and (11.18) yield the identical result

$$c_p - c_v = T\left(\frac{\partial v}{\partial T}\right)_p \left(\frac{\partial p}{\partial T}\right)_v \qquad (11.19)$$

But

$$(\partial p/\partial T)_v(\partial T/\partial v)_p(\partial v/\partial p)_T = -1, \text{ or } (\partial p/\partial T)_v = -(\partial v/\partial T)_p(\partial p/\partial v)_T$$

so that

$$c_p - c_v = -T\left(\frac{\partial v}{\partial T}\right)_p^2 \left(\frac{\partial p}{\partial v}\right)_T = \frac{vT\beta^2}{\kappa} \qquad (11.20)$$

Equation (11.20) is an important relation in thermodynamics. Not only does it allow c_v to be obtained from the experimental measurements of c_p, β, and κ, but it shows that c_p can never be less than c_v, because while the quantity $(\partial v/\partial T)^2_p$ is positive, the quantity $(\partial p/\partial v)_T$ is always negative (since all substances decrease in volume when the pressure is increased). Thus, $c_p - c_v$ can never be negative and c_p can never be less than c_v. The only exception is when $c_p = c_v$, such as when water has its maximum density at 4° Centigrade. Equation (11.20) also shows that as $T \to 0$, $c_p \to c_v$, which means that, at absolute zero, the two heat capacities are equal.

Returning to the two Tds equations, namely,

$$Tds = c_v dT + T\left(\frac{\partial p}{\partial T}\right)_v dv$$

$$Tds = c_p dT - T\left(\frac{\partial v}{\partial T}\right)_p dp$$

another useful relation between specific heats may be obtained by setting $ds = 0$:

$$c_v(dT)_s = -T\left(\frac{\partial p}{\partial T}\right)_v (dv)_s$$

$$c_p(dT)_s = T\left(\frac{\partial v}{\partial T}\right)_p (dp)_s$$

Dividing the latter equations by each other gives

$$\frac{c_p}{c_v} = \gamma = -\frac{(\partial v/\partial T)_p}{(\partial p/\partial T)_v}(dp/\partial v)_s$$

and using the cyclic relation to replace

$$-\frac{(\partial v/\partial T)_p}{(\partial p/\partial T)_v} \quad \text{by} \quad -(\partial v/\partial p)_T$$

this becomes

$$\frac{c_p}{c_v} = \gamma = \frac{(\partial p/\partial v)_s}{(\partial p/\partial v)_T} \tag{11.21}$$

Equations (11.20) and (11.21) are relations involving the difference in heat capacities and the ratio of heat capacities. Additional relations, involving each heat capacity, may be obtained as follows: For any reversible cycle, $dq = Tds$. At constant volume, this becomes $(dq)_v = T(ds)_v$. Division by $(dT)_v$ gives

$$\frac{(dq)_v}{(dT)_v} = T\frac{(ds)_v}{(dT)_v}$$

or

$$c_v = T\left(\frac{\partial s}{\partial T}\right)_v \tag{11.22}$$

Differentiating both sides of Eq. (11.22) while holding T constant gives

$$\left(\frac{\partial c_v}{\partial v}\right)_T = \left[\frac{\partial}{\partial v}T\left(\frac{\partial s}{\partial T}\right)_v\right]_T = T\left[\frac{\partial}{\partial v}\left(\frac{\partial s}{\partial T}\right)_v\right]_T$$

$$= T\left[\frac{\partial}{\partial T}\left(\frac{\partial s}{\partial v}\right)_T\right]_v$$

Making use of Maxwell's equation, $(\partial s/\partial v)_T = (\partial p/\partial T)_v$, this becomes

$$\left(\frac{\partial c_v}{\partial v}\right)_T = T\left[\frac{\partial}{\partial T}\left(\frac{\partial p}{\partial T}\right)_v\right]_v$$

$$= T\left(\frac{\partial^2 p}{\partial T^2}\right)_v = T\left[\frac{\partial}{\partial T}\left(\frac{\beta}{\kappa}\right)\right]_v \tag{11.23}$$

Similarly, $dq = Tds$ applied to a constant pressure process gives

$$(dq)_p = T(ds)_p$$

or, upon division by $(dT)_p$,

$$c_p = T\left(\frac{\partial s}{\partial T}\right)_p \qquad (11.24)$$

From this, differentiation at constant T gives

$$\left(\frac{\partial c_p}{\partial p}\right)_T = \left[\frac{\partial}{\partial p}T\left(\frac{\partial s}{\partial T}\right)_p\right]_T = T\left[\frac{\partial}{\partial T}\left(\frac{\partial s}{\partial T}\right)_p\right]_T = T\left[\frac{\partial}{\partial T}\left(\frac{\partial s}{\partial p}\right)_T\right]_p$$

and, upon replacement of $(\partial s/\partial p)_T$ by $-(\partial v/\partial T)_p$,

$$\left(\frac{\partial c_p}{\partial p}\right)_T = -T\left[\frac{\partial}{\partial T}\left(\frac{\partial v}{\partial T}\right)_p\right]_p$$

$$= -T\left(\frac{\partial^2 v}{\partial T^2}\right)_p = -T\left[\frac{\partial}{\partial T}(v\beta)\right]_p \qquad (11.25)$$

The specific heat relations obtained above clearly show the thermodynamic consistency that must be satisfied between thermal data and the equation of state.

Example 11.2. Over a considerable range of temperature and pressure, the coefficient of volume expansion β and the compressibility κ of a solid are constant. (a) Show that in such a case the equation of state may be written as

$$v = v_0 + v_0\beta(T - T_0) - v_0\kappa(p - p_0)$$

where v_0 is the specific volume at the temperature T_0 and the pressure p_0. (b) Show that c_v is a function of T only.

Solution. (a) Consider v a function of T and p. Then

$$dv = \left(\frac{\partial v}{\partial T}\right)_p dT + \left(\frac{\partial v}{\partial p}\right)_T dp = v\beta dT - v\kappa dp$$

or

$$v = v_0 + \int_{T_0}^T v\beta dT - \int_{p_0}^p v\kappa dp$$

where the first integral is evaluated at the pressure p and the second at the temperature T. Since β and κ for liquids and solids are often of small magnitude, the specific volume v changes only slightly, and v may be assumed constant and equal to v_0 in the above integrations. Thus, in the first approximation, the equation of state is

$$v = v_0 + v_0\beta(T - T_0) - v_0\kappa(p - p_0)$$

(b) From Eq. (11.23),

$$\left(\frac{\partial c_v}{\partial v}\right)_T = T\left(\frac{\partial^2 p}{\partial T^2}\right)_v$$

But $(\partial^2 p/\partial T^2)_v = 0$ as seen from the equation of state. Thus,

$$\left(\frac{\partial c_v}{\partial v}\right)_T = 0$$

i.e. c_v is independent of v. That c_v is also independent of p may be shown by writing

$$\left(\frac{\partial c_v}{\partial v}\right)_T = 0 = \left(\frac{\partial c_v}{\partial p}\right)_T \left(\frac{\partial p}{\partial v}\right)_T$$

As $(\partial p/\partial v)_T \neq 0$ from the equation of state, the only remaining possibility is that

$$\left(\frac{\partial c_v}{\partial p}\right)_T = 0$$

and consequently c_v is function of T only.

It is of interest to discuss briefly the specific heat data of substances. Figure 11.2 shows the variation of c_v for a diatonic gas based on kinetic

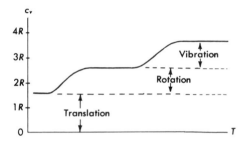

Fig. 11.2   Specific Heat, c_v for Diatomic Gas.

theory (see Chap. 14). At low temperatures, $c_v = 3/2R$; at intermediate temperatures, $c_v = 5/2R$; and at high temperatures, $c_v = 7/2R$. At low temperatures, only the energy of translation contributes to the specific heat. At intermediate temperatures, the energy of rotation (about the axis connecting the atoms) makes its contribution, and at high temperatures, the energy of vibration (along the line connecting the atoms) must also be added. These energies are all shown schematically in Fig. 11.2.

Figure 11.3(a) shows c_v vs. temperature for several solids. Notice that, as the temperature increases, c_v approaches a value of 6 Btu/mole °R for all substances. This observation, first made by Dulong and Petit, is sometimes referred to as the law of Dulong and Petit.

Debye, with the aid of statistical mechanics, developed the following relation for the specific heat at constant volume:

$$c_v = 3Rf(T/\Theta) \tag{11.26}$$

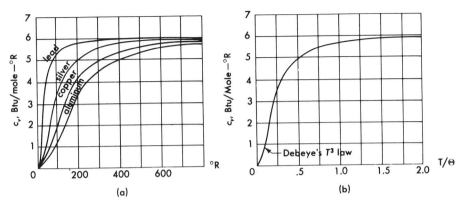

Fig. 11.3 Temperature Variation of c_v for Solids.

where R is the universal gas constant (1.986 Btu/mole-°R), Θ is a constant for each substance, known as the Debye temperature, and f is a function which is the same for all substances. The plot of Debye's equation is shown in Fig. 11.3(b). The Dulong and Petit value arises from the fact that in Debye's formula, $f(T/\Theta) \to 1$ as $T/\Theta \to \infty$. This gives $c_v = 3R$ or 5.964 Btu/mole—°R. Notice also that as $T/\Theta \to 0$, Debye's equation becomes

$$c_v = AT^3 \tag{11.27}$$

where A is a constant which is function of Θ. Equation (11.27) is known as Debye's T^3 law. For isotropic non-metals, it is quite accurate; for metals, a correction must be made.

11.5 Joule-Thomson Coefficient

Section 6.6 introduced the *Joule-Thomson effect* or *porous plug experiment*. This is a process in which a gas is allowed to seep through a porous plug from a region of higher pressure to a region of lower pressure. It was shown that the specific enthalpy of the gas was the same in both regions.

Suppose that a series of Joule-Thomson experiments are performed in the following manner: The pressure and temperature on the high-pressure side of the plug are arbitrarily chosen and maintained at p_i and T_i. The pressure p_f on the other side of the plug is set as a value less than p_i, and the temperature T_f of the gas measured. Keeping p_i and T_i the same, let p_f be changed to another value and the corresponding T_f measured. The result is a set of discrete points on a temperature-pressure diagram as shown in Fig. 11.4(a), one point being p_i, T_i, and the others being the various pairs of p_f's and T_f's (numbered 1, 2, 3, etc.). The specific enthalpy

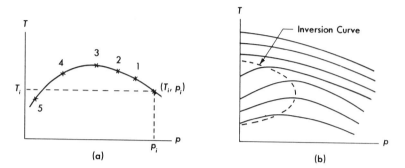

Fig. 11.4 Isenthalpic Curve and Inversion Curve for Joule-Thomson Experiment.

is the same at all the points 1, 2, 3, . . . and a curve drawn through these points thus represents a constant enthalpy curve (Note, however, that such a curve does *not* represent the throttling process undergone by the gas, since the process is not reversible and the intermediate states traversed by the gas cannot be described by means of thermodynamic coordinates. All that the porous-plug experiments provides are a few discrete equilibrium points through which a reasonably smooth *isenthalpic* curve may be drawn.) The curve shows that, if a throttling process takes place between (T_i, p_i) and p_{f_2}, there is a rise in temperature, whereas a throttling process between (T_i, p_i) and p_{f_5} yields a drop in temperature.

If a series of experiments is performed, with the initial (p_i, T_i) the same in each series, but varying (p_i, T_i) from one series to another, a number of curves (each corresponding to a different value of h) would be obtained. Such a family of curves is shown in Fig. 11.4(b), and is typical of most gases. It is seen that each curve passes through a maximum, called the *inversion point*. The locus of all the inversion points is then called the *inversion curve*.

The slope of an isenthalpic curve at any point is called the Joule-Thomson coefficient, denoted by

$$\mu = \left(\frac{\partial T}{\partial p}\right)_h \tag{11.28}$$

The region inside the inversion curve where μ is positive is the cooling region; that region outside the inversion curve where μ is negative is the heating region.

The Joule-Thomson coefficient can be computed if the equation of state is known. But first, a relation for enthalpy must be developed. For any reversible process, the first and second laws combine to give $Tds = dh - vdp$. Considering T and p as independent variables, this may be written as

$$dh = T\left[\left(\frac{\partial s}{\partial T}\right)_p dT + \left(\frac{\partial s}{\partial p}\right)_T dp\right] + vdp$$

$$= T\left(\frac{\partial s}{\partial T}\right)_p dT + T\left[\left(\frac{\partial s}{\partial p}\right)_T + v\right]dp$$

But $T(\partial s/\partial T)_p = c_p$ by Eq. (11.24), and $(\partial s/\partial p)_T = -(\partial v/\partial T)_p$ by Maxwell's equations, so that

$$dh = c_p dT + \left[v - T\left(\frac{\partial v}{\partial T}\right)_p\right]dp = c_p dT + v(1 - T\beta)dp$$

This equation may be solved for dT:

$$dT = \frac{1}{c_p}dh + \frac{1}{c_p}T\left[\left(\frac{\partial v}{\partial T}\right) - v\right]dp$$

Regarding T as a function of h and p, it is seen that

$$\frac{1}{c_p} = \left(\frac{\partial T}{\partial h}\right)_p$$

and that

$$\frac{1}{c_p}\left[T\left(\frac{\partial v}{\partial T}\right)_p - v\right] = \left(\frac{\partial T}{\partial p}\right)_h = \mu \qquad (11.29)$$

Equation (11.29) is the expression for the Joule-Thomson coefficient in terms of the tabulated properties of a substance. It can be written more compactly as

$$\mu = \left(\frac{\partial T}{\partial p}\right)_h = \frac{T^2}{c_p}\left[\frac{\partial}{\partial T}\left(\frac{v}{T}\right)\right]_p \qquad (11.30)$$

Example 11.3. Determine the Joule-Thomson coefficient for an ideal gas and a van der Waals gas respectively.

Solution. For an ideal gas: $pv = RT$; Eq. (11.30) gives

$$\mu = \frac{T^2}{c_p}\left[\frac{\partial}{\partial T}\left(\frac{v}{T}\right)\right]_p = \frac{T^2}{c_p}\left[\frac{\partial}{\partial T}\left(\frac{R}{p}\right)\right]_p = 0$$

Since the Joule-Thomson coefficient is zero, an ideal gas shows no temperature drop on passage through a porous plug.

From a van der Waals gas, $(p+a/v^2)(v-b) = RT$. It is more convenient to use Eq. (11.29) for computing the Joule-Thomson coefficient, since v/T cannot be obtained explicitly from the equation of state. Thus,

$$\mu = \frac{1}{c_p}\left[T\left(\frac{\partial v}{\partial T}\right)_p - v\right] = \frac{v}{c_p}(T\beta - 1)$$

Now β for a van der Waals gas was calculated in Sec. 9.6 to be

$$\beta = \frac{Rv^2(v-b)}{RTv^3 - 2a(v-b)^2}$$

The Joule-Thomson coefficient is then

$$\mu = \frac{v}{c_p}(T\beta - 1) = \frac{v}{c_p}\left[\frac{RTv^2(v-b)}{RTv^3 - 2a(v-b)^2} - 1\right]$$

$$= \frac{v}{c_p}\left[\frac{RTv^2(v-b) - RTv^3 + 2a(v-b)^2}{RTv^3 - 2a(v-b)^2}\right]$$

$$= \frac{v}{c_p}\frac{2a(v-b)^2 - RTbv^2}{RTv^3 - 2a(v-b)^2}$$

Example 11.4. By means of the Joule-Thomson coefficient, derive a correction term which must be applied to a constant-pressure gas thermometer using an actual gas in order to obtain values of temperature consistent with the thermodynamic temperature scale.

Solution. For a perfect gas, $\mu = 0$, so that Eq. (11.29) gives

$$T\left(\frac{\partial V}{\partial T}\right)_p - V = 0$$

or

$$\left(\frac{\partial V}{\partial T}\right)_p = \frac{V}{T}$$

and, at p = constant

$$\frac{\partial T}{v} = \frac{\partial T}{T}$$

Integration gives

$$\ln T = \ln KV$$

or

$$T = KV$$

i.e. the temperature is proportional to the reading on the constant pressure gas thermometer.

For an actual gas, $\mu \neq 0$, and Eq. (11.29) gives, at constant pressure

$$T\left(\frac{dV}{dT}\right) - V = \mu C_p$$

or

$$\frac{dT}{T} = \frac{dV}{V - \mu C_p}$$

Integration gives

$$\frac{T}{T_0} = \frac{V - \mu C_p}{V_0 - \mu C_p}$$

Thus, a correction term μC_p must be applied to V in order to obtain values of temperature which are consistent with the thermodynamic temperature scale.

11.6 Relations for Internal Energy

In order to obtain energy quantities from experimental measurements of p, v, T and the specific heats, it is first necessary to know how the energy quantities are related to these properties. In Sec. 5.13, a number of relations for the internal energy were systematically derived. Not having the benefit of the Maxwell equations and the Tds equations, the development was understandably long and roundabout. The derivation of these relations could be repeated here with considerable dispatch, but this will be left to the student. Instead, attention is focused on obtaining relations for $(\partial u/\partial v)_T$ and $(\partial u/\partial p)_T$.

The combined first and second law statement

$$ds = \frac{du}{T} + p\frac{dv}{T}$$

and the fact that s may be regarded as a function of two variables, as for example T and v, leads to the relation

$$ds = \frac{1}{T}\left(\frac{\partial u}{\partial T}\right)_v dT + \frac{1}{T}\left[\left(\frac{\partial u}{\partial v}\right)_T + p\right]dv \qquad (11.31)$$

The quantity $[(\partial u/\partial v)_T + p]$ occurs so often that it is helpful to be able to rewrite it in standard form.* Accordingly, the condition for a total differential is applied to Eq. (11.31):

$$\frac{\partial}{\partial v}\left[\frac{1}{T}\left(\frac{\partial u}{\partial T}\right)_v\right]_T = \frac{\partial}{\partial T}\left\{\frac{1}{T}\left[\left(\frac{\partial u}{\partial v}\right)_T + p\right]\right\}_v$$

This gives

$$\frac{1}{T}\frac{\partial^2 u}{\partial v\,\partial T} = \frac{1}{T}\left[\frac{\partial^2 u}{\partial T\partial v} + \left(\frac{\partial p}{\partial T}\right)_v\right] - \frac{1}{T^2}\left[\left(\frac{\partial u}{\partial v}\right)_T + p\right]$$

---

* Recall that "standard form" means in terms of p, v, T, and their partial derivatives.

and, upon simplification

$$\left(\frac{\partial u}{\partial v}\right)_T = T\left(\frac{\partial p}{\partial T}\right)_v - p = T\frac{\beta}{\kappa} - p \qquad (11.32)$$

since $(\partial p/\partial T)_v$ may be eliminated in favor of β/κ by means of the cyclic relation $(\partial p/\partial T)_v(\partial T/\partial v)_p(\partial v/\partial p)_T = -1$. Equation (11.32) is an important relation in thermodynamics. It enables internal energy change to be calculated with respect to volume change at constant temperature from the equation of state. Conversely, if u is known, a differential equation may be written whose solution is none other than the equation of state.

Similarly, if s is taken to be function of T and p, then

$$ds = \frac{1}{T}du + \frac{p}{T}dv$$

$$= \frac{1}{T}\left[\left(\frac{\partial u}{\partial T}\right)_p dT + \left(\frac{\partial u}{\partial p}\right)_T dp\right] + \frac{p}{T}\left[\left(\frac{\partial v}{\partial T}\right)_p dT + \left(\frac{\partial v}{\partial p}\right)_T dp\right]$$

$$= \frac{1}{T}\left[\left(\frac{\partial u}{\partial T}\right)_p + p\left(\frac{\partial v}{\partial T}\right)_p\right] dT + \frac{1}{T}\left[\left(\frac{\partial u}{\partial p}\right)_T + p\left(\frac{\partial v}{\partial p}\right)_T\right] dp$$

Differentiating the coefficient of dT with respect to p and that of dp with respect to T gives

$$\frac{\partial}{\partial p}\left[\left(\frac{\partial u}{\partial T}\right)_p + p\left(\frac{\partial v}{\partial T}\right)_p\right]_T = \frac{\partial}{\partial T}\left[\left(\frac{\partial u}{\partial p}\right)_T + p\left(\frac{\partial v}{\partial p}\right)_T\right]_p$$

which, upon expansion and simplification may be written as

$$\left(\frac{\partial u}{\partial p}\right)_T = -T\left(\frac{\partial v}{\partial T}\right)_p - p\left(\frac{\partial v}{\partial p}\right)_T = -vT\beta + pv\kappa \qquad (11.33)$$

Example 11.5. Determine the general form of the equation of state of a substance whose internal energy is a function of temperature only.

Solution. If u is a function of T only, then Eq. (11.32) becomes

$$\left(\frac{\partial u}{\partial v}\right)_T = 0 = T\left(\frac{\partial p}{\partial T}\right)_v - p$$

or

$$\frac{1}{p}\left(\frac{\partial p}{\partial T}\right)_v = \frac{1}{T}$$

Integration with respect to T gives

$$\ln p = \ln T + \psi(v)$$

which may be written as

$$p = T\phi(v)$$

whereupon

$$\frac{p}{T} = \phi(v) \tag{11.34}$$

Thus, the condition for u to be a function of T only is that p/T be a function of v only. If, in addition, pv is a function of T only (Boyle's Law), then

$$pv = \xi(T) \tag{11.35}$$

Eqs. (11.34) and (11.35) give

$$T\phi(v) = \frac{1}{v}\xi(T)$$

or

$$v\phi(v) = \frac{1}{T}\xi(T)$$

the only way this can be satisfied is to have

$$\phi(v) = \frac{\text{constant}}{v}$$

$$\xi(T) = (\text{constant})(T)$$

so that Eqs. (11.34) and (11.35) both give

$$pv = (\text{constant})(T) = RT \tag{11.36}$$

where R is constant which varies from gas to gas.

11.7   Relations for Enthalpy and Entropy

While it is convenient to deal with the internal energy in processes taking place at constant volume, the same statement does not hold true for processes taking place at constant pressure. Instead, it is preferable to work with h, the enthalpy. This is particularly true in chemistry problems, for the heat taken in during a reaction at constant pressure is $h_2 - h_1$, where h_1 and h_2 are the original and final values of the enthalpy. Since dh is an exact differential, it is to be expected that some interesting and useful relationship exists between h and other thermodynamic quantities.

From the definition of enthalpy: $h = u + pv$, differentiation gives $dh = du + pdv + vdp$. Replacing $du + pdv$ by Tds, this becomes

$$dh = Tds + vdp$$

Considering T and p as independent variables, this can be written as

$$dh = T\left(\frac{\partial s}{\partial T}\right)_p dT + T\left[\left(\frac{\partial s}{\partial p}\right)_T + v\right]dp$$

But $T(\partial s/\partial T)_p = c_p$ by Eq. (11.24), and $(\partial s/\partial p)_T = -(\partial v/\partial T)_p$ by Maxwell's equations, so that

$$dh = c_p dT + \left[v - T\left(\frac{\partial v}{\partial T}\right)_p\right]dp = c_p dT + (v - T\beta)dp \qquad (11.37)$$

Equation (11.37) gives the partial derivatives for the enthalpy as

$$\left(\frac{\partial h}{\partial T}\right)_p = c_p \qquad (11.38)$$

$$\left(\frac{\partial h}{\partial p}\right)_T = v - T\beta \qquad (11.39)$$

As for the entropy, similar treatment yields the following results:

$$\left(\frac{\partial s}{\partial T}\right)_p = \frac{c_p}{T} \qquad (11.40)$$

$$\left(\frac{\partial s}{\partial p}\right)_T = -\frac{v\beta}{T} \qquad (11.41)$$

These relations have already been derived in Sec. 9.6. They can, however, be derived in much simpler fashion by using Maxwell's equations (see Prob. 11.1).

Example 11.6. Calculate the enthalpy for an ideal gas and a van der Waals gas respectively.

Solution. For an ideal gas, $pv = RT$, $\beta = R/p$. Equation (11.37) gives

$$dh = c_p dT + \left[v - \frac{RT}{p}\right]dp = c_p dT$$

or

$$h = h_0 + \int_{T_0}^{T} c_p dT$$

This is function of T only, because, for thermodynamic consistency, c_p must obey Eq. (11.25), which is

$$\left(\frac{\partial c_p}{\partial p}\right)_T = -T\left(\frac{\partial^2 v}{\partial T^2}\right)_p$$

The right-hand side of this equation is zero by virtue of the equation of state. Therefore, $(\partial c_p/\partial p)_T = 0$, which means that c_p is independent of p.
Similarly, by writing

$$\left(\frac{\partial c_p}{\partial p}\right)_T = \left(\frac{\partial c_p}{\partial v}\right)_T\left(\frac{\partial v}{\partial p}\right)_T = 0$$

it is seen that $(\partial c_p/\partial v)_T = 0$, because $(\partial v/\partial p)_T = 0$. Thus, for a perfect gas, c_p is function of T only.

For a van der Waals gas having the equation of state

$$\left(p+\frac{a}{v^2}\right)(v-b) = RT$$

it is recalled that β, as previously calculated, is

$$\beta = \frac{Rv^2(v-b)}{RTv^3-2a(v-b)^2}$$

Equation (11.37) then gives

$$dh = c_p dT + [v - T\beta]dp$$

$$= c_p dT + \left[v - \frac{RTv^2(v-b)}{RTv^3-2a(v-b)^2}\right]dp$$

This result, however, is not easy to handle; it is easier to backtrack and obtain the enthalpy in some other way. From the definition of enthalpy, $h = u + pv$, it is seen that, if u is known, the enthalpy can be readily obtained by simply adding the product pv to u. Now, in Ex. 5.10, du for a van der Waals' gas was calculated to be

$$du = c_v dT + \frac{a}{v^2}dv$$

This integrates to

$$u = u_0 + \int_{T_0}^{T} c_v dT - \left(\frac{a}{v} - \frac{a}{v_0}\right)$$

The enthalpy is then obtained by adding pv to the internal energy:

$$h = u_0 + \int_{T_0}^{T} c_v dT - \left(\frac{a}{v} - \frac{a}{v_0}\right) + pv \tag{11.42}$$

To further illustrate the calculation of thermodynamic properties and to get experience in working with a medium other than the perfect gas, let a van der Waals gas be considered, and a number of relations be obtained. For instance, Eq. (11.32):

$$\left(\frac{\partial u}{\partial v}\right)_T = T\left(\frac{\partial p}{\partial T}\right)_v - p$$

when applied to the van der Waals equation of state $(p + a/v^2)(v-b) = RT$,

gives

$$\left(\frac{\partial u}{\partial v}\right)_T = \frac{a}{v^2}$$

Integration of this equation gives

$$u = -\frac{a}{v} + f(T) \tag{11.43}$$

Now, if it is recalled that, by definition, $(\partial u/\partial T)_v = c_v$, it is seen that

$$\left(\frac{\partial u}{\partial T}\right)_v = c_v = f'(T)$$

and furthermore, if c_v is considered constant, then Eq. (11.43) yields

$$u = -\frac{a}{v} + c_v T + \text{constant} \tag{11.44}$$

Equation (11.44) is interesting: it shows that as $v \to \infty$, the internal energy approaches that of an ideal gas. This is in line with the fact that, at low pressures, all gases tend to behave ideally.

To obtain the entropy of a van der Waals gas, start with the total differential

$$ds = \left(\frac{\partial s}{\partial T}\right)_v + \left(\frac{\partial s}{\partial v}\right)_T dv$$

and make use of the fact that $(\partial s/\partial T)_v = c_v/T$ and Maxwell's equation

$$\left(\frac{\partial s}{\partial v}\right)_T = \left(\frac{\partial p}{\partial T}\right)_v$$

in conjunction with the equation of state to obtain

$$ds = \frac{c_v}{T} dT + \frac{R}{v-b} dv$$

Assuming c_v to be constant, this integrates into

$$s = c_v \ln T + R \ln(v-b) + \text{constant} \tag{11.45}$$

Equation (11.45) should be compared to the corresponding equation for a perfect gas. Once again, it will be noticed that as $v \to \infty$, the entropy approaches that of the perfect gas, since b becomes negligible compared with v under these circumstances.

The preceding relations obtained from a van Waals gas are fairly simple in form because T and v are chosen as independent variables. If T and p are chosen as independent, the treatment becomes much less tractable, and approximations must be made to avoid unduly complicated expressions. It is not unusual, therefore, to write van der Waals' equation in the approximate form of

$$pv = RT + \left(b - \frac{a}{RT}\right)p \tag{11.46}$$

Equation (11.46) is valid for low pressures, and has the merit that it can be solved for v and substituted into Eq. (11.39) to give

$$\left(\frac{\partial h}{\partial p}\right)_T = b - \frac{2a}{RT} \tag{11.47}$$

This is integrated to give

$$h = \left(b - \frac{2a}{RT}\right)p + g(T) \tag{11.48}$$

where $g(T)$ is a function of T. The specific heat at constant pressure is then given by

$$c_p = \left(\frac{\partial h}{\partial T}\right)_p = \frac{2ap}{RT^2} + g'(T) \tag{11.49}$$

11.8 Characteristic Functions

In the evaluation of the entropy of a pure substance from $p\text{-}v\text{-}T$ and specific heat data, the entropy may be considered as a function of any two of the properties: p and v, p and T, and v and T. The partial derivatives of s which are involved are therefore $(\partial s/\partial p)_v$, $(\partial s/\partial v)_p$, $(\partial s/\partial p)_T$, $(\partial s/\partial T)_p$, $(\partial s/\partial v)_T$, $(\partial s/\partial T)_v$. Each of the derivatives can be expressed in terms of p, v, T, and the specific heats by means of the relations developed in this chapter. The results, as can be verified, are

$$\left(\frac{\partial s}{\partial p}\right)_v = \frac{c_v}{T}\left(\frac{\partial T}{\partial p}\right)_v \qquad\qquad \left(\frac{\partial s}{\partial T}\right)_p = \frac{c_p}{T}$$

$$\left(\frac{\partial s}{\partial v}\right)_p = \frac{c_p}{T}\left(\frac{\partial T}{\partial v}\right)_p \qquad\qquad \left(\frac{\partial s}{\partial v}\right)_T = \left(\frac{\partial p}{\partial T}\right)_v$$

$$\left(\frac{\partial s}{\partial p}\right)_T = -\left(\frac{\partial v}{\partial T}\right)_p \qquad\qquad \left(\frac{\partial s}{\partial T}\right)_v = \frac{c_v}{T}$$

It is noticed, however, that only the derivatives of the entropy have been expressed in terms of $p\text{-}v\text{-}T$ and specific heat data. Entropy values are obtained by integration, so that "constants of integrations," which cannot be evaluated from $p\text{-}v\text{-}T$ data alone, are introduced. The same difficulty is encountered in trying to evaluate u, h, a, or g from $p\text{-}v\text{-}T$ data. An equation for a substance such as

$$\phi(p, v, T) = 0$$

is therefore *not* a characteristic function. On the other hand, if a relation such as

$$\psi(u, v, s) = 0$$

is known, p, T, h, a, and g can be completely determined from $u\text{-}v\text{-}s$ data alone. This is easily seen from Eq. (11.1), $du = Tds - pdv$, which gives

$$T = \left(\frac{\partial u}{\partial s}\right)_v ; \qquad p = -\left(\frac{\partial u}{\partial v}\right)_s \tag{11.50}$$

The enthalpy $(h = u + pv)$, Helmholtz function $(a = u - Ts)$, and Gibbs function $(g = h - Ts)$ are therefore

$$h = u - v\left(\frac{\partial u}{\partial v}\right)_s \tag{11.51}$$

$$a = u - s \left(\frac{\partial u}{\partial s}\right)_v \tag{11.52}$$

$$g = u - v \left(\frac{du}{\partial v}\right)_s - s \left(\frac{\partial u}{\partial s}\right)_v \tag{11.53}$$

Equations (11.50) through (11.53) show that p, T, h, a and g are completely determined once u–v–s data is known. Thus, the relation $\psi(u, v, s) = 0$ is said to be a *characteristic function*. In other words, a characteristic function is one from which all properties of a substance can be obtained by differentiation alone, so that no arbitrary functions or constants requiring additional data for their evaluation is needed. Other characteristic functions are obtained from h–p–s, a–v–T, and g–p–T data. Unfortunately, none of these groups represent all three properties that are directly or easily measurable.

PROBLEMS

11.1. Among the eight properties p, v, T, u, s, h, a, g, select possible pairs of variables such as p and v, p and T, etc. and in each case consider the remaining properties as functions of the chosen pair of variables. Develop and briefly discuss the various relations between partial derivatives thus obtained. What comment should be made about the choice of the pairs T and u, T and h, and u and h?

11.2. For a pure substance, the entropy is a function of any two properties such as p and v, p and T, etc. By means of Maxwell's relations, derive the following Tds equations:

$$Tds = c_v dT + T\frac{\beta}{\kappa}dv$$

$$Tds = c_p dT - v\beta dp$$

$$Tds = \frac{\kappa c_v}{\beta}dp + \frac{c_p}{v\beta}dv$$

Compare the derivation with that given in Sec. 9.6 without the use of Maxwell's equations. Which is easier?

11.3. Derive the following partial derivatives of the internal energy:

$$\left(\frac{\partial u}{\partial T}\right)_v = c_p - \frac{vT}{\kappa}\beta; \qquad \left(\frac{\partial u}{\partial T}\right)_p = c_p - pv\beta$$

$$\left(\frac{\partial u}{\partial p}\right)_v = \frac{c_p}{\beta}\kappa - vT\beta; \qquad \left(\frac{\partial u}{\partial p}\right)_T = pv\kappa - vT\beta$$

$$\left(\frac{\partial u}{\partial v}\right) = \frac{\beta}{\kappa} - p; \qquad \left(\frac{\partial u}{\partial v}\right)_p = \frac{c_p}{v\beta} - p$$

11.4. Derive the following relations involving the enthalpy:

$$\left(\frac{\partial h}{\partial s}\right)_p = T; \qquad \left(\frac{\partial h}{\partial p}\right)_s = v$$

$$\left(\frac{\partial h}{\partial p}\right)_T = -T\left(\frac{\partial v}{\partial T}\right)_p + v$$

$$\left(\frac{\partial h}{\partial v}\right)_T = T\left(\frac{\partial p}{\partial T}\right)_v + v\left(\frac{dp}{dv}\right)_T$$

$$\left(\frac{\partial h}{\partial s}\right)_v = T - v\left(\frac{\partial T}{\partial v}\right)_s$$

$$\left(\frac{\partial h}{\partial v}\right)_s = v\left(\frac{\partial p}{\partial v}\right)_s; \qquad \left(\frac{\partial h}{\partial T}\right)_s = v\left(\frac{\partial p}{\partial T}\right)_s$$

$$\left(\frac{\partial h}{\partial s}\right)_T = T - v\left(\frac{\partial T}{\partial v}\right)_p$$

11.5. Derive the following relations for the Helmholtz function and the Gibbs function:

$$\left(\frac{\partial a}{\partial v}\right)_T = -p; \qquad \left(\frac{\partial a}{\partial T}\right)_v = -s$$

$$u = a - T\left(\frac{\partial a}{\partial T}\right)_v; \qquad c_v = -T\left(\frac{\partial^2 a}{\partial T^2}\right)_v$$

$$\left(\frac{\partial g}{\partial T}\right)_p = -s; \qquad \left(\frac{\partial g}{\partial p}\right)_T = v$$

$$h = g - T\left(\frac{\partial g}{\partial T}\right)_p; \qquad c_p = -T\left(\frac{\partial^2 g}{\partial T^2}\right)_p$$

11.6. Show that for a van der Waals gas,

$$du = c_v dT + \frac{a}{v^2}\, dv$$

$$ds = \frac{c_v}{T}\, dT + \frac{R\, dv}{v - b}$$

and compare these with the corresponding relations for an ideal gas.

11.7. Develop an expression for the enthalpy change of a gas which follows the equation of state $p(v - b) = RT$.

11.8. Determine the isothermal compressibility of a perfect gas, a van der Waals gas, and a Clausius gas respectively.

11.9. The isothermal compressibility and the adiabatic compressibility are defined respectively as

$$\kappa_T = -\frac{1}{v}\left(\frac{\partial v}{\partial p}\right)_T; \qquad \kappa_s = -\frac{1}{v}\left(\frac{\partial v}{\partial p}\right)_s$$

(a) Show that the isothermal compressibility is always greater than or equal to the adiabatic compressibility.

(b) Show that if $\gamma = c_p/c_v$, then

$$\gamma = \frac{\kappa_T}{\kappa_s}$$

11.10. Derive the following relations for the specific heats:

$$c_p - c_v = T\left(\frac{\partial p}{\partial T}\right)_v\left(\frac{\partial v}{\partial T}\right)_p = -T\left(\frac{\partial p}{\partial v}\right)_T\left(\frac{\partial v}{\partial T}\right)_p^2$$

$$\frac{c_p}{c_v} = \gamma = \frac{(\partial p/\partial v)_s}{(\partial p/\partial v)_T}$$

$$\left(\frac{\partial c_v}{\partial v}\right)_T = T\left(\frac{\partial^2 p}{\partial T^2}\right)_v; \qquad \left(\frac{\partial c_p}{\partial p}\right)_T = -T\left(\frac{\partial^2 v}{\partial T^2}\right)_p$$

11.11. (a) Show that $(\partial c_v/\partial v)_T = 0$ for a van der Waals gas.

(b) Calculate the entropy change $s_2 - s_1$ for a van der Waals gas undergoing a transformation from v_1, T_1, to v_2, T_2, assuming the specific heat at constant volume to be

$$c_v = a + bT + cT^2$$

where a, b and c are constants.

11.12. Show that for any substance, $c_p - c_v$ can never be negative, and therefore c_p can never be less than c_v.

11.13. From the definition of the Joule-Thomson coefficient, $\mu = (\partial T/\partial p)_h$, calculate μ for a gas obeying the equation of state

$$p(v - b) = RT$$

where R and b are constants.

11.14. Show that $\mu = -(\partial h/\partial p)_T/(\partial h/\partial T)_p$ and consequently,

$$\left(\frac{\partial h}{\partial p}\right)_T = -\mu c_p$$

Hint: Make use of the cyclic relation.

11.15. Show that the Joule-Thomson coefficient of a van der Waals gas is

$$\mu = \frac{v}{c_p}\left[\frac{2a(v-b)^2 - RTbv^2}{RTv^3 - 2a(v-b)^2}\right]$$

and determine the equation of the inversion curve.

Hint: Set $\mu = 0$ and obtain $T_i = [2a(v-b)^2]/(Rv^2b)$. Eliminate v between this equation and the equation of state to get the equation connecting T_i and p_i.

11.16. A certain liquid at a temperature of 495 °R has a specific volume of 0.016 cu ft/lbm, a specific heat at constant pressure of 1 Btu/lbm-°R, and a coefficient of volume expansion $\beta = -2.7 \times 10^{-5}/°R$. Determine the value of the Joule-Thomson coefficient.

11.17. Water, at a temperature of 50 °F, has a coefficient β of approximately $5 \times 10^{-6}/°F$. What is the final temperature if water in a hydraulic press is compressed adiabatically and reversibly from 1 atm to 900 atm?

11.18. Show that for a liquid or solid under hydrostatic pressure, the volume change $v - v_0$ corresponding to a temperature change $T - T_0$ and a pressure change $p - p_0$ is given by

$$v - v_0 = v_0\beta(T - T_0) + v_0\kappa(p - p_0)$$

11.19. Show that, for a solid or liquid, the heat absorbed, the change in internal energy, the change in entropy, and the work done in an isothermal process are, respectively

$$q = v_0 T \beta (p - p_0)$$

$$u - u_0 = -v_0 T \beta (p - p_0) + \frac{v_0}{2} \kappa (p^2 - p_0^2)$$

$$s - s_0 = -v_0 \beta (p - p_0)$$

$$w = -\frac{v_0}{2} \kappa (p^2 - p_0^2)$$

11.20. (a) Show that if $\tau = 1/T$,

$$\left(\frac{\partial h}{\partial p} \right)_T = \left(\frac{\partial (v\tau)}{\partial \tau} \right)_p$$

(b) If the specific heat at constant pressure is known at all temperatures for the pressure p_0, show that the enthalpy at pressure p and temperature T is

$$h = \int_{T_0}^{T} c_p \, dT + \int_{p_0}^{p} \left[\frac{\partial (v\tau)}{\partial \tau} \right]_p dp + h_0$$

where h_0 is the enthalpy at pressure p_0 and temperature T_0.

11.21. From experimental data on steam, a family of specific volume vs. temperature curves for various pressure values ranging from 10 psia to 100 psia were plotted. From these curves, the following slopes for a temperature of 600 °F at various pressures were obtained:

Pressure (psia)	Value of $\left(\dfrac{\partial v}{\partial T} \right)_p$ at 600 °F; (ft^3/lbm °R)
10	0.05990
20	0.03013
40	0.01523
60	0.01028
80	0.00781
100	0.00633

Using the above data, calculate the entropy change for one pound of steam in an isothermal process at 600 °F from 10 psia to 100 psia. Hint: Make use of the Tds equation in terms of p and T as independent variables.

11.22. The pressure on a block of copper is increased at a constant temperature of 60 °F from 1 atm to 100 atm. If $\beta = 2.8 \times 10^{-5}$ increase in volume per degree Rankine, $\kappa = 5.9 \times 10^{-8}$ contraction in volume per psi, and the specific volume at 60 °F and 1 atm is 1.82×10^{-3} cu ft, what is the heat transferred and the work done per unit mass?

11.23. Give the restrictions, if any, under which each of the following relations is valid:

$$h_2 - h_1 = c_p(T_2 - T_1) \qquad\qquad c_p - c_v = \frac{v\,T\beta^2}{\kappa_T}$$

$$du = c_v\,dT \qquad\qquad \gamma = \frac{\kappa_T}{\kappa_s}$$

$$c_p - c_v = R \qquad\qquad pv^\gamma = \text{constant}$$

$$Tds = dh - v\,dp \qquad\qquad du = Tds - p\,dv$$

$$w = \int p\,dv \qquad\qquad \left(\frac{\partial h}{\partial s}\right)_p = T$$

$$a = u + T\left(\frac{\partial a}{\partial T}\right)_v \qquad\qquad da = -p\,dv - s\,dT$$

$$w = \int v\,dp + \Delta(KE) + \Delta(PE) \qquad\qquad dg = v\,dp - s\,dT$$

11.24. As part of outside reading, consider the following methods for the evaluation of partial derivatives of thermodynamic functions: (a) Bridgman's tables, (b) Shaw's Jacobian method, (c) Tobolsky's method and (d) McKay's method. Select a particular method, and read the paper pertaining to it. Prepare a digest of the paper, along with some example calculation. Discuss the applicability of the method. The following references are given: (a) Bridgman, P. W., *Phys. Rev.*, 2nd series, 3, 273 (1914), also Harvard University Press, 1925, (b) Shaw, A. N., *Phil. Trans. Roy. Soc.* (London), A234, 299 (1935), (c) Tobolsky, A. V., *J. Chem. Phys.*, 10, 644 (1942), (d) McKay, H. A. C., *J. Chem. Phys.*, 3, 715 (1935).

PART II

STATISTICAL MECHANICS AND KINETIC THEORY

CHAPTER 12

Entropy and Probability; Introduction to Statistical Mechanics; Third Law of Thermodynamics

12.1 Introduction

So far, the study of thermodynamics has been based entirely upon large-scale properties of systems, such as experimental data on compressibilities, coefficients of expansion, specific heats, and upon generalizations known as the first and second laws. Essentially, this is the classical and historical treatment of the subject.

Having achieved this much understanding, the reader is now in a position to realize that a more fundamental and satisfying view of thermodynamics can be obtained from a treatment based on the statistical study of the individual particles (molecules, atoms, etc.) which make up a system. The

285

development of this approach, known as *statistical thermodynamics* is carried out in this and the succeeding chapters.

12.2 Microstate, Macrostate,* and Probability

In Chap. 9, the concept of entropy was developed as a logical outgrowth of the postulate of the second law. This existence of the entropy function was demonstrated without recourse to any molecular model; thus, from the point of view of classical or phenomenological thermodynamics, entropy is entirely meaningful even with no knowledge of the particle structure of systems. Nevertheless, the molecular picture contributes immeasurably to the understanding of the entropy function by attaching to it a probability concept. It will shortly be shown that the entropy of a system in a given state is a function of the probability of occurrence of the particular state.

To establish a working knowledge of probability, some terminology is first defined by means of a few examples: Consider an ordinary coin being tossed into the air. There are two possible ways the coin may land: heads up or tails up. Intuitively, it can be said that the probability of heads or tails is 1/2. More precisely, if the coin is tossed a *large* number of times, the ratio of heads to the number of tosses will become 1/2. Thus, the *probability* of an event may be defined as *the ratio of the number of ways the event can occur to the total number of ways all possible events can occur.* A probability of unity means certainty of occurrence, while a probability

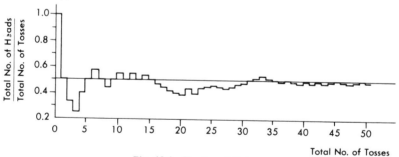

Fig. 12.1 Tossing of Coins.

---

* A macrostate of a system is a state which is observed by the experimenter. Its description need not be given to the ultimate limit of detail, but only to the degree of accuracy of laboratory equipment. A microstate of a system specifies the state of the system to the ultimate limit of detail. (A complete specification of the co-ordinates and momenta of all the molecules comprising the system would define a microstate of the system.) The best way for the reader to grasp the notion of microstate and macrostate is to work out fully the illustrations given in this section and at the beginning of the next chapter (example 13.1).

of zero corresponds to non-occurrence. Note that the ratio of heads to the total number of tosses is 1/2 only after a large number of tosses. This is shown in Fig. 12.1. The value of the ratio of heads to the total number of tosses approaches 1/2 as the number of tosses is increased, even though the difference between the number of heads actually obtained and one-half the number of tosses can become large as the number of tosses becomes large. For example, after 100 tosses, there may occur 55 heads and 45 tails, giving a difference of 5 between the number of heads obtained and one-half of the total number of tosses. After 1000 tosses, there may occur 510 heads and 490 tails, giving a difference of 10 betwen the number of heads obtained and one-half the total number of tosses.

Consider next a box which is partitioned off into two equal compartments as shown in Fig. 12.2. Let there be a hole in the partition, and let a

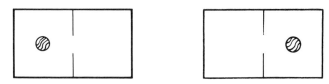

Fig. 12.2 System with Two Possible Arrangements.

small ball be placed in the box. If the box is shaken (assuming the ball is small enough to pass through the hole) there would be equal probability of finding the ball in one compartment or the other. There are two possible arrangements, as shown schematically in Fig. 12.3: the ball (labeled *a*) is either in the left compartment or the right compartment. There is only

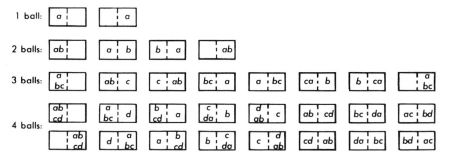

Fig. 12.3 Microstates of a System.

one way the ball can be in the right compartment and only one way the ball can be in the left compartment. The probability that the ball will be in the right (or left) compartment is 1/2. The total probability, of course, is unity, since the ball must be found in one compartment or the other.

Now, let there be two balls (labeled a and b) in the box. Let the box be shaken and the position of each ball examined. Referring to Fig. 12.3, there are four possible arrangements or microstates ($2^2 = 4$): both a and b can be in the left compartment, a can be in the left compartment and b in the right compartment, b can be in the left compartment and a in the right compartment, both a and b can be in the right compartment. However, if both balls are identical, and cannot be told apart, two of the microstates $\boxed{a \mid b}$ and $\boxed{b \mid a}$ become identical and form one macrostate, and the situation where there is one ball in each compartment has a probability of $2 \times 1/4 = 2/4$ (since there are now 2 ways of realizing this), whereas the situation where both balls are in the right or left compartment is, respectively, 1/4.

In the case of three balls, there are eight possible microstates ($2^3 = 8$), defined by the location of each ball, but if the balls are identical, to anyone viewing the situation macroscopically, i.e., not identifying the balls, there are only 4 macrostates, and the probabilities corresponding to these are (as seen in Fig. 12.3) 1/8, 3/8, 3/8, and 1/8 respectively.

For the case of 4 balls, the number of possible microstates becomes $2^4 = 16$, but if the balls are indistinguishable from each other, there will be 5 macrostates, with respective probabilities of 1/16, 4/16, 6/16, 4/16, and 1/16. Every time a ball is added, the number of ways of locating the balls is doubled. In the general case of N balls, the number of microstates is 2^N.

Several conclusions derive from the foregoing study: (1) As the number of balls increases, the most probable macrostates are those with an equal number of balls in each compartment. (2) There are two least probable macrostates: they correspond to the situation where all the balls are in one compartment or the other. The probability of this happening is $1/2^N$. That it is indeed small may be seen from the fact that, with 10 balls, there is only one chance in 1024 of finding all 10 balls in one compartment or the other. With 20 balls, there is only one chance in a million, with 40 balls, one chance in 10^{12} and with a very large number of balls, the probability becomes so small that the occurrence can be considered an impossibility.

12.3   Statistical Interpretation of Entropy

The situation described in the preceding section is similar to the case of the molecules of a perfect gas in a container (divided into two compartments), except that the molecules mix through their thermal agitation;

the balls mix only when the container is shaken. The molecules move randomly, and are all identical. Suppose that, at the start, one compartment is evacuated, and the other contains all the molecules (N in number). Let the arrangement wherein all molecules are in one compartment or the other be defined as *order*, and the arrangements wherein the molecules are in various combinations in both compartments be defined as *disorder*. Then, as time goes by, there will be a tendency for the molecules to arrange themselves in a state of maximum disorder. As N (the number of molecules) increases, the probability of disorderly macrostates increases, and that of orderly macrostates decreases. The very high probability of a state of disorder is apparent when it is realized that, in a mole of gas, there are $N = 6.02 \times 10^{23}$ molecules.

The existence of a relation between probability and entropy is suggested by the fact that, from the thermodynamic viewpoint, the entropy of an isolated system always tends to a maximum value (see Sec. 9.7), just as, from the statistical viewpoint, the equilibrium state of a system is that macrostate of maximum probability. This leads to the assumption, subject to later verification by experiment, that there is a functional relationship

$$s = f(W) \qquad (12.1)$$

between the entropy, S, of a system, and the thermodynamic probability, W, of its macrostate.* The function itself, once its existence has been postulated, is readily determined from the extensive property of entropy (i.e., if two identical systems are combined into a single system, the entropy of the combination is the sum of the entropies of the two components), and the multiplicative property of probability (i.e., the probability of realizing a combination of systems is equal to the product of the probabilities of realizing the separate systems). In other words, the function f in Eq. (12.1) must be such that

$$s = f(W) = f(W_1) + f(W_2) = f(W_1 W_2) \qquad (12.2)$$

The only way to obtain this agreement is to choose a logarithmic function and to set the entropy to be proportional to the logarithm of the thermodynamic probability:

$$s = k \ln W \qquad (12.3)$$

where k, the constant, is to be obtained by comparison with experiment (it will turn out to be the gas constant per molecule, known as Boltzmann's constant). Equation (12.3) is the famous postulate of statistical thermo-

---

* The *thermodynamic probability*, W, of a macrostate, is the number of microstates belonging to it. A thermodynamic probability is never less than unity, whereas an ordinary probability is never greater than unity.

dynamics; it gives values for entropies that are consistent with those obtained from thermal measurements.

From the above developments, it can be seen that the principle of entropy increase (and consequently the second law of thermodynamics) is essentially a *statistical* law. Faced with a choice of "orderly" or "disorderly" states, a system always behaves as if the most disorderly state were the only possible one that can be attained in the end. This is because the thermodynamic probability of the system in an orderly state is very small compared to the thermodynamic probability of the system in a disorderly state. Only orderly states, however, have potential for doing useful work, and it is for this reason that the tendency of a system toward a state of maximum disorder is often called *the principle of degradation of energy.*

Example 12.1. From statistical considerations, show that the entropy change attending the free expansion of one mole of ideal gas from an initial volume V_1 to a final volume V_2 is given by

$$S_2 - S_1 = \bar{R} \ln \frac{V_2}{V_1}$$

where $\bar{R}$ is the gas constant per mole.

Solution. Let N be the number of molecules in a mole of gas (Avogadro's number: 6.02×10^{23} molecules/mole). When the gas is expanded to V_2, it becomes evenly distributed in that space, and the probability of finding all N molecules in V_2 is unity (since any molecules must be somewhere within V_2). The probability of finding all N molecules within V_1, however, is $(V_1/V_2)^N$, so that the ratio of the probability of finding all the molecules within the total enclosure to the probability of finding all the molecules within V_1 is

$$\frac{1^N}{(V_1/V_2)^N} = \left(\frac{V_2}{V_1}\right)^N$$

In other words, the thermodynamic probabilities W_1 and W_2 are related by

$$W_2 = W_1 \left(\frac{V_2}{V_1}\right)^N$$

Applying Eq. (12.3), the entropy change is thus

$$S_2 - S_1 = k \ln W_2 - k \ln W_1 = k \ln \frac{W_2}{W_1} = k \ln\left(\frac{V_2}{V_1}\right)^N = Nk \ln \frac{V_2}{V_1}$$

Now, if the constant k is taken to be the gas constant per molecule, this becomes

$$S_2 - S_1 = \bar{R} \ln \frac{V_2}{V_1}$$

where $\bar{R}$ is the gas constant per mole. Equation (12.4) checks with the result previously obtained in Ex. 9.7. This is precisely one of the reasons for choosing k as the gas constant/molecule (Boltzmann's constant).

For the special case where the final volume is twice the initial volume, the entropy change becomes

$$S_2 - S_1 = Nk \ln 2 = \bar{R} \ln 2$$

Example 12.2. A certain mass m is dropped from a height z onto a surface. Considering the process to be adiabatic and the mass to be non-elastic, determine the probability of the mass jumping back to its initial height.

Solution. The decrease in potential energy is converted to enthalpy:

$$\frac{mgz}{g_c J} = m c_p \Delta T$$

or

$$\Delta T = \frac{gz}{g_c J c_p} \tag{12.4}$$

The entropy change, as calculated from the Tds equation, Eq. (9.50), with $dp = 0$ (the dropping of the mass is under a constant pressure environment), is

$$\Delta S = m c_p \ln \frac{T_2}{T_1} = m c_p \ln \left(1 + \frac{\Delta T}{T_1}\right) \tag{12.5}$$

since $T_2 = T_1 + \Delta T$. The entropy change, however, can also be calculated by means of Eq. (12.3):

$$\Delta S = k \ln \frac{W_2}{W_1} \tag{12.6}$$

where W_1 denotes the probability at the beginning of the process (the mass is up in the air) and W_2 the probability at the end of the process (the mass is on the ground).

So far as the first law is concerned, there is no prohibition on the mass jumping back into the air, provided it conserves energy by cooling off in the process. It is the second law which says that this is not likely to occur. By setting the two expressions for the entropy change, namely Eqs. (12.5) and (12.6), equal to each other, the probability that the mass will jump back may be calculated:

$$m c_p \ln \left(1 + \frac{\Delta T}{T_1}\right) = k \ln \frac{W_2}{W_1}$$

or

$$\ln \frac{W_2}{W_1} = \frac{m c_p}{k} \ln \left(1 + \frac{\Delta T}{T_1}\right)$$

Replacing ΔT by its expression as given by Eq. (12.4), this becomes

$$\ln \frac{W_2}{W_1} = \frac{m c_p}{k} \ln \left(1 + \frac{z}{J c_p T_1}\right)$$

But $k = \bar{R}/N$ where N = Avogadro's number. Thus,

$$\ln \frac{W_2}{W_1} = \frac{N m c_p}{\bar{R}} \ln \left(1 + \frac{gz}{g_c J c_p T_1}\right)$$

or

$$\frac{W_2}{W_1} = \left(1 + \frac{gz}{g_c J c_p T_1}\right)^{N m c_p / \bar{R}}$$

$$= 1 + \frac{g N m z}{g_c J \bar{R} T_1} + \dots \tag{12.7}$$

By way of numerical illustration, consider a mass of one pound at a height of 5 feet and a temperature of 60 °F. Then, with $N = 6.02 \times 10^{23}$ molecules/mole, and $\bar{R} = 1.96$ Btu/mole-°R,

$$\frac{W_2}{W_1} = 1 + \frac{(6.02 \times 10^{23})(1)(5)}{(778)(1.96)(520)} = 3.77 \times 10^{18}$$

or

$$\frac{W_1}{W_2} = 2.65 \times 10^{-17}$$

It is seen that the probability for an inelastic system of unit mass (which has exchanged its potential energy for thermal energy) to bounce back to its original height is small indeed! The probability, of course, gets slightly bigger if the mass is asked to jump back a smaller distance. For example, the height to which the mass would have a probability $1/3$ of jumping back can be obtained by setting $W_1/W_2 = 1/3$ in Eq. (12.7), and solving for z:

$$3 = 1 + \frac{(6.02 \times 10^{23})(1)(z)}{(778)(1.96)(520)}$$

or

$$z = 2.63 \times 10^{-18} \text{ ft}$$

In other words, z is of the order of a molecular dimension; the mass remains essentially on the ground.

12.4   Third Law of Thermodynamics

Experimental evidence shows that the coefficient of expansion β and the specific heat c_p at low temperatures both tend toward zero as the first or higher power of T. The compressibility, κ, however, remains greater than zero. These facts enable the entropy change near absolute zero to be calculated. From Maxwell's relations, Eqs. (11.7) and (11.8), it can be seen that

$$\left(\frac{\partial s}{\partial v}\right)_T = \left(\frac{\partial p}{\partial T}\right)_v = \frac{\beta}{\kappa} \tag{12.8}$$

$$\left(\frac{\partial s}{\partial p}\right)_T = -\left(\frac{\partial v}{\partial T}\right)_p = v\beta \tag{12.9}$$

Since $\beta = 0$ as $T \to 0$, the above relations show that the entropy is independent of either volume or pressure at absolute zero. The dependence of entropy on the temperature, however, is given by

$$c_p = \left(\frac{dq}{dT}\right)_p = T\left(\frac{\partial s}{\partial T}\right)_p$$

which, upon replacement of c_p by CT^α (with $\alpha > 1$), integrates into

$$s = s_0 + \frac{CT^\alpha}{\alpha} \tag{12.10}$$

Equation (12.10) shows that the entropy approaches a constant value, at least as rapidly as T, independently of the pressure or volume, as absolute zero is approached. Furthermore, it is found that this constant value at absolute zero is the same, regardless of the chemical state. For example, ice at absolute zero may be warmed to the melting point, melted, warmed to the boiling point, vaporized, heated further until the steam is dissociated to hydrogen and oxygen and then the gases separated and cooled to solid hydrogen and oxygen at absolute zero. The net entropy change throughout this cycle is found to be zero, which means that the entropies of hydrogen plus oxygen, in suitable proportions, are equal to the entropy of the ice which they might form by combination. These facts led Nernst to state that *the entropy change associated with any isothermal, reversible process of a condensed system approaches zero as the temperature approaches zero.* The change in question may be a chemical reaction, a change in physical state, or in general any change that can be carried out reversibly in principle. This is known as the Nernst heat theorem, and is stated mathematically as

$$\lim_{T \to 0} \Delta s = 0 \tag{12.11}$$

Later, Planck concluded that the entropy of all crystalline solids is the same at absolute zero; since Eq. (12.10) contains an arbitrary constant of integration, this value of the entropy at absolute zero can be taken as zero.* In other words, *the entropy of a perfect crystal at absolute zero is zero.* This statement, credited to Planck, is known as the *third law* of thermodynamics.

The postulate that the entropy is zero at absolute zero is in line with the thesis that entropy is a measure of a system's disorder. For it is noted that, in Eq. (12.3), zero entropy is obtained when there is only one microstate possible ($W = 1$, $s_0 = \ln W = \ln 1 = 0$). This condition exists at a

---

* The experimental data on which Nernst based his heat theorem was for condensed systems. The restriction, however, should not be troublesome, for all known systems in the neighbourhood of absolute zero are condensed at finite pressure.

temperature of absolute zero, where a system is in the state of least energy (crystalline configuration). Because of the cessation of translational molecular motion, the positions of the atoms may be fixed uniquely, so that the probability of this state becomes unity. With $W = 1$ at absolute zero of temperature, Planck merely thought it logical to assign zero entropy to a system exhibiting a maximum state of order and minimum thermal motion.

12.5   Use of the Third Law; Heat Capacity at Absolute Zero

The third law of thermodynamics enables the absolute entropies of pure substances at any temperature to be calculated from their specific heats and heats of transition. A solid material at temperature T, for instance, will have an entropy given by

$$s = \int_0^T \frac{c_p}{T} dT \tag{12.12}$$

A liquid material, on the other hand, will have an entropy given by the expression

$$s = \int_0^{T_m} \frac{c_{p(s)}}{T} dT + \frac{h_{if}}{T_m} + \int_{T_m}^T \frac{c_{p(l)}}{T} dT \tag{12.13}$$

in which T_m is the melting temperature, $c_{p(s)}$ is the specific heat of the solid, h_{if} is the latent heat of fusion, and $c_{p(l)}$ is the specific heat of the liquid.

The extension to gases (obviously involving the entropy change associated with evaporation) is

$$s = \int_0^{T_m} \frac{c_{p(s)}}{T} dT + \frac{h_{if}}{T_m} + \int_{T_m}^{T_b} \frac{c_{p(l)}}{T} dT + \frac{h_{fg}}{T_b} + \int_{T_b}^T \frac{c_{p(g)}}{T} dT \tag{12.14}$$

where T_b denotes the boiling temperature, h_{if} and h_{fg} denote the heats of solidification and vaporization respectively, and $c_{p(g)}$ denotes the specific heat of the gas.

The quantities needed for the numerical evaluation of entropy include the specific heat (as a function of temperature from absolute zero to a given temperature T). Measurements of specific heats of solids in the neighborhood of absolute zero reveal that

$$\lim_{T \to 0} \left(\frac{c_p}{T} \right) = 0 \tag{12.15}$$

The data, extended to absolute zero, is as shown in Fig. 12.4. Since $c_p \approx c_v$

for solids, Debye and Einstein developed the following relation for the specific heats of solids:

$$c_p \approx c_v = aT^3 \qquad (12.16)$$

where a is a characteristic constant, but different for each substance. Equation (12.16) is valid for a temperature range up to 20 °K.

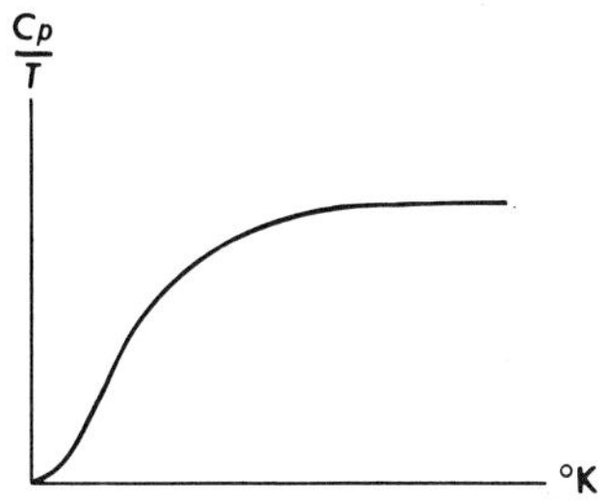

That Eq. (12.15) follows from the third law of thermodynamics ($s_0 = 0$), may be shown as follows: When a simple substance is heated at constant pressure, the increase in entropy is given by

$$ds = \frac{c_p}{T}dT \qquad (12.17)$$

Fig. 12.4 Variation of c_p/T with Temperature.

If Eq. (12.17) is integrated between absolute zero temperature (where $s = 0$) and temperature T (where $s = s$), the result is

$$s = \int_0^T \frac{c_p}{T}dT \qquad (12.18)$$

It is seen that c_p cannot remain finite but must approach zero as T approaches zero, otherwise the integral would become equal to infinity. A similar reasoning at constant volume shows that c_v must also approach zero. The above conclusions may be expressed by means of the single equation

$$\lim_{T \to 0} c_p = c_v = 0 \qquad (12.19)$$

Note that it is satisfied by the Debye-Einstein equation.

Example 12.3. A certain compound has the following values of specific heats, determined by calorimetric methods from 18.3 °K to 290.1 °K:

Temperature °K	Phase	$\bar{c}$ cal/mole	Temperature °K	Phase	$\bar{c}$ cal/mole
18.28	crystalline	1.695	136.78	crystalline	24.71
27.11	crystalline	3.819	180.86	crystalline	29.77
49.92	crystalline	8.670	229.64	liquid	46.75
60.97	crystalline	12.68	240.19	liquid	48.06
76.52	crystalline	15.80	260.70	liquid	50.00
103.26	crystalline	19.95	290.01	liquid	55.56

In addition, it is found that the melting point of the compound is 225.8 °K, and that the enthalpy of fusion is 3767 cal/mole. Determine $\bar{s}_{298}$, the absolute entropy of the compound at 298 °K.

Solution. The value of $\bar{s}_{298}$ includes four terms:

$$\bar{s}_{298} = \int_0^{18.28} \frac{\bar{c}_p dT}{T} + \int_{18.28}^{225.8} \frac{\bar{c}_p dT}{T} + \frac{\bar{h}_{if}}{T} + \int_{225.8}^{298} \frac{\bar{c}d_p T}{T}$$

Since no data are available below 18.28 °K, the first integral will be computed by means of Eq. (12.16), with $a = 1.695/(18.28)^3 = 1/3600$. Thus,

$$\bar{s}_{298} = \frac{1}{3600} \int_0^{18.28} \frac{T^3 dT}{T} + \int_{18.28}^{225.8} \frac{\bar{c}_p dT}{T} + \frac{3767}{225.8} + \int_{22.58}^{298} \frac{\bar{c}_p dT}{T}$$

The integrals

$$\int_{18.58}^{225.8} \frac{\bar{c}_p dT}{T} \quad \text{and} \quad \int_{225.8}^{298} \frac{\bar{c}_p dT}{T}$$

are best evaluated graphically by plotting $\bar{c}_p/T$ versus T. The integration is left to the student.

12.6 Further Consequences of the Third Law

It was stated earlier that one consequence of the third law is that the specific heats c_p and c_v tend to zero as T tends to zero. Other consequences are developed and discussed below.

For a constant-temperature process near 0 °K, the entropy change is given by

$$\Delta S = \int \left(\frac{\partial S}{\partial p}\right)_T dp \tag{12.20}$$

Since $\Delta S = 0$ at $T = 0$ from the third law, Eq. (12.20) gives

$$\lim_{T \to 0} \left(\frac{\partial S}{\partial p}\right) = 0 \tag{12.21}$$

But $(\partial S/\partial p)_T = -(\partial V/\partial T)_p$ from Maxwell's equation, Eq. (11.8). Thus, Eq. (12.21) becomes

$$\lim_{T \to 0} \left(\frac{\partial V}{\partial T}\right)_p = 0 \tag{12.22}$$

Equation (12.22) says that the coefficient of volume expansion β vanishes as T approaches zero. In other words, near absolute zero, the volume remains constant so long as the pressure remains constant, irrespective of temperature. Similarly, it can be shown that, near absolute zero,

$$\lim_{T \to 0} \left(\frac{\partial S}{\partial V} \right)_T = 0 \qquad (12.23)$$

$$\lim_{T \to 0} \left(\frac{\partial p}{\partial T} \right)_V = 0 \qquad (12.24)$$

The above results are in accord with experimental evidence. For example, Buffington and Latimer found that the coefficients of expansion of a number of crystalline solids approach zero. Also, when a system containing solid and liquid helium at low temperature is subjected to pressure, the change with temperature of the equilibrium pressure tends toward zero, so that the equilibrium pressure at low temperatures approaches a constant value that is independent of the temperature.

A final consequence of the third law is the *unattainability* of absolute zero. Consider the field of research in low temperatures. Here, the Joule-Thomson effect is used to produce liquid helium at a temperature below 5 °K. This is followed by rapid adiabatic vaporization to give temperatures in the neighborhood of 1 °K. Still lower temperatures can be obtained by cyclic magnetization and demagnetization as shown in Fig. 12.5.

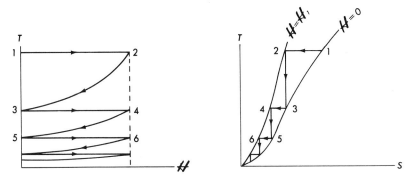

Fig. 12.5 Cyclic Magnetization–Demagnetization.

Starting with an original isothermal magnetization, shown by the line 1–2, the first adiabatic demagnetization 2-3 provides material at temperature T_3 to serve as a heat reservoir for the next isothermal magnetization 3-4. This is followed by another adiabatic demagnetization 4-5, and so on. Experimental evidence indicates that the temperature attained by any adiabatic demagnetization from a given initial temperature is one-half that at the start. Thus, the lower the temperature attained, the less there is possibility of going still lower. In other words, quite aside from practical difficulties, an infinite number of adiabatic demagnetizations would be required to reach absolute zero.

12.7 Discussion of the Third Law

The most convincing test of the validity of the third law lies in the comparison of the entropies obtained from thermal data and those calculated from spectroscopic data by the methods of quantum statistics. Within limits of experimental error, the measurements show that $\Delta S = 0$ at absolute zero temperature. There are, however, some cases of discrepancy, and the third law has often been stated in a number of ways so as to eliminate these cases. A universally accepted formulation of the third law is perhaps not as important as an appreciation of the types of systems to which the law does not apply. Some of these are briefly discussed here:

(1) Substances in a metastable disordered state: This is a disordered arrangement originally at high temperatures which persists at low temperature because of a slow rate of equilibrium attainment. Such a system does not attain the ordered state required by the third law.

(2) Incorrect extrapolation: In order to evaluate

$$S = \int_0^T \frac{C_p}{T}\, dT = \int_0^T C_p\, d\ln T$$

from $0\,°K$ to the lowest temperature at which C_p has been measured, an extrapolation involving Debye functions is required. (Debye, with the aid of statistical mechanics, developed a relation for the heat capacity in terms of a function which is the same for all substances, but which is rather complicated.) Since the Debye function represents only the lattice heat capacity, extrapolation would not take into account the entropy change associated with an order–disorder transition occurring at temperatures lower than those studied experimentally.

(3) Solid solutions: These are not pure substances; consequently, they do not obey the third law.

(4) Entropy contributions not obtainable in calorimetric determinations: The entropy contributions of isotope mixing and nuclear spin are neither obtained nor tabulated in calorimetric data. They do not, however, affect ΔS for a standard chemical change in state, and their omission is thus taken without much concern.

In conclusion, it may be said that the Nernst heat theorem is supported by a wealth of experimental evidence and that occasional discrepancies do not destroy its validity or usefulness.

PROBLEMS

12.1. Thermodynamics is an experimental science which deals only with the macroscopic behavior of matter. If it is to be explained further, the statistical behavior of the particles making up the matter must be taken into account. These particles are restricted to certain discrete energy levels, the smallest allowable level known as the *ground level*. What effect does the size of the volume available to a particle have on its energy levels? Why does a gas appear, macroscopically, to have a continuous energy distribution? Why do lower energy levels always have the heaviest population?

12.2. What is the difference between a microstate and a macrostate? Give examples of a macrostate and microstate.

12.3. A bridge hand in which all 13 cards are specified is a microstate. What is the likelihood of a hand consisting of 13 spades as compared with that of a hand in which all 13 cards are specified? What is the likelihood of a hand consisting of 4 hearts, 3 spades, 2 diamonds, and 4 clubs? Is the latter hand a microstate or a macrostate?

12.4. A complete specification of the state of a gas, from the microscopic viewpoint, calls for a knowledge of the position and velocity of each molecule. In other words, the six quantities $x, y, z, \mathscr{V}_x, \mathscr{V}_y, \mathscr{V}_z$ must be specified for each molecule. Geometrically, these quantities form a six-dimensional hyperspace or phase space. Let this space be subdivided into small elements of volume or cells with side lengths $dx, dy, dz, d\mathscr{V}_x, d\mathscr{V}_y, d\mathscr{V}_z$. A specification of the six co-ordinates of each molecule within the limits of the dimensions of a cell then defines a microstate. How would a macrostate be defined? Do the observable properties of the gas, such as density, pressure, etc., depend on which molecules lie in each cell of phase space or on how many molecules lie in each cell? Can it be said that, over a long period of time, any one microstate occurs as often as another?

12.5. Many different microstates go to make up a macrostate. Thus, any shift of the molecules of a gas which does not change the number of points in each volume element of phase space leaves unaltered the macrostate of the gas. Suppose that there is a particular macrostate for which there are many more microstates than any other. Will this macrostate be the only one ever observed? Will other macrostates be occasionally observed? In the light of this, study and discuss the phenomenon of Johnson noise in an electrical circuit.

12.6. Consider the distribution of two balls called X and Y, in a box partitioned into two equal compartments. The possible microstates are the following:

Microstate	Balls in left compartment	Balls in right compartment
1	X, Y	
2	X	Y
3	Y	X
4		X, Y

What is the probability of each microstate? If the balls are indistinguishable from each other, the possible macrostates are

Macrostate	Number of balls in left compartment	Number of balls in right compartment
a	2	0
b	1	1
c	0	2

What is the probability of each macrostate? Do the same thing for three balls.

12.7. Let a container be subdivided into two equal compartments. Each single molecule of a gas has, therefore, 2 ways of realizing a system, i.e., it can be either in one compartment or in the other. For N molecules, the number of ways becomes 2^N, so that the probability of finding all N molecules in one compartment is $(1/2)^N$. These results are summarized below:

Number of molecules, N	Number of ways of molecules in a compartment	Number of ways in which the molecules in a compartment is exactly $0.5N$	Relative number of ways in which molecules are exactly *divided* between the two compartments
1	2		
2	4	2	0.500
3	8		
4	16	6	0.375
5	32		
10	1024	252	0.250
20	1.049×10^6	0.1848×10^6	0.176
30	1.074×10^9	0.1551×10^9	0.145
100	1.268×10^{30}	0.1009×10^{30}	0.080

(a) Complete the table by carrying on the calculations for $N = 1$ to $N = 10$ by increments of 1, and from $N = 10$ to $N = 100$ by increments of 10.

(b) Notice that, as N increases, the fraction of arrangements in which the division of molecules is *exactly* even between compartments decreases. Does this also mean that the certainty of an *essentially* even distribution decreases? (An essentially even distribution means that a leeway of say, 10 or 20 per cent fluctuation from the even distribution is permitted.) Explain.

12.8. Consider N balls to be tossed into a box partitioned into two compartments. If a 20 per cent fluctuation from the even distribution is permitted, i.e., if the number of balls in one compartment or the other is between $0.4N$ and $0.6N$, and 10 balls are present, show that the probability is $672/1024 = 0.656$. Show that for 20 balls present, this probability becomes $733,000/1,049,000 = 0.74$.

12.9. Entropy is an extensive property depending on the amount of substance in a system. Thus, if two systems of a single substance with entropies S_1 and S_2 respectively are combined into one system, the entropy of this system is the sum

$$S = S_1 + S_2$$

From a statistical point of view, however, if two systems with probabilities W_1 and W_2 respectively are combined into one system, the probability of this system is

$$W = W_1 W_2$$

(a) Show that the entropy and the probability can be related by the equation

$$S = k \ln W$$

where k is a proportionality constant. What are the dimensions of k? (b) Show that the postulate of $S = k \ln W$ anticipates the third law of thermodynamics by noticing that it contains an additive constant.

12.10. Show that

$$\frac{\partial^2 S}{\partial T \partial V} = \frac{1}{T}\left(\frac{\partial C_v}{\partial V}\right)_T; \qquad \frac{\partial^2 S}{\partial T \partial p} = \frac{1}{T}\left(\frac{\partial C_p}{\partial p}\right)_T$$

$$p = T\frac{dS}{dV} - \frac{dU}{dV}; \qquad V = \frac{dH}{dp} - T\frac{dS}{dp}$$

$$\left(\frac{\partial S}{\partial V}\right)_T = \left(\frac{\partial p}{\partial T}\right)_v; \qquad \left(\frac{\partial S}{\partial p}\right)_T = -\left(\frac{\partial V}{\partial T}\right)_p$$

12.11. The Nernst heat theorem states that there is no entropy change for reactions at absolute zero of temperature. This means that all condensed systems at absolute zero have the same entropy value (not necessarily zero). However, according to statistical theory, the entropy is related to the probability by

$$S = k \ln W$$

Now, as a result of cessation of translational molecular motion at absolute zero, the positions of the atoms become uniquely fixed so that the probability of this state becomes unity and consequently $S_0 = \ln 1 = 0$. This led Planck to propose that zero be a common value for the entropy of all substances at absolute zero.

(a) Which of the two proposals is the stronger? Can the Nernst heat theorem be obtained from Planck's formulation?

(b) Can chemical reactions provide a direct proof for $S_0 = 0$ at absolute zero?

(c) What limitations (or exemptions) did Planck give for the third law?

12.12. (a) Can the entropy of a *mixture* of substances be zero at absolute zero?

(b) Investigate the behavior of a glass or supercooled fluid in the neighborhood of absolute zero and see if the third law applies without modification.

12.13. The Nernst heat theroem implies that no simple adiabatic process can lead

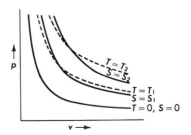

Fig. 12.6 Isotherms and Adiabats near Absolute Zero.

from a nonzero to a zero temperature. In other words, it identifies the isotherm $T = 0$ as being coincident with the adiabat $S = 0$, although other isotherms and adiabats are distinct. This is shown schematically in Fig. 12.6. Can an adiabatic process initiated at nonzero temperature lead to zero temperature?

12.14. The determination of entropies based on the third law is simple in principle. Since $ds = c/(dT/T)$, it follows that

$$s = \int_0^T c \frac{dT}{T}$$

where the appropriate heat capacity is usually c_p. The integration is often carried out graphically by plotting c_p/T vs. T as shown in Fig. 12.7. Notice that at some points the specific heat changes discontinuously. To what is this due? What is the amount of contribution of each phase change to the entropy?

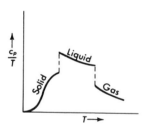

Fig. 12.7

Variation of c_p/T versus T.

12.15. Using the Debye formula for the specific heat of a solid, show that the entropy of a solid at low temperatures is equal to one-third of its specific heat.

12.16. Show that for a solid whose equation of state is

$$pv + f = ku$$

where f is a function of volume only and k is a constant, c_v approaches zero as T approaches zero.

12.17. A well-known equation relating property changes during a phase change of a pure substance is the Clapeyron equation (derived and discussed in Chap. 15):

$$\frac{dp}{dT} = \frac{\Delta h}{T \Delta v}$$

where Δh and Δv are the latent heat and volume change of the phase change, and dp/dT is the slope of the saturation pressure-temperature line. Applying the third law of thermodynamics to Clapeyron's equation, show that

$$\lim_{T \to 0} \frac{dp}{dT} = 0$$

12.18. Calculate the entropy of gaseous sulfur dioxide at its boiling and 1 atm. pressure using the following data from Giauque and Stephenson [*J. Am. Chem. Soc.* 60, 1389 (1938)]:

Temperature °K	c_p cal/mole-deg	Temperature °K	c_p cal/mole-deg
15 (solid)	0.83	110	11.97
20	1.66	120	12.40
25	2.74	130	12.83
30	3.79	140	13.31
35	4.85	150	13.82
40	5.78	160	14.33
45	6.61	170	14.85
50	7.36	180	15.42
60	8.62	190	16.02
70	9.57	200 (liq.)	20.97
80	10.32	220	20.86
90	10.93	240	20.76
100	11.49	260	20.66

The latent heat of fusion is 1,769 cal/mol at 197.64 °K, and the heat of vaporization is 5960 cal/mole at 263.08 °K. (Make use of graphical integration and Debye's formula for the specific heat of solids.)

12.19. A solid of constant specific heat c is to be cooled from temperature T_1 to temperature T_2 by means of a reversible refrigerating machine operating from a heat sink which is at the constant temperature T_0. Show that the work required is

$$w = cT_0 \ln\frac{T_1}{T_2} - c(T_1 - T_2)$$

How much work is required to bring the solid to absolute zero?

12.20. (a) Derive Eq. (12.23) and (12.24).

(b) Show that

$$\lim_{T \to 0}\left(\frac{\partial B}{\partial T}\right)_v = 0$$

where B is the isothermal bulk modulus.

CHAPTER 13

Maxwell–Boltzmann Statistics; Quantum Statistics; Information Theory

13.1 Statistical Method

In the previous chapter, the connection between entropy and probability was introduced. The postulate, $s = k \ln W$, was seen to be the bridge that connects phenomenological (macroscopic) thermodynamics with probability and molecular structure. It is the purpose of the present chapter to inquire more systematically into this relationship, and to show that a rational foundation for thermodynamics can be provided by *statistical mechanics* and by *information theory*.

Statistical mechanics is concerned with interpreting and predicting the macrocopic properties of a substance in terms of the elementary particles

304

(atoms, molecules, ions, electrons, etc.) which compose the substance. The subject was first developed during the latter part of the nineteenth century, largely by Maxwell, Boltzmann, and Gibbs. Its history is typical of many other branches of theoretical physics. Early work led to results that were in part in good agreement with experiment, while in other parts, the agreement was not so good. Later, a newer theory (quantum statistics) was introduced, with the result that the older theory fell into its rightful place as a limiting case. Following historical order (and also for pedagogical reasons), the classical or Maxwell–Boltzmann statistics will be presented first. Later, the subject of quantum statistics will be introduced.

If a deck of cards were to be shuffled and a single card be drawn at random, it is not possible to predict what that card will be. Nevertheless, certain significant statements can be made regarding the result of the drawing. For example, the probability of drawing an ace is one in thirteen; the probability of drawing a diamond is one in four; the probability of drawing the ace of hearts is one in fifty-two. Similarly a life insurance company can predict quite accurately the percentage of its policy holders who will die at each age, if it has enough policy holders. However, the same company could not safely base its insurance premiums on only one person, because no one can predict when one person will die. In many instances, it is impossible to forecast the outcome of an individual event, but, if a large number of similar events are considered, a statement based on probability laws can safely be made.

Since particles are extremely small, any macroscopic body contains an enormous number of them. Although it is impossible to keep track of each individual particle by giving its position and velocity at any instant, the methods of statistics, when applied to a large number of molecules, yield results which have a surprising certainty. In other words, the very fact that a system contains a large number of particles makes its behaviour practically indistinguishable from that predicted by statistics. From the molecular point of view, the second law of thermodynamics is a statistical law; it expresses the drive toward randomness or disorder in a system containing a large number of particles. Applied to an individual molecule it has no meaning, but applied to a large number of molecules, it makes possible the distinction between heat (disordered energy) and work (ordered energy). In the following sections, attention will be centered on systems which are in equilibrium (these are the systems treated in classical thermodynamics), although the restriction is not a prerequisite of the statistical method. Situations in which a system is changing with time or rate processes are outside the scope of this text.

13.2   Probability of a Macrostate

As previously stated, W, the thermodynamic probability, is the number of different ways in which a statistical state can be realized. Consider a system of N objects whatever, which may be atoms, molecules, coins, or dice. As an illustration, take the case of a coin: it can turn up heads or tails; therefore, it is said to have two possible aspects. A dice, on the other hand, can turn up any of six faces; it has six possible aspects. In the case of atoms or molecules, these aspects are represented by the possible quantum states and energy levels (accepted as a result of quantum mechanics). By definition, the statistical state of a system is the specification of the number of objects in the system which exhibit each aspect. Thus, the statistical state of a system of ten coins is completely specified if six of them show heads and four show tails.

For illustrative purposes, consider first the tossing of a single coin. Let H represent the probability of turning up heads, and T represent the probability of turning up tails. If the coin is well balanced, $H = 1/2$, $T = 1/2$, and

$$1 = (H + T) \tag{13.1}$$

Now, consider the tossing of two coins (1 and 2). Coin 1 has a probability of turning up heads $H_1 = 1/2$, and a probability of turning up tails $T_1 = 1/2$, so that $H_1 + T_1 = 1$. Similarly, for coin 2, $H_2 = 1/2$, $T_2 = 1/2$, $H_2 + T_2 = 1$. The states that are possible as result of tossing two coins can be obtained from simple probability theory (multiplication theorem) by writing

$$\begin{aligned} 1 &= (H_1 + T_1)(H_2 + T_2) \\ &= H_1 H_2 + H_1 T_2 + T_1 H_2 + T_1 T_2 \end{aligned} \tag{13.2}$$

which becomes, with $H_1 = H_2 = H$, and $T_1 = T_2 = T$,

$$1 = H^2 + 2HT + T^2 = 1\left(\frac{1}{4}\right) + 2\left(\frac{1}{4}\right) + 1\left(\frac{1}{4}\right) \tag{13.3}$$

The coefficients 1, 2 and 1 in Eq. (13.3) are precisely the thermodynamic probabilities of the states consisting of all heads, a head and a tail, and all tails. The absolute probabilities of these states are, of course, 1/4, 1/2, and 1/4 respectively.

In the case of tossing three coins, the equation for possible states is

$$1 = (H_1 + T_1)(H_2 + T_2)(H_3 + T_3) \tag{13.4}$$

and, if the coins are all identical (honest coins),

$$1 = (H + T)^3 = H^3 + 3H^2 T + 3HT^2 + T^3 \tag{13.5}$$

The coefficients 1, 3, 3, and 1 are again, the thermodynamic probabilities of the states consisting of all heads, two heads and a tail, two tails and a head, and all tails. The absolute probabilities are 1/8, 3/8, 3/8, and 1/8 respectively.

The foregoing development can be extended to a system of N identical coins in which H and T represent the probabilities of heads and tails:

$$1 = (H+T)^N = H^N + NH^{N-1}T + \ldots$$

$$= \sum_{i=0}^{N} \frac{N!}{(N-i)!i!} H^{N-i}T^i \qquad (13.6)$$

In this summation, a particular term represents the absolute probability of realizing $(N-i)$ heads and i tails; the thermodynamic probability is given by the coefficient

$$\frac{N!}{(N-i)!i!}$$

Equation (13.6) can be written in a more symmetrical form if $(N-i)$ is replaced by N_1 to denote the number of heads, and i is replaced by N_2 to denote the number of tails. Thus,

$$1 = (H+T)^N = \sum \frac{N!}{N_1!N_2!} H^{N_2}T^{N_2} \qquad (13.7)$$

In Eq. (13.7), the set of numbers (N_1, N_2) ranges from (N, O), corresponding to all heads and no tails, to (O, N), corresponding to all tails and no heads. The coefficient

$$W = \frac{N!}{N_1!N_2!} \qquad (13.8)$$

is the *thermodynamic probability* for the particular state consisting of N_1 heads and N_2 tails.

Equation (13.8) is for a system of N objects (coins) having only two aspects (heads or tails). For the general case of a system composed of N objects (such as atoms, molecules, electrons, or ions) having s possible aspects, Eq. (13.8) becomes

$$W = \frac{N!}{N_1!N_2! \ldots N_s!} = \frac{N!}{\prod_{i=1}^{s} N_i!} \qquad (13.9)\dagger$$

---

† In essence, this formula gives the number of ways N objects may be placed in s piles N_1 in the first pile, N_2 in the second pile, $\ldots N_s$ in the sth pile.

This is a most important relation. It is the basis of a kind of statistics known as *Maxwell–Boltzmann statistics*. Its validity rests on the assumption that the objects, though identical, are *distinguishable* from one another. (This is not always the case, and a new kind of statistics will be introduced later.)

Example 13.1. Consider a gas in a container which is subdivided by imaginary boundaries into a very large number of small and equal volumes, henceforth called cells. A complete specification of which molecules (in different numbers) are in each cell is called a microstate. A specification of only how many molecules are in each cell is called a macrostate. Equation (13.9) gives the thermodynamic probability or number of microstates corresponding to a given macrostate. As a simple example, let there be four molecules (a, b, c, d) and two cells (1, 2). If N_1 and N_2 denote the number of molecules in cells 1 and 2, the possible macrostates are

N_1	4	3	2	1	0
N_2	0	1	2	3	4

For each of the macrostates, calculate the thermodynamic probability.

Solution. Consider the particular macrostate $N_1 = 3$, $N_2 = 1$. The microstates corresponding to this macrostate are shown in Fig. 13.1. The number of

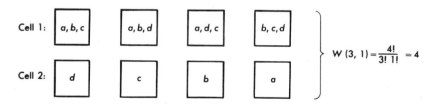

Fig. 13.1   Microstates of a Macrostate.

microstates or thermodynamic probability of the macrostate, as obtained from Equation (13.9), is $4!/3!1! = 4$. This can be verified by actual counting. Note that changing the order within a particular cell such as $\boxed{a, b, c}$ and $\boxed{a, c, b}$ is not considered a change in microstate.

The thermodynamic probabilities of the remaining macrostates are: $W(4, 0) = = 4!/4!0! = 1$, $W(2, 2) = 4!/2!2! = 6$, $W(1, 3) = 4!/1!3! = 4$, and $W(0, 4) = = 4!/0!4! = 1$. Altogether, there are sixteen microstates corresponding to the five macrostates. *All the microstates are equally probable* (this is one of the fundamental hypotheses of statistical mechanics). As time goes on, the molecules are continually shifting around, so that one microstate after another turns up. The macrostate that occurs most frequently, however, is that for which there is the largest number of microstates.

13.3 Stirling's Approximation for ln N!

In evaluating W for a gas, where the number N and all the N_i's is very large, it is convenient to have an approximate expression for $N!$ that can be differentiated and manipulated like any ordinary function. This is provided by Stirling's formula for ln $N!$, derived below.

Consider Fig. 13.2, in which ln x is plotted against x; in addition there are plotted steps, both above and below the curve, having heights equal to ln 2, ln 3, etc.

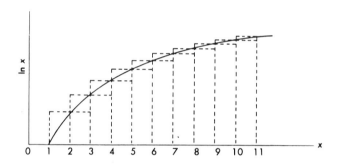

Fig. 13.2 Approximation for Area under ln x.

The area under the smooth curve from $x = 1$ to $x = N$ is

$$\int_1^N \ln x\, dx = N \ln N - N + 1 \qquad (13.10)$$

where integration has been obtained by parts. This area can be approximated by adding the areas of the rectangles whose tops lie above the curve: ln 2, ln 3, etc. This gives

$$\ln 2 + \ln 3 + \ldots + \ln N = \ln N! \qquad (13.11)$$

On the other hand, if the areas of the rectangles whose tops lie below the curve (ln 1, ln 2, etc.) are chosen, the result is

$$\ln 1 + \ln 2 + \ldots + \ln(N-1) = \ln(N-1)!$$
$$= \ln N! - \ln N \qquad (13.12)$$

Clearly, the answer given by Eq. (13.10) must lie between the answers given by Eqs. (13.11) and (13.12). In other words,

$$\ln N! - \ln N < N \ln N - N + 1 < \ln N!$$

Subtracting $\ln N! + N \ln N - N + 1$ and reversing signs gives

$$N \ln N - N + 1 < \ln N! < (N+1)\ln N - N + 1 \qquad (13.13)$$

If N is very large, the 1 can be neglected in Eq. (13.13), so that the upper and lower limits for $\ln N!$ become identical, and consequently

$$\ln N! = N \ln N - N \qquad (13.14)$$

This is Stirling's approximation† for $\ln N!$. It will be used to good advantage in the next section.

13.4 Maximum Probability with One Constraint

It was previously mentioned that the entropy, S, is related to the thermodynamic probability, W, by the equation

$$S = k \ln W \qquad (13.15)$$

Substitution of Eq. (13.9) into Eq. (13.15) would thus give the entropy of a system under any conceivable state. For a state of equilibrium, however, the maximum probability must be used. This is because the entropy (and hence the thermodynamic probability) of an isolated system strives for a maximum. When this maximum is reached, the system is said to be in a state of equilibrium, and the entropy of the system is given by

$$S = k \ln W_{\text{max}} \qquad (13.16)$$

The next task is therefore very clear: the function in Eq. (13.9) must be maximized. Now, it will be observed that this function is discontinuous (because factorial quantities are defined only for whole numbers). In dealing with atomic or molecular systems, however, the number of particles is so large that, from a practical point of view, the problem of finding the maximum thermodynamic probability can be considerably simplified by expressing the factorial function as a continuous function that is amenable to differentiation. (This is why Stirling's approximation is used.)

---

† A more exact analysis gives

$$\ln N! = \tfrac{1}{2} \ln 2\pi + \tfrac{1}{2} \ln N + N \ln N - N$$

When N is very large compared with unity, the first two terms are negligible, so Eq. (13.14) is again obtained.

Consider a system of N identical but distinguishable objects (such as atoms, molecules, etc.) to be distributed among s aspects. What is the state of maximum thermodynamic probability? The answer is obtained by applying the calculus of variations to Eq. (13.9). Now, a continuous function will exhibit a maximum under the same conditions as its logarithm; hence, if $\ln W$ is maximized, W will be maximized. Therefore, take the logarithm of W, and make use of Stirling's approximation, Eq. (13.14), to obtain

$$\ln W = \ln N! - \sum_{i=1}^{s} \ln N_i!$$

$$= N \ln N - N - \sum_{i=1}^{s} (N_i \ln N_i - N_i) \tag{13.17}$$

The problem consists of adjusting the N_i's to make $\ln W$ a maximum while keeping constant the total number of particles, N. In other words, the relation of the dependent variables $N_1, N_2, \ldots$ to be independent variable N must be found that will render $\ln W$ a maximum. This requires that the variation of $\ln W$ from Eq. (13.17) be zero:

$$\delta \ln W = \delta \left[N \ln N - N - \sum_{i=1}^{s} \left(N_i \ln N_i - N_i \right) \right] = 0 \tag{13.18}$$

The symbol δ in the above equation denotes an arbitrary variation. Now,

$$N = N_1 + N_2 + \ldots + N_s = \sum_{i=1}^{s} N_i,$$

and, since the total number of particles remains constant,

$$\delta N = \delta N_1 + \delta N_2 + \ldots + \delta N_s = \sum_{i=1}^{s} \delta N_i = 0 \tag{13.19}$$

Therefore, Eq. (13.18) becomes

$$\delta \ln W = -\sum_{i=1}^{s} N_i \delta \ln N_i - \sum_{i=1}^{s} \ln N_i \delta N_i = 0 \tag{13.20}$$

But

$$\sum_{i=1}^{s} N_i \delta \ln N_i = \sum_{i=1}^{s} N_i \frac{\delta N_i}{N_i} = 0,$$

so that Eq. (13.20) further reduces to

$$\delta \ln W = -\sum_{i=1}^{s} \ln N_i \delta N_i = -(\ln N_1 \delta N_1 + \ln N_2 \delta N_2 + \ldots) = 0 \tag{13.21}$$

The quantities $\delta N_1, \delta N_2, \ldots$ in Eq. (13.21) are the small increases or decreases in the members $N_1, N_2 \ldots$ as a result of molecular motion or collision. If all the δN_i's were independent, the coefficient of each would have to be zero separately, and this information would be of no help. But the δN_i's are not independent, since any increases in populations of some cells must be balanced by decreases in the populations of others, according to Eq. (13.19), which is called a *condition equation*. Employing the method of *Lagrangian multipliers*,† Eq. (13.19) is first multiplied by a parameter, λ (as yet undetermined):

$$\lambda\delta N = \lambda\delta N_1 + \lambda\delta N_2 + \ldots \sum_{i=1}^{s} \lambda\delta N_i = 0 \qquad (13.22)$$

Eq. (13.22) is then added term by term to Eq. (13.21) to give

$$\delta \ln W + \lambda\delta N = \sum_{i=1}^{s} (- \ln N_i + \lambda)\delta N_i = 0 \qquad (13.23)$$

The idea is now to regard the variations as independent rather than subject to the condition of constraint; the added degree of freedom being compensated by the introduction of the multiplier, λ. The coefficients of each of the variations in Eq. (13.23) are therefore set to zero:

$$\left. \begin{array}{c} - \ln N_1 + \lambda = 0 \\ - \ln N_2 + \lambda = 0 \\ \cdot \quad \cdot \quad \cdot \quad \cdot \quad \cdot \\ \cdot \quad \cdot \quad \cdot \quad \cdot \quad \cdot \\ - \ln N_s + \lambda = 0 \end{array} \right\} \qquad (13.24)$$

Eqs. (13.24) yield

$$N_1 = N_2 = \ldots = N_s = e^\lambda \qquad (13.25)$$

In other words, the state of maximum probability is that for which the molecules are equally distributed among the s states. The multiplier λ is determined by noting that

$$N_1 + N_2 + \ldots + N_s = se^\lambda = N$$

or

$$e^\lambda = \frac{N}{s} \qquad (13.26)$$

---

† *Lagrange's method of undetermined multipliers* is the standard method for treating maxima problems involving constraints. When there is only one condition of constraint, as in the present problem, the use of multipliers is not particularly necessary. In the case of two or more constraints, however, the multiplier method allows greater simplification. It is for this reason (and because problems involving more than one constraint will shortly appear) that the method is introduced at this stage.

Replacing this in Eq. (13.25) gives

$$N_1 = N_2 = \ldots N_s = \frac{N}{s} \qquad (13.27)$$

Equation (13.27) is a very special and simple case of *Maxwell–Boltzmann statistics*. The fundamental problem of this kind of statistics is the following: given a large number of objects, as for example, molecules of a gas, it is desired to distribute these with respect to some property they all possess, e.g. position in space, velocity, or kinetic energy. It is convenient to think of this property as associated with a set of boxes, with a definite value of the property attached to each box. A distribution law is then obtained. This law involves the distribution of molecules in terms of both N, the total number of molecules, and ϵ_i, the allowable energy levels of the system.

13.5 Maximum Probability with Two Constraints

The preceding section dealt with the distribution of a large number of molecules among a number of boxes. It was shown that the state of maximum thermodynamic probability, under the stipulation that the total number of molecules remain the same, is attained when the same number of molecules is in each of the boxes. A similar problem, this time involving two constraints, is treated. These constraints are:

constancy of total number: $\sum_i N_i = N$ (13.28)

constancy of total energy: $\sum_i N_i \epsilon_i = U$ (13.29)

where ϵ_1, ϵ_2, . . . denote energy levels of the molecules, and U is the internal energy of the system. The problem of distributing molecules among various quantized energy levels is analogous to the following mechanical situation: A number of boxes are placed at different levels in a gravitational field and a number of marbles are to be distributed among these boxes, under the stipulation that the total potential energy is constant, although the potential energy of any marble will, of course, depend upon the height of each box.

The condition for maximum W is that the variation of W, and hence of $\ln W$, be zero; therefore start with the logarithm of both sides of Eq. (13.9):

$$\ln W = \ln N! - \sum_i \ln N_i!$$

Setting $\delta \ln W = 0$, (and noting that $N!$ is a constant) gives

$$\delta \ln W = 0 = - \sum_i \delta \ln N_i! \tag{13.30}$$

Using Stirling's approximation for $\ln N_i!$ this becomes

$$- \sum_i \delta(N_i \ln N_i - N_i) = 0 \tag{13.31}$$

But

$$\sum_i \delta N_i \ln N_i = \sum_i N_i \delta \ln N_i + \sum_i \ln N_i \delta N_i =$$

$$= \sum_i N_i \frac{\delta N_i}{N_i} + \sum_i \ln N_i \delta N_i = 0 + \sum_i \ln N_i \delta N_i,$$

while

$$\sum_i \delta N_i = 0,$$

so that Eq. (13.31) simplifies to

$$- \sum_i \ln N_i \delta N_i = 0 \tag{13.32}$$

Now, the two constraints, Eq. (13.28) and (13.29), may be written as

$$\sum_i \delta N_i = 0 \tag{13.33}$$

$$\sum_i \epsilon_i \delta N_i = 0 \tag{13.34}$$

Multiplying Eq. (13.33) by λ, Eq. (13.34) by μ, and subtracting from Eq. (13.32) gives

$$\sum_i (- \ln N_i - \lambda - \mu \epsilon_i) \delta N_i = 0 \tag{13.35}$$

The variation δN_i may now be considered to be perfectly arbitrary (the restraining conditions being removed by the introduction of the multipliers), so that for Eq. (13.35) to hold, the coefficient of each term is set to zero:

$$- \ln N_i - \lambda - \mu \epsilon_i = 0$$

This gives

$$N_i = e^{-\lambda - \mu \epsilon_i} \tag{13.36}$$

Equation (13.36) known as the *Maxwell–Boltzmann distribution law*, is a very important result in statistical mechanics.

It is of interest at this point to extend the distribution law to *degenerate* systems. Sometimes it happens that certain of the energy levels ϵ_1, ϵ_2 , .

can be realized in more than one way, e.g., through more than one combination of quantum numbers. In a mechanical analogue, this is equivalent to having several boxes at the same height. The number of boxes at any one height, or the number of combinations of quantum numbers corresponding to a given energy level, is said to be the degree of degeneracy of the energy level. When a situation of this kind occurs, it is necessary to assign a statistical weight, g_i, equal to the number of superimposed boxes at a given energy level ϵ_i. In other words, g_i represents the number of energy cells at the energy levels ϵ_i. Energy states with $g = 1$ are *nondegenerate;* those with $g > 1$ are *degenerate.* Thus, each of the N particles is equally likely to be in any one of the g_i states or boxes, so that the total number of distinct distributions of the N_i particles among the g_i states at the energy level ϵ_i is $g_i^{N_i}$. Consequently the thermodynamic probability for the system of N particles becomes

$$W = N! \prod_i \frac{g_i^{N_i}}{N_i!} \tag{13.37}$$

to which corresponds the distribution

$$N_i = g_i e^{-\lambda - \mu \epsilon_i} \tag{13.38}$$

This is the most general form of the Maxwell–Boltzmann law. It is also sometimes termed a *canonical distribution.*

13.6   Identification of μ

Equation (13.38), the distribution law, is stated in terms of two multipliers, λ and μ. The constant λ is evaluated from the condition

$$\sum_i N_i = N,$$

whence

$$\sum_i g_i e^{-\lambda - \mu \epsilon_i} = N$$

or

$$e^{-\lambda} = \frac{N}{\sum_i g_i e^{-\mu \epsilon_i}}$$

Thus, Eq. (13.38) becomes

$$N_i = \frac{N g_i e^{-\mu \epsilon_i}}{\sum_i g_i e^{-\mu \epsilon_i}} \tag{13.39}$$

The expression

$$\sum_i g_i e^{-\mu \epsilon_i}$$

in the denominator of Eq. (13.39) plays an important role in statistical mechanics. Called the *partition function*, or sum-over-states, it is usually represented by the letter z (German, *Zustandssumme*):

$$z = \sum_i g_i e^{-\mu \epsilon_i} \tag{13.40}$$

The partition function depends on μ (shortly identified as $1/kT$) and on the way in which the energy ϵ_i of a particle varies from level to level. It must be evaluated for each particular system. In terms of the partition function, the distribution of particles at equilibrium becomes

$$N_i = \frac{N g_i}{z} e^{-\mu \epsilon_i} \tag{13.41}$$

The average energy $\bar{\epsilon}$ of a particle is

$$\bar{\epsilon} = \frac{U}{N} = \frac{\sum_i N_i \epsilon_i}{\sum_i N_i} = \frac{\sum_i \epsilon_i g_i e^{-\mu \epsilon_i}}{\sum_i g_i e^{-\mu \epsilon_i}} \tag{13.42}$$

Equation (13.42) shows that since μ depends only on the average molecular energy, it must be an intensive property. To further identify μ, we must first consider its relationship to the entropy. Since $S = k \ln W$, Eq. (13.37) gives (using Stirling's approximation),

$$\ln W = N \ln N - N + \sum_i (N_i \ln g_i - N_i \ln N_i + N_i)$$

$$= N \ln N + \sum_i N_i \ln g_i - \sum_i N_i \ln N_i \tag{13.43}$$

Now, from Eq. (13.41),

$$\ln N_i = \ln N - \ln z + \ln g_i - \mu \epsilon_i.$$

Replacing this in Eq. (13.43) gives

$$\ln W = N \ln N + \sum_i N_i \ln g_i - \sum_i N_i (\ln N - \ln z + \ln g - \mu \epsilon_i)$$

$$= N \ln N - \ln N \sum_i N_i + \ln z \sum_i N_i + \mu \sum_i N_i \epsilon_i \tag{13.44}$$

Since

$$\sum_i N_i = N,$$

the first two terms on the right-hand side cancel out. Furthermore,

$$\sum_i N_i \epsilon_i = U,$$

so that Eq. (13.44) becomes

$$\ln W = N \ln z + \mu U \tag{13.45}$$

From this, the entropy ($S = k \ln W$) is readily obtained:

$$S = k \ln W = Nk \ln z + \mu k U \tag{13.46}$$

Now, from classical thermodynamics, $(dQ)_V = T(ds)_V = (dU)_V$, so that

$$\left(\frac{\partial S}{\partial U}\right)_V = \frac{1}{T} \tag{13.47}$$

This is to be compared with the result of partial differentiation (with respect to U at constant V) taken from Eq. (13.46):

$$\left(\frac{\partial S}{\partial U}\right)_V = \frac{Nk}{z} \cdot \frac{dz}{d\mu} \cdot \left(\frac{\partial \mu}{\partial U}\right)_V + \mu k + k U \left(\frac{\partial \mu}{\partial U}\right)_V \tag{13.48}$$

Since

$$z = \sum_i g_i e^{-\mu \epsilon_i},$$

$$\frac{dz}{d\mu} = -\sum_i g_i \epsilon_i e^{-\mu \epsilon_i},$$

and by Eq. (13.42),

$$\frac{dz}{d\mu} = -\frac{Uz}{N},$$

so that the first and last terms on the right-hand side of Eq. (13.48) cancel out, leaving

$$\left(\frac{\partial S}{\partial U}\right)_V = \mu k \tag{13.49}$$

Equations (13.49) and (13.47) show that, if the results of statistical mechanics are to be consistent with those of classical thermodynamics, the constant μ must be

$$\mu = \frac{1}{kT} \tag{13.50}$$

With this information, the Maxwell–Boltzmann distribution law is now rewritten in the usual form of

$$N_i = g_i e^{-\lambda} e^{-\epsilon_i / kT} = g_i \frac{N}{z} e^{-\epsilon_i / kT} \tag{13.51}$$

Example 13.2. Determine the distribution for the following systems: (a) N particles and two cells or energy levels ϵ_1 and ϵ_2 such that $\epsilon_1 = \epsilon_2 = \epsilon$, (b) N particles and two energy levels such that $\epsilon_1 = 0$ and $\epsilon_2 = \epsilon$.

Solution. (a) From Eqs. (13.40) and (13.50), the partition function is

$$z = \sum_i e^{-\epsilon_i/kT} = 2e^{-\epsilon/kT}$$

The distribution, according to Eq. (13.51), is

$$N_1 = N_2 = \frac{N}{z}e^{-\epsilon/kT} = \frac{Ne^{-\epsilon/kT}}{2e^{-\epsilon/kT}} = \frac{N}{2}$$

In other words, the particles are uniformly distributed between the two cells, as would be expected. This result is true for any number of cells of equal energy.

(b) For the case of $\epsilon_1 = 0$, $\epsilon_2 = \epsilon$, the partition function is

$$z = e^{-\epsilon_1/kT} + e^{-\epsilon_2/kT} = 1 + e^{-\epsilon/kT}$$

The distribution is therefore

$$N_1 = \frac{Ne^{-\epsilon_1/kT}}{1+e^{-\epsilon/kT}} = \frac{N}{1+e^{-\epsilon/kT}}$$

$$N_2 = \frac{Ne^{-\epsilon_2/kT}}{1+e^{-\epsilon/kT}} = \frac{Ne^{-\epsilon/kT}}{1+e^{-\epsilon/kT}} = \frac{N}{1+e^{\epsilon/kT}}$$

The quantity ϵ/k has the dimension of a temperature; it is, in fact, called the *characteristic temperature*. At temperatures that are small compared to the characteristic temperature, ϵ/kT is large compared to unity, $e^{-\epsilon/kt}$ is small, and $e^{\epsilon/kt}$ is large. Then N_1 becomes nearly equal to N, and N_2 is small. That is, nearly all the particles are in cell 1 (low energy). At temperatures which are large compared with the characteristic temperature, ϵ/kT is small compared to unity, and N_1 and N_2 are very nearly equal to each other. Note that when $T = \epsilon/k$, $N_1 = 0.73N$, and $N_2 = 0.27N$, so that, even at very high temperatures, a sizeable number of particles still remain in the state of zero energy.

13.7 Relation of Partition Function to Thermodynamic Properties

Having found the distribution, we can now make use of this to calculate the various functions of thermodynamics. The preceding section already established the relation for the entropy, namely,

$$S = Nk \ln z + \mu k U = Nk \ln z + \frac{U}{T} \tag{13.52}$$

Similar relations in terms of the partition function may be obtained for other properties. For example, the internal energy u of a particle is

$$\bar{\epsilon} = u = \frac{\sum\limits_i N_i \epsilon_i}{\sum\limits_i N_i} = \frac{\sum\limits_i \epsilon_i g_i e^{-\epsilon_i/kT}}{\sum\limits_i g_i e^{-\epsilon_i/kT}} = kT^2 \frac{\partial \ln z}{\partial T} \qquad (13.53)$$

For a system consisting of N particles, this becomes

$$U = NkT^2 \frac{\partial \ln z}{\partial T} \qquad (13.54)$$

The Helmholtz function, $A = U - TS$, is seen to be

$$A = U - T\left(Nk \ln z + \frac{U}{T}\right) = -NkT \ln z \qquad (13.55)$$

Since $dA = dU - TdS - SdT = -pdV - SdT$, or $p = -(\partial A/\partial V)_T$, it follows that

$$p = -\left(\frac{\partial A}{\partial V}\right)_T = NkT\left[\frac{\partial(\ln z)}{\partial V}\right]_T \qquad (13.56)$$

Thus, we see that, once the partition function is known, all the thermodynamic properties of a system can be calculated. The following table summarizes the thermodynamic laws from the classical and statistical points of view.

TABLE 13.1

SUMMARY OF THERMODYNAMIC LAWS

	Classical	Statistical
First law	$dU = dQ - dW$	$dU = \Sigma \epsilon_i dN_i + \Sigma N_i d\epsilon_i$
Second law	$dS = \left(\dfrac{dQ}{T}\right)_{rev}$	$dS = kd \ln W$
Third law	$S_0 = 0$ at absolute zero for perfect crystal	$S_0 = k \ln W_0$; for perfect crystal, $W_0 = 1$, and $S_0 = 0$

Example 13.3. From $S = k \ln W$, derive and discuss the statistical analog to the equation

$$dU = TdS$$

as applied to a constant-volume process.

Solution. First, the equation

$$S = Nk \ln z + \mu k U$$

must be derived. This is done in the text. Now, it should be mentioned that the energy levels ϵ_i are fixed by quantum mechanical theory. The Schrödinger equation, from which the ϵ's are calculated, involves the number of particles, their masses, and the potential energy of the system as a function of its co-ordinates. The permissible solutions are restricted by boundary conditions (as for example, the dimensions of a container in which a gas is enclosed). The ϵ's change only when the potential energy or the boundary conditions change. But changing either potential energy or boundary conditions involve the performance of work on or by the system. Thus, it follows that a process involving no work is a process at constant ϵ's.

Now, differentiate $S = Nk \ln z + \mu k U$, keeping the ϵ's constant, so that z is a function of μ only. This gives

$$dS = Nk \frac{\partial \ln z}{\partial \mu} d\mu + \mu k dU + k U d\mu \tag{13.57}$$

At the constant ϵ's, the term $\partial \ln z / \partial \mu$ becomes, with the aid of Eq. (13.40) and (13.42),

$$\left(\frac{\partial \ln z}{\partial \mu} \right)_{\epsilon_i} = \frac{- \sum\limits_i g_i \epsilon_i e^{-\mu \epsilon_i}}{z} = - \frac{U}{N}$$

Thus, Eq. (13.57) becomes

$$dS = -k U d\mu + \mu k dU + k U d\mu = \mu k dU$$

or

$$dU = \frac{1}{\mu k} dS \tag{13.58}$$

This is the analog to the classical equation $dU = Tds$ for a constant volume process. Since Eq. (13.42), which assumed equilibrium distribution, was used in deriving Eq. (13.58), the latter thus applies to a reversible process.

The Maxwell–Boltzmann distribution law is one of the most important and useful relations in statistical mechanics and physical chemistry. It is remarkably universal in its applicability, frequently turning up in problems which are at first not explicitly connected with statistical mechanics. For example, the barometric equation or pressure of an ideal gas in an isothermal atmosphere subject to the earth's gravitational field can be derived from Eq. (13.51) by replacing ϵ_i by $(mg/g_c)h$, the potential energy of a molecule of mass m at height h above the earth's surface. This, and many other applications of the Maxwell–Boltzmann law, will be discussed in the next chapter.

13.8   Quantum Statistics

In deriving the Boltzmann statistics, it was assumed that the individual particles were *distinguishable* from each other and that *any* number of particles could be assigned to an energy level. In *quantum statistics*, the first of these assumptions is invalid (identical particles cannot be distinguished from one another). The second assumption is also invalid if dealing with particles such as electrons and protons. In that case, the Pauli Exclusion principle requires that no more than one particle occupy a given energy cell. On the other hand, particles such as deuterons and photons may occupy a given energy cell in any number.

The essential difference between the newer theory (quantum statistics) and the older theory (Maxwell–Boltzmann statistics) lies in the method of defining a microstate and of counting the number of microstates associated with a particular macrostate. Quantum statistics, which include Maxwell–Boltzmann statistics as a limiting case, considers particles as belonging to any one of *three* types, each type having a different expression for the thermodynamic probability. The development of this probability follows.

(a) *Identical Distinguishable Particles.* This is the case leading to the Maxwell–Boltzmann distribution law. It was developed in the preceding sections that the number of microscopic arrangements or thermodynamic probability for the system is given by

$$W = N! \prod_i \frac{g_i^{N_i}}{N_i!} \qquad (13.59)$$

where N_i is the number of particles in the ith energy state, and g_i is the degeneracy or number of energy cells at this ith level. (Recall that the entire energy range is divided into contiguous levels or states $\epsilon_1, \epsilon_2, \ldots \epsilon_i, \ldots$ and that each state, however, is still large enough that a number g_i of energy cells may be contained within it.)

(b) *Identical, Indistinguishable Particles of Integral Spin.*† An essential feature of quantum statistics is that it considers the particle to be indistinguishable. It is therefore not possible to identify particles as a, b, c, etc. as was done in Ex. 13.1, but instead, a somewhat different counting procedure is required to determine the number of microstates corresponding to a macrostate. The following simple pictorial device is helpful in studying the number of ways the N_i particles can be placed among the g_i energy levels of the ith cell: Consider the ith cell to consist of an array of N_i particles (denoted by $\otimes$) and $g_i - 1$ partitions (denoted by $|$). The $g_i - 1$ partitions are just sufficient to separate the entire cell into g_i intervals (energy levels), so that the N_i particles when placed into groups by the partitions, represent possible distributions of the particles among the energy levels. Figure

---

† The type of statistics obeyed by a system of particles depends upon the spin properties of the particles. If the nuclear spin is an even multiple of $\frac{1}{2}$, Bose–Einstein statistics applies. If the nuclear spin is an odd multiple of $\frac{1}{2}$, Fermi–Dirac statistics holds. The following are examples of systems and the statistics they obey: ideal gas (Maxwell–Boltzmann), electrons in conductors (Fermi–Dirac), black-body radiation (Bose–Einstein).

13.3 shows a cell consisting of $g_i = 16$ energy levels populated by $N_i = 24$ particles. The particular distribution illustrated here consists of 3 particles in the first energy level, 1 in the second, 4 in the third, 1 in the fourth, 0 in the fifth, 0 in the sixth, 2 in the seventh, and so on.

To obtain the number of possible distinct arrangements of the N_i particles among the g_i energy levels of a cell, let the particles and the partitions be considered as an array of $N_i + g_i - 1$ objects to be permuted. The number of permutations, if the objects were distinguishable, is $(N_i + g_i - 1)!$ However, because of the indistinguishability of particles as well as partitions, a permutation of the particles among themselves or of the partitions among themselves does not lead to a distinguishably different arrangement. Thus, the number of arrangements $(N_i + g_i - 1)!$ must be divided by

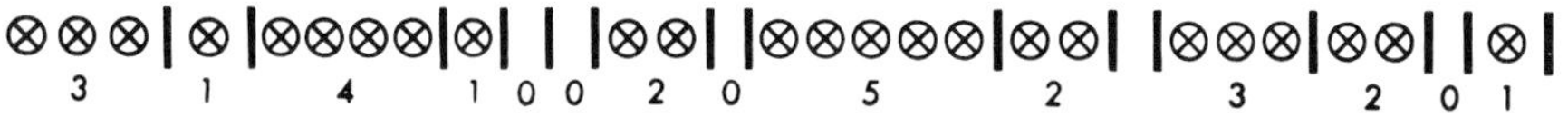

⊗⊗⊗| ⊗ |⊗⊗⊗⊗|⊗| | |⊗⊗| |⊗⊗⊗⊗⊗|⊗⊗| |⊗⊗⊗|⊗⊗| |⊗|
 3   1   4   1 0 0   2 0   5   2   3   2 0 1

Fig. 13.3 Distribution of Particles among Energy Levels of a Cell.

$N_i!$, the number of permutations among the N_i particles and by $(g_i - 1)!$, the number of permutations among the $g_i - 1$ partitions to give the number of distinct arrangements or thermodynamic probability for the ith cell:

$$W_i = \frac{(N_i + g_i - 1)!}{N_i!(g_i - 1)!}$$

As for the number of ways of distributing a total of N particles among various cells, it is

$$W = W_1 W_2 \ldots = \prod_i W_i$$

$$= \prod_i \frac{(N_i + g_i - 1)!}{N_i!(g_i - 1)!} \tag{13.60}$$

This is known as *Bose–Einstein statistics*.

(c) *Identical, Indistinguishable Particles of Half-Integral Spin.*   Here, an exclusion principle (known as the Pauli exclusion principle) acts to limit the occupancy of a given energy level to not more than one particle. The number of distinguishable arrangements of the N_i particles among the g_i energy levels of the ith cell is then found as follows: If the particles were distinguishable, the "first" particle could be placed in any one of the g_i levels, and for each one of these choices, the "second" particle could be placed in any one of the $(g_i - 1)$ remaining levels, and so on. The number of arrangements in the case of distinguishable particles is thus

$$g_i(g_i - 1) \ldots (g_i - N_i + 1) = \frac{g_i!}{(g_i - N_i)!}$$

In the case of indistinguishable particles, this answer must be divided by $N_i!$, the number of permutations of the N_i particles among themselves. The thermodynamic probability for the ith cell is thus

$$W_i = \frac{g_i!}{N!(g_i - N_i)!}$$

For the various cells taken together, the probability is

$$W_t = W_1 W_2 \ldots = \prod_i W_i$$

$$= \prod_i \frac{g_i!}{N!(g_i - N_i)!} \tag{13.61}$$

This is known as *Fermi–Dirac statistics*.

To illustrate the difference in counting between Maxwell–Boltzman statistics, Bose-Einstein statistics, and Fermi–Dirac statistics, consider the case of two particles (represented by letters) to be distributed among three energy levels (represented by horizontal lines). The possible distributions are as follows:

Maxwell–Boltzmann (particles identical but distinguishable)

a b	___	___	a	b
___	a b	___	b	a
___	___	a b	___	___

a	b	___	___
___	___	a	b
b	a	b	a

Bose–Einstein (particles identical but indistinguishable)

a a	___	___	a	a
___	a a	___	a	___
___	___	a a	___	a

___
a
a

Fermi–Dirac (particles identical and indistinguishable, but limited to one per energy cell)

a	a	

a		a

	a	a

13.9   Bose–Einstein and Fermi–Dirac Distributions

Having developed the expression for the thermodynamic probability in all three cases, there remains, in the case of Bose–Einstein statistics and Fermi–Dirac statistics, the problem of maximizing W, subject to the conditions

$$\sum_i N_i = \text{constant} = N \qquad (13.62)$$

$$\sum_i N_i \epsilon_i = \text{constant} = U \qquad (13.63)$$

Because of the large number of particles ($N \approx 10^{23}$) and energy levels in a single cell ($g_i \approx 10^8$), Eqs. (13.60) and (13.61), as well as Eq. (13.59) may be regarded as continuous functions of the continuous variables N_i, so that the problem is treated in exactly the same manner as that developed for Maxwell–Boltzmann statistics. For the sake of uniformity, the following intermediate steps are sketched out for all three statistics.

First, the logarithm of W is taken:
Case (a):

$$\ln W = \ln N! + \sum_i (N_i \ln g_i - \ln N_i!)$$

Case (b):

$$\ln W = \sum_i [\ln (N_i + g_i - 1)! - \ln N_i! - \ln (g_i - 1)!]$$

Case (c):

$$\ln W = \sum_i [\ln g_i! - \ln N_i! - \ln (g_i - N_i)!]$$

This is to be maximized with respect to all small variations of the cell populations which can occur while satisfying Eqs. (13.62) and (13.63).

In other words, for each N_i which changes by a small amount δNi, the following equations must be satisfied:

$$\delta(\ln W) = 0 \tag{13.64}$$

$$\sum_i \delta N_i = 0 \tag{13.65}$$

$$\sum_i \epsilon_i \delta N_i = 0 \tag{13.66}$$

The problem is solved by means of Lagrange's method of undetermined multipliers. Using λ and μ as multipliers, we obtain

$$\delta(\ln W) - \lambda \sum_i \delta N_i - \mu \sum_i \epsilon_i \delta N_i = 0 \tag{13.67}$$

This gives the maximum value of $\ln W$ as the one defined by the distribution $N_i(\epsilon_i)$, λ, and μ which satisfy the following relations:
Case (a):

$$\ln g_i - \ln N_i - \lambda - \mu \epsilon_i = 0$$

Case (b):

$$\ln(N_i + g_i) - \ln N_i - \lambda - \mu \epsilon_i = 0$$

Case (c):

$$-\ln N_i + \ln(g_i - N_i) - \lambda - \mu \epsilon_i = 0$$

The above equations are solved for $N_i(\epsilon_i)$ to yield the three distribution laws:
Case (a):

$$N_i = \frac{g_i}{e^{\lambda + \mu \epsilon_i}} \qquad\qquad \textit{Maxwell–Boltzmann}$$

Case (b):

$$N_i = \frac{g_i}{e^{\lambda + \mu \epsilon_i} - 1} \qquad\qquad \textit{Bose–Einstein}$$

Case (c):

$$N_i = \frac{g_i}{e^{\lambda + \mu \epsilon_i} + 1} \qquad\qquad \textit{Fermi–Dirac}$$

The parameters λ and μ are evaluated by inserting each of the distribution laws into Eqs. (13.62) and (13.63). It may be shown (see Prob. 13.28) that μ has a universal character closely related to the temperature, independent of the particular type of particle. In fact, $\mu = 1/kT$ for all three types of particles. These results are summarized in Table 13.2.

The parameter μ has the same value $(1/kT)$ in all three cases. Also, in almost every case, the exponential term is large compared to unity, so that the Boltzmann statistics become fairly good approximations for most systems.

It is instructive to examine some of the more general properties exhibited by the three distributions: As previously stated, μ is a universal quantity, independent of the nature of the particular system. It is essentially a measure of the temperature of the system. Therefore, μ is the same for various systems in contact with one another (i.e., systems which can exchange energy between them, as for example a mixture of particles of different types).

TABLE 13.2

SUMMARY OF CLASSICAL AND QUANTUM STATISTICS†

Statistics	W	N_i
Maxwell–Boltzmann	$W = N! \prod_i \dfrac{g_i{}^{N_i}}{N_i!}$	$N_i = g_i e^{-\lambda - \epsilon_i/kT}$
Bose–Einstein	$W = \prod_i \dfrac{(N_i + g_i - 1)!}{N!(g_i - 1)!}$	$N_i = \dfrac{g_i}{e^{\lambda + \epsilon_i/kT} - 1}$
Fermi–Dirac	$W = \prod_i \dfrac{g_i!}{N_i!(g_i - N_i)!}$	$N_i = \dfrac{g_i}{e^{\lambda + \epsilon_i/kT} + 1}$

An additional way of bringing out the similarities and differences of the three distributions is to plot the quotient N_i/g_i, which is called the *occupation index*. This is the average number of particles per energy level (at the energy ϵ), and is plotted versus energy for various temperatures, as shown in Figure 13.4.

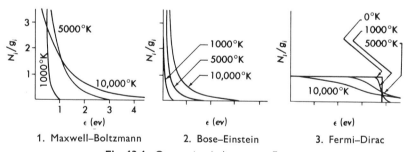

1. Maxwell–Boltzmann   2. Bose–Einstein   3. Fermi–Dirac

Fig. 13.4 Occupation Index versus Energy.

The Maxwell–Boltzmann distribution gives a pure exponential curve at all temperatures and for all values of ϵ. The Bose–Einstein distribution differs significantly from the Maxwell–Boltzmann distribution mainly for $N_i/g_i \gg 1$. A case of fundamental interest is that of a photon gas, for which

---

† Depending upon the type of statistics they obey, particles are often referred to as *boltzons, bosons,* and *fermions.*

$\lambda = 0$. The Fermi–Dirac distribution is characterized by an occupation index which can never exceed unity. At very low temperatures, the occupation index is equal to unity for energies less than a certain energy ϵ_m, and equal to zero for energies greater than ϵ_m. At higher temperatures, the index drops from unity toward zero as shown in Fig. 13.4. A common property shared by all three distributions is that, at sufficiently high energies, each distribution becomes essentially a Maxwell–Boltzmann distribution. In many situations, this fact is of great utility in deducing the relative occupation indices of any two levels which lie in this high energy range.

13.10   Information Theory

An interesting feature in the concept of entropy is that the term is used both in *statistical mechanics* (*thermodynamics*) and in *communication theory*. The latter is concerned with the development of mathematical laws pertaining to systems designed to communicate or manipulate information. In communication theory, the amount of information, H, is given by the expression

$$H = - \sum_i p_i \log_2 p_i \qquad (13.68)$$

where p_i is the probability of the ith possible state of the system. This equation is identical in form with the (Boltzmann) equation representing entropy in statistical mechanics and suggests that there may be some deep-lying connection between thermodynamics and information theory. The quantity H may be considered as a measure of the *uncertainty* existing about a message before its reception just as the thermodynamic entropy is, in a sense, a measure of the disorder (uncertainty) pertaining to the microscopic state in which a system may be found at a given time.

The name *entropy* itself is used in information theory (communication theory) for Eq. (13.68). The amount of information conveyed by a message increases as the amount of uncertainty as to what the message actually will be produced becomes greater. Consider a message source, such as a writer or a speaker which may produce on a given occasion any one of many possible messages. Thus, a message which is one out of a thousand possible messages conveys a greater amount of information than a message which is one out of ten possible messages. The more it is known about what message a source will produce, the less the uncertainty, and the less the information conveyed. The entropy of communication theory is a measure of this uncertainty and is taken as the amount of information conveyed by a message from a source.

Although some of the ideas pertaining to communication theory go back to the electrical telegraph (Morse code), the theory, in its broader applications, sets up quantitative measures of information and of the capacity of various systems to transmit, store, and otherwise process information. It deals with such things as finding the best method of utilization, the best method of separating signal from noise, and determining the upper bounds of a given channel. Information is interpreted to include the messages occurring in any of the standard communication media such as telegraphy, radio or television, the signals involved in electronic computing machines, servo systems, and other data processing devices, and even signals occurring in the nerve networks of animal and man. The development of communication theory has proceeded along two main lines. The first line stems from the work of Norbert Wiener, presented in his book "Cybernetics," the second line stems from the work of Claude Shannon, presented in his paper "A Mathematical Theory of Communication." These key contributions originated in part, from wartime research on automatic fire control and on secrecy codes. While it is not the intention of this text to take up the subject of communication theory in detail, it is nevertheless of interest to discuss in the next sections some aspects of the theory which have a relation to thermodynamics.

13.11　Model of Communication System

The block diagram of Fig. 13.5 illustrates a typical communication

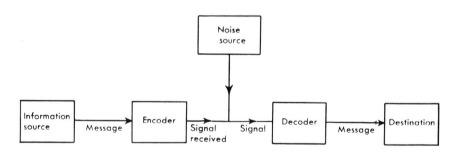

Fig. 13.5　Diagram of a Communication System.

system. The box marked "information source" stands for the person or device that generates the information to be transmitted. This may be a man speaking into a telephone, a scene picked up by a television camera, or a girl operating a teletypewriter. The "encoder" represents a device which transforms the output from the source into a signal suitable for transmission through the prescribed channel. For example, the encoder transforms the source output into a sequence of binary digits, from which the decoder will in turn generate an acceptable reproduction of the source output. The fact that such a binary representation of the information to be transmitted can be assumed without loss of generality is by no means obvious, but it is one of the major results of information theory. The "channel" is the means by which the encoded information or signal is transmitted to the receiver which decodes the received signal to recover the original message. Some obvious examples of communication channels are: a pair of wires connected at one end to a voltage source and at the other end to a recording instrument; two antennas together with the space between them; a sailor waving a pair of semaphore flags from the deck of a ship and another sailor observing them with a pair of binoculars. During transmission, the signal may be perturbed by noise, as indicated schematically by the box labeled "noise source." Finally, the box marked "destination" represents the person or device which uses the information. The purpose of a communication system such as that illustrated in Fig. 13.5 is to make the source output available to the user at a place convenient to the user.

A basic concept in communication theory is that information can be treated very much like a physical quantity, i.e., it can be measured in suitable units and produced at a certain rate by a given information source. The communication system shown in Fig. 13.5 is thus analogous to a transportation system. Imagine, for example, a lumbermill producing lumber at a certain locality, and this lumber is to be transported to another locality by a conveyor. In such a situation, there are two important parameters: the rate R (cu ft/sec) at which lumber is produced at the mill, and the capacity C (cu ft/sec) at which the conveyor can handle lumber. If R is greater than C, it will be impossible to transport all the lumber produced. If, on the other hand, R is less than or equal to C, it may or it may not be possible to transport all the output of the lumbermill, depending upon the efficiency of the conveyor. If the anology is correct, it will be possible to set up a quantity R in suitable units indicating the rate at which information is produced by a source, and a second quantity C denoting the capacity of a channel for transmitting information. Furthermore, the analogy would show that by suitable coding or modulation, information can be transmitted over a channel only if R is not greater than C. Information theory shows that it is indeed possible to set up quantities R and C having this property.

13.12   Measurement of Information

From the transmission standpoint, the most significant aspect of information is the fact that one particluar message is chosen from a set of possible messages. What is transmitted is the specification of the particular message chosen by the information source so that the original message can be reconstructed at the receiving point based on this specification. In other words, information is related to the notion of a choice from a set of possibilities, each possibility having its own probability. This is illustrated by the "tree of choice" shown in Fig. 13.6.

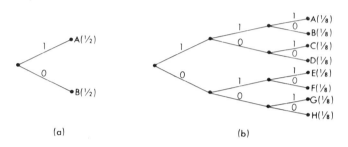

(a)   (b)

Fig. 13.6   Tree of Choice.

Consider, as in Fig. 13.6a, the simplest type of choice, which is a choice between two possibilities, each with probability 1/2. Such a situation occurs when, for example, a coin is tossed which is equally likely to come up heads (A) or tails (B). The message source chooses repeatedly between A and B, each choice being uninfluenced by any previous choice (ergodic process). If p_1 is the probability that the coin will turn up heads, and p_2 is the probability that the coin will turn up tails, and if p_1 and p_2 do not change with time (ergodic source), then the entropy or amount of information produced is, according to Eq. (13.68),

$$H = -(p_1 \log_2 p_1 + p_2 \log_2 p_2)$$
$$= -(\tfrac{1}{2} \log \tfrac{1}{2} + \tfrac{1}{2} \log \tfrac{1}{2}) = 1 \text{ bit per toss}$$

In other words, it takes 1 bit of information to convey whether heads or tails has turned up, if the message source is the sequence of heads and tails obtained by tossing a coin. It is convenient to use the amount of information produced by such a choice as the basic unit, and this has been called a binary digit or, more briefly, a *bit*. The reason for this is that in order for the sender to indicate to the receiver which message he has chosen, he must use some sort of signal. One form of signal is a series of pulses or absences of pulses, yeses or noes, heads or tails, etc. These patterns can be represented by the digits 1 and 0 in the binary system of notation. Thus, a pulse or a space (lack of pulse) in one interval of time is equivalent to one binary digit.

When there are N possibilities, all equally likely, as in Fig. 13.6b, each 0 or 1 can be regarded as expressing an elementary choice between two possibilities. Proceeding outward from the center to the twigs, let 1 signify that the upper branch is taken and 0 signify that the lower branch is taken. Then 011 means message E. Thus, by means of a sequence of elementary choices, a large number of alternatives can be selected. When these choices are made known to the recipient of the message, he can find out which alternative was chosen. These elementary choices are called bits of information. In the present case, the amount of information is 3, as can be seen from Eq. (13.68):

$$H = -(\tfrac{1}{8} \log_2 \tfrac{1}{8} + \tfrac{1}{8} \log_2 \tfrac{1}{8} + \ldots)$$
$$= - \log_2 \tfrac{1}{8} = 3 \text{ bits per message}$$

More generally, for a source which chooses at each junction or level of decision with equal likelihood among N outcomes or messages, the probability of any one particular outcome turning up is $1/N$, and entropy the or amount of information is

$$H = -\left(\frac{1}{N} \log_2 \frac{1}{N} + \frac{1}{N} \log_2 \frac{1}{N} + \ldots\right) = - \log_2 \frac{1}{N} =$$

$$= \log_2 N \text{ bits per message.}$$

If the probabilities are not all equal, but each outcome has a probability of its own, Eq. (13.68) gives the amount of information as

$$H = -(p_1 \log_2 p_1 + p_2 \log_2 p_2 + p_3 \log_3 p_3 + \ldots) \text{ bits per message.}$$

For example, in the case of a message source which produces a string of 1's and 0's by tossing a coin so weighted that it turns up heads 3/4 of the time and tails 1/4 of the time, the amount of information is

$$H = -\left(\frac{3}{4} \log_2 \frac{3}{4} + \frac{1}{4} \log_2 \frac{1}{4}\right) = -\left[\frac{3}{4}(-0.415) + \frac{1}{4}(-2)\right] =$$

$$= 0.811 \text{ bits per toss.}$$

Note that this is less than the 1 bit per toss obtained in the case of a coin having equal probabilities of turning up heads or tails. This is because in the case of a coin which turns up heads more often than tails, there is a constraint to choose heads more often than tails and therefore more is known about the outcome than otherwise. The more an outcome is known a priori, the less information is conveyed in a message.

13.13 Shannon's Formula

The preceding section has established the fact that a message source chooses randomly one among many possible messages for transmission.

Prior to the receipt of the message, the recipient is uncertain as to which among the many messages the source will choose, and the entropy or information is a measure of the uncertainty of the recipient as to which message will be received. Thus, for the case of a message source which produces one among N symbols or messages, with probabilities which are independent of previous choice, the entropy or information is defined as

$$H \equiv I = - \sum_{i=1}^{N} p_i \log_2 p_i \quad \text{bits per symbol}$$

The logarithm to the base 2 is customary, though not essential, in communication theory. The equation given is due to Shannon.

It is of interest to state the reasons that lead Shannon to select such an expression to be used as a measure of uncertainty: (1) the uncertainty H about an even A with possible outcomes N_1, N_2 . . . should depend upon the probabilities $p_1, p_2, \ldots$ of these outcomes:

$$H = H(p_1, p_2, \ldots p_N)$$

(2) The uncertainty about two independent events A and B taken together as one should be the sum of the uncertainties about A and B taken separately:

$$H(AB) = H(A) + H(B)$$

(3) The uncertainty should be a monotonically increasing function of N, the number of outcomes. These criteria lead to the use of a logarithmic function, and consequently Shannon defined information as

$$H \equiv I = - K \sum_{i=1}^{N} p_i \ln p_i \tag{13.69}$$

where K is a constant, and the logarithm is to the base e. A derivation of this equation follows.

Consider an event to occur and a message is to be transmitted telling about the occurrence. Let the amount of information received in the message be defined as

$$I = \log \left[\frac{\text{probability of the event after the message is received}}{\text{probability of the event before the message is received}} \right]$$

For a *noiseless* channel, the receiver is certain that the message is correct. Therefore, the probability of the event after the message is received is unity and the definition reduces to

$$I = - \log [\text{probability of the event before the message is received}]$$

As an example, if a coin has just been tossed and the question is asked, "What is the outcome?" The answer: "It's heads," denotes an amount of information equal to

$$I = - \log\frac{1}{2}$$

The numerical value of the amount of information depends upon what logarithmic base is used. If 10 is used as the base, the unit of information is called a decimal digit. If 2 is used as the base, the unit of information is called a binary digit or bit. In any event, the measure of information may be written as

$$I = - K \ln p \qquad (13.70)$$

where p denotes the probability prior to the receipt of the message. Note that the use of the logarithmic function obviously satisfies the requirement for additivity, since, if p_A is the probability assigned to event A, and p_B is the probability assigned to event B, then for the compound event A and B of probability $p_A p_B$, the uncertainty or information is

$$I(AB) = - K \ln(p_A p_B) = - K \ln p_A - K \ln p_B$$
$$= I(A) + I(B)$$

Consider now the problem of determining the information content in a set of symbols with different *a priori probabilities*. As illustration, consider the English language, which uses an alphabet of 27 symbols (26 letters plus the "blank" or spacing between words). These symbols have a probability of occurrence given in Table 13.3.†

How many possible messages could be sent, using N symbols from this supply, the relative number of each symbol being according to Table 13.3? For example, N could be a total of 10,000 symbols, of which N_1 are letters A, N_2 are letters B, and so on. The problem is to find the number of permutations of N things, of which N_1 are alike, N_2 are alike, etc., and for which

$$N = N_1 + N_2 + \ldots$$

This problem has already been discussed in the preceding sections on statistical mechanics. However, for the sake of completeness, its solution is restated here: The number of ways in which N things can be arranged in sequence, or the number of permutations, is $N!$ There are N choices for the first, $(N-1)$ for the second, $(N-2)$ for the third, and so on up to 1 for the last. However, since N_1 things are alike, N_2 things are alike, etc.

---

† From L. Brillouin's book *Science and Information Theory*, Academic Press Inc., 1956.

TABLE 13.3
PROBABILITY OF OCCURRENCE AND POSSIBLE CODING OF ENGLISH
LANGUAGE

Symbol or Letter	Probability p_i	Possible binary code	Symbol or Letter	Probability, p_i	Possible binary code
A	0.063	10000	N	0.059	10100
B	0.0105	1110000	O	0.0654	1100
C	0.023	111000	P	0.0175	1011000
D	0.035	110000	Q	0.001	10101100
E	0.105	100	R	0.054	11100
F	0.0225	111100	S	0.052	101000
G	0.011	1101100	T	0.072	1000
H	0.047	101100	U	0.0225	1010000
I	0.055	11000	V	0.008	1110100
J	0.001	10101000	W	0.012	1101000
K	0.003	1111000	X	0.002	1111100
L	0.029	110100	Y	0.012	1011100
M	0.021	1010100	Z	0.001	10110000
			Blank	0.20	000

the total number of permutations, $N!$, must be divided by the permutations $N_1!$ (which are all alike), $N_2!$ (which are all alike), etc. Thus, the number of distinct messages is

$$\frac{N!}{N_1! N_2! \ldots} = \frac{N!}{\prod_i N_i!}$$

and the probability of any one message is the reciprocal of this, so that Eq. (13.70) gives

$$I = -K \ln \frac{\prod_i N_i!}{N!} = -K \sum_i \ln N_i! + K \ln N!$$

Assuming N and N_i to be large, Stirling's formula ($\ln N! \doteq N \ln N - N$) can be used, and therefore

$$I = -K \left[\sum_i N_i \ln N_i - \sum N_i - N \ln N + N \right]$$

Noting that

$$N = \sum_i N_i,$$

this gives

$$I = -K\left[\sum_i N_i \ln N_i - N \ln N\right] = -K\left[\sum_i N_i \ln N_i - \sum_i N_i \ln N\right]$$

$$= -K \sum_i N_i \ln \frac{N_i}{N} \tag{13.71}$$

Dividing both sides by N and noting that $N_i/N = p_i$ is the probability of the ith symbol, Eq. (13.71) gives the *average information per symbol as*

$$I = -K \sum_i \frac{N_i}{N} \ln \frac{N_i}{N} = -K \sum_i p_i \ln p_i \tag{13.72}$$

This is precisely *Shannon's formula.*

13.14   Properties of $-K\sum_i p_i \ln p_i$

As previously shown, the average information per symbol for an event having $1, 2, \ldots N$ possible outcomes or symbols is given by

$$I = -K \sum_i p_i \ln p_i$$

where $p_1, p_2 \ldots p_N$ are the a priori probabilities for the symbols $1, 2, \ldots N$. It is instructive to discuss some properties† of this equation.

Theorem I. If a choice is broken down into successive choices, then the information is the weighted sum of the individual informations. This statement is best explained by means of the following diagrams.

Fig. 13.7 Probabilities of Reaching Outcomes with Intermediate Points.

Consider, as in Fig. 13.7a, that the probability of going from O to A is $1/2$, from O to B is $1/3$, and from O to C is $1/6$. If an intermediate point P is used such that the probability of going from O to P is $1/2$, then the probability of going from P to B must be $2/3$, and from P to C must be

_____

† These properties are proved in the manner given in Brillouin's book *Science and Information Theory.*

1/3. Theorem I states that

$$I\left(\frac{1}{2}, \frac{1}{3}, \frac{1}{6}\right) = I\left(\frac{1}{2}, \frac{1}{2}\right) + \frac{1}{2} I\left(\frac{2}{3}, \frac{1}{3}\right)$$

where I (1/2, 1/2) is the information corresponding to paths OA and OP, and I (2/3, 1/3) is the information corresponding to paths PB and PC. To show that the above relation is true, expand the left-hand side:

$$I\left(\frac{1}{2}, \frac{1}{3}, \frac{1}{6}\right) = -K\left[\frac{1}{2}\ln\frac{1}{2} + \frac{1}{3}\ln\frac{1}{3} + \frac{1}{6}\ln\frac{1}{6}\right]$$

$$= -K\left[\frac{1}{2}\ln\frac{1}{2} + \frac{1}{2}\cdot\frac{2}{3}\ln\left(\frac{1}{2}\cdot\frac{2}{3}\right) + \frac{1}{2}\cdot\frac{1}{3}\ln\left(\frac{1}{2}\cdot\frac{1}{3}\right)\right]$$

$$= = K\left[\left(\frac{1}{2}\ln\frac{1}{2} + \frac{1}{2}\ln\frac{1}{2}\right) + \frac{1}{2}\left(\frac{2}{3}\ln\frac{2}{3} + \frac{1}{3}\ln\frac{1}{3}\right)\right]$$

$$= -K\left[\frac{1}{2}\ln\frac{1}{2} + \frac{1}{2}\ln\frac{1}{2}\right] + \frac{1}{2}\left[-K\left(\frac{2}{3}\ln\frac{2}{3} + \frac{1}{3}\ln\frac{1}{3}\right)\right]$$

$$= I\left(\frac{1}{2}, \frac{1}{2}\right) + \frac{1}{2}I\left(\frac{2}{3}, \frac{1}{3}\right)$$

This last expression shows that the original information is the weighted sum of the informations for paths OA, OP, and PB, PC.

Theorem II. If p_i is the probability of the ith outcome, and q_i is another probability such that

$$\sum_i q_i = \sum_i p_i = 1,$$

then

$$-K\sum_i p_i \ln q_i \geqslant -K\sum_i p_i \ln p_i$$

To show this, write

$$q_i = p_i + u_i = p_i\left(1 + \frac{u_i}{p_i}\right)$$

where the u_i's satisfy the condition

$$\sum_i u_i = 0$$

Replacing q_i by the above value in

$$\sum_i p_i \ln q_i$$

gives

$$\sum_i p_i \ln q_i = \sum_i p_i \ln\left[p_i\left(1+\frac{u_i}{p_i}\right)\right]$$

$$= \sum_i p_i \ln p_i + \sum_i p_i \ln\left(1+\frac{u_i}{p_i}\right) \qquad (13.73)$$

If u/p and $\ln(1+u/p)$ are plotted versus u/p as shown in Fig. 13.8, it is seen that

$$\frac{u}{p} \geqslant \ln\left(1+\frac{u}{p}\right)$$

wherever $\ln(1+u/p)$ is defined. Thus, Eq. (13.73) gives

$$\sum_i p_i \ln q_i \leqslant \sum_i p_i \ln p_i + \sum_i p_i\left(\frac{u_i}{p_i}\right)$$

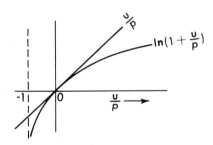

Fig. 13.8 Graphs of $\frac{u}{p}$ and $\ln\left(1+\frac{u}{p}\right)$ versus $\frac{u}{p}$.

Since

$$\sum_i p_i\left(\frac{u_i}{p_i}\right) = \sum_i u_i = 0,$$

this becomes

$$\sum_i p_i \ln q_i \leqslant \sum_i p_i \ln p_i \qquad (13.74)$$

Equation (13.74), upon multiplication by $-K$ yields the desired result:

$$-K\sum_i p_i \ln q_i \geqslant -K\sum_i p_i \ln p_i \qquad (13.75)$$

Theorem III. $-K\sum_i p_i \ln p_i$ is a maximum when all the probabilities are equal. This is first demonstrated for the case of two possibilities:

$$I = - K[p_1 \ln p_1 + p_2 \ln p_2] = - K[p_1 \ln p_1 + (1-p_1) \ln(1-p_1)]$$

Computing I for various values of p_1 and plotting a graph of I versus p_1 (or p_2) gives the curve shown in Fig. 13.9. It is seen that I is zero when p_1 is 0 or 1, and a maximum when

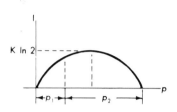

$$p_1 = p_2 = \frac{1}{2}$$

For three possibilities,

$$I = - K[p_1 \ln p_1 + p_2 \ln p_2 + p_3 \ln p_3];$$
$$p_1 + p_2 + p_3 = 1$$

Fig. 13.9 Information as Function of $p_1 = 1 - p_2$.

Since only two of p_1, p_2, p_3 are independent, a point corresponding to a set of numbers p_1, p_2, and p_3 may be represented on a two-dimensional diagram as shown in Fig. 13.10a. Consider three directions making angles of $2\pi/3$ with one another. Taking a length p_1 in the first direction, a length p_2 in

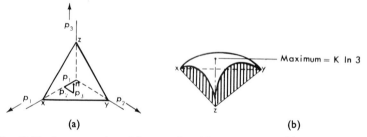

(a)   (b)

Fig. 13.10   Representation of (p_1, p_2, p_3) and Representation of I versus p_1, p_2, p_3.

the second direction, and a length p_3 in the third direction obtains a point M. This point M remains within the equilateral triangle XYZ by virtue of the constraint $p_1 + p_2 + p_3 = 1$. Point X, for example, corresponds to $p_1 = 1$, $p_2 = p_3 = 0$. Line XY corresponds to $p_1 + p_2 = 1$, $p_3 = 0$. Thus, each point within the triangle XYZ corresponds to a set of numbers p_1, p_2, p_3, and the triangle may be used as a base to plot the information I in a direction perpendicular to the plane of the triangle. The result is the surface shown, in perspective, in Fig. 13.10b. The maximum of the surface is at the center of the triangle, for which

$$p_1 = p_2 = p_3 = \frac{1}{3}$$

13.15   Principle of Minimum Prejudice

It is no coincidence that the function

$$H \equiv I = -K \sum_i p_i \ln p_i$$

has been given the name "entropy" in communication theory. It was previously pointed out that this function is identical in form to the expression in statistical mechanics for the thermodynamic entropy. The question arises: Is there any connection between thermodynamics and information theory? Heretofore, the fields of classical thermodynamics and information theory have gone their separate ways. Recently, however, Tribus[†] has suggested that information theory can be used as the basis for the development of thermodynamics. This is reported below.

Tribus' suggestion stems from Jaynes' paper,[‡] which showed that the measure of uncertainty,

$$-K \sum_i p_i \ln p_i,$$

can be used as a basis for statistical inference. The situation is as follows: "Frequency" refers to a set of measurements that have been made; "probability" refers to measurements which have not yet been made. The problem of statistical inference is to find a method for assigning probabilities that is least prejudiced, i.e., using only available information and not assuming more than is actually known. To elaborate: suppose that in the past the frequency of certain events were observed and found to be of magnitude f_i. Then, it is only rational procedure to assign for the future $p_i = f_i$. But what happens if the frequencies are not available or measurable? The answer, according to Jaynes, is to assign that set of values to p_i which is consistent with the given information and which maximizes the uncertainty. This is known as the *Principle of Minimum Prejudice*.

As an illustration of Jaynes' principle, consider the throwing of two coins: one a dime and the other a nickel. Each coin has two aspects: heads or tails. For convenience, let heads be assigned a numerical value 1, and tails a numerical value 2. The four possible microstates are as follows:

---

† Myron Tribus: "Information Theory as the Basis for Thermostatics and Thermodynamics," ASME Paper No. 60–WA–23.

‡ E. T. Jaynes: "Information Theory and Statistical Mechanics." *The Physical Review*, Vol. 106, 108, 1957.

Microstate	Description	Total Value
1	(Dime: head), (Nickel: head)	2
2	(Dime: tails), (Nickel: head)	3
3	(Dime: head), (Nickel: tails)	3
4	(Dime: tails), (Nickel: tails)	4

Suppose that it is given that in a sequence of tosses the average value for the simultaneous tosses of the two coins is $\bar{V} = 3.1$. What is the least prejudiced value for $p_D(H)$, the probability of a head in the toss of the dime? Now, the given information is summarized by the following set of equations:

$$f_D(H) + f_D(T) = 1$$

$$f_N(H) + f_N(T) = 1$$

$$f_D(H) + f_N(H) + 2f_D(T) + 2f_N(T) = \bar{V} = 3.1$$

There are three equations and four unknowns and a deterministic solution cannot, therefore, be found. The problem is one of statistical inference, i.e., it is only possible to infer probabilities from the given information. Applying Jaynes' formalism, the following is to be maximized:

$$S \equiv H = -K[p_D(H) \ln p_D(H) + p_D(T) \ln p_D(T)]$$
$$- K[p_N(H) \ln p_N(H) + p_N(T) \ln p_N(T)] \qquad (13.76)$$

Subject to

$$p_D(H) + p_D(T) = 1 \qquad (13.77)$$

$$p_N(H) + p_N(T) = 1 \qquad (13.78)$$

$$p_D(H) + p_N(H) + 2p_D(T) + 2p_N(T) = <V> = 3.1 \qquad (13.79)$$

where $<V>$ denotes the *expected value* of the tosses. Differentiation of the above equations gives

$$\frac{dS}{K} = [\ln p_D(H) + 1]dp_D(H) + \ldots + [\ln p_N(T) + 1]dp_N(T) = 0 \quad (13.80)$$

$$dp_D(H) + dp_D(T) = 0 \qquad (13.81)$$

$$dp_N(H) + dp_N(T) = 0 \qquad (13.82)$$

$$dp_D(H) + dp_N(H) + 2dp_D(T) + 2p_N(T) = 0 \qquad (13.83)$$

Multiplying Eqs. (13.81), (13.82), (13.83), by $(\lambda_D - 1)$, $(\lambda_N - 1)$, and μ, respectively, and adding to Eq. (13.80) yields

$$p_D(H) = e^{\lambda_D - \mu}; \quad p_D(T) = e^{-\lambda_D - 2\mu} \tag{13.84}$$

$$p_N(H) = e^{\lambda_N - \mu}; \quad p_N(T) = e^{-\lambda_N - 2\mu} \tag{13.85}$$

Replacing these into Eqs. (13.77) and (13.78) gives

$$\lambda_D = \lambda_N = \ln(e^{-\mu} + e^{-2\mu}) \tag{13.86}$$

With λ_D and λ_N alike, the least prejudiced assignment of probabilities is, according to Eqs. (13.84) and (13.85), one of symmetry: $p_D(H) = p_N(H)$; $p_D(T) = p_N(T)$, and thus Eqs. (13.77), (13.78), and (13.79) combine to give $p_D(H) = 0.45$. Note that the condition of the symmetry, i.e., the coins being alike, was not assumed outright, but comes out of the application of Jaynes' formalism. The result should not be interpreted as saying "We don't know anything better, so let's go ahead and guess that the coins are alike."†

13.16 Information Theory and Thermodynamics

To relate more closely and systematically information theory with thermodynamics, consider a thermodynamic system to be made up of a large number of particles. This number is an integer, which means that matter is considered particulate. By the same token, it is assumed that the energy of the system can change only in quanta or discrete manner. A "state" of the system is taken to mean a microscopic description, that is, a message containing a number of symbols sufficient to describe in detail what is going on inside the system. For example, if the system contains N atoms, a message would be

$$(x_1, y_1, z_1, \dot{x}_1, \dot{y}_1, \dot{z}_1, ; \ldots x_N, y_N, z_N, \dot{x}_N, \dot{x}_N, \dot{y}_N, \dot{z}_N)$$

stating the three coordinates of position and velocity for each particle. Associated with this message i is an energy ϵ_i which is a function of the quantum index and the external co-ordinates. In other words,

$$\epsilon_i = \epsilon(i, X_1, X_2, \ldots X_k) \tag{13.87}$$

where $X_1, \ldots X_k$ denote external co-ordinates such as length, volume, strain, electric or magnetic field, or any other constraint imposed by the surroundings, and i is a sequence of allowed states which is determined from quantum theory when the X's and the number of different particles

---

† This quotation, as well as the example just discussed, is from M. Tribus' book: *Thermostatics and Thermodynamics*, D. Van Nostrand Co., 1961.

are specified. The allowed energy levels $\epsilon_i = \epsilon(i, X_1, X_2, \ldots X_K)$ are found from quantum theory.

The system is described as follows. Let p_i represent the probability that the system is in the quantum state i. Then the given information is:

$$\sum_i p_i = 1; \text{ the system is in some state} \tag{13.88}$$

$$\sum_i p_i \epsilon_1 = <E>; \text{ the system has energy} \tag{13.89}$$

The question is this: What values should be assigned to the p_i, the probability of the ith state? The answer, according to the Principle of Minimum Prejudice, is that values of p_i should be assigned that make the uncertainty a maximum, i.e., that assumes the least. Accordingly,

$$S = -K \sum_i p_i \ln p_i \tag{13.90}$$

is to be maximized, subject to Eqs. (13.88) and (13.89). Differentiating and multiplying Eqs. (13.88) and (13.89) by $(\lambda - 1)$ and μ, and adding to $dS/K = 0$ gives

$$p_i = e^{-\lambda - \mu \epsilon_i} \tag{13.91}$$

$$\lambda = \ln \sum_i e^{-\mu \epsilon_i} \tag{13.92}$$

$$S = K[\lambda + \mu <E>] \tag{13.93}$$

$$<E> = -\frac{\partial \lambda}{\partial \mu} \tag{13.94}$$

$$\frac{\partial^2 \lambda}{\partial \mu^2} = \sigma^2(E) \tag{13.95}$$

where $\sigma^2(\epsilon)$ is the variance or square deviation defined as

$$\sigma^2(E) = \sum_i p_i(\epsilon_i - <E>)^2. \tag{13.96}$$

Note that these results resemble those obtained in previous sections on statistical mechanics.

As in the case of statistical thermodynamics, the parameter μ is related to the concept of thermal equilibrium. In fact, it has been given the designation "temper" by Tribus. For, as shown in the example of the tossing of a dime and a nickel (Section 13.15), if two probability distributions are to be considered together in the case a given information does not permit them to be treated separately, the two distributions will have a common Lagrangian multiplier. In other words, if systems A and B, with energies $<E_A>$ and $<E_B>$ are allowed to interact with each other, but not with other systems, the system C, of A and B taken together, has an energy $<E_C> = <E_A> + <E_B>$, and a least prejudiced description requires the maximization of

$$S_C = -K\left[\sum p_A \ln p_A + \sum p_B \ln p_B\right] \tag{13.97}$$

subject to the constraints

$$\sum p_A = 1 \tag{13.98}$$

$$\sum p_B = 1 \tag{13.99}$$

$$\sum p_A E_A + \sum p_B E_B = <\epsilon_A> + <\epsilon_B> \tag{13.100}$$

In the process of maximization, Lagrangian multipliers λ_A, λ_B, and μ_C are introduced, so that both systems A and B will be described by the same temper. More generally stated, if a system A with $\mu = \mu_A$ and energy $<E_A>$ is allowed to interact with a system B with $\mu = \mu_B$ and energy $<E_B>$, both systems after a time adopt a common value of $\mu = \mu_C$. It can be further shown that

$$\mu = \frac{1}{kT} \tag{13.101}$$

where k is the Boltzmann constant.

Classical thermodynamics (which makes up the first part of this book) usually treats the concepts of heat and work as primitive. Information theory, however, considers heat and work as derived quantities. Since

$$<E> = \sum_i p_i \epsilon_i,$$

differentiation gives

$$d<E> = \sum_i \epsilon_i dp_i + \sum_i p_i d\epsilon_i \tag{13.102}$$

Eq. (13.102) shows that the energy of a closed system may be changed in two fundamentally different ways. Let the following quantities be defined:

$$dQ_r \equiv \sum_i \epsilon_i dp_i \tag{13.103}$$

$$dW_r \equiv -\sum_i p_i d\epsilon_i \tag{13.104}$$

Then Eq. (13.102) becomes

$$d<E> = dQ_r - dW_r \tag{13.105}$$

To give an interpretation of dQ_R and dW_R, let the energy,

$$\epsilon_i = \epsilon(i, X_1, X_2, \ldots X_K)$$

associated with each quantum state i, be plotted against the index i. Similarly, let the probabilities p_i, and also the product $p_i\epsilon_i$, be plotted against i. This gives the three diagrams shown in Fig. 13.11. A change of the

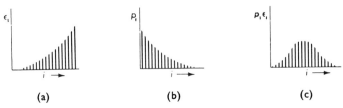

(a)   **(b)**   **(c)**

Fig. 13.11 Plot of ϵ_i, p_i, $p_i\epsilon_i$ versus i.

type dQ_r causes a change in Fig. 13.11b, since

$$dQ_r = \sum_i \epsilon_i dp_i.$$

It also causes a change in the uncertainty

$$S = -K\sum_i p_i \ln p_i.$$

A change of the type dW_r is associated with a change in Fig. 13.11a, since

$$dW_r = -\sum p_i d\epsilon_i.$$

But it gives rise to no change in S, because the p_i's are unchanged. Either type of change, however, causes a change in Fig. 13.11c, where the lengths of the lines add up to the expected value of the energy. The quantities dQ_r and dW_r are equivalent to reversible heat and work transfer respectively. Now, according to Eq. (13.92),

$$\lambda = \ln \sum_i e^{-\mu\epsilon_i}$$

and since $\epsilon_i = \epsilon(i, X_1, X_2, \ldots X_K)$, this means that λ depends upon μ and the external co-ordinates X_K. Furthermore, $<E> = -\partial\lambda/\partial\mu$ (Equation 13.94). Consequently, $<E> = \epsilon(\mu, X_K)$. This gives, for a cyclic transformation in which μ and the external co-ordinates X_K resume their original values,

$$\oint d<E> = 0 \qquad\qquad (13.106)$$

Equation (13.106) is equivalent to the *first law* of thermodynamics.

The *second law* of thermodynamics is equivalent to the statement that "the entropy of an isolated system does not decrease spontaneously." This conclusion is immediate, since entropy and uncertainty are synonymous in information theory. It simply means that knowledge of an isolated system becomes more vague as time goes by. As for the third law of thermodynamics, it may be obtained by applying Eq. (13.91),

$$p_i = e^{-\lambda - \mu \epsilon_i}$$

to two states i and j. This gives

$$\frac{p_i}{p_j} = e^{-\mu(\epsilon_i - \epsilon_j)} \qquad (13.107)$$

Let ϵ_i be greater than ϵ_j. As $\mu(= 1/kT)$ is increased to infinity, the ratio of p_i to p_j goes to zero. This means that as the absolute temperature drops to zero, only the lowest energy level has a probability of being occupied, the other energy levels having comparatively small probabilities. Since the sum of all the probabilities must be unity, the probability at the lowest energy level may be taken to be $p \cong 1$, so that $S = -K[1 \ln 1 + +0 \ln 0 + \ldots]$. Thus,

$$\lim_{T \to 0} S = 0 \qquad (13.108)$$

This is recognized as the *third law* of thermodynamics.

PROBLEMS

13.1. (a) Define the "statistical state" of a system. Illustrate this for a system consisting of 10 coins.

(b) Does the statistical state specify which coins show heads and which show tails?

13.2. To help understand the concept of probability, consider all possible outcomes of an experiment as represented by a space of unit area as shown in Fig. 13.12. An event A is then some subspace within this area, and its probability, $P(A)$, is denoted by a number between 0 and 1 (equal in magnitude to the area of the subspace). Similarly, subspace B represents the probability of an event B. Let $P(A+B)$ denote the probability of either event A or B occurring and $P(A \cdot B)$ denote the probability of both A and B occurring simultaneously. Show that

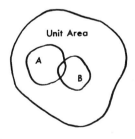

Fig. 13.12

$$P(A+B) = P(A)+P(B)-P(A\cdot B)$$

which, for the case of mutually exclusive events, i.e., $P(A\cdot B) = 0$, becomes

$$P(A+B) = P(A)+P(B) \tag{1}$$

Let $P(A/B)$ denote the probability of event A occurring, given the occurrence of event B. (This is often called conditional probability). Similarly, let $P(B/A)$ denote the probability of B occurring given the occurrence of A. Show that

$$P(A/B) = \frac{P(A\cdot B)}{P(B)}$$

$$P(B/A) = \frac{P(A\cdot B)}{P(A)}$$

and therefore

$$P(A\cdot B) = P(A/B)\times P(B) = P(B/A)\times P(A)$$

For the case of mutually independent events, $P(A/B) = P(A)$, $P(B/A) = P(B)$, so that this becomes

$$P(A\cdot B) = P(A)\times P(B) \tag{2}$$

Equations (1) and (2) are respectively known as the *addition theorem* and the *multiplication theorem* in probability theory.

13.3. (a) What is the probability of obtaining a pair of heads when two coins are tossed? Consider the coins to be "honest".

(b) What is the probability of obtaining either two heads or two tails when two coins are tossed?

13.4. A pair of "honest" dice are tossed.

(a) What is the probability for the first die to yield one and the second to yield six?

(b) What is the probability for the first die to yield three and the second to yield four?

(c) What is the probability of occurrence of "seven"?

13.5. How many ways can a state of three heads occur in eight tosses of a coin? Consider the problem as that of combining three of one kind of object with five of another kind.

13.6. Two observers, Smith and Jones, independently cover a certain event and report it in the same fashion. What is the probability that their report is correct if Smith is known to be correct four-fifths of the time and Jones is known to be correct three-quarters of the time?

13.7. The number of arrangements or permutations of N *distinguishable* objects on N sites is $N!$, for the first object can be put in any one of N places, the second in any one of the $(N-1)$ remaining ones, and so on, up to one for the last. The total number of arrangements is therefore

$$N(N-1)(N-2)\ldots 1 = N!$$

Similarly, the number of permutations of N *distinguishable* objects taken R at a time is

$$N(N-1)\ldots(N-R+1) = \frac{N!}{(N-R)!}$$

What is the number of arrangements of N objects taken R at a time, irrespective of the sequence in which the objects can appear?

13.8. Let there be N coins, each having two possible states or aspects, i.e. heads or tails. Show that the frequency of having R coins (out of the total number N) exhibiting heads is

$$\left[\frac{N!}{(N-R)!R!}\right](2)^{-N}$$

Compare this result with Eq. (13.7) developed in the text.

13.9. (a) Consider a system made up of N objects, each of which has two aspects (coins). If p_1 is the probability of a head and p_2 is that for a tail (only in the case of well-balanced coins will $p_1 = p_2 = 1/2$), show that

$$1 = (p_1+p_2)^N = \Sigma \, \frac{N!}{N_1!N_2!}p_1{}^{N_1}p_2{}^{N_2}$$

where N_1 and N_2 represent the numbers of heads and tails respectively, with $N_1+N_2 = N$.

(b) Generalize this to a system composed of N objects each of which has six aspects (dice), with $p_1, p_2, \ldots p_6$ being the probabilities of these aspects, and obtain

$$1 = (p_1+p_2+ \ldots p_6)^N$$
$$= \Sigma\,\Sigma\,\Sigma\,\Sigma\,\Sigma \, \frac{N!}{N_1!N_2!\ldots N_6!}p_1{}^{N_1}p_2{}^{N_2}\ldots p_6{}^{N_6}$$

where N_i is the number of objects showing the ith aspect, and

$$\Sigma \, N_i = N.$$

(c) What is the thermodynamic probability for the state of a system composed of N objects to be distributed among aspects, with N_i objects in the ith aspect? Does the answer depend upon whether the objects are distinguishable from each other?

13.10. Consider a microstate represented by the following bridge hand:

Spades: K, Q, 10, 5
Hearts: A, J, 4
Diamonds: 10, 9, 6
Clubs: J, 10, 8

What is the probability of occurrence of this microstate as compared to that of a 13-spade hand?

13.11. A total of 30 particles is distributed among three cells, the energies of which are $\epsilon_1 = 2$ joules, $\epsilon_2 = 4$ joules, and $\epsilon_3 = 6$ joules, such that $N_1 = N_2 = N_3 = 10$. If $\delta N_3 = -2$, what is δN_1 and δN_2?

13.12. From Eq. (13.13), show that

$$\ln N! = N \ln N + \frac{1}{2} \ln N - N + 1$$

and write this in the non-logarithmic form of

$$N! = e\sqrt{N}\left(\frac{N}{e}\right)^{N}$$

Hint: Consider ln $N!$ to be halfway between the upper and lower limits given by Eq. (13.13).

13.13. Apply the result expressed by Eq. (13.27) to some familiar examples, such as a large number of coins ($s = 2$), a large number of dice, a large number of molecules in a container subdivided into imaginary compartments of equal volume, etc.

13.14. Consider a system of 20×10^6 particles and a phase space of 5×10^5 cells. If ϵ_i is the same for all cells, what is the thermodynamic probability of:
(a) the most probable distribution,
(b) the least probable distribution?

13.15. A mechanical analogue to the problem of distributing atoms or molecules among quantized energy levels is to have a number of boxes placed at different heights and to distribute among these boxes a number of marbles of uniform mass. The potential energy of any one marble depends upon the height of the box in which it is placed, but the total potential energy of the marbles is fixed, and the distribution of the marbles among the boxes is subject to this overall energy constraint. What is the mechanical analogue when certain of the energy levels are *degenerate*, i.e., can be realized through more than one combination of quantum numbers?

13.16. One way of carrying out the distribution problem for degenerate systems is to start with the thermodynamic probability in the form of Eq. (13.9), which is valid for non-degenerate systems:

$$W = N! \prod_i \frac{1}{N_i!}$$

This is just the formula for the number of ways in which N distinguishable objects can be placed in an array of boxes, with N_1 in the first box, N_2 in the second box, or N_i in the ith box. Now, N_i distinguishable particles can be placed in g_i energetically equivalent boxes in $g_i^{N_i}$ different ways, because for each particle there are g_i ways in which it can be placed. Thus, the thermodynamic probability for degenerate systems is

$$W = N! \prod_i \frac{g_i^{N_i}}{N_i!}$$

Applying Stirling's approximation for the logarithm of W, and using λ and μ as Lagrangian multipliers, maximize W as expressed by the above equation, subject to the constraints involving total number of particles and total energy, and obtain the Maxwell–Boltzmann distribution law for a degenerate system:

$$N_i = g_i e^{-\lambda - \mu \epsilon_i}$$

13.17. (a) From the equation for the thermodynamic probability,

$$W = N! \prod_i \frac{g_i{}^{N_i}}{N_i!}$$

obtain

$$\ln W = N \ln N - N + \sum_i (N_i \ln g_i - N_i \ln N_i + N_i)$$

(b) Multiplying this by k and replacing $\ln N_i$ by $\ln g_i - \lambda - \mu\epsilon_i$ (from the distribution law $N_i = g_i e^{-\lambda - \mu\epsilon_i}$), obtain for the entropy,

$$S = k \ln W = Nk \ln N - Nk + k \sum_i N_i(\lambda + \mu\epsilon_i + 1)$$

$$= k \ln N! + Nk\lambda + k\mu U + Nk$$

(c) Differentiate S while keeping N and all the ϵ_i's constant (from the quantum mechanics point of view, the statement that ϵ_i is constant means that the dimensions of the container are fixed or that the volume of the system is constant. This gives

$$dS = Nk d\lambda + k U d\mu + k\mu dU$$

Making use of

$$N = \sum_i N_i = \sum_i g_i e^{-\lambda - \mu\epsilon_i},$$

obtain

$$dN = 0 = - \sum_i N_i(d\lambda + \epsilon_i d\mu) = -Nd\lambda - Ud\mu,$$

and hence

$$(dS)_{V, N} = k\mu(dU)_{V, N}$$

or

$$\left(\frac{\partial S}{\partial U}\right)_{V, N} = \frac{1}{T} = k\mu$$

Compare this with Eq. (13.49) derived alternatively in the text.

13.18. (a) Show that the Maxwell–Boltzmann distribution law may be written as

$$N_i = C_i e^{-\epsilon_i/kT}$$

where $c_i = e^{-\lambda} g_i$.

(b) Show that if N_0 is the number of molecules in a given reference state ($\epsilon_0 = 0$), the number N of molecules in a state whose energy is ϵ above that of the reference state is given by

$$N = N_0 e^{-\epsilon/kT}$$

13.19. (a) Show that

$$N = N_0 Z$$

where Z is the partition function, and N_0 is the number of molecules in the ground state.

(b) Show that

$$\frac{dZ}{dT} = \frac{1}{kT^2} \sum \epsilon_i g_i e^{-\epsilon_i/kT}$$

Are the energy differences and the quantum weights of the various cells functions of temperature? Is the population distribution of the molecules function of the temperature?

13.20. From

$$U - U_0 = (N_0 g_0)(o) + N_0 \epsilon_1 g_1 e^{-\epsilon_1/kT} + N_0 \epsilon_2 g_2 e^{-\epsilon_2/kT} + \dots$$

show that

$$U - U_0 = N \frac{\sum\limits_i \epsilon_i g_i e^{-\epsilon_i/kT}}{\sum\limits_i g_i e^{-\epsilon_i/kT}} = NkT^2 \frac{\partial \ln Z}{\partial T}$$

where

$$Z = \sum_i g_i e^{-\epsilon_i/kT}$$

is the general molecular partition function. The preceeding equations are for N molecules of gas. For 1 mole of gas, N becomes equal to the Avogadro number and Nk becomes $\bar{R}$. Thus, for 1 mole,

$$U - U_0 = \bar{R}T^2 \frac{\partial \ln Z}{\partial T}$$

and consequently, the molar specific heat is

$$C_V = \frac{\partial}{\partial T}\left(\bar{R}T^2 \frac{\partial \ln Z}{\partial T}\right) = -\bar{R}\left[\frac{\partial}{\partial T}\left(\frac{\partial \ln Z}{\partial [1/T]}\right)\right]$$

13.21. Consider every molecule of a gas to have its representative point in phase space. The co-ordinates of a point in this space are x, y, z, p_x, p_y, p_z, where x, y, z are the rectangular co-ordinates of ordinary space, and p_x, p_y, p_z are the rectangular components of momentum mv_x, mv_y, mv_z. A "cell" is a small subdivision of the phase space having a volume $dx\, dy\, dz\, dp_x\, dp_y\, dp_z$ such that dx, dy, dz are small compared with the linear dimensions of the system, and dp_x, dp_y, dp_z are small compared with the range of momenta of the particles Can a cell be taken to be smaller than h^3, where h is the Planck constant $(= 6.6237 \times 10^{-34}$ joule-sec)? Discuss this in relation to *Heisenberg's uncertainty principle.* Is the ratio

$$\frac{dx\, dy\, dz\, dp_x\, dp_y\, dp_z}{h^3}$$

usually a large number? Discuss this in relation to Stirling's approximation for $\ln N_i$!

13.22. Determine the number of possible deals at bridge. This is the thermodynamic probability corresponding to a 13–13–13–13 macrostate. Consider the 52 cards of the deck to be dealt into four hands by tossing the cards into a box containing four compartments.

13.23. Consider four particles or phase points to be distributed among two cells, i and j, each cell having four energy levels, i.e., being subdivided into four compartments as shown in Fig. 13.13. Consider the particular macrostate $N_i = 3$, $N_j = 1$. Without making use of the identities of the particles, but denoting instead each particle by a dot, complete the number of possible arrangements of the particles in each cell. What is the thermodynamic probability of each cell? What is the thermodynamic probability of the macrostate $N_i = 3$, $N_j = 1$? Check this with the formula developed for Bose–Einstein statistics.

Cell i: --- $w_i = ?$

Cell j: --- $w_j = ?$

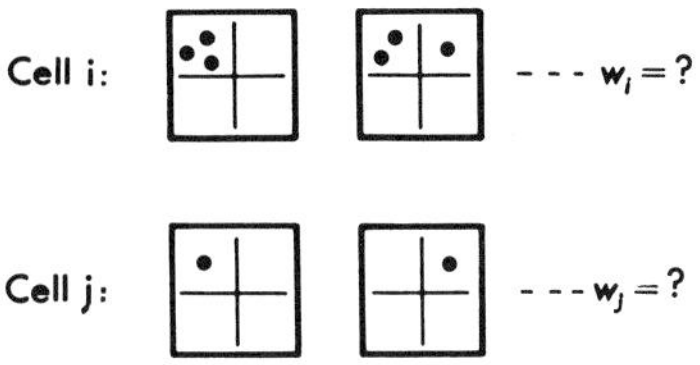

Fig. 13.13

13.24. Complete the steps sketched out in Sec. 13.9 and obtain, for the case of Bose–Einstein statistics, the following distribution law:

$$N_i = \frac{g_i}{ce^{\mu\epsilon_i} - 1}$$

Show that if N_i is very much smaller than g_i, i.e., if the density of phase points in phase space is very small, the distribution goes over to the Maxwell–Boltzmann distribution. Hint: divide both sides of the Bose–Einstein distribution by g_i and neglect the term -1 in comparison with $ce^{\mu\epsilon_i}$.

13.25. Consider four particles to be distributed among two cells, i and j, each cell having four energy levels as shown in Fig. 13.14. For the particular macrostate of $N_i = 3$, $N_j = 1$, and with-out making use of the identities of the particles, complete the number of possible arrangements of the particles in each cell, subject to the stipulation that no more than one particle be allowed per compartment. What is the thermodynamic probability of each cell? What is the thermodynamic probability of the macrostate $N_i = 3$, $N_j = 1$? Check this with the formula developed for Fermi–Dirac statistics.

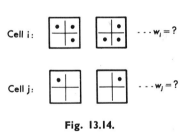

Cell i: --- $w_i = ?$

Cell j: --- $w_j = ?$

Fig. 13.14.

13.26. Complete the steps sketched out in Sec. 13.9 and obtain, for the case of Fermi–Dirac statistics, the following distribution law:

$$N_i = \frac{g_i}{e^{\lambda + \mu\epsilon_i} + 1} = \frac{g_i}{e^{\lambda + \epsilon_i/kT} + 1}$$

For most Fermi–Dirac systems, λ becomes negative and rather large at very low temperatures. Show that at these temperatures, the occupation index N_i/g_i (= average number of particles per energy level at the energy ϵ) is essentially equal to unity for energies less than $-\lambda kT$. The quantity $-\lambda kT$ is called the *Fermi level* and is designated ϵ_m.

13.27. At very high temperatures, λ becomes positive and large. Show that in this case the Fermi–Dirac distribution approaches a Maxwell–Boltzmann distribution.

13.28. To show that μ has a universal character closely related to the thermodynamic temperature, independent of the type of particle, consider a system composed of a mixture of two different kinds of identical particles. Divide the energy range into cells $\Delta\epsilon_i$ for the first kind of particle, $\Delta\epsilon_j$ for the second kind of particle, and maximize the joint probability $W(N_i, N_j) = W(N_i) W(N_j)$ subject to the conditions

$$\sum_i N_i = \text{constant} = N_1 \tag{1}$$

$$\sum_j N_j = \text{constant} = N_2 \tag{2}$$

$$\sum_i N_i\epsilon_i + \sum_j N_j\epsilon_j = \text{constant} = U \tag{3}$$

where N_1 and N_2 are the numbers of the two kinds of particles present in the mixture and U is the total energy of the system. Apply the method of undetermined multipliers, using three multipliers: λ_1 and λ_2 for conditions (1) and (2), and μ for condition (3). Show that this leads to distributions for the two kinds of particles which are similar in form to those obtained previously, each distribution involving a different λ, but precisely the same μ.

13.29. The quantity given by Eq. (13.92):

$$\lambda = \ln \sum_i e^{-\mu\epsilon_i},$$

is often called the *Massieu function*. It enables the macroscopic properties of a system to be evaluated if $\lambda(\mu, x_k)$ and $\epsilon_i(x_k)$ are known. Show that

$$\langle E \rangle = -\frac{\partial\lambda}{\partial\mu}$$

$$\sigma^2(E) = \frac{\partial^2\lambda}{\partial\mu^2}$$

$$S = k\left[\lambda - \mu\frac{\partial\lambda}{\partial\mu}\right]$$

$$T = -\frac{1}{k\mu}$$

$$\langle p \rangle = \frac{1}{\mu}\left(\frac{\partial\lambda}{\partial V}\right)$$

$$\langle A \rangle \equiv \langle E \rangle - TS = -\frac{\lambda}{\mu}$$

$$C_V \equiv \left[\frac{\partial\langle E \rangle}{\partial T}\right]_{x_k} = k\mu^2\left(\frac{\partial^2\lambda}{\partial\mu^2}\right)$$

$$H = \left(\frac{V}{\mu}\right)\left(\frac{\partial\lambda}{\partial V}\right) - \left(\frac{\partial\lambda}{\partial\mu}\right)$$

CHAPTER 14

Kinetic Theory of Ideal Gas

14.1 Introduction

Thermodynamics is a macroscopic science, dealing with properties of systems without seeking to inquire further into the nature of those quantities. Assumptions regarding the ultimate structure of matter are not necessary, since the laws of thermodynamics are based solely on macroscopic observations and in no way depend on molecular theory.

Kinetic theory, on the other hand, does seek to explain physical phenomena on the basis of molecular behaviour. It regards both temperature and pressure as manifestations of molecular motion. Temperature is a measure of the average translational kinetic energy of the molecules, whereas pressure is the effect of the average force resulting from repeated impacts of molecules with the containing walls. Having developed the essentials of Maxwell–Boltzmann statistics in Chap. 13, we will apply these statistics in the present chapter to the translational properties of ideal gases. This kind of treatment describes quite adequately the high-temperature behavior of monoatomic gases (such as helium, neon, and argon). It also proves useful in describing the behavior of diatomic and poly-atomic molecules, though it provides only a partial description of their behavior, since these molecules can undergo rotations and vibrations as well as translations. Before applying the Maxwell–Boltzmann law, however, a few properties of an ideal gas will first be presented.

14.2 Ideal Gas

There are, in engineering applications, many substances whose state may be considered to fall into two regions: (a) the region of high tempera-ture (where the temperature is in excess of twice the critical temperature), and, (b) the region of low pressure, where the pressure is 1 atm or less. The behavior of substances in these two regions then approaches closely the behavior of a hypothetical fluid known as a *perfect* or *ideal gas*, a very useful concept in thermodynamics.

The laws pertaining to the gaseous state are particularly simple when the density of the gas is very much less than that of the corresponding liquid or solid. These laws are called ideal-gas laws. They are very good approxima-tions for ordinary gases if the gas density is one thousandth of that of the corresponding liquid. In that case, the deviation of the actual behavior from the ideal behavior is in the order of a few tenths of one per cent.

Boyle's Law: If the temperature remains constant, the volume of a given mass of gas is inversely proportional to the pressure. Thus, between any two states 1 and 2 of a gas at the same temperature,

$$\frac{v_1}{v_2} = \frac{p_2}{p_1} \tag{14.1}$$

where v = specific volume, p = absolute pressure. Boyle's law for gases corresponds to Hooke's law for solids; both are good approximations in the limit of low pressures.

Charles' Law: This law, also known as Gay-Lussac's law, is in two parts:

If the pressure is held constant, the volume of a gas varies directly as the absolute temperature:

$$\frac{v_1}{v_2} = \frac{T_1}{T_2} \tag{14.2}$$

If the volume is held constant, the pressure of a gas varies directly as the absolute temperature:

$$\frac{p_1}{p_2} = \frac{T_1}{T_2} \qquad (14.3)$$

A relation between all three variables: p, v, and T may be obtained by combining Boyle's law and Charles' law. Referring to Fig. 14.1, let an ideal gas be in state 1, and let the gas undergo an arbitrary change to state 2. From state 1, draw a constant pressure line; from state 2, draw a constant temperature line. The two lines intersect at point A. Applying Charles' law to the process 1-A, we obtain

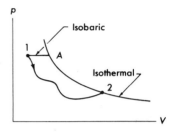

$$\frac{v_1}{v_A} = \frac{T_1}{T_A}$$

or

Fig. 14.1

Demonstration of Charles' Law.

$$v_A = \frac{T_A v_1}{T_1} = \frac{T_2 v_1}{T_1} \qquad (14.4)$$

Similarly, Boyle's law applied to the process 2-A, gives

$$\frac{v_2}{v_A} = \frac{p_A}{p_2}$$

or

$$v_A = \frac{p_2 v_2}{p_A} = \frac{p_2 v_2}{p_1} \qquad (14.5)$$

Eqs. (14.4) and (14.5) yield the following result:

$$\frac{T_2 v_1}{T_1} = \frac{p_2 v_2}{p_1}$$

or

$$\frac{p_1 v_1}{T_1} = \frac{p_2 v_2}{T_2}$$

Since points 1 and 2 can be selected at random, it follows that a like relation may be written for any other pair of points, so that

$$\frac{p_1 v_1}{T_1} = \frac{p_2 v_2}{T_2} = \ldots = \frac{pv}{T} = R$$

or

$$pv = RT \tag{14.6}$$

where R is a constant for a particular gas. In the engineering system of units, it has the units of ft lbf/lbm–°R. Equation (14.6) is the equation of state of an ideal gas; it is written for a unit mass of gas. For a system consisting of m pounds of gas, it becomes $pV = mRT$, and, for a system consisting of N moles, it becomes

$$pV = N\bar{R}T \tag{14.7}$$

where $\bar{R}$ is a universal gas constant (to be discussed shortly).

Equation (14.6) defines a surface called the p–v–T surface if the three variables p, v, and T are plotted along three mutually perpendicular lines as shown in Fig. 14.2. It can be seen that lines of intersection with planes perpendicular to the temperature axis yield isothermal lines which have the form of hyperbolas.

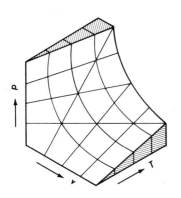

Avogadro's Law: According to Avogadro's hypothesis, all ideal gases at a particular pressure and temperature have the same number of molecules in a given volume. Since the molecular weight of a gas is an index to the weight of a molecule of that gas, it follows from Avogadro's law that the density is proportional to the molecular weight, i.e.,

Fig. 14.2
p–v–T Surface for Ideal Gas.

$$\frac{\rho_A}{\rho_B} = \frac{M_A}{M_B} \tag{14.8}$$

where ρ_A and ρ_B are the densities, and M_A and M_B are the molecular weights of gases A and B, respectively. Since the densities are inversely proportional to the specific volumes, Eq. (14.8) may be written as

$$\frac{v_B}{v_A} = \frac{M_A}{M_B}$$

or

$$M_A v_A = M_B v_B \tag{14.9}$$

Because A and B may be any two gases, Eq. (14.9) states that the product Mv is the same for all ideal gases at any particular temperature and pressure. Mv is called the *mole volume*. At 14.7 psia and 32 °F, it is 359 cu ft.

Let both sides of Eq. (14.6) be multiplied by M, the molecular weight. This gives

$$Mpv = MRT \qquad (14.10)$$

Since Mv is the mole volume (usually denoted as $\bar{v}$), Eq. (14.10) may be written as

$$p\bar{v} = MRT$$

or

$$MR = \frac{p\bar{v}}{T} \qquad (14.11)$$

Since $\bar{v}$ is the same for all ideal gases at the same pressure and temperature, The product MR (denoted by $\bar{R}$), which is called the *universal gas constant*, is the same for all ideal gases, and has the value of

$$
\left.
\begin{aligned}
\bar{R} &= 1445 \text{ ft lbf/lb mole-}^\circ\text{R} \\
&= 1.986 \text{ Btu/lb mole-}^\circ\text{R} \\
&= 1.986 \text{ cal/g mole-}^\circ\text{K}
\end{aligned}
\right\} \qquad (14.12)
$$

The individual gas constant R of any gas may be found by dividing the universal gas constant $\bar{R}$ by the molecular weight of that gas.

14.3 Internal Energy and Enthalpy of Ideal Gas

A consequence of the fact that a perfect gas obeys the equation of state $pv = RT$ is that the internal energy is function of temperature only. This may be readily shown as follows: Recall that in Sec. 5.12, there was derived the relation

$$du = c_v dT + \left[\frac{c_p - c_v}{v\beta} - p \right] dv$$

From this, it is seen that

$$\left(\frac{\partial u}{\partial v} \right)_T = \frac{c_p - c_v}{v\beta} - p \qquad (14.13)$$

Now,

$$\beta = \frac{1}{v}\left(\frac{\partial v}{\partial T} \right)_p = \frac{1}{v}\left[\frac{\partial}{\partial T}\left(\frac{RT}{p} \right) \right]_p = \frac{1}{v}\left(\frac{R}{p} \right) = \frac{1}{T}$$

for an ideal gas. As for $c_p - c_v$, it can be calculated from the relation (developed in Sec. 11.4):

$$c_p - c_v = T\left(\frac{\partial p}{\partial T}\right)_v \left(\frac{\partial v}{\partial T}\right)_p$$

which, for a gas obeying equation of state $pv = RT$ becomes

$$c_p - c_v = T\left(\frac{R}{v}\right)\left(\frac{R}{p}\right) = \frac{TR^2}{pv} = R$$

Thus, for a perfect gas, Eq. (14.13) gives

$$\left(\frac{\partial u}{\partial v}\right)_T = \frac{R}{v(1/T)} - p = \frac{RT}{v} - p = 0$$

which means that u is independent of v. That u is also independent of p may be shown by writing

$$\left(\frac{\partial u}{\partial v}\right)_T = 0 = \left(\frac{\partial u}{\partial p}\right)_T \left(\frac{\partial p}{\partial v}\right)_T$$

Since

$$\left(\frac{\partial p}{\partial v}\right)_T = -\frac{RT}{v^2} = -\frac{p}{v}$$

and therefore is not zero, it follows that

$$\left(\frac{\partial u}{\partial p}\right)_T = 0 \qquad\qquad (14.14)$$

That the internal energy of a perfect gas is function of temperature only was demonstrated by Joule in one of the famous experiments of thermo-dynamics. Two vessels, A and B, shown in Fig. 14.3, are connected by a pipe and a valve, and immersed in a water bath. The water itself is in an insulated container, so that the whole apparatus may be considered an isolated system. One of the vessels holds air at a pressure of 22 atm, and the other is evacuated. The temperature of the water bath is measured, the valve opened, and the air expanded without doing work until both containers are filled. As no work is done, and no heat transferred, the first law gives $U = Q - W = 0$, i.e.,

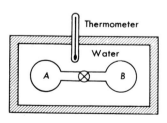

Fig. 14.3 Joule's Experiment.

there is no change in internal energy. Since the pressure and the volume change during the experiment, Joule concluded that the internal energy is not a function of pressure or volume, but a function of temperature only. Thus, the difference in internal energy of an ideal gas in any two states may be written in differential form as

$$du = \left(\frac{\partial u}{\partial v}\right)_T dv + \left(\frac{\partial u}{\partial T}\right)_v dT = 0 + \left(\frac{\partial u}{\partial T}\right)_v dT$$

or

$$du = c_v dT \tag{14.15}$$

where

$$c_v = \left(\frac{\partial u}{\partial T}\right)_v$$

is the specific heat at constant volume.

As for the enthalpy, it follows from its definition and the use of the equation of state that

$$h = u + pv = u + RT \tag{14.16}$$

Since R is a constant, and u is a function of temperature only, it is seen from the above equation that the enthalpy of a perfect gas is also a function of temperature only. The enthalpy change between two states infinitesimally apart may thus be written as

$$dh = \left(\frac{\partial h}{\partial p}\right)_T dp + \left(\frac{\partial h}{\partial T}\right)_p dT = 0 + \left(\frac{\partial h}{\partial T}\right)_p dT$$

But $(\partial h/\partial T)_p = c_p$ by definition, so that

$$dh = c_p dT \tag{14.17}$$

Example 14.1. A certain mass of gas in an initial state $p_1 = 70$ psia and $V_1 = 4.8$ cu ft undergoes a change to a state $p_2 = 25$ psia and $V_2 = 8.3$ cu ft, during which the enthalpy decreases by 60 Btu. If the specific heat at constant volume for the gas is $c_v = 0.754$ Btu/lbm–°R, determine: (a) the change in internal energy during the process, (b) the gas constant R, (c) the ratio of specific heats $\gamma = c_p/c_v$.

Solution. (a) From the definition of enthalpy: $H = U + pV$,

$$\Delta H = \Delta U + \Delta(pV)$$

or

$$-60 = \Delta U + \frac{144}{778}[(25)(8.3) - (70)(4.8)]$$

whence

$$\Delta U = -36.2 \text{ Btu}$$

(b) The method of solution for R is not immediately apparent; however, it is helpful to write down the general relation

$$\Delta U = mc_v(T_2 - T_1)$$

In this last equation, c_v is known, and ΔU has been calculated from part (a) The unknown temperatures T_1 and T_2 may be eliminated in favor of pressure, volume, and R by applying the equation of state and writing $T_1 = (p_1V_1)/mR$; $T_2 = (p_2V_2)/mR$. Thus,

$$\Delta U = mc_v(T_2 - T_1) = mc_v\left(\frac{p_2V_2}{mR} - \frac{p_1V_1}{mR}\right)$$

$$= \frac{c_v}{R}(p_2V_2 - p_1V_1)$$

or

$$-36.2 = \left(\frac{0.754}{R}\right)(144)[(25)(8.3) - (70)(4.8)]$$

whence

$$R = 386 \text{ ft lbf/lbm-°R}$$

(c) The ratio of specific heats is

$$\gamma = \frac{c_p}{c_v} = \frac{c_p \Delta T}{c_v \Delta T} = \frac{\Delta H}{\Delta U} = \frac{-60}{-36.2} = 1.66$$

14.4 Specific Heats of Ideal Gas

Since the internal energy and the enthalpy of an ideal gas are functions of temperature only, it follows that the specific heat at constant volume and the specific heat at constant pressure are also functions of temperature only, i.e.,

$$c_v = c_v(T) \tag{14.18}$$

and

$$c_p = c_p(T) \tag{14.19}$$

Because all gases approach ideal gas behaviour at low pressures, Eqs. (14.18) and (14.19) define what is known as the constant zero pressure specific heat $c_p{}^o$ and the constant infinite volume (zero pressure) specific heat $c_v{}^\infty$. Figure 14.4 shows the zero pressure specific heat $\bar{c}_p{}^o$ (per mole) of

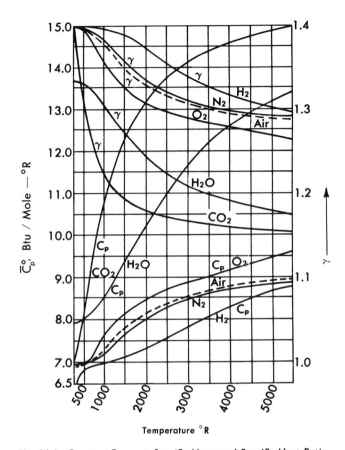

Fig. 14.4 Constant-Pressure Specific Heats and Specific Heat Ratio.

various gases plotted against temperature. It also gives the ratio of specific heats, so that it is not necessary to plot $\bar{c}_v{}^\infty$. While no simple equation can fit any one curve over a wide range of temperatures, the specific heat at zero pressure may nevertheless be represented by an equation of the form

$$\bar{c}_p{}^o = A + BT + CT^2 + \frac{D}{\sqrt{T}}$$

where A, B, C, and D are constants (different for different gases).

It is of interest to calculate the difference in specific heats for an ideal gas: Eq. (14.16) gives

$$h = u + RT$$

or

$$dh = du + RdT$$

But $dh = c_p dT$, and $du = c_v dT$; thus,

$$c_p dT = c_v dT + RdT$$

whence

$$c_p = c_v + R$$

or

$$c_p - c_v = R \qquad (14.20)$$

In other words, the *difference* in specific heats for an ideal gas is the same at all temperatures and is equal to R, even though the specific heat at constant pressure and the specific heat at constant volume may vary with temperature. For example knowing the constant-pressure specific heat at zero pressure, the constant-volume specific heat at zero pressure may be readily obtained:*

$$\bar{c}_v{}^\infty = \bar{c}_p{}^o - \bar{R}$$

or

$$\bar{c}_v{}^\infty = A + BT + CT^2 + \frac{D}{\sqrt{T}} - \bar{R}$$

It should also be pointed out that from the definition of $\gamma = c_p/c_v$ and $R = c_p - c_v$, the specific heat at constant pressure and the specific heat at constant volume for an ideal gas may each be written as

$$c_p = \frac{\gamma R}{\gamma - 1} \qquad (14.21)$$

and

$$c_v = \frac{\gamma R}{\gamma - 1} \qquad (14.22)$$

Example 14.2. A certain gas has a specific heat at constant pressure of

$$\bar{c}_p{}^o = 11.5 - \frac{172}{\sqrt{T}} + \frac{1530}{T}$$

---

* The student should always keep in mind dimensional consistency. Thus, if R is given in units of ft lbf/lbm-°R, it should be divided by 778 ft lbf/Btu in any relation involving specific heats.

where $\bar{c}_p^{\,0}$ = Btu/lb mole-°R, and T = °R. Determine: (a) the change of enthalpy when one pound is heated from 140 °F to 1540 °F, (b) the average specific heat for the process. The gas has a molecular weight of 32.

Solution.

$$\Delta \bar{h} = \int_{600}^{2000} \overline{c_p^{\,0}}\, dT = \int_{600}^{2000} \left(11.5 - \frac{172}{T^{1/2}} + \frac{1530}{T}\right) dT$$

$$= \left[11.5(T_2 - T_1) - (172)(2)(T_2^{1/2} - T_1^{1/2}) + 1530 \ln \frac{T_2}{T_1}\right]_{600}^{2000}$$

$$= 11.5(1400) - 344(44.7 - 24.5) + 1530 \ln 3.34$$

$$\Delta \bar{h} = 10{,}998 \text{ Btu/lb mole}$$

or

$$\Delta h = \frac{10998}{32} = 343 \text{ Btu/lbm}$$

(b) The average specific heat for the process is

$$(\bar{c}_p)_{\text{av}} = \frac{\displaystyle\int_{T_1}^{T_2} c_p\, dT}{T_2 - T_1} = \frac{10{,}998}{2000 - 600}$$

$$= 7.85 \text{ Btu/lb mole-°R}$$

or

$$(c_p)_{\text{av}} = \frac{7.85}{32} = 0.246 \text{ Btu/lbm-°R}$$

14.5 Entropy of Ideal Gas

The entropy change of an ideal gas may be calculated by means of the relations developed in Sec. 9.6. For example, from $Tds = du + pdv$ and $du = c_v dT$, the entropy change for a gas obeying $pv = RT$ is

$$ds = c_v \frac{dT}{T} + pdv$$

$$= c_v \frac{dT}{T} + R\frac{dv}{v}$$

or

$$s_2 - s_1 = \int_1^2 c_v \frac{dT}{T} + R \ln \frac{v_2}{v_1} \tag{14.23}$$

Alternate expressions for the entropy change in terms of (T, p) and (p, v) as pairs of independent variables are

$$s_2 - s_1 = \int_1^2 c_p \frac{dT}{T} - R \ln \frac{p_2}{p_1} \tag{14.24}$$

and

$$s_2 - s_1 = c_v \ln \frac{p_2}{p_1} + c_p \ln \frac{v_2}{v_1} \qquad (14.25)$$

They are readily obtained from the Tds equations developed in Sec. 9.6.

Changes in entropy and calculations pertaining to isentropic processes of ideal gases with variable specific heats involve trial and error solution, especially if one of the terminal temperatures is unknown. The following numerical example illustrates this fact.

Example 14.3. Four pounds of an ideal gas having variable specific heats undergo an isentropic expansion from 100 psia and 1540 °F to 20 psia. Determine the work done if the constant-pressure specific heat is given by

$$\bar{c}_p{}^o = 0.340 - 0.36 \times 10^{-5} T + 0.616 \times 10^{-9} T^2 - \frac{3.19}{\sqrt{T}}$$

where $\bar{c}_p{}^o$ = Btu/lbm-°R, and T = degrees Rankine. The gas constant is $R = 48.2$ ft lbf/lbm-°R.

Solution. In Fig. 14.5, the work done in the isentropic expansion 1–2 is obtained from the first law:

$$Q = 0 = \Delta U + W,$$

which gives

$$W_{1-2} = m\Delta u = -m \int_{2000}^{T_2} c_v dT$$

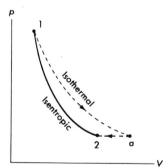

Fig. 14.5 Isothermal and Isentropic of Ideal Gas.

Since T_2 is unknown, it must be calculated beforehand. To this effect, let an isothermal $1-a$ and an isobaric $a-2$ be drawn. Entropy being a point function, its change between two states is the same irrespective of paths. Thus,

$$(\Delta s)_{1-2} = 0 = (\Delta s)_{1-a} + (\Delta s)_{a-2}$$

$$= R \ln \frac{p_1}{p_a} + \int_a^2 c_p \frac{dT}{T} = \frac{48.2}{778} \ln \frac{100}{20} + \int_{2000}^{T_2} c_p \frac{dT}{T}$$

$$= 0.09987 + \int_{2000}^{T_2} c_p \frac{dT}{T}$$

whence

$$\int_{T_2}^{2000} \left(0.340 - 0.36 \times 10^{-5} T + 0.616 \times 10^{-9} T^2 - \frac{3.19}{\sqrt{T}} \right) \frac{dT}{T} = 0.09987$$

or

$$0.340 \ln \frac{2000}{T_2} - 36 \times 10^{-5}(2000 - T_2) + \frac{0.616}{2} \times 10^{-9}(\overline{2000^2} - T_2{}^2) +$$

$$+2\times3.19\left(\frac{1}{\sqrt{2000}}-\frac{1}{\sqrt{T_2}}\right) = 0.09987$$

Solution for T_2 is by trial and error. An approximate value for T_2, however, is first obtained by assuming the gas to have a constant specific ratio of $\gamma = 1.35$ (which it does not):

$$T_2 \approx 2000\left(\frac{20}{100}\right)^{(1.35-1)/1.35} = 1320\ ^\circ R$$

A more accurate solution then gives $T_2 = 1350\ ^\circ R$.

Knowing T_2, the work can be obtained by calculating the change in internal energy:

$$W_{1-2} = -m \int_{2000}^{T_2} c_v dT = -m \int_{2000}^{1350} (c_p - R) dT$$

$$= -4 \int_{2000}^{1350} \left(0.340 - 0.36\times10^{-5}T + 0.616\times10^{-9}T^2 - \frac{3.19}{\sqrt{T}} - \frac{48.2}{778}\right)dT = 501\ \text{Btu}$$

14.6 Gas Tables

The integration of specific heat equations, as shown in the preceding example, is a time-consuming process. For this reason, the modern trend is to use the gas tables by Keenan and Kaye. These tables, which take into account the variation of specific heats with temperature, give the enthalpy and internal energy of a number of gases, including air. In effect, the values of enthalpy and internal energy at a given temperature are obtained by integrating the zero-pressure specific heat equations from absolute zero to the given temperature, the enthalpy and internal energy being assumed to be zero at absolute zero.*

Since the perfect-gas equation of state $pv = RT$ is assumed, the enthalpy and internal energy are functions of temperature only, and a table for these need have only one independent parameter, temperature. Entropy, however, is a function of two independent properties, for example pressure and temperature. Referring to Eq. (14.24), the entropy change between any two states is

$$s_2 - s_1 = \int_{T_1,\ p_1}^{T_2,\ p_2} ds = \int_{T_1}^{T_2} c_p \frac{dT}{T} - R \ln\frac{p_2}{p_1}$$

Let the zero of entropy be assigned to an arbitrary reference state where the temperature is T_0 and the pressure is unity. Then the entropy s_1 at a given temperature T_1 and pressure p_1 is

---

* An abstract of the gas tables is given in the appendix.

$$s_1 - 0 = \int_{T_0}^{T_1} c_p \frac{dT}{T} - R \ln p_1 \qquad (14.26)$$

Similarly, the entropy s_2 at a temperature T_2 and a pressure p_2 is

$$s_2 - 0 = \int_{T_0}^{T_2} c_p \frac{dT}{T} - R \ln p_2 \qquad (14.27)$$

From Eqs. (14.26) and (14.27), the entropy change between states 1 and 2 then becomes

$$s_2 - s_1 = \int_{T_0}^{T_2} c_p \frac{dT}{T} - \int_0^{T_1} c_p \frac{dT}{T} - R \ln \frac{p_2}{p_1} \qquad (14.28)$$

In the gas tables the quantity

$$\phi = \int_{T_0}^{T} c_p \frac{dT}{T} \qquad (14.29)$$

is tabulated as a function of temperature, the argument. The entropy change between any two states is thus

$$s_2 - s_1 = \phi_2 - \phi_1 - R \ln \frac{p_2}{p_1} \qquad (14.30)$$

Since ϕ_2 and ϕ_1 are read directly from the tables, there are no tedious calculations. Equation (14.30) holds for all processes, both reversible and irreversible.

Example 14.4. Find the change in entropy for a pound of air as it undergoes a change in state from $p_1 = 100$ psia, $t_1 = 1540$ °F, to $p_2 = 20$ psia, $t_2 = 1140$ °F.

Solution. From the gas tables, corresponding to $T_1 = 2000$ °R and $T_2 = 1600$ °R,

$$\phi_1 = 0.93205 \text{ Btu/lbm-°R}; \quad \phi_2 = 0.87130 \text{ Btu/lbm-°R}$$

From Eq. (14.30),

$$s_2 - s_1 = 0.87130 - 0.93205 - \frac{53.3}{778} \ln \frac{20}{100}$$

$$= 0.04958 \text{ Btu/lbm-°R}$$

14.7   Reversible Adiabatic Process with Variable Specific Heats

The equation for a reversible adiabatic process involving a perfect gas with *constant* specific heats is $pv^\gamma = $ constant. In the case of a perfect gas with *variable* specific heats, no such simple relation exists. The gas tables, however, may be used for reversible adiabatic processes by introducing a relative pressure, p_r, and a relative specific volume, v_r. The definition and use of these terms follow:

For a reversible adiabatic process, the combined first and second laws give

$$Tds = 0 = du + pdv = dh - vdp$$

or

$$dh = vdp$$

Replacing dh by $c_p dT$ and v by RT/p, this becomes

$$c_p dT = RT \frac{dp}{p}$$

or

$$\frac{d_p}{p} = \frac{c_p}{R} \frac{dT}{T}$$

This relation can be integrated between a reference state (T_0, p_0) and a given state (T, p):

$$\ln \frac{p}{p_0} = \frac{1}{R} \int_{T_0}^{T} \frac{c_p \, dT}{T} \tag{14.31}$$

The right side of Eq. (14.31) is function of temperature only. Let a relative pressure p_r, be defined as

$$\ln p_r = \ln \frac{p}{p_0} = \frac{1}{R} \int_{T_0}^{T} c_p \frac{dT}{T} \tag{14.32}$$

Then, p_r can be tabulated in terms of temperature as the argument. Now, consider two states, 1 and 2, along a reversible adiabatic line. It follows from Eq. (14.32) that

$$\frac{p_{r_1}}{p_{r_2}} = \frac{p_1/p_0}{p_2/p_0} = \frac{p_1}{p_2} \tag{14.33}$$

i.e., the ratio of the relative pressures for two states having the same entropy is equal to the ratio of the absolute pressures.

Similarly, the relative specific volume v_r, is defined by

$$\ln v_r = \ln \frac{v}{v_0} = -\frac{1}{R} \int_{T_0}^{T} c_v \frac{dT}{T} \tag{14.34}$$

or, alternately, by

$$v_r = \frac{RT}{p_r} \tag{14.35}$$

so that it follows, for any two states along an isentropic line:

$$\frac{v_{r_1}}{v_{r_2}} = \frac{v_1}{v_2} \qquad (14.36)$$

Example 14.5. Air initially at 100 psia and 1000 °F expands isentropically to 15 psia. Determine the change of enthalpy and of specific volume by: (a) using perfect gas laws with constant specific heat, (b) using the gas tables.

Solution. (a) Using perfect gas laws: $p_1 v_1{}^\gamma = p_2 v_2{}^\gamma$

$$v_2 = v_1 \left(\frac{p_1}{p_2}\right)^{1/\gamma} = \frac{RT_1}{p_1}\left(\frac{p_1}{p_2}\right)^{1/\gamma}$$

$$= \frac{(53.3)(1460)}{(100)(144)}\left(\frac{100}{15}\right)^{1/1.4} = 20.95 \text{ cu ft/lbm}$$

$$\Delta v = v_2 - v_1 = 20.95 - \frac{RT_1}{p_1}$$

$$= 20.95 - 5.40 = 15.55 \text{ cu ft/lbm}$$

From $\qquad\qquad\qquad \dfrac{p_1 v_1}{T_1} = \dfrac{p_2 v_2}{T_2},$

$$T_2 = T_1 \frac{p_2 v_2}{p_1 v_1} = (1460)\frac{(15)(20.95)}{(100)(540)} = 849 \text{ °R} = 389 \text{ °F}$$

$$\Delta h = c_p \, \Delta T = (0.24)(389 - 1000) = -146.6 \text{ Btu/lbm}$$

(b) Using the gas tables, at $T_1 = 1460$ °R, $h_1 = 358.6$ Btu/lbm, and $p_{r_1} = 50.3$. For an isentropic process,

$$p_{r_2} = p_{r_1}\left(\frac{p_2}{p_1}\right) = 50.3\left(\frac{15}{100}\right) = 7.55$$

Corresponding to $p_{r_2} = 7.55$, the gas tables give $T_2 = 873$ °R, $h_2 = 209.8$ Btu/lbm. Thus,

$$\Delta h = 209.8 - 358.6 = -148.8 \text{ Btu/lbm}$$

From $p_2 v_2 = RT_2$,

$$v_2 = \frac{RT_2}{p_2} = \frac{(53.34)(873)}{(15)(144)} = 21.55 \text{ cu ft/lbm}$$

The change in specific volume is

$$\Delta v = 21.55 - 5.40 = 16.15 \text{ cu ft/lbm}$$

Example 14.6. A pound of air is compressed adiabatically in steady flow from 15 psia and 80 °F with a compression ratio of 5 (i.e. the volume at the end of compression is one-fifth of the initial volume). The compression efficiency is 80 per cent (meaning that the actual work required is 1.25 times the isentropic work). Determine: (a) the actual amount of work required, (b) the increase in entropy and the increase in unavailable energy $T_0 \Delta s$ referred to a surroundings temperature of 60 °F.

Solution. (a) From the gas tables, at 540 °R: $h_1 = 129.06$, $v_{r_1} = 144.32$, $p_{r_1} = 1.3860$, $\phi_1 = 0.60078$. For a compression ratio of 5, in an isentropic process,

$$\left(\frac{v_1}{v_2}\right)_s = 5 = \frac{v_{r_1}}{v_{r_2}}$$

or

$$v_{r_2} = \frac{v_{r_1}}{5} = \frac{144.32}{5} = 28.85$$

Corresponding to $v_{r_2} = 28.85$, the gas tables give $h_2 = 245.12$, $p_{r_2} = 13.059$, $T_2 = 1016.8$ °R. The work required for isentropic compression is

$$w_s = h_2 - h_1$$
$$= 245.12 - 129.06 = 116.06 \text{ Btu/lbm}$$

The work required for actual compression is

$$w = h_{2'} - h_1 = \frac{h_2 - h_1}{0.80}$$

$$= \frac{116.06}{0.80} = 145 \text{ Btu/lbm}$$

(b) From $h_{2'} - h_1 = 145$,

$$h_{2'} = h_1 + 145 = 129.06 + 145 = 274.06 \text{ Btu/lbm}$$

From the gas tables, corresponding to $h_{2'} = 274.06$, read $T_{2'} = 1132$ °R, $\phi_{2'} = 0.78148$. From $p_1 v_1 / T_1 = p_{2'} v_{2'} / T_{2'}$,

$$p_{2'} = p_1 \left(\frac{v_1}{v_{2'}}\right)\left(\frac{T_{2'}}{T_1}\right) = 15(5)\left(\frac{1132}{540}\right)$$

$= 157.2$ psia (actual discharge pressure)

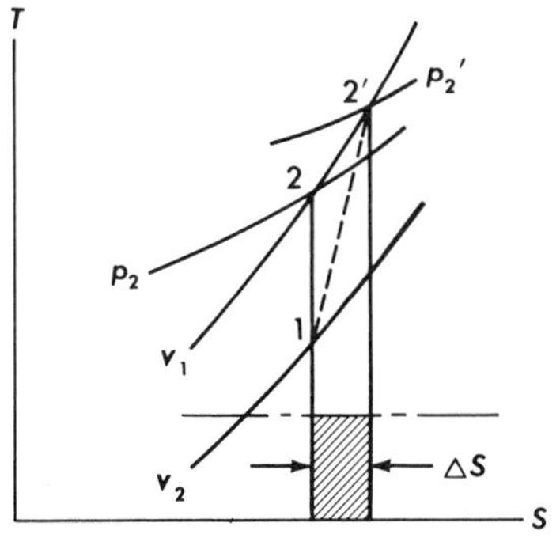

The increase in entropy at 2′ is obtained from Eq. (14.30):

$$\Delta s = \phi_{2'} - \phi_1 - R \ln \frac{p_{2'}}{p_1}$$

$$= 0.78148 - 0.60078 - \frac{53.34}{778} \ln \frac{157.2}{15}$$

$$= 0.0196 \text{ Btu/lbm-°R}$$

The increase in unavailable energy is thus

$$T_0 \Delta s = 520(0.0196) = 10.04 \text{ Btu/lbm}$$

Fig. 14.6 Reversible and Irreversible Adiabatic Compression.

14.8 Kinetic Theory of Gases

Having introduced a working knowledge of ideal gases in the preceding sections, the behavior of an ideal gas will now be presented in terms of kinetic theory. In essence, this is the study of the properties of a large assembly of like particles and it will be seen that the distribution of velocities and energies follows the laws of classical statistics.

It was previously pointed out that thermodynamics makes no hypotheses about the nature of the matter, and that while it can predict many relations between the properties of a substance, such as the difference between the specific heats c_p and c_v, it does not lead to the derivation of the equation of state for the substance.

It is, however, possible to go beyond the limitations of pure thermodynamics by making hypotheses regarding the nature of matter. By far the most fruitful of such hypotheses is the atomic-molecular concept of matter. Modern scientists agree with Democritus (400 B.C.) that all matter is not continuous in structure, but composed of particles called *molecules*. A *molecule* is an aggregate of atoms, from one atom up. The atoms, in turn, are composed of electric charges held together by forces which are primarily electric and magnetic in nature. A perfect gas is composed of a large number of molecules, subject to the following postulates:

1. All molecules are identical and have the same mass and size.
2. The molecules are in a state of chaotic motion, during which they collide with each other and with the sides of the container.
3. These collisions are elastic, like billiard balls bumping into each other. No kinetic energy is lost due to friction.
4. At low pressures the molecules are far apart compared to their diameters so that attractive forces between molecules are considered negligible.
5. At low pressures the volume occupied by the molecules is negligible compared to the volume of the container.
6. The absolute temperature is a function of the average kinetic energy of all the molecules.
7. Pressure is caused by collisions of the molecules with the side of the container. For example, any solid surface placed in a gas is bombarded by many molecules. Each molecule that strikes the surface undergoes a change in momentum (since its velocity changes direction) and therefore imparts an impulse to the surface as shown in Fig. 14.7(a).

When the impulse curve for all the collisions occurring on a surface are plotted, the result is as it appears in Fig. 14.7(b). Although each impulse is of different size because each molecule has a different velocity as it hits the surface, the sum of all the individual impulse curves is very nearly a straight line, representing steady force against the surface.

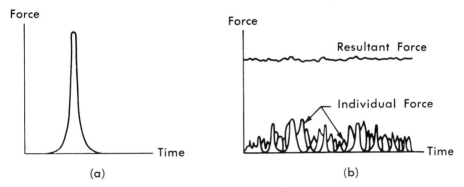

Fig. 14.7 Impulse Curves and Resultant Steady Force for Perfect Gas.

To calculate the pressure in terms of molecular quantities, let a volume of gas within a cubic box of side l be considered. The velocity $\mathscr{V}$ of any molecule may be resolved into components $\mathscr{V}_x$, $\mathscr{V}_y$, and $\mathscr{V}_z$ so that its magnitude is given by

$$\mathscr{V}^2 = \mathscr{V}_x^2 + \mathscr{V}_y^2 + \mathscr{V}_z^2 \tag{14.37}$$

If collisions between molecules and the walls are assumed to be elastic, the angle of incidence equals the angle of reflexion, and the velocity changes in direction but not in magnitude. Thus, at each collision with a wall perpendicular to the x-axis, the velocity component $\mathscr{V}_x$ changes sign from $\mathscr{V}_x$ to $-\mathscr{V}_x$, or vice versa. The momentum component of the molecule changes from $m\mathscr{V}_x$ to $-m\mathscr{V}_x$, or vice versa, and therefore the magnitude of change in momentum is $2m\mathscr{V}_x$. Since the number of collisions in unit time with the two walls perpendicular to the x-axis is $\mathscr{V}_x/l$, the change in the x-component of momentum in unit time is

$$2m\mathscr{V}_x\left(\frac{\mathscr{V}_x}{l}\right) = \frac{2m\mathscr{V}_x^2}{l}$$

where m is the mass of a molecule. Now, there are n molecules in the box, so that the change in the x-component in unit time becomes

$$\frac{2nm\overline{\mathscr{V}_x^2}}{l}$$

where $\overline{\mathscr{V}_x^2}$ is the average value of the square of the velocity component

$\mathscr{V}_x$. This rate of change of momentum is the force exerted by the molecules colliding against the two walls perpendicular to the x-direction. The pressure (force/unit area) is the rate of momentum change divided by the area of the walls ($2l^2$):

$$p = \frac{2nm\overline{\mathscr{V}_x^2}}{l} \cdot \frac{1}{2l^2} = \frac{nm\overline{\mathscr{V}_x^2}}{V} \tag{14.38}$$

where V is the volume of the box.

Since there is nothing to distinguish the magnitude of one particular velocity component from another,

$$\overline{\mathscr{V}_x^2} = \overline{\mathscr{V}_y^2} = \overline{\mathscr{V}_z^2}$$

and Eq. (14.37) becomes

$$\overline{\mathscr{V}^2} = 3\overline{\mathscr{V}_x^2} = 3\overline{\mathscr{V}_y^2} = 3\overline{\mathscr{V}_z^2}$$

or

$$\overline{\mathscr{V}_x^2} = \overline{\mathscr{V}_y^2} = \overline{\mathscr{V}_z^2} = \frac{\overline{\mathscr{V}^2}}{3} \tag{14.39}$$

Equations (14.38) and (14.39) combine to give

$$p = \frac{nm\overline{\mathscr{V}^2}}{3V} \tag{14.40}$$

where the quantity $\overline{\mathscr{V}^2}$ (not to be confused with $[\overline{\mathscr{V}}]^2$) is called the *mean square speed*. Equation (14.40)* is of fundamental importance in kinetic theory. It may be written as

$$pV = \frac{1}{3}nm\overline{\mathscr{V}^2} = \frac{2}{3}\left(\frac{nm\overline{\mathscr{V}^2}}{2}\right) \tag{14.41}$$

The quantity in parentheses represents the kinetic energy of translation of all the molecules in the volume V. If the temperature remains constant, the kinetic energy remains constant (postulate 6), so that Eq. (11.41) gives, at constant temperature,

$$pV = \text{constant}$$

This is precisely *Boyle's law*.

---

* A more sophisticated deviation would show Eq. (14.40) to be

$$p = \frac{nm}{3V} \int_0^\infty \mathscr{V}^2 f(\mathscr{V}) d\mathscr{V} = \frac{nm\overline{\mathscr{V}^2}}{3V}$$

where $f(\mathscr{V})$ is a function describing the velocity distribution of the molecules, and the quantity

$$\int_0^\infty \mathscr{V}^2 f(\mathscr{V}) \, d\mathscr{V} = \overline{\mathscr{V}^2}$$

is the *mean square speed* of the molecules. This is discussed in Sec. (14.11).

To deduce the experimental ideal-gas law, consider Eq. (14.7), which is written for N moles of gas as

$$pV = N\bar{R}T$$

Since $N = n/n_0$, where n is the number of molecules within a volume V, and n_0 is Avogadro's number (number of molecules per mole), the above equation may be written as

$$pV = \frac{n}{n_0}\bar{R}T \qquad (14.42)$$

Comparison of Eq. (14.42) with Eq. (11.41) shows that

$$\frac{2}{3}\left(\frac{nm\overline{\mathscr{V}^2}}{2}\right) = \frac{n}{n_0}\bar{R}T$$

or

$$\frac{m\overline{\mathscr{V}^2}}{2} = \frac{3}{2}\frac{\bar{R}}{n_0}T = \frac{3}{2}kT \qquad (14.43)$$

where the quotient, $\bar{R}/n_0 = k$, is the *universal gas constant per molecule*, known as *Boltzmann's constant*.* In terms of Boltzmann's constant, Eq. (14.42) becomes

$$pV = nkT \qquad (14.44)$$

This is the equation of state of an ideal gas as derived from molecular theory.

The fact that many well-established relatious can be deduced from the fundamental kinetic equation is an indication of the usefulness and overall validity of the kinetic theory of gases.

14.9 Specific Heats and Equipartition of Energy

From Eq. (14.43), it is seen that the total translational kinetic energy is

$$\frac{m\overline{\mathscr{V}^2}}{2} = \frac{3}{2}kT$$

Since $\overline{\mathscr{V}^2} = 3\overline{\mathscr{V}_x^2} = 3\overline{\mathscr{V}_y^2} = 3\overline{\mathscr{V}_z^2}$, it follows that

$$\frac{m\overline{\mathscr{V}_x^2}}{2} = \frac{m\overline{\mathscr{V}_y^2}}{2} = \frac{m\overline{\mathscr{V}_z^2}}{2} = \frac{1}{2}kT \qquad (14.45)$$

i.e., the kinetic energy is divided equally among the three translational degrees of freedom.† For each of these degrees of freedom, the average

---

* Boltzmann's constant $k = 1.3893 \times 10^{16}$ erg/molecule-degree is a fundamental constant in physics.

† The degrees of freedom are the number of quantities (such as co-ordinates of position) necessary to describe the condition of a molecule. A monoatomic molecule (atom) has three degrees of freedom.

kinetic energy is $(1/2)kT$. This conclusion, enunciated by Boltzmann, is known as the *principle of equipartition of energy*.

Consider the application of these developments to the calculation of $\bar{c}_v$, the specific heat at constant volume/mole. For a monoatomic gas (such as the metallic vapors or the noble gases helium, argon, krypton, and neon), the internal energy/mole is thus

$$\bar{u} = 3(n_0)\left(\frac{1}{2}kT\right) = \frac{3}{2}\bar{R}T$$

Hence

$$\bar{c}_v = \frac{d\bar{u}}{dT} = \frac{3}{2}\bar{R} \qquad (14.46)$$

The molar specific heat at constant pressure is then

$$\bar{c}_p = \bar{c}_v + \bar{R} = \frac{3}{2}\bar{R} + \bar{R} = \frac{5}{2}\bar{R} \qquad (14.47)$$

from which the ratio of specific heats is

$$\gamma = \frac{\bar{c}_p}{\bar{c}_v} = \frac{(5/2)\bar{R}}{(3/2)\bar{R}} = 1.67 \qquad (14.48)$$

This is in good agreement with experimental observation.

For a diatomic gas (such as hydrogen, oxygen, nitrogen, or carbon monoxide), the molecule has the form of a dumbell, and there are five degrees of freedom (three of translation, and two of rotation). This can be seen from Fig. 14.8. The two additional degrees of freedom are due to the possibility of rotation about two axes mutually perpendicular to each other and to the line connecting the centers of the atoms. The internal energy is then

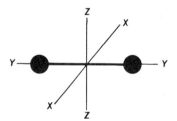

$$\bar{u} = 5(n_0)\left(\frac{1}{2}kT\right)$$

$$= \frac{5}{2}\bar{R}T$$

Fig. 14.8 Dumbbell Molecule.

Hence

$$\bar{c}_v = \frac{d\bar{u}}{dT} = \frac{5}{2}\bar{R} \qquad (14.49)$$

and

$$\bar{c}_p = \frac{5}{2}\bar{R} + \bar{R} = \frac{7}{2}\bar{R} \tag{14.50}$$

whereupon

$$\gamma = \frac{\bar{c}_p}{\bar{c}_v} = \frac{(7/2)\bar{R}}{(5/2)R} = 1.\overset{.}{4} \tag{14.51}$$

This is also in good agreement with observation.

For triatomic gases (O_3, CO_2, etc.), the number of degrees of freedom is six (three of translation and three of rotation); therefore

$$\bar{c}_v = \frac{6}{2}\bar{R} \tag{14.52}$$

$$\bar{c}_p = \frac{8}{2}\bar{R} \tag{14.53}$$

$$\gamma = 1.33 \tag{14.54}$$

As the number of atoms in a molecule increases, the number of degrees of freedom not only increases, but vibrational and rotational energies must be taken into account. The result is that the specific heats increase and γ decreases. The exact behavior of specific heats with temperature, however, cannot be explained solely in terms of the simple theory above, and recourse must be made to quantum mechanics.

14.10 Law of Atmospheres

The distribution of velocities and hence of kinetic energies among the molecules of a gas form one of the most important parts of kinetic theory. The molecules in their constant motion collide with one another; as a result, the velocities of individual molecules are continually changing. Although most molecules have velocities with magnitudes close to the average, some have velocities much above, and others have velocities much below this average. The distribution law for molecular velocities is first introduced by developing the barometric formula. Later, it is confirmed by applying the Maxwell–Boltzmann statistics.

Consider a column of gas extending upward into the atmosphere as shown in Fig. 14.9. It is of interest to derive a formula for the variation of gas pressure in the gravitational field. Let dz be a thin layer of gas of unit area cross section. The weight of the layer is $\rho(g/g_c)dz$, where ρ is the density of the gas. The difference in pressure between the top and bottom of the layer is $-dp$, and this must be equal to the weight of the layer $\rho(g/g_c)dz$. Thus,

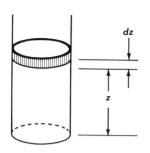

Fig. 14.9   Derivation
of Barometric Formula.

$$-dp = \rho \frac{g}{g_c} dz \qquad (14.55)$$

For an ideal gas, $p = \rho RT$, or $\rho = p/RT$, so that Eq. (14.55) becomes

$$-\frac{dp}{p} = \frac{1}{RT} \cdot \frac{g}{g_c} dz \qquad (14.56)$$

Assuming the temperature to be constant and integrating between the limits $p = p_0$ at $z = 0$, and $p = p$ at $z = z$ gives

$$-\ln \frac{p}{p_0} = \frac{1}{RT} \frac{g}{g_c} z$$

or

$$p = p_0 e^{-gz/RTg_c} \qquad (14.57)$$

But $(g/g_c)z$ is simply the gravitational potential energy of a unit mass of gas at elevation z, and if this potential energy is represented by e_p, Eq. (14.57) becomes

$$p = p_0 e^{-e_p/RT} \qquad (14.58)$$

If, instead of using the macroscopic energy e_p, the molecular potential energy is used, Eq. (14.58) becomes

$$p = p_0 e^{-\epsilon_p/kT} \qquad (14.59)$$

where k is the gas constant per molecule or Boltzmann constant. Equation (14.59) is known as the barometric formula or law of atmospheres. It is of interest to compare it with the Maxwell–Boltzmann distribution law of the preceding chapter, which may be written as

$$n = n_0 e^{-\epsilon/kT} \qquad (14.60)$$

Equation (14.60) states that if n_0 is the number of molecules in any given state, the number n in a state whose energy is ϵ above that of the given state is $n = n_0 \exp(-\epsilon/kT)$. Thus, it is seen that Eq. (14.59) is essentially a special case of the Maxwell–Boltzmann law applied to the potential energy ϵ_p. That a similar analogy holds for the case of the kinetic energy ϵ_k is discussed in the next section.

14.11   Distribution of Velocities and Kinetic Energy

The Maxwell–Boltzmann law is a statistics law of general validity. As to be expected, it applies equally well to kinetic energies. In other words, the distribution of kinetic energies, ϵ_k, among molecules follows an exponential law as does the distribution of potential energies. Consider first the x-component of velocity: the fraction of molecules having a velocity between $\mathscr{V}_x$ and $\mathscr{V}_x + d\mathscr{V}_x$ is written, from analogy with Eq. (14.60), as

$$\frac{dn}{n_0} = Ae^{-\epsilon_k/kT} \, d\mathscr{V}_x = Ae^{-m\mathscr{V}_x^2/2kT} \, d\mathscr{V}_x \qquad (14.61)*$$

where A is a constant whose value will be determined shortly. Note that the distribution law is unaffected by collisions between molecules (since a collision between two molecules merely results in an interchange of velocity components between these molecules). Note also that distributions similar to Eq. (14.61) may be written for the y-component and the z-component of velocity.

The constant A in Eq. (14.61) is evaluated from the fact that the sum of all the fractions of molecules in the whole velocity range of $\mathscr{V}_x = -\infty$ to $\mathscr{V}_x = +\infty$ must be equal to unity. In other words,

$$A\int_{-\infty}^{+\infty} e^{-m\mathscr{V}_x^2/2kT} \, d\mathscr{V}_x = 1 \qquad (14.62)$$

Letting

$$\frac{m\mathscr{V}_x^2}{2kT} = x^2$$

Equation (14.62) becomes

$$A\left(\frac{2kT}{m}\right)^{1/2} \int_{-\infty}^{+\infty} e^{-x^2} \, dx = 1$$

and, since

$$\int_{-\infty}^{+\infty} e^{-x^2} \, dx = \sqrt{\pi},$$

this gives

$$A = \left(\frac{m}{2\pi kT}\right)^{1/2}$$

Thus, Eq. (14.61) yields

$$\frac{dn}{n_0} = \left(\frac{m}{2\pi kT}\right)^{1/2} e^{-m\mathscr{V}_x^2/2kT} \, d\mathscr{V}_x \qquad (14.63)$$

---

* It is desirable to use the absolute system of units for the remainder of the chapter. For this reason, the constant g_c is not carried along in the expression for the kinetic energy.

or

$$\frac{dn}{d\mathscr{V}_x} = n_0\left(\frac{m}{2\pi k T}\right)^{1/2} e^{-m\mathscr{V}_x^2/2kT} \tag{14.64}$$

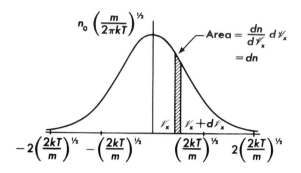

Fig. 14.10   Distribution for x-Component of Velocity.

This is plotted in Fig. 14.10. Note that the average x-component of velocity is zero, and that the curve is symmetric. The number of molecules with velocity components in the x direction between $\mathscr{V}_x$ and $\mathscr{V}_x + d\mathscr{V}_x$ is represented by the area of a vertical strip between $\mathscr{V}_x$ and $\mathscr{V}_x + d\mathscr{V}_x$.

The above development is for a one degree of freedom of translation (namely in the x direction). For translation in two directions, the probability of a molecule having a given velocity $\mathscr{V}_y$ in the y direction in no way depends on the value in the x direction. The fraction of the molecules having simultaneously velocity components between $\mathscr{V}_x$ and $\mathscr{V}_x + d\mathscr{V}_x$, and $\mathscr{V}_y$ and $\mathscr{V}_y + d\mathscr{V}_y$ is therefore the product of the two individual probabilities, or

$$\frac{dn}{n_0} = \left(\frac{m}{2\pi k T}\right) e^{-m(\mathscr{V}_x^2 + \mathscr{V}_y^2)/2kT} d\mathscr{V}_x d\mathscr{V}_y \tag{14.65}$$

For the general case of translation in three dimensions, the fraction of the molecules having simultaneously velocity components between $\mathscr{V}_x$ and $\mathscr{V}_x + d\mathscr{V}_x$, $\mathscr{V}_y$ and $\mathscr{V}_y + d\mathscr{V}_y$, and $\mathscr{V}_z$ and $\mathscr{V}_z + d\mathscr{V}_z$ is

$$\frac{dn}{n_0} = \left(\frac{m}{2\pi k T}\right)^{3/2} e^{-m(\mathscr{V}_x^2 + \mathscr{V}_y^2 + \mathscr{V}_z^2)/2kT} d\mathscr{V}_x d\mathscr{V}_y d\mathscr{V}_z \tag{14.66}$$

Equation (14.66) may be transformed by replacing $\mathscr{V}_x$, $\mathscr{V}_y$, and $\mathscr{V}_z$ in terms of polar co-ordinates $\mathscr{V}$, θ, and ϕ so defined that $\mathscr{V}_x = \mathscr{V} \sin \theta \cos \phi$, $\mathscr{V}_y = \mathscr{V} \sin \theta \sin \phi$, and $\mathscr{V}_z = \mathscr{V} \cos \theta$, where $\mathscr{V} = \sqrt{\mathscr{V}_x^2 + \mathscr{V}_y^2 + \mathscr{V}_z^2}$. The result (see Prob. 14.36) is

$$\frac{dn}{n_0} = \left(\frac{m}{2\pi k T}\right)^{3/2} e^{-m\mathscr{V}^2/2kT} \mathscr{V}^2 \sin\theta d\mathscr{V} d\theta d\phi \qquad (14.67)$$

Since the kinetic energy does not depend upon θ or ϕ, this is readily integrated with respect to θ and ϕ over the ranges $0 \leqslant \theta \leqslant \pi$, and $0 \leqslant \phi \leqslant 2\pi$ to give

$$\frac{dn}{n_0} = 4\pi\mathscr{V}^2 \left(\frac{m}{2\pi k T}\right)^{3/2} e^{-m\mathscr{V}^2/2kT} d\mathscr{V} \qquad (14.68)$$

or

$$\frac{dn}{d\mathscr{V}} = 4\pi n_0 \mathscr{V}^2 \left(\frac{m}{2\pi k T}\right)^{3/2} e^{-m\mathscr{V}^2/2kT} \qquad (14.69)$$

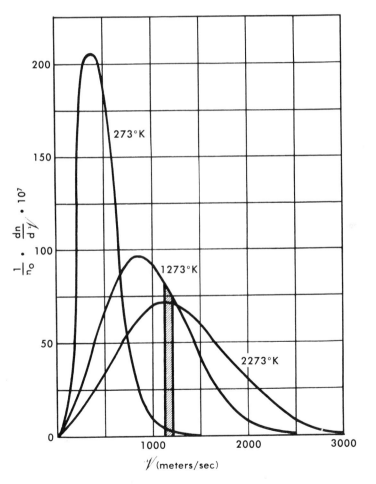

Fig. 14.11 Distribution for Kinetic Energies.

Equation (14.69) is plotted in Fig. 14.11. The number of molecules with speeds between $\mathscr{V}$ and $\mathscr{V}+d\mathscr{V}$ is represented by the area of a vertical strip between $\mathscr{V}$ and $\mathscr{V}+d\mathscr{V}$. Note that, unlike Fig. 14.10, the curve in Fig. 14.11 is zero when $\mathscr{V}=0$, rises to a maximum, then decreases with increasing $\mathscr{V}$. The difference between the curves of Fig. 14.10 and Fig. 14.11 may seem puzzling at first, but an examination of Fig. 14.12

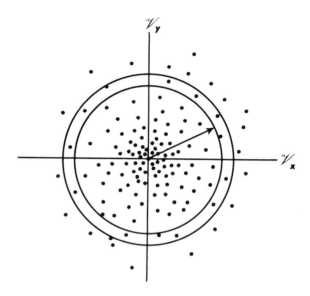

Fig. 14.12   Distributional in Two-Dimensional Velocity Space.

only confirms this. Consider, in two-dimensional space, a plot in which each point represents a combination of $\mathscr{V}_x$ and $\mathscr{V}_y$ for a particular molecule of the gas. The magnitude of the velocity $\mathscr{V}$ is the length of a line drawn from the origin to the point. Note that, although there are many points with $\mathscr{V}_x$ near zero, there are very few points with $\mathscr{V}$ near zero. In other words, the greatest occurrence of sets of *simultaneous* values of $\mathscr{V}_x$ and $\mathscr{V}_y$ is not at the origin, but in the annular region shown. The same situation holds in three-dimensional space: the largest number of points having simultaneous values of $\mathscr{V}_x$, $\mathscr{V}_y$, and $\mathscr{V}_z$ is within a spherical shell.

14.12 Average Speed; Root-Mean-Square Speed; Most Probable Speed

The *average molecular speed*, $\mathscr{V}_{av}$, is

$$\mathscr{V}_{av} = \frac{1}{n_0} \int_0^\infty \mathscr{V} \, dn$$

Replacing dn by its value from Eq. (14.68), this becomes

$$\mathscr{V}_{av} = 4\pi \left(\frac{m}{2\pi k T} \right)^{3/2} \int_0^\infty e^{-m\mathscr{V}^2/2kT} \mathscr{V}^3 d\mathscr{V} \qquad (14.70)$$

The evaluation of this integral is obtained by noting that

$$\int_0^\infty e^{-ax^2} x^3 dx = \frac{1}{2a^2} \qquad (14.71)*$$

Making the appropriate substitutions in Eq. (14.70), the latter gives

$$\mathscr{V}_{av} = \sqrt{\frac{8}{\pi} \cdot \frac{kT}{m}} \qquad (14.72)$$

Similarly, the *mean square speed* is

$$\overline{\mathscr{V}^2} = \frac{1}{n_0} \int_0^\infty \mathscr{V}^2 dn = 3\frac{kT}{m} \qquad (14.73)$$

If the square root of this is taken, the *root-mean-square speed* is

$$\mathscr{V}_{rms} = \left[\overline{\mathscr{V}^2} \right]^{1/2} = \sqrt{3\frac{kT}{m}} \qquad (14.74)$$

Finally, the *most probable speed*, $\mathscr{V}_{mp}$, is that corresponding to the radius of the spherical shell in velocity space containing the largest number of points. It is obtained by setting the derivative of the speed distribution

---

* This can be verified by writing

$$\int_0^\infty e^{-ax^2} x^3 dx = -\frac{d}{da} \int_0^\infty e^{-ax^2} dx$$

Letting $z^2 = $,

$$\int_0^\infty e^{-ax^2} x \, dx = \frac{1}{2} \int_0^\infty e^{-az} dz = \frac{1}{2} \left[\frac{e^{-az}}{-a} \right]_0^\infty = \frac{1}{2a}$$

Thus

$$\int_0^\infty e^{-ax^2} x^3 dx = -\frac{d}{da} \left(\frac{1}{2a} \right) = \frac{1}{2a^2}$$

function equal to zero. Now, the speed distribution function, as given in Eq. (14.68), is

$$4\pi\mathscr{V}^2\left(\frac{m}{2\pi kT}\right)^{3/2}e^{-m\mathscr{V}^2/2kT}$$

Therefore,

$$\frac{d}{d\mathscr{V}}\left[4\pi\mathscr{V}^2\left(\frac{m}{2\pi kT}\right)^{3/2}e^{-m\mathscr{V}^2/2kT}\right]=0$$

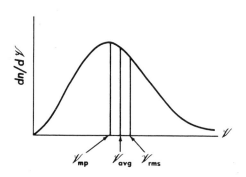

Solving this for the most probable speed gives

$$\mathscr{V}_{mp}=\sqrt{2\frac{kT}{m}} \qquad (14.75)$$

Note that the relative magnitudes of the most probable speed, the average speed, and the root-mean-square speed are

$$\mathscr{V}_{mp}:\mathscr{V}_{av}:\mathscr{V}_{rms}=$$
$$1:1.128:1.224$$

Fig. 14.13 Representation of Most Probable Speed, Mean Speed, and Root-Mean-Square Speed.

The plot of these speeds is shown in Fig. 14.13.

14.13   Translational Partition Function of Monoatomic Gas

The discussion of ideal gases will be brought to a close by the calculation of the partition function for an ideal monatomic gas. Consider, for example, a particle of mass m constrained to move between walls a distance l apart. Quantum mechanics (i.e., the solution of Schrödinger's wave equation with the appropriate boundary conditions) establishes the allowable translational energy levels as

$$\epsilon=\frac{n^2h^2}{8ml^2} \qquad (14.76)$$

where h is Planck's constant (6.22×10^{-27} erg sec), and n is a quantum number. Taking the statistical weight of each level to be unity, the molecular partition function as developed in the preceding chapter becomes

$$z = \sum \exp\left(-\frac{n^2 h^2}{8ml^2} \cdot \frac{1}{kT}\right) \tag{14.77}$$

Because of the extremely small value of h^2, the energy levels are so closely packed together that they can be considered to be continuous; the summation in Eq. (14.77) can thus be replaced by an integration:

$$z = \int_0^\infty \exp\left(-\frac{n^2 h^2}{8ml^2} \cdot \frac{1}{kT}\right) dn$$

Letting

$$x^2 = \frac{n^2 h^2}{8ml^2 kT},$$

this becomes

$$z = \frac{l}{h}(8mkT)^{1/2} \int_0^\infty e^{-x^2} dx$$

Now

$$\int_0^\infty e^{-ax^2} dx = \frac{1}{2}\left(\frac{\pi}{a}\right)^{1/2},$$

so that

$$z = \frac{(2\pi mkT)^{1/2}l}{h} \tag{14.78}$$

Equation (14.78) is for one degree of translational freedom. For three degrees of translational freedom, the expression for z must be cubed (since the energy is $\epsilon = \epsilon_x + \epsilon_y + \epsilon_z$; to this corresponds the partition function $z = z_x z_y z_z$). Thus,

$$z = \frac{(2\pi mkT)^{3/2}}{h^3} l^3 = \frac{(2\pi mkT)^{3/2} V}{h^3} \tag{14.79}$$

where $V = l^3$. Having evaluated the partition function, we may calculate all the thermodynamic properties of interest. For example, the internal energy, as derived in Chapter 13, is

$$U = NkT^2\frac{\partial(\ln z)}{\partial T} = \bar{R}T^2\frac{\partial(\ln z)}{\partial T} = RT^2 \cdot \frac{3}{2} \cdot \frac{1}{T}$$

$$= \frac{3}{2}\bar{R}T \tag{14.80}$$

The entropy (previously obtained in Chapter 13), is

$$S = \frac{U}{T} + k \ln Z \qquad (14.81)$$

The quantity Z is the molar function, i.e., the partition function for the system of N molecules. For an ideal monoatomic gas, the relation between Z and z, the partition function for a single molecule is

$$Z = \frac{z^N}{N!} \qquad (14.82)$$

Thus, Eq. (14.81) becomes

$$S = \frac{3}{2}\bar{R} + k \ln \frac{1}{N!} \left[\frac{(2\pi m k T)^{3/2} V}{h^3} \right]^N$$

Using Stirling's formula, $\ln N! = N \ln N - N$, this gives

$$S = \frac{3}{2}\bar{R} + k \left[N \ln \frac{(2\pi m k T)^{3/2} V}{h^3} - (N \ln N - N) \right]$$

$$= \frac{3}{2}\bar{R} + Nk \ln \frac{(2\pi m k T)^{3/2} V}{h^3} - Nk \ln N + Nk$$

$$= \frac{3}{2}\bar{R} + \bar{R} \ln \frac{(2\pi m k T)^{3/2} V}{h^3} - \bar{R} \ln N + \bar{R}$$

$$= \bar{R} \left[\frac{5}{2} + \ln \frac{(2\pi m k T)^{3/2} V}{N h^3} \right] \qquad (14.83)$$

Equation (14.83) is the famous *Sackur-Tetrode equation*, named in honor of the men who originally derived it.

PROBLEMS

14.1. An ideal gas is defined as one obeying the equation of state

$$pv = RT$$

where R is a constant which is different for each gas. Its value is related to the universal gas constant $\bar{R}$ by

$$R = \frac{\bar{R}}{M}$$

where M is the molecular weight of the gas. Select a number of gases, and make a collection of pressure, molal volume, and temperature data over a wide range. For each gas at a given temperature, plot ratios pv/T as ordinates against pressure as abscissa. Connect the points so obtained by a smooth curve and denote each curve by its temperature. What remarkable features do these curves display? Determine the point of convergence of these curves on the vertical axis and verify the value of the universal gas constant as

$$\bar{R} = 1544 \text{ ft–lbf/mole} - R = 1.986 \text{ Btu/mole} - R$$
$$= 1.986 \text{ cal/g mole} - K$$

14.2. Verify that at "standard" conditions ($p = 1$ standard atmosphere $= 1.01325 \times 10^3$ newtons/m², $T = 273.16$ °K $= 0$ °C) the molal specific volume of an ideal gas is 22.4146 m³/kgm-mole.

14.3. Discuss the construction of an ideal gas thermometer scale defined by the equation

$$\frac{T_2}{T_1} = \left(\frac{p_2}{p_1}\right)_{\substack{v = \text{const} \\ p_1 \to 0}}$$

14.4. (a) Show that for any substance which obeys the equation of state $pv = RT$,

$$\left(\frac{\partial u}{\partial v}\right)_T = 0$$

(b) Show that for an ideal gas,

$$c_p - c_v = R$$

$$c_p = \frac{\gamma R}{\gamma - 1}$$

$$c_v = \frac{R}{\gamma - 1}$$

where

$$\gamma = \frac{c_p}{c_v}.$$

14.5. Determine the general form which must be taken by the equation of state of a substance in order that the internal energy u be a function of the temperature T only. Hint: Make use of the following relation (developed in Chap. 11):

$$\left(\frac{\partial u}{\partial v}\right)_T = T\left(\frac{\partial p}{\partial T}\right)_v - p$$

and obtain

$$\frac{1}{p}\left(\frac{\partial p}{\partial T}\right)_v = \frac{1}{T}$$

Solve this by integrating with respect to T to give

$$\ln p = \ln T + \phi(v)$$

or

$$\frac{p}{T} = \psi(v)$$

Show that if, in addition, pv is a function of T only (Boyle's law) then

$$\psi(v) = \frac{\text{constant}}{v} = \frac{R}{v}$$

and the equation of state thus becomes

$$pv = RT$$

14.6. An insulated 20 cu ft vessel contains air at 80 °F and 14.7 psia. It is to be evacuated until the pressure is 5 psia. Assuming air to be a perfect gas and the surroundings to be at 14.7 psia, find the isentropic work required and the final temperature in the vessel.

14.7. Show that $(\partial p/\partial p)_s = \gamma(\partial p/\partial p)_T$ and verify this for a perfect gas having constant specific heats.

14.8. The products of combustion from a boiler reach the base of a stack at 510 °F. At the top of the stack, the temperature is 250 °F. Neglecting the slight pressure change between bottom and top of stack, determine the ratio of areas between top and bottom to give equal velocities at the sections.

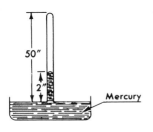

Fig. 14.14

14.9. In Fig. 14.14, nitrogen at a pressure of 14.7 psia and 200 °F is enclosed in a 50 inch long tube. One end is closed, the other end is stuck into a pool of mercury as shown. The tube is in a vertical position. Determine: (a) The p–v relation of the nitrogen as it cools. Does the relation fit the polytropic family? (b) The height the mercury has risen when the nitrogen has cooled to 100 °F.

Hint: For part (a) the pressure and volume of the nitrogen are respectively:

$$p = 14.7\left(1 - \frac{z}{29.92}\right); \quad \frac{v}{v_1} = \frac{50-z}{50}$$

where z is the height of the mercury in inches. For part (b) the ideal gas relation for nitrogen may be written as

$$\frac{p_1 V_1}{p_2 V_2} = \frac{660}{560}$$

14.10. A pound of air at 400 °F and 100 psia expands into an evacuated insulated container so that its volume doubles. Calculate the increase in entropy. Does the answer depend on the initial pressure and temperature?

14.11. Air expands through an adiabatic turbine. Measurements at various stages show that the states lie on the line

$$pv^{1.25} = \text{constant}$$

Show that the shaft work per pound of air is

$$w_{\text{shaft}} = \frac{\gamma}{\gamma-1}p_1v_1\left[1-\left(\frac{p_2}{p_1}\right)^{1/5}\right]$$

where $\gamma = c_p/c_v$.

Hint: Neglecting potential and kinetic energy changes, the work is given by

$$h_2-h_1 = c_p(T_2-T_1) = \frac{\gamma}{\gamma-1}(p_2v_2-p_1v_1)$$

Why is work not equal to

$$-\int_1^2 v\,dp\,?$$

14.12. (a) Show that for a reversible adiabatic process of an ideal gas with constant specific heats, the relation between T and v is given by

$$Tv^{\gamma-1} = \text{constant}$$

(b) For the same process, show that the work done by an ideal gas with constant specific heat is

$$w = c_v(T_1-T_2)$$
$$= \frac{p_1p_1}{\gamma-1}1-\left(\frac{p_2}{p_1}\right)^{(\gamma-1)\gamma}$$

14.13. Air enters a compressor at a temperature of 80 °F and a pressure of 14.7 psia. The oil used to lubricate the compressor has a flash-point temperature of 355 °F. If compression follows the law $pv^{1.3} = $ constant, what is the maximum attainable pressure if the maximum allowable temperature is not to exceed 50 °F below the flash-point temperature of the oil? Consider air to be ideal and to have constant specific heats.

14.14. Show that for a perfect gas, the slope of a reversible adiabatic is

$$\left(\frac{\partial p}{\partial v}\right)_s = -\gamma\frac{p}{v}$$

and the slope of a reversible isothermal is

$$\left(\frac{\partial p}{\partial v}\right)_T = -\frac{p}{v}$$

14.15. A 60 cu ft vessel contains air at a pressure of 5 psia and a temperature of 65 °F. Atmospheric air at a pressure of 14.7 psia and a temperature of 65 °F leaks into the vessel. When the pressure in the vessel has risen to 10 psia, the leak is discovered and stopped. The temperature of the air in the vessel is found to be 100 °F. Determine: (a) the mass of air leaked into the vessel, (b) the heat transferred through the vessel walls.

14.16. Considering air as a perfect gas with constant specific heats, determine the difference in the work required to compress one pound of air from 14.7 psia and 80 °F to successive pressures of 25, 50, 75 and 100 psia. Plot a curve of this difference against pressure and try to express it by means of a simple equation.

14.17. Air is expanded isentropically from a temperature of 1200 °F to a temperature of 800 °F. Find the pressure ratio and the volume ratio, (a) assuming constant specific heats, (b) using the gas tables.

14.18. Air at a pressure of 1 atm and a temperature of 70 °F is compressed in a steady flow process to a pressure of 5 atm. Assuming perfect gas behavior, but variable specific heats, determine: (a) the isentropic work per pound of air, (b) the actual work per pound of air for a compression efficiency of 65 per cent. The compression efficiency is defined here as the ratio of isentropic work to actual work.

14.19. Using the gas tables, determine the entropy change per pound of air for a process between a pressure and temperature of 15 psia and 50 °F and a pressure and temperature of 30 psia and 100 °F.

14.20. (a) Considering air to be a perfect gas with variable specific heats, show that for a constant pressure process the change in entropy is given by

$$\Delta s = \Delta \phi$$

where

$$\phi = \int_{T_0}^{T} c_p \frac{dT}{T}$$

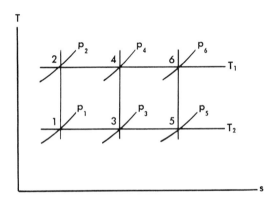

Fig. 14.15

(b) Show that for any isentropic path between T_1 and T_2 in Fig. 14.15, the ratio of the pressures is the same, even though the pressures are different:

$$\ln \frac{p_2}{p_1} = \frac{1}{R} \int_{T_1}^{T_2} c_p \frac{dT}{T}$$

or

$$\frac{p_2}{p_1} = \frac{p_4}{p_3} = \ldots = f(T_1, T_2)$$

14.21. Eight cu ft of oxygen at an initial pressure of 14.7 psia and temperature of 60 °F are compressed according to the relation

$$pv^{1.3} = \text{constant}$$

If the final volume is 1.5 cu ft, what is the work done, the heat transferred, and the entropy change if the gas is considered as an ideal gas with *variable* specific heats?

14.22. The earliest and simplest method of measuring the specific heat ratio of an ideal gas is that of Clément and Désormes: Let the gas be contained in a vessel at temperature T_1 equal to room temperature, and pressure p_1 slightly above atmospheric (p_0). Let the stopcock on the vessel be opened and closed rapidly: the gas expands adiabatically to atmospheric pressure, and its temperature drops to slightly below room temperature. Let the gas be allowed to stand for a few minutes at constant volume until it resumes room temperature, thus causing the pressure to rise to a final value p_2 which is accurately measured. From the sequence of operations, develop the following expression for the specific heat ratio:

$$\gamma = \frac{\ln(p_1/p_0)}{\ln(p_1/p_2)}$$

Hint: Consider the initial volume V_1 of a mass of gas. During rapid opening and closing of the stopcock, the mass may be assumed constant and the expansion to be reversible adiabatic:

$$p_1 V_1^\gamma = p_2 V_2^\gamma$$

Eliminate V_1 and V_2 from the two equations and solve for γ.

14.23. (a) It is customary, in elementary kinetic theory of gases, to consider a molecule as a rigid elastic sphere or billiard ball. Would it be better to replace this simple model by the more realistic picture of a particle surrounded by a short range force field? Discuss.

(b) Do the molecules of a gas preserve their mean speeds and kinetic energies throughout the innumerable collisions that they make with each other and with the walls of the container? Supplement your answer by means of an illustrative example.

14.24. Calculate the value of kT at room temperature (290 °K) and at the temperature of thermionic emission (1200 °K to 2700 °K). Give the answers in electron volts (1 e.v. = 1 volt $\times 1.6 \times 10^{-19}$ coulomb = 1.602×10^{-19} joule) and compare these with the kinetic energy of an·electron in a radio tube which is accelerated through a potential difference of 200 volts. Can the energy of random motion be neglected in comparison to voltages commonly used to accelerate electrons?

14.25. Equation (14.43) shows that the mean kinetic energy of molecules of different gases are all the same at the same temperature, despite the disparity in their masses. Taking oxygen as an example, compute the energy at a temperature of 300 °K, and find the rms speed. Compare this with the speed of sound in the air at standard conditions (1100 fps), and the speed of a .30 caliber bullet (2700 fps).

14.26. Does thermal energy in a gas depend exclusively on the kinetic energy of translation of the molecules? Discuss this in terms of the internal structure of the molecule. Does the equipartition theorem take into account the quantization of the internal degrees of freedom? In what temperature range are the results of classical kinetic theory accurate?

14.27. The mean kinetic energy of a gas molecule,

$$\frac{1}{2}m\overline{\mathscr{V}^2} = \frac{3}{2}kT$$

serves to define a quantity $\frac{1}{2}m\overline{\mathscr{V}^2}$ which is the mean kinetic energy associated with the x-components of velocities:

$$\frac{1}{2}m\overline{\mathscr{V}_x^2} = \frac{1}{2}kT$$

This equation is of far-reaching implications and can be applied to electrical engineering in the theory of *thermal noise*. If a resistance R (or impedance with real part equal to R) is connected to the input of a large-gain radio receiver, fluctuations in the output of the receiver are observed. These fluctuations or noise are inconsequential at low frequencies (up to 10 megacycles) because of the relatively large amount of noise contributed by atmospheric static and man-made interference. At higher frequencies, however, thermal noise dominates, and the average square of the thermal noise voltage developed across a resistance R is

$$\overline{V^2} = 4kTR\Delta f$$

where $\overline{V^2}$ is in (volts)^2, kT is in joules, R is in ohms, and Δf is in cycles. This equation has been experimentally verified by Johnson. (a) Discuss how thermal noise sets a lower limit to the signal strength that a radio receiver can detect. (b) Discuss how the equation can be used to measure k, and compare the accuracy of this method with that of obtaining k by measuring the gas constant and Avogadro's number.

14.28. As a result of collisions, there exists a distribution of velocities among the molecules of a gas. Most molecules have velocities with magnitudes close to the average, but a few have velocities rather above or below the average. If the change of a lucky hit is $1/c$, show that the change p of n hits in row is

$$p = e^{-an}$$

where $a = -\ln(1/c)$ is a constant. Similarly, the probability of a molecule having an energy ϵ above the average energy is proportional to $e^{-b\epsilon}$.

14.29. For the case of gas molecules which are not acted upon by any forces except when they collide with each other or with the walls, the density does not vary from point to point. For the case of gas molecules which are acted upon by a gravity force $-mg/g_c$, where m is the mass of a molecule and g is the acceleration of gravity, develop the following expression for the number of molecules per unit volume at height z;

$$n = n_1 e^{-(mg/g_c kT)(z-z_1)}$$

where n_1 is the density of molecules at height z_1. Also, obtain the companion equation

$$p = p_1 e^{-(mg/g_c kT)(z-z_1)}$$

which is known as the *law of atmospheres*.

14.30. Consider a velocity space formed by transferring the velocity vectors of all the molecules of a gas to a common origin. Let the three axes of the rectangular co-ordinate system represent the velocity components $\mathscr{V}_x, \mathscr{V}_y$, and $\mathscr{V}_z$ respectively, and let $\mathscr{V}$ represent the magnitude of the velocity or speed. Give the appropriate expression for each of the following: (a) the number of molecules with velocity vectors terminating in a volume element $d\mathscr{V}_x d\mathscr{V}_y d\mathscr{V}_z$ of velocity space, (b) the number of molecules with velocity vectors terminating in a thin spherical shell of radius $\mathscr{V}$ and thickness $d\mathscr{V}$, (c) the number of molecules with velocity vectors terminating in a thin slice of thickness $d\mathscr{V}_x$ parallel to the $\mathscr{V}_y - \mathscr{V}_z$ plane at a distance $\mathscr{V}_x$ from this plane.

14.31. Compute: (a) the mean speed, $\mathscr{V}$, (b) the square of the mean speed, $(\overline{\mathscr{V}})^2$, and (c) the mean value of the square of the speed, $\overline{\mathscr{V}^2}$, for the following distribution: 2 molecules with speeds of 3.25 fps, 4 molecules with speeds of 6.5 fps, 3 molecules with speeds of 4.6 fps.

14.32. Calculate the average speed, the root-mean-square speed, and the most probable speed in cm/sec and ft/sec for hydrogen and for oxygen at $0°$ C and 1000 °C respectively.

14.33. From the predicted value of the specific heat ratio

$$\gamma = \frac{f+2}{f}$$

where f is the number of degrees of freedom, show that γ can never be greater than 1.67 or less than 1.

14.34. Determine, from Eq. (14.68), the fractional number of molecules of a gas with speeds between $\mathscr{V}_{mp}$ and $1.2\ \mathscr{V}_{mp}$, letting: (a) $\mathscr{V} = \mathscr{V}_{mp}$ and $d\mathscr{V} = 0.2\ \mathscr{V}_{mp}$, and (b) $\mathscr{V} = 1.1\ \mathscr{V}_{mp}$ and $d\mathscr{V} = 0.2\ \mathscr{V}_{mp}$.

14.35. In accordance with the Maxwell–Boltzmann distribution law, the number of molecules having velocity components in the ranges from $\mathscr{V}_x$ to $\mathscr{V}_x + d\mathscr{V}_x$, from $\mathscr{V}_y$ to $\mathscr{V}_y + d\mathscr{V}_y$, and from $\mathscr{V}_z$ to $\mathscr{V}_z + d_z$ is given by

$$dn = ce^{-m(\mathscr{V}_x^2 + \mathscr{V}_y^2 + \mathscr{V}_z^2)/2kT} d\mathscr{V}_x d\mathscr{V}_y d\mathscr{V}_z$$

Integration over all conceivable values of the velocity components gives

$$n = c \int_{-\infty}^{\infty} \int_{-\infty}^{\infty} \int_{-\infty}^{\infty} e^{-m(\mathscr{V}_x^2 + \mathscr{V}_y^2 + \mathscr{V}_z^2)/2kT} d\mathscr{V}_x d\mathscr{V}_y d\mathscr{V}_z$$

Using appropriate tables, evaluate the definite integrals and obtain

$$c = n\left(\frac{m}{2\pi kT}\right)^{3/2}$$

14.36. Let the rectangular co-ordinates x, y, z of a point be expressed as functions of u, v, w, by the transformation

$$x = x(u, v, w), y = y(u, v, w), z = z(u, v, z)$$

It is shown in calculus that, when transforming multiple integrals from rectangular to orthogonal curvilinear co-ordinates, the volume element $dxdydz$ is replaced by $h_1 h_2 h_3 du dv dw$ or the equivalent $J[(x, y, z)/(u, v, w)]dx dv dw$, where J is the Jacobian of the transformation from x, y, z to u, v, w. The Jacobian of x, v, z with respect to u, v, w is the determinant

$$J = \frac{\partial(x, y, z)}{\partial(u, v, w)} = \begin{vmatrix} \dfrac{\partial x}{\partial u} & \dfrac{\partial x}{\partial v} & \dfrac{\partial x}{\partial w} \\[2mm] \dfrac{\partial y}{\partial u} & \dfrac{\partial y}{\partial v} & \dfrac{\partial y}{\partial w} \\[2mm] \dfrac{\partial z}{\partial u} & \dfrac{\partial z}{\partial v} & \dfrac{\partial z}{\partial w} \end{vmatrix} = h_1 h_2 h_3$$

In particular, consider the case of spherical co-ordinates and apply this to the result obtained from Prob. 14.35:

$$dn = n \left(\frac{m}{2\pi k T} \right)^{3/2} e^{-m(\mathscr{V}_x^2 + \mathscr{V}_y^2 + \mathscr{V}_z^2)/2kT} \, d\mathscr{V}_x d\mathscr{V}_y d\mathscr{V}_z$$

Replacing $\mathscr{V}_x, \mathscr{V}_y$ and $\mathscr{V}_z$ by $\mathscr{V}$, θ, and ϕ, so defined that $\mathscr{V}_x = \mathscr{V} \sin \theta \cos \phi$, $\mathscr{V}_y = \mathscr{V} \sin \theta \sin \phi$, and $\mathscr{V}_z = \mathscr{V} \cos \theta$ make the appropriate Jacobian transformation and verify the following answer given in text:

$$dn = n \left(\frac{m}{2\pi k T} \right)^{3/2} e^{-m\mathscr{V}^2/2kT} \mathscr{V}^2 \sin \theta \, d\mathscr{V} d\theta d\phi$$

14.37. From

$$dn = n \left(\frac{m}{2\pi k T} \right)^{3/2} e^{-m\mathscr{V}^2/2kT} \mathscr{V}^2 \sin \theta \, d\mathscr{V} d\theta d\phi$$

show that the number of molecules having energies in the range from ϵ to $\epsilon + d\epsilon$ is

$$dn_\epsilon = \frac{2n}{\sqrt{\pi}(k T)^{3/2}} e^{-\epsilon/kT} \sqrt{\epsilon} d\epsilon$$

Does the distribution with respect to energies depend on the molecular weight?

14.38. It is shown in Prob. 14.37 that the number of molecules having energies in the range from ϵ to $\epsilon + d\epsilon$ is given by

$$dn_\epsilon = \frac{2n}{\sqrt{\pi}(k T)^{3/2}} e^{-\epsilon/kT} \sqrt{\epsilon} d\epsilon$$

Calculate the translational energy of an ideal gas by multiplying dn_ϵ by ϵ and integrating the result over all conceivable values, i.e., show that

$$U = \int \epsilon \, dn_\epsilon = \int_0^\infty \frac{2n}{\sqrt{\pi}(kT)^{3/2}} e^{-\epsilon/kT} \epsilon^{3/2} d\epsilon = \frac{3}{2} nk T$$

Thus, if n is chosen as Avogadro's number, then $nk = \bar{R}$, and the translational energy of a mole of ideal gas is $U = (3/2)\bar{R}T$. This gives a specific heat at constant volume attributable to translational effects as simply $(3/2)\bar{R}$ per mole of gas. What assumption is implied by the use of the integration process? Strictly speaking, are translational energies, like other energies, subject to quantization? What is the size of separation between translational energy levels in ordinary systems compared with kT? Does $E = (3/2)nkT$ hold for extremely low temperatures?

CHAPTER 15

Thermodynamic Properties of Liquids, Vapors, and Real Gases

15.1 Introduction

In this chapter, the tabulated properties of fluids† will be introduced. In order to successfully apply the principles of thermodynamics to the solution of actual problems, it is necessary to have access to a great deal of information pertaining to the properties of a working fluid. In the case of a one-component system, the important properties are: temperature, pressure, specific volume, specific internal energy, specific enthalpy, and

---

† The word *fluid* is used in a general sense to mean a thermodynamic medium. This medium may be in the liquid, vapor, or gaseous state.

specific entropy. In the case of a multi-component system, the concentration (composition) must also be known. It is the purpose of the following sections to discuss the way in which thermodynamic properties of a fluid are tabulated and used. For illustrative purposes, the discussion will center around the steam tables.

15.2 p–v–T Surface

It is well known that substances can exist in three different states of aggregation or phases: gaseous, liquid, and solid. In some cases, pure material of definite chemical composition may exist in several solid modifications, each possessing a different crystal structure. The word *phase* may be defined by means of the following statement: *If a system is uniform throughout, both in chemical composition and physical state, then it is said to be homogeneous or to consist of only one phase.*

Let the state of a substance be described in terms of the pressure, specific volume, and temperature plotted along three mutually perpendicular axes as shown in Fig. 15.1, the result is a surface which represents all possible equilibrium states of the particular substance.† Any line on the p–v–T surface represents a possible reversible process, i.e., a succession of equilibrium processes.

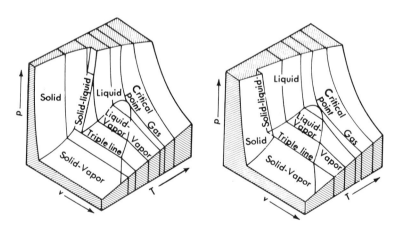

Fig. 15.1 The p–v–T Surface.

Examination of Fig. 15.1† reveals that there are regions labeled solid, liquid, and gas where only one phase can exist, and regions labeled solid–liquid, solid–vapor, and liquid–vapor, where two phases can exist simul-

---

† The surface on the left is for a substance which contracts on freezing; that on the right is for a substance which expands on freezing.

taneously in equilibrium. Along the triple line (a line of constant temperature and pressure) all three phases can coexist. On those portions of the surface where two phases can coexist, a straight-edge parallel to the v-axis makes contact with the surface at all points. For this reason, they are called *ruled surfaces*.

15.3 p–v and p–T Diagrams

The p–v–T surface of Fig. 15.1 may be projected onto the p–v and the p–T planes, thus obtaining p–v and p–T diagrams. The result is as shown in Fig. 15.2.

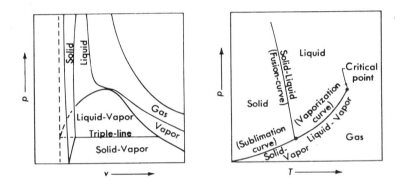

Fig. 15.2 p–v and p–T Diagrams for Water.

Projections such as the ones just described are sometimes called *equilibrium* or *phase diagrams*. The points on the p–T diagram representing the coexistence of solid and vapor phases lie on the *sublimation curve;* those representing the coexistence of liquid and vapor phases lie on the *vaporization curve;* and those representing the coexistence of liquid and solid phases lie on the *fusion curve*. All of those curves are known as *saturation curves*. The line representing the equilibrium between solid and liquid phases slopes upward to the left. This is characteristic of substances that expand when freezing. This same line slopes upward to the right for substances that contract when freezing.

The triple line of Fig. 15.1 projects onto the p–T diagram as a point called the *triple point*. This is the pressure and temperature at which all three phases of a pure substance may coexist. Only on the p–T diagram is the triple line represented by a point. On the p–v diagram, it is denoted by a line, on the u–v diagram by a triangle.

The *critical point* marks the termination of any distinction between liquid and gaseous phases. If a liquid phase and a vapor phase are maintained in equilibrium in a heavy glass tube while the temperature and pressure are raised, the attainment of the critical state would be marked by the disappearance of the meniscus that identifies the presence of the two phases. In the vicinity of the critical point, the two phases tend to merge into a single phase without forming a two-phase mixture. The p–T diagram of Fig. 15.2 shows that, when the temperature and pressure are above the critical values, the liquid and gaseous phases cannot be identified separately.

The p–v and p–T diagrams just discussed are only two examples of a vast number of property representations. Any two co-ordinates may be chosen to yield a particular diagram for a particular purpose. For instance, a T–v diagram may be constructed as follows:

Consider a system, composed of one pound of water at constant pressure, in a container of the piston-cylinder arrangement. Let the piston and weight maintain a constant pressure equivalent to 14.7 lbf/in². Starting from a temperature of 60 °F, let heat be transferred at constant pressure to the water. The temperature and specific volume increase. When the temperature reaches 212 °F, a change of phase begins to occur. At the saturation temperature of 212 °F and the saturation pressure of 14.7 lbf/in², the substance becomes a *saturated liquid*. The process of heating a liquid at constant pressure from a given initial temperature to the saturation temperature is represented by line *A–B* in Fig. 15.3. Additional heating brings about vaporization at constant temperature. When all of the liquid has vaporized, the state of the substance becomes known as *saturated vapor*, represented by point *C*. Further transfer of heat increases the temperature along the line *C–D*, and the substance becomes known as *superheated vapor*. If the substance is very much superheated at low pressure, it is commonly called gas; its behaviour approaches that of the hypothetical ideal gas.

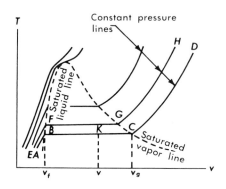

Fig. 15.3 *T-v* Diagram for Water.

Similar constant pressure heating processes at different values of pressure are shown by lines *E–F–G–H*, etc. The locus of all saturated-liquid points such as *B*, *F*, etc., is called the *saturated liquid line*; the locus of saturated-vapor points such as *C*, *G*, etc., is called the *saturated vapor line*. At any state (such as *K*) between saturated points *B* and *C*, liquid and vapor are in equilibrium. Let v_f and v_g represent, respectively, the specific volumes of the saturated liquid and saturated vapor. Let m be the total mass of the system, m_1 the amount of mass in the liquid phase, and m_2 the amount of mass in the vapor phase. Then, for a state of the system such as that represented by point K, the total volume of the mixture is the sum of the volume occupied by the liquid and that occupied by the vapor, or

$$mv = m_1 v_f + m_2 v_g \tag{15.1}$$

The ratio of the amount of saturated vapor to the total amount of mixture is called the *quality* of the mixture, usually designated by the symbol $x (= m_2/m)$. Equation (15.1) may be written in terms of the quality as

$$v = v_f + x(v_g - v_f) = v_f + x v_{fg} \tag{15.2}$$

where v_{fg} denotes the specific volume change from liquid to vapor.

15.4   T–s Diagram

Having found by experiment the relationship between the primary properties p, v, and T, we must now determine the internal energy, enthalpy, and entropy. This is accomplished by supplementing the p–v–T data with data on specific heats or internal energy. The relations developed in Chap. 11 then allow the calculation of any other property without further experimentation. The results may be tabulated or plotted in any convenient way. For example, the entropy may be represented by a surface such as that shown in Fig. 15.4(a), where s, p, and T have been selected as coordinates. The surface resembles somewhat a p–v–T surface, but it can be drawn more to scale because the entropy increase between liquid and vapor phases is relatively smaller than the volume increase between the same phases in the case of a p–v–T representation.

Just as the p–v–T surface can be projected onto the p–v and p–T planes to obtain p–v and p–T diagrams, so can the s–p–T surface be projected onto the T–s and p–s planes to obtain T–s and p–s diagrams. The most useful diagram by far, however, is the T–s diagram, illustrated in Fig. 15.4(b). Here, a typical constant pressure heating process is represented by line A–B–C–D. Its shape is similar to the corresponding line on the T–v diagram previously discussed. The area under the isothermal line B–C represents the heat of vaporization. The shape of the diagram indicates that the heat of vaporization decreases as the temperature rises, becoming zero at the critical point. Also shown in Fig. 15.4(b) are lines of constant quality and constant superheat. The quality of a mixture is as previously defined, and the *degree of superheat* is the difference between the existing temperature of a point such as D and the saturation tempera-

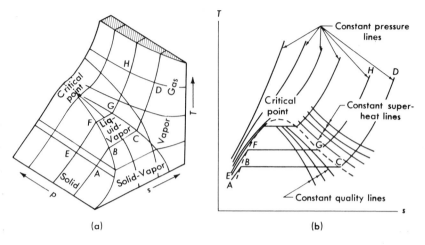

(a)   (b)

Fig. 15.4 $s-p-T$ Surface and $T-s$ Diagram.

ture corresponding to the existing pressure, namely the temperature at point C.

Consider a typical isobaric line such as $A-B-C-D$. The entropy change from A to B is given by

$$s_B - s_A = \int_A^B \frac{c_p \, dT}{T} \tag{15.3}$$

From B to C, the entropy change is given by

$$ds = \frac{dq}{T} = \frac{du + p \, dv}{T} = \frac{dh}{T} \tag{15.4}$$

since $du + p \, dv = d(u + pv) = dh$ for a constant pressure process. Furthermore, if the temperature is constant, the entropy change between B and C becomes

$$s_C - s_B = \frac{h_C - h_B}{T} = \frac{\text{latent heat}}{T} \tag{15.5}$$

Note that we have calculated the entropy change and not the absolute entropy of a system. For convenience, an arbitrary standard state is usually chosen, and the entropy change is calculated from this state. In the case of water, the standard state chosen is that of saturated liquid at 0.01 °C.

The preceding sections have dealt with the presentation of properties of a substance from a general point of view. For extensive or repetitive calculations such as those in engineering design, recourse is made to tables or diagrams giving enthalpy, entropy, internal energy, and other properties of various working substances over a wide range of pressures and temperatures. Tables of this sort are available for water, air, ammonia, carbon dioxide, sulphur dioxide, and other thermodynamic media commonly in use in engineering. The following sections discuss the use of steam tables.

15.5 Steam Tables

In general, all tables of thermodynamic properties have the same form. It is therefore only necessary to discuss the steam tables. Once the steam tables* are understood, the student will readily be able to use tables pertaining to other substances.

Tables 1 and 2 of *Thermodynamic Properties of Steam* by J. H. Keenan and F. G. Keyes give the properties of saturated liquid and saturated vapor as functions of temperature and pressure. In Table 1, the properties are given as a function of saturation temperature; in Table 2, the properties are given as a function of saturation pressure. The information contained in the two tables is essentially the same, the choice of the one used is simply a matter of convenience. Referring to Table 1, the first column after the temperature gives the saturation pressure in inches of mercury and in lbf/in² absolute. The next three columns give, respectively the specific volume of the saturated liquid, v_f, the increase in specific volume when the substance changes from saturated liquid to saturated vapor, v_{fg}, and the specific volume of the saturated vapor, v_g. Notice that

$$v_g = v_f + v_{fg} \qquad (15.6)$$

Succeeding columns give the specific enthalpy of saturated liquid, h_f, the latent heat of evaporation, h_{fg}, the specific enthalpy of saturated vapor h_g, and likewise for the entropy. These saturated properties are related in the following manner:

$$h_g = h_{fg} + h_f \qquad (15.7)$$

$$s_g = s_f + s_{fg} \qquad (15.8)$$

Notice that the datum of both enthalpy and entropy is saturated liquid at 32 °F, i.e., $h_f = 0$, $s_f = 0$ at 32 °F.

The specific volume of a mixture of vapor and liquid is stated in terms of its *quality*. As previously defined, quality is the ratio of the mass of vapor to the total mass of liquid plus vapor. For a unit of mass mixture having quality x, the specific volume is the sum of the volume of the vapor, xv_g, and the volume of the liquid, $(1-x)v_f$. Thus, if v denotes the specific volume,

$$v = xv_g + (1-x)v_f \qquad (15.9)$$

---

* An abstract of the steam tables is given in the appendix.

or, alternatively,

$$v = v_f + x v_{fg} \qquad (15.10)$$

$$v = v_g - (1-x)v_{fg} \qquad (15.11)$$

since $v_f + v_{fg} = v_g$. Similar expressions hold for enthalpy and entropy. In other words,

$$h = h_f + x h_{fg} \qquad (15.12)$$

$$s = s_f + x s_{fg} \qquad (15.13)$$

Referring to Table 2, the first column after the pressure gives the saturation temperature as a function of pressure. Succeeding columns give the same data as in Table 1, except that v_{fg} is not listed for low pressures. When necessary, v_{fg} can always be found by subtracting v_f from v_g.

Table 3 lists the properties of superheated vapor. In order to define the state of a substance in the superheat region, it is necessary to specify two properties. While any two may be used, the most common procedure is to give the pressure and temperature. Thus, values of v, h, and s are given in terms of the set of independent variables p and T.

Table 4 lists data pertaining to compressed liquid. If the pressure on a liquid is greater than the saturation pressure corresponding to its temperature, the liquid is known as *compressed liquid* or *subcooled liquid*. In Fig. 15.5, point 3 represents the state of a compressed liquid. Point 1 represents the state of a saturated liquid at the same temperature as 3,

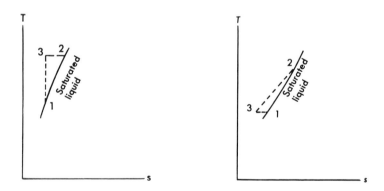

Fig. 15.5 Compressed (Subcooled) Liquid.

and point 2 represents the state of saturated liquid at the same pressure as 3. Although there is little information in general about properties of liquids in the compressed or subcooled region, the Keenan and Keyes tables give enough data to enable the specific volume of a compressed liquid to be determined. Consider, for example, one pound of saturated liquid at 200 °F (its properties are given in Table 1) and a pressure of 11.53 lbf/in². Suppose that the pressure is increased to 1000 lbf/in² with the temperature held at 200 °F. The difference in specific volume between the compressed liquid and the saturated liquid at the same temperature is given in Table 4 as

$$(v - v_f)10^5 = -5.4 \text{ ft}^3/\text{lbm}; \ v_f = 0.016634 \text{ ft}^3/\text{lbm}$$

whereupon

$$v = 0.016634 - 0.000054 = 0.016580 \text{ ft/lbm}$$

Similarly, Table 4 also gives values for $(h - h_f)$ and $(s - s_f) \cdot 10^3$. On the same page with the table of compressed liquid properties is a chart giving the enthalpy change of isentropically compressed water.

Table 5 gives the properties of a saturated solid and a saturated vapor in equilibrium. The first column lists the temperature; the second column lists the corresponding saturation pressure. The next two columns give the respective specific volumes of the saturated solid and saturated vapor.

The steam tables also include a number of diagrams. Chief among these are the specific-heat charts and the Mollier diagram. The specific-heat charts give the variation of c_p with T and p for water and steam. The Mollier diagram, shown in Fig. 15.6, is perhaps one of the most widely used diagrams in engineering applications. It consists of a family of constant-pressure and constant-temperature lines plotted on h–s co-ordinates. The Mollier diagram (Fig. 15.6b) is actually a portion of the

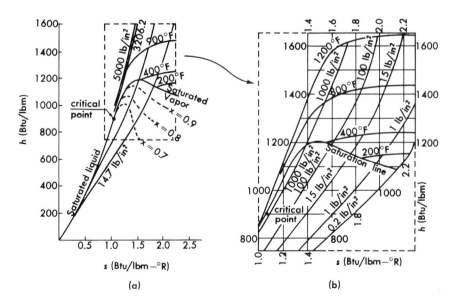

Fig. 15.6 Mollier Diagram.

overall h–s diagram which has been enlarged for convenience. The heavy line is the boundary of the liquid-vapor region. The constant pressure lines (straight lines in the wet region) merge into a single saturated liquid line, as shown in Fig. 15.6a. Constant dryness fraction lines and constant superheat lines are also included, so that the Mollier diagram has indeed a wide range of usefulness.

Example 15.1. What is the internal energy of (a) saturated liquid (water) at 32 °F? (b) superheated steam at 100 psia and 600 °F? (c) Determine the entropy of steam at 297 psia and 512 °F.

Solution. (a) Since the enthalpy of water at 32 °F is set as zero, the internal energy of the saturated liquid is given by

$$h_f = 0 = u_f + p_f v_f$$

From Table 1,

$$0 = u_f + \frac{(0.08854)(144)(0.01602)}{778}$$

or

$$u_f = -0.0026 \text{ Btu/lbm}$$

(b) From Table 3, $h = 1329.1$, $v = 6.218$. Thus,

$$u = h - pv = 1329.1 - \frac{(100)(144)(6.218)}{778}$$

$$= 1214 \text{ Btu/lbm}$$

(c) To arrive at the answer, a double interpolation is performed. From Table 3,

At 500 °F and 295 psia, $s = 1.5725$ ⎫
At 500 °F and 300 psia, $s = 1.5701$ ⎬ At 500 °F and 297 psia, $s = 1.571\underset{\cdot}{5}$
      Difference   = 0.0024 ⎪
      2/5 (0.0024) = 0.0009 ⎭

At 520 °F and 295 psia, $s = 1.5847$ ⎫
At 520 °F and 300 psia, $s = 1.5824$ ⎬ At 520 °F and 297 psia, $s = 1.5838$
      Difference   = 0.0023 ⎪
      2/5 (0.0023) = 0.0009 ⎭

At 297 psia and 500 °F, $s = 1.5715$ ⎫
At 297 psia and 520° F, $s = 1.5838$ ⎪ At 297 psia and 512 °F,
      Difference   = 0.0123 ⎬ $s = 1.5789$ (Answer)
      12/20 (0.0123) = 0.0074 ⎭

Example 15.2. A vessel having a volume of 11 cu ft contains 3.2 lbm of a mixture of liquid water and water vapor in equilibrium at a pressure of 100 psia. Find: (a) the volume and mass of liquid, (b) the volume and mass of vapor.

Solution. The specific volume of the mixture is first calculated: $v = 11/3.2$ = 3.44 ft³/lbm. The quality of the mixture is found by using Eq. (15.9):

$$v = 3.44 = x(4.432) + (1-x)(0.01774)$$

from which

$$x = 0.78 \text{ or } 78 \text{ per cent}$$

The amount of saturated liquid is $(3.2)(1-0.78) = 0.705$ lbm. Its volume is $(0.705)(0.01774) = 0.0125$ ft³.

The amount of saturated vapor is $(3.2)(0.78) = 2.5$ lbm. Its volume is $(2.5)(4.432) = 11.05$ ft³.

15.6 Vapor Processes

The process relations introduced in Chap. 5 may be applied to processes of vapors as well as to processes of gases. The only difference is that the assumption of a perfect gas ($pv = RT$) no longer holds. The following examples illustrate the use of steam tables to vapor processes.

Constant-Pressure Process. For purposes of illustration, consider a system of unit mass being heated in a non-flow constant-pressure process from a state in the wet region to a state in the superheated region, as shown in Fig. 15.7. The work done is

$$\int p\,dv = p(v_2 - v_1)$$

where the specific volume v_2 of the superheated vapor is taken directly from the superheat tables, and the specific volume v_1 of the wet mixture is calculated from the known quality x_1 of the mixture, i.e., $v_1 = v_f x_1 v_{fg}$.

The heat transferred is

$$q = \Delta u + \int p\,dv = u_2 - u_1 + p(v_2 - v_1)$$

$$= u_2 - u_1 + p_2 v_2 - p_1 v_1$$

$$= h_2 - h_1 \qquad (15.14)$$

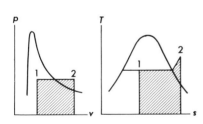

Fig. 15.7
Constant-Pressure Process.

where h_2 is taken from the superheat tables, and h_1 is calculated from $h_1 = h_f + x_1 h_{fg}$.

The change of internal energy is found from the enthalpies:

$$u_2 - u_1 = (h_2 - p_2 v_2) - (h_1 - p_1 v_1) \qquad (15.15)$$

Constant-Volume Process. Consider, for example, a constant-volume process from a state in the superheat region to a state in the wet region as shown in Fig. 15.8. Here, $\int p\,dv$ is zero, and the energy relation becomes

$$q = \Delta u = u_2 - u_1 = (h_2 - p_2 v_2) - (h_1 - p_1 v_1) \qquad (15.16)$$

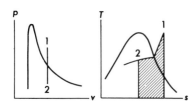

Fig. 15.8 Constant-Volume Process.

The specific enthalpy h_1 is read directly from the superheat tables. To find h_2, the quality x_2 is first obtained by setting

$$v_2 = v_1 = v_f + x_2 v_{fg}$$

Knowing x_2, the specific enthalpy h_2 may be calculated from

$$h_2 = h_f + x_2 h_{fg}$$

Constant-Temperature Process. Consider a non-flow isothermal addition of heat from a state in the wet region to a state in the superheat region as shown in Fig. 15.9. The heat added is

$$q = \int_1^2 T\,ds = T(s_2 - s_1)$$

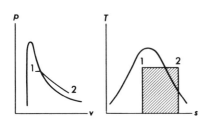

Fig. 15.9 Isothermal Process.

This is represented by the area under 1–2 on the T–s diagram. The entropy s_2 is found in the superheat tables; the entropy s_1 is calculated from

$$s_1 = s_f + x_1 s_{fg}$$

The change in internal energy is

$$\Delta u = (h_2 - p_2 v_2) - (h_1 - p_1 v_1)$$

$$(15.17)$$

The work is obtained from the first law relation

$$w = q - \Delta u = T(s_2 - s_1) = u_1 - u_2 \qquad (15.18)$$

Isentropic Process. Consider a non-flow reversible-adiabatic expansion from a state in the superheat region to a state in the wet region as shown in Fig. 15.10. Since the process is adiabatic and reversible,

$$q = T\,ds = 0;\ ds = 0$$

The governing relation is thus $s_2 = s_1$, and this enables the quality x_2 to be calculated

$$s_2 = s_1 = s_f + x_2 s_{fg}$$

Knowing x_2, we can obtain the specific volume and the specific enthalpy at state 2 by setting

$$v_2 = v_f + x_2 v_{fg}$$

$$h_2 = h_f + x_2 h_{fg}$$

The work done is given by

$$q = 0 = \Delta u + w$$

or

$$w = -\Delta u = u_1 - u_2$$

$$= (h_1 - p_1 v_1) - (h_2 - p_2 v_2) \qquad (15.19)$$

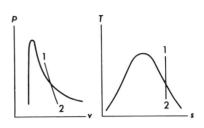

Fig. 15.10

Isentropic Process for Vapor.

Reversible Polytropic Process. Note that, except for the process p = constant, the work was not calculated by means of $\int p\,dv$, because vapors, in general, do not obey simple equations of state. However, if a reversible non-flow process can be defined by the equation

$$pv^n = \text{constant},$$

the process is known as a polytropic process.

The work done in a polytropic process is given by

$$\int_1^2 p\,dv = \frac{p_2 v_2 - p_1 v_1}{1 - n}$$

The heat transferred is

$$q = \Delta u + \int_1^2 p\,dv$$

$$= u_2 - u_1 + \frac{p_2 v_2 - p_1 v_1}{1 - n} \qquad (15.20)$$

For a reversible steady-flow polytropic process, the work done is given by

$$-\int_1^2 v\,dp = \frac{n(p_2 v_2 - p_1 v_1)}{1 - n}$$

and the heat transferred is

$$q = \Delta h - \int_1^2 v\,dp$$

$$= h_2 - h_1 + \frac{n(p_2 v_2 - p_1 v_1)}{1 - n} \qquad (15.21)$$

Throttling Process. For a reversible or irreversible adiabatic steady-flow of any fluid between states 1 and 2 without work, the energy equation is

$$u_1 + p_1 v_1 + \frac{\mathcal{V}_1^2}{2g_c} + \frac{g}{g_c} z_1 = u_2 + p_2 v_2 + \frac{\mathcal{V}_2^2}{2g_c} + \frac{g}{g_c} z_2$$

Neglecting kinetic energy and elevation changes, this becomes

$$u_1 + p_1 v_1 = u_2 p_2 v_2$$

or

$$h_1 = h_2 \tag{15.22}$$

Equation (15.22) defines a throttling process as a free expansion from a region of higher pressure to a region of lower pressure, during which no work is done and no heat is transferred.

The process is commonly used in pratice to determine the quality of wet steam. Suppose we wish to know the quality of steam in a steam main (state 1, Fig. 15.11). A sample of steam is allowed to flow into a throttl-ing calorimeter wherein it is expanded to atmospheric pressure. As the

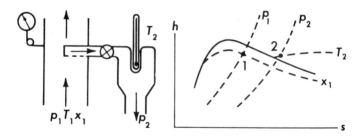

Fig. 15.11   Throttling Calorimeter and Throttling Process.

steam becomes superheated, its state 2 can be precisely located by measuring its pressure and temperature. The enthalpy h_2 can then be obtained from the superheat tables, and the quality x_1 of the steam may be calculated by setting

$$h_1 = h_2 = h_f + x_1 h_{fg} \tag{15.23}$$

Example 15.3. Four pounds of steam expand isentropically from a pressure of 300 psia and a temperature of 700 °F to a temperature of 200 °F. Determine the work done if (a) the process is non-flow, (b) the process is steady-flow.

Solution. In Fig. 15.12, point 1 is in the superheat region; point 2 is in the wet region (corresponding to a temperature of 200 °F and a pressure of 11.53 psia). From Table 3, corresponding to 300 psia and 700° F, $s_1 = 1.6751$, $h_1 = 1368.3$, $v_1 = 2.227$. Setting $s_2 = s_1$, the quality x_2 can be determined:

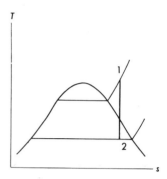

$$s_2 = 1.6751 = s_f + x_2 s_{fg} = 0.2938 + x_2 \,(1.4824)$$

where s_f and s_{fg} are values taken from Table 1 corresponding to $t_2 = 200$ °F. Solving for x_2 gives $x_2 = 0.932$ or 93.2 per cent quality. The specific enthalpy at point 2 is

$$h_2 = h_f + x_2 h_{fg}$$

$$= 167.99 + 0.932(977.9) = 1079.2$$

The specific volume at point 2 is

Fig. 15.12

Isentropic Expansion of Steam.

$$v_2 = v_f + x_2 v_{fg}$$

$$= 0.01663 + 0.932(33.62) = 31.35$$

(a) The work done in a non-flow isentropic process is

$$w = -\Delta u = u_1 - u_2$$

$$= (h_1 - p_1 v_1) - (h_2 - p_2 v_2)$$

$$= \left[1368.3 - \frac{(300)(144)(2.227)}{778}\right]$$

$$- \left[1079.2 - \frac{(11.53)(144)(31.35)}{788}\right]$$

$$= 232.3 \text{ Btu/lbm}$$

or, for 4 pounds,

$$W = 4(232.3) = 929.2 \text{ Btu}$$

(b) The work done in a steady-flow isentropic process may be obtained from the energy equation (neglecting kinetic energy and elevation changes):

$$u_1 + p_1 v_1 = u_2 + p_2 v_2 + w$$

or

$$w = (u_1 + p_1 v_1) - (u_2 + p_2 v_2)$$
$$= h_1 - h_2 = 1368.3 - 1079.2 = 289.1 \text{ Btu/lbm}$$

and for 4 pounds,

$$W = 4(289.1) = 1156.4 \text{ Btu}$$

Example 15.4. For an irreversible adiabatic expansion, the entropy increases, and work is lost. Consider an irreversible adiabatic expansion from the same initial state as in Ex. 15.3, namely $p_1 = 300$ psia, $t_1 = 700$ psia, to a pressure $p_2 = 11.53$ psia. If the temperature t_2 is 210 °F, find the lost work and the increase of unavailable energy.

Solution. Since expansion is not reversible, the actual point 2′ is to the right of point 2 (there is an increase in entropy). This is shown in Fig. 15.13. Considering a steady-flow process, the work for a reversible expansion is

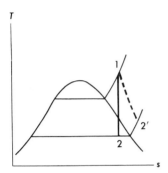

$$w_{rev} = h_1 - h_2$$

The work for an irreversible steady-flow expansion is

$$w_{irrev} = h_1 - h_2'$$

The *lost work* is therefore

$$w_{rev} - w_{irrev} = (h_1 - h_2) - (h_1 - h_2')$$
$$= h_2' - h_2$$

Fig. 15.13 Reversible and Irreversible Expansion.

For the case at hand, $h_2' = 1150.7$ (corresponding to 11.53 psia and 210 °F), $h_2 = 1079.2$ (from Ex. 15.3), so that the lost work amounts to $1150.7 - 1079.2 = 71.5$ Btu/lbm.

The increase in unavailable energy (referred to a datum temperature $t_0 = 200$ °F) is given by

$$T_0(\Delta s) = 660(s_2' - s_2)$$
$$= 660(1.7836 - 1.6751) = 71.5 \text{ Btu/lbm}$$

Note that when point 2′ falls in the wet region, the lost work is the same as the increase in unavailable energy.

15.7 Dependence of Transition Pressure on Temperature; Clapeyron Equation

Having discussed the various plots of thermodynamic properties, we wish at this stage to inquire more deeply into the nature of the lines separating the regions of the phase diagram. In other words, the dependence of the equilibrium pressure on the temperature is to be sought.

When a system undergoes a change of phase such as vaporization or condensation, the temperature and pressure are no longer independent of each other: at any given pressure the change of phase occurs at a definite temperature and vice versa. This is illustrated in Fig. 15.14 where, corresponding to a given pressure, the change of phase takes place at a definite temperature (called the saturation temperature).

Consider a system composed of one constituent in two different states which can change into each other, as for example, a liquid in equilibrium with its vapor (such a system is usually referred to as a two-phase system).

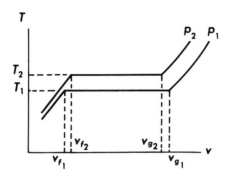

Fig. 15.14 Dependence of Vapor Pressure on Temperature.

During a change of phase (say, evaporation) the heat supplied to the liquid is taken up in doing work against forces holding the molecules to the liquid and in doing work of expansion through the increased volume of the vapor produced. The first appears as an increase in internal energy; the second as the product $p\Delta v$. If u_f and u_g are the specific internal energies, and v_f and v_g are, respectively, the specific volumes of liquid and vapor, the heat required to change a unit mass of liquid to vapor at constant pressure is equal to

$$(u_g - u_f) + p(v_g - v_f) = (u_g + pv_g) - (u_f + pv_f)$$
$$= h_g - h_f$$

since $p_g = p_f = p$. The quantity $h_g - h_f$ is the latent heat of evaporation. Now, the process of evaporation may be readily reversed by moving a piston in and out of a cylinder kept at constant temperature, so that $Tds = dq = h_g - h_f$, and therefore

$$s_g - s_f = \frac{h_g - h_f}{T} \tag{15.24}$$

where s_f and s_g are the respective entropies of the liquid and vapor. Thus,

$$T(s_g - s_f) = h_g - h_f$$

which may be written as

$$h_g - Ts_g = h_f - Ts_f$$

or

$$g_g = g_f \tag{15.25}$$

since $T_g = T_f = T$. Thus the liquid and vapor phase of a substance are in equilibrium only if the Gibbs function of each is equal. A similar statement applies to any two phases in equilibrium, or even three phases in equilibrium (triple point).

Consider now a liquid and its vapor in equilibrium at a pressure p and a temperature T and let g_f and g_g be the Gibbs functions of the liquid and vapor respectively. Let the temperature be changed to $T+dT$, the pressure to $p+dp$, and the Gibbs functions to g_f+dg_f and g_g+dg_g. Since the liquid and vapor are in equilibrium at the new temperature and pressure, it follows that

$$g_f+dg_f = g_g+dg_g$$

since $g_f = g_g$, this reduces to

$$dg_f = dg_g \tag{15.26}$$

Now, it was shown in Sec. 11.2 that $dg = vdp - sdT$. Therefore, Eq. (15.26) can be written as

$$v_f dp - s_f dT = v_g dp - s_g dT$$

or

$$(v_g - v_f)dp = (s_g - s_f)dT \tag{15.27}$$

But $s_g - s_f = s_{fg} = h_{fg}/T$. Thus, Eq. (15.27) becomes

$$(v_f - v_f)dp = \frac{(h_{fg})dT}{T}$$

or

$$\frac{dp}{dT} = \frac{h_{fg}}{(v_g - v_f)T} \tag{15.28}$$

Equation (15.28) is known as *Clapeyron's equation*. It allows the latent heat h_{fg} to be determined from measurements of v_f, v_g, and the saturation temperature at two nearby pressures. The equation is applicable to any change of state: fusion, vaporization, sublimation, and changes between crystalline forms, provided the appropriate latent heats and volume changes are employed.

15.8   Consequences of the Clapeyron Equation

The Clapeyron equation can be applied in numerous ways to physical-chemical problems. It can be used, for example, in predicting the effect of pressure on melting points. Consider the equilibrium between ice and liquid water: since ice is less dense than water, Δv for the melting process is negative. Moreover, since Δh, the heat of fusion, is positive, it is concluded from the Clapeyron equation that dp/dT must be a negative quantity. This means that the slope of the solid-liquid line in Fig. 15.15 must be negative, i.e., the melting point of ice is decreased by increasing the pressure.

This is the reason a piece of ice at or below its normal melting point can be melted by sufficient extra pressure, a fact which makes ice skating possible. Such a behavior is rather unusual, for, among common substances, only bismuth and antimony behave similarly. These substances expand on freezing.

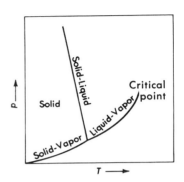

Fig. 15.15

p–T Diagram for Water.

Several approximations of the Clapeyron equation are possible, leading to a simpler equation than Eq. (15.28). Perhaps the most widely known is the application to the change "liquid$\rightleftharpoons$vapor". In this case, the volume of the liquid may be neglected in comparison with that of the vapor; this is equivalent to saying that Δv is simply equal to v_g, the volume of the vapor. If, furthermore, the vapor is taken to behave as an ideal gas, v_g can be replaced by RT/p, in which case Eq. (15.28) becomes, upon rearrangement,

$$\frac{d \ln p}{dT} = \frac{h_{fg}}{RT^2} \qquad (15.29)$$

Equation (15.29) is known as the *Clausius–Clapeyron equation*. If h_{fg} is regarded as independent of pressure, the equation may be integrated to give

$$\ln \frac{p_2}{p_1} = \int_{T_1}^{T_2} \frac{h_{fg}}{RT^2} dT \qquad (15.30)$$

If furthermore, h_{fg} is assumed constant, Eq. (15.30) simplifies to

$$\ln \frac{p_2}{p_1} = \frac{h_{fg}}{R} \left(\frac{1}{T_1} - \frac{1}{T_2} \right) \qquad (15.31)$$

which is the relation between two vapor pressures and the corresponding temperatures. The integration of Eq. (15.30) may also be carried out indefinitely, in which case

$$\ln p = -\frac{h_{fg}}{RT} + \text{constant} \qquad (15.32)$$

Equation (15.32) suggests that, if the logarithm of the vapor pressure is plotted against the reciprocal of the absolute temperature, a straight line with slope equal to $-h_{fg}/R$ is obtained. It is observed experimentally that the vapor pressures of most substances agree with such a conclusion.

15.9   Degrees of Freedom; Phase Rule

In discussing phase equilibria, it is important to consider intensity factors such as temperature, pressure, and composition. Of these variables a certain number may be varied independently, but the rest are fixed by the values chosen for the independent variables. The number of intensive properties that can be independently varied without changing the number of phases is called the *degrees of freedom* or *variance* of the system.

For example, when a system consists of only a single substance all in one phase (such as a pure gas), it is called a *homogeneous* system (in contrast to a heterogeneous system, such as a two-phase system consisting of water in equilibrium with water vapor). The state of a homogeneous system is specified completely by any two variables, such as pressure and temperature. If these two variables are known, then any other variable may be calculated. Such a system therefore has two degrees of freedom, and is called a *bivariant* system.

A two-phase, one-component system, on the other hand, requires only one variable to specify its state. In the example of water in equilibrium with water vapor, if the temperature is arbitrarily fixed, the pressure is automatically fixed, since, for a given temperature, there is but one pressure at which the two phases are in equilibrium. The system therefore has one degree of freedom and is said to be *univariant*

In general, for a system having C components and P phases, the degree of freedom F is given by

$$F = C + 2 - P \qquad (15.33)$$

This relation, of great fame and importance in physical chemistry, is known as the Gibbs phase rule. It is more fully discussed in Chapter 18.

15.10   Real Gases

So far in the discussion of tabulated properties of fluids, mention has been made of the gas tables (Sec. 14.6) and the steam tables (Sec. 15.5). The former deals with perfect gases having variable specific heats, and the latter with water vapor in various degrees of superheat. There is, however, a large class of gases whose properties, although not tabulated with such care and precision, must nevertheless be evaluated by some means (usually approximate). These are the so-called *real gases* or *non-ideal gases*. The evaluation of their properties is usually based on that of an ideal gas, with a correction factor thrown in. There are essentially two approaches to the treatment of non-ideal gases: (1) employ some form of the equation of state, (2) use the law of corresponding states. These approaches are discussed immediately below.

All equations involving only p, v, T, and constants are called *equations of state*. Whether they are empirical or theoretical, it is desirable that they be solvable for p and v without too much difficulty, because, in order to evaluate the quantities du, dh, ds, etc., it is necessary to evaluate such partial derivatives as

$$\left(\frac{\partial p}{\partial T}\right)_v, \ \left(\frac{\partial v}{\partial p}\right)_T, \text{ and } \left(\frac{\partial v}{\partial T}\right)_p.$$

Listed below are some of the more popular equations of state, presented on a mole basis.

(1) *van der Waals:*

$$\left(p + \frac{a}{\bar{v}^2}\right)(\bar{v} - b) = \bar{R}T \tag{15.34}$$

(2) *Dieterici:*

$$p(\bar{v} - b)e^{a/\bar{v}\bar{R}T} = \bar{R}T \tag{15.35}$$

(3) *Beattie-Bridgman:*

$$p\bar{v}^2 = \bar{R}T\left[\bar{v} + B_0\left(1 - \frac{b}{\bar{v}}\right)\right]\left(1 - \frac{c}{\bar{v}T^3}\right) - A_0\left(1 - \frac{a}{\bar{v}}\right) \tag{15.36}$$

In the above equations, $\bar{v}$ is the volume per mole, and $\bar{R}$ is the universal gas constant (the same for all gases). The other constants must be determined separately for each gas from experimental data. Constants for some of the more common gases are available in technical periodicals. Of the various equations of state, only the van der Waals equation will be discussed in some detail.

Van der Waals' equation represents one of the earliest attempts to develop an equation of state more accurate than the perfect-gas law. It takes into account the effect of attractive forces between molecules by introducing the term $a/\bar{v}^2$, and the effect of finite size of molecules by introducing the term b. The result, on a mole basis, is

$$\left(p + \frac{a}{\bar{v}^2}\right)(\bar{v} - b) = \bar{R}T$$

where the constants a and b are different for different gases. Written for N moles of gas, van der Waals' equation takes the form

$$\left(p + \frac{N^2 a}{V^2}\right)(V - Nb) = N\bar{R}T$$

where V is the total volume corresponding to N moles. Note that, if a and b are zero, the equation becomes identical to that for a perfect gas.

The p–v–T surface and the isotherms for a van der Waals gas are shown in Fig. 15.16. Note the similarity and difference with the corresponding data for a perfect gas.

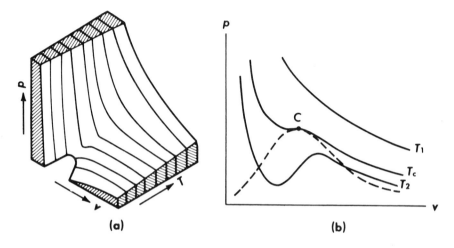

Fig. 15.16   Isotherms and p–v–T Surface for van der Waals Gas.

At temperatures far above condensation, the relationship between pressure and volume (as seen by the isotherm T_1) approaches that of a perfect gas, namely a rectangular hyperbola. As the temperature is lowered, the relationship between pressure and volume departs from that of a perfect gas. At the critical temperature, the isotherm T_c displays an inflection point. At temperatures below the critical, isotherms such as T_2 display a maximum and a minimum in the two-phase region. This is witnessed by the fact that van der Waals' equation is cubic in v, and therefore, it has three roots (three values of the volume) for a given pressure. However, two of the roots may be conjugate imaginaries, leaving only one root real. This is the case of the T_1 isotherm. On the other hand, the isotherm T_2 will give three distinct roots for a value of p in the wet region.

One way of determining the constants a and b in van der Waals' equation is to substitute measured values of p, v, and T for a gas in two different states. The two equations may then be solved simultaneously for a and b. The resulting van der Waals equation will then decribe the behavior of the gas reasonably well near the two chosen states. A better way of determining a and b, however, is to make use of the fact that the critical isotherm has an inflection point: Differentiating Eq. (15.34) at constant temperature gives:

$$\left(\frac{\partial p}{\partial \bar{v}}\right)_T = -\frac{\bar{R}T}{(\bar{v}-b)^2} + \frac{2a}{\bar{v}^3} \tag{15.37}$$

Differentiating once more at constant temperature yields:

$$\left(\frac{\partial^2 p}{\partial \bar{v}^2}\right)_T = \frac{2\bar{R}T}{(\bar{v}-b)^3} - \frac{6a}{\bar{v}^4} \tag{15.38}$$

Since the critical point is a point of inflection, the critical volume may be obtained by setting Eqs. (15.37) and (15.38) equal to zero and solving simultaneously for v_c. The result is

$$\frac{\bar{v}_c - b}{2} = \frac{\bar{v}_c}{3}$$

or

$$\bar{v}_c = 3b \tag{15.39}$$

Substituting this into Eq. (15.37) gives

$$T_c = \frac{2a(\bar{v}_c - b)^2}{\bar{v}_c^3 \bar{R}} = \frac{(2a)(4b^2)}{27b^3 \bar{R}}$$

$$= \frac{8}{27}\frac{a}{b\bar{R}} \tag{15.40}$$

Replacing $\bar{v}_c$ and T_c by these values in Eq. (15.34) gives

$$p_c = \frac{1}{27}\frac{a}{b^2} \tag{15.41}$$

Eqs. (15.40) and (15.41) are then solved for a and b to obtain

$$a = \frac{27}{64}\frac{\bar{R}^2 T_c^2}{p_c} \tag{15.42}$$

$$b = \frac{1}{8}\frac{\bar{R}T_c}{p_c} \tag{15.43}$$

In a similar manner, the constants, a and b, in the Dieterici equation are found to be

$$a = \frac{4}{e^2} \frac{\bar{R}^2 T_c^{\ 2}}{p_c} \tag{15.44}$$

$$b = \frac{\bar{R} T_c}{e^2 p_c} \tag{15.45}$$

where e is the base of natural logarithms, 2.718.

Before closing the discussion on equations of state, one type of equation, called the *virial type*, should be mentioned:

$$p\bar{v} = \bar{R}T + Ap + Bp^2 + Cp^3 + \ldots \tag{15.46}$$

where the virial constants A, B, C, ... are functions of temperature that must be determined experimentally. The chief characteristic of a virial equation of state is that it may be made to conform with experimental data as closely as desired by increasing the number of constants. Virial equations of state with ten or more constants have been used in composing tables of properties for steam and refrigerants.

Example 15.5. A 1.25 cu ft rigid-walled steel vessel contains one pound of oxygen at a temperature of 100 °F. Calculate the pressure within the vessel using (a) The perfect gas law, (b) The van der Waals equation, (c) The Beattie-Bridgman equation. The critical pressure and temperature for oxygen are 49.7 atm and 154 °K respectively. The constants in the Beattie-Bridgman equation are, in metric units: $a = 0.02562$ liters/gm-mole, $A_0 = 1.4911$ (atm) (liters)^2/gm-mole, $b = 0.004208$ liters/gm-mole, $B_0 = 0.04624$ liters/gm-mole, $c = 4.8 \times 10^4$ liters ($°K$)^3/gm-mole, $\bar{R} = 0.0821$ (liters) (atm)/(gm-mole) ($°K$).

Solution. The molecular weight of oxygen being 32, a pound of oxygen represents 1/32 mole. (a) Using the perfect gas law: $pV = N\bar{R}T$, where N is the number of moles,

$$p = \frac{N\bar{R}T}{V} = \frac{1}{32} \frac{(1545)(560)}{(144)(1)}$$

$$= \frac{1}{32} \frac{(10.73)(560)}{(1)} = 188 \text{ psia}$$

(b) Using the van der Waals equation: $(p + a/\bar{v}^2)(\bar{v} - b) = \bar{R}T$, the constants a and b are first calculated from Eqs. (15.42) and (15.43):

$$a = \frac{27}{64} \frac{\bar{R}^2 T_c^2}{p_c} = \frac{27}{64} \cdot \frac{(10.73)^2 (277)^2}{(730)}$$

$$= 5110 \text{(psi)(cu ft)}^2/\text{(lb mole)}^2$$

$$b = \frac{1}{8} \frac{\bar{R} T_c}{p_c} = \frac{1}{8} \cdot \frac{(10.73)(277)}{(730)} = 0.509 \text{ cu ft/lb mole}$$

Note that the critical temperature and pressure were first converted into degree Rankine and pounds per square inch so as to obtain a and b in English units. Van der Waals' equation becomes, with $\bar{v} = (1.25)\,(32) = 40$ cu ft/lb mole,

$$\left(p + \frac{5110}{40^2}\right)(40 - 0.509) = (10.73)(560)$$

$$p = 148.8 \text{ psia}$$

(c) Using the Beattie-Bridgman equation, the constants a, A_0, b, B_0, c and $\bar{R}$ can all be converted into English units, or they can be retained as such, and the answer changed to English units. Choosing the latter procedure, the mole volume is first determined to be

$$\bar{v} = \frac{(40)(28.32)}{(454)} = 2.49 \text{ liters/g mole}$$

Eq. (15.36) then gives

$$p\bar{v}^2 = RT\left[\bar{v} + B_0\left(1 - \frac{b}{\bar{v}}\right)\right]\left(1 - \frac{c}{\bar{v}T^3}\right) - A_0\left(1 - \frac{a}{\bar{v}}\right)$$

or

$$p(2.49)^2 = (0.0821)(315)\left[(2.49) + (0.04624)\left(1 - \frac{0.004208}{2.49}\right)\right]\left(1 - \frac{4.8 \times 10^4}{(2.49)(315)^3}\right)$$
$$- (1.4911)\left(1 - \frac{0.02562}{2.49}\right)$$

whence

$$p = 10.32 \text{ atm} = 151.9 \text{ psia}$$

15.11 Law of Corresponding States

The second approach to the treatment of non-ideal gases is to use *compressibility charts* based on the *law of corresponding states*.

When a gas is not ideal, pv does not equal RT. However, the quantity RT may be multiplied by a correction factor so that, for one mole of gas

$$p\bar{v} = Z\bar{R}T \tag{15.47}$$

or, for N moles,

$$pV = ZN\bar{R}T \tag{15.48}$$

The constant Z is called the "compressibility factor". It is not really a constant, since it is different for each gas, and varies with both temperature and pressure. It has, however, been found from experience that when different gases are at the same reduced temperature and reduced pressure, their compressibility factors are very nearly the same. *Reduced* temperature, pressure, and volume are defined as the ratio of the actual temperature, pressure, and volume to the temperature, pressure, and volume at the critical point. In other words,

$$T_R = \frac{T}{T_c}; \; p_R = \frac{p}{p_c}; \; v_R = \frac{v}{v_c} \qquad (15.49)$$

The degree to which a gas deviates from ideal gas behavior depends upon its reduced temperature and pressure, but at equal reduced conditions the deviation is the same for *all* gases. The statement to this effect is called the *law of corresponding states*. This rule is an empirical one, but it can be applied to most gases with a fair degree of accuracy. The result is that a compressibility chart may be plotted, giving the value of the compressibility factor for any gas as a function of reduced pressure and temperature. Such a chart is shown in Fig. 15.17. The compressibility factor Z is plotted

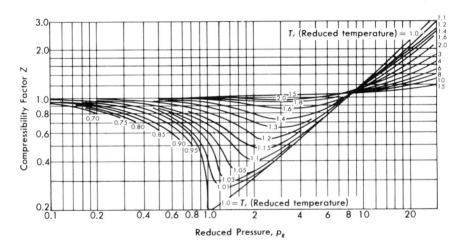

Fig. 15.17 Generalized Compressibility Chart.

against the reduced pressure p_R with the reduced temperature T_R as parameter. Note that, as the pressure approaches zero, Z approaches unity. This is as expected, since the postulates of a perfect gas (no attractive forces between the molecules and negligible volume of the molecules) are essentially fulfilled at very low pressures.

Example 15.6. Using the generalized compressibility chart, find the volume occupied by a pound of ethylene at 140 °F and 950 psia. Compare this with the answer obtained by using the ideal gas law. The critical pressure and temperature for ethylene are 50.9 atm and 9.7 °C respectively.

Solution. $p_c = 50.9$ atm $= 749$ psia; $T_c = 9.7$ °C $= 509$ °R; $p_R = 950/749$ $= 1.27$; $T_R = 600/509 = 1.18$. From the compressibility chart corresponding to $p_R = 1.27$ and $T_R = 1.18$, read $Z = 0.7$. Thus,

$$\bar{v} = \frac{Z\bar{R}T}{p} = \frac{(0.7)(1545)(600)}{(950)(144)}$$

$$= 4.75 \text{ cu ft/lb mole}$$

$$= \frac{4.75}{28} = 0.1696 \text{ cu ft/lbm}$$

Note: Sometimes, the constant $\bar{R}$ is given as 0.729 cu ft-atm/lb mole-°R. Using this value, the mole volume may also be found to be

$$\bar{v} = \frac{Z\bar{R}T}{p} = \frac{(0.7)(0.729)(600)}{64.6}$$

$$= 4.75 \text{ cu ft/lb mole}$$

If the ideal gas law had been used, the volume would have been 6.79 cu ft/lbm mole, and the error would have been 42.5 per cent.

15.12 Enthalpy and Entropy of Non-Ideal Gas

It was previously shown that the enthalpy of a perfect gas is a function only of temperature. For a real gas, this is not the case, and the effect of pressure must be taken into account. Although the effect of pressure on enthalpy is small for solids and liquids, it is large for gases, and in many cases the neglect of this correction can lead to errors.

The relations upon which an enthalpy correction chart may be constructed is a good example of the utility of partial derivatives. The reasoning is as follows: as the pressure of a gas decreases, it approaches ideal behavior. At zero pressure, all gases are ideal. The deviation is thus a function of pressure. To obtain a correction, an equation stating how enthalpy varies with pressure at a constant temperature is needed. Starting with

$$dh = d(u+pv) = du + pdv + vdp$$

$$= Tds + vdp$$

this can be written as

$$dh = T\left[\left(\frac{\partial s}{\partial p}\right)_T dp + \left(\frac{\partial s}{\partial T}\right)_p\right]dT + vdp$$

$$= \left[T\left(\frac{\partial s}{\partial p}\right)_T + v\right]dp + \left(\frac{\partial s}{\partial T}\right)_p dT$$

The change of enthalpy with pressure at constant temperature is thus

$$\left(\frac{\partial h}{\partial p}\right)_T = T\left(\frac{\partial s}{\partial p}\right)_T + v \tag{15.50}$$

The term $(\partial s/\partial p)_T$ can be written in terms of p, v, and T by means of one of Maxwell's relations: $(\partial s/\partial p)_T = -(\partial v/\partial T)_p$. Thus,

$$\left(\frac{\partial h}{\partial p}\right)_T = -T\left(\frac{\partial v}{\partial T}\right)_p + v \tag{15.51}$$

From the equation of state for real gases: $pv = ZRT$,

$$v = \frac{ZRT}{p} \tag{15.52}$$

and, upon differentiation with respect to T, holding p constant:

$$\left(\frac{\partial v}{\partial T}\right)_p = \frac{R}{p}\left[Z + T\left(\frac{\partial Z}{\partial T}\right)_p\right] \tag{15.53}$$

Equation (15.51) may be rewritten, with the substitutions for v and $(\partial v/\partial T)_p$ from Eqs. (15.52) and (15.53), as

$$\left(\frac{\partial h}{\partial p}\right)_T = -T\left(\frac{R}{p}\right)\left[Z + T\left(\frac{\partial Z}{\partial T}\right)_p\right] + \frac{ZRT}{p}$$

$$-\frac{ZRT}{p} - \frac{RT^2}{p}\left(\frac{\partial Z}{\partial T}\right)_p + \frac{ZRT}{p}$$

$$= -\frac{RT^2}{p}\left(\frac{\partial Z}{\partial T}\right)_p \tag{15.54}$$

Equation (15.54) is integrated at constant temperature into

$$\int_{h^*}^{h} dh = -RT^2\int_0^p \left(\frac{\partial Z}{\partial T}\right)_p \frac{dp}{p} \tag{15.55}$$

where h^* (corresponding to $p = 0$) is the enthalpy of the ideal gas, and h (corresponding to $p \neq 0$) is the enthalpy of the real gas.

Equation (15.55) can be used as such if values of Z as a function of p and T are available for an individual gas. However, since this is not often the case, it is put in terms of reduced temperature and pressure so that values of Z from the generalized compressibility-factor chart may be used. Since $p_R = p/p_c$ and $T_R = T/T_c$, $dp = p_c\,dp_R$ and $dT = T_c dT_R$. Thus, Eq. (15.55) becomes

$$\int_{h^*}^{h} dh = -RT_R^2 T_c^2 \int_0^{p_R} \frac{1}{T_c}\left(\frac{\partial Z}{\partial T_R}\right)_{p_R} \frac{dp_R}{p_R}$$

or, reversing the limits of integration on the left-hand side of the equation, and changing the sign on the right-hand side:

$$h^* - h = RT_R^2 T_c^2 \int_0^{p_R} \frac{1}{T_c}\left(\frac{\partial Z}{\partial T_R}\right)_{p_R} \frac{dp_R}{p_R} \qquad (15.56)$$

Since different gases have different critical temperatures, Eq. (15.56) is made more general by dividing through by T_c:

$$\frac{h^* - h}{T_c} = RT_R^2 \int_0^{p_R} \left(\frac{\partial Z}{\partial T_R}\right) \frac{dp_R}{p_R} \qquad (15.57)$$

Equation (15.57) is the basis of the enthalpy correction chart shown in Fig. 15.18 where the correction $(h^* - h)/T_c$ has been evaluated on a mole

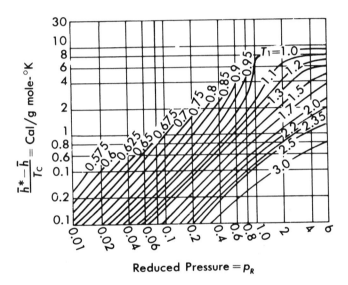

Fig. 15.18 Generalized Enthalpy Correction Chart.

basis. The use of the chart is a simple matter: Suppose that we wish to calculate the enthalpy of a mole of methane at 110°F and 490 psia. First, the enthalpy of the methane is calculated at 110 °F as though it were an ideal gas. This gives $\bar{h}^*$. The reduced temperature and pressure are then evaluated, and the point corresponding to these values is located on the chart to give the correction $(\bar{h}^* - \bar{h})/T_c$. Since $\bar{h}^*$ and T_c are known, the enthalpy $\bar{h}$ of the real gas is obtained.

A technique similar to the above is used to obtain the entropy of a real gas. The starting point is, again, Maxwell's equation:

$$\left(\frac{\partial s}{\partial p}\right)_T = -\left(\frac{\partial v}{\partial T}\right)_p$$

This can be written, with the aid of Eq. (15.53), as

$$\left(\frac{\partial s}{\partial p}\right)_T = -\frac{R}{p}\left[Z + T\left(\frac{\partial Z}{\partial T}\right)_p\right]$$

which integrates at constant temperature into

$$(\Delta s)_T = -R\int_{p_1}^{p_2}\left[Z + T\left(\frac{\partial Z}{\partial T}\right)_p\right]\frac{dp}{p}$$

$$= -R\int_{p_{R_1}}^{p_{R_2}}\left[Z + T_R\left(\frac{\partial Z}{\partial T_R}\right)_{p_R}\right]\frac{dp_R}{p_R} \tag{15.58}$$

Now, the entropy change for a perfect gas at constant temperature is

$$(\Delta s^*)_T = -R\int_{p_1}^{p_2}\frac{dp}{p} = -R\int_{p_{R_1}}^{p_{R_2}}\frac{dp_R}{p_R} \tag{15.59}$$

Subtraction of Eq. (15.59) from Eq. (15.58) gives

$$(\Delta s)_T - (\Delta s^*)_T = -R\int_{p_{R_1}}^{p_{R_2}}\left[(Z-1) + T_R\left(\frac{\partial Z}{\partial T_R}\right)_{p_R}\right]\frac{dp_R}{p_R} \tag{15.60}$$

Noting that the behavior of a real gas approaches that of an ideal gas as the pressure decreases, i.e., as $p \to 0$, $Z = 1$, $(\partial Z/\partial T_R)_{p_R} = 0$, $(\Delta s)_T - (\Delta s^*)_T = (s_{T,p} - s_{T,p\to 0}) - (s^*_{T,p} - s^*_{T,p\to 0}) = s_{T,p} - s^*_{T,p}$, Eq. (15.60) may be integrated from a lower limit of $p = 0$ to give

$$s^*_{T,p_R} - s_{T,p_R} = R\int_0^{p_R}\left[(Z-1) + T_R\left(\frac{\partial Z}{\partial T_R}\right)_{p_R}\right]\frac{dp_R}{p_R}$$

or, on a mole basis,

$$\frac{\bar{s}^*_{T,p_R} - \bar{s}_{T,p_R}}{\bar{R}} = \int_0^{p_R}\left[(Z-1) + T_R\left(\frac{\partial Z}{\partial T_R}\right)_{p_R}\right]\frac{dp_R}{p_R} \tag{15.61}$$

Equation (15.61) is the basis of the entropy correction chart shown in Fig. 15.19, where the entropy correction $(\bar{s}^* - \bar{s})$ has been plotted against p_R, with T_R as parameter.

In calculating the entropy change of a real gas between two states (T_1, p_1) and (T_2, p_2), it is convenient to adopt the following sequence:

(1) from T_1, p_1 (real gas) to T_1, p_1 (ideal gas)
(2) from T_1, p_1 (ideal gas) to T_2, p_2 (ideal gas)
(3) from T_2, p_2 (ideal gas) to T_2, p_2 (real gas).

Steps (1) and (3) are read off the chart. Step (2) is straightforward procedure based on standard relations developed earlier in the text.

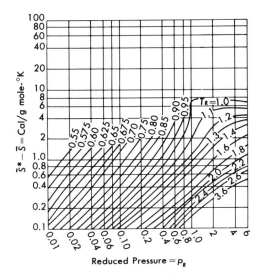

Fig. 15.19 Generalized Entropy Correction Chart.

Example 15.7. Determine the change in enthalpy and entropy of isobutane vapor when it is compressed isothermally from 40 psia and 130 °F to 100 psia. The critical temperature and pressure of isobutane are, respectively, 407 °K (= 732 °R) and 37 atm (544 psia). The molecular weight of isobutane is 58.

Solution. The reduced temperature and pressure at states 1 and 2 are

$$T_{R_1} = T_{R_2} = \frac{590}{732} = 0.805; \quad p_{R_1} = \frac{40}{544} = 0.0735; \quad p_{R_2} = \frac{100}{544} = 0.184$$

From Fig. 15.18, corresponding to $T_{R_1} = 0.805$ and $p_{R_1} = 0.0735$, read

$$\frac{\bar{h}^* - \bar{h}}{T_c} = 0.2 \text{ cal/(g mole)-°K}$$

Similarly, corresponding to $T_{R_2} = 0.805$ and $p_{R_2} = 0.184$, read

$$\frac{\bar{h}^* - \bar{h}}{T_c} = 1.1 \text{ cal/(g mole)-°K}$$

Thus,

$$\frac{\Delta\bar{h}}{T_c} = 0.2 - 1.1 = -0.9 \text{ cal/(g mole)-°K}$$

$$\Delta h = -(0.9)(407) = -367 \text{ cal/g mole}$$
$$= -(367)(1.8) = -660 \text{ Btu/lb mole}$$

or

$$\Delta h = -\frac{660}{58} = -17.4 \text{ Btu/lbm}$$

As for the change in entropy $\bar{s}_{p_2} - \bar{s}_{p_1}$, this can be written as

$$\bar{s}_{p_2} - \bar{s}_{p_1} = (\bar{s}^*_{p_2} - \bar{s}^*_{p_1}) - (\bar{s}^*_{p_2} - \bar{s}_{p_2}) + (\bar{s}^*_{p_1} - \bar{s}_{p_1})$$

The term $(\bar{s}^*_{p_2} - \bar{s}^*_{p_1})$ represents the entropy change between two pressures p_1 and p_2 as though the gas were perfect, i.e.,

$$\bar{s}^*_{p_2} - \bar{s}^*_{p_1} = -R \ln\frac{p_2}{p_1}$$

$$= -(1.98) \ln\frac{100}{40} = -1.81 \text{ cal/(g mole)-}^\circ\text{K}$$

The terms $(\bar{s}^*_{p_2} - \bar{s}_{p_2})$ and $(\bar{s}^*_{p_1} - \bar{s}_{p_1})$ represent deviations from perfect gas behaviour; they are read from Fig. 15.19, corresponding to $p_{R_2} = 0.184$ and $p_{R_1} = 0.0735$, each at $T_R = 0.805$;

$$\bar{s}^*_{p_2} - \bar{s}_{p_2} = 1.1 \text{ cal/(g mole)-}^\circ\text{K}$$

$$\bar{s}^*_{p_1} - \bar{s}_{p_1} = 0.38 \text{ cal/(g mole)-}^\circ\text{K}$$

Thus

$$\bar{s}_{p_2} - \bar{s}_{p_1} = -1.81 - 1.1 + 0.38$$

$$= -2.53 \text{ cal/g mole-}^\circ\text{K}$$

$$= -2.53 \text{ Btu/lb mole-}^\circ\text{R}$$

or

$$s_{p_2} - s_{p_1} = -\frac{2.53}{58} = 0.0436 \text{ Btu/lbm-}^\circ\text{R}$$

PROBLEMS

15.1. (a) Show that during an evaporation or condensation process, $dh = Tds$, and consequently $dg = 0$. (b) The vapor pressure of many substances can be represented by the equation

$$\ln p = a - \frac{b}{T}$$

Assuming that the vapor obeys the perfect gas relation, what is the equation of the condensation curve on a $p - v$ plot?

15.2 (a) Using the steam tables, find the density of water at the following states: (1) saturated liquid at 60 °F, (2) subcooled liquid at 60 °F and 14.7 psia,

(3) saturated liquid at 14.7 psia, (4) saturated liquid at 100 psia. Compare the answer in each case with the usual 62.4 lbm/cu ft. (b) Plot the following vapor pressure curves (saturation pressure versus saturation temperature): (1) water, from -30 °F to 100 °F, (2) water, from 5 psia to 3000 psia.

15.3 (a) Using steam tables, make a plot on $T-s$ co-ordinates of a constant pressure line (100 psia). Measure the subtangent, and compare this value with the c_p obtained from steam tables. (b) Using steam tables, construct a $u-v$ diagram for water. Show lines of constant temperature and constant pressure. Show that the triple point is represented by an area.

15.4. At a certain instant a 2 cu ft radiator of a heating system contains saturated steam at 18 psia. The valves are then closed on the radiator, and as a result of heat transfer to surroundings, the pressure drops to 16 psia. Determine: (a) the temperature in the final state, (b) the quality in the final state, (c) the mass of liquid and vapor in the final state.

15.5. What must be the proportions by volume of liquid and vapor at 14.7 psia if water in a rigid vessel is to pass through the critical state when it is heated?

15.6. Using the steam tables, construct a skeleton $p-h$ chart for steam. Plot lines of constant p, constant h, constant s, constant T, and constant v. Include the saturation curves for liquid and vapor.

15.7. A throttling calorimeter is used to measure the quality of steam in a steam main. The calorimeter readings are: pressure, 14.7 psia, temperature, 248 °F, main pressure, 86 psia. Find the quality of the steam.

15.8. Show that $(\partial h/\partial s)_p$, the slope of a constant-pressure line on the Mollier chart is equal to T and therefore, constant-pressure lines are straight lines in the wet region. Hint: The increase of enthalpy from a saturated liquid state to a state of quality x at the same pressure is xh_{fg}.

15.9. A Carnot cycle carried out with steam as the working medium operates between the temperature limits of 500 °F and 90 °F. The isothermal expansion at the high-temperature changes the specific volume of steam from 0.3 to 5 cu ft. Determine: (a) the heat added, the heat rejected, and the work output per pound of steam, (b) the thermal efficiency of the cycle.

15.10. A boiler feed pump delivers 500,000 pounds of water per hour at a pressure of 1100 psia and 460 °F. Calculate the volume rate of flow in cfm by: (a) assuming saturated water at 460 °F, (b) by using table 4 of the steam tables.

15.11. Wet steam from a steam main flows steadily through a partially open valve into a pipeline in which is fitted an electric coil. The mass flow rate is 0.95 lbm/min; the coil takes 3.7 amps at 220 volts. The pressure in the main is 40 psia. Conditions downstream of the coil are 20 psia and 309 °F. Determine the condition of the steam in the main.

15.12. Two boilers deliver steam into the same main at 200 psia. The output of one is 2900 lbm/hr at 98 per cent quality, the output of the other is 23,000 lbm/hr at 480 °F. Determine: (a) the condition of the mixture in the main, (b) the increase in unavailable energy referred to a surroundings temperature $t_0 = 80°F$. Why is there an increase in unavailable energy?

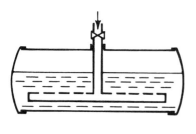

Fig. 15.20

15.13. A steam accumulator (Fig. 15.20) contains 2,500 cu ft of water and 2500 cu ft of steam in thermal equilibrium at 40 psia. Steam at 220 psia and 500 °F flows through a valve into the accumulator at the rate of 10 pounds per minute. Assuming the accumulator to be insulated, find: (a) the time required to raise the accumulator to 100 psia, (b) the volumes finally occupied by water and steam, respectively. Hint: Write equations for a mass balance and an energy balance.

15.14. Often small plant auxiliaries require saturated steam from a steam generator which produces superheated steam. The saturated steam can be obtained by use of a spray-type desuperheater, wherein the superheat of the steam is reduced by the injection of water. If steam leaving the steam generator is at 400 psia and 640 °F, what mass of spray water at 70 °F would be required per pound of steam?

15.15. An insulated tank having a total volume of 3.5 cu ft is divided into two halves by a membrane. One half contains steam at 20 psia and 400 °F; the other half contains steam at 60 psia and 360 °F. The membrane is broken, and pressure and temperature equalize within the tank. Determine the final temperature and pressure. Hint: $Q = 0$; $W = 0$: $\Delta U = 0$: $\Delta H = \Delta(pV)$.

15.16. A vessel is divided by a partition into two parts of 9 cu ft each. One part contains steam at 290 psia and 500 °F; the other part contains saturated steam at 20 psia. The partition is broken, and the two parts mix. During the process, the tank loses 50 Btu to the surroundings. Determine the final temperature and pressure of the mixture.

15.17. Steam at 100 psia and 400 °F expands isentropically in a frictionless nozzle to a pressure of 15 psia. The mass rate of flow is 9 lbm/sec. What is the required discharge area if (a) an equilibrium state exists between vapor and liquid in the wet region, (b) a metastable (super-saturation) state exists in the wet region. The appropriate value of γ in $pv^\gamma = $ constant may be obtained from Fig. 8 of the Keenan and Keyes steam tables.

15.18. From experimental data on steam, a family of specific volume vs. temperature curves for various pressure values ranging from 10 psia to 100 psia are plotted. From these curves, the following slopes for a temperature of 600 °F at various pressures are obtained:

Pressure (psia)	Value of $(dv/dT)_p$ at 600 °F; $(ft^3/lbm\text{-}°R)$
10	0.05990
20	0.03013
40	0.01523
60	0.01028
80	0.00781
100	0.00633

Using the above data, calculate the entropy change for one pound of steam in an isothermal process at 600 °F from 10 psia to 100 psia. Hint: Make use of the Tds equation in terms of p and T as independent variables.

15.19. A rigid tank containing CO_2 is heated until a pressure of 215 psia and a temperature 160 °F is attained. What is the original condition of the CO_2 in the tank if a heat input of 75 Btu per pound of CO_2 is required?

15.20. Water, at a temperature to 50 °F, has a coefficient β of approximately $9 \times 10^{-6}/°F$. What is the final temperature, if water in a hydraulic press is compressed adiabatically and reversibly from 1 atm to 900 atm?

15.21. Assuming that the vapor in equilibrium with a liquid at a given temperature and pressure behaves as an ideal gas, show that Clapeyron's equation may be written as

$$\frac{d(\ln p)}{dT} = \frac{\Delta h}{RT^2}$$

This equation, known as the *Clausius–Clapeyron equation,* is valid for evaporation and sublimation processes. If, furthermore, Δh is constant, the relation becomes

$$\ln p = -\frac{\Delta h}{RT} + \text{constant}$$

Thus, if the logarithm of the vapor pressure is plotted vs. the reciprocal of the absolute temperature, a straight line with slope equal to $-(\Delta h/R)$ is obtained. Verify this result experimentally for a number of substances by means of data available from the Bureau of Standards.

15.22. (a) Determine the amount the melting-point temperature of ice is lowered for an increase in pressure of 1 atm. The specific volumes of ice and water at 32 °F are 0.0175 and 0.0160 cu ft/lbm respectively. (Make use of Clapeyron's equation.) (b) What relation does this problem have on, say, the act of ice skating?

15.23. Derive Clapeyron's equation by considering a Carnot engine operating between two reservoirs differing infinitesimally in temperature and letting the working substance undergo a phase change.

15.24. From the following data for water:

Saturation Temperature ($°F$)	Saturation pressure ($psia$)	Volume of liquid (ft^3/lbm)	Volume of vapour (ft^3/lbm)
228	20.016	0.01683	20.07
230	20.780	0.01684	19.38
232	21.567	0.01686	18.72

compute the latent heat of evaporation of water at 230 °F (use Clapeyron's equation).

15.25. (a) Show that $(\partial c_v/\partial v)_T = 0$ for a van der Waals gas.

(b) Calculate the entropy change $s_2 - s_1$ for a van der Waals gas undergoing a transformation from v_1, T_1, to v_2, T_2, assuming the specific heat at constant volume to be

$$c_v = a + bT + cT^2$$

where a, b and c are constants.

15.26. Show that the Joule–Thomson coefficient of a van der Waals gas is

$$\mu = \frac{v}{c_p} \frac{2a(v-b)^2 - RTbv^2}{RTv^3 - 2a(v-b)^2}$$

and determine the equation of the inversion curve. Hint: Set $\mu = 0$ and obtain

$$T_i = \frac{2a(v-b)^2}{Rv^2b}.$$

Eliminate v between this equation and the equation of state to get the equation connecting T_i and p_i.

15.27. Equations 15.40 to 15.42 may be obtained in an alternate manner from that presented in the text: Since van der Waals' equation is cubic in v, it follows that for $p = p_c$ and $T = T_c$, it must have a triple root $v = v_c$. Write the equation in the form

$$p_c v^3 - (p_c b + RT_c)v^2 + av - ab = 0$$

Since v_c is a triple root, the left-hand side must be of the form $p_c(v - v_c)^3$. By comparison, find

$$v_c{}^3 = \frac{ab}{p_c}; \quad 3v_c{}^2 = \frac{a}{p_c}; \quad 3v_c = \frac{p_c b + RT_c}{p_c}$$

Solve these three equations for v_c, p_c and T_c.

15.28. (a) Show that for a van der Waals gas, the work done during an isothermal process is

$$RT \ln\left(\frac{v_2-b}{v_1-b}\right) + a\left(\frac{1}{v_2} - \frac{1}{v_1}\right)$$

(b) Treating nitrogen as a van der Waals gas, determine the work done per pound in compressing isothermally nitrogen from 15 psia and 60 °F to 850 psia.

15.29. Dieterici's equation:

$$p = \frac{RT}{v-b} e^{-a/vRT}$$

represents facts more closely than the perfect-gas law. Because of its exponential form, however, it has not been popular with engineers. Making use of the fact that the isotherm passing through the critical point has zero slope at that point, and that the critical point is also a point of inflection, i.e.,

$$\left(\frac{\partial p}{\partial v}\right)_T = 0, \quad \left(\frac{\partial^2 p}{\partial v^2}\right)_T = 0,$$

show that

$$a = \frac{4R^2 T_c^2}{e^2 p_c}; \quad b = \frac{RT_c}{e^2 p_c}$$

15.30. Consider the isotherm for a van der Waals gas as shown in Fig. 15.21.
At any temperature below the critical, the portion of the isotherm to the left of the minimum point represents liquid states and that to the right of the maximum point represents vapor states. The portion between the maximum and minimum represents unstable states.

Given a van der Waals isothermal let us determine what the pressure of the saturated vapor is when its temperature is equal to that of the given isothermal. In other words, where should the horizontal line A—B be sketched? Show that its position should be such that the areas $AA'O$ and $BB'O$ are equal.

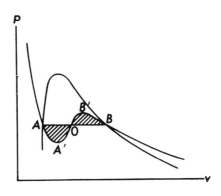

Fig. 15.21

Hint: Consider the isothermal $A - A' - O - B' - B - A$ by which the system can return to its original state. Since only one level of temperature is involved, the net work done by the system must be zero, i.e.,

$$\oint p dv = 0.$$

15.31. Show that for a gas obeying the Berthelot equation of state

$$p = \frac{RT}{v-b} - \frac{a}{v^2 T}$$

the internal energy and entropy change are given by

$$d = c_v dT + \frac{2a}{v^2 T} dv$$

$$ds = c_v \frac{dT}{T} + \left(\frac{R}{v-b} + \frac{a}{v^2 T^2}\right) dv$$

CHAPTER 16

Non-Reactive Mixtures

16.1 Mixtures of Perfect Gases

Up to this point, our discussions have been concerned chiefly with one-component systems, e.g., systems containing a single gas. Many thermodynamic calculations, however, involve a homogeneous mixture of different gases. Such a case is air, which is a mixture of nitrogen and oxygen, with a small trace of argon and other gases present. A homogeneous mixture of gases can be regarded as a single substance if the constituents do not react chemically with one another. The problem is simply to determine the thermodynamic properties of a mixture of perfect gases from the properties of the individual constituents.

Consider the rigid vessel shown in Fig. 16.1. Let it be first evacuated, then connected by pipes fitted with stopcocks to storage bottles containing

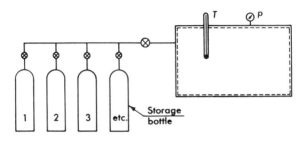

Fig. 16.1 Mixture of Gases.

various ideal gases labeled 1, 2, 3, etc. Let each of the stopcocks be opened for a short period. As a result, the vessel now contains a mixture of gases 1, 2, 3, etc. If the gases mix completely and have no tendency to react chemically with each other, the contents of the vessel will be uniform in pressure and temperature, and uniform and invariant in composition and chemical aggregation. This means that the system can be treated as a pure substance, even though it is not chemically pure.

The thermometer and pressure gage shown in Fig. 16.1 indicate the temperature T and pressure p of the mixture. The total mass m of the mixture is the sum of the mass of individual constituents:

$$m = m_1 + m_2 + m_3 + \ldots \qquad (16.1)$$

A description of the mixture may be given by a *gravimetric analysis* of it; this is the percentage by weight of each constituent. For example, the gravimetric percentage of gas i in a mixture is

$$g_i = \frac{m_i}{m_1 + m_2 + \ldots} = \frac{m_i}{\sum_i m_i} \qquad (16.2)$$

A description of the mixture may also be given by a *volumetric analysis* of it. Referring to Fig. 16.2, this is the percentage of the total volume that each component would occupy if the various gases were placed in separate compartments at the pressure p and the temperature T of the mixture. Each of the components would then occupy a certain percentage of the entire volume, i.e.,

$$v_1 = x_i V$$

or

$$x_i = \frac{v_i}{v}$$ (16.3)

where v_i is the partial volume of the ith constituent, and x_i is its mole fraction.

The gravimetric analysis g_i and the volumetric analysis x_i are related by the following equations, which the reader can easily verify:

$$g_i = \frac{x_i M_i}{\sum\limits_i x_i M_i}$$ (16.4)

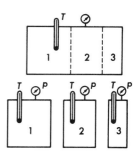

Fig. 16.2
Concept of Partial Volume.

$$x_i = \frac{g_i/M_i}{\sum\limits_i (g_i/M_i)}$$ (16.5)

where M_i is the molecular weight of the ith gas. Equation (16.4) enables the gravimetric analysis to be calculated if the volumetric analysis is known; Equation (16.5) gives the volumetric analysis from a knowledge of the gravimetric analysis.

Besides the gravimetric analysis and the volumetric analysis, the notion of *partial pressure* is often used in connection with a mixture of gases. Referring to Fig. 16.3, the partial pressure of any constituent is that pressure of the constituent if it alone occupied the vessel at the temperature of the mixture. Thus, the partial pressure of the ith gas in a mixture is p_i; it is the pressure exerted by the single ith gas. The ratio of the pressure of any component to the pressure of the mixture is then p_i/p.

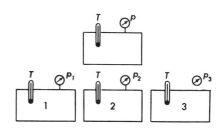

Fig. 16.3 Concept of Partial Pressure.

16.2 Gibbs–Dalton Law

The thermodynamic properties of a mixture of perfect gases may be calculated from the properties of the individual gases by means of the Gibbs–Dalton law. This law is in two parts: the first is concerned with the intensive property, pressure; the second with the extensive properties, internal energy, enthalpy, and entropy.

(a) *The pressure of a mixture of perfect gases is equal to the sum of the partial pressures that each component would exert if it alone occupied the volume of the mixture at the temperature of the mixture.* Mathematically, this is expressed as

$$p = p_1 + p_2 + p_3 + \ldots = \sum_i p_i \tag{16.6}$$

(b) *The internal energy, the enthalpy, and the entropy of a mixture of perfect gases are respectively equal to the sums of the internal energies, the enthalpies, and the entropies that each component would have, if it alone occupied the volume of the mixture at the temperature of the mixture.* Mathematically, this is expressed as

$$U = U_1 + U_2 + U_3 + \ldots = \sum_i U_i \tag{16.7}$$

$$H = H_1 + H_2 + H_3 + \ldots = \sum_i H_i \tag{16.8}$$

$$S = S_1 + S_2 + S_3 + \ldots = \sum_i S_i \tag{16.9}$$

As a consequence of the Gibbs–Dalton law of partial pressures, the gas constant of a mixture of perfect gases may be easily calculated. Consider three different gases 1, 2, and 3 all at the same temperature T and each occupying the same volume V. The equation of state for each of the gases may be written as

$$p_1 V = m_1 R_1 T; p_2 V = m_2 R_2 T; p_3 V = m_3 R_3 T$$

The pressure of the individual gases are, respectively,

$$p_1 = \frac{m_1 R_1 T}{V}; p_2 = \frac{m_2 R_2 T}{V}; p_3 = \frac{m_3 R_3 T}{V}$$

The pressure of the mixture, according to the Gibbs–Dalton law, is

$$p = p_1 + p_2 + p_3$$

$$= (m_1 R_1 + m_2 R_2 + m_3 R_3) \frac{T}{V}$$

whence

$$pV = (m_1 R_1 + m_2 R_2 + m_2 R_3) T = \left(\sum_{i=1}^{3} m_i R_i \right) T \tag{16.10}$$

Comparing Eq. (16.10) with the equation of state written for m pounds of mixture, $pV = mRT$, it is seen that the gas constant R of the mixture is given by

$$R = \frac{m_1 R_1 + m_2 R_2 + m_3 R_3}{m} = \frac{\sum_{i=1}^{3} m_i R_i}{m} \qquad (16.11)$$

Another consequence of Dalton's law of partial pressures is that the mole fraction and the partial pressure ratio are numerically equal for a mixture of perfect gases. Let n_1, n_2, n_3 be the number of moles of each constituent present in the mixture. The equation of state for each constituent then becomes

$$p_1 V = n_1 \bar{R} T; \; p_2 V = n_2 \bar{R} T = p_3 V = n_3 \bar{R} T$$

where R is the universal gas constant (same for each gas).† The pressure of the mixture, according to Dalton's law, is

$$p = p_1 + p_2 + p_3 = (n_1 + n_2 + n_3)\frac{\bar{R} T}{V}$$

$$= \left(\sum_{i=1}^{3} n_i\right) \frac{\bar{R} T}{V} \qquad (16.12)$$

The partial pressure ratio is then

$$\frac{p_i}{p} = \frac{(n_i \bar{R} T)/V}{\left(\sum_i n_i\right) \bar{R} T / V} = \frac{n_i}{\sum_i n_i} = x_i \qquad (16.13)$$

where x_i is the mole fraction of the ith constituent. In other words, the ratio of the partial pressure of a constituent gas in a mixture to the total pressure of the mixture is equal to the mole fraction of that constituent.

In connection with mixtures, it is also convenient to speak of the equivalent molecular weight of a mixture. This is the ratio of the total mass of the mixture to the number of moles of mixture. Let, M_1, $M_2 \ldots$ be the respective molecular weights of each constituent. The total mass of the mixture is then

$$n_1 M_1 + n_2 M_2 + \ldots$$

where n_1, n_2, $\ldots$ are the number of moles of each constituent present in the mixture. Now, the total number of moles of mixture is equal to the sum of the moles of individual gases:

$$n_1 + n_2 + \ldots$$

---

† Recall that $\bar{R} = 1545$ ft lbf/mole-°R $= 1.986$ Btu/mole-°R.

The equivalent molecular weight M of the mixture is thus

$$\frac{n_1 M_1 + n_2 M_2 + \cdots}{n_1 + n_2 + \cdots} = x_1 M_1 + x_2 M_2 + \cdots = \sum_i x_i M_i \qquad (16.14)$$

where x_i is the mole fraction of the ith constituent.

Example 16.1. A 4 cu ft tank contains a mixture of 3.5 pounds of CO_2 and 2 pounds of N_2 at a temperature of 80 °F. Determine: (a) the pressure of the mixture, (b) the specific gas constant of the mixture, (c) the molecular weight of the mixture, (d) the specific enthalpy of the mixture, (e) the specific internal energy of the mixture, (f) the specific entropy of the mixture.

Solution. (a) The specific volume of the carbon dioxide is $4/3.5 = 1.143\ \text{ft}^3/\text{lbm}$, its temperature is 80 °F. Its pressure can thus be found from the perfect gas law:

$$P_{CO_2} = \frac{(34.9)(540)}{(1.143)(144)} = 114.3\ \text{psia}$$

Similarly, the specific volume of the nitrogen being $4/2 = 2\ \text{ft}^3/\text{lbm}$, its temperature being 80 °F, its pressure is

$$P_{N_2} = \frac{(55.2)(540)}{(2)(144)} = 103.5\ \text{psia}$$

The pressure of the mixture is thus

$$p = p_{CO_2} + p_{N_2} = 114.3 + 103.5 = 217.8\ \text{psia}$$

(b) The specific gas constant for the mixture is

$$R = \frac{1}{m}(m_{CO_2} R_{CO_2} + m_{N_2} R_{N_2})$$

$$= \frac{1}{5.5}(3.5 \times 34.9 + 2 \times 55.2) = 42.3\ \text{ft lbf/lbm-}°\text{R}$$

(c) The molecular weight of the mixture is

$$M = \frac{m}{m_{CO_2}/M_{CO_2} + m_{N_2}/M_{N_2}} = \frac{5.5}{3.5/44 + 2/28} = 36.3$$

(d) The specific enthalpy of the mixture is given by

$$mh = m_{CO_2} h_{CO_2} + m_{N_2} h_{N_2}$$

where h_{CO_2} and h_{N_2} are read from the gas tables† to be 92.2 Btu/lbm and 134 Btu/lbm respectively. Thus,

$$h = \frac{(3.5)(92.2) + (2)(134)}{5.5} = 107\ \text{Btu/lbm}$$

(e) The specific internal energy of the mixture is given by

$$mu = m_{CO_2} u_{CO_2} + m_{N_2} u_{N_2}$$

---

† The use of gas tables was discussed in Sec. 14.6.

From the gas tables, $u_{CO_2} = 67.8$ Btu/lbm, $u_{N_2} = 95.4$ Btu/lbm. Thus,

$$u = \frac{(3.5)(67.8)+(2)(95.4)}{5.5} = 78 \text{ Btu/lbm}$$

(f) The specific entropy of the mixture is given by

$$ms = m_{CO_2}s_{CO_2}+m_{N_2}s_{N_2}$$

whence

$$s = \frac{m_{CO_2}s_{CO_2}+m_{N_2}s_{N_2}}{m}$$

To find s_{CO_2} and s_{N_2} from the gas tables, note that any entropy change may be given by

$$ds = \frac{c_p}{T}dT - R\frac{dp}{p}$$

If the zero of entropy is chosen at 0 °F absolute and one atmosphere, the entropy at any state is then

$$s = \int_0^T \frac{c_p}{T}dT - R \ln p = \phi - R \ln p$$

The quantity ϕ is listed in the gas tables against temperature as argument. Thus,

$$s_{CO_2} = \phi_{CO_2}-R_{CO_2} \ln p = 1.16 - \frac{34.9}{778} \ln 7.79$$

$$= 1.069 \text{ Btu/lbm-}°R$$

$$s_{N_2} = \phi_{N_2}-R_{N_2} \ln p = 1.63 - \frac{55.2}{778} \ln 7.04$$

$$= 1.49 \text{ Btu/lbm-}°R$$

and the entropy of the mixture is

$$s = \frac{(3.5)(1.069)+(2)(1.49)}{5.5} = 1.22 \text{ Btu/lbm-}°R$$

16.3 Amagat–Leduc Law

It has been previously stated that the partial volume of a constituent in a mixture of perfect gases is the volume that would be occupied by that constituent at the same temperature and same total pressure as that of the mixture. The *Amagat-Leduc law* states that *the volume of a mixture of perfect gases is equal to the sum of partial volumes of the constituent gases.* This may be shown as follows:

Let a mixture at pressure p and temperature T consist of three different gases in the amounts of n_1, n_2, and n_3 moles each. Let V_1, V_2, and V_3 denote the partial volumes. The equation of state for each constituent gas may be written as

$$pV_1 = n_1\bar{R}T; \quad pV_2 = n_2\bar{R}T; \quad pV_3 = n_3\bar{R}T$$

or

$$V_1 = \frac{n_1\bar{R}T}{p}; \quad v_2 = \frac{n_2\bar{R}T}{p}; \quad v_3 = \frac{n_3\bar{R}T}{p}$$

Adding the partial volumes gives

$$V_1 + V_2 + V_3 = (n_1 + n_2 + n_3)\frac{\bar{R}T}{p} = \left(\sum_{i=1}^{3} n_i\right)\frac{\bar{R}T}{p}$$

But

$$\left(\sum_i n_i\right)\frac{\bar{R}T}{p} = V,$$

the volume of the mixture, by Eq. (16.12), and the above relation becomes

$$V_1 + V_2 + V_3 = V$$

or, more generally,

$$\sum_i V_i = V \qquad (16.15)$$

which is the mathematical statement of the *Amagat-Ludec law*.

It is of interest to note that the mole fraction of any constituent gas is numerically equal to the ratio of the partial volume of that constituent to the total volume of the mixture. This can be shown as follows: Since $pV_i = n_i\bar{R}T$, it follows that $n_i = (pV_i)/\bar{R}T$, and consequently

$$x_i = \frac{n_i}{\sum_i n_i} = \frac{(pV_i)/\bar{R}T}{\sum_i (pV_i)/\bar{R}T} = \frac{V_i}{\sum_i V_i} \qquad (16.16)$$

Equations (16.16) and (16.13) show that the mole fraction, the volume fraction, and the partial pressure ratio are all equal for a mixture of perfect gases.

16.4 Specific Heats of a Gaseous Mixture

The specific heats at constant volume and pressure are respectively the differentials with respect to temperature of the internal energy and enthalpy:

$$c_v = \left(\frac{\partial u}{\partial T}\right)_v \; ; \; c_p = \left(\frac{\partial h}{\partial T}\right)_p$$

Now, Eq. (16.7) may be written as

$$mu = m_1 u_1 + m_2 u_2 + m_3 u_3 + \ldots = \sum_i m_i u_i$$

Differentiating this with respect to temperature gives

$$m\left(\frac{\partial u}{\partial T}\right)_v = m_1\left(\frac{\partial u_1}{\partial T}\right)_v + m_2\left(\frac{\partial u_2}{\partial T}\right)_v + \ldots = \sum_i m_i\left(\frac{\partial u_i}{\partial T}\right)_v$$

or

$$mc_v = m_1 c_{v_1} + m_2 c_{v_2} + m_2 c_{v_2} + \ldots = \sum_i m_i c_{v_i} \qquad (16.17)$$

Equation (16.17) gives the specific heat at constant volume of a mixture in terms of the individual specific heats.

The preceding development may be put on a molar basis if Eq. (16.17) is written as

$$n\bar{u} = n_1 \bar{u}_1 + n_2 \bar{u}_2 + \ldots = \sum_i n_i \bar{u}_i$$

The molar specific heat of the mixture would be then given by

$$n\bar{c}_v = n_1 \bar{c}_{v_1} + n_2 \bar{c}_{v_2} + \ldots = \sum_i n_i \bar{c}_{v_i}$$

or

$$\bar{c}_v = \frac{n_1}{n}\bar{c}_{v_1} + \frac{n_2}{n}\bar{c}_{v_2} + \ldots$$

$$= x_1 \bar{c}_{v_1} + x_2 \bar{c}_{v_2} + \ldots = \sum_i x_i \bar{c}_{v_i} \qquad (16.18)$$

Similarly, the specific heat at constant pressure is derived from Eq. (16.8) to give

$$mc_p = m_1 c_{p_1} + m_2 c_{p_2} + \ldots = \sum_i m_i c_p \qquad (16.19)$$

or, per mole basis,

$$\bar{c}_p = x_1 \bar{c}_{p_1} + x_2 \bar{c}_{p_2} + \ldots = \sum_i x_1 \bar{c}_{p_i} \qquad (16.20)$$

It is understood, of course, that the specific heats under discussion are those of a perfect gas; in other words, the c_v's and c_p's are those at zero pressure.

Equations (16.17) and (16.19) enable the internal energy and enthalpy of a mixture of perfect gases to be calculated in terms of the specific heats of the constituents. The entropy change may also be readily obtained from the relations developed so far. Selecting, for example, T and p as independent variables, the entropy change of a mixture is given by

$$ds = c_p \frac{dT}{T} - R \frac{dp}{p}$$

and, by use of Eqs. (16.19) and (16.11),

$$ds = \frac{1}{m}(m_1 c_{p_1} + m_2 c_{p_2} + \ldots) \frac{dT}{T}$$

$$- \frac{1}{m}(m_1 R_1 + m_2 R_2 + \ldots) \frac{dp}{p}$$

$$= \left(\sum_i g_i c_{p_i}\right) \frac{dT}{T} - \left(\sum_i g_i R_i\right) \frac{dp}{p} \qquad (16.21)$$

where g_i is the gravimetric proportion of each constituent. On a mole basis Eq. (16.21) would be written as

$$d\bar{s} = (x c_{1_{p_1}} + x_2 \bar{c}_{p_2} + \ldots) \frac{dT}{T} - \bar{R} \frac{dp}{p}$$

$$= \left(\sum_i x_i \bar{c}_{p_i}\right) \frac{dT}{T} - \bar{R} \frac{dp}{p} \qquad (16.22)$$

Similarly, it may be easily shown (see the problems section at the end of the chapter) that

$$ds = \left(\sum_i g_i c_{v_i}\right) \frac{dT}{T} + \left(\sum_i g_i R_i\right) \frac{dv}{v} \qquad (16.23)$$

$$d\bar{s} = \left(\sum_i x_i \bar{c}_{v_i}\right) \frac{dT}{T} + \bar{R} \frac{dv}{v} \qquad (16.24)$$

$$ds = \left(\sum_i g_i c_{v_i}\right) \frac{dp}{p} + \left(\sum_i g_i c_{p_i}\right) \frac{dv}{v} \qquad (16.25)$$

$$d\bar{s} = \left(\sum_i x_i \bar{c}_{v_i}\right) \frac{dp}{p} + \left(\sum_i x_i \bar{c}_{p_i}\right) \frac{dv}{v} \qquad (16.26)$$

Example 16.2. Determine the entropy increase when n_A moles of gas A at a given pressure and temperature mix adiabatically with n_B moles of gas B at the same pressure and temperature.

Solution. Recall that the entropy change in terms of T and p as independent variables is given by

$$\Delta \bar{s} = \bar{c}_p \ln \frac{T_2}{T_1} - \bar{R} \ln \frac{p_2}{p_1}$$

Since no work is done and the mixing process is adiabatic, the internal energy remains unchanged, and it follows that the temperature of the mixture will be the same as the original temperature of the constituents. Thus, when the gases mix, the pressure of each gas changes from p to the partial pressures p_A and p_B respectively, but there is no change in temperature, so that the entropy change for each gas reduces to

$$\Delta S_A = -n_A \bar{R} \ln \frac{p_A}{p} = -n_A \bar{R} \ln x_A$$

$$\Delta S_B = -n_B \bar{R} \ln \frac{p_B}{p} = n_B \bar{R} \ln x_B$$

where x_A and x_B are the mole fractions of each gas. The total change in entropy is thus

$$\Delta S = -\bar{R}(n_A \ln x_A + n_B \ln x_B)$$

For the general case of mixing any number of gases,

$$\Delta S = -\bar{R}(n_A \ln x_A + n_B \ln x_B + \ldots)$$

$$= -\bar{R} \sum_i n_i \ln x_i$$

It is seen that the result depends only on the number of moles of component gases and not on the nature of the gases. In other words, if one mole of oxygen and one mole of nitrogen are mixed, the resultant increase in entropy is the same as if one mole of hydrogen and one mole of nitrogen are mixed. This has given rise to what is known as *Gibbs' paradox,* because when one mole of, say, oxygen is mixed with another mole of oxygen, there is no increase in entropy. The explanation lies in the fact that when it is impossible to distinguish between gases, there is no increase in entropy.

Example 16.3. A 100-cu ft container is divided into two separate compartments by means of a partition. One compartment contains 0.61 moles of oxygen at 100 psia and 760 °R; the other contains 0.27 moles of carbon dioxide at 30 psia and 520 °R. The partition is removed, and the gases mix. Assuming the process to be adiabatic, determine the equilibrium temperature and pressure of the mixture and the entropy–change. The molar specific heats at constant volume for O_2 and CO_2 are 5.0 Btu/mole-°R and 6.8 Btu/mole-°R respectively.

Solution. Let T_e be the equilibrium temperature. Since W and Q are zero, the total internal energy of the system must remain constant. Initially, the internal energy (reckoned from an arbitrary T_0) is

$$(0.61)(5.0)(760 - T_0) + (0.27)(6.8)(5.20 - T_0)$$

After mixing, the internal energy (reckoned from the same arbitrary T_0) is

$$(0.61 + 0.27)(c_v)_m(T_e - T_0)$$

where $(c_v)_m$, the specific heat at constant volume of the mixture is given by

$$(c_v)_m = \frac{(0.61)(5.0)+(0.27)(6.8)}{0.61+0.27}$$

The internal energy of the mixture is thus

$$[(0.61)(5.0)+(0.27)(6.8)](T_e - T_0)$$

Equating the initial and final internal energies and rearranging gives

$$(0.61)(5.0)(760 - T_e) = (0.27)(6.8)(T_e - 520)$$

or

$$T_e = 670\,°R$$

The equilibrium pressure may be obtained by writing $pV = n\bar{R}T$ for the mixture:

$$(p)(144)(100) = (0.61+0.27)(1545)(670)$$

whence

$$p = 64\text{ psia}$$

The change in entropy is the sum of the entropy-change of each constituent. For oxygen, this is (recalling the Tds equation with T and v as independent variables):

$$(\Delta S)_{O_2} = 0.61\left(5.0 \ln \frac{670}{760} + 1.986 \ln \frac{100}{V_{O_2}}\right)$$

where V_{O_2} is the initial volume of the oxygen (easily computed from the given data). Similarly, the entropy change for the carbon dioxide is

$$(\Delta S)_{CO_2} = 0.269\left(6.7 \ln \frac{760}{520} + 1.986 \ln \frac{100}{V_{CO_2}}\right)$$

where V_{CO_2} is the initial volume of the carbon dioxide. The remaining computation is left to the student.

16.5 Mixtures of Ideal Gas and Condensable Vapor

With respect to mixtures, it frequently happens that one of the components is a vapor. The most important engineering example of mixtures of ideal gases with a condensable vapor is the air-steam mixture. Such a mixture is not a pure substance in the thermodynamic sense of the word. Instead, three properties are needed to fix its state, as for example, temperature, specific volume, and composition.

Since the pressure of the vapor in a mixture is its partial pressure, and the latter is quite low, the vapor may be treated as an ideal gas. However, when the temperature of the mixture is lowered sufficiently, some of the vapor may condense or solidify out of the mixture. Conversely, if the temperature of the mixture is raised sufficiently, some of the liquid may evaporate, or some of the solid may sublime. In other words, the composition of the gaseous mixture changes as the vapor component condenses or evaporates. Taking air as an example, a number of definitions is first introduced:

Atmospheric air has a volumetric composition of 20.99 per cent oxygen, 78.03 per cent nitrogen, and traces of other gases such as argon, carbon dioxide, helium, hydrogen, neon, and water vapor. For engineering purposes, it is sufficiently accurate to consider air as composed of

21 per cent oxygen, 79 per cent nitrogen, *by volume*

23.2 per cent oxygen, 76.8 per cent nitrogen, *by mass*

Saturated air is a mixture of dry air and saturated water vapor. Note that it is the water vapor which is saturated, not the air.

The *dew point* of a gas-vapor mixture is the temperature at which the vapor condenses when it is cooled at constant pressure. Referring to Fig. 16.4, let the temperature of the mixture and the partial pressure of the vapor in the mixture be such that the vapor is initially superheated (state 1). If the mixture is cooled at constant pressure, the partial pressure of the vapor remains constant until state 2 is reached, at which point condensation will begin. The temperature at state 2 is known as the dew point temperature. This is the temperature at which the vapor (and therefore the mixture) becomes saturated.

Relative humidity, ϕ, is defined as the ratio of the partial pressure of the vapor as it exists (state 1), to the saturation pressure of the vapor at the same temperature (p_g)

$$\phi = \frac{p_1}{p_g} \qquad (16.27)$$

Because its pressure is very low, water vapor may be regarded as a perfect gas, i.e., $p_1 = \rho_1 R T_1$; $p_g = \rho_g R T_g$, so that, in the first approximation, Eq. (16.27) becomes

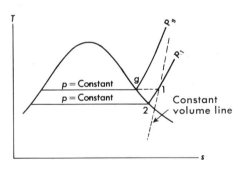

Fig. 16.4 Representation of Dew Point.

$$\phi = \frac{\rho_1 R T_1}{\rho_g R T_g} = \frac{\rho_1}{\rho_g} = \frac{v_g}{v_1} \qquad (16.28)$$

since $T_g = T_1$. Thus, the relative humidity may also be defined in terms of density or specific volume.

Humidity ratio (or *specific humidity*), is the ratio of the mass of water vapor m_v, to the mass of dry air, m_a. It is often expressed as the number of pounds of vapor per pound of dry air:

$$\omega = \frac{m_v}{m_a} \tag{16.29}$$

where the subscripts v and a refer to vapor and air respectively. Since

$$m_v = \frac{p_v V}{R_v T}, \; m_a = \frac{p_a V}{R_a T}$$

(both vapor and air occupy the same volume V, and are at the same temperature T), Eq. (16.29) becomes

$$\omega = \frac{(p_v V)/(R_v T)}{(p_a V)/(R_a T)} = \frac{R_a}{R_v}\frac{p_v}{p_a}$$

But $p_v + p_a = p_m$ where p_m is the pressure of the mixture. Thus,

$$\omega = \left(\frac{R_a}{R_v}\right)\left(\frac{p_v}{p_m - p_v}\right) \tag{16.30}$$

For an air-water vapor mixture, $R_a = 53.3$ ft lbf/lbm-°R, $R_v = 85.7$ ft lbf/lbm-°R, so that Eq. (16.29) reduces to

$$\omega = \frac{53.3}{85.7}\frac{p_v}{p_m - p_v}$$

or

$$\omega = 0.622\frac{p_v}{p_m - p_v} \tag{16.31}$$

Example 16.4. An air water-vapor mixture has a relative humidity of 70 per cent at 14.7 psia and 85 °F. Determine: (a) the dew-point, (b) the humidity ratio, (c) the mass of dry air and mass of vapor per 1000 cu ft of mixture, (d) the amount of water-vapor condensed per pound of dry air if the mixture is processed in an air-conditioner to 60°F and 80 per cent relative humidity.

Solution. (a) Let p_{v_1} denote the pressure of the water vapor at state 1 (Fig. 16.4). From the definition of the relative humidity Eq. (16.27),

$$\phi = 0.70 = \frac{p_{v_1}}{0.5959}$$

or

$$p_{v_1} = (0.70)(0.5959) = 0.418 \text{ psia}$$

The dew point is the saturation temperature corresponding to this pressure, which is 74.2 °F.

(b) The humidity ratio is the amount of water-vapor per pound of dry air. It is given by Eq. (16.31):

$$\omega_1 = 0.622 \frac{p_{v_1}}{p_m - p_{v_1}} = 0.622 \frac{0.418}{14.7 - 0.418} = 0.0182$$

(c) Using the perfect gas relation, the mass of dry air per 1000 cu ft of mixture is

$$m_a = \frac{p_a V}{R_a T} = \frac{(14.282)(1000)}{(53.3)(545)} = 70.6 \text{ lbm}$$

Similarly, the mass of water vapor per 1000 cu ft of mixture is

$$m_v = \frac{p_v V}{R_v T} = \frac{(0.418)(1000)}{(85.7)(545)} = 1.29 \text{ lbm}$$

this can also be checked by using

$$m_v = \omega m_a = (0.0182)(70.6) = 1.29 \text{ lbm}$$

(d) The amount of water vapor condensed per pound of dry air is equal to the difference of the humidity ratios entering and leaving the conditioner. The humidity ratio entering the conditioner was found to be $\omega_1 = 0.0182$. The humidity ratio ω_2 leaving the conditioner is given by Eq. (16.31) as

$$\omega_2 = 0.622 \frac{p_{v_2}}{p_m - p_{v_2}}$$

Now, $p_{v_2} = 0.80 \times 0.2563 = 0.205$ psia, Thus,

$$\omega_2 = 0.622 \frac{0.205}{14.7 - 0.205} = 0.0088$$

The amount of water vapor condensed per pound of dry air is then $0.0182 - 0.0088 = 0.0094$ lbm.

16.6 Adiabatic Saturation

Consider the process shown in Fig. 16.5(a). An air-water vapor mixture of temperature t_1 and relative humidity less than 100 per cent enters a

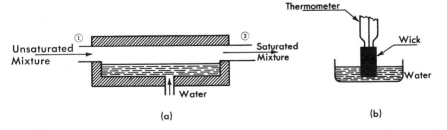

Fig. 16.5 Adiabatic Saturator and Wet Bulb Thermometer.

device known as an adiabatic saturator. It leaves as saturated mixture (100 per cent relative humidity) at temperature t_2. Make up water at temperature t_2 enters the saturator at the same rate that water is evaporated. The device is insulated, and the process is considered to be adiabatic. As the unsaturated mixture passes over the water surface, some of the water is evaporated. The energy for evaporation comes from both the air-vapor mixture and the water in the chamber. Since the system is isolated from heat transfer, the temperature of the air decreases from t_1 (known as the dry bulb temperature and measured by an ordinary thermometer) to t_2 (known as the wet bulb temperature and measured by a wet-bulb thermometer). This may be shown on the $T-s$ diagram of Fig. 16.6,

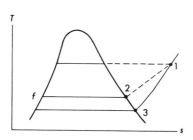

Fig. 16.6 Adiabatic Saturation Process.

where the irreversible process of adiabatic saturation is shown by the dotted line 1–2. Note that the wet-bulb temperature is above the dew point temperature (t_3), and that the humidity ratio increases.

Considering the process to be a steady-flow adiabatic, and neglecting changes in kinetic and potential energy, application of the first law gives

$$h_{a_1} + \omega_1 h_{v_1} + (\omega_2 - \omega_1)h_{f_2} = h_{a_2} + \omega_2 h_{v_2}$$

$$(16.32)$$

where h_{a_1} is the specific enthalpy of dry air entering the saturator, ω_1 the mass of water-vapor per unit mass of entering dry air, h_{v_1} the specific enthalpy of water vapor at entrance conditions, h_{f_2} the specific enthalpy of injected water, h_{a_2} the specific enthalpy of dry air leaving the saturator, ω_2 the specific humidity leaving the saturator, and h_{v_2} the specific enthalpy of water vapor leaving the saturator. Equation (16.32) may be simplified somewhat by noting that $h_{a_1} - h_{a_2} = c_p(t_1 - t_2)$ and that $h_{v_2} - h_{f_2} = h_{fg_2}$. Thus,

$$c_p(t_1 - t_2) + \omega_1(h_{v_1} - h_{f_2}) = \omega_2 h_{fg_2}$$

or

$$\omega_1 = \frac{\omega_2 h_{fg_2} - c_p(t_1 - t_2)}{h_{v_1} - h_{f_2}} \qquad (16.33)$$

Equation (16.33) gives the humidity ratio of the original atmospheric air (dry air + moisture) in terms of the temperature and pressure of the mixture entering and leaving the saturator. From this, the relative humidity of an original atmospheric air may be calculated.

The exact determination of the thermodynamic wet-bulb temperature is not practical. However, a good approximation may be obtained by means of a wet-bulb thermometer as shown in Fig. 16.5(b). This thermometer is similar to an ordinary thermometer except that the bulb is covered with a water-moistened wick. The temperature read from a wet-bulb thermometer is called the *wet-bulb temperature*, whereas the temperature read from an ordinary thermometer is often called *dry-bulb temperature*. A sling psychrometer (consisting of a dry-bulb and a wet-bulb thermometer attached to the same holder) will also give a good approximation of the thermodynamic wet-bulb temperature and thus provide a means for determining relative humidities. W. H. Carrier developed from Eq. (16.33), a semi-empirical expression for determining the partial pressure of water vapor in atmospheric air. His derivation† yields

$$p_v = p_{w.b} - \frac{(p_m - p_{w.b.})(t_{d.b.} - t_{w.b.})}{2800 - 1.3 t_{w.b.}} \tag{16.34}$$

where p_v is the pressure of the water vapor at the dry-bulb temperature, $p_{w.b.}$ the pressure of the water vapor at the wet-bulb temperature, p_m the pressure of the mixture (barometric pressure), $t_{d.b.}$ the dry-bulb temperature, and $t_{w.b.}$ the wet-bulb temperature.

Example 16.5. Atmospheric air at 14.7 psia has a dry-bulb temperature of 85 °F and a wet-bulb temperature of 75 °F. Determine: (a) the relative humidity, (b) the specific humidity, (c) the density of the dry air in the mixture, (d) the density of the vapor in the mixture, (e) the enthalpy of the mixture per pound of dry air.

Solution. (a) From Eq. (16.34), the vapor pressure is

$$p_v = 0.4298 - \frac{(14.7 - 0.4298)(85 - 75)}{2800 - 1.3 \times 75} = 0.377 \text{ psia}$$

The relative humidity is then

$$\phi = \frac{0.377}{0.5959} = 0.632 \text{ or } 63.2 \text{ per cent}$$

(b) From Eq. (16.31), the humidity ratio is

$$\omega = 0.622 \frac{0.377}{(14.7 - 0.377)} = 0.0164 \text{ lbm vapor/lbm dry air}$$

(c) From the perfect gas law, the density of the dry air is

$$\rho_a = \frac{(14.7 - 0.377)(144)}{(53.3)(545)} = 0.071 \text{ lbm/cu ft}$$

(d) The density of the vapor is

$$\rho_v = \frac{(0.377)(144)}{(85.7)(545)} = 0.00116 \text{ lbm/cu ft}$$

---

† W. H. Carrier, *Rational Psychrometric Formulae*, A.S.M.E. Transactions 33, 1005, 1911.

This answer could also be obtained as follows:

$$\rho_v = \left(0.0164\frac{\text{lbm vapor}}{\text{lbm dry air}}\right)\left(0.071\frac{\text{lbm dry air}}{\text{cu ft}}\right)$$

$$= 0.00116 \text{ lbm vapor/cu ft}$$

(e) The enthalpy of the mixture is equal to the sum of the enthalpy of one pound of dry air and that of the accompanying vapor:

$$h = h_a + \omega h_v = c_p t + \omega h_v$$

where t is the dry-bulb temperature, ω the humidity ratio, and h_v the enthalpy of the water vapor.† Since water vapor at low pressures behaves like a perfect gas, its enthalpy can be considered as a function of temperature only, and the enthalpy of slightly superheated water vapor may be taken equal to the enthalpy of saturated vapor at the same temperature. Thus, using values from the steam tables,

$$h = 0.24(85) + 0.0164(1098.8)$$

$$= 38.4 \text{ Btu/lbm dry air}$$

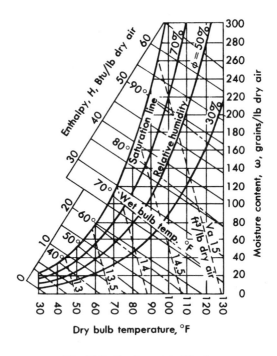

Fig. 16.7 Psychometric Chart.

---

† It should be noted that, in the air conditioning field, it is traditional to have the enthalpy of dry air reckoned from 0°F, while the enthalpy of water vapor as read from steam tables is reckoned from saturated liquid at 32°F.

16.7 Fundamentals of Psychrometrics

Because of the importance of air water-vapor mixtures in air conditioning and manufacturing processes, a special field of study called *psychrometrics* has evolved. While it is not intended to be comprehensive, the following discussion will nevertheless serve to introduce the subject. The the properties of air water-vapor mixtures may be conveniently presented in a graphical form known as psychrometric charts. Figure 16.7 illustrates an example of such a chart. Basically, this is a plot of specific humidity *vs.* dry bulb temperatures. Thus, if the total pressure for which the chart is to be constructed (usually atmospheric) is fixed, lines of constant relative humidity, constant specific volume, and constant wet-bulb and enthalpy may be drawn. Psychrometric charts are usually prepared for one particular barometric pressure, but correction curves are often available for other barometric pressures. Enthalpy values are given on the basis of one pound of dry air, with the enthalpy of dry air taken to be zero at 0 °F, and the enthalpy of water vapor (read from steam tables) reckoned from saturated liquid at 32 °F. Most air conditioning processes can be conveniently expressed on the psychrometric chart. A number of these are shown in the figures below:

Adiabatic Mixing. Consider two streams of air which mix adiabatically and emerge as a single stream. This is shown graphically in Fig. 16.8. The original states of the two streams are shown by points 1 and 2. A straight line is drawn between these two points and divided into segments inversely proportional to the relative masses of the two streams. Point 3 represents the resultant state of the emerging stream.

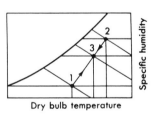

Fig. 16.8 Mixing Process.

Humidification with Cooling. If an air water-vapor mixture is passed through a spray chamber where a large quantity of water is circulated, the mixture will leave in a saturated or near saturated state, as shown in Fig. 16.9. The increase in specific humidity is equal to the quantity of circulating water which is evaporated per pound of dry air. Since no heat transfer takes place between the chamber and the surroundings, the process is adiabatic, and the energy required for evaporation is supplied by the air passing through the chamber. As a result, the dry bulb temperature of the air is lowered as it picks up moisture.

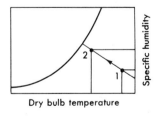

Fig. 16.9
Evaporative Humidification.

Humidification with Heating. A simple example of humidification and heating occurs in a conventional warm-air furnace provided with a humidifier, such as an open pan of water. The process is shown in Fig. 16.10.

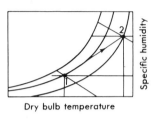

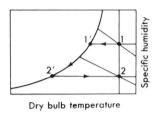

Fig. 16.10

Humidification with Heating.

Fig. 16.11

Dehumidification.

The specific numidity of the heated air is increased and its relative humidity is decreased as it flows over the humidifier.

Dehumidification. Moisture may be removed from an air water-vapor mixture by cooling the mixture below the dew point. This is shown in Fig. 16.11, where a mixture at state 1 is cooled (at constant specific humidity) to the dew-point temperature 1'. Upon further cooling, condensation of moisture occurs until point 2' is attained. From 2' to 2, the mixture is heated at constant specific humidity to whatever dry-bulb temperature is desired.

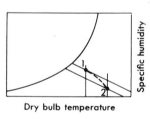

Fig. 16.12 Chemical Drying.

Chemical Drying. (Figure 16.12.) Dehumidification of air water-vapor mixtures can also be accomplished by use of *adsorbents* such as silica gel or activated alumina; the moisture is caught and retained in the pores of the agent used. The action is due to the difference in vapor pressure of the water condensed in the pores and the vapor pressure of the air mixture. Chemical changes take place during the process of adsorption, but heat is liberated; consequently the dry bulb temperature of the mixture is increased. Dehumidification may also be accomplished by use of *absorbents*, such as solutions of chlorides and bromides. Absorbents, however, undergo both physical as well as chemical change during the process.

Example 16.6. A lecture room occupied by 100 people is to be kept at a dry-bulb temperature of 74 °F and a wet-bulb temperature of 62 °F by circulated air. The sensible heat and moisture from the occupants amount to 27,500 Btu/hr and 86,000 grains/hr respectively.† If air is to be supplied at a dry-bulb temperature of 64 °F, determine: (a) the pounds of air per hour required, (b) the wet-bulb temperature of the supply air.

Solution. (a) The amount of air to satisfy the sensible load is calculated from

$$Q_{\text{sensible}} = mc_p(T_2 - T_1)$$
$$27,500 = m(0.24)(74 - 64)$$
$$m = 11,450 \text{ lbm/hr}$$

(b) To absorb 86,000 grains of moisture with 11,270 pounds of air, each pound must absorb

$$\frac{86,000}{11,450} = 7.5 \text{ grains/lbm dry air}$$

From the psychrometric chart, the auditorium air, which is at 74 °F dry-bulb and 62 °F wet-bulb, has a humidity ratio of 64 grains/lbm dry air. The supply air, whose temperature is 64 °F, must therefore have a humidity ratio of

$$64 - 7.64 = 57.36 \text{ grains/lbm dry air}$$

From the psychrometric chart, this corresponds to a wet-bulb temperature of 57 °F.

Example 16.7. A cooling tower is a device that utilizes the phenomenon of evaporative cooling to cool warm water below the dry-bulb temperature of the air. Figure 16.13 shows two types of cooling towers: a natural-draft cooling tower

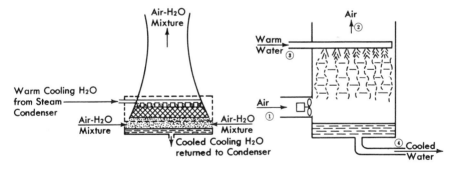

Fig. 16.13 Cooling Tower.

and an induced-draft cooling tower. Water which is to be cooled is introduced at the top of the tower and sprayed over baffles, thus presenting a large surface for evaporation. Atmospheric air is circulated through the water, leaving at the top in a nearly saturated state. Consider the following installation: water enters a cooling tower at 110 °F and leaves at 75 °F. Air enters the tower at a dry-bulb

---

† In air conditioning work, it is often convenient to give the amount of moisture in terms of "grains." There are 7000 grains in a pound.

temperature of 70 °F and a wet-bulb temperature of 58 °F. It leaves the tower as saturated mixture at a dry-bulb temperature of 105 °F. Determine: (a) the mass flow rate of atmospheric air required to cool 250,000 pounds of water per hour, (b) the rate at which water is evaporated. Assume the atmospheric pressure to be 14.7 psia throughout.

Solution. (a) The vapor pressure of the moisture in the entering air is given by Eq. (16.34),

$$p_v = 0.2386 - \frac{(14.7 - 0.2386)(70 - 58)}{2800 - 1.3(58)} = 0.175 \text{ psia}$$

Since the air leaving the cooling tower is saturated, the vapor pressure of the moisture is obtained directly from the steam tables corresponding to a temperature of 105 °F, i.e., $p_{v_2} = 1.102$ psia.

The humidity ratio of the air entering the cooling tower is

$$\omega_1 = 0.622 \frac{0.175}{(14.7 - 0.1770)} = 0.00749 \text{ lbm vapor/lbm dry air}$$

The humidity ratio of the air leaving the cooling tower is

$$\omega_2 = 0.622 \frac{1.102}{(14.7 - 1.102)} = 0.0504 \text{ lbm vapor/lbm dry air}$$

Referring to Fig. 16.13b, an energy and mass balance yields the two relations:

$$\begin{cases} h_{a_1} + \omega_1 h_{v_1} + \omega_{f_3} = h_{a_2} + \omega_2 h_{v_2} + \omega_{f_4} h_{f_4} \\ \omega_{f_3} - \omega_{f_4} = \omega_2 - \omega_1 \end{cases}$$

which, in the present problem, become

$$\begin{cases} 0.24(70) + 0.00749(1092.3) + \omega_{f_3}(77.94) = 0.24(105) \\ \qquad\qquad + 0.0504(1107.4) + \omega_{f_4}(42.98) \\ \omega_{f_3} - \omega_{f_4} = 0.0504 - 0.00749 \end{cases}$$

Simultaneous solution of the two equations gives

$$W_{f_3} = 1.552 \text{ lbm water/lbm dry air}$$

$$W_{f_4} = 1.509 \text{ lbm water/lbm dry air}$$

In other words, for each pound of dry air, 1.552 pounds of warm water enter the cooling tower, and 1.509 pounds of cool water leave the tower, leaving 0.043 pounds to be picked up by the air. The mass rate of atmospheric air (dry air + vapor) to cool 250,000 pounds of water per hour is thus

$$\frac{250,000}{1.552} + 0.00749 \left(\frac{250,000}{1.552} \right)$$

$$= 162,200 \text{ lbm atmospheric air/hr}$$

(b) The rate at which water is evaporated is

$$0.043 \left(\frac{250,000}{1.552} \right) = 6,910 \text{ lbm/hr}$$

Make-up water of this amount will therefore be required.

16.8   Real-Gas Mixtures

So far, the discussion of mixtures has been confined to mixtures of perfect gases. In the case of mixtures of real gases, the ratio, p_i/p, is not necessarily equal to the mole fraction x_i, although Dalton's law,

$$p = \sum_i p_i$$

holds true even though the individual gases are not ideal. Mixtures of real gases, however, may often be conveniently treated by introducing a compressibility-factor for the mixture, just as a compressibility-factor was introduced for each individual gas. Thus, for a mixture at pressure p, volume V, and temperature T,

$$pV = nZ\bar{R}T \qquad (16.35)$$

where n is the number of moles of mixture, and $Z = Z(p, T, x_i)$ is the compressibility-factor of the mixture. It depends on the pressure, temperature, and composition of the mixture.

Now, each ith component of the mixture obeys the relation

$$p_i V = n_i Z_i \bar{R}T \qquad (16.36)$$

Furthermore,

$$p = \sum_i p_i, \; n = \sum_i n_i$$

so that Eq. (16.35) becomes

$$(p_1 + p_2 + \ldots)V = (n_1 + n_2 + \ldots)Z\bar{R}T$$

This is rewritten with the aid of Eq. (16.36), as

$$(n_1 Z_1 + n_2 Z_2 + \ldots)\bar{R}T = (n_1 + n_2 + \ldots)Z\bar{R}T$$

whence

$$Z = \frac{n_1 Z_1 + n_2 Z_2 + \ldots}{n_1 + n_2 + \ldots}$$
$$= x_1 Z_1 + x_2 Z_2 + \ldots = \sum_i x_i Z_i \qquad (16.37)$$

Eq. (16.37) enables the overall compressibility-factor to be calculated in terms of the individual compressibility-factors.

Example 16.8. Show that for a mixture of gases, each obeying van der Waals' equation of state, the over-all pressure of the mixture is

$$p = RT \sum_i \frac{x_i}{\bar{v} - x_i b_i} - \frac{1}{\bar{v}^2} \sum_i (a_i x_i^2)$$

Solution. Consider a unit mole of mixture. The volume of the mixture is thus $\bar{v}$. Let there be x_1 moles of gas 1, x_2 moles of gas 2, . . . x_i moles of gas i in the mixture. Note that

$$\sum_i x_i = 1$$

Now, van der Waals' equation, written for N moles is

$$\left(p + \frac{N^2 a}{V^2}\right)(V - Nb) = N\bar{R}T$$

This becomes, for x_1 moles of gas 1 occupying a volume $\bar{v}$,

$$\left(p_1 + \frac{x_1^2 a_1}{\bar{v}^2}\right)(\bar{v} - x_1 b_1) = x_1 \bar{R} T$$

Similarly, for x_2 moles of gas 2,

$$\left(p_2 + \frac{x_2^2 a_2}{\bar{v}^2}\right)(\bar{v} - x_2 b_2) = x_2 \bar{R} T$$

and in general, for x_i moles of gas i,

$$\left(p_i + \frac{x_i^2 a_i}{\bar{v}^2}\right)(\bar{v} - x_i b_i) = x_i \bar{R} T$$

Solving for the p's gives

$$p_1 = \frac{x_1 \bar{R} T}{\bar{v} - x_1 b_1} - \frac{x_1^2 a_1}{\bar{v}^2}$$

$$p_2 = \frac{x_2 \bar{R} T}{\bar{v} - x_2 b_2} - \frac{x_2^2 a_2}{\bar{v}^2}$$

$$\cdots \quad \cdots \quad \cdots \quad \cdots$$

$$p_i = \frac{x_i \bar{R} T}{\bar{v} - x_i b_i} - \frac{x_i^2 a_i}{\bar{v}^2}$$

Application of Dalton's law $\;(p = \sum_i p_i)\;$ gives

$$p = p_1 + p_2 + \cdots$$

$$= \bar{R} T\left(\frac{x_1}{\bar{v} - x_1 b_1} + \frac{x_2}{\bar{v} - x_2 b_2} + \cdots\right) - \frac{1}{\bar{v}^2}(x_1^2 a_1 + x_2^2 a_2 + \cdots)$$

or

$$p = \bar{R} T\sum_i \left(\frac{x_i}{\bar{v} - x_i b_i}\right) - \frac{1}{\bar{v}^2}\sum_i (a_i x_i^2)$$

16.9   Ideal Solutions; Raoult's Law

Having discussed the properties of gaseous mixtures, the properties of solutions should now be considered to some extent. A solution is, by definition, any phase containing more than one component; this phase may be gaseous, liquid, or solid. In fact, mixtures of gases at equilibrium are solutions, for gases are miscible in all proportions. The following sections discuss the behavior of solutions of non-reacting materials, beginning first with the notion of an *ideal solution*.

Just as the concept of an ideal gas is helpful in the study of gases, so the concept of an ideal solution is helpful in the discussion of solutions. Ideality in a gas implies a complete absence of cohesive forces. Ideality in a solution is characterized by complete uniformity of cohesive forces. In other words, if there are two components A and B, the forces between A and A, B and B, and A and B are the same.

Among the properties of importance in the discussion of solutions is the partial vapor pressure of a component above the solution. The partial vapor pressure is, in a sense, a measure of the constituent's "tendency to escape" from the solution. A solution is said to be *ideal* if *the vapor pressure of each component is proportional to the mole fraction of that component in the solution.* Consider, for example, a liquid mixture of two components A and B, with mole fractions x_A and x_B. If the solution is ideal, a molecule of A will have the same tendency to escape into the vapor, whether it is surrounded entirely by other A molecules, entirely by B molecules, or partly by A and partly by B molecules. Since the inter-molecular forces between all molecules are the same, it is immaterial to the behavior of a molecule what sort of neighbours it has. Under these circumstances, the partial vapor pressure of component A is the same as that of the pure liquid A, except that it is proportionately reduced on account of the lowered fraction of A molecules in the solution. This is expressed mathematically by the simple relationship

$$p_A = x_A p_A^o \qquad (16.38)$$

where p_A is the partial vapor pressure of A above the solution, x_A is the mole fraction of A, and p_A^o is the vapor pressure of pure liquid A at the same temperature. Equation (16.38) is known as *Raoult's law*. A similar equation applies to component B, or to each of several components (if the solution is made up of more than two components). Equation (16.38) can also be expressed in terms of the relative lowering of the vapor pressure of pure A due to the addition of B:

$$\frac{p_A^o - p_A}{p_A^o} = 1 - x_A \qquad (16.39)$$

Raoult's law does not hold exactly for all combinations of liquids; nevertheless, it is a useful idealization that can be applied to some combinations (e.g., mixtures of hydrocarbons). A binary liquid mixture obeying Raoult's law has vapor pressures which are straight lines when plotted against mole fractions. This is shown in Fig. 16.14. The lines refer, of course, to pressures observed at a given temperature, for as the temperature is changed, the slopes of the partial-pressure lines will change. Solutions

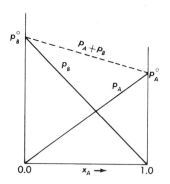

Fig. 16.14 Representation of Raoult's Law.

which obey Raoult's law are distinguished by the fact that the enthalpy change and the volume change attending the mixing of the pure liquids are zero. In other words, for an ideal solution, there is no heat solution and no volume change on mixing.

16.10 Statistical Mechanics of Mixing Liquids

Recall from Ex. 16.2 that, when n_A moles of gas A are mixed with n_B moles of gas B, each at a pressure p and a temperature T, the entropy change upon mixing is

$$\Delta S_{\text{mix}} = -n_A \bar{R} \ln x_A - n_B \bar{R} \ln x_B$$

This result, obtained for a mixture of ideal gases, will be shown to hold true for ideal solutions.

Consider N_A molecules of type A and N_B molecules of type B mixed to form a liquid solution. Assume that the forces operating between A molecules are the same as those operating between B molecules or between A and B molecules. Assume also that the volume occupied by a molecule A is the same as that occupied by a molecule B. Imagine a liquid to be represented by a lattice or assembly of sites each occupied by a molecule. Pure liquid A consists of N_A sites, each occupied by a molecule A. Since the molecules are indistinguishable, the thermodynamic probability, W_A, as far as lattice sites are concerned, is simply unity. Similarly, the thermodynamic probability, W_B, of pure liquid B, is also unity.

The mixture, on the other hand, has a different thermodynamic probability, since there are now $N_A + N_B$ total sites available. The problem is one of calculating the number of ways in which N_A indistinguishable molecules of type A are distributed among these sites, with the remaining sites filled by molecules of type B. Imagine the mixture to be constructed by successively placing the molecules of type A one by one into the available sites. The first molecule has $N_A + N_B$ possible locations, leaving $N_A + N_B - 1$ sites available for the second molecule. After the second molecule has been placed in the lattice, there remains $N_A + N_B - 2$ sites for the location of the third molecule, and so on. The total number of ways in which the N_A molecule of type A can be placed in the lattice is then given by the continued product:

$$(N_A + N_B)(N_A + N_B - 1)(N_A + N_B - 2) \ldots$$

$$(N_A + N_B - N_A + 1) = \frac{(N_A + N_B)!}{N_B!}$$

But, since the molecules of type A are indistinguishable, the above expression must be divided by $N_A!$ to give the number of different ways in which N_A molecules can be placed among $N_A + N_B$ sites. Thus, the thermodynamic probability for the mixture is

$$W_{mix} = \frac{(N_A + N_B)!}{N_A! \, N_B!} \tag{16.40}$$

From the statistical definition for entropy, $S = k \ln W$, the entropy change upon mixing is then given by

$$\Delta S_{mix} = k \ln W_{mix} - k \ln W_A W_B$$

$$= k \ln \frac{(N_A + N_B)!}{N_A! \, N_B!} - k \ln 1$$

$$= k \ln \frac{(N_A + N_B)!}{N_A! \, N_B!} \tag{16.41}$$

Using Stirling's approximation ($\ln N! = N \ln N - N$), Eq. (16.41) simplifies to

$$\Delta S_{mix} = - N_A k \ln \frac{N_A}{N_A + N_B} - N_B k \ln \frac{N_B}{N_A + N_B}$$

$$= - n_A \bar{R} \ln x_A - n_B \bar{R} \ln x_B \tag{16.42}$$

where n_A and n_B are the moles of constituents A and B respectively, x_A and x_B are the mole fractions of these constituents, and $\bar{R}$ is the gas constant per mole. Equation (16.42) is seen to be full in agreement with the result previously obtained for a mixture of perfect gases.

16.11 Henry's Law

Not many solutions obey Raoult's law over the complete range of concentrations. In actual liquid mixtures, the departure from Raoult's law is of two general types, shown in Fig. 16.15.

Figure 16.15(a) is for a mixture which exhibits positive deviations from Raoult's law, so designated because the partial pressures are in excess of those predicted for ideal solutions. Figure 16.15(b) depicts a system having negative deviations from Raoult's law, so called because the vapor pressures are below those for ideal solutions. Regardless of the type of departure, careful examination of the experimental curves show that (1) as the composition approaches that of a pure liquid, the partial pressure of the nearly pure compound becomes tangent to the line representing Raoult's law, (2) the partial pressure of the dilute component, on the other hand, is

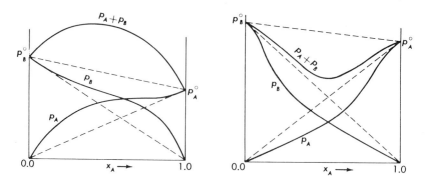

Fig. 16.15 Deviations from Raoult's Law.

seen to be a straight line with a slope different from that expressed by Raoult's law. The vapor pressure of the dilute component is said to obey *Henry's law*, which is expressed as follows:

$$p_B = kx_B \qquad (16.43)$$

In other words, in a solution which is sufficiently diluted and in which A is the solvent and B is the solute,[†] the escaping tendency of B from its uniform environment is proportional to its mole fraction. For dilute solutions, the solvent obeys Raoult's law, and the solute obeys Henry's law.

16.12 Vaporization and Condensation of Mixtures

When binary liquid solutions are distilled at constant pressure, their behaviour falls into the following types:

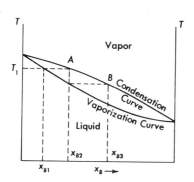

Fig. 16.16 Temperature-Composition Diagram for Ideal Solution.

(a) Solutions whose boiling points are intermediate between the boiling points of the pure components. A temperature-composition diagram for a solution of this type is shown in Fig. 16.16. The lower curve represents the boiling temperatures of all mixtures of A and B for a given pressure. The upper curve represents the composition of the vapor in equilibrium with the solution. A solution of initial mole fraction x_{B_1} has the initial vaporization temperature T_1. The vapor com-

---

† In discussing solutions, it is often convenient to call the component in excess the *solvent* and the other component the *solute*.

ing off at this temperature, represented by point A, has the composition x_{B_2}, which is richer in the more volatile component B. If this vapor is cooled until it liquefies, and then boiled, the vapor that comes off, represented by point B, has the composition x_{B_3}. Thus, by continued condensation and distillation, it is possible to obtain pure component B in the distillate and pure component A in the residue. In practice, these successive condensations and vaporizations are automatically carried out in a fractionating or distilling column.

(b) Solutions whose boiling points show a maximum which is greater than the boiling point of either pure component.

(c) Solutions whose boiling points show a minimum which is less than the boiling point of either pure component.

The temperature-composition for these types of solution are shown in Fig. 16.17. In Fig. 16.17(a), when liquid of composition x_{B_1} is distilled, the first vapor coming off has the composition x_{B_2}, which is richer in

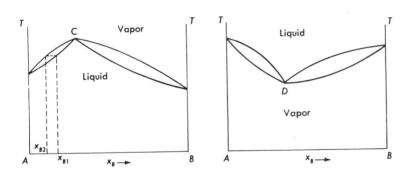

Fig. 16.17 Temperature-Composition Diagrams for Solutions Deviating from Raoult's Law.

component A than the original liquid. The residual solution therefore becomes richer in B. If the vapor is continuously removed, the boiling point of the residue rises (since the residue is richer in B) until liquid of composition x_C remains in the flask. Both liquid and vapor now have the same composition (point C), and the distillation proceeds until all the residue has boiled away. A solution that distills without change in composition and temperature is called an *azeotrope*. If fractional distillation is carried out, separation into pure component A and the azeotropic solution can be obtained. Similar remarks apply to the diagram of Fig. 16.17(b), except that the residue tends toward a pure component and the distillate tends toward an azeotropic composition.

PROBLEMS

16.1. A 5 cu ft tank contains 3 pounds of CO_2 and 3 pounds of N_2 at 80 °F. Determine: (a) the partial pressure of each constituent, (b) the partial volume of each constituent, (c) the pressure of the mixture, (d) the mole fraction of each constituent, (e) the gas constant of the mixture, (f) the molecular weight of the mixture, (g) the enthalpy and entropy of the mixture by using the gas tables.

16.2. From the definition of the specific ratio for a mixture:

$$\gamma = \frac{c_p}{c_v} = \frac{m_1 c_{p_1} + m_2 c_{p_2} + \ldots}{m_1 c_{v_1} + m_2 c_{v_2} + \ldots}$$

show that during a reversible adiabatic process, the mixture obeys the relation

$$pv^\gamma = \text{constant}$$

16.3. From Dalton's law, show that the entropy of a mixture of gases is

$$s_m = \frac{S_m}{m_m} = \frac{m_1 s_1 (T_m, V_m) + m_2 s_2 (T_m, V_m) + \ldots}{m_m}$$

where the constituent entropies are evaluated at the temperature and volume of the mixture. How does the entropy of any constituent at the volume and temperature of the mixture (and hence at its partial pressure) compare with its entropy at the pressure and temperature of the mixture (and hence at its partial volume)?

16.4. A 15 cu ft tank is divided into two compartments of 10 cu ft and 5 cu ft by a partition. The 10 cu ft compartment contains nitrogen at a temperature of 130 °F and a pressure of 100 psia. The 5 cu ft compartment contains CO_2 at a temperature of 55 °F and a pressure of 140 psia. The partition is removed, and the gases mix. Determine: (a) the temperature and pressure of the resulting mixture, (b) the entropy change. Consider the mixing to be adiabatic.

16.5. The pseudocritical method of computing properties of a gas mixture consists of defining a pseudocritical temperature and a pseudocritical pressure by means of

$$T'_c = x_1 T_{c_1} + x_2 T_{c_2} + \ldots = \sum_i x_i T_{c_i}$$

$$p'_c = x_1 p_{c_1} + x_2 p_{c_2} + \ldots = \sum_i x_i p_{c_i}$$

From these, the pseudoreduced temperature T'_R and the pseudoreduced pressure p'_R may be calculated to obtain the factor Z from the generalized compressibility chart. A certain mixture, leaving a reactor in a chemical plant, has the following volumetric analysis

Component	Mole fraction	T_c (°K)	p_c (atm)
Ethylene	0.70	282.5	50
Ethyl ether	0.15	467	35.6
Water	0.10	647.3	218.4
Ethyl Alcohol	0.05	516	63

Determine the specific volume of the mixture if it is at 300 °F and 270 psia. The critical temperature and pressure of the components are as shown.

16.6. In a mixture of perfect gases, the change of entropy of the ith constituent is given by

$$ds_i = c_{p_i} \frac{dT}{T} - R_i \frac{dp_i}{p}$$

Substituting this into

$$ms = \sum_i m_i s_i$$

and restricting the mixture to two components, show that

$$ds = \frac{1}{m}(m_1 c_{p_1} + m_2 c_{p_2}) \frac{dT}{T} - (m_1 R_1 + m_2 R_2) \frac{dp}{p}$$

$$= (x_1 c_{p_1} + x_2 c_{p_2}) \frac{dT}{T} - \bar{R} \frac{dp}{p}$$

16.7. Show that for a mixture restricted to two constituent gases, the following expressions of entropy change are equivalent:

$$ds = (x_1 c_{p_1} + x_2 c_{p_2}) \frac{dT}{T} - \bar{R} \frac{dp}{p}$$

$$ds = (x_1 c_{v_1} + x_2 c_{v_2}) \frac{dT}{T} + \bar{R} \frac{dv}{v}$$

$$ds = (x_1 c_{p_1} + x_2 c_{p_2}) \frac{dv}{v} + (x_1 c_{v_1} + x_2 c_{v_2}) \frac{dp}{p}$$

16.8. Air has a gravimetric analysis of 76.7 per cent nitrogen and 23.3 per cent oxygen. Assuming constant specific heats, calculated the entropy of air at 200 °F and 30 psia. Assume the entropy of oxygen and nitrogen to be both zero at 14.7 psia and 0 °F absolute. Compare the result with the gas tables.

16.9. A mixture consisting of nitrogen and hydrogen in equal amounts at 90 °F and 30 psia is cooled at constant pressure to 45 °F. Determine the change in internal energy, enthalpy, and entropy per pound of mixture. The zero of enthalpy and internal energy is 0 °F absolute. The zero of entropy is 0 °F absolute and a pressure of 1 atmosphere.

16.10. Consider the mixture of different gases initially at different temperatures and pressures. When diffusion is completed and equilibrium is established,

$$mu = \sum_i m_i u_i$$

i.e., the internal energy of the mixture before and after mixing is constant, since no external work or heat transfer takes place. For a mixture of ideal gases, show that

$$T = \frac{m_1 c_{v_1} T_1 + m_2 c_{v_2} T_2 + \cdots}{m_1 c_{v_1} + m_2 c_{v_2} + \cdots} = \frac{p_1 V_1 + p_2 V_2 + \cdots}{mR}$$

$$p = \frac{p_1 V_1 + p_2 V_2 + \cdots}{V}$$

16.11. Determine the entropy increase when 0.232 pounds of oxygen and 0.768 pounds of nitrogen mix adiabatically at 60 °F and 14.7 psia to form air. Is mixing an irreversible process? Discuss this in light of a hypothetical piston permeable to all except one gas, so as to extract work from the interpenetration of the gases. Does actual mixing make use of this work?

16.12. Show that relative humidity ϕ and humidity ratio ω are connected by

$$\phi = \frac{\omega p_a}{0.622 p_g}$$

where p_a refers to the pressure of dry air, and p_g to the saturation pressure of the vapor at the same temperature.

16.13. An 8 cu ft tank contains atmospheric air initially compressed to 100 psia, 300 °F, and a relative humidity of 5 per cent. The air is allowed to cool in the receiver to 80 °F. Calculate: (a) the initial dew point, (b) the temperature at which condensation begins, (c) the partial pressures after cooling, (d) the amount of moisture condensed per pound of dry air, (e) the heat transferred. Hint: Each constituent changes state at constant volume. The moisture which remains as vapor is in the saturated vapor state at the final temperature of the mixture. The heat transferred is the change of internal energy of the system (dry air + H$_2$O).

16.14. The dew point of a gas-vapor mixture is the temperature at which the vapor condenses or solidifies when it is cooled at constant volume instead of constant pressure. Show that the condensation point is of slightly lower temperature than the dew point temperature.

16.15. An air-fuel mixture in an intake manifold consists of air and octane (C$_8$H$_{18}$). The mixture is at a temperature of 120 °F and a pressure of 12 psia. The relative humidity of the mixture (with respect to octane) is 22 per cent. Determine: (a) the dew point of the mixture, (b) the air–fuel ratio, (c) the density of the mixture. Octane has a gas constant of 13.5 ft lbf/lbm-°R, and its saturated vapor pressure vs. temperature curve is shown in Fig. 16.18.

16.16. The wall of a room is found to have a surface temperature of 49 °F. The air in the room has a dry-bulb temperature of 70 °F. What is the highest relative humidity at which condensation on the wall can be avoided? Consider the barometer to be standard.

16.17. An air-vapor mixture of 60 °F and 70 per cent relative humidity is compressed isothermally from 14.7 psia to 35 psia. Determine: (a) the amount of vapor condensed per pound of dry air, (b) the relative humidity at the end of the

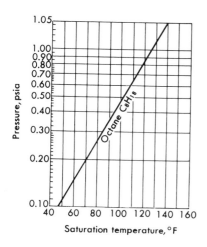

Fig. 16.18

process, (c) the work done and the heat transferred per pound of dry air. Compare the answers in part (c) with those obtained when compressing isothermally dry air under the same conditions.

16.18. It is known that the pressure–altitude relation for atmospheric air is

$$p = 30 - 9 \times 10^{-4}z$$

where p = inches Hg, and z = feet above sea level. Let a stream of air at 50 °F and 80 per cent relative humidity be flowing in from an ocean. Let it pass over a mountain range. Assuming a reversible adiabatic change (with $\gamma = 1.4$), determine the height of the mountain range to cause formation of clouds at the peaks.

16.19. Two streams of air are mixed at 14.7 psia in an insulated duct. One stream flows at the rate of 250 cu ft/min at 60 °F and 60 per cent relative humidity, the other at the rate of 1000 cu ft/min at 80 °F and 70 per cent relative humidity. Find the dry-bulb temperature, wet-bulb temperature, relative humidity, specific humidity, and density of the resultant stream.

16.20. Atmospheric air of 86 °F and 80 per cent relative humidity flows at a rate of 10,000 cfm over cooling coils. Condensed vapor is removed at 45 °F. The air then flows over heating coils, and leaves with a dry-bulb temperature of 68 °F and a relative humidity of 60 per cent. (a) Represent the sequence of operations on the psychrometric chart. (b) Compute the individual heat transfers for the cooling and heating processes and check the net heat transfer with the psychrometric chart. Consider the barometric pressure to be 14.7 psia throughout.

16.21. A natural-draft cooling tower is illustrated in Fig. 16.13. Water enters the tower at 72 °F and leaves at 50 °F. The air enters at 45 °F and 51 per cent relative humidity. It leaves, saturated, at 66 °F. Assuming a pressure of 14.7 psia to exist throughout, determine: (a) the ratio of mass flow rates of entering water and air, (b) the percentage of entering water leaving with the air.

16.22. Consider the effect of air leakage on the design and performance of a steam condenser. Besides reducing the rate of heat transfer per unit area per unit temperature difference between steam and cooling water by forming a non-condensable gas boundary-layer, the most obvious consequence of air leakage is the necessity for a pump of sufficient capacity to extract the air continuously in order to maintain the vacuum in the condenser. Since some of the steam mixes with it and the air cannot be separated from it, this entails a loss of condensate. Furthermore, the presence of air results in undercooling, i.e., the condensate is cooled below the saturation temperature of the incoming steam, and this necessitates an increased supply of heat in the boiler.

Suppose a condenser is required to handle 10,000 lbm/hr of steam at 100 °F and 95 per cent quality. If the estimated air leakage is 10 lbm/hr, what amount of vapor is carried away with the air for condensate temperature of 98 °F, 95 °F, and 85 °F respectively? Also, determine the capacity of air pump required in each case. Plot the results against condensate temperature. Note that, as the mixture of air and steam flows through the condenser, some of the steam condenses, so that the partial pressure of the air increases. But the total pressure is constant, which means that there is a decrease in the saturation pressure, and hence temperature, of the steam. In other words, the temperature of the condensate falls progressively below that of the incoming steam as condensation proceeds.

16.23. Benzene and toluene form nearly a completely miscible pair, i.e. they form solutions which obey Raoult's law. At 30 °C the vapor pressures of pure benzene and pure toluene are 119 and 37 mm respectively. At what composition would a solution have a total vapor pressure of 90 mm?

16.24. When Raoult's law holds, the free energy or Gibbs function of mixing is given by

$$\Delta G_{\text{mix}} = \sum_i n_i \bar{R} T \ln x_i \tag{1}$$

where n_i is the number of moles of a particular component i, $\bar{R}$ a universal gas constant, and x_i the mole fraction of the component. It will be shown in Chap. 18 that the change of free energy in a process is related to the enthalpy change by the Gibbs–Helmholtz equation

$$\frac{\partial}{\partial T}\left(\frac{\Delta G}{T}\right) = -\frac{\Delta H}{T^2} \tag{2}$$

Using the result given by Eq. (1), show that the enthalpy of mixing is in accordance with Eq. (2).

$$\Delta H_{\text{mix}} = -T^2 \frac{\partial}{\partial T}\left(\frac{\Delta G_{\text{mix}}}{T}\right) = 0$$

What is the volume change attending the mixing of liquids which form solutions obeying Raoult's law?

16.25. Consider the temperature-composition diagram shown below; it is characteristic of pairs of completely miscible substances such as benzene and toluene. T_A and T_B represent the boiling points of pure A and pure B respectively. The lower curve gives the boiling point for any mixture composition. Thus, if a liquid mixture of state i is heated, it will boil upon reaching state j. The composition of the liquid is x'_j and that of the vapor is x''_k (by convention, the the composition of the liquid phase is denoted by x' and that of the vapor phase by x''). At temperature T_1 the mixture consists of a liquid phase in state m (of composition x'_m) and a vapor phase in state n (of composition x''_n.) The total amount of components A and B in the system, however, remains the same, so that the overall composition remains the same as the original, i.e. $x_l = x_i$. For a state of the mixture, such as that represented by point l, the relative amounts of liquid and vapor present are indicated by the lengths l–n and l–m respectively. Upon further heating, the compositions of the liquid and vapor phases change until the temperature T_0 is reached, whereupon the liquid phase disappears and the composition of the vapor phase x''_0 is the same as that of the mixture x_i. Additional heating of the mixture results in a single phase superheated vapor represented by point q.

If a mixture of A and B such as benzene and toluene is heated to the boiling point and the vapor is removed, the liquid becomes richer in B and the vapor richer in A. This principle is used in the rectification process to obtain separation of a mixture into its components. Referring to Fig. 16.19, the liquid mixture at

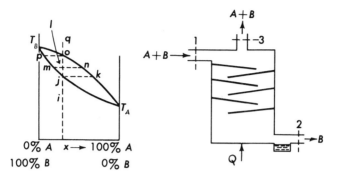

Fig. 16.19 Temperature-Composition Diagram and Partial Rectification.

state i or j enters the rectifying tower at section 1 and flows downward over large trays while heat is added at the bottom of the tower. The vapor initially driven off is in state k, whereas the remaining liquid is in state j. The liquid is thus richer in B, raising its boiling point. As it proceeds downward, its temperature rises, evaporation continues, and its B concentration increases, so that it is possible to withdraw pure B at section 2. The vapor leaves at section 3. The maximum yield of pure B per unit amount of mixture can be determined by means of a mass balance and temperature-composition data. If x'_A denotes the mass fraction of A in the liquid phase, m_1 the flow rate at section 1, m_3 the flow rate at section 3, and if the liquid entering at 1 is assumed to be in equilibrium with the vapor leaving at 3, i.e. $x''_{A_1} = x''_{A_3}$, show that

$$\frac{M_{B_2}}{M_1} = 1 - \frac{M_3}{M_1} = 1 - \frac{M_{A_3}}{M_1 x''_{A_3}} = 1 - \frac{x'_{A_1}}{x''_{A_1}}$$

PART III

REPRESENTATIVE
APPLICATIONS

CHAPTER 17

Reactive Systems; Combustion

17.1 Introduction

So far, only non-reactive systems have been considered, i.e., previous chapters have been concerned wholly with the behaviour of substances which remained in the same chemical state throughout a process. In this chapter the thermodynamics of reactive systems are discussed. A *chemical reaction* can be defined as *the rearrangement of atoms due to a redistribution of electrons.* The discussion will be primarily concerned with the thermodynamic aspects of a particular type of reaction, namely combustion.

The term *combustion* refers to a fairly rapid reaction, usually accompanied by a flame, which occurs between a fuel and an oxygen carrier

469

(air). The molecules of fuel have a certain amount of energy stored in the bonds between the atoms (a form of internal energy which has not been discussed so far because it remains constant in all processes not involving chemical reactions). When new molecules are formed by the combustion reaction, this "chemical" energy is usually at a lower level, and the energy thus released is transferred to the surroundings in the form of heat.

In dealing with chemical reactions, the three important things from the standpoint of engineering are: (1) What direction and how far will the reaction go? (2) How much heat will be given off or absorbed? (3) How fast will the reaction go? The first two questions comprise chemical thermodynamics, and is the only aspect of chemical change which is discussed in the present text. The third question involves rates. It is known as *chemical kinetics*, and is beyond the scope of the text. From the thermodynamics standpoint, three major aspects are to be considered, corresponding to the three natural laws: the law of conservation of matter, the law of conservation of energy, and the second law of thermodynamics. The first aspect is known as *stoichiometry*; it is concerned with the relationship between the composition of the reactants and the composition of the products. The second aspect involves the application of the first law of thermodynamics to systems which are not pure substances (because the chemical state of the system changes). The third aspect involves prediction about chemical reactions. By distinguishing between reversible and irreversible processes, the second law provides information as to whether a given reaction will go forwards or backwards. Also, the second law makes it possible to determine how much work can be obtained from the combustion of a given mass of fuel; this provides a standard of comparison for the performance of actual power plants.

17.2   Fuels

Most fuels consist of hydrogen and carbon, whether they be solid (e.g., coal), liquid (e.g., petroleum), or gaseous (e.g., coal gas). The chemical analysis of solid and liquid fuels is usually given in terms of the percentage by weight of each chemical element in the fuel (ultimate analysis). Analysis of gaseous fuels, on the other hand, is given in terms of the percentage by volume of each type of hydrocarbon present.

Coal is the remains of vegetation deposits of past geological ages. Its combustible constituents are chiefly carbon (C), hydrogen (H), and, to a small extent, sulphur (S). Its incombustible constituents are nitrogen (N), moisture (H_2O), and ash. The *proximate analysis* of coal gives the percentage of moisture, volatile matter, fixed carbon, and ash. The procedure used in obtaining such an analysis is outlined in ASTM bulletins (Standards on Coal and Coke). The *ultimate analysis* gives the percentage of carbon, hydrogen, oxygen, sulphur, nitrogen and ash. It may be on a "as received" basis or on a "dry" basis, i.e. with the moisture as determined by proximate analysis being excluded.

Petroleum oil is a complex mixture of a large number of hydrocarbons. These hydrocarbons are commonly classified into several groups: the paraffins (C_nH_{2n+2}), olefins and naphthenes (C_nH_{2n}), and aromatics (C_nH_{2n-2}). Most liquid fuels are mixtures of hydrocarbons which are derived from crude oil through distillation and cracking. Thus, from a given crude oil, a number of different fuels can be produced such as gasoline, kerosene, Diesel fuel, and fuel oil. The difference between these types of fuels is given by the corresponding distillation curves in Fig. 17.1.

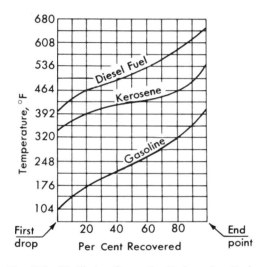

Fig. 17.1 Distillation Curves for Hydrocarbon Fuels.

A distillation curve is obtained by slowly heating a sample of fuel so that it vaporizes, then condensing and measuring the vapor.

Gaseous fuels are obtained from natural gas wells and manufacturing processes. Some hydrocarbons in petroleum deposits exist in the gaseous phase at atmospheric pressure. Methane (CH_4) is the most common; it is known as marsh gas. The most widely used gaseous fuels, however, are formed by heating coal.

17.3 Stoichiometric Relations

As previously stated, a chemical reaction is the process in which the interatomic bonds in the reactant molecules are broken, followed by the rearrangement of the atoms in new molecular combinations. In other words, new chemical substances appear, old ones disappear, and actual atoms remain the same.

A chemical equation expresses the principle of conservation of mass in terms of the conservation of atoms. Consider, for example, the change in composition in the stoichiometric combustion of a hydrocarbon fuel such as methane, or for that matter, any other fuel.† A stoichiometric combustion is one in which all the hydrogen atoms are converted to H_2O and all the carbon atoms are converted to CO_2. Thus, in the case of methane,

$$CH_4 + 2O_2 \rightarrow CO_2 + 2H_2O \qquad (17.1)$$

Equation (17.1) states that one mole of methane reacts with two moles of oxygen to form one mole of carbon dioxide and two moles of water. The water may be in the vapor, liquid or solid phase, depending on the temperature and pressure of the products of combustion. Merely writing an equation, of course, tells little about the reaction itself, not even whether it is possible that it should proceed in the direction indicated. Questions of possibility must be discussed in terms of the second law. For the present, however, it is taken that combustion reactions in which hydrocarbon fuels are completely oxidized can always proceed spontaneously if sufficient oxygen is provided.

In most combustion processes the oxygen is supplied as air rather than as pure oxygen. Assuming that air is 21 per cent oxygen and 79 per cent nitrogen by volume (i.e., for each mole of oxygen, there is $79/21 = 3.76$ moles of nitrogen present), the preceding reaction would be written as

$$CH_4 + 2O_2 + 2(3.76)N_2 \rightarrow CO_2 + 2H_2O + 7.52\ N_2 \qquad (17.2)$$

Note that all the carbon atoms are converted to CO_2 and all the hydrogen atoms are converted to H_2O by combination with the oxygen in the air; the nitrogen does not enter into the reaction at all. The minimum amount of air which supplies sufficient oxygen for the complete oxidation of all the carbon, hydrogen, and other combustible elements in a fuel is called the *theoretical air*. In practice, however, it is found that complete combustion is not likely to be achieved unless the amount of air supplied is somewhat greater than the theoretical amount. An important parameter in the study of combustion is the *air-fuel ratio,* the ratio of the mass of air to the mass of fuel. When the air-fuel ratio is *less* than the theoretical or stoichiometric air-fuel ratio for complete conbustion, some of the carbon unites with oxygen to form carbon monoxide instead of carbon dioxide.

---

† It is useful to remember that the combustible elements in any fuel are essentially the following: carbon, which burns to CO_2, hydrogen which burns to H_2O, and sulfur, which burns to SO_2.

Although it is undesirable to supply much more than the stoichiometric quantity of air (the excess air merely lowers the gas temperature and therefore the heat transfer rate), 20 per cent excess air is usually regarded as the minimum acceptable amount of air. Gas turbines often operate with 300 per cent excess air to avoid the melting of turbine blades.

Example 17.1. (a) Determine the stoichiometric air/fuel ratio and the products for the combustion of octane, C_8H_{18}. (b) Compare the molal analysis of the products of combustion with that obtained when C_1H_{18} is burned with 200 per cent theoretical air.

Solution. (a) The stoichiometric or theoretical air/fuel ratio is obtained from the equation

$$C_8H_{18}+12.5\ O_2+12.5(3.76)\ N_2 \to 8\ CO_2+9\ H_2O+47\ N_2$$

The amount of air to the amount of fuel is

$$\frac{12.5\times32+47\times28}{114} = 15\ \text{lbm air/lbm fuel}$$

The molal analysis of the products corresponding to stoichiometric combustion is

	Number of moles	Percentage by volume
CO_2	8	12.5
H_2O	9	14
N_2	47	73.5
	——	
	64	

(b) The equation for combustion with 200 per cent theoretical air is

$$C_8H_{18}+2(12.5)\ O_2+2(12.5\times3.76)\ N_2 \to 8\ CO_2+9\ H_2O+12.5\ O_2+94\ N_2$$

The corresponding volumetric analysis of the products of combustion is

	n	x_i
CO_2	8	6.5
H_2O	9	7.3
O_2	12.5	10.1
N_2	94	76.1
	———	
	123.5	

Example 17.2. The volumetric analysis of a producer gas is 26 per cent CO, 12 per cent H_2, 7 per cent CO_2 and 55 per cent N_2. Air in the amount of 1.2 cu ft

is supplied for each cubic foot of gas. What is the minimum temperature allowable for any surface in contact with the flue gas if condensation is not to occur? Consider the flue gas to be at 14.7 psia.

Solution. The reactions are:

0.26 moles of $CO + 0.13$ moles of O_2 = 0.26 moles of CO_2

0.12 moles of $H_2 + 0.06$ moles of O_2 = 0.12 moles of H_2O

The products of combustion are thus:

CO_2: 0.26 moles (from combustion of CO) + 0.07 moles (supplied with fuel)
  $= 0.33$ moles

H_2O: 0.12 moles (from combustion of H_2)

O_2: 1.2×0.21 moles (supplied with air)—0.19 moles (consumed in oxidation of CO and H_2) = 0.062 moles

N_2: 1.2×0.79 moles (supplied with air) + 0.55 moles (supplied with fuel)
  = 1.499 moles

Total moles of products = $0.33 + 0.12 + 0.062 + 1.499 = 2.011$ moles.
The partial pressure of H_2O vapor is thus

$$\frac{0.12}{2.011} \times 14.7 = 0.876 \text{ psia}$$

From the steam tables, this corresponds to a saturation temperature of 97 °F. Thus, no part of any surface should fall below 97 °F.

17.4 Analysis of Products of Combustion

The actual amount of air supplied in a combustion process can be calculated from an analysis of the products of combustion. This analysis is usually made with an Orsat apparatus, shown in Fig. 17.2.

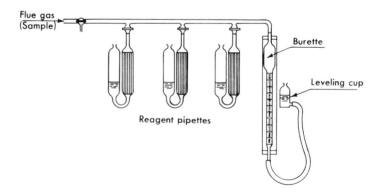

Fig. 17.2 Orsat Apparatus.

The Orsat apparatus makes use of the concept of partial volume. A measured volume of combustion gases (usually 100 cc) is successively passed through a number of chemical solutions; the decrease in volume being recorded each time. This is done by lowering the levelling cup to introduce 100 cc of flue gas into the measuring burette, then forcing the gas (by raising the levelling cup) to bubble through various reagent pipettes. The first pipette contains a 20 per cent solution of potassium hydroxide which absorbs the CO_2 in the flue gas. The second pipette contains an alkaline solution of pyrogallic acid which absorbs the O_2. The third pipette contains an acid solution of cuprous chloride which absorbs CO. Since the major components of flue gas are usually CO_2, CO, O_2 and N_2, the remainder is N_2. The analysis obtained from the Orsat apparatus is on a dry basis, i.e., the water formed during combustion does not appear in the results. This is because the procedure is conducted at room temperature, which is considerably below the dew point of the products of combustion of most hydrocarbon fuels. The method of calculating the actual air-fuel ratio from the Orsat analysis is illustrated in the following example:

Example 17.3. Methane (CH_4) is burned with atmospheric air. The Orsat analysis of the products of combustion is as follows: 10 per cent CO_2, 2.4 per cent O_2, 0.5 per cent CO, 87.1 per cent N_2. Determine the actual air/fuel ratio.

Solution. Let the combustion equation be written for say, 100 moles of dry products. Since it is not known *a priori* how much reactants and in what proportions were consumed in order to obtain the 100 moles of dry products, unknown coefficients a, b, c . . . will be used:

$$aCH_4 + bO_2 + b(3.76)N_2 \longrightarrow$$

$$10CO_2 + 0.5CO + 2.4O_2 + cH_2O + 87.1N_2$$

The coefficients a, b, c are easily determined by the following mass balance:

Nitrogen balance: $3.76b = 87.1$; $b = 23.16$

Carbon balance: $a = 10 + 0.5 = 10.5$

Hydrogen balance: $4a = 4(10.5) = 2c$; $c = 21$

The combustion equation is thus

$$10.5CH_4 + 23.16O_2 + 87.1N_2 \longrightarrow$$

$$10CO_2 + 0.5CO + 2.4O_2 + 21H_2O + 87.1N_2$$

The actual air-fuel ratio is

$$\frac{(23.16 \times 32) + (87.1 \times 28)}{10.5 \times 16} = 18.9 \text{ lbm air/lbm fuel}$$

17.5 First Law Analysis of Chemical Reaction

When a system undergoes a chemical reaction, the first law of thermo-dynamics applies, as for any other process. From a thermodynamics viewpoint, a chemical reaction is but a change of phase in the system so to speak, analogous to a physical change of phase such as vaporization. There is, however, a difference in treatment between a *pure substance* (a system of fixed composition with no chemical reaction occurring) and a *chemical substance* (a system of homogeneous composition, but changing due to chemical reaction). Whereas all the properties of a pure substance, including its internal energy and enthalpy, are fixed by specifying *two* independent properties (such as pressure and specific volume), this is not true for a chemical substance. In the latter case, the state of chemical aggregation must be specified as well. Consequently, it is *not* possible, when dealing with chemical reactions, to choose independently the zeros of internal energies and enthalpies of chemical substances which may be transformed into each other by reaction. This will become clearer in the development that follows.

Isometric-Isothermal Reaction. When a chemical reaction takes place, there is usually an evolution or absorption of heat. This is because the energy of the products of a reaction is usually *different* from that of the reactants, even when both are at the same temperature. Consider a chemical substance which changes composition from a reactant to a product by chemical reaction at constant volume and temperature.† The internal energy of the system in the product state, U_p, is related to the internal energy in the reactant state, U_r, through the first law:

$$Q = (U_p - U_r) + W$$

For a constant-volume reaction ($W = 0$) this becomes

$$Q = U_p - U_r = \Delta U \tag{17.3}$$

Since the chemical states of the products and of the reactants are different, the problem of evaluating ΔU is no longer as simple as in the case of a pure substance (which doesn't change in chemical composition). In other words, the state of zero internal energy cannot be arbitrarily chosen for each reactant and product, otherwise $U_p - U_r$ could have any value what-ever. This is shown in Fig. 17.3(a), where the upper curve represents the internal energy of the reactants, and the lower curve that of the products. Here, U has been plotted against T, with a zero of U taken arbitrarily

---

† What is really meant is that the temperature should return to its initial value. It is not required that the temperature be constant throughout the entire reaction.

for both reactants and products. For a process involving a change from a reactant state to a product state, the two curves must be shifted into

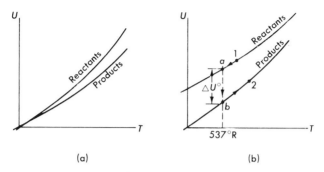

(a)   (b)

Fig. 17.3 Internal Energy of Reactants and Products versus Temperature.

proper relative position by allowing the reaction to be carried out in a closed rigid vessel (bomb calorimeter) and measuring the heat transfer required to bring the products back to the initial temperature of the reactants. Thus, the internal energy change ΔU° at a standard base temperature T_0 (usually 77 °F) is determined, and the curves can be drawn in proper position, as in Fig. 17.3(b). Having accomplished this, the internal energy change for any process which begins with the reactants at state 1 and with the products at state 2 can then be easily found by writing

$$U_p - U_r = U_2 - U_1 = (U_2 - U_b) + (U_b - U_a) - (U_1 - U_a)$$

$$= (U_2 - U_b) + \Delta U^\circ + (U_1 - U_a)$$

$$= \Big[U_{\text{products}} \Big]_{T_b}^{T_2} + \Delta U^\circ - \Big[U_{\text{resultants}} \Big]_{T_a}^{T_1} \qquad (17.4)$$

The full use of Eq. (17.4) will be illustrated as soon as the general discussion on reactions is completed.

Isobaric-Isothermal Reaction. A similar discussion applies to a chemical reaction occurring at constant pressure and temperature. In this case, the first law gives

$$Q = (U_p - U_r) + W \qquad (17.5)$$

For a constant pressure process, $W = \int p\,dV = p(V_p - V_r)$, where the subscripts r and p denote, as usual, reactants and products. Equation (17.5) thus becomes

$$Q = (U_p - U_r) + p(V_p - V_r) = (U_p + pV_p) - (U_r + pV_r)$$

$$= H_p - H_r = \Delta H \qquad (17.6)$$

Just as the internal energy of the products of a reaction is usually different from that of the reactants, so the enthalpy of the products of a reaction is usually *different* from that of the reactants, even though the products and reactants are at the same temperature. The enthalpy change of a reaction is equal to the heat absorbed or evolved. In an *endothermic* reaction, the enthalpy of the products is *greater* than that of the reactants, and heat is absorbed. In an *exothermic* reaction, the enthalpy of the products is *less* than that of the reactants, and heat is evolved.

The relationship between the enthalpy of the reactants and that of the products is obtained by carrying out a steady-flow reaction at a standard base temperature in a Junker calorimeter. This gives $\Delta H°$, the standard heat of reaction, and enables the enthalpy curves to be drawn in proper relation as in Fig. 17.4.

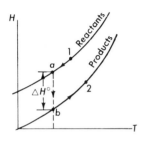

Fig. 17.4 Enthalpy of Reactants and Products versus Temperature.

Example 17.4. The internal energy of reaction for the combustion of carbon to carbon dioxide at 68 °F is $-14,085$ Btu/lbm of carbon. What is the heat transferred when a system composed of 1 lbm of carbon and 4 lbm of oxygen at 100 °F burns at constant volume to a mixture of CO_2 and O_2 at a temperature of 400 °F?

Solution. Referring to Fig. 17.3 (b) the heat transferred is

$$Q = U_2 - U_1$$

To evaluate this, it is convenient to choose a path composed of the three steps $1-a$, $a-b$, $b-2$. Thus

$$Q = U_2 - U_1 = (U_a - U_1) + (U_b - U_a) + (U_2 - U_b)$$

The reaction equation on the basis of a unit mass of carbon is

$$1 \text{ lbm C} + 4 \text{ lbm O}_2 \rightarrow 3.67 \text{ lbm CO}_2 + 1.33 \text{ lbm O}_2$$

Assuming $c_v = 0.165$ Btu/lbm–°F for CO_2, $c_v = 0.155$ Btu/lbm–°F for O_2, and $c_v = 0.17$ Btu/lbm–°F for C,

$$U_a - U_1 = (1)(0.17)(68 - 100) + (4)(0.155)(68 - 100)$$

$$= -25.28$$

$$U_b - U_a = -14,085$$

$$U_2 - U_b = (3.67)(0.165)(400 - 68) + (1.33)(0.155)(400 - 68)$$

$$= 269.4$$

Thus,

$$Q = -25.28 - 14,085 + 269.4 = -13,841 \text{ Btu/lbm C}$$

The minus sign implies that heat is transferred *out* of the system.

17.6 Enthalpy of Formation

It was pointed out in the preceding section that, in a system of fixed composition (no chemical reaction), thermodynamic properties can always be tabulated relative to some arbitrarily assumed base. For example, in the steam tables, the enthalpy of saturated liquid at 32 °F is assumed to be zero. It was also pointed out that this procedure is inadequate when dealing with a chemical reaction, because the composition of the system changes during the process.

When designating heats of reaction, a definite temperature and the physical state of each component must be specified. These physical states are called standard states, and the corresponding heat of reaction is known as the standard heat of reaction. The most often specified base temperature is 25 °C (77 °F).† Consider, for example, the reaction of hydrogen and oxygen to form liquid water:

$$H_2(g) + \tfrac{1}{2}O_2(g) = H_2O(l)$$

Let the process be carried out at 77 °F and one atmosphere pressure in a steady-flow device such as a Junker calorimeter. If the heat transfer is carefully measured, it is found to be $-122{,}891$ Btu/lb-mole of liquid H_2O (the minus sign indicates that heat was removed in order to restore the system to its original temperature of 77 °F). The first law in the guise of Eq. (17.6) gives

$$Q = \Delta H = H_p - H_r$$

$$= \bar{h}_{H_2O} - (\bar{h}_{H_2} + \tfrac{1}{2}\bar{h}_{O_2}) \tag{17.7}$$

where $\bar{h}_{H_2O}$, $\bar{h}_{H_2}$, and $\bar{h}_{O_2}$ are the enthalpies per mole of H_2O, H_2, and O_2 respectively. Since enthalpies can be reckoned from any arbitrary base, the technique resorted to is to set the enthalpy of all the elements to zero at the reference state. In other words, $\bar{h}_{H_2} = 0$, $\bar{h}_{O_2} = 0$ at 77 °F and one atmosphere. Thus, Eq. (17.7) becomes

$$Q = \Delta H° = -122{,}891 = \bar{h}_{H_2O}$$

The enthalpy of H_2O at 77 °F and one atmosphere pressure (with the enthalpy of elements assumed to be zero) is called the *enthalpy of formation*. It is, as seen from the above development, equal to the heat of reaction

---

† The value at 25 °C (77 °F) has become widely accepted in recent thermodynamics data. Earlier tabulations such as that of Bichowsky & Rossini have been based upon 18 °C. In most engineering applications this difference in reference temperature is unimportant.

at the base temperature of 77 °F. (More precisely, *the enthalpy of formation of a chemical compound is the enthalpy of the compound formed in a constant-pressure isothermal reaction in which the compound is the only product and the reactants are the chemical elements in their datum states of zero enthalpy.*) For this reason, it is usually written with a subscript 0 to denote that it is taken at the reference temperature of t_0 ($= 77$ °F):

$$\bar{h}^{\circ}{}_{f,\mathrm{H_2O}} = 122{,}891 \text{ Btu/lb mole}$$

The definition of the enthalpy of formation of a compound enables the standard heat of reaction to be easily calculated by taking the difference between the enthalpies of formation of products and reactants. This is shown schematically in Fig. 17.5

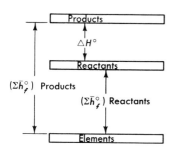

Fig. 17.5
Enthalpy Levels in a Reaction.

$$\Delta H^{\circ} = \left(\sum \bar{h}^{\circ}{}_{f}\right)_{p} - \left(\sum \bar{h}^{\circ}{}_{f}\right)_{r} \quad (17.8)$$

where $\bar{h}^{\circ}{}_{f}$ denotes enthalpy of formation per mole, and the subscripts p and r refer to products and reactants respectively. The concept of enthalpy of formation is further illustrated in the example below. Before that, however, it is useful to list the enthalpy of formation of various substances which may be encountered in the present chapter:

TABLE 17.1
ENTHALPY OF FORMATION *

Compound	State	$\bar{h}^{\circ}_{f}$ Btu/lb mole	Compound	State	$\bar{h}^{\circ}_{f}$ Btu/lb mole
Carbon, C	Graphite	0			
	Diamond†	815			
Carbon dioxide, CO₂	Gas	− 169,182	Ethylene, C₂H₂ (Ethene)	Gas	22,478
Carbon monoxide, CO	Gas	− 47,517			
			Ethane, C₂H₆	Gas	− 36,401
Water, H₂O	Gas	− 103,968	Propane, C₃H₈	Gas	− 44,647
	Liquid	− 122,891	Butane, C₄H₁₀	Gas	− 54,234
Sulfur dioxide, SO₂	Gas	− 127,644			
			Benzene, C₆H₆	Gas	35,653
Methane, CH₄	Gas	− 32,179	Octane, C₈H₁₈	Gas	− 89,617
Acetylene, C₂H₂	Gas	97,485		Liquid	− 107,462

† Relative to graphite.

* Data is converted from *National Bureau of Standards Circular* 500, 1952.

Example 17.5. The heat of combustion, heat of solution, heat of dilution, and heat of formation are merely specialized forms of heat of reaction; more specifically, if a chemical reaction is an oxidation process, the heat of reaction is called *heat of combustion.* Consider the steady-flow calorimeter of Fig. 17.6 in which the following reaction occurs:

$$CH_4(g) + 2 O_2(g) \rightarrow CO_2(g) + 2 H_2O(l)$$

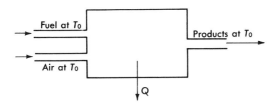

Fig. 17.6 Constant-Pressure Calorimeter.

The reactants at temperature t_0 ($= 77$ °F) and one atmosphere pressure enter the calorimeter where combustion takes place; heat is transferred at such a rate that the products also leave at temperature t_0. Determine the heat transfer per mole of fuel.

Solution. The heat transferred is equal in magnitude to the heat of reaction which in this case is $\Delta H°$, and may be obtained from a knowledge of the heats of formation (Table 17.1). Thus

$$Q = \Delta H° = (\bar{h}°_{f,CO_2} + 2\bar{h}_{f,H_2O}) - (\bar{h}°_{f,CH_4} + 2\bar{h}°_{f,O_2})$$
$$= [-169,182 + 2(-122,891)] - [-32,179 + 2(0)] = -382,785 \text{ Btu/lb mole } CH_4$$

In this example, the heat of reaction $\Delta H°$ at the reference temperature t_0 is called the heat of combustion, for it is the change in enthalpy during the combustion process. Note that it is equal to the heat transfer per unit mass of fuel and is usually given in Btu/mole or in Btu/lbm. The term *heating value* is defined as the heat *evolved* per pound of fuel. Thus, heating value and heat of combustion have the same magnitude but opposite sign; heating value is always regarded as heat transferred *from* the products of combustion.

Fig. 17.7
Constant-Volume
Calorimeter.

17.7 Relation between $\Delta U°$ and $\Delta H°$

A reaction similar to that of Ex. 17.5 may be carried out in a closed vessel at a given reference temperature t_0. This is shown in Fig. 17.7.

where the reaction is initiated by means of a spark or a hot wire, and the products of combustion are cooled to the initial temperature. The first law of thermodynamics gives

$$Q = \Delta U^{\circ} = U_p - U_r$$

where the subscripts p and r refer to products and reactants respectively. Q is called the heat of reaction at constant volume. If the reaction is a heat-producing one, Q is negative, and the internal energy of the products is lower than that of the reactants, both at the same temperature. The constant-volume heating value of a fuel is defined as the heat transferred from the products in order to restore the system to its initial temperature t_0. Thus, the heat of reaction ΔU° and the constant-volume heating value have the same magnitude, but opposite sign.

It is of interest to determine the difference between the heat of reaction at constant volume ΔU° and the heat of reaction at constant pressure ΔH°. From the definition of enthalpy ($h = u + pv$),

$$\Delta H^{\circ} = H_p - H_r = (U_p + pV_p) - (U_r + pV_r)$$
$$= (U_p - U_r) + (pV_p - pV_r)$$

or

$$\Delta H^{\circ} = \Delta U^{\circ} + \Delta(pV) \qquad (17.9)$$

Thus, the difference between the constant-pressure heat of reaction and the constant-volume heat of reaction depends on the difference between the pV term of the products and the pV term of the reactants. Consider, in a reaction, those constituents which are gases (since the pV of liquids and solids is usually much less than the pV of gases), and assume the behavior of the gases to be ideal. Then

$$pV_p = n_p \bar{R} T_0; \quad pV_r = n_r \bar{R} T^{\circ}$$

where n_p and n_r are the number of moles of *gaseous* products and reactants respectively, and T_0 is the absolute temperature at which the reaction is carried out. Equation (17.9) thus becomes

$$\Delta H^{\circ} = \Delta U^{\circ} + (n_p - n_r)\bar{R} T_0 = \Delta U^{\circ} + (\Delta n)\bar{R} T_0 \qquad (17.10)$$

where Δn represents the change in the number of moles occurring during the reaction. Equation (17.10) indicates that the difference $\Delta H^{\circ} - \Delta U^{\circ}$ between the constant-pressure heat of reaction and the constant-volume heat of reaction depends on this change in the number of moles of gaseous constituents. *When a reaction is such that the number of moles of gaseous products is equal to the number of moles of gaseous reactants, the change Δn is zero, and ΔH° and ΔU° are numerically equal.*

Example 17.6. The enthalpy of reaction for

$$CO(g) + \tfrac{1}{2} O_2(g) = CO_2(g)$$

is $-4,348$ Btu/lbm of CO at 77 °F. What is the internal energy of reaction $\Delta U°$?

Solution. The number of moles of gaseous reactants is $n_r = 1 + 1/2 = 1.5$; the number of moles of gaseous products is $n_p = 1$. Thus $\Delta n = 1 - 1.5 = -0.5$, and $(\Delta n)\bar{R}T_0 = -(0.5)(1.986)(537) = -533$ Btu/mole of CO. Eq. (17.10) gives, on the basis of one mole of CO:

$$-4,348 \times 28 = \Delta U° - 533$$

or

$$\Delta U° = -121,210 \text{ Btu/lb mole of CO}$$
$$= -4,300 \text{ Btu/lbm of CO}$$

Note that n_r and n_p are the number of moles of *gaseous* constituents present. If any of the reactants or products are present as liquids or solids, they are ignored in computing Δn. For example, in the reaction

$$C(s) + O_2(g) = CO_2(g)$$

$n_r = 1$ and $n_p = 1$, so that $\Delta U° = \Delta H°$.

17.8 Heating Value of Fuels

The heating value of a fuel is generally defined as the heat of reaction at 77 °F and a pressure of 1 atmosphere. It is expressed as Btu/lbm of fuel, Btu/mole of fuel, or Btu/cu ft of fuel according to convenience. Reference to a unit mass of fuel makes it unnecessary to specify the amount of air to be mixed with the fuel, as long as it exceeds the stoichiometric quantity for complete combustion. It is likewise unnecessary to specify whether air or pure oxygen is the oxidant.

It is sometimes necessary to distinguish between a constant-pressure heat value $-\Delta H°$, and a constant-volume heating value $-\Delta U°$, although they may be equal, as in the case of carbon, since the reaction

$$C(s) + O_2(g) \rightarrow CO_2(g)$$

has one mole of gas on each side of the equation. A more important distinction, however, is between the higher heating value (HHV) and the lower heating value (LHV). This refers to fuels which contain hydrogen: the water formed in the products may be either liquid or vapor. Suppose the hydrogen is burned to water under such conditions that all the water vapor formed is condensed to the liquid state. The chemical equation for the reaction at 77 °F is

$$H_2(g) + \tfrac{1}{2} O_2(g) \rightarrow H_2O(l); \quad \Delta H = -122,891 \text{ Btu/lb mole}$$

This gives the higher heating value because it includes the heat transferred from the system as the result of the condensation of the H_2O. It is larger than if the state of H_2O in the products had been vapor. On a pound basis, the higher and lower heating value are related by

$$HHV = LHV + mh_{fg} \qquad (17.11)$$

where m is the mass of H_2O produced per pound of fuel, and h_{fg} is the latent heat of vaporization of water at the reaction temperature ($h_{fg} \approx 1050$ Btu/lbm at 77 °F). A similar distinction can be made for a reaction occurring at constant volume, in which case the higher and lower heating value at constant volume are related by

$$HHV = LHV + mu_{fg} \qquad (17.12)$$

In discussing heating values, the following remarks are of interest: (1) Although the higher heating value gives an indication of the maximum amount of heat that could be transferred in a given reaction, in practice, however, the heat of vaporization of H_2O in the products of combustion is seldom utilized because serious corrosion problems would arise if moisture is permitted to condense from the flue gas. (2) Some fuels may be supplied either as a gas or as a liquid. In such cases the heating value for the gas and the heating value for the liquid differ by the latent heat of vaporization of the fuel. Usually, this is a smaller difference than that resulting from the latent heat of vaporization of the H_2O in the products of combustion.

17.9 Energy Relations for Reactions in General

The reactions discussed so far have been those in which the reactants and products are at the same temperature. The evaluation of enthalpy or internal energy change for the general case of a reaction in which the reactants and products are not necessarily at the same temperature is now discussed.

First, it should be mentioned that the heat of reaction at constant volume $\Delta U°$ and the heat of reaction at constant pressure $\Delta H°$ depend on the conditions of the reaction, chiefly on the reference temperature t_0. As previously pointed out, the temperature and the physical state for each component must be specified when speaking of heat of reaction. Although the effect of pressure on the heat of reaction is small and is often neglected (for ideal gases, the heat of reaction is not affected by pressure), the effect of temperature on the heat of reaction is significant and cannot be ignored in most cases. This is shown in Fig. 17.8, where the internal energy and

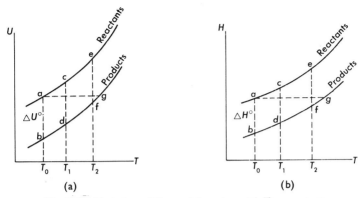

Fig. 17.8 Variation of Heats of Reaction with Temperature.

the enthalpy of the reactants and products have been plotted against temperature. Now, an isothermal reaction corresponds to the passage from an upper curve (reactants) to a lower curve (products) along a vertical line. It will be noticed that ΔU° and ΔH° (represented by the vertical spacing between the curves) varies with the location of the temperature t_0, being in fact less at a higher temperature than at a lower temperature. (The distance between the curves changes because the specific heats of the products differ from those of the reactants). Values of ΔU° and ΔH° at a standard temperature t_0, (usually 77 °F), are known respectively as standard heat of reaction at constant volume and standard heat of reaction at constant pressure. They are most often tabulated for low pressures, where gases may be taken to be ideal. With such information available, the enthalpy and internal energy changes for any reaction (isothermal or not) can be evaluated in the manner given below. The discussion will be illustrated by means of a constant-pressure reaction. However, the method applies equally well to a constant-volume reaction. There are four cases of interest; these are:

(1) *Isothermal Reaction at Standard Temperature.* The reactants enter and the products leave at the reference temperature (usually 77 °F) for which the heat of reaction is given, i.e., the process is the following:

$$\text{Reactants} \longrightarrow \text{Products}$$
$$(\text{at } T_0) \qquad\qquad (\text{at } T_0)$$

The enthalpy change ΔH for the reaction is simply the standard heat of reaction ΔH° as shown in Fig. 17.8(b).

(2) *Isothermal Reaction at Temperature Different from Standard.* The reactants and products enter and leave at the same, but not standard (77 °F), temperature, i.e.,

$$\text{Reactants} \longrightarrow \text{Products}$$
$$\text{(at } T_1) \qquad\qquad \text{(at } T_1)$$

Referring to Fig. 17.8(b), this is the case corresponding to a reaction taking place at temperature T_1 instead of T_0. The enthalpy change $H_d - H_c$ for the reaction may be computed by taking the equivalent path c–a, a–b, b–d. Thus,

$$\Delta H = H_d - H_c = (H_d - H_b) + (H_b - H_a) + (H_a - H_c)$$
$$= \int_{T_b}^{T_d} \sum n_p(\bar{c}_p)_p dT + \Delta H^\circ + \int_{T_c}^{T_a} \sum n_r(\bar{c}_p)_r dT \qquad (17.13)$$

where $\Sigma n_p(\bar{c}_p)_p$ is the sum of the enthalpies of all the products, and $\Sigma n_r(\bar{c}_p)_r$ is the sum of the enthalpies of all the reactants.

(3) *Non-Isothermal Reaction.* The reactants enter at temperature T_1 and the products leave at temperature T_2, i.e.,

$$\text{Reactants} \longrightarrow \text{Products}$$
$$\text{(at } T_1) \qquad\qquad \text{(at } T_2)$$

The enthalpy change $H_f - H_e$ for the reaction is computed by taking the equivalent path c–a, a–b, b–f:

$$\Delta H = H_f - H_e = (H_f - H_b) + (H_b - H_a) + (H_a - H_e)$$
$$= \int_{T_b}^{T_f} \sum n_p(\bar{c}_p)_p dT + \Delta H^\circ + \int_{T_c}^{T_a} \sum n_r(\bar{c}_p)_r dT \qquad (17.14)$$

where $\Sigma n_p(\bar{c}_p)_p$ and $W n_r(\bar{c}_p)_r$ have the same meaning as before.

(4) *Adiabatic Reaction.* This is the case in which the enthalpy change ΔH is zero (since no heat is transferred). The reaction proceeds along a–g, reaching a temperature T_g (called the adiabatic flame temperature):

$$\text{Reactants} \longrightarrow \text{Products}$$
$$\text{(at } T_0) \qquad \text{(at } T_g = \text{adiabatic)}$$

Here, T_g is the item of interest; it is calculated from the equivalent path a–b, b–g, i.e.,

$$\Delta H = (H_g - H_b) + (H_b - H_a) = 0$$

or

$$0 = \int_{T_b}^{T_g} \sum n_p(\bar{c}_p)_p dT + \Delta H^\circ \qquad (17.15)$$

Equation (17.15) enables the theoretical flame temperature T_g to be calculated either by trial and error or by use of the gas tables.

Example 17.7. As a further illustration of the application of the first law to combustion, consider the steady-flow process shown in Fig. 17.9. Liquid octane (C_8H_{18}) is burned with 200 per cent theoretical air. The octane enters at 200 °F; the air at 400 °F. The products of combustion leave at 1600 °F. (a) Determine the relationship between heat transferred, work done, and enthalpy change. (b) Calculate the heat transferred per pound of fuel if no work is done and kinetic energies are neglected.

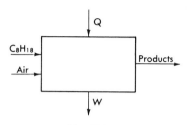

Fig. 17.9

Steady-Flow Combustion Process.

Solution. (a) The relationship between heat transferred, work done, and change of state is obtained by writing the first law in the form of the steady-flow energy equation:

$$H_r + \left(\frac{\mathscr{V}^2}{2g_c}\right)_r + Q = H_p + \left(\frac{\mathscr{V}^2}{2g_c}\right)_p + W$$

or

$$H_p - H_r = Q - W + \left(\frac{\mathscr{V}^2}{2g_c}\right)_r - \left(\frac{\mathscr{V}^2}{2g_c}\right)_p \tag{17.16}$$

where the subscripts p and r refer to products and reactants respectively. Since this is the case of a non-isothermal reaction, the enthalpy change $H_p - H_r$ is obtained from Eq. 17.14, with $T_b = 537$ °R, $T_f = 2060$ °R, $T_a = 537$ °R, and $T_c = 860$ °R. Thus,

$$\int_{537}^{2060} \sum n_p (\bar{c}_p)_p dT + \Delta H° + \int_{660}^{537} n_{C_8H_{18}} (\bar{c}_p)_{C_8H_{18}} dT + \int_{860}^{537} n_{\text{air}} (\bar{c}_p)_{\text{air}} dT$$

$$= Q - W + \left(\frac{\mathscr{V}^2}{2g_c}\right)_r - \left(\frac{\mathscr{V}^2}{2g_c}\right)_p \tag{17.17}$$

Eq. (17.17) enables the heat transfer or the work to be evaluated in terms of the standard heat of reaction $\Delta H°$ and the heat capacities of the reactants and products.

(b) In the absence of shaft work, and neglecting kinetic energies, the heat transferred, Q, is simply equal to the left-hand side of Eq. 17.17. To evaluate this, the combustion equation for C_8H_{18} with 200 per cent theoretical air is first written:

$$C_8H_{18} + 2(12.5)\,O_2 + 2(12.5 \times 3.76)\,N_2 = 8\,CO_2 + 9\,H_2O + 12.5\,O_2 + 94\,N_2$$

The quantity

$$\int_{537}^{2060} \sum n_p (\bar{c}_p)_p dT$$

representing the enthalpy of the products is best evaluated by using enthalpy values from the gas tables:

Products	n	$\bar{h}$ (from gas tables)		$n(\bar{h}_{2060} - \bar{h}_{537})$
		at 2060 °R	at 537 °R	
CO_2	8	21,818	4,030	142,300
H_2O	9	18,054	4,258	124,200
O_2	12.5	15,671	3,725	149,200
N_2	94	15,013	3,730	1,060,500
				1,476,200 Btu/mole C_8H_{18} = 12,920 Btu/lbm C_8H_{18}

The standard heat of reaction $\Delta H°$ is obtained by use of the enthalpies of formation listed in Table 17.1:

$$C_8H_{18}(l) + 25\ O_2(g) + 94\ N_2(g) \rightarrow 8\ CO_2(g) + 9\ H_2O(g) + 12.5 O_2(g) + 94\ N_2(g)$$

$$\Delta H° = (8\bar{h}°_{f,CO_2} + 9\bar{h}°_{f,H_2O} + 12.5\bar{h}°_{f,O_2} + 94\bar{h}°_{f,N_2}) - (\bar{h}°_{f,C_8H_{18}} + 25\bar{h}°_{f,O_2} + 94\bar{h}°_{f,N_2})$$

$$= [8(-169,182) + 9(-103,968)] - [(-107,462)]$$

$$= -2,181,706 \text{ Btu/mole } C_8H_{18} = -19,100 \text{ Btu/lbm } C_8H_{18}$$

Note that the standard heat of reaction depends only upon the reacting substances and is independent of the amount of non-reacting substances such as excess air. As for quantities

$$\int_{660}^{537} n_{C_8H_{18}}(\bar{c}_p)_{C_8H_{18}} dT \quad \text{and} \quad \int_{860}^{537} n_{air}(\bar{c}_p)_{air} dT,$$

they are calculated by assuming $c_p = 0.5$ Btu/lbm-°R for liquid octane and by using enthalpy values for air from the gas tables. Thus, on the basis of one mole of C_8H_{18} and 119 moles of air (200 per cent theoretical air):

$$\int_{660}^{537} n_{C_8H_{18}}(\bar{c}_p)_{C_8H_{18}} dT + \int_{860}^{537} n_{air}(\bar{c}_p)_{air} dT$$

$$(1)(114)(0.5)(537 - 660) + (119)(28.95)(128.34 - 206.46) = -282,000 \text{ Btu/mole } C_8H_{18}$$

$$= -2470 \text{ Btu/lbm } C_8H_{18}$$

The heat transfer is then

$$Q = 12,920 - 19,100 - 2470 = -8650 \text{ Btu/lbm } C_8H_{18}$$

17.10   Adiabatic Flame Temperature

If a reaction goes to completion and no heat is withdrawn, the products will reach a high temperature labeled the *adiabatic flame temperature*. It is often of interest to know this temperature. For example, in the case of a gas turbine, the maximum permissible temperature is limited by metallurgical considerations and it becomes important to know the adiabatic or theoretical flame temperature for a given air/fuel ratio.

Neglecting the effect of dissociation (to be discussed in the next chapter), the theoretical flame temperature may be calculated using Eq. (17.15). The value thus obtained differs from the measured value by about 10 per cent. (The actual flame temperature is always less than the theoretical temperature, because there is always some heat transferred during the combustion process, and because the reaction is less than complete.) As an example of adiabatic flame temperature calculation, consider the case of liquid octane C_8H_{18} at 77 °F being burned adiabatically with 400 per cent theoretical air:

$$C_8H_{18} + 4(12.5)O_2 + 4(12.5 \times 3.76)N_2 = 8\ CO_2 + 9\ H_2O + 37.5\ O_2 + 188N_2$$

According to Eq. (17.15), the enthalpy change of the products of reaction from T_b to T_g, plus the heat of reaction, must be equal to zero. Now, the heat of reaction $\Delta H°$ for liquid octane was calculated in Ex. 17.7 to be $-2,181,706$ Btu/mole C_8H_{18}. As for the enthalpy change of the products, from the base temperature $T_b = 537$ °R to the unknown adiabatic flame temperature T_g, this is evaluated from the gas tables as follows:

Products	n	$\bar{h}$ from (gas tables)		$n(\bar{h}_{T_g} - \bar{h}_{537})$
		T_g	at 537 °R	
CO_2	8	?	4,030	8 (?–4,030)
H_2O	9	?	4,258	9 (?–4,258)
O_2	37.5	?	3,725	37.5(?–3,725)
N_2	188	?	3,730	188 (?–3,730)
				$\Sigma = 2,181,706$

The procedure is to assume a certain T_g. This enables the enthalpy values at T_g to be read off the gas tables and $\Sigma n(\bar{h}_{T_g} - \bar{h}_{537})$ to be obtained. If the sum equals 2,181,706, the assumed value of T_g is the adiabatic flame temperature. The reader will find the answer to be approximately 1730 °F.

Because of dissociation, only about 80 per cent of the C_8H_{18} may react, and the actual flame temperature will most likely be less than 1730 °F. The new adiabatic flame temperature may be found in the following manner:

$$0.8\ C_8H_{18} + 4(12.5)\ O_2 + 4(12.5 \times 3.75)\ N_2 + 0.2\ C_8H_{18}$$

$$= 0.8(8)\ CO_2 + 0.8(9)\ H_2O + 0.2\ C_8H_{18} + 40\ O_2 + 188\ N_2$$

The heat released is 0.8 (2,181,706) = 1,745,365 Btu/mole C_8H_{18}, and this must equal the enthalpy change of the new products from the base temperature of 77 °F to the new adiabatic flame temperature. The latter will be less than the original adiabatic flame temperature.

17.11   Explosion Pressure

A procedure similar to the one just described may be used to calculate a pressure known as *explosion pressure*. Here, combustion takes place essentially at constant volume, for the reacting mixture is assumed to burn fast, much faster than any increase in volume. Consequently, pressure is generated. The heat released by the reaction is equal to the change in internal energy ΔU, rather than ΔH (as in the preceding section), and specific heat capacities c_v's rather than c_p's are used. Thus, Eq. (17.15) applied to a constant-volume process gives

$$\Delta U = (U_g - U_b) + (U_b - U_a) = 0$$

or

$$0 = \int_{T_b}^{T_g} \sum n_p (\tilde{c}_v)_p \, dT + \Delta U^\circ \qquad (17.18)$$

where T_g, the theoretical flame temperature at constant volume, is calculated in the same manner as before. Assuming ideal gas behavior, the explosion pressure is then obtained by considering the volume to remain constant at the volume initially occupied by the reactants.

Example 17.8. A 50 per cent mixture of carbon monoxide in standard air has a calculated adiabatic flame temperature of 3920 °F. What is the theoretical explosion pressure?

Solution. The reacting mixture (on the basis of one mole of CO) consists of

$$1 \text{ mole CO} + 1 \text{ mole air} = \begin{cases} 1 \text{ mole CO} \\ 0.79 \text{ mole } N_2 \\ 0.21 \text{ mole } O_2 \end{cases}$$

Since one mole of CO requires one-half mole of O_2 for complete combustion, there is an insufficiency of oxygen, and oxygen is the limiting reactant. From the equation $(\frac{1}{2})O_2 + CO \rightarrow CO_2$ it is seen that

$$0.21 \; O_2 + 0.42 \; CO \rightarrow 0.42 \; CO_2$$

In other words, only 0.42 moles of CO react, and the products of reaction consist of 0.58 moles of CO, 0.42 moles of CO_2, 0.79 moles of N_2, giving a total of 1.79 moles.

Now, originally, there were 2 moles of reactants, so that the original volume (at standard conditions) is $2(359) = 718$ cu ft. The explosion pressure is that pressure which corresponds to a volume of 718 cu ft occupied by 1.79 moles of products mixture at 3920 °F:

$$p = \frac{(1.79)(1545)(3920 + 460)}{(718)(144)} = 117 \text{ psia}$$

17.12   Work Done by Chemically-Reacting System

The occurrence of a chemical reaction is one means by which a heat reservoir may be created to produce work in a thermodynamic cycle. Heat is transferred from this reservoir, and, as a result, the products undergo a decrease in temperature until, in the limit, the products are reduced to the temperature of the surroundings. The heat transferred from the heat reservoir to a thermodynamic cycle, however, cannot be entirely transformed into work because of the limitation placed by the second law. It is of interest to know the maximum amount of work obtainable from a chemical reaction.

Consider first a non-flow process. The first law ($Q = \Delta U + W$) gives

$$W = -(\Delta U - Q) \qquad (17.19)$$

The maximum work is obtained when the process is reversible, in which case $Q = \int T dS$, so that

$$W_{max} = -(\Delta U - \int T dS) \qquad (17.20)$$

For a non-flow reversible isothermal process, Eq. (17.20) becomes

$$W_{max} = -(\Delta U - T \Delta S) \qquad (17.21)$$

Similarly, for a flow process, the first law ($Q = \Delta H + W$) gives

$$W = -(\Delta H - Q) \qquad (17.22)$$

and, for a reversible isothermal process ($Q = T \Delta S$),

$$W_{max} = -(\Delta H - T \Delta S) \qquad (17.23)$$

Equations (17.21) and (17.22) may be written in terms of the potential or work functions $A \equiv U - TS$ and $G \equiv H - TS$ as follows:

$$W_{max} = -\Delta A; \text{ for non-flow, isothermal process}$$

$$W_{max} = -\Delta G; \text{ for steady-flow, isothermal process}$$

Note that these results are consistent with those obtained in Chap. 10, where it was pointed out that the maximum work obtainable in an isothermal non-flow process and an isothermal steady-flow process is equal to the decrease of the Helmholtz function and the Gibbs function respectively. Table 17.2 gives the standard *Gibbs function* change at $t_0 (= 77\ °F)$, better known as the *free energy of formation*.

TABLE 17.2
FREE ENERGY OF FORMATION

Compound	State	$\bar{g}_f^{\circ}$ $Btu/lb\ mole$	Compound	State	$\bar{g}_f^{\circ}$ $Btu/lb\ mole$
Carbon, C	Graphite	0	Ethylene, C_2H_4	Gas	29,288
	Diamond *	1,232	(Ethene)		
Carbon dioxide, CO_2	Gas	$-169,556$			
			Ethane, C_2H_6	Gas	$-14,139$
Carbon monoxide, CO	Gas	$-59,015$	Propane, C_3H_8	Gas	$-10,099$
Water, H_2O	Gas	$-98,279$	Butane, C_4H_{10}	Gas	$-7,375$
	Liquid	$-101,975$			
Sulfur dioxide, SO_2	Gas	$-129,137$	Benzene, C_6H_6	Gas	55,744
Methane, CH_4	Gas	$-21,838$	Octane, C_8H_{18}	Gas	7,105
Acetylene, C_2H_2	Gas	$-89,941$		Liquid	2,842

* Relative to graphite

Example 17.9. Ethylene (C_2H_4) at 77 °F and 1 atmosphere is burned with 400 per cent theoretical air in an isothermal constant pressure process. Assuming complete combustion, determine: (a) the maximum useful work obtainable from the reaction, (b) the availability of the products of combustion referred to surroundings at 77 °F and 1 atmosphere. (Consider steady flow conditions.)

Solution. The reaction, with 400 per cent theoretical air, is

$$C_2H_4(g)+12\ O_2(g)+12(3.76)\ N_2(g)\to 2\ CO_2(g)+2\ H_2O(g)+9\ O_2(g)+45.1\ N_2(g)$$

(a) The maximum useful work obtainable from the combustion process is equal to the decrease in the Gibbs function or free energy during the reaction. Using values from Table 17.2:

$$W_{max} = -\Delta G^{\circ}$$
$$= (\bar{g}_{f,C_2H_4}^{\circ}+12\bar{g}_{f,O_2}^{\circ}+45.1\bar{g}_{f,N_2}^{\circ})-(2\bar{g}_{f,CO}^{\circ}+2\bar{g}_{f,H_2O}^{\circ}+9\bar{g}_{f,O_2}^{\circ}+45.1\bar{g}_{f,N_2}^{\circ})$$
$$= (29,288+0+0)-[2(-169,556)+2(-98,279)+0+0]$$
$$= 564,958\ Btu/lb\text{-mole}\ C_2H_4 = 20,000\ Btu/lbm\ C_2H_4$$

(b) To determine the availability of the products of combustion *after* the reaction has taken place, the adiabatic flame temperature must first be calculated. From Eq. (17.15),

$$\int_{T_b}^{T_g} \Sigma\ n_p(c_p)_p dT = -\Delta H^{\circ}$$

The left-hand side is the enthalpy change of the products from the base temperature of 77 °F to the unknown adiabatic flame temperature T_g; the right-hand side is the negative of the standard heat of reaction which is calculated from Table 17.1:

$$\Delta H^{\circ} = (2\bar{h}_{f,CO_2}^{\circ}+2\bar{h}_{f,H_2O}^{\circ})-\bar{h}_{f,C_2H_4}^{\circ}$$
$$= [2(-169,182)+2(-103,968)]-22,478$$
$$= 568,778\ Btu/lb\text{-mole}\ C_2H_4 = -20,300\ Btu/lbm\ C_2H_4$$

The enthalpy change of the products of combustion is best obtained with the aid of Table 4 of the gas tables. This table lists, among other things, the enthalpy of the products of combustion of a hydrocarbon with 400 per cent theoretical air. The enthalpy of the products at the base temperature of 537 °R is given as 3746.8 Btu/mole of products. Since there are 58.1 moles of products $(2+2+9+45.1 = 58.1)$, the enthalpy of the products at the unknown adiabatic flame temperature is thus given by

$$(H_{\text{products at } Tg}) - 3746.8 = -\left(-\frac{568{,}778}{58.1}\right)$$

whence

$$H_{\text{products at } Tg} = 13{,}506 \text{ Btu/mole}$$

Corresponding to this value of the enthalpy, Table 4 of the gas tables gives an adiabatic flame temperature of 1829 °R.

The availability of the products of combustion is the maximum work obtainable in bringing (reversibly) the products of combustion from the adiabatic flame temperature of 1829 °R to the surroundings temperature of 77 °F. Considering steady-flow, the availability of the products is, according to Sec. 10.9:

$$\bar{b}_1 - \bar{b}_2 = (\bar{h} - T_0 \bar{s})_{1829°\text{R}} - (\bar{h} - T_0 \bar{s})_{537°\text{R}}$$

$$= (\bar{h}_{1829°\text{R}} - \bar{h}_{537°\text{R}}) - T_0(\bar{s}_{1829°\text{R}} - \bar{s}_{537°\text{R}})$$

Since constant pressure conditions prevail, the entropy change per mole of products $(\bar{s}_{1829°\text{R}} - \bar{s}_{537°\text{R}})$ is, according to Sec. 14.5, simply equal to the difference $\bar{\phi}_{1829°\text{R}} - \bar{\phi}_{537°\text{R}}$ read off the gas tables. Thus,

$$\bar{b}_1 - \bar{b}_2 = (13{,}506 - 3746.8) - 537(55.44 - 46.32)$$

$$= 4{,}930 \text{ Btu/mole of products}$$

$$= \frac{(4{,}930)(58.1)}{28} = 10{,}200 \text{ Btu/lbm of } C_2H_4$$

Two important remarks should be made concerning the above example: First, the maximum useful work obtainable from the reaction, 20,200 Btu, is very nearly equal to the heat of reaction, 20,200 Btu (and therefore to the heating value in the case of a combustion reaction). Second, the availability of the products, *after* an adiabatic combustion, 10,200 Btu, is much less than the heat of reaction. This is indicative of the irreversible nature of combustion processes, and raises the question as to the possibility of chemical reactions approaching reversibility by having them take place in an electrolytic cell. When the applied potential just equals the electromotive force of the cell, no reaction takes place. By increasing or decreasing the applied potential slightly, the reaction can be made to proceed in one or the other direction. This is why so much effort is being directed toward the development of fuel cells, in which carbon, hydrogen, or hydrocarbons react with oxygen to produce electricity directly.

PROBLEMS

17.1. (a) Fifty pounds of carbon are burned in 360 pounds of air. Determine the masses of CO and CO_2 formed. (b) Find the amount of air required to burn 1 lbm of carbon to equal masses of CO and CO_2.

17.2. A certain coal has the following ultimate analysis: 88 per cent carbon, 5.5 per cent hydrogen, 4.5 per cent oxygen, 1 per cent nitrogen, 1 per cent sulfur. Find the equivalent formula for the coal if the latter is to be represented by $C_a H_b S_s O_d N_e$. Also, determine the complete-combustion equation for this coal. Can the oxygen, hydrogen, and sulfur in the coal be neglected for simplicity?

17.3. The dry products of combustion of a hydrocarbon fuel have the following Orsat analysis: 8 per cent CO_2, 1 per cent CO, 8.8 per cent O_2, and 82.2 per cent N_2. Determine the actual air/fuel ratio and the composition of the fuel. The formula for a hydrocarbon is of the form $C_x H_y$.

17.4. Derive the following expression for the pounds of dry products of combustion per pound of carbon:

$$\frac{44 n_{CO_2} + 32 n_{O_2} + 28 n_{CO} + 28 n_{N_2}}{12 (n_{CO_2} + n_{CO})}$$

17.5. Ethyl alcohol has the chemical formula $C_2 H_6 O$. Calculate the stoichiometric air/fuel ratio by weight and the corresponding volumetric analysis of the products of combustion.

17.6. Determine the stoichiometric air/fuel ratio for: (a) gasoline with a gravimetric analysis of 86 per cent carbon and 14 per cent hydrogen, (b) natural gas with a volumetric analysis of 85.3 per cent methane, 12.6 per cent ethane, 1.7 per cent nitrogen, 0.3 per cent oxygen, and 0.1 per cent carbon dioxide.

17.7. Consider a mixture of CO_2, N_2, and H_2O at constant temperature and atmospheric pressure in an Orsat apparatus. The CO_2 and H_2O are absorbed in the first pipette. However, the partial pressure of the saturated water vapor is constant since the temperature is constant during the test. Thus,

$$p_{H_2O} = \left(\frac{n_{H_2O}}{n_{H_2O} + n_{CO_2} + n_{N_2}} \right)(14.7) = \left(\frac{n'_{H_2O}}{n'_{H_2O} + n_{N_2}} \right)(14.7) \tag{1}$$

where n_{H_2O} is the number of moles of water vapor in the original mixture, and n'_{H_2O} is the number of moles of water vapor remaining after absorption of the carbon dioxide. The Orsat reading for the percentage absorption of CO_2 is thus equal to

$$\%CO_2 = \frac{n_{CO_2} + (n_{H_2O} - n'_{H_2O})}{n_{H_2O} + n_{CO_2} + n_{N_2}} \tag{2}$$

Show that Eqs. (1) and (2) combine to give

$$\%CO = \frac{n_{CO_2}}{n_{CO_2} + n_{N_2}}$$

which is the *dry* percentage of CO_2 in the original mixture.

17.8. Consider the process wherein octane is burned with 85 per cent theoretical air. Assuming that the only combustibles in the products are CO and CH_4 which appear in equal volumes, determine the gravimetric analysis of the exhaust-gas.

17.9. In industrial installations, the CO_2 content of the exhaust gas is conveniently used to determine the amount of excess air in a combustion. If y denotes the per cent excess air in the reaction:

$$(CH_2)_n + 1.5n(1+y) O_2 + 5.67n(1+y) N_2 = n CO_2 + n H_2O + 1.5ny O_2 + 5.17n(1+y) N_2$$

show that the mole fraction of CO_2, upon condensation of H_2O in the products, is

$$x_{CO_2} = \frac{n}{n+1.5ny+5.67n(1+y)} = \frac{1}{6.67+7.17y}$$

and therefore knowledge of x_{CO_2} enables y to be determined.

17.10. The ultimate analysis of a bituminous coal as fired is: 79 per cent carbon, 4.3 per cent hydrogen, 1.3 per cent nitrogen, 3.6 per cent oxygen, 1.2 per cent sulfur, 3.8 per cent moisture, and the remainder ash. (a) Convert the analysis to a dry basis, (b) Determine the air/fuel ratio on a dry basis and on an "as fired" basis.

17.11. The volumetric analysis of the dry products of combustion of a certain fuel is 79.5 per cent nitrogen, 13 per cent carbon dioxide, 7 per cent oxygen, and 0.5 per cent carbon monoxide. The fuel is coal, whose partial gravimetric analysis is 75 per cent carbon and 6 per cent ash. The refuse from the ash-pit has a gravimetric analysis of 80 per cent ash and 20 per cent carbon. Determine the weight of carbon burned per pound of fuel.

17.12. Liquid C_8H_{18} is burned at a total pressure of 30 in. Hg abs, and a temperature of 77 °F. Combustion air of 45 per cent relative humidity is supplied. Determine the amount of heat to be removed per pound of fuel to cool the products of combustion to 150 °F if there is 50 per cent excess air supplied.

17.13. A system composed of 1 lbm of carbon and 20 lbm of air undergoes a constant-volume combustion process from 100 °F to 900 °F. What is the amount of heat transferred if the change in internal energy for the oxidation of carbon to carbon dioxide at 68 °F is $-14,087$ Btu/lbm of carbon? The specific heat of carbon is 0.17 Btu/lbm °F.

17.14. Determine the constant-volume heating value and the constant-pressure heating value of CO at a temperature of 1000 °F. Is the heating value of this fuel at a given temperature affected by the amount of excess air?

17.15. (a) Calculate the higher constant-volume heating value of gaseous octane at 77 °F for the reaction

$$C_8H_{18}(g) + 12.5 O_2 + 47 N_2 \to 8 CO_2 + 9 H_2O(l) + 47 N_2$$

if it is known that the higher constant-pressure heating value at 77 °F is $\Delta H° = -2,369,860$ Btu/mole C_8H_{18}. Consider the volume of the liquid to be negligible. This gives a value of Δn for the reaction of -5.5. (b) Calculate the lower constant-volume heating value of gaseous octane at 77 °F. The value of u_{fg} is calculated from the steam tables as

$$u_{fg} = h_{fg} - pv_{fg} = 1050.4 \frac{(0.4593)(144)(694.9)}{778.2} = 991 \text{ Btu/lbm}$$

(c) Calculate the lower constant-volume heating value of gaseous octane at 1000 °R. Is it necessary to consider the nitrogen in the calculations?

17.16. Liquid hydrogen peroxide (H_2O_2) is to be used as a source of oxygen for a torpedo power plant according to the reaction

$$C + 2 H_2O_2 \to 2 H_2O + CO_2$$

What is the heat of reaction at constant pressure, Btu/lbm of carbon, at 68 °F, if the enthalpies of formation at 68 °F are as follows: H_2O_2 (liquid) = $-44,500$ cal/g-mole, H_2O (liquid) = $-68,320$ cal/g-mole, and CO_2 (gas) = $-94,050$ cal/g-mole? Consider the H_2O in the products to be liquid.

17.17. (a) Given the two reactions

$$H_2 + \tfrac{1}{2}O_2 = H_2O + 122,967$$

$$CO + \tfrac{1}{2}O_2 = CO_2 + 121,721$$

show that, for the water-gas reaction,

$$CO + H_2O = CO_2 + H_2 - 1,246$$

The above procedure represents *Hess' law,* which may be stated as follows: Since enthalpy is a state function and thus is independent of path, any series of reactions between the same end states must have the same value of enthalpy change. (b) Calculate the heat of reaction at constant pressure for a fuel consisting of 28 per cent CO and 72 per cent H_2 by volume.

17.18. The heat of reaction depends on the temperature at which reaction takes place. Show that

$$\frac{\partial}{\partial T}(\Delta H) = (c_p)_{\text{products}} - (c_p)_{\text{reactants}}$$

$$\frac{\partial}{\partial T}(\Delta U) = (c_v)_{\text{products}} - (c_v)_{\text{reactants}}$$

or

$$(\Delta H)_T - (\Delta H)_{T_0} = \int_{T_0}^{T} (c_p)_{\text{products}}\, dT - \int_{T_0}^{T} (c_p)_{\text{reactants}}\, dT$$

$$(\Delta U)_T - (\Delta U)_{T_0} = \int_{T_0}^{T} (c_v)_{\text{products}}\, dT - \int_{T_0}^{T} (c_v)_{\text{reactants}}\, dT$$

i.e., the heat of reaction at temperature T equals that at temperature T_0 plus the effect of changes in heat capacity of the products relative to the heat capacity of the reactants. Hint: this can be proved very simply by writing

$$\frac{\partial}{\partial T}(\Delta H) = \Delta\left(\frac{\partial H}{\partial T}\right) = \Delta c_p$$

$$\frac{\partial}{\partial T}(\Delta U) = \Delta\left(\frac{\partial U}{\partial T}\right) = \Delta c_v$$

Figs. 17.3 and 17.4 show this to be so.

17.19. Given $-\Delta H = 1,363,544$ Btu/mole for gaseous benzene (C_6H_6) at 77 °F, and the latent heat of vaporization of benzene at 77 °F to be 14,606 Btu/mole, determine the four heating values of liquid benzene at 77 °F. Hint: The enthalpy of a liquid fuel is correspondingly less than the enthalpy of the gaseous fuel by an amount equal to the latent heat of vaporization of the fuel. The four heating values are: lower constant-pressure heating value, higher constant-pressure heating value, lower constant-volume heating value, and higher constant-volume heating value.

17.20. Consider the reaction

$$C_2H_4(g) + H_2O(g) \rightleftarrows C_2H_5\,OH(g)$$

For which the thermal data are as follows:

	$(\bar{h}^\circ{}_f)_{298°K}$	$\bar{s}^\circ{}_{298°K}$
	cal/g–mole	cal/g mole-°K
$C_2H_4(g)$	12,496	52.45
$H_2O(g)$	−57,798	45.11
$C_2H_5OH(g)$	−56,240	67.4

Determine $\Delta S^\circ{}_{298°K}$ and the change in Gibbs function ΔG° by the third law method.

17.21. It is often of interest to know the temperature at which the driving force ΔG° for a reaction becomes zero. Show that a rough estimate is

$$T = \frac{\Delta H^\circ}{\Delta S^\circ}$$

17.22. Given the following values of entropy:

Substance	$S^\circ{}_{298}$ cal/mole-°K
C (graphite)	1.36
$CO_2(g)$	51.06
$CO(g)$	47.30

Calculate the standard entropy change $\Delta S^\circ{}_{298}$ for the reaction

$$C + CO_2(g) = 2\,CO(g)$$

17.23. Carbon burns to carbon dioxide in a steady-flow process using stoichiometric air. Assuming the initial conditions to be 77 °F and 1 atm and the products of combustion to have constant specific heats, determine the adiabatic flame temperature.

17.24. Determine the adiabatic flame temperature and explosion pressure resulting from the constant-volume combustion of CO with 80 per cent excess air. Assume the temperature and pressure at beginning of combustion to be 537 °R and 15 psia, and neglect dissociation.

17.25. Compare the maximum theoretical temperatures of combustion for methane (CH_4) in a constant pressure process and in a constant volume process respectively. Assume stoichiometric combustion and constant specific heats. Choose initial conditions of 77 °F and 14.7 psia. From the results would it be preferable to use constant volume combustion whenever possible? Discuss the improvement of diesel engines by modifying the combustion process from constant pressure to constant volume.

17.26. (a) Calculate the standard heat of reaction $-\Delta H°$ for the following reactions at 77 °F (25 °C):

$$Cl_2 + H_2 \rightarrow 2 \, HCl$$

$$Ca \, CO_3 \rightarrow CaO + CO_2$$

(b) Calculate the change in the Standard Gibbs function for the water–gas reaction

$$CO + H_2O \rightarrow CO_2 + H_2$$

17.27. A mixture of 1 lbm of C_3H_8 and stoichiometric air at 77 °F and 14.7 psia burns adiabatically according to the process 1–2–3 as shown in Fig. 17.10. If peak pressure is limited to 300 psia, what is the final temperature? Hint:

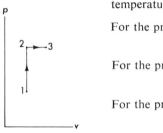

For the process 1–2,

$$Q_{1-2} = U_2 - U_1$$

For the process 2–3,

$$Q_{2-3} = H_3 - H_2$$

For the process 1–2–3,

$$Q = H_3 - H_2 + U_2 - U_1$$

$$= H_3 - p_2 V_1 - U_1$$

Fig. 17.10

since $H_2 = U_2 + p_2 V_2$ and $V_2 = V_1$. For adiabatic combustion, $Q = 0$.

17.28. Determine the maximum work theoretically obtainable from a flow process for the reaction of pure carbon and atmospheric air at 77 °F. The standard free energy change $\Delta G°$ is known to be $-169,557$ Btu/lb mole of carbon for the reaction

$$C(s) + O_2 + 3.76 \, N_2 = CO_2 + 3.76 \, N_2$$

Consider the air to enter the control volume (Fig. 17.11) at unit pressure, and

Fig. 17.11

therefore $p_{N_2} = 0.79$ atm, $p_{O_2} = 0.21$ atm. Note that the standard free energy change is defined as the change in G between the products in their *standard* states and the reactants in their *standard* states. The free energy change for the system illustrated is slightly different from the standard free energy change $\Delta G°$, because the nitrogen and oxygen are not in their standard states, and the following corrections must be added to $\Delta G°$:

$$\text{For } N_2: \quad -n_{N_2} \bar{R} T \ln \frac{0.79}{1} = -(3.76)(1.986)(537) \ln 0.79$$

$$\text{For } O_2: \quad -n_{O_2} \bar{R} T \ln \frac{0.21}{1} = -(1)(1.986)(537) \ln 0.21$$

Note finally that the maximum obtainable work will be slightly less than the negative of the heat of reaction.

17.29. Gaseous propane is burned with theoretical air at 1 atm and 77 °F in a constant-pressure process. The products leave at 77 °F. Determine the change in Gibbs function for the two following cases: (a) The reactants and products are separated into their various constituents, and each constituent is at 1 atm and 77 °F. (b) The reactants and products each consist of a mixture at a total pressure of 1 atm and 77 °F.

17.30. A certain pound of carbon burns at constant pressure so that 0.9 pounds goes into carbon dioxide, 0.05 pounds goes into carbon monoxide, and the remainder emerges as unburned carbon. Determine the efficiency of the combustion process. Here, the efficiency is defined as the ratio of the heat of reaction of the actual combustion process to the heat of reaction of the stoichiometric combustion process.

17.31. A boiler produces 12,000 lbm/hr of saturated steam at 160 psia. In addition, there is a "blow down" of 500 lbm/hr of saturated liquid at 160 psia (this is water which carries with it dissolved solids which would otherwise accumulate and precipitate as scale). Feed water is supplied to the boiler at 210 °F. Fuel oil having a heating value of 19,500 Btu/lbm is burned at the rate of 740 lbm/hr. Determine the efficiency of the boiler. Hint: The rate of heat transferred to the water can be obtained from the steady-flow energy balance

$$m_1 h_1 + Q = m_2 h_2 + m_3 h_3$$

where m_1 = mass rate of feed water, m_2 = mass rate of steam, m_3 = mass rate of "blow down," and h_1, h_2 and h_3 are the corresponding specific enthalpies.

17.32. A gas turbine prime mover develops 6200 hp and has a specific fuel consumption of 0.78 lbm of fuel per hp. Determine the efficiency of the prime mover if the fuel used has a higher heating value of 18,300 Btu/lbm. The efficiency of an "open cycle" prime mover is usually defined as the ratio of the shaft work to the heating value.

CHAPTER 18

Homogeneous Equilibrium

18.1 Second Law Analysis of Chemical Reaction

So far, nothing has been said about the direction and possibility of a given reaction. It was assumed that the reactions under consideration simply took place. In other words, the analysis of chemical reactions has been based solely on the first law of thermodynamics. Yet, quite aside from the question of how much heat is given off or absorbed in a reaction, the question of how far and in what direction a reaction will proceed is of equal interest to the engineer. This latter question will now be discussed.

The possibility of a given reaction can be determined by applying the second law of thermodynamics to the reaction. It was pointed out in

500

Sec. 9.7 that the entropy of an adiabatic system can only increase; consequently, any chemical system which reacts readily under adiabatic conditions is irreversible, and the entropy after the reaction is greater than the entropy before the reaction. Specifically, it was shown that, for any process,

$$dS \geqslant \frac{dQ}{T} \tag{18.1}$$

where dQ is an infinitesimal transfer of heat, T is the temperature of the system, and dS is the entropy change of the system.

For an isothermal constant-volume reaction, $dQ = dU$, and Eq. (18.1) becomes

$$dS \geqslant \frac{dU}{T}$$

or

$$dU - TdS \leqslant 0$$

This may be written (keeping in mind that T = constant) as

$$d(U - TS) \leqslant 0 \tag{18.2}$$

Similarly, for an isothermal constant-pressure reaction, $dQ = dH$, and Eq. (18.1) gives

$$dS \geqslant \frac{dH}{T}$$

or

$$dH - TdS \leqslant 0$$

and with T a constant, this may be written as

$$d(H - TS) \leqslant 0 \tag{18.3}$$

Equations (18.2) and (18.3) give the *criterion* for the possibility of isothermal reactions. This criterion may be stated as follows: *An isothermal constant-volume chemical reaction is possible if the Helmholtz function $A(\equiv U - TS)$ for the products is less than the Helmholtz function for the reactants. An isothermal constant-pressure chemical reaction is possible if the Gibbs function $G(\equiv H - TS)$ for the product is less than the Gibbs function for the reactants.*

The situation has the mechanical analogy shown in Fig. 18.1. Here a ball is shown in three positions: at rest on a horizontal plane, balanced on the crest of a hill, and at rest at the base of a trough between hills.

The change in potential energy for a finite displacement of the sphere is respectively zero, negative, and positive. The position on the horizontal plane corresponds to neutral equilibrium, that on the crest to unstable

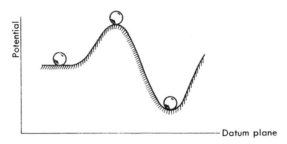

Fig. 18.1   Representation of Equilibrium.

equilibrium, and that in the trough to stable equilibrium. The criterion of equilibrium for a *mechanical system* in terms of potential energy is

Δ(P.E.) = 0: Neutral equilibrium

Δ(P.E.) < 0: Spontaneous change or unstable equilibrium

Δ(P.E.) > 0: Stable equilibrium

The analogous relations for a *chemical system* are, in the case of constant pressure and temperature,

$(\Delta G)_{p,T}$ = 0: Neutral equilibrium

$(\Delta G)_{p,T}$ < 0: Spontaneous change or unstable equilibrium

$(\Delta G)_{p,T}$ > 0: Stable equilibrium

Similar relations, involving the Helmholtz function, hold for a chemical system at constant volume and temperature. Knowledge of the change in Helmholtz function and Gibbs function thus becomes useful in predicting chemical reactions, for if the ΔA or the ΔG of a given reaction is negative, that reaction will tend to take place spontaneously.† $\Delta G°$, the change in Gibbs function at t_0 (= 77 °F), is called the *standard free energy change* by chemists. It is easily calculated from the free energy of formation $\bar{g}_f^°$ given in Table 17.2. For example, the standard free energy change for the reaction

$$CO(g) + \tfrac{1}{2}O_2(g) \rightarrow CO_2(g)$$

---

† If $\Delta G° < 0$, the reaction is promising; if $0 < \Delta G° < 10,000$, the reaction is of doubtful promise; if $\Delta G° > 0$, the reaction is possible only under unusual conditions.

is

$$\Delta G^\circ = \bar{g}^\circ_{f}, _{CO_2} - (\bar{g}^\circ_{f}, _{CO} + \tfrac{1}{2}\bar{g}^\circ_{f}, _{O_2})$$
$$= 169{,}556 - (-59{,}015 + 0) = -110{,}541 \text{ Btu/lb mole CO}$$

The large negative value of ΔG° indicates that a large driving force exists which should make the reaction spontaneous. Remember, however, that thermodynamics does not tell anything about rates (this is a subject for chemical kinetics). It merely provides information that a driving force exists. Carbon monoxide and oxygen, for example, may be mixed at room temperature and pressure and remain as a mixture for years with no reaction taking place at appreciable speed. Such a condition is sometimes referred to as *frozen equilibrium*. If, however, the reaction is started by such means as heat or a suitable catalyst, it is observed to proceed always in the direction predicted by the above calculations.

18.2   Equilibrium

Consider the equilibrium of a mixture of ideal gases capable of undergoing a chemical reaction, and let the reaction be represented by the following balanced chemical equation:

$$aA + bB + \ldots \rightarrow eE + fF + \ldots$$

Now, reactions are seldom complete. They proceed towards an equilibrium state which is attained when opposing changes take place at the same rate. Initially, as reactants A and B begin to mix, the rate of the forward reaction is fast and the rate of the reverse reaction is zero, because no E and F are present. After E and F are formed, the reverse reaction begins to take place, and the forward reaction slows down (since there is less of the reactants left). The rate of the forward reaction continues to decrease and the rate of the reverse reaction continues to increase until the two rates become equal, offsetting each other. No further change in composition takes place, and the system is said to be in a state of chemical equilibrium. We shall investigate, in this chapter, how far such a reaction will go.

The study of chemical equilibrium is best approached by the use of the thermodynamic potential functions A and G, because, as stated in the preceding section, the Helmholtz function of a system undergoing an isothermal constant volume reaction can only decrease, reaching a minimum when the equilibrium state is attained. Similarly, the Gibbs function of a system undergoing an isothermal constant pressure reaction can only decrease, reaching a minimum when equilibrium is attained. In other words, if a change of state can occur at constant T and p, which would decrease the Gibbs function of a system, a net driving force exists, and the change will take place spontaneously. If dG for the given change is found to be equal to zero, the system is in a state of equilibrium (so far as that change is concerned). This is illustrated in Fig. 18.2, where the Gibbs function for the system is plotted against the composition expressed in terms of relative proportions of the various constituents. A similar plot could also be drawn for a constant-volume isothermal reaction. It is seen that, essentially, the Helmholtz and Gibbs functions play a role in thermodynamics similar to that of potential energy in mechanics; recall that, in

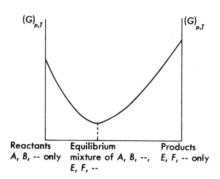

Fig. 18.2 Variation of Gibbs Function in a Chemical Reaction.

mechanics, the condition for equilibrium of a conservative system is that the potential energy shall be at a minimum.

Example 18.1. As a simple application of the preceding developments, consider the equilibrium between two phases of a pure substance: When the liquid and vapor phases are at the same pressure and temperature, they are in equilibrium, and accordingly, the Gibbs function for the liquid and the vapor must be equal. Using the data from the steam tables, verify this for the case of water at atmospheric pressure.

Solution. For the saturated liquid:

$$g_f = h_f - Ts_f = 180.70 - (460 + 212)(0.312)$$
$$= -29.5 \text{ Btu/lbm}$$

For the saturated vapor:

$$g_g = h_g - Ts_g = 1150.4 - (460 + 212)(1.757)$$
$$= -29.5 \text{ Btu/lbm}$$

In other words, $g_f = g_g$. This could have been predicted from the combined first law and second law statement

$$Tds = du + pdv = dh - vdp$$

Since the change of phase takes place at constant pressure and temperature, this relation becomes

$$Tds = dh$$

which is integrates into

$$T(s_g - s_f) = h_g - h_f$$
$$h_f - Ts_f = h_g - Ts_g$$

or

$$g_f = g_g$$

This is precisely the same idea that was used in deriving Clapeyron's equation in Sec. 15.7.

Example 18.2. (a) Show that the change in specific Gibbs function for a solid undergoing an isothermal process is

$$dg = v_0(1 - p\kappa)dp$$

where v_0 is the specific volume at one atmosphere, and κ is the isothermal compressibility.

(b) The specific volume for graphite and for diamond is 0.00712 and 0.00456 cu ft/lbm respectively; the isothermal compressibility for graphite and for diamond is 3×10^{-6} and 0.16×10^{-6} atm^{-1} respectively. What pressure is required to convert graphite into diamond at a temperature of 77 °F?

Solution. (a) From

$$dv = \left(\frac{\partial v}{\partial p}\right)_T dp + \left(\frac{\partial v}{\partial T}\right)_p dT,$$

the volume change at constant temperature is given by

$$v - v_0 = \int_{p=1}^{p} \left(\frac{\partial v}{\partial p}\right)_T dp = -\int_{p=1}^{p} v\kappa dp$$

Taking $v \approx v_0$ and κ to be constant, this becomes

$$v - v_0 = -v_0\kappa(p - 1)$$

or, with $p \gg 1$,

$$v = v_0(1 - p\kappa) \tag{18.4}$$

Now, $g = h - Ts = u + pv - Ts$, and therefore

$$dg = du + pdv + vdp - Tds - sdT$$
$$= vdp - sdT$$

At constant temperature, this becomes

$$dg = vdp \tag{18.5}$$

Replacing v by its value from Eq. (18.4) into Eq. (18.6) gives the desired result,

$$dg = v_0(1 - p\kappa)dp$$

(b) Integration at constant temperature of the above expression between limits of $p = 1$ and $p = p$ gives

$$g = g° = v_0(p - 1) - v_0\kappa\frac{(p^2 - 1)}{2}$$

where $g°$ is the Gibbs function at the reference pressure of 1 atm and 77 °F. With $p \gg 1$, this reduces to

$$g - g° = v_0\left(p - \frac{\kappa p^2}{2}\right) \tag{18.6}$$

Equation (18.6) will now be applied to give the Gibbs function for diamond and for graphite. The basic idea is this: When different phases of a pure substance are in equilibrium, each phase must have the same value of the Gibbs function per unit mass. Thus, diamond and graphite will exist in equilibrium if their values of the Gibbs function are the same. The Gibbs function for diamond at a pressure p is

$$g_{\text{diamond}} = g°_{\text{diamond}} + v_0\left(p - \frac{\kappa p^2}{2}\right)$$

The value of $g°$ is obtained from Table 17.2; the values of v_0 and κ are given in the data. Thus

$$g_{\text{diamond}} = \frac{(1.232)(778)}{(12)(14.7)(144)} + 0.0045\left(p - \frac{0.16 \times 10^{-6} p^2}{2}\right)$$

Similarly, the Gibbs function for graphite is

$$g_{\text{graphite}} = g°_{\text{graphite}} + v_0\left(p - \frac{\kappa p^2}{2}\right)$$

$$= 0 + 0.00712\left(p - \frac{3.0 \times 10^{-6} p^2}{2}\right)$$

Setting $g_{\text{diamond}} = g_{\text{graphite}}$ and solving for p gives

$$p = 15,500 \text{ atm}$$

In other words, at 15,500 atm and 77 °F, graphite and diamond exist in equilibrium, and it is possible to convert one into the other.

18.3   Equilibrium Constant

Having illustrated the concept of equilibrium for a pure substance, we will now proceed to discuss systems of variable composition. From the point of view of the chemist, the most important way of producing a change in composition is through a chemical reaction. The development that follows pertains to a constant-temperature constant-pressure reaction, since chemical equilibria are usually studied under conditions of constant specified temperature and pressure.

It has been shown that the criterion of equilibrium for a chemical reaction at constant pressure and temperature is that the change in free energy or Gibbs function be zero. This criterion will now be used to introduce a quantity called the *equilibrium constant*. Consider the balanced chemical reaction involving reactants $A, B, \ldots$ and products $E, F, \ldots$.

$$aA + bB + \ldots \rightleftharpoons eE + fF + \ldots \tag{18.7}$$

where the stoichiometric coefficient $a, b, \ldots$ and $e, f, \ldots$ are the moles of each constituent in accordance with the reaction. The double arrow indicates that, when equilibrium is reached, all the constituents will be present in some degree. At equilibrium a certain amount of each constituent will be present, and each constituent will exist at its partial pressure.

Let the system be in the neighbourhood of the equilibrium condition, and let differential amounts dn_A, dn_B, ... of the reactants be converted into dn_E, dn_F, ... of the products. The change in Gibbs function for the reaction is then

$$\Delta G = \Delta G_{\text{products}} - \Delta G_{\text{reactants}}$$

$$= (\bar{g}_E dn_E + \bar{g}_F dn_F + \ldots) - (\bar{g}_A dn_A + \bar{g}_B dn_B + \ldots)$$

The criterion of equilibrium, $\Delta G = 0$, gives

$$(\bar{g}_E dn_E + \bar{g}_F dn_F + \ldots) - (\bar{g}_A dn_A + \bar{g}_B dn_B + \ldots) = 0$$

If this is divided by dn_A, the result is

$$\left(\bar{g}_E \frac{dn_E}{dn_A} + \bar{g}_F \frac{dn_F}{dn_A} + \ldots\right) - \left(\bar{g}_A + \bar{g}_B \frac{dn_B}{dn_A} + \ldots\right) = 0 \qquad (18.8)$$

Now, the relative amounts which react are not independent, but are related to one another through the coefficients of the balanced chemical equation as follows:

$$\frac{dn_E}{dn_A} = \frac{e}{a}, \quad \frac{dn_F}{dn_A} = \frac{f}{a}, \quad \ldots \frac{dn_B}{dn_A} = \frac{b}{a} \qquad (18.9)$$

Thus, Eq. (18.8) becomes, upon multiplication by a

$$(e\bar{g}_E + f\bar{g}_F + \ldots) - (a\bar{g}_A + b\bar{g}_B + \ldots) = 0 \qquad (18.10)$$

Equation (18.10) is a result of great importance, for the quantity

$$(e\bar{g}_E + f\bar{g}_F + \ldots) - (a\bar{g}_A + b\bar{g}_B + \ldots)$$

is known as the *reaction potential*. Equation (18.10) states that, when the reaction potential or driving force is zero, equilibrium is reached. It is also seen that the reaction potential is the sum of the chemical potentials† of the products less that of the reactants, each potential being multiplied by the coefficient of the corresponding substance in the balanced chemical reaction.

Equation (18.10) will now be applied to *homogeneous gas reactions*, i.e., reactions taking place entirely between gaseous products and reactants. Many important applications of equilibrium theory are in this field. From the definition, $g = u + pv - Ts$, it is seen that

$$dg = du + pdv + vdp - Tds - sdT = vdp - sdT \qquad (18.11)$$

---

† The subject of chemical potentials will be more fully discussed in Sec. 18.9.

Assume that each constituent is an ideal gas and that, for each constituent, the Gibbs function or free energy at all temperatures and a pressure of one atmosphere is known, and let this value of the Gibbs function be denoted by $g°$. In other words, $g°$ is a function of temperature, but it is at the standard pressure of one atmosphere. At any given constant temperature T. the variation of the Gibbs function with pressure is given by

$$dg = v\,dp = RT\,d\ln p \tag{18.12}$$

Integrating this at constant temperature from $g°$ (the Gibbs function in the standard state of $p = 1$ atm) to g, the Gibbs function at T and p yields

$$g - g° = RT[\ln p]_1^p = RT\ln p$$

or

$$g = g° + RT\ln p \tag{18.13}$$

Using this expression for the Gibbs function, Eq. (18.10) thus becomes

$$e(\bar{g}_E° + \bar{R}T\ln p_E) + f(\bar{g}_F° + \bar{R}T\ln p_F) + \dots$$
$$- a(\bar{g}_A° + \bar{R}T\ln p_A) - b(\bar{g}_B° + \bar{R}T\ln p_B) - \dots = 0$$

or, upon collecting terms

$$(e\bar{g}_E° + f\bar{g}_F° + \dots - a\bar{g}_A° - b\bar{g}_B°)$$
$$+ \bar{R}T(e\ln p_E + f\ln p_F + \dots - a\ln p_A - b\ln p_B - \dots) = 0 \tag{18.14}$$

The first group of terms represents the change in Gibbs function or free energy which would occur if all reactants and products were in their standard states (pressure of one atmosphere). It is known as the *standard free energy change* of the reaction, and is denoted by the symbol $\Delta G°$. The second group of terms may be simplified by noting that $e\ln p_E = \ln p_E^e$, $f\ln p_F = \ln p_F^f$, $a\ln p_A = \ln p_A^a$, $\dots$. Thus, Eq. (18.14) becomes

$$\Delta G° + \bar{R}T\ln \frac{p_E^e\,p_F^f\cdots}{p_A^a\,p_B^b\cdots} = 0$$

or

$$\frac{p_E^e\,p_F^f\cdots}{p_A^a\,p_B^b\cdots} = \exp\left(-\frac{\Delta G°}{RT}\right) \tag{18.15}$$

The quantity

$$\frac{p_E^e p_F^f\cdots}{p_A^a\,p_B^b\cdots} = K_p \tag{18.16}$$

is called the *equilibrium constant*.† Stated verbally, Eq. (18.15) says that a unique value is attached to the partial pressures of a mixture of perfect gases capable of interacting chemically, but which are in chemical equilibrium at temperature T and a total pressure p ($= p_A + p_B + \ldots + p_E + p_F + \ldots$). This unique value depends on the temperature only, since the right-hand side of Eq. (18.15) depends on the temperature only. Figure (18.3)

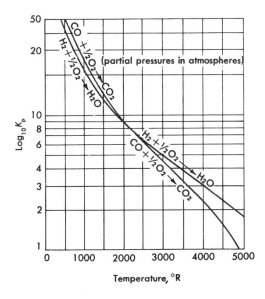

Fig. 18.3 Equilibrium Constants.

shows a plot of the equilibrium constant for a number of common reactions. There are several important observations regarding K_p: First, as noted above, it is independent of pressure and is a function of temperature only. This is because $\Delta G°$ is independent of pressure and is a function of temperature only. Second, the magnitude of K_p depends on the unit selected for pressures. Most values given for K_p are based on pressures in atmospheres. Finally, the equilibrium constant as defined by Eq. (18.16) has the partial pressures of the products in the numerator and the partial pressures of

---

† The subscript p in the equilibrium constant K is to indicate that this particular equilibrium constant is expressed in terms of pressures. The equilibrium constant for the most general case, valid for solids, liquids, or gases, is in terms of activities (see Sec. 18.9). For a reaction involving ideal gases, $K_a = K_p$.

the reactants in the denominator. This is the usual procedure for listing equilibrium constants, but it is not always adhered to. Consequently, when reading values of equilibrium constants from tables or charts, attention should be given to the way the reaction and the equilibrium constants are written.

Example 18.3. The equilibrium constant K_p at a temperature of 5040 °R for the reaction

$$CO + \tfrac{1}{2}O_2 \rightarrow CO_2$$

is 6.44. Determine the composition and partial pressures of the equilibrium mixture at this temperature if the total pressure is (a) 1 atm, (b) 10 atm.

Solution. (a) Let x be the fraction of 1 mole of CO_2 that dissociates. In other words, we consider the reaction to have formed 1 mole of CO_2, then, of this mole of CO_2, x amount will dissociate back into x moles of CO and $x/2$ moles of O_2. The result of this sequence of events can be expressed by saying that the actual reaction is

$$CO + \frac{1}{2}O_2 \rightarrow (1-x)CO_2 + x\,CO + \frac{x}{2}O_2$$

The total number of moles at equilibrium is thus $1 - x + x + (x/2) = 1 + (x/2)$, and the partial pressures of the constituents are

$$p_{CO_2} = \frac{1-x}{1+x/2}$$

$$p_{CO} = \frac{x}{1+x/2}$$

$$p_{O_2} = \frac{x/2}{1+x/2} = \frac{x}{2+x}$$

From the definition for the equilibrium constant

$$Kp = \frac{(1-x)/(1+x/2)}{[x/(1+x/2)][(x/2)/(1+x/2)]^{1/2}} = \frac{(1-x)(2+x)^{1/2}}{x^{3/2}} = 6.44$$

or

$$(1-x)(2+x)^{1/2} = 6.44x^{3/2}$$

Squaring both sides and solving for x gives

$$x = 0.3$$

The composition of the equilibrium mixture, in mole fractions, is thus

$$x_{CO_2} = \frac{1-0.3}{1+0.15} = 0.609$$

$$x_{CO} = \frac{0.3}{1+0.15} = 0.261$$

$$x_{O_2} = \frac{0.3/2}{1+0.15} = 0.130$$

and the partial pressures for CO_2, CO, and O_2 are 0.609 atm, 0.261 atm, and 0.130 atm respectively.

(b) When the total pressure is increased to 10 atm, the partial pressures become

$$p_{CO_2} = \frac{10-10x}{1+x/2}$$

$$p_{CO} = \frac{10x}{1+x/2}$$

$$p_{O_2} = \frac{10x/2}{1+x/2}$$

and similar calculations as above give $x = 0.16$, i.e., the reaction is more complete (since a smaller fraction of CO_2 dissociates back to CO and O_2). Thus, increasing the total pressure causes the reaction

$$CO + \tfrac{1}{2}O_2 \rightarrow CO_2$$

to proceed further to the right, because, in the case of the present reaction, the volume of the products is less than the volume of the reactants, and an increase in pressure tends to drive the reaction in the direction of smaller volume.

18.4 Relation between K_p and K_x

The equilibrium constant developed in the preceding section is expressed in terms of partial pressures. It is possible to express a similar constant in terms of mole fractions. Consider the chemical reaction

$$aA + bB + \ldots \rightleftarrows eE + fF + \ldots$$

The equilibrium mixture at a particular temperature and pressure will most likely include all of the components. If the mixture consists of ideal gases, the partial pressure of each component is equal to the total pressure multiplied by the mole fraction of that component. Thus

$$\left. \begin{array}{l} p_A = x_A p, \quad p_B = x_B p, \ldots \\ p_E = x_E p, \quad p_F = x_F p, \ldots \end{array} \right\} \tag{18.17}$$

where

$$x_A = \frac{n_A}{n_A + n_B + \ldots + n_E + n_F + \ldots}, \quad x_B = \frac{n_B}{n_A + n_B + \ldots + n_E + n_F + \ldots},$$

$$x_E = \frac{n_E}{n_A + n_B + \ldots + n_E + n_F + \ldots}, \quad x_F = \frac{n_F}{n_A + n_B + \ldots + n_E + n_F + \ldots}, \ldots$$

are the mole fractions of each constituent. Substitution of Eq. (18.17) into Eq. (18.16) gives

$$K_p = \frac{x_E^e \, x_F^f \cdots}{x_A^a \, x_B^b \cdots} \, p^{(e+f+\ldots)-(a+b+\ldots)}$$

or

$$K_p = K_x p^{\Delta n} \tag{18.18}$$

where

$$K_x = \frac{x_E^e \, x_F^f \cdots}{x_A^a \, x_B^b \cdots} \tag{18.19}$$

is an equilibrium constant expressed in terms of mole fractions, and

$$\Delta n = (e+f+\ldots)-(a+b+\ldots) \tag{18.20}$$

is the number of moles of products less that of reactants in the stoichiometric equation for the reaction. Equation (18.18) is known as the *law of mass action.*† It predicts what effect the temperature and pressure have on the equilibrium composition. The influence of temperature on the equilibrium composition lies in the value of K_p, since K_p for ideal gases is a function of temperature only. The influence of pressure on the equilibrium composition lies in the term $p^{\Delta n}$. If $\Delta n = 0$, there is no change in the total number of moles, consequently no change in volume during the reaction, and the pressure has no effect on the equilibrium composition. If $\Delta n \neq 0$, there is a change in the number of moles, consequently a change in volume, and it is seen from Eq. (18.18) that the effect of increasing the pressure is to drive the reaction in the direction which has the smaller volume.

Example 18.4. One mole of CO is burned with 100 per cent excess air in a steady-flow process at a pressure of 1 atm. The carbon monoxide and the air are both supplied at 77 °F, and the products leave at 4580 °F. Determine the degree of reaction and the amount of heat transferred.

Solution. The reaction (with 100 per cent excess air) may be written as

$$CO+O_2+3.76\,N_2 \rightleftarrows CO_2+\tfrac{1}{2}O_2+3.76\,N_2$$

Consider the reaction to first give a mole of CO_2 and that subsequently some of this CO_2 dissociates back into CO and O_2. Let x be the fraction of 1 mole of CO_2 dissociated. The mixture at equilibrium is then

$$(1-x)\,CO_2+x\,CO+\frac{x}{2}\,O_2+\frac{1}{2}\,O_2+3.76\,N_2$$

---

† Enunciated by Gulberg and Waage, Norwegian chemists, in 1863.

and the total number of moles is

$$1-x+x+\frac{x}{2}+\frac{1}{2}+3.76 = 5.26+\frac{x}{2}$$

The partial pressures are

$$p_{CO_2} = \frac{1-x}{5.26+0.5x}; \quad p_{CO} = \frac{x}{5.26+0.5x}$$

$$p_{O_2} = \frac{0.5x+0.5}{5.26+0.5x}; \quad p_{N_2} = \frac{3.76}{5.26+0.5x}$$

In Ex. 18.3, the equilibrium constant for the reaction

$$CO+\tfrac{1}{2}O_2 \rightarrow CO_2$$

was given as $K_p = 6.44$ at 4580 °F. Making use of this,

$$K_p = \frac{[(1-x)/(5.26+0.5x)]}{[x/(5.26+0.5x)][(0.5x+0.5)/(5.26+0.5x)]^{1/2}} = 6.44 \qquad (18.21)$$

Notice that the presence of nitrogen affects the reaction only to the extent to which the reaction proceeds, but does not change the equilibrium constant. In other words, the equilibrium constant depends only upon the particular reaction for which it is listed, and not on the various amounts of constituents actually present. Equation (18.21) gives, upon squaring both sides,

$$K_p^2 = \frac{(1-x)^2(5.26+0.5x)}{x^2(0.5x+0.5)} = \overline{6.44}^2 = 41.5$$

or

$$x = 0.31$$

This is the degree of dissociation. The degree of reaction is $(1-x) = 0.69$.
To find the amount of heat transferred, consider the reaction to be as follows:

$$CO+O_2+3.76\ N_2 \rightarrow 0.69\ CO_2+0.31\ CO+\left(\frac{0.31}{2}+0.5\right)O_2+3.76\ N_2$$

In Fig. 18.4, the reactants enter at 77 °F (537 °R) and the products leave at 4580 °F (5040 °R). The heat transferred is thus given by

$$Q = (H_{\text{products at } 5040°R} - H_{\text{products at } 537°R}) + \Delta H°$$

$$= \int_{537}^{5040} \Sigma\, n_p(\bar{c}_p)_{\text{products}} dT + \Delta H°$$

The enthalpy change of the products is calculated from the values for enthalpies listed in the gas tables:

$$\int_{537}^{5040} \Sigma\, n_p(\bar{c}_p)_{\text{products}}\, dT = 0.69(\bar{h}_{CO_2}^{5040} - \bar{h}_{CO_2}^{537})$$

$$+0.31(\bar{h}_{CO}^{5040} - \bar{h}_{CO}^{537})$$

$$+\left(\frac{0.31}{2}+0.5\right)(\bar{h}_{O_2}^{5040} - \bar{h}_{O_2}^{537})$$

$$+3.76(\bar{h}_{N_2}^{5040} - \bar{h}_{N_2}^{537})$$

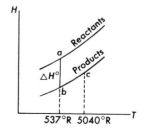

Fig. 18.4
Enthalpy-Temperature Diagram
for Chemical Reactions.

$$= 0.69(64,596-4039)+0.31(40,757-3730)+0.66(42,463-3725)$$
$$+3.76(40,432-3730)$$
$$= 213,000$$

As for the enthalpy of reaction, $\Delta H°$, this is calculated from the enthalpies of formation (Table 17.1):

$$\Delta H° = 0.69(\bar{h_f°})_{CO_2}+0.31(\bar{h_f°})_{CO}+0.66(\bar{h_f°})_{O_2}+3.76(\bar{h_f°})_{N_2}-(\bar{h_f°})_{CO}-3.76(\bar{h_f°})_{N_2}$$
$$= 0.69(-169,182)+0.31(-47,517)+0+0-(-47,517)-0$$
$$= -83,700$$

The heat transferred is therefore

$$Q = 213,000-83,700 = 129,300 \text{ Btu}$$

18.5 Temperature Dependence of Equilibrium Constant; Gibbs–Helmholtz Equation

It was earlier pointed out that the equilibrium constant K_p is a function of temperature. To find its variation with respect to temperature, the variation of $\Delta G°$ with respect to temperature will first be derived, since, according to Eq. (18.15), $K_p = \exp(-\Delta G°/RT)$.

From the definition of the Gibbs function, $G = H-TS = U+pV-TS$, it follows that $dG = dU+pdV+Vdp-Tds-SdT = Vdp-SdT$; therefore

$$\left(\frac{\partial G}{\partial T}\right)_p = -S \tag{18.22}$$

Consider now a chemical reaction at constant temperature and pressure represented as follows:

$$\text{Reactants} \longrightarrow \text{Products}$$
$$\text{at } p, T \qquad\qquad \text{at } p, T$$

Associated with this process is a change in the Gibbs function

$$\Delta G = G_{products} - G_{reactants} \tag{18.23}$$

Equation (18.23) may be expressed in the manner of

$$\Delta G = (H-TS)_{products}-(H-TS)_{reactants}$$
$$= (H_{products}-H_{reactants}) - T(S_{products}-S_{reactants})$$
$$= \Delta H-T\Delta S \tag{18.24}$$

On the other hand, if the partial derivative of Eq. (18.23) with respect to T is taken:

$$\left(\frac{\partial \Delta G}{\partial T}\right)_p = \left(\frac{\partial G_{\text{products}}}{\partial T}\right)_p - \left(\frac{\partial G_{\text{reactants}}}{\partial T}\right)_p$$

This may be expressed with the aid of Eq. (18.22) as

$$\left(\frac{\partial \Delta G}{\partial T}\right)_p = -S_{\text{products}} + S_{\text{reactants}} = -\Delta S \qquad (18.25)$$

Eliminating ΔS from Eqs. (18.24) and (18.25) results in

$$\Delta G = \Delta H + T\left(\frac{\partial \Delta G}{\partial T}\right)_p$$

or

$$\left(\frac{\partial \Delta G}{\partial T}\right)_p = \frac{\Delta G - \Delta H}{T} \qquad (18.26)$$

Equation (18.26) is the famous *Gibbs–Helmholtz equation*. It gives the dependence of ΔG on the temperature. In other words, if the ΔG of a chemical reaction were to be measured at a series of different, but constant, temperatures (always under the same pressure), the observed values of ΔG would depend upon the temperature in the manner of Eq. (18.26). In particular, if Eq. (18.26) is applied to an isothermal reaction at standard-state pressure (one atmosphere), then

$$\left(\frac{\partial \Delta G^\circ}{\partial T}\right)_p = \frac{\Delta G^\circ - \Delta H^\circ}{T} \qquad (18.27)$$

where ΔG° and ΔH° are the standard free energy change and enthalpy change respectively.

Equation (18.27) will now be used to find the variation of the equilibrium constant K_p with respect to temperature. Since

$$\frac{d}{dT}\left(\frac{\Delta G^\circ}{T}\right) = \frac{1}{T}\frac{d(\Delta G^\circ)}{dT} - \frac{\Delta G^\circ}{T^2}$$

it follows that

$$\left[\frac{\partial}{\partial T}\left(\frac{\Delta G^\circ}{T}\right)\right]_p = \frac{1}{T}\left(\frac{\partial \Delta G^\circ}{\partial T}\right)_p - \frac{\Delta G^\circ}{T^2} \qquad (18.28)$$

Now $(\partial \Delta G^\circ / \partial T)_p$ may be eliminated from Eqs. (18.27) and (18.28) to give

$$\left[\frac{\partial}{\partial T}\left(\frac{\Delta G^\circ}{T}\right)\right]_p = -\frac{\Delta H^\circ}{T^2} \qquad (18.29)$$

But $\Delta G^\circ/T = -\bar{R}\ln K$ from Eq. (18.15),* so that Eq. (18.29) becomes

$$\left(\frac{\partial \ln K}{\partial T}\right)_p = \frac{\Delta H^\circ}{\bar{R}T^2} \tag{18.30}$$

For the case of reactions involving ideal gases, Eq. (18.30) simplifies to

$$\frac{d \ln K_p}{dT} = \frac{\Delta H^\circ}{\bar{R}T^2} \tag{18.31}$$

Equation (18.31) is known as the *van't Hoff equation* or *van't Hoff isobar*. Since $d(1/T) = -dT/T^2$, it can be written as

$$\frac{d \ln K_p}{d(1/T)} = -\frac{\Delta H^\circ}{\bar{R}} \tag{18.32}$$

Equation (18.32) allows $\ln K_p$ to be plotted against $1/T$. The slope of the curve at any point is equal to $-\Delta H^\circ/\bar{R}$. The result is almost a straight line, shown in Fig. 18.5, because ΔH° is approximately constant for a reaction over a wide temperature range.

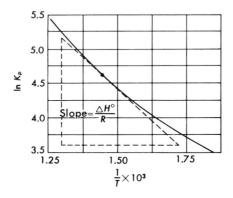

Fig. 18.5 Variation of K_p with Temperature.

Note also that it is possible to measure the equilibrium constant at one temperature, and, with a value of ΔH° obtained from thermochemical data, to calculate the constant at another temperature. Thus, if $K_p(T_1)$ is known, $K_p(T_2)$ may be obtained from the integration of Eq. (18.31):

---

* It was pointed out in Sec. 18.3 that for the general case, $\Delta G^\circ/T = -\bar{R}\ln K$, where K, is an equilibrium constant in terms of activities.

$$\ln \frac{K_p(T_2)}{K_p(T_1)} = \int_{T_1}^{T_2} \frac{\Delta H^\circ}{\bar{R}T^2} dT \tag{18.33}$$

which, over a short temperature range (ΔH° = constant), may be written as

$$\ln \frac{K_p(T_2)}{K_p(T_1)} = -\frac{\Delta H^\circ}{\bar{R}}\left(\frac{1}{T_2} - \frac{1}{T_1}\right) \tag{18.34}$$

18.6 Determination of Equilibrium Constants from Free Energy Data; Third Law of Thermodynamics

The equilibrium constant for a particular reaction can be obtained by measuring experimentally the reaction conversion at one or more temperatures, but this is not very often feasible. A better way is to calculate it from a knowledge of free energy data, because the equilibrium constant K_p and the standard free energy change ΔG° are related by Eq. (18.15). Since

$$\Delta G^\circ = \Delta H^\circ - T\Delta S^\circ \tag{18.35}$$

for an isothermal reaction, the problem resolves to determining ΔH° and ΔS°. Both ΔH° and ΔS° may be determined from calorimetric measurements alone. The measurement of ΔH° is in general not complicated and requires no elaboration. The determination of ΔS°, however, requires the application of the *third law of thermodynamics*. To illustrate, consider the process

$$\text{Reactants} \longrightarrow \text{Products}$$

The entropy change is

$$\Delta S = S_p - S_r = (S_p - S_{p,0^\circ R}) - (S_r - S_{r,0^\circ R}) + (S_{p,0^\circ R} - S_{r,0^\circ R}) \tag{18.36}$$

where the subscripts p and r denote products and reactants respectively, and $0\,^\circ R$ refers to conditions at a temperature of absolute zero. But $(S_p - S_{p,\,0^\circ R}) - (S_r - S_{r,\,0^\circ R})$ is the change in $(S - S_{0^\circ R})$ of the reaction, and $(S_{p,\,0^\circ R} - S_{r,\,0^\circ R})$ is the entropy change ΔS of the reaction at $0\,^\circ R$. Thus, Eq. (18.36) may be written as

$$\Delta S = \Delta(S - S_{0^\circ R}) - (\Delta S)_{0^\circ R} \tag{18.37}$$

Making use of the third law, which says that the entropy change of a reaction is zero at absolute zero, Eq. (18.37) becomes

$$\Delta S = \Delta(S - S_{0^\circ R}) \tag{18.38}$$

Now, $(S - S_{0^\circ R})$ is an experimentally measurable quantity, and, according to Eq. (18.38), values of this quantity can be used to determine the entropy change of a reaction, provided that the entropies $S_{p,\,0^\circ R}$ and $S_{r,\,0^\circ R}$ are so chosen that $(\Delta S)_{0°R} \equiv S_{p,\,0°R} - S_{r,\,0°R} = 0$. The choice that Planck made in 1912, and which has been universally adopted, is to set $S_{p,\,0°R} = S_{r,\,0°R} = 0$. In other words, *the entropy of a pure substance in its most stable state is zero at absolute zero temperature.* This is the *third law of thermodynamics.*

The first experimental evidence of the third law was found by Nernst in his study of data on reactions between solids and liquids at low temperature. Nernst observed that the values of ΔG and ΔH for any reaction involving solids and liquids approach each other asymptotically as the temperature approaches absolute zero. This is shown in Fig. 18.6, and the results may be expressed mathematically as

$$\lim_{T \to 0} (\Delta G - \Delta H) = 0 \qquad (18.39)$$

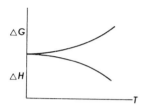

Fig. 18.6
Behavior of ΔG and ΔH
near Absolute Zero.

Now, Eq. (18.26), the Gibbs–Helmholtz equation, is

$$T\left(\frac{\partial \Delta G}{\partial T}\right)_p = \Delta G - \Delta H$$

Furthermore, it was shown in Eq. (18.25) that

$$\left(\frac{\partial \Delta G}{\partial T}\right)_p = -\Delta S$$

Thus,

$$\lim_{T \to 0} (\Delta G - \Delta H) = 0$$

is equivalent to

$$\lim_{T \to 0} \Delta S = 0 \qquad (18.40)$$

Equation (18.40), proposed by Nernst in 1906, is known as the *Nernst heat theorem.* It states that the entropy change associated with an isothermal reaction approaches zero as the temperature approaches zero.

18.7   Dissociation and Flame Temperature

It was previously explained that the theoretical flame temperature is the temperature calculated for conditions in which a fuel is burned so that all of its heat of combustion goes into raising the sensible energy of the combustion gases. This is the highest temperature for which a combustion chamber need be designed. If the effect of dissociation is neglected, the calculated theoretical flame temperature differs from the measured one by about 10 per cent. There are, however, engineering applications where further refinement is desired and the effect of dissociation must be considered. This is especially true when temperatures higher than 2500 °F must be maintained, as in the case of rocket engines. When dissociation is taken into account, the calculated temperature will be somewhat less than for that obtained in a combustion without dissociation, because dissociation reactions are endothermic in nature, and the full heating value of the fuel will not be obtained.

For example, at high temperatures, the products of combustion (steam and carbon dioxide) dissociate into their elements:

$$H_2O(g) \rightleftarrows H_2(g) + \tfrac{1}{2}O_2(g)$$

$$CO_2(g) \rightleftarrows CO(g) + \tfrac{1}{2}O_2(g)$$

The elements, hydrogen and oxygen, may also dissociate:

$$H_2 \rightleftarrows 2H$$

All these reactions absorb energy and they tend to lower the adiabatic flame temperature.

The general method for calculating flame temperatures when taking dissociation into account is as follows: (1) Determine the equilibrium composition of the combustion products at some selected trial temperature. (2) Determine, by means of an energy balance, the temperature to which the energy released would bring these products. (3) Repeat these determinations until the trial temperature and the computed temperature agree. It is seen that, in general, the coefficients in the reaction must be determined before an energy balance can be made. This is essentially a stoichiometric problem involving the use of equilibrium constants. It is discussed for the following cases which are of importance in the field of combustion.

(a) *Theoretical Combustion.* Consider the reaction of one mole of hydrocarbon fuel with the correct amount of air:

$$\text{Hydrocarbon} + aO_2 + (3.76)(a)N_2 \longrightarrow xCO_2 + yH_2O + (3.76)(a)N_2$$

where a, the correct amount of air, is given, and x and y are unknowns which have to be determined by a mass balance. Here, the stoichiometric calculations are relatively simple and no further elaboration is needed (see Ex. 17.1). Having balanced the equation, the degree of dissociation of CO_2 and H_2O may be obtained from a knowledge of their respective equilibrium constants (see Ex. 18.3).

(b) *Rich-Mixture Combustion.* This is the case of a deficiency of air. The combustion equation for one mole of hydrocarbon with a certain amount of air may be written as

$$\text{Hydrocarbon} + a\text{O}_2 + (3.76)(a)\text{N}_2 \rightarrow x\text{CO}_2 + y\text{H}_2\text{O} +$$
$$+ z\text{CO} + w\text{H}_2 + (3.76)(a)\text{N}_2$$

where a is given, and x, y, ... are unknown coefficients. Here, a balance of elements taking part in the reaction, namely, carbon, hydrogen, oxygen, and nitrogen, is not sufficient to determine the coefficients. An additional equation is required; it is provided by, say, the water–gas reaction:

$$\text{CO} + \text{H}_2\text{O} \rightleftharpoons \text{CO}_2 + \text{H}_2$$

The K_p for this reaction (assumed to be available) is used to establish the required additional equation.

(c) *Lean-Mixture Combustion.* In the case of excess air, the equilibrium composition of the products would be CO_2, CO, H_2, H_2O, H_2, and O_2. The combustion equation may be written as

$$\text{Hydrocarbon} + a\text{O}_2 + (3.76)(a)\text{N}_2 \rightarrow x\text{CO}_2 + y\text{H}_2\text{O} +$$
$$+ z\text{CO} + w\text{H}_2 + v\text{O}_2 + (3.76)(a)\text{N}_2$$

Here, in addition to a balance of elements (still four in number), two additional equations are required. Since the constituents for the full CO reaction, the full H_2 reaction, and the water–gas reaction are present in the products, any two of the following equations may be used:

$$\text{CO} + \tfrac{1}{2}\text{O}_2 \rightleftharpoons \text{CO}_2$$
$$\text{H}_2 + \tfrac{1}{2}\text{O}_2 \rightleftharpoons \text{H}_2\text{O}$$
$$\text{CO} + \text{H}_2\text{O} \rightleftharpoons \text{CO}_2 + \text{H}_2$$

The above illustrations involve fairly simple chemical reactions. At high temperatures such as those encountered in rocket engines or jet propulsion devices, the combustion would more likely be according to the equation

$$\text{Hydrocarbon} + m\text{O}_2 + 3.76m\text{N}_2 \rightarrow a\text{CO}_2 + b\text{H}_2\text{O} + c\text{CO}$$
$$+ d\text{H}_2 + e\text{O}_2 + f\text{H} + g\text{O} + h\text{CH}_4 +$$
$$+ i\text{N} + j\text{NO} + 3.76m\text{N}_2$$

and the calculation of the equilibrium composition would involve 10 simultaneous equations. Problems of this type are treated in specialized books on combustion.†

---

† See for example, Hottel, Williams and Satterfield, *Thermodynamic Charts for Combustion Processes* (New York, John Wiley & Sons, Inc., 1949).

Example 18.5. Iso-octane, C_8H_{18}, is burned with 79 per cent theoretical air. Determine the equilibrium composition and the products of combustion at 4 atm and 3000 °R.

Solution. This is the case of a rich mixture. For ideal combustion, the reaction would be

$$C_8H_{18}+12.5\ O_2+(12.5)(3.76)\ N_2 \rightarrow 8\ CO_2+9\ H_2O+(12.5)(37.6)\ N_2$$

For an air supply of 79 per cent of ideal, the reaction becomes

$$C_8H_{18}+9.9\ O_2+(9.9)(3.76)\ N_2 \rightarrow x\ CO_2+y\ H_2O+z\ CO+w\ H_2+37.6\ N_2$$

Whatever distribution may be attained at equilibrium, it must be in conformity with the law of conservation of mass. Thus,

$$\text{balance in carbon:} \quad 8 = x+z \tag{18.41}$$

$$\text{balance in hydrogen:} \quad 18 = 2y+2w \tag{18.42}$$

$$\text{balance in oxygen:} \quad 9.9 = x+y/2+z/2 \tag{18.43}$$

There are four unknowns: x, y, z and w. An additional equation is therefore required. The water–gas reaction:

$$CO+H_2O \rightleftarrows CO_2+H_2$$

of known $K_p = 0.30$ at 3000 °R provides the additional relation. The partial pressures at equilibrium being proportional to the mole fraction of each constituent, the equilibrium constant may be written, with the aid of Eq. (18.18), as

$$K_p = 0.30 = \frac{x^1 w^1}{z^1 y^1}\left(\frac{4}{x+y+z+w+37.6}\right)^{1+1-1-1} \tag{18.44}$$

Equations (18.41) through (18.44) are solved by means of successive approximations, beginning with an initial estimate for y. This is because hydrogen exhibits a particular avidity for oxygen, and the coefficient y would be expected to be fairly close to the value of $0.79(18/2) = 7.19$. The trial and error solution is tabulated below:

y (Assumed)	w From Eq. (18.42)	z From Eq. (18.43)	x From Eq. (18.41)	$\dfrac{xw}{zy} = K_p$
7.2	1.8	3.2	4.8	0.375
7.4	1.6	3.4	4.6	0.292
7.37	1.63	3.37	4.63	0.302

The third attempt gives $K_p = 0.302$, which is close enough to the known value of 0.30 at 3000 °R. The reaction is thus

$$C_8H_{18}+9.9\ O_2+37.2\ N_2 \rightarrow 4.63\ CO_2+7.37\ H_2O+3.37\ CO+1.63\ H_2+37.6\ N_2$$

Example 18.6. Solve the preceding example using an air supply 20 per cent in excess of the theoretical requirement.

Solution. This is the case of a lean-mixture combustion. The reaction is

$$C_8H_{18}+15\ O_2+15(3.76)\ N_2 \rightarrow x\ CO_2+y\ H_2O+z\ CO+w\ H_2+v\ O_2+15(3.76)\ N_2$$

The requirements of conservation of mass give:

$$\text{balance in carbon:} \quad 8 = x+z \tag{18.45}$$

$$\text{balance in hydrogen:} \quad 18 = 2y+2w \tag{18.46}$$

$$\text{balance in oxygen:} \quad 30 = 2x+y+z+2v \tag{18.47}$$

There are three equations and five unknowns. Consequently, two more equations are needed. Selecting the reactions $CO_2 \rightleftarrows CO +(1/2)O_2$ and $H_2+(1/2)O_2 \rightleftarrows H_2O$ with known values of K_p at 3000 °R of 2.37 and 7.76 respectively, the additional equations are

$$\frac{(x)^{1.0}}{(z)^{1.0}(v)^{0.5}}\left[\frac{4}{x+y+z+w+v+(15)(3.76)}\right]^{-0.5} = 2.37 \tag{18.48}$$

$$\frac{(y)^{1.0}}{(w)^{1.0}(v)^{0.5}}\left[\frac{4}{x+y+z+w+v+(15)(3.76)}\right]^{-0.5} = 7.76 \tag{18.49}$$

Equations (18.45) through (18.49) are solved by successive approximation.

Example 18.7. Iso-octane, C_8H_{18}, is burned at 1 atm pressure with 80 per cent of theoretical air. Determine the adiabatic flame temperature, taking dissociation effects into account. Assume the air and fuel to be supplied at the reference temperature of 77 °F. The lower heating value of C_8H_{18} is 2,200,000 Btu/lb mole, and those for CO and H_2 are, respectively, 121,000 and 108,000 Btu/lb mole.

Solution. As mentioned earlier, the procedure consists in starting with an assumed temperature and finding the equilibrium composition that corresponds to it. Let 3000 °R be the assumed temperature (to take advantage of the calculation already done in Ex. 18.5). Then the material balance may be written as

$$C_8H_{18}+9.9\ O_2+37.2\ N_2 \rightarrow 4.63\ CO_2+7.37\ H_2O+3.37\ CO+1.63\ H_2+37.2\ N_2$$

The enthalpy change upon combustion of one mole of C_8H_{18} (with due accounting of the energy that fails to be released because of the presence of H_2 and CO in the combustion products) is:

$$2,200,000-1.63 \times 108,000-3.37 \times 121,000 = 1,617,200\ \text{Btu}$$

The enthalpy change (relative to 77 °F) of the products is best calculated using Tables 11 through 21 of the gas tables:

$$4.63(34,806-4030)-7.37(28,386-4258)$$
$$+3.37(22,973-3730)+1.63(21,577-3640)+37.2(22,762-3730)+$$
$$= 1,135,800\ \text{Btu}$$

This, being much lower than the 1,617,200 Btu released during combustion, indicates that the assumed temperature of 3000 °R is too low. Another trial temperature (3500 °R) is therefore assumed, and a new material balance obtained:

$$C_8H_{18}+9.9\ O_2+37.2\ N_2 \rightarrow 0.28\ CO_2+7.72\ H_2O+3.72\ CO+1.28\ H_2+37.2\ N_2$$

The heat of combustion corresponding to this reaction is

$$2,200,000 - 1.28 \times 108,000 - 3.72 \times 121,000 = 1,611,640 \text{ Btu}$$

The enthalpy changes of the products are

$$4.28(48,646 - 4030) + 7.72(39,989 - 4258) + 3.72(31,256 - 3730) +$$
$$+ 1.28(29,370 - 3640) + 37.2(30,983 - 3730) = 1,626,700 \text{ Btu}$$

This is more in agreement with the 1,611,640 Btu released during combustion, and the adiabatic flame temperature would therefore be taken to be slightly below 3500 °R.

18.8 Equilibrium Constant for Non-Ideal Gases; Fugacity

So far, the expressions developed for the equilibrium constant pertain to ideal gases only. To extend the use to non-ideal gases, a new function, *fugacity*, is introduced, so that when substituted for the pressure in the equations for the equilibrium constant, these become applicable to real gases as well.

Recall [see Eq. (18.12)] that the change in Gibbs function for an isothermal process is

$$dg = v dp$$

For an ideal gas($pv = RT$) this becomes

$$dg_{\text{ideal}} = v_{\text{ideal}} \, dp = RTd(\ln p) \qquad (18.50)$$

Now, for real gases, this relation does not hold, but it is nevertheless possible to retain the simplicity of Eq. (18.50) by defining a new thermodynamic function which, when substituted for the pressure will make Eq. (18.50) valid for real gases. Consequently, the fugacity, f, is defined by the equation

$$dg_{\text{real}} = RTd(\ln f) = v_{\text{real}} dp \qquad (18.51)$$

Subtracting Eq. (18.50) from Eq. (18.51) gives

$$RTd(\ln f) - RTd(\ln p) = v_{\text{real}} dp - v_{\text{ideal}} dp$$

or

$$d\left(\ln \frac{f}{p}\right) = \frac{1}{RT}(v_{\text{real}} - v_{\text{ideal}})dp$$

and, upon integration at constant temperature,

$$\int d\left(\ln \frac{f}{p}\right) = \frac{1}{RT} \int (v_{\text{real}} - v_{\text{ideal}})dp \qquad (18.52)$$

If a gas is ideal, $v_{\text{real}} = v_{\text{ideal}}$, and therefore $f = p$. Since a real gas approaches ideal gas behaviour at low pressures, it is natural to choose $p = 0$ for the lower limit of the integration. Thus,

$$\int_0^p d\left(\ln \frac{f}{p}\right) = \frac{1}{RT} \int_0^p (v_{real} - v_{ideal})dp$$

With $f = p$ as $p \to 0$, this becomes

$$\ln \frac{f}{p} = \frac{1}{RT} \int_0^p (v_{real} - v_{ideal})dp \qquad (18.53)$$

Knowing the deviation $(v_{real} - v_{ideal})$, the right-hand side of Eq. (18.53) can be integrated and the value of the fugacity determined. Note that fugacity has the same dimensions as pressure, and that it is an intensive property.

When pressures are high enough so that significant deviations from ideal gas behavior occurs, the relation for the equilibrium constant given by Eq. (18.15) no longer holds, and fugacities must be substituted for partial pressures. This can be seen from Eq. (18.51), which gives the Gibbs function of a real gas as

$$dg = RT \, d(\ln f)$$

The change in Gibbs function or free energy between a given state and a standard state (1 atm) at the same temperature is therefore

$$g - g° = RT \ln \frac{f}{f°}$$

or

$$g = g° + RT \ln \frac{f}{f°} \qquad (18.54)$$

and a development similar to that of Sec. 18.3 yields

$$\Delta G° + \bar{R}T \ln \frac{f_E^e \, f_F^f \cdots}{f_A^a \, f_B^b \cdots} - \bar{R}T \ln \frac{(f_E°)^e (f_F°)^f \cdots}{(f_A°)^a (f_B°)^b \cdots} = 0 \qquad (18.55)$$

If the standard state is chosen as that in which the fugacity of the pure gas is equal to unity (this would mean setting the fugacity of a pure gas at 1 atm pressure equal to unity), Eq. (18.55) simplifies to

$$\Delta G° + \bar{R}T \ln \frac{f_E^e \, f_F^f \cdots}{f_A^a \, f_B^b \cdots} = 0$$

or

$$\frac{f_E^e \, f_F^f \cdots}{f_A^a \, f_B^b \cdots} = K_f = \exp\left(-\frac{\Delta G^\circ}{RT}\right) \qquad (18.56)$$

where K_f is the equilibrium constant defined in terms of fugacities.

Finally, it should also be mentioned that an equilibrium constant applicable to *all* cases, whether involving solids, liquids, or gases, may be developed. To this effect, G. N. Lewis defined the term *activity* as

$$a = \frac{f}{f^\circ} \qquad (18.57)$$

This is the fugacity of a substance at a given state to the fugacity of the substance in the standard state at the same temperature. In other words, Eq. (18.54) is replaced by

$$g = g^\circ + RT \ln a \qquad (18.58)$$

and the relation for the equilibrium constant becomes

$$\Delta G^\circ + \bar{R} T \ln \frac{a_E^e \, a_F^f \cdots}{a_A^a \, a_B^b \cdots}$$

or

$$\frac{a_E^e \, a_F^f \cdots}{a_A^a \, a_B^b \cdots} = K_a = \exp\left(-\frac{\Delta G^\circ}{\bar{R} T}\right) \qquad (18.59)$$

where K_a is the equilibrium constant in terms of activities. Since the standard state for a gas is that of unit fugacity, the activity and the fugacity are equal for a gas. It follows that, for *gaseous* reactions, $K_a = K_f$. For ideal solutions, $a = c$, where c is the molar concentration, and $K_a = K_c$.

Example 18.8. (a) Develop a relation between the fugacity and the compressibility factor Z. (b) Find the fugacity of ammonia gas at 250 °F and 1000 psig.

Solution. (a) Fugacity is really another measure of the deviation of a gas from ideality. Therefore, it is to be expected that a relationship exists between fugacity and compressibility factor. From Eq. (18.53):

$$\ln \frac{f}{p} = \int_0^p \left(\frac{v_{\text{real}}}{RT} - \frac{v_{\text{ideal}}}{RT}\right) dp$$

Now, $v_{\text{ideal}}/RT = 1/p$ whereas $v_{\text{real}}/RT = z/p$ (from the definition of the compressibility factor). Thus,

$$\ln \frac{f}{p} = \int_0^p (Z-1)\frac{dp}{p} \qquad (18.60)$$

Equation (18.60) can be expressed in more usable form by writing the definition for reduced pressure, p_R:

$$p_R = \frac{p}{p_c} \qquad (18.61)$$

where p_c is the critical pressure. Since $(dp/p_c) = dp_R$ and $(dp/p) = (dp_R/p_R)$, Eq. (18.60) can be written as

$$\ln \frac{f}{p} = \int_0^{p_R} (Z-1)\frac{dp_R}{p_R} \qquad (18.62)$$

Equation (18.62) is integrated with the aid of the generalized compressibility chart of Sec. 15.11. The result is plotted in the form of the generalized fugacity coefficient chart shown in Fig. 18.7.

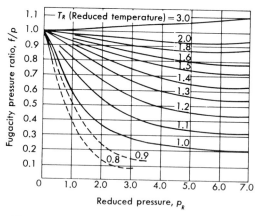

Fig. 18.7 Generalized Fugacity Coefficient Chart.

(b) To find the fugacity of ammonia gas at 250 °F and 1000 psig, the critical temperature and pressure for ammonia must first be known; they are

$$T_c = 132.4 \,^\circ C \,(= 720 \,^\circ R); \quad p_c = 111.5 \, atm$$

The reduced pressure and temperature are then

$$p_R = \frac{(1000+14.7)}{(14.7)(111.5)} = 0.618$$

$$T_R = \frac{(250+460)}{720} = 0.986$$

Corresponding to these values of p_R and T_R, the fugacity coefficient is read off the chart as

$$\frac{f}{p} = 0.78$$

whence

$$f = 0.78 \frac{(1000+14.7)}{(14.7)} = 792 \text{ psia}$$

18.9 General Treatment of Chemical Equilibrium; Chemical Potential

The discussion in the present chapter has been concerned primarily with *homogeneous* equilibrium, i.e., equilibrium involving gases. A more general treatment of chemical equilibrium is in terms of chemical potentials. The study of equilibrium between mixtures of different substances in more than one phase is an important problem, and in this section of the chapter a short introduction to *heterogeneous* equilibrium is given.

Consider a phase† composed of several constituents, of which there are n_1 moles of substance 1, n_2 moles of substance 2, n_3 moles of substance 3, etc. Since there is change in composition, the internal energy, enthalpy, Helmholtz function, and Gibbs function now depend on the n_i's as well as on p, V, and T, so that, for example, $G = G(T, p, n_1, n_2, \ldots)$, and consequently

$$dG = \left(\frac{\partial G}{\partial T}\right)_{p,n_1,n_2,\ldots} dT + \left(\frac{\partial G}{\partial p}\right)_{T,n_1,n_2,\ldots} dp + \left(\frac{\partial G}{\partial n_1}\right)_{T,p,n_2,\ldots} dn_1 +$$

$$+ \left(\frac{\partial G}{\partial n_2}\right)_{T,p,n_2\ldots} dn_2 + \ldots \tag{18.63}$$

In particular, consider a process in which all the dn's are zero, i.e., the composition and the mass of the phase remain constant; for such a case, it was shown [see Eq. (11.4)] that

$$dg = -s\,dT + v\,dp$$

It follows, therefore, that

$$\left(\frac{\partial G}{\partial T}\right)_{p,n_1,n_2,\ldots} = -S$$

$$\left(\frac{\partial G}{\partial p}\right)_{T,n_1,n_2,\ldots} = V$$

---

† Recall that a phase is a portion of a system, set off by definite boundaries, and having uniform intensive properties.

and Eq. (18.63) may be written as

$$dG = -SdT + Vdp + \left(\frac{\partial G}{\partial n_1}\right)_{T,p,n_2,\,\ldots} dn_1 + \left(\frac{\partial G}{\partial n_2}\right)_{T,p,n_1,\,\ldots} dn_2$$

$$= -SdT + Vdp + \sum_i \left(\frac{\partial G}{\partial n_i}\right)_{T,p,nj} dn_i \qquad (18.64)$$

The coefficient $(\partial G/\partial n_i)_{T,p,n_j}$, first introduced by Gibbs, has been given a special name because of its great importance in thermodynamics. It is called the *chemical potential*, and is denoted by the symbol μ. Thus, for each constituent

$$\mu_i = \left(\frac{\partial G}{\partial n_i}\right)_{T,p,nj} \qquad (18.65)$$

This is the change of free energy with respect to the number of moles n_i of the *i*th component; the temperature, pressure, and number of moles of the other constituents being kept constant. In terms of the chemical potential, Eq. (18.64) becomes

$$dG = -SdT + Vdp + \mu_1 dn_1 + \mu_2 dn_2 + \ldots \qquad (18.66)$$

Consider now the chemical reaction represented by

$$aA + bB + \ldots \longrightarrow eE + fF + \ldots \qquad (18.67)$$

At any instant, the system can be specified by stipulating T, p, n_A, n_B, $\ldots$ n_E, n_F, $\ldots$, which are the moles of material present. In accordance with Eq. (18.66), the change in free energy of the system at constant T and p is

$$dG = (a\mu_E dn_E + f\mu_F dn_F + \ldots) - (a\mu_A dn_A + b\mu_B dn_B + \ldots)$$

and an analysis similar to that of Sec. 18.3 shows that, at equilibrium

$$e\mu_E + f\mu_F + \ldots = a\mu_A + b\mu_B + \ldots \qquad (18.68)$$

Equation (18.68) is the general equation for chemical equilibrium, for, in deriving it, there was no stipulation, as in Sec. 18.3, that the constituents be ideal gases.

The remaining problem is in the determination of the μ_i's, the chemical potentials, which are different for different classes of reactions. This is a subject in physical chemistry, outside the scope of this text. It will be shown, however, that for ideal gases, the chemical potential μ_i of the *i*th constituent is

$$\mu_i = \bar{g}_i + \bar{R}T \ln p_i$$

so that, upon replacement in Eq. (18.67), the earlier result for the equilibrium constant is obtained. Before proceeding with the discussion of determining chemical potentials, a short digression on homogeneous functions is necessary.

The function

$$G = G(T, p, n_1, n_2, \ldots) \tag{18.69}$$

is said to be a *homogeneous function* of the first degree in the n_i's because if each n_i is say, doubled, the value of G is doubled. In other words, G is an extensive property which depends on the amount of material present. In general, a function $f(x, y, z)$ is said to be homogeneous of degree n in the variables x, y, z, if

$$f(\lambda x, \lambda y, \lambda z) = \lambda^n f(x, y, z) \tag{18.70}$$

Homogeneous functions possess a remarkable property discovered by Euler: If Eq. (18.70) is differentiated partially with respect to λ, the result is

$$x\frac{\partial f}{\partial(\lambda x)} + y\frac{\partial f}{\partial(\lambda y)} + z\frac{\partial f}{\partial(\lambda z)} = n\lambda^{n-1}f \tag{18.71}$$

Now, Eq. (18.71) is valid for all values of λ; it must, therefore, be valid for the particular value of $\lambda = 1$. With λ set equal to unity, Eq. (18.71) becomes

$$x\frac{\partial f}{\partial x} + y\frac{\partial f}{\partial y} + z\frac{\partial f}{\partial z} = nf \tag{18.72}$$

Equation (18.72) is known as *Euler's theorem for homogeneous functions*. It applies to any number of variables.

Returning to the equation for the Gibbs function, $G = G(T, p, n_1, n_2 \ldots)$, let Euler's theorem be applied to it. This gives

$$G = n_1\left(\frac{\partial G}{\partial n_1}\right)_{T,p,n_2,\ldots} + n_2\left(\frac{\partial G}{\partial n_2}\right)_{T,p,n_1,\ldots} + \cdots$$

$$= \sum_i n_i\left(\frac{\partial G}{\partial n_i}\right)_{T,p,n_j}$$

or by definition of the chemical potential,

$$G = \sum_i \mu_i n_i \tag{18.73}$$

Let this be compared with the expression for the Gibbs function of a mixture of perfect gases: In Chap. 16, it was shown that for a mixture containing n_i moles of perfect gases, the enthalpy is given by

$$H = \sum_i n_i \bar{h}_i,$$

and the entropy is given by

$$S = \sum_i n_i(\bar{s}_i - \bar{R} \ln p_i)$$

The Gibbs function, $G = H - TS$, is thus given by

$$G = \sum_i n_i(\bar{h}_i - T\bar{s}_i + \bar{R}T \ln p_i)$$

$$= \sum_i n_i(\bar{g}_i + \bar{R}T \ln p_i) \qquad (18.74)$$

Comparison of Eq. (18.73) with (18.74) shows that, as stated earlier

$$\mu_i = \bar{g}_i + \bar{R}T \ln p_i \qquad (18.75)$$

18.10   The Phase Rule

This chapter, and indeed the presentation of the fundamentals of thermodynamics, will fittingly come to a close with a discussion of the phase rule of Gibbs. In 1875, J. W. Gibbs published his first of a series of papers on the equilibrium of heterogeneous systems. In these papers Gibbs presented the general question of equilibrium between phases in systems made up of more than one substance with a beauty and preciseness seldom seen in thermodynamic studies. The phase rule, named in honor of Gibbs, provides the relationship among the degrees of freedom of a system F, the number of phases P, and the number of components C. This relationship is

$$F = C + 2 - P$$

It is derived and discussed below.

The state of a system containing P phases and C components is specified if the temperature, the pressure, and the relative amounts of each component in each phase is specified. Let the phases be numbered 1, 2, 3, ... P, and let T_j and p_j denote the temperature and the pressure of the jth phase. Now, if all the phases were separated from one another, and if there were no equilibria between phases, each phase would have $C + 1$ degrees of freedom, representing temperature, pressure, and $C - 1$ mole fractions (note that a phase having C components has only $C - 1$ mole fractions). A system of P separate phases, each consisting of C components would therefore have $P(C + 1)$ degrees of freedom. If, however, the phases are in equilibrium, the P temperatures and the P pressures are all equal, and since this assertion requires $2(P - 1)$ equations, the number of degrees of freedom is now reduced to $P(C + 1) - 2(P - 1) = P(C - 1) + 2$.

In addition to the thermal and mechanical conditions stated above, the condition of chemical equilibrium with respect to chemical potentials must be expressed. This condition is that, if the several phases are all in equilibrium, the chemical potentials of each component must be the *same* in every phase. To show this, consider a system with phases 1 and 2 maintained at constant temperature and pressure, and denote by $n_i^{(1)}$, $n_i^{(2)}$ the moles of some particular component i in the two phases (the phases are designated by superscripts). The condition of equilibrium ($dG = 0$) is

$$dG^{(1)} + dG^{(2)} = 0 \qquad (18.76)$$

Suppose that dn_i moles of component i were taken from phase 1 and added to phase 2, then, by virtue of Eq. (18.66) at constant T and p, Eq. (18.76) becomes

$$-\mu_i^{(1)}dn_i + \mu_i^{(2)}dn_2 = 0 \qquad (18.77)$$

or

$$\mu_i^{(1)} = \mu_i^{(2)} \qquad (18.78)$$

In other words, for any component i, the value of the chemical potential μ_i must be the same in every phase. For a system of P phases and C components, this is expressed by the following set of equations:

$$\left.\begin{array}{l}\mu_1^{(1)} = \mu_1^{(2)} = \mu_1^{(3)} = \ldots = \mu_1^{(P)} \\[4pt] \mu_2^{(1)} = \mu_2^{(2)} = \mu_2^{(3)} = \ldots = \mu_2^{(P)} \\[4pt] \cdot \quad \cdot \quad \cdot \quad \cdot \quad \cdot \quad \cdot \quad \cdot \quad \cdot \\[4pt] \cdot \quad \cdot \quad \cdot \quad \cdot \quad \cdot \quad \cdot \quad \cdot \quad \cdot \\[4pt] \mu_C^{(1)} = \mu_C^{(2)} = \mu_C^{(3)} = \ldots = \mu_C^{(P)}\end{array}\right\} \qquad (18.79)$$

Each equality sign in the set of Eqs. (18.79) represents a condition imposed on the system, decreasing its variance or freedom by one. It is seen that there are $C(P-1)$ of these conditions.

Altogether, the number of degrees of freedom for a system consisting of P phases and C components is thus

$$F = P(C-1) + 2 - C(P-1)$$

or

$$F = C + 2 - P \qquad (18.80)$$

Equation (18.80) is the famous *Phase Rule* of Gibbs. That such a simple relationship exists is all the more remarkable, not so much because it is observed in nature, but because its derivation is essentially based on the first and second laws of thermodynamics.

18.11 Application of Phase Rule to One- and Two-Component Systems

Let the phase rule be applied first to a *one-component* system. With $C = 1$, $F = 3 - P$, there are three different cases which are possible:

$P = 1$, $F = 2$. This is known as a *bivariant* system. There is only one phase present, such as superheated vapor of a pure substance. Here, two intensive properties may be varied independently, i.e., two independent properties determine the state of the system. This is illustrated by the superheated section of the steam tables already familar to the reader.

$P = 2$, $F = 1$. This is a *univariant* system. There are two phases of a pure substance in equilibrium such as saturated liquid and saturated vapor. In this case, temperature and pressure can no longer be varied independently, but for each value of temperature, the saturation pressure is fixed, and vice versa.

$P = 3$, $F = 0$. This is an *invariant* system. It corresponds to the triple point of a pure substance, where three phases coexist. There are no degrees of freedom. That is, the temperature and pressure of the triple point are fixed, and neither can be varied without causing the disappearance of one of the phases.

Now, let the phase rule be applied to a *two-component* system. With $C = 2$, $F = 4 - P$, there are four possible cases; they are discussed below:

$P = 1$, $F = 3$. This is a *trivariant* system. If a two-component system were to exist in only one phase, the three degrees of freedom can be chosen as temperature, pressure, and mole fraction of one of the components.

$P = 2$, $F = 2$. This is a *bivariant* system. Since the system exists in two phases, the number of degrees of freedom is reduced to two, and these can be chosen as temperature and pressure. In other words, specifying the temperature and pressure completely determines the state of the system and hence the composition of each phase. An example of such a system is a binary mixture of ammonia and water existing in the liquid and vapor phases.

$P = 3$, $F = 1$. This is a *univariant* system. It has one degree of freedom so that the equilibrium temperature is a function of the equilibrium pressure. An example of this is a system comprised of liquid mercury, liquid water, and vapor. The water and mercury are immiscible and so form two liquid phases, in addition to the vapor phase. The two components are H_g and H_2O. At a given pressure, there is only one temperature at which the three phases can coexist, with the composition of the vapor being fixed under these conditions.

$P = 4$, $F = 0$. This is an *invariant* system. It can exist in equilibrium at only one temperature, pressure and composition for all four phases.

PROBLEMS

18.1. Carbon dioxide at 77 °F and one atmosphere is heated in a constant pressure steady-flow process to 3000 °R. Determine the equilibrium composition and the heat transfer per mole of CO_2.

18.2. Compare the degrees of dissociation of CO_2 at 5160 °R for total pressures of 1 and 10 atm respectively. Does an increase in pressure tend to shift the equilibrium to a smaller volume?

18.3. Experimental measurements show that H_2O is 5 per cent dissociated into hydrogen and oxygen at a pressure of 10 atm and a temperature of 5150 °R. Calculate the equilibrium constant and compare with the value given in the Appendix.

18.4. (a) If the equilibrium constants for the following reactions are available:

$$C_2H_4 = 2\,C + 2\,H_2; \quad K_1 = \frac{(f_{H_2})^2}{(f_{C_2H_4})}$$

$$C_2H_2 = 2\,C + H_2; \quad K_2 = \frac{(f_{H_2})}{(f_{C_2H_2})}$$

what is the equilibrium constant for the catalytic hydrogenation of acetylene to ethylene ($C_2H_2 + H_2 = C_2H_4$)?
(b) If $K_p = 6.4$ at 5040 °R for the reaction

$$CO + \tfrac{1}{2}O_2 \rightarrow CO_2$$

what are the respective values of K_p for the reactions

$$2\,CO + O_2 \rightarrow 2\,CO_2$$

$$CO_2 \rightarrow CO + \tfrac{1}{2}O_2$$

at 5040 °R?

18.5. What is the maximum possible conversion of carbon dioxide to carbon monoxide in the presence of graphite at a pressure of 1 atm and a temperature of 1500 °F? The reaction $CO_2 + C \rightarrow 2\,CO$ has an equilibrium constant of $K_p = 10$ at 1500 °F.

18.6. The equilibrium constant may also be derived from kinetics: Consider that the rate of a reaction to be directly proportional to the driving force and inversely proportional to the retarding force. For example, in the case of the water–gas reaction:

$$CO_2 + H_2 \rightleftarrows CO + H_2O$$

the rate of reaction dR/dt is, according to the law of mass action:

$$\frac{dR}{dt} = k_1\frac{Fd}{Fr} = k_1\frac{[CO_2][H_2]}{Fr}$$

Where F_d is the driving force and F_r the retarding force. The rate of reverse action is

$$\frac{dR_r}{dt} = k_2 \frac{[CO_2][H_2]}{F_r'}$$

Equilibrium results when the two rates are equal. Setting $dR/dt = dR_r/dt$ and combining k_1, k_2, F_r, and F_r' into a single coefficient K, develop the equation for the equilibrium constant.

18.7. Iso-octane (C_8H_{18}) is burned with 120 per cent theoretical air. Calculate the equilibrium composition of the products of combustion at 5 atm total pressure and 5000 °R.

18.8. One mole of water vapor at atmospheric pressure and 800 °R is heated to 3500 °R in a constant pressure process. Determine the final composition and the heat transfer.

18.9. In the case of combustion processes wherein the products are at a temperature not greater than 2500 °F, the effects of dissociation are ignored. Is this justified as regards CO_2 and H_2O?

18.10. The change in Gibbs function for the reaction

$$C_2H_4(g) + H_2O(g) \rightleftarrows C_2H_5\,OH(g)$$

is $\Delta G° = 300$ cal/g mole at 100 °C. Determine the equilibrium yield of ethanol at 1 atm and 100 °C. Hint: The equilibrium constant is $e^{-300/1.987 \times 373}$. Consider the fraction x of 1 mole of C_2H_4 to be converted to C_2H_5OH.

18.11. Determine the fraction of steam decomposed in the water–gas reaction

$$CO(g) + H_2O(g) \rightarrow CO_2(g) + H_2(g)$$

for the following cases: (a) The reactants (1 mole of CO and 1 mole of H_2O) are at 3000 °R and a total pressure of 1 atm. (b) The reactants are at 3000 °R and a total pressure of 8 atm. (c) Same as b, except that 3 moles of N_2 are included in the reactants. (d) Same as (a), except that the number of moles of H_2O in the reaction is increased to 2.5.

18.12. What is the percentage dissociation of CO_2 at 5170 °R and 1 atm total pressure if three times the correct amount of oxygen is supplied in burning CO? Does the presence of excess oxygen drive the reaction farther toward completion?

18.13. One mole of carbon monoxide at 77 °F reacts with one mole of oxygen at 77 °F in a certain steady-flow process at a total pressure of 1 atm. There is no heat transfer from the system, and the final pressure is 1 atm. Determine the equilibrium composition and the flame temperature considering dissociation. Assume the products to consist of a mixture of CO, CO_2, and O_2.

18.14. If solid chloride (NH_4Cl) were heated in a closed container at 1000 °R, what pressure would be developed? Hint: the pressure developed would be due to the NH_3 and HCl gases formed, for the NH_4Cl would decompose until the equilibrium partial pressures of the gases are attained. Write the equation

$$NH_4Cl(s) \rightleftarrows NH_3(g) + HCl(g); \quad K = \frac{(f_{NH3})(f_{HCl})}{(a_{NH_4HCl})} = 200$$

Consider $a_{\mathrm{NH_4Cl}} = 1$, since $\mathrm{NH_8Cl}$ remains a pure solid, and the gases to be ideal $(f = p)$. Thus,

$$(p_{\mathrm{NH_3}})^2 = (p_{\mathrm{HCl}})^2 = K = 200$$

18.15. The products of combustion of a hydrocarbon fuel and air when at 1 atm pressure and a certain temperature are

$$9.01\ \mathrm{CO_2} + 2.99\ \mathrm{CO} + 5.72\ \mathrm{H_2O} + 0.28\ \mathrm{H_2} + 1.6350_2 + 56.4\ \mathrm{N_2}$$

Determine the equilibrium constants (based on pressures in atmospheres) for the reactions

$$\mathrm{CO_2} \rightleftarrows \mathrm{CO} + \tfrac{1}{2}\mathrm{O_2} \quad \text{and} \quad \mathrm{H_2O} \rightleftarrows \mathrm{H_2} + \tfrac{1}{2}\mathrm{O_2}$$

18.16. The following process takes place at constant volume in an engine: 0.005 moles of fuel (assume pure carbon and 0.03 moles of air) initially at 65 °F are burned adiabatically in a 1 cu ft cylinder volume. Assuming perfect gas behavior, calculate: (a) the composition and temperature at equilibrium, (b) the pressure at equilibrium. Hint: Since there is excess of oxygen and the equilibrium constants for the burning of carbon are high, it is safe to assume that all of the carbon will be burned. At equilibrium, the only pertinent reaction is thus $\mathrm{CO} + (1/2)\mathrm{O_2} \rightleftarrows \mathrm{CO_2}$. The final temperature is determined by a simultaneous solution of the equation for K_p and for the energy balance. As for the pressure, it can be obtained by applying $pV = n\bar{R}T$ to the products of combustion.

18.17. (a) Make a plot of $\log_{10} K_p$ versus $1/T$ for the reaction

$$\mathrm{CO_2} \rightleftarrows \mathrm{CO} + \tfrac{1}{2}\mathrm{O_2}$$

(b) Write the equation for $\log_{10} K_p$ as function of temperature.

18.18. Determine the adiabatic flame temperature for the combustion reaction

$$\mathrm{CO} + \tfrac{1}{2}\mathrm{O_2} \rightleftarrows \mathrm{CO_2}$$

Consider the reactants to be initially at 77 °F and the total pressure to be 5 atm. Assume values of T and calculate values of x which satisfy the equation for the equilibrium constant. Plot the curve of T vs. x. Obtain a second curve of T vs. x by substituting the assumed values of T in the energy equation and solving for x. The intersection of the two curves gives the values of T and x which satisfy the equilibrium constant and the energy equation.

18.19. (a) Show that the Gibbs–Helmholtz equation may be written as

$$\left[\frac{\partial(\Delta G/T)}{\partial(1/T)} \right]_p = \Delta H$$

(b) Verify that the differential equation of part (a) has the integrating factor of

$$e^{-\int (1/T)dt} = \frac{1}{T}$$

and integrate it to give

$$\frac{\Delta G^\circ}{T} = -\int \frac{\Delta H^\circ}{T^2} dT$$

18.20. Air enters the combustion-chamber of a gas turbine at 5.8 atm, 400 °F, and at the rate of 55 lbm/sec. Methane ($\mathrm{CH_4}$) at 77 °F is added for combustion.

Determine the rate of CH_4 required if the final temperature is 1350 °F.

18.21. Starting with the Gibbs–Helmholtz equation:

$$\left(\frac{\partial \Delta G}{T}\right)_p = \frac{\Delta G - \Delta H}{T}$$

show, by means of the third law, that

$$\lim_{T \to 0} \Delta c_p = 0$$

Hint: As T approaches zero, the right-hand side of the Gibbs–Helmholtz equation assumes the indeterminate value 0/0. This is resolved by differentiating the numerator and denominator of the right-hand side to give

$$\lim_{T \to 0} \left(\frac{\partial \Delta G}{\partial T}\right)_p = \lim_{T \to 0} \left(\frac{\partial \Delta G}{\partial T}\right)_p - \lim_{T \to 0} \left(\frac{\partial \Delta H}{\partial T}\right)_p$$

Make use of

$$\lim_{T \to 0} \left(\frac{\partial \Delta G}{\partial T}\right)_p = -\Delta S° \text{ and } \left(\frac{\partial \Delta H}{\partial T}\right)_p = \Delta c_p$$

18.22. Determine the maximum adiabatic-flame temperature resulting from the constant-volume combustion of CO if dissociation of CO_2 is considered. Assume the reaction to start with the reactants at a total pressure of 1 atm and a temperature of 77 °F. Hint: the flame temperature must satisfy the equation for the equilibrium constant and the energy equation ($U_{\text{reactants}} = U_{\text{products}}$).

18.23. (a) The Clausius–Clapeyron equation for a vapor behaving as an ideal gas may be written as

$$\frac{d \ln p}{dT} = \frac{\Delta H}{\bar{R}T^2}$$

Compare this with the van't Hoff equation

$$\frac{d \ln K_p}{dT} = \frac{\Delta H}{\bar{R}T^2}$$

by applying the latter to the change of phase from liquid water to vapor (in which case K_p is equal to the pressure of the water p). Can the latent heat be compared to a simple heat of reaction in the absence of chemical change, and can the van't Hoff equation be considered as a generalization of the Clausius–Clapeyron equation?

(b) Given $\Delta H° = -11,870$ Btu/lb mole at 77 °F for the water-gas reaction

$$CO + H_2O \to CO_2 + H_2$$

what is the equilibrium constant at 1000 °R? Use van't Hoff's equation, and neglect any slight variation of $\Delta H°$.

18.24. (a) The general equation for fugacity may be written as

$$\ln f = \ln \frac{f^*}{p^*} + \ln p + \int_{p^*}^{p} \left(\frac{v}{RT} - \frac{1}{p}\right) dp \tag{1}$$

where the starred quantities denote values at the reference state. Show that when $p*$ approaches zero,

$$\ln f = \ln p + \int_0^p \left(\frac{v}{RT} - \frac{1}{p}\right) dp \tag{2}$$

(b) A gas obeys the equation of state

$$pv(1 - \beta p) = RT \tag{3}$$

in which β is a function of T. Solving for v and substituting into Eq. (2), show that the fugacity becomes

$$f = \frac{p}{1 - \beta p}$$

18.25. A gas obeys the equation of state

$$pv = RT + \alpha p$$

where α is a function of temperature. Show that for such a gas, the fugacity is

$$f = p \exp\left(\frac{\alpha p}{RT}\right)$$

If α is small, this becomes

$$f \approx p(1 + p/RT) \approx \frac{p}{1 - \alpha p/RT}$$

What is the relationship between α and β if the expression for the fugacity is to be compatible with that obtained in Prob. 18.24?

18.26. Using the equation

$$RT \ln \frac{f}{f*} = \int_{p*}^p v \, dp = pv - p*v* - \int_{v*}^v p \, dv$$

evaluate the fugacity of a van der Waals gas $\left(p = \dfrac{RT}{v - b} - \dfrac{a}{v^2}\right)$ and show that

$$RT \ln \frac{f}{f*} = pv - p*v* - RT \ln \frac{v - b}{v* - b} - \frac{a}{v} - \frac{a}{v*}$$

or

$$RT \ln f = RT \ln \frac{f*}{p*} + RT \ln p*(v* - b) - p*v* + \frac{a}{v*} + pv - RT \ln (v - b) - \frac{a}{v}$$

When $p* \to 0$, $v* \to \infty$ and $p*v* \to RT$. Hence,

$$\ln p = \ln \frac{RT}{v - b} - \frac{2a}{vRT} + \frac{b}{v - b}$$

This last equation can also be used to calculate fugacities of liquids to the extent that van der Waals' equation can be used to describe a liquid.

18.27. Given the following functions:

$$f(x, y) = \frac{ax^2}{y^2} + b\left(\sqrt{\frac{\bar{x}}{y}} + \frac{y}{x}\right)$$

$$f(x, y) = ax^2y + by^2x + cy^3 \tan^{-1}\left(\frac{y}{x}\right)$$

test them for homogeneity and verify the validity of Euler's theorem

$$x\frac{\partial f}{\partial x} + y\frac{\partial f}{\partial y} = nf$$

18.28. Consider the following homogeneous function of the first degree in terms of masses $m_1, m_2, \ldots$:

$$G = G(m_1, m_2, \ldots)$$

Let each mass m_i be replaced by a homogeneous function of the first degree in another set of variables, $\xi_1, \xi_2, \ldots$, such that $m_i = m_i(\xi_1, \xi_2, \ldots)$. Show that G becomes a homogeneous function of the first degree in $\xi_1, \xi_2, \ldots$, and that

$$G = \xi_1\left(\frac{\partial m_1}{\partial \xi_1}\frac{\partial G}{\partial m_1} + \frac{\partial m_2}{\partial \xi_1}\frac{\partial G}{\partial m_2} + \ldots\right) + \xi_2\left(\frac{\partial m_1}{\partial \xi_2}\frac{\partial G}{\partial m_1} + \frac{\partial m_2}{\partial \xi_2}\frac{\partial G}{\partial m_2} + \ldots\right) + \ldots$$

18.29. Consider any extensive property $G = G(T, p, n_1, n_2, \ldots)$ which is homogeneous of the first degree with respect to the number of moles n_i. Show that the partial molar quantity

$$G_i = \left(\frac{\partial G}{\partial n_i}\right)_{T, p, n_1, n_2, \ldots}$$

is homogeneous of degree zero and therefore an intensive property, depending on the ratios of the n_i's and not on their absolute values. Hint: If a function $f(x, y, z)$ is homogeneous of degree n in the variables x, y, z, then

$$f(\lambda x, \lambda y, \lambda z) = \lambda^n f(x, y, z)$$

Differentiating with respect to λx gives

$$\frac{\partial f(\lambda x, \lambda v, \lambda z)}{\partial(\lambda x)} = \lambda^{n-1}\frac{\partial f}{\partial x}$$

But this is precisely the condition which must be fulfilled if $(\partial f)/(\partial x)$ is to be homogeneous of degree $(n - 1)$.

18.30. In applying the phase rule, it is important to know how to determine the components of a system. The constituents of a system are the various chemical substances comprising it. The components of a system, however, are the *independently* variable constituents from which the system in any of its states can be prepared. Thus, a system composed of ice, liquid water, and water vapor has only one component: water. The constituents hydrogen and oxygen cannot both be regarded as components since they must be combined in definite proportions and cannot vary independently. In each of the following systems, discuss and determine the number of components: (a) system consisting of calcium carbonate, calcium oxide, and carbon dioxide, (b) system formed by water and the two salts NaCl and KBr.

CHAPTER 19

Power and Refrigeration Cycles; Thermoelectric, Thermionic, and Other Direct Conversion Methods

19.1   Introduction

One of the most important applications of thermodynamics (certainly the most important from the engineering standpoint) is the continuous, though not complete, conversion of heat into work. The method by which this is done is the use of a power cycle. This is a series of processes which periodically returns a system (working fluid) to its original state. An alternate method is to replace the system periodically. The apparatus which enables a power cycle to be carried out is called a *heat engine*.

Another important application of thermodynamics is refrigeration. This consists of abstracting heat from a low-temperature source (the space to be refrigerated) and rejecting it to a higher-temperature sink (such as the atmosphere). Both of these applications are studied in this chapter, with emphasis on thermodynamic analysis rather than on description or operation of equipment. Because of the large number of power and refrigeration cycles in engineering, the chapter will, of necessity, be fairly lengthy. Furthermore, it will be subdivided into three different sections: *vapor power cycles, gas power cycles,* and *refrigeration cycles.*

VAPOR POWER CYCLES

19.2 Carnot Cycle Using Steam

In many power cycles, the working fluid is H_2O, which is alternately vaporized and condensed. These cycles are called steam cycles; they generate not only a major fraction of the electric power produced in the world, but are often combined with the use of steam for space heating or process heating. Steam cycles are also basically the same, whether heat is supplied from the burning of a fuel in a conventional furnace or from the fission process in a nuclear reactor.

The Carnot cycle (cf. Chap. 8), a reversible cycle with the highest efficiency between two given temperature limits, provides a good starting point and basis of comparison for the study of power cycles. In theory, the most convenient way of accomplishing a Carnot cycle using steam is as shown in Fig. 19.1. Starting at state 1, wet steam is compressed isentropically to a saturated state 2, whereupon it is vaporized in a boiler at constant temperature and pressure to saturated steam at state 3. This is followed by an isentropic expansion through a turbine to state 4. The steam then flows into a condenser where it is condensed to state 1. Heat is added to the system or working fluid at constant temperature T_2 in the boiler, and removed at constant temperature T_1 in the condenser. The thermal efficiency of the cycle is

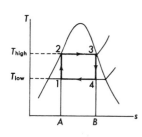

Fig. 19.1
Carnot Cycle Using Steam.

$$\eta = \frac{w_{net}}{q_{added}} = \frac{\text{area } 1\text{-}2\text{-}3\text{-}4}{\text{area } A\text{-}2\text{-}3\text{-}B} = \frac{(T_2 - T_1)(s_B - s_A)}{T_2(s_B - s_A)}$$

$$= \frac{T_2 - T_1}{T_2} = \frac{T_{high} - T_{low}}{T_{high}} \tag{19.1}$$

The Carnot cycle, however, is impractical to carry out, because of the difficulties involved in compressing isentropically a wet vapor (state 1) to saturated vapor (state 2) and in controlling the quality of the condensate coming out of the condenser so that state 1 is exactly obtained.

19.3 Rankine Cycle

Modern steam power generation is based on the Rankine cycle,† which is a practical modification of the Carnot cycle. The Rankine cycle for a simple steam power plant is as shown in Fig. 19.2.

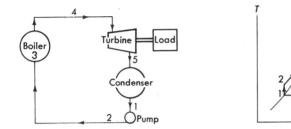

Fig. 19.2 Simple Rankine Cycle.

Consider first an ideal cycle in which steam is not superheated. Starting at state 1, working fluid is pumped isentropically to state 2 into a boiler where it is heated at constant pressure to saturated steam (state 4). The steam then expands isentropically through a turbine (or other prime mover such as a steam engine) to state 5. The wet vapor is next liquefied (by means of the process in the condenser) to the saturated liquid state (point 1) to renew the cycle. The pump work required per pound of working fluid is

$$w_{\text{pump}} = h_2 - h_1$$

The heat input per pound of working fluid is

$$q_{\text{in}} = h_4 - h_5$$

The work output per pound of steam is

$$w_{\text{turbine}} = h_4 - h_5$$

The heat removed by the condenser is

$$q_{\text{out}} = h_5 - h_1$$

---

† Named after William John Rankine (1820–1872), professor at the University of Glasgow and contemporary with Joule, Thomson, Clausius, and Maxwell. It was largely due to the efforts of these men that the laws of thermodynamics were formulated and interpreted. Rankine played no small part in these developments, for he was a man of versatile genius who not only contributed greatly to the engineering and scientific literature of his day, but was also a composer of music and a good vocalist.

The thermal efficiency of the cycle is thus

$$\eta = \frac{w_{\text{turbine}} - w_{\text{pump}}}{q_{\text{in}}} = \frac{(h_4 - h_5) - (h_2 - h_1)}{h_4 - h_2} \qquad (19.2)$$

In the case of a Rankine cycle with superheat (which is advisable in order to prevent erosion of the low-pressure end of the turbine due to excessive liquid content at the end of the expansion process), the cycle takes on the form shown in Fig. 19.3. Also, the use of higher operating temperatures is achieved, without increasing the maximum pressure of the cycle, by having the steam further heated in a superheater. The boiler and the superheater are often combined in a single unit called the *steam generator*.

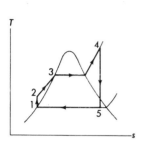

Fig. 19.3
Rankine Cycle with Superheat.

Note that, in the above analysis, changes in potential and kinetic energies from one point of the cycle to another have been neglected. This is usually a reasonable assumption. Note also that a Rankine cycle has lower efficiency than a Carnot cycle with upper and lower temperatures equal to the maximum and minimum temperatures of the Rankine cycle.

Example 19.1. (a) Determine the efficiency of a Rankine cycle employing steam as the working fluid in which the boiler pressure is 300 psia and the exhaust pressure is atmospheric. Consider the steam leaving the boiler as saturated. (b) Repeat (a), with the exception that the exhaust pressure is lowered to 2 psia by means of a condenser.

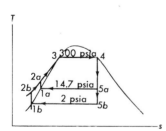

Fig. 19.4 Rankine Cycle with Successively Lower Exhaust Pressures.

Solution. (a) Referring to Fig. 19.4, the efficiency of the cycle $1a-2a-3-4-5a$ having an exhaust pressure of 14.7 psia is

$$\eta = \frac{(h_4 - h_{5a}) - (h_{2a} - h_{1a})}{(h_4 - h_{2a})}$$

From the steam tables, $h_{1a} = 180.1$ Btu/lbm, $s_{1a} = 0.3120$ Btu/lbm-°R, $h_{2a} = 180.9$ Btu/lbm, $h_4 = 1202.8$ Btu/lbm, $s_4 = 1.5104$ Btu/lbm-°R. To obtain the enthalpy at state $5a$, the quality x_{5a} must first be determined. Since

$$s_4 = s_{5a} = s_{1a} + x_{5a}s_{fg}$$

the quality x_{5a} is found to be

$$x_{5a} = \frac{s_{5a} - s_{1a}}{s_{fg}} = \frac{1.5104 - 0.3120}{1.4446} = 0.829$$

It follows that the enthalpy h_{5a} is

$$h_{5a} = h_{1a} + x_{5a}h_{fg} = 180.1 + (0.829)(970.3) = 985.1$$

This result may easily be checked by means of the Mollier chart. The efficiency of the cycle is then

$$\eta = \frac{(1202.8 - 985.1) - (180.9 - 180.1)}{(1202.8 - 180.9)} = 0.212 \text{ or } 21.2 \text{ per cent}$$

(b) The cycle is now $1b$–$2b$–3–4–$5b$, so that the efficiency is

$$\eta = \frac{(h_4 - h_{5b}) - (h_{2b} - h_{1b})}{(h_4 - h_{2b})}$$

This comes out to be around 29 per cent. Thus, it is seen that lowering the exhaust pressure and temperature (by using a condenser) increases the thermal efficiency of the cycle. Furthermore, if several efficiencies were to be calculated using successively lower pressures than atmospheric, and the results plotted against exhaust temperature, the graph of Fig. 19.5 would be obtained. It is seen that decreasing the sink temperature increases the Rankine cycle efficiency in a nearly linear manner.

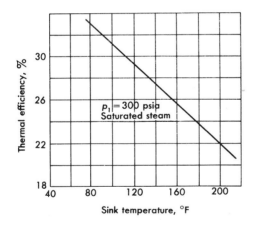

Fig. 19.5 Variation of Thermal Efficiency with Sink Temperature.

19.4 Reheat Cycle

The efficiency of a Rankine cycle is increased by increasing the pressure or the temperature at which heat is added. For a given maximum temperature (usually limited by the strength characteristics of construction materials), increasing the steam-generating pressure decreases the quality of the steam leaving the turbine.† To obtain the advantage of increased efficiency with higher pressure and yet avoid excessive moisture in the low pressure stages of the turbine, the reheat cycle is developed. This is shown in Fig. 19.6. Steam is expanded to some intermediate pressure in the tur-

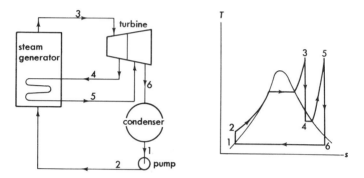

Fig. 19.6 Reheat Cycle.

bine, fed back to the boiler where it is reheated (usually to the original temperature), and then expanded through the turbine to the exhaust pressure. The chief advantage of using reheat is not so much in the gain of thermal efficiency as in maintaining low moisture content at exhaust. In practice reheat is economically justifiable only in large capacity plants, in conjunction with several stages of regeneration. The regenerative cycle is discussed in the next section. Referring to Fig. 19.6, the efficiency of the reheat cycle is

$$\eta = \frac{(h_3 - h_4) + (h_5 - h_6) - (h_2 - h_1)}{(h_3 - h_2) + (h_5 - h_4)} \qquad (19.3)$$

19.5 Regenerative Cycle

The previous modifications of the basic Rankine cycle with superheat and reheat have been directed toward increasing the mean effective temperature at which heat is added by supplying a greater proportion of heat near the superheat region. However, the mean effective temperature can also be raised by raising the temperature at which the working liquid enters the

---

† A moisture content of more than 10 per cent would cause erosion of the turbine blades.

boiler. This is done in the regenerative cycle which, by means of feedwater heaters, eliminates some of the irreversible heat flow taking place when condensed liquid is pumped directly into the boiler.

Consider the idealized regenerative cycle shown in Fig. 19.7. The main feature as compared to the basic Rankine cycle is that, after leaving the pump, the working fluid (flowing counter to the direction of the vapor flow

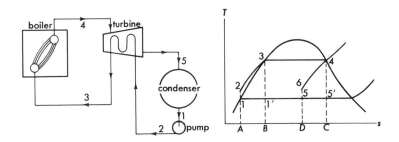

Fig. 19.7 Ideal Regenerative Cycle.

in the turbine) receives heat (represented by the area A–2–3–B) from the vapor expanding through the turbine. The heat given up by the vapor is represented by the area 4–6–D–C. On the T–s diagram, the line 4–6–5, representing the states of the vapor, is essentially parallel to the line 1–2–3, representing the states of the liquid. Note that the areas A–2–3–B and D–6–4–C are congruent and equal. Note also that heat is transferred in the boiler to the working fluid at constant temperature (process 3–4), while heat is abstracted in the condenser from the working fluid at constant temperature (process 5–1). Since the area 5–1–A–D–5 is equal to the area 5'–1'–B–C–5', which is the heat rejected in the corresponding Carnot cycle 1'–3–4–5'–1', the regenerative cycle has the same thermal efficiency as a Carnot cycle operating between the same temperature limits.

In actual practice, the idealized cycle just described is replaced by a more realistic cycle employing feedwater heaters. Vapor is extracted from the turbine at different points along its expansion and used to heat the liquid flowing into the boiler. This is illustrated by means of the example shown in Fig. 19.8. Consider a unit mass of steam upon its entrance to the turbine (state 8). After expansion to state 9, some of the steam is extracted and enters the first feedwater heater† where it is used to heat the condensate

---

† Feedwater heaters used in regenerative cycles are *open* or *closed*, depending on whether the bled steam and the condensate are allowed to mix or are kept separate. The type illustrated here is the open feedwater heater.

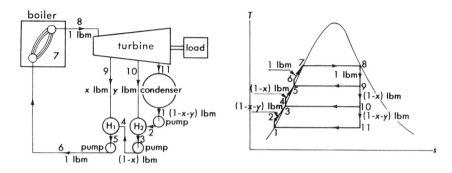

Fig. 19.8 Actual Regenerative Cycle.

to state 5. The amount of steam extracted (x pounds) is calculated to be just sufficient to cause the liquid leaving the feedwater heater to be in the saturated state. The liquid is then raised to a pressure p_6 (equal to boiler pressure) by means of a pump. Proceeding with the flow of the steam through the turbine: after state 9, there remains $(1-x)$ pounds of steam to expand to state 10. At this point, y pounds are extracted for use in the second feed-water to heat the condensate to state 3. The remainder, $(1-x-y)$ pounds, expands to exhaust pressure, and is represented by state 11 on the T–s diagram. The calculation of x and y is done by expressing mathematically the fact that in each feedwater heater, the heat given up by the steam equals that gained by the water. Thus,

$$\left.\begin{array}{l} x(h_9 - h_5) = (1-x)(h_5 - h_4) \\ y(h_{10} - h_3) = (1-x-y)(h_3 - h_2) \end{array}\right\} \tag{19.4}$$

After x and y have been determined, the pump work can be obtained from

$$W_{\text{pump}} = (1-x-y)(h_2 - h_1) + (1-x)(h_4 - h_3) + (1)(h_6 - h_5) \tag{19.5}$$

The turbine work is

$$W_{\text{turbine}} = (1)(h_8 - h_9) + (1-x)(h_9 - h_{10}) + (1-x-y)h_{10} - h_{11}) \tag{19.6}$$

The heat supplied in the boiler to the cycle is

$$Q_{\text{added}} = (1)(h_8 - h_6) \tag{19.7}$$

The heat abstracted (in the condenser) is

$$Q_{\text{rejected}} = (1-x-y)(h_{11} - h_1) \tag{19.8}$$

Eqs. (19.7) and (19.8) enable the thermal efficiency of the regenerative cycle to be obtained:

$$\eta = \frac{Q_{added} - Q_{rejected}}{Q_{added}}$$

$$= \frac{(1)(h_8 - h_6) - (1 - x - y)(h_{11} - h_1)}{(1)(h_8 - h_6)} \tag{19.9}$$

The above illustration employs two feedwater heaters. Note from the T–s diagram that, as more extraction points and heaters are added, the temperature of the liquid entering the boiler (T_6) approaches the highest temperature of the cycle (T_7). However, the reduction of irreversibility with each addition of heaters becomes progressively smaller, so that a point is reached where any further increase in the number of heaters is no longer economically justified. (This occurs when the addition of one more heater would increase the fixed charges more than it would decrease the fuel costs.) Usually seven or eight heaters are the maximum number, and this is employed only in large installations.† The regenerative cycle is subject to the same limitations of moisture content at exhaust as in the other cycles previously discussed. It is therefore often necessary to superheat the steam, or, if a high vaporization pressure is used, to reheat the steam. A reheat-regenerative cycle is shown in Fig. 19.9. This particular cycle has five closed feedwater heaters and one open feedwater heater.

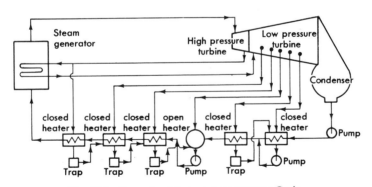

Fig. 19.9 Example of Reheat-Regenerative Cycle.

Example 19.2. An ideal regenerative cycle is operated with 125,000 lbm/hr of steam supplied by the boiler at 900 psia and 900 °F. Extraction from the turbine for feedwater heating occurs at 700 °F and again at 500 °F, with the re-

---

† The bleeding points are usually chosen so that the temperature difference between inlet and exhaust is divided into equal steps.

maining steam expanding to a saturation pressure corresponding to 100 °F. Determine: (a) the hourly amounts of steam extracted at both temperatures, (b) the turbine horsepower, and (c) the thermal efficiency of the cycle.

Solution. In Fig. 19.10, let x be the amount of steam extracted at point 9, and y be the amount of steam extracted at point 10. An energy balance in the first heater gives

$$x(h_9 - h_5) = (1-x)(h_5 - h_4)$$

and, using enthalpy values from the steam tables or the Mollier chart:

$$x = \frac{h_5 - h_4}{h_9 - h_4} = \frac{436.6 - 354.0}{1360.0 - 354.0} = 0.0822$$

For a supply of 125,000 lbm/hr of steam from the boiler, the amount of steam extracted at point 9 is

$$(0.0822)(125,000) = 10,270 \text{ lbm/hr}$$

An energy balance in the second heater gives

$$y(h_{10} - h_3) = (1-x-y)(h_3 - h_2)$$

With $x = 0.0822$ and values of enthalpies read from the steam tables, y is found to be

$$y = \frac{(1-x)(h_3 - h_2)}{h_{10} - h_2} = \frac{(1-0.0822)(353.2 - 68.6)}{(1269.2 - 68.6)} = 0.2175$$

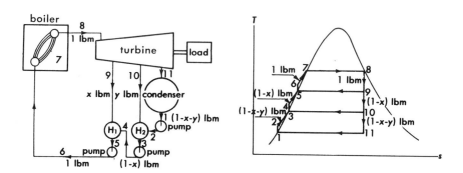

Fig. 19.10

For a steam-supply of 125,000 lbm/hr, this corresponds to

$$(0.2175)(125,000) = 27,200 \text{ lbm/hr}$$

(b) The turbine work is

$$\begin{aligned}
W_{\text{turbine}} &= (1)(h_8 - h_9) + (1-x)(h_9 - h_{10}) + (1-x-y)(h_{10} - h_{11}) \\
&= (1)(1451.8 - 1360.1) + (0.9178)(1360.1 - 1269.2) \\
&\quad + (0.7003)(1269.2 - 904.5) \\
&= 91.7 + 83.4 + 255.5 = 430.6 \text{ Btu/lbm of steam supplied.}
\end{aligned}$$

The turbine horsepower is thus

$$HP_{turbine} = \frac{(430.6 \text{ Btu/lbm/hr})}{(2545 \text{ Btu/hp hr})} = 21,150 \text{ hp}$$

(c) The thermal efficiency of the cycle may be obtained from Eq. (19.9):

$$\eta = \frac{(1)(h_8 - h_6) - (1 - x - y)(h_{11} - h_1)}{(1)(h_8 - h_6)}$$

$$= \frac{(1)(1451.8 - 438.2) - (1 - 0.0822 - 0.2175)(904.5 - 68.0)}{(1)(1451.8 - 438.2)}$$

$$= 0.422 \text{ or } 42.2 \text{ per cent}$$

19.6 Binary Cycle

A binary cycle utilizes two different fluids to obtain more nearly optimum conditions than could be attained by using a single working fluid.

Consider the characteristics of a cycle employing a single fluid: the maximum allowable temperature is determined by metallurgical considerations, which is at present around 1150 °F, well above the critical temperature of water. It is common practice for steam power plant engineers to speak of "going to higher temperatures and pressures" to raise the thermal efficiency. However, higher temperatures mean higher pressures and larger amounts of superheat in the case of steam. The higher the pressure, the lower the maximum temperature a given metal can stand. This is shown in Fig. 19.11(a), where the dotted line represents the states of steam associated with the metallurgical limitations. It is seen that, with steam, the latent heat of vaporization decreases as the pressure increases and that the moisture problem in the turbine becomes more acute at higher pressures.

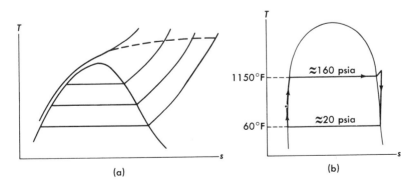

(a) (b)

Fig. 19.11 Limitations of an Actual Fluid and Characteristics of an Ideal Fluid.

Another disadvantage with steam is that the saturation pressures corresponding to the temperatures at which heat is rejected (usually between 40 to 120 °F) is much less than atmospheric. This means that the condenser is operating at a vacuum, and elaborate steps must be taken to prevent leakage of air into it.

The above remarks lead to the concept of an ideal fluid which would have the characteristics shown in Fig. 19.11(b): Saturation pressures corresponding to temperatures at which heat is added would be relatively low, while saturation pressures corresponding to temperatures at which heat is rejected would be above atmospheric. Unfortunately, no single fluid meets these requirements, and it is necessary to employ two fluids so that advantage may be taken of the favorable characteristics of each.

A binary cycle using mercury and steam as working fluids has been successfully operated in a number of power plants. In Fig. 19.12, heat is supplied from an external source to vaporize mercury (process 1–2–3). After expanding in a "topping" turbine, the mercury is condensed in a condenser-boiler where it transfers its heat to the steam. The steam leaves the condenser-boiler as saturated vapor, is fed into the mercury boiler and comes out in a superheated state. It then expands in a turbine of its own and goes through a regular cycle.

To determine the thermal efficiency of the binary cycle, consider a unit mass of steam undergoing its cycle, and let x be the amount of mercury undergoing its cycle for each pound of steam. An energy balance for the condenser-boiler gives

$$xh_4 + h_6 = xh_5 + h_8$$

or

$$x = \frac{h_8 - h_6}{h_4 - h_5} \tag{19.10}$$

Knowing x, the thermal efficiency is then obtained from

$$\eta = \frac{W_{\text{turbines}} - W_{\text{pumps}}}{Q_{\text{added}}}$$

$$= \frac{x(h_3 - h_4) + (h_9 - h_{10}) - x(h_1 - h_5) - (h_6 - h_{11})}{x(h_3 - h_1) + (h_9 - h_8)} \tag{19.11}$$

Note that, in essence, the mercury and steam each undergo a Rankine cycle. The chief advantage is that the average temperature at which heat is supplied can be much higher than for a cycle utilizing steam only, without having to resort to high pressures. The disadvantage, of course, is that mercury is expensive and highly toxic.

Example 19.3. In a certain mercury-steam cycle, saturated mercury vapor enters the mercury turbine at 60 psia and is exhausted into the condenser-boiler at 1 psia. Saturated steam at 360 psia is generated in the condenser-boiler, and expands through a steam turbine to 1.5 psia. Determine: (a) the work of the two turbines per 120,000 lbm/hr of steam generated, (b) the thermal efficiency of the binary cycle. The properties of mercury are as follows: at 60 psia: $h_g = 150.96$ Btu/lbm, $s_g = 0.12779$ Btu/lbm-°R; at 1 psia: $h_f = 13.96$ Btu/lbm, $h_{f_g} = 126.72$ Btu/lbm, $s_f = 0.02045$ Btu/lbm-°R, and $s_{f_g} = 0.13814$ Btu/lbm-°R.

Solution. (a) Referring to Fig. 19.12, let x be the amount of mercury undergoing a cycle for each pound of steam generated. An energy balance for the condenser-boiler gives

$$xh_4 + (1)h_6 = xh_5 + (1)h_8$$

This is solved for x, using enthalpy values for mercury given in the data and enthalpy values for steam given in the steam tables:

$$x = \frac{h_8 - h_6}{h_4 - h_5} = \frac{1204.1 - 84.6}{112.46 - 13.96} = 11.37 \text{ lbm mercury/lbm steam}$$

The work output of the mercury turbine and the steam turbine is

$$w_{\text{turbines}} = x(h_3 - h_4) + (h_9 - h_{10})$$

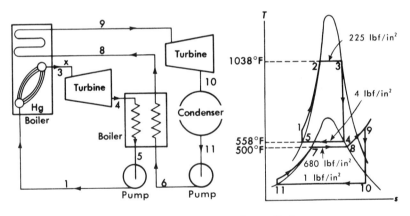

Fig. 19.12 Mercury-Steam Binary Cycle.

Note that, in the present case, point 9 coincides with point 8, since the steam cycle operates without superheat. Thus

$$w_{\text{turbines}} = (11.37)(150.96 - 112.46) + (1204.1 - 853.6)$$
$$= 787.5 \text{ Btu/lbm steam}$$

and, for a steam rate of 120,000 lbm/hr

$$W_{\text{turbines}} = (787.5)(120,000) = 94,500,000 \text{ Btu/hr}$$

This is equivalent to $94,500,000/2545 = 37,100$ hp.

(b) The thermal efficiency of the cycle is

$$\eta = \frac{W_{\text{turbines}} - W_{\text{pumps}}}{q_{\text{added}}}$$

$$= \frac{787.5 - [x(h_1 - h_5) + (1)(h_6 - h_{11})]}{x(h_3 - h_1)}$$

$$= \frac{787.5 - [11.37(13.97 - 13.96) + (1)(84.6 - 83.6)]}{11.37(150.96 - 13.97)}$$

$$= 0.505 \text{ or } 50.5 \text{ per cent}$$

19.7 Deviations from Ideal Cycle

The discussion in the preceding sections pertains mainly to ideal cycles. Actual cycles differ somewhat from ideal cycles in a number of details, the most important being the following:

(a) *Non-Isentropic Expansion in Turbine.* Because of friction, turbulence, and residual velocity, the expansion in the turbine is non-isentropic, and the state of the steam at exhaust is 2′ rather than 2. This is shown in Fig. 19.13. The ideal work would be $h_1 - h_2$ whereas the actual work is $h_1 - h_2'$. The efficiency of the turbine is thus

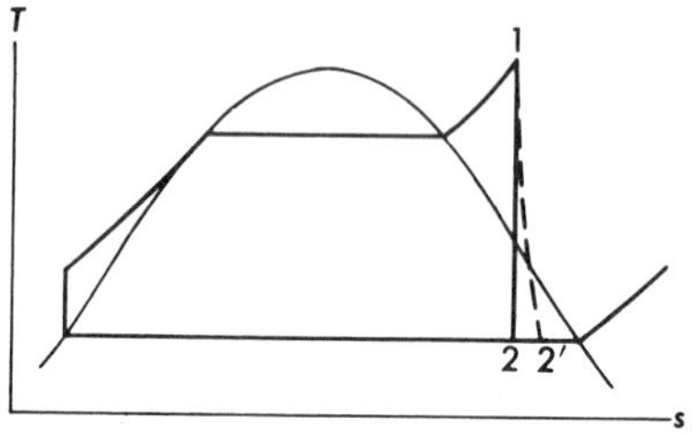

$$\eta_{\text{turbine}} = \frac{h_1 - h_2'}{h_1 - h_2} \quad (19.12)$$

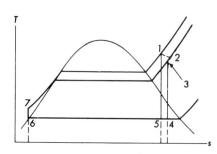

Fig. 19.13
Irreversible Expansion in Turbine.

Fig. 19.14
Representation of Piping Loss.

(b) *Piping Losses.* Because of friction and heat loss to surroundings, the pressure at entrance to the turbine is lower than that existing in the boiler. This is shown in Fig. 19.14. The state of the steam leaving the boiler is represented by point 1. Due to friction, the state of the steam entering the turbine is represented by point 2. If, furthermore, heat is transferred to the surroundings at constant pressure, the steam assumes a state represented by point 3. Both the pressure drop and the heat loss result in a decrease in the "availability" of the steam entering the turbine. This is seen in Fig. 19.13. Operation of the cycle without line losses yields a work output of (h_1-h_5) Btu/lbm of steam, whereas, in the case of line losses, the output is (h_3-h_4), which is obviously less.

(c) *Condenser Losses.* Condenser losses are relatively minor, the chief loss being the cooling of the condensate below the saturation temperature corresponding to exhaust pressure. This is a loss, because additional heat transfer is necessary to bring the working liquid back to saturation temperature.

(d) *Pump Losses.* Pump losses are similar to those occurring in the turbine. They are due to non-isentropic compression, but are often neglected because they are relatively small.

Example 19.4. A steam generator delivers steam at 550 psia and 500 °F. Due to friction in the steam line and to throttling at the turbine because of reduced load, the steam enters the turbine nozzles at 470 psia. The temperature in the condenser is 105 °F. Determine the loss of Rankine work per pound of steam.

Solution. In Fig. 19.14, the difference between point 1 and point 3 is due to friction in the steam line and throttling at the turbine because of reduced load. The loss of Rankine work per pound of steam is

$$(h_1-h_5)-(h_3-h_4)$$

Assuming the frictional and throttling process to be one of constant enthalpy (i.e., $h_3 = h_1$), this becomes

$$(1223.7-828.0)-(1223.7-836.5) = 8.5 \text{ Btu/lbm steam}$$

Note that, although point 3 has the same enthalpy as point 1, it is at a lower pressure and therefore has less potential for doing useful work. Note also that the answer could equally well have been obtained by computing $T_0 \Delta s = T_0(s_4-s_5)$. This is because the difference in the availability functions (see Sec. 10.7) for points 1 and 3 is

$$b_1-b_3 = (h_1-T_0 s_1)-(h_3-T_0 s_3) = T_0(s_3-s_1)$$
$$= T_0(s_4-s_5)$$

19.8 Second Law Analysis of Power Cycles

It was pointed out previously that the second law requires a heat engine to operate between a high-temperature source and a low-temperature sink. Since the source must be maintained by some continuous reaction (such as combustion) which releases energy, it is important that, as nearly as possible, all the energy released appears as heat added to the cycle. For example, when a fuel is burned, maximum flame temperatures of the order of 3500 °F may be attained. It would be desirable that all the heat be added to the working fluid at this temperature. Unfortunately this is not the case, for the working fluid must be conducted through steel pipes which, because of metallurgical considerations, limit the temperature to a maximum not much higher than 1150 °F. Thus, it is seen that an analysis of the power cycle alone can be rather misleading if the irreversibilities incurred in the transfer of heat from the source to the working fluid are not taken into account.

The starting point in the second law analysis of a power cycle is the calculation of the *availability* of the source. This is the maximum work obtainable when the gases are cooled reversibly to the temperature of the surroundings (the atmosphere). The power cycle, however, operates between temperature limits of its own, with its high temperature much lower than that of the source. The maximum work obtainable from the cycle is thus much less than that obtainable from the source. The ratio of the two works is then a measure of the effectiveness of the cycle.

Example 19.5. Considering an adiabatic flame temperature of 3500 °F and an atmospheric temperature of 60 °F, what is the degree of effectiveness of a Carnot cycle operating between 900 °F and 60 °F? Assume that the products of combustion have the same properties as air.

Solution. The availability of the source is found by means of Eq. (10.29):

$$\text{maximum work} = b_1 - b_2 = (h_1 - T_0 s_1) - (h_2 - T_0 s_2)$$
$$= (h_1 - T_0 \phi_1) - (h_2 - T_0 \phi_2)$$

since for the constant-pressure process under consideration, Δs is equal to the change in the function ϕ of the gas tables (see Sec. 14.5). Thus,

$$\text{maximum work} = (1076.2 - 520 \times 1.13) - (124.3 - 520 \times 0.592)$$
$$= 672 \text{ Btu/lbm of combustion gas}$$

For a Carnot cycle operating between 900 °F and 60 °F, and being supplied with heat from the combustion gases, the lowest temperature to which the gases can be cooled is 900 °F. The heat added in the Carnot cycle is thus

$$\Delta h = 1076.2 - 332.5 = 743.7 \text{ Btu/lbm gas}$$

The thermal efficiency of the Carnot cycle is

$$\frac{1360 - 520}{1360} = 0.618 \text{ or } 61.8 \text{ per cent}$$

The work obtainable from the Carnot cycle is

$$0.618 \times 743.7 = 460 \text{ Btu/lbm gas}$$

The degree of effectiveness of the cycle is then

$$\frac{460}{672} = 0.684 \text{ or } 68.4 \text{ per cent}$$

GAS POWER CYCLES

19.9   Air Standard Power Cycles

The cycles discussed in the preceding sections all utilize a vapor as the working fluid. A large class of engines, however, utilize a working fluid which is a gas. The automobile engine is a familiar example, and the same is true of the diesel engine and gas turbine. In all of these engines the supply of heat is by means of the combustion of a suitable mixture of air and fuel within the confines of the engine. There is no external source of heat, and for this reason the engines are called *internal combustion engines*. Also, the working fluid does not go through a complete cycle (because of the chemical change due to combustion), even though the engines operate in a mechanical cycle, so that internal combustion engines are said to operate in an *open cycle*. For purposes of analysis, however, an internal combustion engine may be imagined to operate in a *closed cycle* with a fixed mass of air which experiences *no* chemical change. Also, the combustion process is replaced by an *equivalent* heat transfer process from an external source. These two assumptions constitute what is known as *air standard analysis* of gas power cycles.

Internal combustion engines are usually classified as *reciprocating* or *gas-turbine* types. Reciprocating engines are in turn classified as *spark-ignition* or *compression ignition* types. The cycle pertaining to each type of engine is analyzed in the following sections. For convenience, ideal conditions are assumed throughout.

19.10   Otto Cycle

The air standard Otto Cycle† is the idealized cycle which is closely approximated by a spark ignition engine. The engine in Fig. 19.15 operates in the

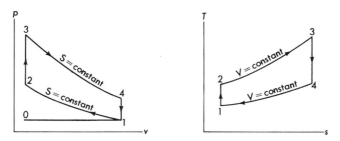

Fig. 19.15   Air-Standard Otto Cycle.

---

† Named after Nikolaus A. Otto (1832–1891), who with his partner Eugen Langen built a gas engine in 1867 and began marketing it. The principle of the four-stroke cycle, however, was worked out in 1862 by a Frenchman, Alphonse Beau de Rochas.

following sequence, starting with the position of the piston at top dead center: (a) A mixture of air and vaporized fuel is drawn into the cylinder by the intake stroke of the piston, 0–1. (b) The mixture is compressed on the return stroke of the piston, 1–2. (c) The mixture is ignited by a spark, and combustion takes place at constant volume, 2–3. (d) The hot gases expand, giving rise to a power stroke, 3–4. (e) The exhaust valve is opened, and the products of combustion flow out at constant volume, 4–1. (f) Combustion gases in the cylinder, when pressure equilibrium with atmosphere is reached, are further pushed out by the exhaust stroke that returns the piston to top dead center, with the exception of a small quantity of products which remains in the clearance space.

Note that the sequence just described takes four strokes of the piston or two revolutions of the crankshaft to be completed. An engine operating in this manner is called a four-stroke engine. If the cycle is carried out in two strokes of the piston, the engine is called a two-stroke engine. In the latter case, the suction and exhaust strokes are omitted, and other means are provided for injecting the fuel and air and for scavenging the cylinder of the products of combustion.

The thermal efficiency of a spark-ignition engine is given by

$$\eta = \frac{Q_{added} - Q_{rejected}}{Q_{added}} = 1 - \frac{Q_{rejected}}{Q_{added}}$$

$$= 1 - \frac{m(u_4 - u_1)}{m(u_3 - u_2)}$$

or, assuming constant specific heat for air,

$$\eta = 1 - \frac{mc_v(T_4 - T_1)}{mc_v(T_3 - T_2)} \tag{19.13}$$

If both compression and expansion are isentropic and of equal volume ratios, then

$$\frac{T_1}{T_2} = \left(\frac{v_2}{v_1}\right)^{\gamma-1} = \left(\frac{v_3}{v_4}\right)^{\gamma-1} = \frac{T_4}{T_3}$$

or

$$\frac{T_4}{T_1} = \frac{T_3}{T_2}$$

From this,

$$\frac{T_4}{T_1} - 1 = \frac{T_3}{T_2} - 1 = \frac{T_4 - T_1}{T_1} = \frac{T_3 - T_2}{T_2}$$

or

$$\frac{T_4 - T_1}{T_3 - T_2} = \frac{T_1}{T_2} \qquad (19.14)$$

Equation (19.14) enables Eq. (19.13) to be written as

$$\eta = 1 - \frac{T_1}{T_2} = 1 - \frac{T_4}{T_3} \qquad (19.15)$$

or, in alternate form,

$$\eta = 1 - (r_v)^{1-\gamma} = 1 - \frac{1}{(r_v)^{\gamma-1}} \qquad (19.16)$$

where $r_v = v_1/v_2 = v_4/v_3$ is the *compression ratio.* Note that the efficiency of the air-standard Otto cycle is a function of only the compression ratio, and that the efficiency is increased by increasing the compression ratio. This is the reason for the trend toward higher compression ratios.† Thermal efficiencies for an Otto cycle utilizing an ideal gas with constant specific heats are shown in Fig. 19.16 for different values of the compression ratio r_v and of the specific heat ratio γ.

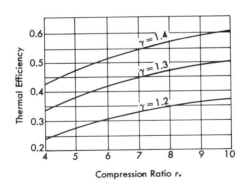

Fig. 19.16 Efficiency of Otto Cycle in Relation to Specific Heat Ratio.

Example 19.6. Consider an ideal Otto cycle in which the working substance is assumed to be ideal air with $\gamma = 1.4$ and $c_p = 0.24$. With these properties, the cycle is known as a *cold-air standard* cycle. Let the compression ratio be 8, the pressure at the beginning of the conpression stroke be 14.7 psia, and the

---

† Too high a compression ratio, however, will give rise to detonation. This is an extremely rapid burning of the fuel characterized by the presence of strong pressure waves. In other words, the engine begins to "knock."

temperature at the beginning of compression be 60 °F. Let the fuel be liquid octane with a lower heating value at constant volume of 19,150 Btu/lbm, and assume that it takes 15 lbm of dry air to burn 1 lbm of the fuel (this is equivalent to assuming 1200 Btu/lbm of working substance). Determine: (a) the pressures and temperatures throughout the cycle, (b) the thermal efficiency and, (c) the mean effective pressure.

Solution. Referring to Fig. 19.15, the temperature at point 1 is 520 °R, and the pressure is 14.7 psia. The specific volume is calculated from the perfect gas law:

$$v_1 = \frac{RT_1}{p_1} = \frac{(53.3)(520)}{(14.7)(144)} = 13.1 \text{ cu ft/lbm}$$

The specific volume at point 2 is then

$$v_2 = \frac{v_1}{8} = \frac{13.1}{8} = 1.64 \text{ cu ft/lbm.}$$

The pressure and temperature at point 2 are calculated from the isentropic-process relations (using a value for γ of 1.4):

$$p_2 = p_1\left(\frac{v_1}{v_2}\right)^{\gamma} = 14.7(8)^{1.4} = 270 \text{ psia}$$

$$T_2 = T_1\left(\frac{p_2}{p_1}\right)^{(\gamma-1)/\gamma} = 520\left(\frac{270}{14.7}\right)^{0.286} = 1196 \text{ °R}$$

The temperature at point 3 is obtained from

$$q_A = 1200 = c_v(T_3 - T_2) = 0.1715(T_3 - 1196)$$

or

$$T_3 = 8196 \text{ °R}$$

From this

$$p_3 = p_2(T_3/T_2) = 270\left(\frac{8196}{1196}\right) = 1852 \text{ psia}$$

Proceeding along the cycle, the pressure and temperature at point 4 are respectively:

$$p_4 = p_3\left(\frac{v_3}{v_4}\right)^{\gamma} = 1852\left(\frac{1}{8}\right)^{1.4} = 100.7 \text{ psia}$$

$$T_4 = T_3\left(\frac{p_4}{p_3}\right)^{(\gamma-1)/\gamma} = 8196\left(\frac{100.7}{1852}\right)^{0.286} = 3570 \text{ °R}$$

(b) To find the thermal efficiency, the heat rejected is first determined:

$$q_R = C_{v4}(T_4 - T_1) = 0.1715(3570 - 520) = 523 \text{ Btu/lbm}$$

The efficiency is then

$$\eta = \frac{q_A - q_R}{q_A} = \frac{1200 - 523}{1200} = 0.565 \text{ or } 56.5 \text{ per cent}$$

The same answer can also be obtained by using Eq. (19.16):

$$\eta = 1 - \frac{1}{(r_v)^{\gamma-1}} = 1 - \frac{1}{(8^{1-1.4})} = 0.565 \text{ or } 56.5 \text{ per cent}$$

(c) The mean effective pressure is the net work divided by the piston displacement:

$$p_m = \frac{q_A - q_R}{v_1 - v_2} = \frac{(1200 - 523)(778)}{(13.1 - 1.64)(144)} = 319 \text{ psi}$$

The above illustrates the usually convenient but approximate method of solving internal combustion engine problems. It is based on the assumption that the engine operates in a closed cycle, that no dissociation occurs, and that specific heats are assumed constant throughout a wide temperature range. In practice, the thermal efficiency and the mean effective pressure would be appreciably lower than those just obtained. A more realistic solution would be to consider the cycle as open and to use the Keenan and Kaye gas tables (which are based on variable specific heats). The corresponding points on the open cycle are shown in Fig. 19.17; starting at point 1:

$$p_1 = 14.7 \text{ psia}; \quad T_1 = 520 \text{ °R}; \quad p_{r1} = 1.2147;$$

$$v_{r1} = 158.58; \quad u_1 = 88.62$$

From the fact that

$$\frac{v_2}{v_1} = \frac{1}{8} = \frac{v_{r2}}{v_{r1}} = \frac{v_{r2}}{158.58},$$

v_{r2} is found to be 19.8. Corresponding to this, the gas tables give

$$T_2 = 1170 \text{ °R}; \quad p_{r2} = 21.85; \quad u_2 = 203.49;$$

$$p_2 = p_1\left(\frac{p_{r2}}{p_{r1}}\right) = 14.7\left(\frac{21.85}{1.2147}\right) = 264 \text{ psia}$$

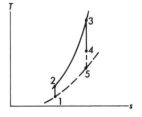

Fig. 19.17
Open-Cycle Analysis of
Otto Engine.

At point 3, the internal energy is obtained by writing the expression for the heat added:

$$q_A = 1200 = u_3 - u_2 = u_3 - 203.49$$

whence

$$u_3 = 1403.49$$

From this, $T_3 = 6460 \text{ °R}$; $p_{r3} = 28,169$; $v_{r3} = 0.08495$. Proceeding to point 4, its properties (calculated from an isentropic expansion process from point 3) are:

$$v_{r4} = (8)(v_{r3}) = (8)(0.08495) = 0.68, \quad T_4 = 3540 \text{ °R}, \quad u_4 = 707.65$$

As for point 5, it is at the same entropy as point 4, and its pressure is 14.7 psia. However, it is not of much concern in the present problem, and its determination is left out. The net work obtained from the open cycle is the difference between the heat added and the heat rejected, or

$$q_A - q_R = (u_3 - u_2) - (u_4 - u_1)$$
$$= (1403.9 - 203.49) - (707.65 - 88.62) = 580.97 \text{ Btu/lbm}$$

The thermal efficiency is then

$$\eta = \frac{w_{net}}{q_A} = \frac{580.97}{1200} = 0.485 \text{ or } 48.5 \text{ per cent}$$

and the mean effective pressure is

$$p_m = \frac{w_{net}}{v_1 - v_2} = \frac{(580.97)(778)}{(13.1 - 1.64)(144)} = 274 \text{ psi}$$

19.11   Diesel Cycle

A compression-ignition reciprocating engine may be constructed to operate on an air-standard Diesel† cycle as shown in Fig. 19.18. This cycle

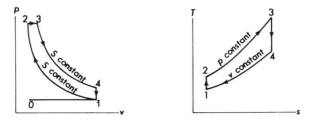

Fig. 19.18   Air-Standard Diesel Cycle.

is used extensively by large and small stationary engines and by engines in locomotives, trucks, buses, surface ships, and submarines. The cycle was evolved from Rudolph Diesel's plan to have air without fuel compressed to high pressure (and therefore high temperature) by using a larger compression ratio than in the Otto cycle. The high temperature would then cause the fuel to ignite when it was injected into the combustion chamber. Diesel originally intended that powdered coal be used as fuel, but liquid fuels proved more suitable. The cycle may be carried out either in two strokes of the piston or in four strokes. Taking the four-stroke engine as an illustration, we see that air is drawn into the cylinder where it mixes with a small amount of residual burned products. The mixture (without fuel) is compressed during the compression stroke, 1–2. Near the end of this stroke, fuel is injected into the cylinder, the fuel burning substantially at constant pressure 2–3. The products of combustion further expand isentropically from 3 to 4. The remainder of the cycle is essentially the same as that for the spark-ignition engine. If the Diesel cycle is carried out in two

---

† Named after Rudolf Diesel (1858–1913), who in 1893 obtained a patent on a compression-ignition engine. Four years later, he produced his first successful engine. He disappeared mysteriously in 1913 while crossing the English Channel.

strokes instead of four, an auxiliary blower may be used to scavenge the cylinder and charge it with air during the period between the end of expansion and the beginning of compression.

Referring to Fig. 19.18, the efficiency of an ideal air-standard Diesel cycle is

$$\eta = \frac{Q_{\text{added}} - Q_{\text{rejected}}}{Q_{\text{added}}}$$

$$= \frac{mc_p(T_3 - T_2) - mc_v(T_4 - T_1)}{mc_p(T_3 - T_2)}$$

$$= 1 - \frac{T_4 - T_1}{\gamma(T_3 - T_2)} \tag{19.17}$$

This may be rewritten as

$$\eta = 1 - \frac{1}{\gamma}\left(\frac{T_1}{T_2}\right)\left(\frac{T_2}{T_1}\right)\left(\frac{T_4 - T_1}{T_3 - T_2}\right)$$

$$= 1 - \frac{1}{\gamma}\left(\frac{T_1}{T_2}\right)\left(\frac{T_4 T_2 - T_1 T_2}{T_1 T_3 - T_1 T_2}\right) = 1 - \frac{1}{\gamma}\left(\frac{T_1}{T_2}\right)\left(\frac{T_4/T_1 - 1}{T_3/T_2 - 1}\right) \tag{19.18}$$

Assuming the working fluid to be an ideal gas,

$$\frac{p_1 v_1}{T_1} = \frac{p_4 v_4}{T_4} \ ; \ \frac{p_2 v_2}{T_2} = \frac{p_3 v_3}{T_3}$$

With $v_1 = v_4$ and $p_3 = p_2$, these relations become

$$\frac{T_4}{T_1} = \frac{p_4}{p_1} \ ; \ \frac{T_3}{T_2} = \frac{v_3}{v_2} = r_c \tag{19.19}$$

where r_c is the ratio of the volume at the end of the constant-pressure process to the volume at the beginning of the process. It is called the *cut-off ratio*. Also, the isentropic relations

$$\frac{p_1}{p_2} = \left(\frac{v_2}{v_1}\right)^{\gamma}; \ \frac{p_4}{p_3} = \left(\frac{v_3}{v_4}\right)^{\gamma}$$

become, with $v_1 = v_4$ and $p_3 = p_2$,

$$\frac{p_4}{p_1} = \left(\frac{v_3}{v_2}\right)^{\gamma} = r_c{}^{\gamma} = \frac{T_4}{T_1} \tag{19.20}$$

whence

$$\frac{T_1}{T_2} = \left(\frac{v_2}{v_1}\right)^{\gamma-1} = \frac{1}{(r_v)^{\gamma-1}} \tag{19.21}$$

where $r_v = v_1/v_2$ is the *compression ratio.* Substitution of Eqs. (19.19), (19.20), and (19.21) into Eq. (19.18) gives

$$\eta = 1 - \frac{1}{(r_v)^{\gamma-1}}\left[\frac{(r_c)^{\gamma}-1}{\gamma(r_c-1)}\right] \qquad (19.22)$$

Equation (19.22) shows that the thermal efficiency of an ideal Diesel cycle using a perfect gas with constant specific heats as the working fluid is increased by increasing the compression ratio r_v, decreasing the cutoff ratio r_c, or using a gas with a larger value of γ. This is illustrated in Fig. 19.19,

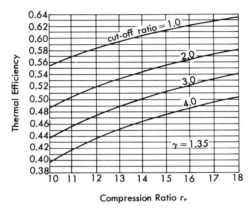

Fig. 19.19   Efficiency of Diesel Cycle in Relation to Specific Heat Ratio.

where the thermal efficiency has been plotted against compression ratio for several values of cut off ratio. Equation (19.22) also shows that, for a given compression ratio, the efficiency of a Diesel cycle is lower than that of an Otto cycle, since the expression in the bracket is always greater than unity. The chief advantage of a Diesel cycle is that since the working fluid during the compression process is all air (and therefore incombustible), a much higher compression ratio can be achieved. The compression ratio used in Diesel engines varies between 14 and 17, as compared to 6 and 10.5 for spark-ignition engines.

19.12   Dual Cycle

In practice, neither the Otto engine nor the Diesel engine operate quite in the manner of the cycles just described. For one thing, the combustion in an actual spark-ignition engine does not occur exactly at constant volume, since a finite time interval must be allowed for the chemical reaction. In order to approximate more closely actual operating conditions, the limited pressure or dual-combustion air cycle has been developed. The pressure-volume and temperature-entropy diagrams for this cycle are in Fig. 19.20.

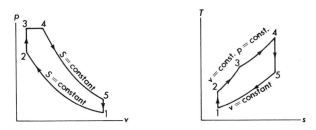

Fig. 19.20 Air-Standard Dual Cycle.

In the dual cycle, heat is first transferred to the working fluid at constant volume and the remainder transferred at constant pressure. In actual practice, injection of fuel starts before the end of the compression stroke and is completed during the early part of the return stroke. A spark plug, glow plug, or hot bulb may be used to aid combustion if the compression ratio is relatively low, or they may be omitted if a higher compression ratio is used. The ratios $r_v = v_1/v_2$, $r_c = v_4/v_3$, and $r_p = p_3/p_2$ are called *compression ratio*, *cut-off ratio*, and *constant-volume pressure ratio* respectively.

Assuming an ideal gas with constant specific heats to be the working fluid, the net work per pound of working substance is

$$w = (u_3 - u_2) + (h_4 - h_3) - (u_5 - u_1)$$
$$= c_v(T_3 - T_2) + c_p(T_4 - T_3) - c_v(T_5 - T_1)$$
$$= c_v(T_3 - T_2 + T_1 - T_5) + c_p(T_4 - T_3) \qquad (19.23)$$

The efficiency of the cycle is

$$\eta = \frac{q_A - q_R}{q_A} = 1 - \frac{q_R}{q_A} = 1 - \frac{u_5 - u_1}{u_3 - u_2 + h_4 - h_3} \qquad (19.24)$$

$$= 1 - \frac{c_v(T_5 - T_1)}{c_v(T_3 - T_2) + c_p(T_4 - T_3)}$$

$$= 1 - \frac{T_5 - T_1}{T_3 - T_2 + \gamma(T_4 - T_3)} \qquad (19.25)$$

Example 19.7. An air-standard dual cycle has a compression ratio of 16.5, and the pressure and temperature at the beginning of compression are 14.7 psia and

80 °F respectively. The temperature after constant-volume combustion is 2140 °F, and 2900 °F after constant-pressure combustion. Determine: (a) the cutoff ratio, (b) the constant-volume pressure ratio, (c) the heat added and rejected per pound of air, and (d) the thermal efficiency.

Solution. (a) In Fig. 19.20, note that $p_1 = 14.7$, $T_1 = 540$ °R, $T_3 = 2600$ °R, $T_4 = 3360$ °R. Since $p_4 = p_3$, the cutoff ratio v_4/v_3 is given by

$$\frac{v_4}{v_3} = \frac{T_4}{T_3} = \frac{3360}{2600} = 1.29$$

(b) The temperature T_2 at the end of the compression process 1–2 is obtained from the gas tables corresponding to $v_{r2} = (1/16.5)v_{r1} = (1/16.5)(144.32) = 8.75$, i.e., $T_2 = 1569$ °R. Since process 2–3 is a constant-volume process, the constant-volume pressure ratio p_3/p_2 is simply

$$\frac{p_3}{p_2} = \frac{T_3}{T_2} = \frac{2600}{1569} = 1.66$$

(c) The heat added per pound of air, using values from the gas tables, is

$$q_A = (u_3 - u_2) + (h_4 - h_3)$$
$$= (496.26 - 279.91) + (896.80 - 674.49) = 438.66 \text{ Btu/lbm}$$

The heat rejected per pound of air is

$$q_R = (u_5 - u_1)$$

However, before this can be obtained, the properties at state 5 must first be found. The specific volume at state 1 is

$$v_1 = \frac{(53.3)(540)}{(14.7)(144)} = 13.6 \text{ cu ft/lbm}$$

At states 2 and 3, it is

$$v_2 = v_3 = \frac{13.6}{16.5} = 0.825 \text{ cu ft/lbm}$$

Now, v_4/v_5, the cutoff ratio, was previously found to be 1.29, so that, at state 4, the specific volume is

$$v_4 = (1.29)(0.825) = 1.06$$

As for the relative volume at state 4, it is read from the gas tables (corresponding to $T_4 = 3360$ °R) as $v_{r4} = 0.8121$. Since process 4–5 is isentropic, the following may be written:

$$\frac{v_{r5}}{v_{r4}} = \frac{v_5}{v_4} = \frac{v_1}{v_4} = \frac{13.6}{1.06} = 12.81$$

Thus

$$v_{r5} = (12.81)(v_{r4}) = (12.81)(0.8121) = 10.4$$

Corresponding to this, read $u_5 = 261.85$. The heat rejected is then

$$q_R = u_5 - u_1 = 261.85 - 92.04 = 169.81 \text{ Btu/lbm}$$

(d) The thermal efficiency is

$$\eta = \frac{q_A - q_R}{q_A} = \frac{438.66 - 169.81}{438.66} = 0.612 = 61.2 \text{ per cent}$$

19.13 Brayton Cycle

The air-standard Brayton† cycle is the cycle for a simple gas turbine. It is shown in Fig. 19.21. The processes, in order, are: isentropic compression 1–2, constant-pressure addition of heat 2–3, isentropic expansion 3–4, and constant-pressure rejection of heat 4–1. They are carried out separately in a compressor, a combustor, and a turbine.

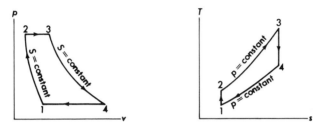

Fig. 19.21 Air-Standard Brayton Cycle.

Under steady-flow conditions, and assuming a working fluid with constant heat capacities, the efficiency of a Brayton cycle is

$$\eta = \frac{Q_{\text{added}} - Q_{\text{rejected}}}{Q_{\text{added}}} = \frac{(h_3 - h_2) - (h_4 - h_1)}{h_3 - h_2}$$

$$= \frac{c_p(T_3 - T_2) - c_p(T_4 - T_1)}{c_p(T_3 - T_2)} = 1 - \frac{T_4 - T_1}{T_3 - T_2} \qquad (19.26)$$

The latter expression may be rewritten (through multiplication and division by T_1/T_2) as

$$\eta = 1 - \frac{T_1(T_4/T_1 - 1)}{T_2(T_3/T_2 - 1)} \qquad (19.27)$$

Since $p_3/p_4 = p_2/p_1$, it follows that

$$\frac{T_3}{T_2} = \frac{T_4}{T_1}$$

and Eq. (19.27) becomes

$$\eta = 1 - \frac{T_1}{T_2} \qquad (19.28)$$

---

† George B. Brayton (1830–1892) was a Boston engineer. His cycle was first used with reciprocating engines, although it is now used only for gas turbines.

Another expression for the thermal efficiency of the Brayton cycle may be obtained by writing

$$\frac{p_2}{p_1} = \left(\frac{T_2}{T_1}\right)^{\gamma/(\gamma-1)}$$

Equation (19.27) then becomes

$$\eta = 1 - \frac{1}{(p_2/p_1)^{(\gamma-1)/\gamma}} = 1 - \frac{1}{(r_p)^{(\gamma-1)/\gamma}} \tag{19.29}$$

where $r_p = p_2/p_1$ is the *pressure ratio*. It is seen that the efficiency of the air-standard Brayton cycle increases as the pressure ratio is increased.

The Brayton cycle may be carried out in the steady-flow arrangement shown in Fig. 19.22, with the work delivered by the turbine being used, in

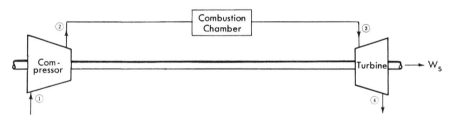

Fig. 19.22 Sample Gas Turbine Plant

part, to drive the compressor. The remainder is the net work of the plant, which is then available for driving an electric generator or for propulsion. For an ideal plant, the compression and expansion processes are isentropic, and there is no pressure drop through the combustion chamber. An actual plant will differ from the ideal plant because of irreversibilities in the compressor and turbine, and because of pressure drop in the flow passages and in the combustion chamber.

It is of interest to determine the value of the pressure ratio r_p $(=p_2/p_1)$ that will give a maximum work output between two given temperature limits. The problem arises from the fact that in practice T_1 is limited to atmospheric temperature (around 520 °R) and T_3 is fixed by the maximum temperature which the highly stressed

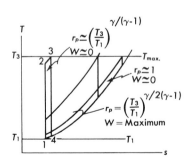

Fig. 19.23 Work Output of Brayton Cycle in Relation to Pressure Ratio.

parts of the turbine can withstand (around 1800 °R). This is shown in Fig. 19.23. Having fixed T_1 and T_3, the *maximum* pressure ratio theoretically possible is

$$\left(\frac{T_1}{T_3}\right)^{\gamma/(\gamma-1)}$$

However, examination of Fig. 19.23 shows that this is not a practical value, because at this pressure ratio the compressor work and the turbine work are equal, and the net work output is *zero*. Similarly, for a pressure ratio of unity, the net output is zero. Between these two extreme values there exists an *optimum pressure ratio* for which the work output is a *maximum*. Since the net work output per unit mass is given by

$$w = c_p(T_3 - T_4) - c_p(T_2 - T_1)$$

$$= -\left[c_p T_1\left(\frac{T_2}{T_1} - 1\right) + c_p T_3\left(\frac{T_4}{T_3} - 1\right)\right] = -\left[c_p T_1\left(\frac{T_2}{T_1} - 1\right) + c_p T_3\left(\frac{T_1}{T_2} - 1\right)\right]$$

$$= -\left\{c_p T_1\left[(r_p)^{(\gamma-1)/\gamma} - 1\right] + c_p T_3\left[\frac{1}{(r_p)^{(\gamma-1)/\gamma}} - 1\right]\right\} \qquad (19.30)$$

the optimum pressure ratio can be obtained by differentiating Eq. (19.30) with respect to r_p (treating T_1 and T_3 as constants), equating to zero, and solving for r_p. The result is

$$(r_p)_{\text{optimum}} = \left(\frac{T_3}{T_1}\right)^{\gamma/2(\gamma-1)} \qquad (19.31)$$

With $T_1 \approx 520$ °R, $T_3 \approx 1800$ °R, the corresponding optimum pressure ratio is around 8.8. For this value of $r_p (= p_2/p_1)$, the flow rate of air for a given horsepower output is a minimum and hence the size of the power plant is a minimum.

Example 19.8. Air enters the compressor of a Brayton cycle at 65 °F and 14.7 psia. It leaves at a pressure of 70 psia. The maximum temperature of the cycle is limited to 1600 °F by metallurgical considerations. Assuming a compressor efficiency of 82 per cent, a turbine efficiency of 85 per cent and a pressure drop of 2 psi between compressor and turbine, determine: (a) the pressure and temperature at each point in the cycle, (b) the net work of the cycle, (c) the thermal efficiency of the cycle, (d) the percentage of the turbine work required to drive the compressor.

Solution. (a) In Fig. 19.24, let 2*i* denote the state at the end of ideal (isentropic) compres-

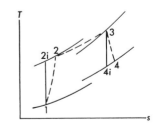

Fig. 19.24 Comparison of Actual Brayton Cycle with Ideal Brayton Cycle.

sion, and 2 denote the state at the end of actual (82 per cent efficiency) compression. The temperature corresponding to $2i$ is first obtained by writing

$$T_{2i} = T_1\left(\frac{p_2}{p_1}\right)^{(\gamma-1)/\gamma} = 525\left(\frac{70}{14.7}\right)^{(1.4-1)/1.4}$$
$$= 821 \ ^\circ\text{R}$$

The actual temperature T_2 is then obtained from the definition of a compressor efficiency:

$$0.82 = \frac{h_{i2}-h_1}{h_2-h_1} = \frac{T_{2i}-T_1}{T_2-T_1} = \frac{821-525}{T_2-525};$$

which gives
$$T_2 = 886 \ ^\circ\text{R}$$

The temperature at state 3 is 2060 °R (given), and the pressure is $p_3 = p_2 - 2 = 70 - 2 = 68$ psia. The temperature at the end of ideal expansion (state $4i$) is given by

$$T_{4i} = T_3\left(\frac{p_4}{p_3}\right)^{(\gamma-1)/\gamma} = 2060\left(\frac{14.7}{68}\right)^{(1.4-1)/1.4} = 1329 \ ^\circ\text{R}$$

The temperature T_4 at the end of actual expansion (85 per cent efficiency) is obtained from

$$0.85 = \frac{h_3-h_4}{h_3-h_{4i}} = \frac{T_3-T_4}{T_3-T_{4i}} = \frac{2060-T_4}{2060-1329}; \ \ T_4 = 1439 \ ^\circ\text{R}$$

(b) The compressor work is 0.24 (886 − 525) = 86.7 Btu/lbm. The turbine work is 0.24 (2060 − 1439) = 149.2 Btu/lbm. The net work of the cycle is thus

$$w_{\text{net}} = 149.2 - 86.7 = 62.5 \ \text{Btu/lbm}$$

(c) The heat added in the cycle is 0.24 (2060 − 886) = 281.5 Btu/lbm. The thermal efficiency is

$$\eta = \frac{w_{\text{net}}}{q_{\text{added}}} = \frac{86.7}{281.5} = 0.222 \ \text{or} \ 22.2 \ \text{per cent}$$

(d) The percentage of the turbine work required to drive the compressor is

$$\frac{w_{\text{compressor}}}{w_{\text{turbine}}} = \frac{86.7}{149.2} = 0.581 \ \text{or} \ 58.1 \ \text{per cent}$$

19.14   Brayton Cycle with Regeneration and Stage Compression

The efficiency of a gas turbine cycle may be improved by regenerative heating, staged compression with intercooling, staged expansion with reheating, or by a combination of all these features. The installation for a closed cycle with a one-stage regenerative heating is shown in Fig. 19.25.

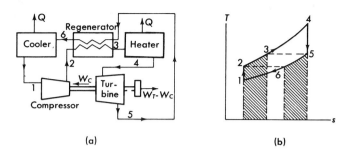

Fig. 19.25 Regenerative Brayton Cycle.

Starting at point 1, the working gas enters the compressor where it is compressed to state 2. The gas is then heated at constant pressure in the regenerator to state 3 by transfer of heat from the hotter gas leaving the turbine. The temperature of the gas leaving the regenerator, T_3, is, in the ideal case, equal to T_5, the temperature of the gas leaving the turbine. The effectiveness, e_r, of the regenerator is thus

$$e_r = \frac{T_3 - T_2}{T_5 - T_6} = \frac{T_3 - T_2}{T_5 - T_2} \qquad (19.32)$$

Additional heat transfer from an external source or heat released through chemical reaction in a combustion increases the temperature to T_4. The gas enters the turbine in state 4 and expands to state 5; it then enters the regenerator where it is cooled at constant pressure to state 6. Further heat rejection (to an external sink) brings it back to state 1.

Per pound of working gas, the heat added, the heat rejected, and the net work are respectively $h_4 - h_3$, $h_6 - h_1$, and $h_4 - h_5 - h_2 + h_1$. The thermal efficiency is thus

$$\eta = 1 - \frac{q_{rejected}}{q_{added}} = 1 - \frac{h_6 - h_1}{h_4 - h_3}$$

$$= 1 - \frac{c_p(T_6 - T_1)}{c_p(T_4 - T_3)} \qquad (19.33)$$

The efficiency of a Brayton cycle may also be improved by using multi-stage compression with intercooling, and multistage expansion with reheating. Figure 19.26 shows such an installation. Here, the working gas is compressed and expanded in two stages.

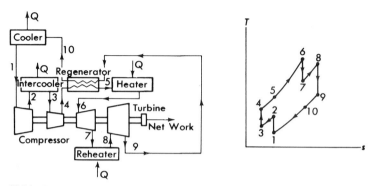

Fig. 19.26 Regenerative Brayton Cycle with Stage Compression and Stage Expansion.

Per pound of working gas, the heat supplied in the heater and reheater is

$$q_{added} = (h_6 - h_5) + (h_8 - h_7)$$

while the heat rejected in the intercooler and gas cooler is

$$q_{rejected} = (h_{10} - h_1) + (h_2 - h_3)$$

The thermal efficiency is thus

$$\eta = 1 - \frac{q_{rejected}}{q_{added}} = 1 - \frac{(h_{10} - h_1) + (h_2 - h_3)}{(h_6 - h_5) + (h_8 - h_7)} \qquad (19.34)$$

or, for an ideal gas with constant specific heats,

$$\eta = 1 - \frac{(T_{10} - T_1) + (T_2 - T_3)}{(T_6 - T_5) + (T_8 - T_7)} \qquad (19.35)$$

Example 19.9.   An air-standard gas-turbine installation operates under the following conditions: Air enters the compressor at 60 °F and 14.7 psia. An intercooler cools the air at 35 psia to 60 °F. It leaves the second stage compressor at 75 psia and flows through a regenerator of effectiveness 0.65. After passage through the heater, it enters the turbine at 1500 °F and expands to 35 psia. It is reheated to 500 °F and finally expanded to 14.7 psia. Assuming isentropic compression and expansion, and neglecting pressure drops, determine: (a) the heat added, (b) the heat rejected, (c) the thermal efficiency, and (d) the ratio of compressor work to turbine output.

Solution.   (a) Referring to Fig. 19.26, the heat added per pound of working fluid is

$$q_{added} = c_p(T_6 - T_5) + c_p(T_8 - T_7)$$

T_6 and T_8 are given, but T_5 and T_7 are not. They are calculated as follows. From the definition of the regenerator effectiveness:

$$e_r = 0.65 = \frac{T_5 - T_4}{T_9 - T_{10}} = \frac{T_5 - T_4}{T_9 - T_4}$$

Neither T_4 nor T_9 are given, but they are easily obtained:

$$T_4 = T_3\left(\frac{p_4}{p_3}\right)^{(\gamma-1)/\gamma} = 520\left(\frac{75}{35}\right)^{0.286} = 646.5\ ^\circ R;\quad T_9 = T_8\left(\frac{p_9}{p_8}\right)^{(\gamma-1)/\gamma}$$

$$= 1960\left(\frac{14.7}{35}\right)^{0.286} = 1528\ ^\circ R$$

Replacing these in the expression for the regenerator effectiveness gives

$$T_5 = T_4 + e_r(T_9 - T_4) = 646.5 + 0.65(1528 - 646.5)$$
$$= 1219.5\ ^\circ R$$

As for T_7, it is given by

$$T_7 = T_6\left(\frac{p_7}{p_6}\right)^{(\gamma-1)/\gamma} = 1960\left(\frac{35}{75}\right)^{0.286} = 1573\ ^\circ R$$

The heat added is thus

$$c_p[(T_6 - T_5) + (T_8 - T_7)] = 0.24[(1960 - 1219.5) + (1960 - 1573)] = 270.5\ \text{Btu/lbm}$$

(b) The heat rejected is

$$c_p(T_2 - T_3) + c_p(T_{10} - T_1)$$

Neither T_2 nor T_{10} are given. The first is calculated from

$$T_2 = T_1\left(\frac{p_2}{p_1}\right)^{(\gamma-1)/\gamma} = 520\left(\frac{35}{14.7}\right)^{0.286} = 666\ ^\circ R$$

The second is obtained from an energy balance around the regenerator:

$$c_p(T_9 - T_{10}) = c_p(T_5 - T_4)$$

or

$$T_{10} = T_9 - T_5 - T_4 = 1528 - (1219.5 - 646.5) = 955\ ^\circ R$$

Thus

$$q_{\text{rejected}} = c_p[(T_2 - T_3) + (T_{10} - T_1)] = 0.24[(666 - 520) + (955 - 520)]$$
$$= 139.6\ \text{Btu/lbm}$$

(c) The thermal efficiency is

$$\eta = \frac{q_{\text{added}} - q_{\text{rejected}}}{q_{\text{added}}} = \frac{270.5 - 139.6}{270.5} = 0.484\ \text{or 48.4 per cent}$$

Compare this with the corresponding answer in Ex. 19.8.

(d) The turbine work is

$$w_{\text{turbine}} = c_p(T_6 - T_7) + c_p(T_8 - T_9)$$
$$= 0.24[(1960 - 1573) + (1960 - 1528)] = 196.6\ \text{Btu/lbm}$$

The compressor work is

$$w_{\text{compressor}} = c_p(T_2 - T_1) + c_p(T_4 - T_3)$$
$$= 0.24[(666 - 520) + (646.5 - 520)] = 65.4 \text{ Btu/lbm}$$

The ratio of compressor work to turbine work is thus

$$\frac{w_{\text{compressor}}}{w_{\text{turbine}}} = \frac{65.4}{196.6} = 1333 \text{ or } 33.3 \text{ per cent}$$

19.15 Other Cycles

As the number of compression and expansion stages increases, the gas-turbine cycle gradually takes on the appearances shown in Fig. 19.27. In the limit, for an infinite number of multistage compression and expansion with intercooling, reheating, and heat exchange, the gas-turbine cycle becomes an Ericcson cycle [Fig. 19.27(c)]. This is a cycle which consists of two isothermals and two isobarics. The importance of this cycle is that its efficiency equals that of a Carnot cycle operating between the same temperatures. This is because all the heat is supplied and rejected isothermally. On the other hand, the Otto, Diesel and mixed (dual) cycles all have efficiencies less than the Carnot efficiency based upon the maximum and minimum temperatures in the cycle. Therefore it would seem that the Ericcson has an important feature to recommend it (in fact it was originally proposed as a basis for a reciprocating engine). However, the practical difficulties of obtaining such a cycle are very great. It is difficult to achieve isothermal compression or expansion in a machine operating at reasonable speeds. Also, there will be pressure drops and a temperature difference between the flowing streams in the generator.

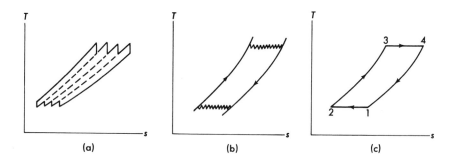

Fig. 19.27 Gas Turbine Cycle Transforming into Ericcson Cycle.

Another cycle which has the same efficiency as that of a Carnot cycle based upon the maximum and minimum temperatures of the cycle is that shown in Fig. 19.28. Consisting of two constant volume processes (2–3 and 4–1) and two isothermals (1–2 and 3–4), it is called the Stirling cycle.

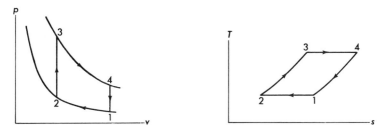

Fig. 19.28 Stirling Cycle.

The heat supplied during process 2–3 is equal to the heat rejected during process 4–1. Ideally, this can be accomplished reversibly in a regenerator consisting of a matrix of small tubes. The only heat added from an external source is that which is transferred during the isothermal process 3–4, and the only heat rejected to an external sink is that transferred during the isothermal process 1–2. Furthermore, the mean effective pressure of this cycle is greater than that of the Carnot cycle (the latter has a mean effective pressure which is very small, thereby detracting from its usefulness as a practical cycle). However, the Stirling cycle is still impracticable because of the difficulty involved in obtaining a regenerator of reasonable size which can operate at temperatures comparable to those found in Otto, Diesel, or mixed engines.

19.16   Compound Power Plants

Compound gas power plants are designed to capitalize on the advantages of both reciprocating engines and gas turbines. Higher maximum gas temperatures can be used in reciprocating engines than in gas turbines because metal parts in a reciprocating engine are in contact with gases at the maximum temperature only during part of the cycle. During much of the cycle, these parts are in contact with relatively cool gases. This is not the case of a gas turbine, where the gas temperature at each point is constant. On the other hand, reciprocating engines are not as good as turbines for expanding gases to low pressures, because the engine size becomes prohibitive. In other words, turbines are much more suited for handling large volumes of gas. To utilize the advantages of both reciprocating engines and turbines, compound engines have been designed in which the high-temperature and high-pressure expansion occurs in a reciprocating engine and the low-temperature, low-pressure expansion occurs in a turbine. In such an installation, exhaust gases from the reciprocating engine drive a turbine which in turn supplies most of the net power output of the plant. This is shown in Fig. 19.29(a).

Figure 19.29(b) shows another arrangement of a compound power plant. Here, the engine and compressor are replaced by a gas generator whose sole function is to supply gas for driving the turbine. The gas generator supplies no work output, but merely consists of a free-piston engine compressor. Air in the bounce cylinders is compressed during the power stroke of the opposed pistons (which are synchronized to each other by suitable linkage) and then expands to move the pistons together to compress the air in the combustion chamber. The hot gas produced at high pressure drives the turbine.

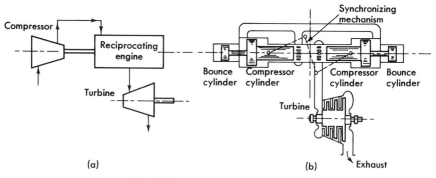

Fig. 19.29   Compound Power Set.

19.17   Jet Engines

The Brayton cycle is the basic cycle for jet engines. The latter may be classified into: (a) ram-jets, (b) pulse-jets, and (c) turbo-jets. They are discussed below.

(a) *Ram-jet.* The main elements of an athodyd or ram-jet engine (shown in Fig. 19.30) are an inlet diffuser, a combustion chamber, and an exit nozzle.

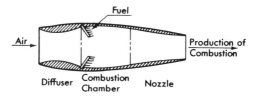

Fig. 19.30   Ram-Jet.

The purpose of the diffuser is to reduce the relative velocity of the inlet air and increase its pressure. In an ideal diffuser, this compression is isentropic. In the combustion chamber or combustor, fuel is burned at constant pressure and the products of combustion leave at high temperature. The products expand in the exit nozzle to ambient pressure with a decrease in enthalpy and an increase in relative velocity. It is seen that the ram-jet operates on an open Brayton cycle.

(b) *Pulse-jet*. The pulse-jet (Fig. 19.31) is an intermittent firing duct system. It was developed from the inability of the ram-jet to be self-starting. The main elements are: inlet diffuser, inlet valve with mechanical control, combustor, and exit nozzle. The engine was first used in the V-1 buzz bomb of World War II. The bomb was launched from a catapult, and started by means of compressed air and electric ignition. In flight, air was forced into the combustor by ram effect through shutters opening against spring pressure. Fuel was injected into the air stream and ignited by residual flame from previous combustion. As the pressure during combustion increased, the shutters

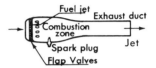

Fig. 19.31 Pulse-Jet.

were closed and the products of combustion expelled through the rear nozzle and tube. Momentary suction created in the combustor by this flow reopened the shutters to start the cycle of events anew. The number of cycles per second was around forty, resulting in an intermittent thrust. The operating cycle was approximated by the *Lenoir cycle:* Constant-pressure admission, constant-volume combustion, isentropic expansion. This cycle, however, is of exceedingly low efficiency.

(c) *Turbo-jet*. The turbo-jet engine is in essence a gas-turbine plant with the plant output in the form of a high-velocity gas stream instead of shaft power. In Fig. 19.32, the main elements are the inlet diffuser, the compressor, the combustor, the gas turbine, and the exit nozzle. The turbine delivers just sufficient power to drive the compressor, so that no net shaft

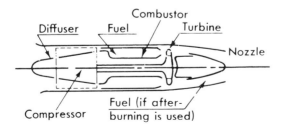

Fig. 19.32 Turbo-Jet Engine.

power is available. The performance of the turbojet engine is computed from the open Brayton cycle.

At low Mach numbers, a turbo-jet is inefficient. This has led to the development of the turbo-prop, shown in Fig. 19.33. Here, the gas turbine, geared to a propeller, develops greater power than the compressor requires. Note that, proceeding from the ram-jet to the turbo-prop jet, the exhaust jet decreases in velocity. This is because, generally, a fast aircraft requires a high-velocity jet and a slow aircraft requires a low-velocity jet.

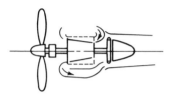

Fig. 19.33 Turbo-Prop Engine.

19.18 Rocket Engine

The rocket engine differs from the previously mentioned propulsion devices in that it carries its own oxidizer, instead of using the surrounding atmospheric air as oxidizer. For this reason it is the only power plant suitable for very high altitudes or for space flight. A typical rocket engine, along with its theoretical cycle, is shown in Fig. 19.34. The rocket engine

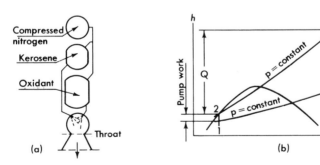

Fig. 19.34 Rocket Engine.

carries both fuel and oxidizer. The two substances together are usually known as the propellants. For short durations, such as those involved in temporary thrust boosting or starting of ram-jet aircraft, solid fuel is used. For longer durations, a liquid fuel (kerosene) and a liquid oxidant (nitric acid or hydrogen peroxide) are preferred. The fuel is either fed into the combustion chamber by mechanical pumps or forced in by compressed nitrogen carried in a separate container.

Combustion takes place at essentially constant pressure (around 300 psia), with the hot gases expanding through the nozzle to a high velocity jet (and therefore a large thrust). The idealized cycle of a rocket [Fig. 19.33(b)] consists of an isentropic compression, a constant-pressure adiabatic combustion, and an isentropic expansion. Actual performance calculations, however, are complicated by the fact that temperatures reached during combustion are quite high (in the neighborhood of 4500 °F), so that dissociation is likely to occur. For this reason, the combustion chamber and nozzle are cooled, usually by the liquid fuel prior to injection, so that the combustion process is not strictly adiabatic. Another unknown item is the extent to which the reactions still continue during the expansion of the hot gases in the nozzle.

Example 19.10. Hot gas (of specific heat ratio $\gamma = 1.25$ and gas constant $R = 51.5$ ft lbf/lbm-°R) enters the nozzle of an ideal rocket engine at stagnation conditions of 280 psia and 5000 °R. It expands isentropically to 14.5 psia at a flow rate of 98 lbm/sec. Determine: (a) the exit velocity, (b) the thrust developed.

Solution. In Fig. 19.33(b), $p_3 = 320$ psia, $T_3 = 5000$ °R. The exit velocity $\mathcal{V}_4$ is obtained from the energy relation for a nozzle:

$$\frac{\mathcal{V}_4^2}{2g_c} = h_3 - h_4$$

For a perfect gas with constant γ, this becomes

$$\frac{\mathcal{V}_4^2}{2g_c} = \left(\frac{R\gamma}{\gamma-1}\right)(T_3 - T_4) = \left(\frac{R\gamma}{\gamma-1}\right)T_3\left(1 - \frac{T_4}{T_3}\right)$$

or, upon replacement of T_4/T_3 by $(p_4/p_3)^{(\gamma-1)/\gamma}$,

$$\frac{\mathcal{V}_4^2}{2g_c} = \left(\frac{R\gamma}{\gamma-1}\right)T_3\left[1 - \left(\frac{p_4}{p_3}\right)^{(\gamma-1)/\gamma}\right]$$

Thus

$$\mathcal{V}_4 = \sqrt{\frac{2g_c R\gamma T_3}{\gamma-1}\left[1 - \left(\frac{p_4}{p_3}\right)^{(\gamma-1)/\gamma}\right]}$$

$$= \sqrt{\frac{2(32.2)(51.5)(1.25)(5000)}{1.25-1}\left[1 - \left(\frac{14.5}{280}\right)^{(1.25-1)/1.25}\right]}$$

$$= 6140 \text{ fps}$$

(b) The thrust† developed is

$$F = \dot{m}\mathscr{V}_4 = \frac{98}{32.2}(6140) = 18,700 \text{ lbf}$$

Note, however, that the thrust is not the most important criterion of performance. Because a large proportion of the total weight of a rocket is comprised of fuel, it is the thrust per pound of products discharged which is really important. This quantity, often called the *specific impulse*, is, in this case, equal to $18,700/98 = 191$ lbf-sec/lbm.

Example 19.11. Air enters the diffuser of a turbo-jet at a relative velocity of 400 mph (587 fps); the turbo-jet is traveling at 400 mph at an altitude of 30,000 ft. Liquid octane at 530 °R is introduced into the stream of compressed air at a rate of 0.0163 pounds for every 0.9837 pounds of air. The turbine produces the same amount of power as that required by the compressor. The products of combustion leave the exit nozzle with a velocity of 2423 fps. Determine: (a) the thrust per pound of air per second, (b) the equivalent horsepower for a flow rate of 40 pounds of air per second, (c) the propulsive efficiency.

Solution. (a) Let m_a denote the mass flow rate of air in pounds per second, and m_f the mass flow rate of fuel in pounds per second. The momentum of the entering stream is $(m_a/J_c)/\mathscr{V}_1$, where $\mathscr{V}_1$ is the velocity of the air entering the diffuser; the momentum of the leaving stream is $[(m_a+m_f)/J_e/\mathscr{V}_2$, where $\mathscr{V}_2$ is the velocity of the combustion products leaving the exit nozzle. The rate of momentum change or thrust is then

$$F = \frac{m_a+m_f}{g_c}\mathscr{V}_2 - \frac{m_a}{g_c}\mathscr{V}_1$$

$$= \frac{m_a}{g_c}\left[\left(1+\frac{m_f}{m_a}\right)\mathscr{V}_2 - \mathscr{V}_1\right]$$

$$= \frac{0.9837}{32.2}\left[\left(1+\frac{0.0163}{0.9837}\right)(2423) - 587\right]$$

and the thrust per pound of air per second (specific impulse) is therefore

$$\frac{F}{0.9837} = \frac{1}{32.2}\left[\left(1+\frac{0.0163}{0.9837}\right)(2423) - 587\right] = 57.1 \text{ lb}_s\text{-sec/lbm}$$

(b) The thrust for a flow rate of air of 40 lbm/sec is

$$(57.1)(40) = 2284 \text{ lbf}$$

† It will be shown in the next chapter that the thrust developed by a rocket is

$$F = \dot{m}\mathscr{V}_e + A_e(p_c - p_a)$$

where $\dot{m}$ is the mass rate of products discharged, $\mathscr{V}_e$ is the exhaust velocity, A_e is the exit area, p_e is the pressure in the exit plane of the nozzle, and p_a is the atmospheric pressure. In the event the pressure in the exit plane equals atmospheric pressure, this reduces to

$$F = \dot{m}\mathscr{V}_e$$

Since the aircraft is moving at a speed of 587 fps, the work done by this thrust is

$$(2,284)(587) = 1,340,000 \text{ ft lbf/sec}$$

This is equivalent to a horsepower of

$$\frac{1,340,000}{550} = 2,440 \text{ hp}$$

(c) The propulsive efficiency, η_p, is the ratio of the propulsive work to the energy input. The propulsive work is $1,340,000/778 = 1,720$ Btu/sec. The energy input from the fuel is $40(0.0163/0.9837)(19,250) = 12,500$ Btu/sec, where 19,250 Btu/lbm is the heating value of octane. The propulsive efficiency is thus

$$\eta_p = \frac{1,720}{12,500} = 0.138 \text{ or } 13.8 \text{ per cent}$$

REFRIGERATION CYCLES

19.19 Refrigeration

The third part of this chapter deals with refrigeration, which is another important application of thermodynamics. Refrigeration is the production and maintenance, within a space, of a temperature lower than that of the surroundings.

Until fairly recent times, refrigeration was accomplished mostly by non-cyclic processes such as the melting of ice or the sublimation of carbon dioxide. Nowadays, a refrigerating installation operates on a cycle, so that by supplying work to the refrigerant, it is possible to abstract heat from the low-temperature source (the space to be refrigerated) and to reject heat to a higher-temperature sink (the surrounding atmosphere). Thus, a refrigerator is essentially the reverse of a heat engine; it operates on a reverse power cycle. The *coefficient of performance* of a refrigerator is the ratio of heat removed from the refrigerated space to the work supplied to do the job.

In other words

$$\text{C O P} = \frac{q_{\text{abstracted}}}{w_{\text{input}}} \tag{19.36}$$

Just as a heat engine operating between two given heat reservoirs cannot have a thermal efficiency greater than a Carnot engine operating between the same reservoirs, so a refrigerating machine operating between two given heat reservoirs cannot have a coefficient of performance greater than that of a Carnot refrigerator operating between these reservoirs. Refer to Fig.

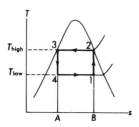

Fig. 19.35
Reversed Carnot Cycle.

19.35 and recall that the coefficient of performance of a Carnot refrigerator is given by

$$\text{C O P} = \frac{q_{\text{abstracted}}}{w_{\text{input}}} = \frac{T_1(s_B - s_A)}{(T_2 - T_1)(s_B - s_A)}$$

$$= \frac{T_1}{T_2 - T_1} = \frac{T_{\text{low}}}{T_{\text{high}} - T_{\text{low}}} \qquad (19.37)$$

The unit of capacity used in rating refrigerating machines is the *ton of refrigeration*. By definition, one ton of refrigeration is equivalent to a heat removal of 12,000 Btu/hr or 200 Btu/min from the refrigerated space. The choice of such a unit has its origin in the fact that, since the latent heat of fusion of ice is 144 Btu/lbm at 32 °F, it takes a heat removal of 12,000 Btu/hr to produce a ton of ice a day. Another measure of performance of refrigerating machines is the ratio of the horsepower required to drive the machine to the refrigerating capacity of the machine. This is called the *horsepower per ton* (*hp/ton*).

Just as power cycles may be classified into vapor power cycles or gas power cycles, depending on the state of the working fluid, so can refrigeration cycles be classified into *vapor refrigeration cycles* and *gas refrigeration cycles*. The following sections present an analysis of some basic refrigeration cycles, beginning with the vapor compression cycle.

19.20   Vapor Compression Refrigeration Cycle

The vapor compression refrigeration cycle is shown in Fig. 19.36. Starting at state 1, saturated (or sometimes superheated) vapor at low pressure enters the compressor and, in the ideal case, is reversibly and adiabatically compressed to state 2. This is followed by heat rejection at constant pressure (process 2–3), with the working fluid (refrigerant) leaving the condenser either as saturated or subcooled liquid. The refrigerant

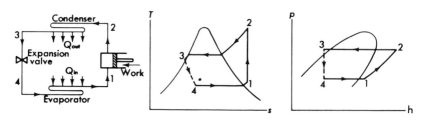

Fig. 19.36   Vapor Compression Refrigeration Cycle.

next enters the throttling valve and leaves at state 4, some of it flashing into vapor during the throttling process. It is then evaporated at constant pressure (process 4–1) in the evaporator where it abstracts heat from the refrigerated space. The latter step supplies the refrigerating effect. The coefficient of performance is

$$\mathrm{C\,O\,P} = \frac{q_{abstracted}}{w_{input}} = \frac{h_1 - h_4}{(h_2 - h_3) - (h_1 - h_4)}$$

$$= \frac{h_1 - h_4}{h_2 - h_1} \qquad (19.38)$$

The cycle just described represents the basic vapor-compression cycle. In practice, refrigerating machines operate on cycles which include many refinements of the basic cycle. An actual refrigerating installation would also differ somewhat from that outlined above in that pressure drops and heat gains and losses would occur in the piping, and that compression would not be isentropic.

Example 19.12. An ice-making refrigerating plant having a capacity of 20 tons operates with ammonia as refrigerant. Chilled brine (obtained by means of the evaporator) is used as an intermediary circuit. The brine leaves the evaporator at 15 °F, and to obtain this temperature, an evaporator temperature of 5 °F is assumed. Cooling water at 68 °F is supplied to the condenser; it leaves at 80 °F, enabling the ammonia to condense at 86 °F. Assuming "dry" and isentropic compression, and neglecting piping losses, determine: (a) the horsepower per ton of refrigeration, (b) the cooling water requirement per ton of refrigeration, (c) the coefficient of performance, (d) the coefficient of performance of a reverse Carnot cycle operating between the same evaporator and condenser temperatures.

Solution. (a) Referring to Fig. 19.36 and using enthalpy values from ammonia tables, the refrigeration effect per pound of refrigerant is

$$h_1 - h_4 = 613.3 - 138.9 = 474.4 \text{ Btu/lbm}$$

The refrigerant flow rate per ton of refrigeration is

$$\frac{200 \text{ Btu/min–ton}}{474.4 \text{ Btu/lbm}} = 0.422 \text{ lb/min–ton}$$

The compressor work per pound of refrigerant is

$$h_2 - h_1 = 713.3 - 613.3 = 100 \text{ Btu/lbm}$$

The horsepower required per ton of refrigeration is thus

$$\frac{(0.422 \text{ lbm/min–ton})(100 \text{ Btu/lbm})}{42.42 \text{ Btu/min–hp}} = 0.995 \text{ hp/ton}$$

(b) On the basis of 1 ton of refrigeration, 0.422 lbm/min of refrigerant enters the condenser with an enthalpy of h_2 Btu/lbm and leaves with an enthalpy of h_3

Btu/lbm. Cooling water enters at 68 °F and leaves at 80 °F. An energy balance at the condenser gives

$$0.422(h_2 - h_3) = 0.422(713.3 - 138.9) = m(1)(80 - 68)$$

where m refers to the mass flow rate of cooling water. Solving for $\dot{m}$ gives

$$m = \frac{0.422(713.3 - 138.9)}{(1)(80 - 68)} = 20.15 \text{ lb/min-ton}$$

(c) The coefficient of performance is

$$COP = \frac{h_1 - h_4}{h_2 - h_1} = \frac{613.3 - 138.9}{713.3 - 613.3} = \frac{474.4}{100} = 4.74$$

(d) The evaporator temperature is 5 °F and the condenser temperature is 86 °F. The coefficient of performance of a reverse Carnot cycle between these temperature limits is

$$COP_{\text{Carnot}} = \frac{T_{\text{evaporator}}}{T_{\text{condenser}} - T_{\text{evaporator}}} = \frac{465}{546 - 465} = 5.74$$

19.21 Volumetric Efficiency

The function of the compressor in a refrigerating installation is to remove refrigerant from the evaporator and deliver it to the condenser. A theoretically perfect compressor would have no clearance (i.e., no space between the end of the cylinder and the piston when the latter is at top dead center), no losses, and would pump on each stroke a quantity of refrigerant equal to the piston displacement. The adiabatic operation of such a compressor is shown in Fig. 19.37(a). The refrigerant is admitted at constant pressure, compressed isentropically, and discharged at constant pressure. The volumetric efficiency (ratio of the actual volume of gas drawn into the compressor on each stroke to the piston displacement) would be unity.

The effect of clearance is shown in Fig. 19.37(b). Let c, the clearance, be expressed as a certain per cent of the piston displacement. The refrigerant gas trapped in the clearance space $V_{2'}$ at the end of the discharge process

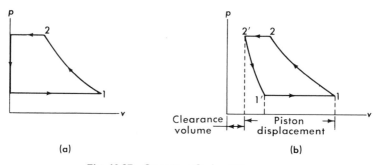

Fig. 19.37 Operating Cycle of Compressor.

expands isentropically to a volume $V_{1'}$ at the suction pressure and, in so doing, reduces the portion of the piston displacement effective in drawing in a new charge of gas. The ratio of the actual volume of new gas to the piston displacement is known as the *clearance volumetric efficiency*:

$$\eta_{cv} = \frac{V_1 - V_{1'}}{V_1 - V_{2'}} \tag{19.39}$$

Equation (19.39) is usually rewritten in terms of the clearance, c, and the pressure ratio, p_2/p_1, by noting that

$$V_1 - V_{1'} = (V_1 - V_{2'}) - (V_{1'} - V_{2'})$$

$$V_{1'} = V_{2'} \left(\frac{p_2}{p_1}\right)^{1/\gamma}$$

$$c = \frac{V_{2'}}{V_1 - V_{2'}}$$

Substitution of these into the equation for the clearance volumetric efficiency gives

$$\eta_{cv} = \frac{(V_1 - V_{2'}) - (V_{1'} - V_{2'})}{(V_1 - V_{2'})} = 1 - \frac{V_{1'} - V_{2'}}{V_1 - V_{2'}}$$

$$= 1 - \frac{V_{2'}(p_2/p_1)^{1/\gamma} - V_{2'}}{V_1 - V_{2'}} = 1 + \frac{V_{2'}}{V_1 - V_{2'}}\left[1 - \left(\frac{p_2}{p_1}\right)^{1/\gamma}\right]$$

$$= 1 + c - c\left(\frac{p_2}{p_1}\right)^{1/\gamma} \tag{19.40}$$

The clearance volumetric efficiency has the effect of increasing the compressor piston displacement required per ton of refrigeration. This is especially so if the compression ratio or spread between condenser and evaporator pressure increases. It has, however, no effect upon the horsepower required per ton of refrigeration, because the alternate compression and expansion of the trapped gas is analogous to the alternate compression and expansion of a spring, and, theoretically, consumes no power.

19.22 Multiple Evaporator and Compressor Systems

In many refrigeration applications, it is necessary to operate several evaporators at different temperatures. Fig. 19.38 shows such a possibility using only one compressor and one condenser. Two evaporators are shown, but more may be used. Between the condenser and each evaporator there is an expansion valve which controls the flow rate of refrigerant. Between

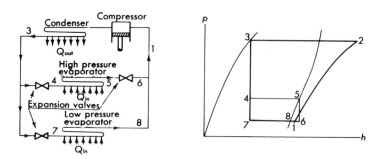

Fig. 19.38   Multiple Evaporator System.

all evaporators, excepting the one operating at the lowest pressure, there is a regulator valve which controls the suction pressure of the compressor. The remainder of the installation is similar to that of the previously mentioned simple cycle.

Use of a single compressor is often limited to systems of small capacity, because of the relatively large adiabatic work required by a single compressor. It is common practice, especially when the compression ratio is large, to reduce the required compressor work by using stage compression with intercooling. An example of this is shown in Fig. 19.39. The re-

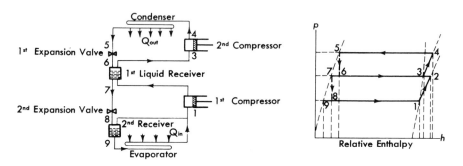

Fig. 19.39   Stage Compression and Expansion Refrigeration Cycle.

frigerant goes through two stages of compression and two stages of expansion (throttling). Two receivers (often called flash intercoolers) are used. The first receiver desuperheats the vapor on its way to the second compressor and also provides only liquid to the second expansion valve. The second receiver serves to relieve the evaporator of the useless flow of refrigerant that is already vaporized.

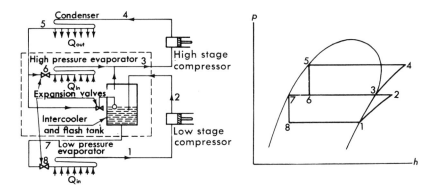

Fig. 19.40 Multiple Evaporator and Compressor Cycle.

Another variation of the basic cycle is shown in Fig. 19.40. It is used in situations requiring concurrent refrigeration at several temperature levels. This is true in many industrial plants, hotels, institutions, large restaurants and food markets. The cycle has two evaporators, two compressors, and one intercooler flash tank. It is best understood by means of the numerical example which follows.

Example 19.13. A multiple evaporator system for a frozen-food plant uses ammonia as the working fluid. It provides 15 tons of refrigeration at $-30\ °F$ to quick-freeze the food and 20 tons of refrigeration at $10\ °F$ to hold the food after it is frozen. Condensing temperature is $90\ °F$ and a two-stage compression with flash intercooling is used. Calculate the horsepower requirements of the cycle.

Solution. In Fig. 19.40, the enthalpies (obtained from ammonia tables) at the various state points are as follows: $h_1 = 601.4$; h_2 (after isentropic compression) $= 657$; $h_3 = 614.9$; h_4 (after isentropic compression) $= 712$; $h_5 = 143.5$; $h_6\ (=h_5) = 143.5$; $h_7 = 53.8$; $h_8\ (= h_7) = 53.8$. Starting at state 1, the mass flow rate through the lowest-temperature evaporator is

$$m_1 = \frac{(15\ \text{tons})(200\ \text{Btu/min–ton})}{[(601.4-53.8)\ \text{Btu/lbm]}} = 5.47\ \text{lbm/min}$$

This is also the flow rate through the low-stage compressor. To calculate the flow rate through the high-stage compressor, consider a portion of the system bounded by the dotted outline. It is seen that $m_2 = m_7 = 5.47$ lbm/min, and that consequently $m_3 = m_5$. Also, an energy balance gives

$$m_5 h_5 + (20)(200) + m_2 h_2 = m_3 h_3 + m_7 h_7$$

Replacing m_5 by m_3, this becomes

$$m_3 h_5 + 4000 + m_2 h_2 = m_3 h_3 + m_7 h_7$$

or

$$m_3(143.5)+4000+(5.47)(657) = m_3(614.9)+(5.47)(53.8)$$

Solving for m_3 gives

$$m_3 = 15.5 \text{ lbm/min}$$

The horsepower requirements are thus

$$\frac{m_1(h_2-h_1)}{42.42} = \frac{5.47(657-601.4)}{42.42} = 7.2 \text{ hp}$$

for the low-stage compressor, and

$$\frac{m_3(h_4-h_3)}{42.42} = \frac{15.5(712-615)}{42.42} = 31.5 \text{ hp}$$

for the high-stage compressor, giving a total of 38.7 hp for the cycle.

19.23   Steam-Jet Refrigeration

For refrigeration at temperature levels above 32 °F (such as in air conditioning) water may be used as the refrigerant. This is shown in Fig. 19.41, where the evaporator of the common vapor-compression system

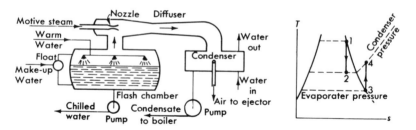

Fig. 19.41   Steam-Jet Refrigeration System.

has been replaced by an insulated flash chamber. Water to be cooled is piped into the evaporation chamber. Here it flashes partly into vapor, cooling both the vapor and the liquid to the saturation temperature corresponding to the pressure in the chamber. This pressure is maintained at the saturation pressure corresponding to the desired temperature of the chilled water. For example, if chilled water at 40 °F is desired, the pressure maintained in the flash chamber would be 0.2478 in. Hg. The chilled water may be used directly or it may cool some other fluid.

The vapor is removed from the flash chamber by the ejector and discharged into the condenser. Make-up water is supplied to replace the water removed. The motive steam is expanded through the nozzle along 1–2 as shown on the $T–s$ diagram, and the vapor from the flash chamber is entrained and compressed in the diffuser along 3–4. Note that the absolute pressure in the condenser is always less than atmospheric. For that reason, the steam-jet refrigeration system is often referred to as a *vacuum refrigeration* system. For an ideal ejector, the amount of motive steam required per pound of flash vapor is given by

$$m_{\text{steam}}(h_1 - h_2) = m_{\text{vapor}}(h_4 - h_3)$$

or

$$m_{\text{steam}} = \frac{h_4 - h_3}{h_1 - h_2}\, m_{\text{vapor}} \qquad (19.41)$$

The efficiency of an actual ejector is the ratio of the ideal amount of steam required to the actual amount of steam required. Starting from a value of 20 per cent for a compression ratio of 4, the efficiency drops to about 5 per cent for a compression ratio of 10.

19.24   Absorption Refrigeration System

In the refrigeration systems discussed so far, the energy required for compressing the refrigerant from the lower pressure to the higher pressure has been supplied in the form of work or in the form of kinetic energy. The work of compression, however, may be regarded as the available portion of a quantity of heat which has been supplied to an engine cycle from a source at a temperature higher than the upper temperature of the refrigeration cycle. The basic difference between an absorption system and a vapor-compression system is that refrigeration is mainly produced by a supply of heat rather than by a supply of work. In Fig. 19.42, the simple absorption

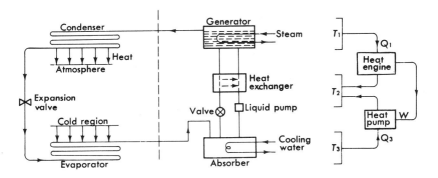

Fig. 19.42 Simple Absorption System.

cycle consists of a condenser, an expansion valve, an evaporator, a pump, and a generator. Heat supplied by the steam causes a vapor mixture of ammonia and water to be boiled off at high pressure in the generator. The vapor mixture, rich in ammonia, is condensed in the water-cooled condenser, and from that point on, the circuit is similar to that of a vapor-compression cycle. The vapor leaving the evaporator enters an absorber, where it is absorbed by aqua ammonia. As the concentration of ammonia in the solution increases, the strong solution is transferred to the generator by means of a liquid pump. The absorber is water cooled so as to remove the heat of solution as well as the heat of condensation.

To obtain the *coefficient of performance* for an absorption refrigeration cycle, let Q_1 be the quantity of heat which is supplied at the generator temperature T_1 to a reversible heat engine. The available portion W is then

$$W = \frac{T_1 - T_2}{T_1} Q_1 \qquad (19.42)$$

where T_2 is the temperature of the surroundings. Now, let a heat pump absorbing energy Q_3 at the cold temperature T_3 be operated by the work output of the heat engine. The work required by the heat pump is

$$W = \frac{T_2 - T_3}{T_3} Q_3 \qquad (19.43)$$

Equations (19.42) and (19.43) give

$$\frac{T_1 - T_2}{T_1} Q_1 = \frac{T_2 - T_3}{T_3} Q_3$$

This is solved for the coefficient of performance Q_3/Q_1:

$$\frac{Q_3}{Q_1} = \frac{T_3}{T_1} \cdot \frac{T_1 - T_2}{T_2 - T_3} \qquad (19.44)$$

The detailed calculation of an absorption cycle requires an understanding of the characteristics of binary mixtures. This is brought out by a discussion of the T–x, h–x, and s–x diagrams for aqua ammonia. Figure 19.43(a) represents a boiling diagram: at any pressure, the boiling temperature of the liquid mixture depends on the concentration x, which is the ratio of the amount of ammonia per unit mass of mixture. Note that when $x = 0$, the boiling temperature is the saturation temperature for water, and when $x = 1$, the boiling temperature is the saturation temperature for ammonia. Note also that the concentration of the vapor phase is not the same as that of the liquid phase with which it is in equilibrium. For example, at a temperature T_1 and pressure p_1, the liquid phase (represented by point A) has a concentration x', whereas the vapor phase (represented by point B)

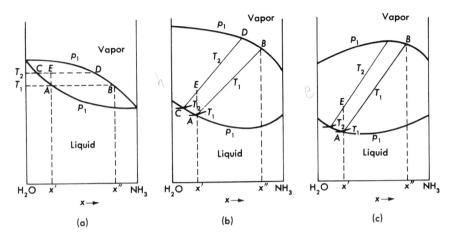

Fig. 19.43 Equilibrium Diagrams for Aqua Ammonia.

has a concentration x''. Figure 19.43(b) is an enthalpy-concentration diagram; it shows the phase boundaries for liquid and vapor at a given pressure. Note the way a constant-temperature line is represented on the diagram. Figure 19.43(c) is an entropy-concentration diagram. Its construction is similar to the enthalpy-concentration diagram.

To illustrate the use of these diagrams, consider a process in which saturated aqua ammonia of concentration x', temperature T_1 and pressure p_1 is heated at constant pressure in an evaporator to a temperature T_2. Starting with the T–x diagram, a horizontal line is drawn at a temperature T_2. This line intersects the p_1 phase boundary lines at points C and D. These points are correspondingly established on the h–x and s–x diagrams. The process on all three diagrams is represented by the line AE, where E is the intersection of the horizontal line at T_2 with the vertical line drawn from the initial point A. It is seen that the liquid and vapor have new compositions given by points C and D.

Absorption refrigeration systems have a coefficient of performance which is lower than that of a mechanical refrigeration system. They are generally used in industrial applications only where heat which would otherwise be wasted is available. The absorption cycle, however, has the advantage over the compression cycle in that it requires relatively little power to operate. As a matter of fact, it is possible to operate an absorption refrigeration machine with no input of work at all. This is done on small installations such as the Servel Electrolux domestic refrigerator. Its operation is based on the principle that a liquid, exposed to an inert atmosphere not already saturated with the vapor of the liquid, will evaporate, thus producing a cooling effect. In Fig. 19.44, an ammonia solution is boiled

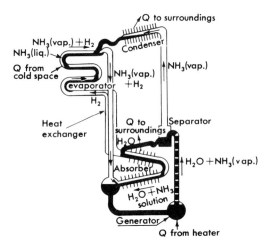

Fig. 19.44 Electrolux Refrigerator.

in the generator and rises to the separator. From here, the water flows to the absorber through a liquid trap and the ammonia vapor rises to the condenser. After condensation, the ammonia flows through a liquid trap to the evaporator coils. In the evaporator there is some hydrogen present, and the ammonia evaporates at a low temperature corresponding to its partial pressure. The mixture of hydrogen and ammonia then flows through a heat exchanger to the absorber, where the ammonia vapor goes into the cold water solution and the hydrogen rises back to the evaporator. The ammonia-in-water solution then flows into the generator to complete the cycle. The total pressure is essentially uniform throughout the plant, but the partial pressure of the ammonia vapor varies, being high in the condenser and low in the evaporator (the variation is accomplished by the presence of hydrogen in the evaporator). Circulation is obtained by density gradients (convection currents) created by the heating.

19.25 Gas-Cycle Refrigeration

Since a low temperature can be arrived at through adiabatic expansion of a gas, the reverse Brayton cycle using air represents another method of refrigeration. Such a system is especially suited for aircraft application because it is light in weight and requires less space than a vapor compression system of equal capacity. Referring to Fig. 19.45, outside air is first compressed (process 1–2). This may be done by means of a compressor or, if the aircraft is powered by a jet or turboprop engine, some air can be bled off the compressor of the engine. After cooling in a heat exchanger (pro-

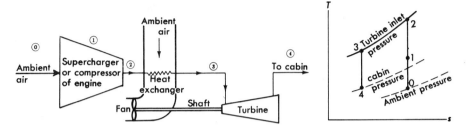

Fig. 19.45 Simple Air Cycle Refrigeration.

cess 2–3), the compressed air enters the turbine and expands to cabin pressure (process 3–4). The work output of the turbine is used to drive a fan which pulls the ambient air over the heat exchanger.

Assuming air to be an ideal gas with constant specific heats, the coefficient of performance of an ideal air-cycle refrigeration system is

$$\text{COP} = \frac{T_1 - T_4}{T_2 - T_1 - T_3 - T_4} \tag{19.45}$$

The work input required is the difference between the compressor work and the turbine work, or per pound of air,

$$w_{\text{net}} = w_{\text{compressor}} - w_{\text{turbine}}$$

$$= c_p(T_2 - T_1 - T_3 + T_4) \tag{19.46}$$

Another instance for the use of a gas cycle is in the production of liquefied gases, the manufacture of solid carbon dioxide (dry ice), and the various studies associated with extremely low temperatures (cryogenics). Of these applications, only the production of carbon dioxide will be discussed here. Carbon dioxide is a non corrosive, non-toxic substance with a triple point at $-70\,°F$ and 5.1 atm. Consequently, it does not exist as a liquid at atmospheric pressure, but instead sublimes at $-109\,°F$. The heat of sublimation (245 Btu/lbm) may be used to maintain products at low temperature. The principal use of dry ice is to preserve perishables such as ice cream and to provide short-time refrigeration in laboratories. The basic cycle for the production of dry ice is shown in Fig. 19.46.

Gaseous carbon dioxide at one atmosphere and room temperature (state 7) is mixed adiabatically with low-temperature vapor leaving the insulated collection chamber. The result of the mixing is state 1. The gas is then compressed† to state 2 at high pressure, after which it is cooled in the

---

† The basic cycle has been shown here using simple compression. In actual dry ice plants, staged compression with intercooling is employed to achieve reduction in the work required.

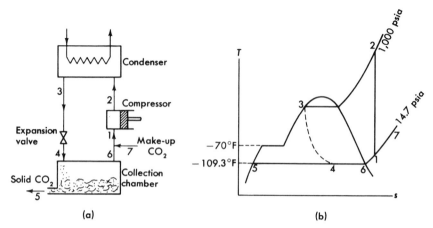

Fig. 19.46 Production of Dry Ice.

condenser to a liquid (state 3). The liquid flows to a throttle valve which expands it to atmospheric pressure (state 4), thus resulting in a mixture of solid and vapor. The solid (state 5) is removed and pressed into blocks, while the vapor (state 6) mixes with the make-up CO_2 to begin the cycle anew.

Example 19.14. The air conditioning unit of an aircraft receives air from the engine superchargers at 15 psia and 95 °F. The air is further compressed to a pressure p by means of a compressor driven by a turbine. It is then cooled at constant pressure before expanding in the turbine to a pressure of 14.6 psia and a temperature of 65 °F. Assuming ideal conditions, determine the pressure p if the turbine is to produce only work sufficient to drive the compressor.

Solution. Let T_1 and T_2 respectively denote the temperatures at inlet and outlet of the compressor. Then

$$T_2 = T_1\left(\frac{p}{15}\right)^{(1.4-1)/1.4} = 555\left(\frac{p}{15}\right)^{0.286}$$

The work required by the compressor is

$$w_{\text{compressor}} = c_p(T_2 - T_1) = 0.24\left[555\left(\frac{p}{15}\right)^{0.286} - 555\right]$$

$$= (0.24)(555)\left[\left(\frac{p}{15}\right)^{0.286} - 1\right]$$

Let T_3 and T_4 denote the temperatures at inlet and outlet of the turbine. Then

$$T_3 = T_4\left(\frac{p}{14.6}\right)^{(1.4-1)/1.4} = 525\left(\frac{p}{14.6}\right)^{0.286}$$

The work output of the turbine is

$$w_{\text{turbine}} = c_p(T_3 - T_4) = 0.24\left[525\left(\frac{p}{14.6}\right)^{0.296} - 525\right]$$

$$= (0.24)(525)\left[\left(\frac{p}{14.6}\right)^{0.286} - 1\right]$$

Since the compressor work and the turbine work must be equal:

$$(0.24)(555)\left[\left(\frac{p}{15}\right)^{0.286} - 1\right] = (0.24)(525)\left[\left(\frac{p}{14.6}\right)^{0.286} - 1\right]$$

This may be solved to give

$$p = 29 \text{ psia}$$

Example 19.15. Dry ice is to be produced at the rate of 400 lbm/hr using the basic cycle shown in Fig. 19.46. The low-pressure is 14.7 psia and the high pressure is 1000 psia. The liquid leaving the condenser is saturated, and make-up carbon dioxide is supplied at 75 °F. Considering the compression to be insentropic, determine the power required.

Solution. In Fig. 19.46, the enthalpies, as obtained from the CO_2 chart, are as follows: $h_7 = 170$, $h_3 = h_4 = 79$, $h_5 = -122$, $h_6 = 132$, all in Btu/lbm. An energy balance for the collection chamber gives

$$m_4 h_4 = m_5 h_5 + m_6 h_6$$

or

$$m_4(79) = 400(-112) + (m_4 - 400)(132)$$

Thus

$$m_4 = \frac{44,800 + 52,800}{53} = 1840 \text{ lbm/hr}$$

The enthalpy at state 1 is obtained from

$$m_1 h_1 = m_6 h_6 + m_7 h_7$$

or

$$1840(h_1) = (1840 - 400)(132) + 400(170)$$

$$h_1 = \frac{1440(132) + 68,000}{1840} = 140 \text{ Btu/lbm}$$

From the CO_2 chart, the enthalpy at state 2 after isentropic compression is read to be 264 Btu/lbm. The power required for compression is thus

$$m_1(h_2 - h_1) = 1840(265 - 140) = 230,000 \text{ Btu/hr}$$
$$= 90.2 \text{ hp}$$

19.26   Heat Pump

A heat pump is a refrigeration system which utilizes the heat rejected at the condenser for heating purposes. Its chief use is to heat homes in localities where electric rates are advantageous.

Since a heat pump must deliver heat to a building during cold weather to keep it warm, a source of heat must be available. Part of the heat comes, of course, from the work of compressing the refrigerant, but the remainder must come from an outside source. The principal sources of heat are the surrounding atmosphere, water from wells or lakes, and the ground. Figure 19.47 shows the basic refrigerant circuit for the heat pump. The hot re-

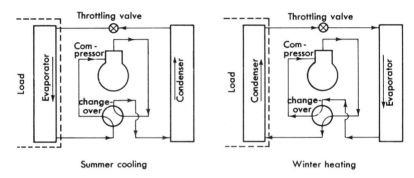

Fig. 19.47   Basic Heat Pump Cycle.

frigerant from the compressor enters a change-over valve which directs the refrigerant to the proper coil. When the heat pump is used to heat a building, the hot refrigerant flows to the indoor coil which serves as a condenser. The refrigerant then goes through the expansion valve and is evaporated in the outdoor coil which serves as an evaporator. When the heat pump is used to cool a building, the indoor coil serves as evaporator, and the outdoor coil as condenser. The coefficient of performance of a heat pump is defined as

$$\text{COP} = \frac{\text{Heat rejected in condenser}}{\text{Work of compression}} \tag{19.47}$$

The proper selection of the size of heat pump is a challenging engineering problem. Ideally, the heat pump should have just enough capacity to satisfy the heat load and just enough cooling capacity to satisfy the cooling load. This might mean a slightly undersized heat pump during cold spells, but it is usually cheaper to handle peak loads by means of separate resistance heaters.

Another interesting application of the heat pump is the vapor-compression still, diagrammed in Fig. 19.48. Its purpose is to produce distilled

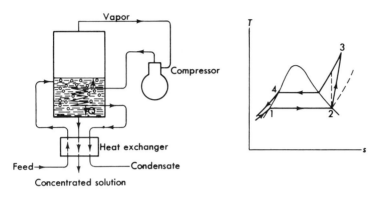

Fig. 19.48 Vapor-Compression Still.

water or a concentrated solution. Entering feed (sea water or perhaps sugar solution) is vaporized in the still by heat transferred from the compressed vapor leaving the still.

It can be seen from the corresponding T–s diagram that, in reality, Rankine-cycle refrigeration is used. Normally, it takes about 20 Btu of work to produce a pound of distilled water.

Example 19.16. A vapor-compression refrigeration system having a rated capacity of 8 tons operates on Freon-12. The evaporator and condenser temperatures are 32 °F and 95 °F respectively, with no superheating of the refrigerant leaving the evaporator and no subcooling of the refrigerant leaving the condenser. Assuming compression to be isentropic, determine: (a). The coefficient of performance of the installation when performing as a refrigerating machine and as a heat pump respectively, (b). the heating capacity (Btu/hr) of the heat pump.

Solution. (a) The installation operates on a simple vapor-compression cycle (previously shown in Fig. 19.36). The enthalpies (obtained from Freon charts) at the various states are: $h_1 = 81.8$, h_2 (after isentropic compression) $= 89.4$, $h_3 = 29.5$, $h_4 (=h_3) = 29.5$. The coefficient of performance of the installation operating as a refrigerating machine is

$$\text{COP}_{\text{refrig. mach.}} = \frac{h_1 - h_4}{h_2 - h_1} = \frac{81.8 - 29.5}{89.4 - 81.8} = 6.90$$

The coefficient of performance when operating as a heat pump is

$$\text{COP}_{\text{heat pump}} = \frac{h_2 - h_3}{h_2 - h_1} = \frac{89.4 - 29.5}{89.4 - 81.8} = 7.98$$

Note that from the way it is defined, the coefficient of performance of the heat pump is always greater than the coefficient of performance of a refrigerating machine between the same temperature limits.

(b) The refrigerant flow rate (lbm/min) is $(8)(200)/(h_1 - h_4)$. Since each pound of refrigerant rejects $(h_2 - h_3)$ Btu at the condenser, the heating capacity is

$$\frac{(8)(200)(h_2 - h_3)}{h_1 - h_4} = \frac{(8)(200)(89.4 - 29.5)}{81.8 - 29.5} = 1,830 \text{ Btu/min}$$

$$= 110,000 \text{ Btu/hr}$$

19.27   Exotic Power

The term exotic power has come into use to denote various concepts (some new, some old) for the direct conversion of heat energy into electricity. Not since atomic energy was released has there been so much excitement about a new technology, even though only a few exotic power units have so far emerged from the laboratory, and these are small devices suitable largely for use in space vehicles. Energy does not occur naturally in the form of electricity. Normally, the chemical and nuclear sources of energy are converted into heat. This heat is then converted into mechanical work of a turbine by steam generation as described in the preceding sections. Then the mechanical work is converted into electrical energy by means of an electric generator (dynamo).

The new conversion concepts do not necessitate the conversion of heat energy into mechanical energy by use of a steam engine or turbine. Instead, the heat or in some cases the chemical energy of the primary fuel is directly converted into electricity. Methods which have been suggested for direct conversion are *thermoelectric, thermionic, magnetohydrodynamic, photo-voltaic* and *fuel cells.* Indeed, many of these methods are used on a small scale to produce electricity for specific purposes. The most common is the primary battery, which is a very useful, though expensive, source of electric power. (In the latter part of the nineteenth century, primary batteries supplied a large percentage of the electrical power available.) The "fuel" consumed by these batteries consists of the metallic electrodes; and obviously, this is expensive when compared with more conventional fuels. Recently, the idea of using batteries with replaceable electrodes has been receiving attention. Such batteries are known as *fuel cells,* and several combinations of possible chemical fuels have been demonstrated. The fuels that have been used to date, however, have been quite expensive as compared with conventional conbustion fuels, so that it still makes good economic sense to use mechanical energy as an intermediate step in the production of electricity. Thermoelectricity has also been tried, and in some cases used rather successfully. The development of thermoelectricity, however, is severely limited by the low efficiency of thermoelectric materials available so that here again large electrodynamic machinery driven by steam turbine or engine cycles proves to be a more economical method of electric power production.

Thus, direct conversion is not a new idea. Nevertheless, two things have happened in recent years which have caused the re-evaluation of the importance of this field. First, good semiconductor materials have not only been fabricated, but their theory of operation is now well understood. Second, the higher temperatures required in thermionic processes are now available as a result of nuclear fission. For applications such as portable power supplies and power for space vehicles, direct conversion is most attractive because it provides a means for reducing the weight and complexity of power plants. In the sections that follow, the physical principles associated with each direct conversion device will be discussed, keeping in mind that the development of new materials and technology will surely increase the performance obtainable today.

19.28 Thermoelectricity

As far back as 1822, the German physicist Seebeck discovered that a voltage was generated in a loop containing two dissimilar metals if the two junctions were maintained at different temperatures. The coefficient of proportionality between voltage and temperature difference is known as the *Seebeck coefficient* and is denoted by the symbol S. This is shown in Fig. 19.49(a) where an open circuit potential difference ΔV is developed as a result of the temperature difference ΔT between the junctions of conductor a to conductor b:

$$S = \lim_{\Delta T \to 0} \frac{\Delta V}{\Delta T} \tag{19.48}$$

In 1834, Peltier, a French watchmaker, discovered a second thermo-electric effect. This is that whenever a current is passed through a junction between two different conductors, there is absorption or generation of heat

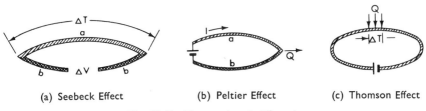

| (a) Seebeck Effect | (b) Peltier Effect | (c) Thomson Effect |

Fig. 19.49 Thermoelectric Effects.†

† A more detailed discussion of thermoelectric effects as well as an analysis of a thermocouple is to be found in Chapter 21.

depending on the direction of the current. In other words, the junction between two dissimilar metals acts as a heat sink or as a heat source, depending on the direction of the electric current. This effect is superimposed upon, but distinct from, the Joule resistance-heating effect usually associated with the passage of an electric current. The strength of the heat sink or heat source is found to be proportional to the current itself. Referring to Fig. 19.49(b), the coefficient of proportionality between the rate of reversible heat flow Q (at $\Delta T = 0$) and current I is known as the *Peltier coefficient* and is denoted by the symbol π:

$$\pi = \frac{Q}{I} \tag{19.49}$$

A few years later, in 1854, the English physicist, Thomson (Lord Kelvin), established from classical thermodynamic considerations, the following relation between the Seebeck and Peltier coefficients:

$$S = \frac{\pi}{T} \tag{19.50}$$

This led him to the conclusion that there must be a third thermoelectric effect, now called the Thomson effect. Referring to Fig. 19.49(c), consider a portion of a conductor having a temperature gradient ΔT. When an electric current is passed, the heat flow Q that must take place laterally along the wire (in addition to the Joulean heat) in order to maintain the same temperature difference that existed in the absence of the electric current, is called the Thomson heat. The *Thomson coefficient,* denoted by the symbol σ, is defined by

$$\sigma = \lim_{\substack{\Delta T \to 0 \\ Q \to 0}} \frac{Q}{I \Delta T} \tag{19.51}$$

Equation (19.51) gives the rate at which heat is absorbed or evolved per unit temperature difference as σI. Note that the Thomson heat, like the Peltier heat, is reversible, whereas the Joulean heat ($I^2 R$) is not.

Despite the fact that thermoelectric effects have been known for a long time, practically the only devices based upon them, which have been of widespread application are thermocouples for the measurement of temperature and thermopiles for the detection of radiant energy. Both of these applications utilize the Seebeck effect; in fact, they involve the thermoelectric generation of electricity from heat. This lack of application, other than for temperature measurement, has been due to the low thermoelectric efficiency of known materials. Altenkirch, in 1909 and 1911 showed that, for both thermoelectric generators and thermoelectric refrigerators, materials with high thermoelectric coefficients, high electrical conductivities, and low thermal conductivities were required. However, it was quite a different matter to obtain materials embodying these specifications.

No serious attempt was made to develop better thermoelectric materials until 1930 when Maria Telkes of the Westinghouse Research Laboratories made a study of the *Pb S–Zn Sb* couple and raised its potential efficiency of thermoelectric conversion by a factor of ten from 0.5 per cent to 5 per cent. The present resurgence of interest in thermoelectricity is due to the advances made in solid state physics since World War II and to the belief of solid state physicists that they can design and fabricate materials of prescribed physical properties. This resurgence of interest first occurred in Russia under the leadership of A. F. Ioffe, whose book *Semiconductor Thermo-elements and Thermoelectric Cooling* has become the Bible of those people working in the field of thermoelectricity. Since then, many people in many countries have undertaken the study of this field. It is the aim of the following sections to give an understanding of some aspects of physical electronics as they relate to semiconductors, since it is only due to the advent of semiconductor thermocouples that reasonably efficient thermoelectric generators and refrigerators have become possible.

19.29 Energy Bands in Semiconductors

In thermoelectricity, the state of matter of most interest is the solid state. From the standpoint of electrical conductivity, solids may be classified as *conductor, insulator,* or *semiconductor.* A conductor is a solid with a relatively large number of current carriers (electrons); this number is independent of temperature. An insulator is a solid with few carriers at ordinary temperatures. A semiconductor is a solid in which the number of current carriers is temperature dependent, being generally large at high temperatures and relatively small at low temperatures. To fully understand the operation of semiconductor devices, it is necessary to discuss the energy band theory of solids. The energy state of an isolated atom is indicated by the potential and kinetic energy possessed by each electron in the atom. Each electron may possess only certain exact amounts of energy, i.e. it may occupy only certain *discrete energy levels* as shown in Fig. 19.50(a).

In an isolated atom there are a finite number of these energy levels; an electron which occupies a lower energy is strongly attached to the atom, while an electron which occupies a high energy level is only feebly attached to the atom. Between the energy levels are forbidden energy gaps in which no electron may remain. An electron, however, may pass from one level to a higher one if it should gain sufficient energy, or it may go to a lower energy level if it should give up enough energy. In the absence of external influences the electrons of an atom fill all the possible energy levels from the bottom up and the atom is said to be in the *normal* state. If one or more

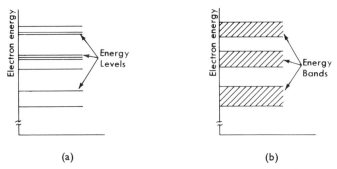

(a)   (b)

Fig. 19.50   Energy Levels in Isolated Atom and Energy Bands in Crystalline Solid.

electrons are raised to a higher than normal energy level, the atom is said to be in an *excited* state.

In the case of a solid, there is an enormous number of atoms per unit volume, and accordingly, there is an enormous number of allowable energy levels. With such a large number of energy levels, and with interaction occurring between the densely packed atoms, the difference between the energy levels becomes very small indeed, and the levels merge, resulting in the formation of energy bands, each band consisting of an enormous (but finite) number of energy levels. Thus, just as the electrons in an isolated atom are restricted to discrete energy levels, so the electrons in a solid are restricted to discrete energy bands, which may overlap or be separated by forbidden gaps. This is shown in Fig. 19.50(b).

In crystalline semiconductor solids, the valence electrons (electrons in the outer shells) normally occupy and completely fill the *valence band* (which is the second highest energy band). The inner electrons fill the energy band below the valence band, and excess electrons, whose existence is the result of imperfections in the crystal, are in the highest band, which is called the *conduction band*. To generate an electron-hole pair in a crystal, it is necessary to supply to an electron in the valence or filled band a sufficient amount of energy to excite it into the conduction or empty band. The result is the creation of a carrier (the electron) in the empty band and a carrier (the hole) in the filled band. The energy required for the generation of the electron-hole pair in this manner is equal to the width of the forbidden gap between the two bands. The conduction of electricity in a crystal arises solely from the presence of excess electrons in the empty band and of holes in the filled band. Indeed, for a study of the electrical properties of a semiconductor, it is only necessary to focus attention on these two bands.

An examination of the energy band diagram of solids serves to explain the electrical behavior of an insulator, a conductor, and a semiconductor.

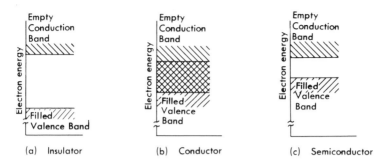

Fig. 19.51   Energy Band Diagram for Insulator, Conductor, and Semiconductor.

Figure 19.51(a) shows the energy band diagram for diamond (a good insulator). The valence band and the conduction band are far apart so that at normal ambient temperatures only a small number of electrons receive enough energy to be excited from the valence band to the conduction band.

Figure 19.51(b) shows the energy band diagram for lead (a conductor). Here the valence band and the conduction band overlap one another, so that the valence electrons are free to move within the lattic structure as "free" electrons. The energy band diagram for germanium [Fig. 19.51(c)] on the other hand, shows the valence band and the conduction band to be separated, but close enough that at room temperature a large number of electrons can be excited into the conduction or empty band, leaving behind them holes in the valence or filled band. The separation of the two bands by a small energy gap (of the order of 1 ev) is typical of semi-conductors.

A semiconductor material with the properties described above is called an *intrinsic semiconductor*. Most engineering applications, however, involve semiconductors which have been "doped" by the intentional addition of small impurities. The presence of these impurities serve to alter the electrical characteristics of semiconductors in the following manner. Consider a crystal of germanium (valence 4) containing a small amount of arsenic (valence 5). The "extra" electrons associated with the arsenic atoms occupy states which lie only a fraction of a volt below the conduction band. This is indicated in Fig. 19.52(b) by the short bars which represent the energy level for the extra electrons of the arsenic atoms. As the temperature is raised, the lattic vibrations become more pronounced and, by absorbing the proper amount of energy, some of the arsenic atoms become ionized, i.e., they release their electrons to the conduction band as shown by the black dots. The arsenic atoms are called *donors* since they give electrons to the conduction band, and a semiconductor with such impurity atoms is known as an *n-type semiconductor* because the excess electrons are negative carriers of current.

If an impurity such as boron (valence 3) is added to a germanium semiconductor, the boron atoms again occupy places in the lattice which, in the pure material, are occupied by germanium atoms. However, there is now a shortage of one electron in the band structure of the crystal, giving rise to a hole. The holes asociated with the impurity atoms occupy an energy level just a few hundredths of an electron volt above the normally filled valence band [dotted line, Fig. 19.52(c)], so that as the temperature is raised, valence electrons are easily excited into these bound holes, with the result that a mobile hole is left behind in the valence band. The bound hole levels are known as *acceptor* levels since they can accept electrons, and the semiconductor with a boron impurity is known as a *p-type semiconductor* indicating that conduction current is carried by positive charges (holes).

It is of interest to point out that the energy required to ionize impurity atoms to generate electrons in *n*-type germanium or holes in *p*-type germanium is much lower than that required to generate electron-hole pairs in intrinsic germanium. This is brought out in Fig. 19.52 which shows that the energy required to generate an electron-hole pair in pure germanium is about 0.7 ev, whereas the energy required to set an electron free from a donor atom or to replace a hole from an acceptor atom is about 0.01 ev.

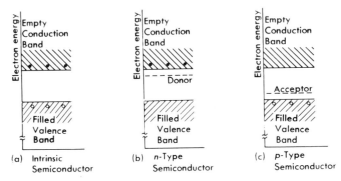

Fig. 19.52 Energy Band Diagram for Intrinsic Germanium, *n*-Type Germanium, and *p*-Type Germanium.

19.30 Energy-Distribution of Electrons in Metal; Fermi Level

As mentioned earlier, the number of energy levels that can be occupied by the electrons in a crystal is very great. In fact, there are more allowable energy levels than there are available electrons in the crystal. At absolute zero temperature, the available electrons fill the lowest allowable energy

levels. At higher temperature, some of the electrons are excited to higher
levels, leaving certain lower levels unfilled. The distribution of the electrons
among the energy levels is described by the *Fermi-Dirac* distribution function which will now be derived.

Consider, as in Sec. 13.8, that the entire energy range is divided into
contiguous levels or cells ϵ_1, ϵ_2, etc., and that each $\Delta\epsilon_i$ is small in comparison
to the error likely to be made in measuring the total energy. Any ith cell,
however, is still large enough that it contains a number g_i of energy states.
Consider a group of N_i electrons ($N_i \ll g_i$). How many ways can these
electrons be distributed among the g_i states at the energy ϵ_i if the Pauli
exclusion principle allows only one or zero electrons per state? The answer
is given by the formula for the number of combinations of g_i things taken
N_i at a time:

$$_{g_i}C_{N_i} = \frac{g_i!}{N_i!(g_i - N_i)!}$$

Figure 19.53 illustrates the situation for the case of two electrons to be
distributed among four states at a given energy. The number of possible
arrangements is

$$\frac{4!}{2!(4-2)!} = 6$$

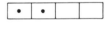

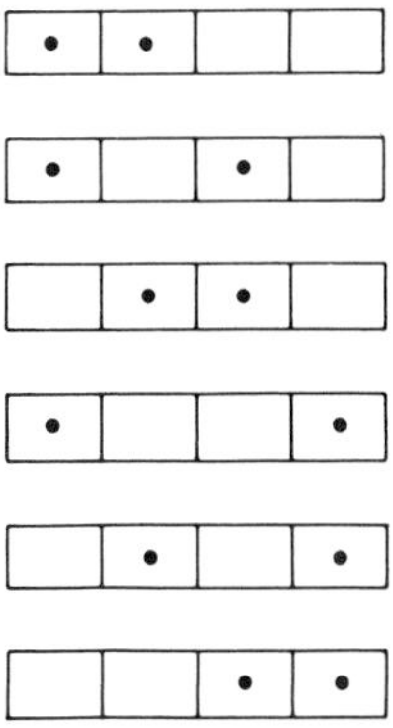

Note that for a Maxwellian distribution, there
would be four additional arrangements, making
a total of ten, since it would be possible to have
both electrons in any one state.

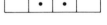

For all the energy levels or cells taken together, the total number of combinations or
thermodynamic probability is

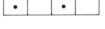

$$W = \prod_i \frac{g_i!}{N_i!(g_i - N_i)!} \qquad (19.52)$$

Fig. 19.53

According to statistical thermodynamics, the
electrons will be in equilibrium when the entropy
($S = k \ln W$) is a maximum. This corresponds to
the maximization of $\ln W$ subject to the conditions
that (1) the total number of electrons remains
constant ($\Sigma N_i = N$) and, (2) the total energy of

Distribution of
Electrons among States
of an Energy Level.

the electrons remains constant ($\Sigma N_i \epsilon_i = E$). The maximization problem
is conveniently expressed by writing

$$\delta \ln W = 0 \qquad (19.53)$$
$$\Sigma \, \delta N_i = 0 \qquad (19.54)$$
$$\Sigma \, \epsilon_i \delta N_i = 0 \qquad (19.55)$$

Using Stirling's approximation ($\ln N_i! \cong N_i \ln N_i - N_i$), Eq. (19.53) becomes

$$\delta \ln W = \delta \ln \prod_i \frac{g_i!}{N_i!(g_i - N_i)!} = \delta \Sigma [\ln g_i! - \ln N_i! - \ln (g_i - N_i)!]$$

$$= \delta \Sigma [g_i \ln g_i - g_i - N_i \ln N_i + N_i - (g_i - N_i) \ln (g_i - N_i) + (g_i - N_i)]$$

$$= \delta \Sigma [g_i \ln g_i - N_i \ln N_i - (g_i - N_i) \ln (g_i - N_i)] = 0$$

Taking $\partial/(\partial N_i)$, this gives

$$\Sigma [-\ln N_i + \ln(g_i - N_i)] \delta N_i = \Sigma \left(\ln \frac{g_i - N_i}{N_i} \right) \delta N_i = 0$$

If this is added to Eq. (19.54) multiplied by $-\lambda$ and to Eq. (19.55) multiplied by $-\mu$ (Lagrange's method of undetermined multipliers), the result is

$$\Sigma \left(\ln \frac{g_i - N_i}{N_i} - \lambda - \mu \epsilon_i \right) \delta N_i = 0$$

From this is obtained

$$\ln \frac{g_i - N_i}{N_i} - \lambda - \mu \epsilon_i = 0$$

or

$$\frac{g_i - N_i}{N_i} = e^{\lambda + \mu \epsilon_i}$$

This gives

$$\frac{N_i}{g_i} = \frac{1}{e^{\lambda + \mu \epsilon_i} + 1} \qquad (19.56)$$

According to kinetic theory (cf. Sec. 13.8), $\mu = 1/kT$, where k is the Boltzmann constant and T is the absolute temperature. Furthermore, if the quantity λ is defined as a reference energy level ϵ_F/kT, Eq. (19.56) becomes, for a sufficient number of energy levels that the energy may be considered continuous,

$$\frac{N_i}{g_i} = \frac{1}{e^{(\epsilon - \epsilon_F)/kT} + 1} = f(\epsilon, T) \qquad (19.57)$$

Equation (19.57) is the expression for the *Fermi-Dirac distribution function*. This function gives the probability of finding an electron at an energy level ϵ at temperature T. The reference energy level ϵ_F, called the *Fermi level*, is the value for which the distribution function has a value of one half.

Figure (19.54) shows graphically the distribution function for three different temperatures. It is seen that at absolute zero temperature, the available electrons fill all the energy levels below ϵ_F, while occupying none of the energy levels above ϵ_F. At a higher temperature, the probability of finding an energy level slightly above ϵ_F occupied by an electron increases. By the same token, the probability of finding an energy level slightly below ϵ_F not occupied by an electron (and therefore occupied by a hole) increases. From symmetry of the curves about the ordinate at ϵ_F, it is seen that at any given temperature the probability of finding an electron at a level ϵ above ϵ_F is the same as that of finding a hole at a level ϵ below ϵ_F.

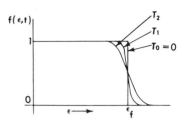

Fig. 19.54 Fermi-Dirac Distribution Function for Different Temperatures.

For intrinsic semiconductors, the Fermi level is situated at the center of the gap between the valence band and the conduction band. For n-type semiconductors the Fermi level lies closer to the conduction band, and for p-type semiconductors the Fermi level is closer to the valence band. The comparison between the three cases is shown in Fig. 19.55.

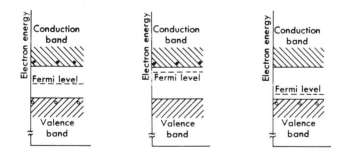

(a) Intrinsic Semiconductor   (b) n-Type Semiconductor   (c) p-Type Semiconductor

Fig. 19.55 Fermi Level for Intrinsic Semiconductor, n-Type Semiconductor, and p-Type Semiconductor.

19.31 Semiconductor Junctions

Conduction in solids may be ascribed to two basic phenomena: drift of charges under the influence of an applied electric field, or diffusion of charges from a region of high-charge density to a region of low-charge density. The first phenomenon is associated with the usual flow of current in conductors, the second phenomenon occurs in semiconductors between regions having abundances and deficiencies of particular types of charge carriers. In the latter case, it would be expected that, given time, the charges would tend to redistribute themselves so as to attain homogeneity. Thus, there is a process of charge diffusion equivalent to current flow across reference planes.

Consider pieces of *n*-type and *p*-type semiconductors as shown in Fig. 19.56(a). There is no net charge in any region of an isolated *n*-type or *p*-type specimen, but the *n*-type material does have high-energy electrons in the conduction band (supplied by the donor atoms) and the *p*-type material does have holes in the valence band (supplied by the acceptor atoms).

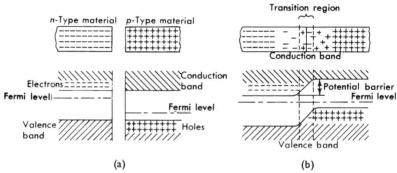

(a)   (b)

Fig. 19.56 Energy Levels in *n* and *p* Materials Before and After Joining.

Let the two blocks be brought together tightly. An important property pertaining to the concept of Fermi level is that when two solids are in contact at thermal equilibrium, the Fermi levels of the two solids come to alignment much as the water levels in connected tanks, so that the energy diagram is as shown in Fig. 19.56(b). Electrons slide down the potential hill from the *n*-type to the *p*-type material, and holes climb the hill from the *p*-type to the *n*-type material. As a result there are more electrons than normal in the *p*-type material and less electrons than normal in the *n*-type material. A potential thus appears across the junction with the *n*-type region positive with respect to the *p*-type region.

By applying an external potential and making the *p*-type region positive with respect to the *n*-type region, more charge carriers are urged across the junction and current will flow from the *p*-type region to the *n*-type region. This situation is called *forward bias* and makes it easier for high-energy electrons and holes to be "emitted" from one material to another. It is shown in Fig. 19.57(a).

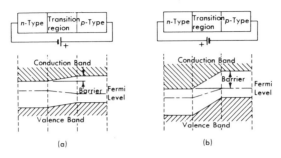

Fig. 19.57 *p–n* Junction with Forward and Reverse Bias.

With a *reverse bias,* as shown in Fig. 19.57(b) the height of the energy barrier is increased and only very few electrons and holes can pass across to carry a small current. The *n–p* diode then acts as a high resistance shunted by a capacitive component.

19.32 Thermoelectric Generator

The preceding sections have shown that in semiconductors there are bands of allowed energy levels for the electrons, and when these bands are nearly full or nearly empty, the electrons can move and carry current. Figure 19.58(a) is a diagram of the energy states in an *n*-type semiconductor. The Fermi level is the highest occupied level at very low tem-

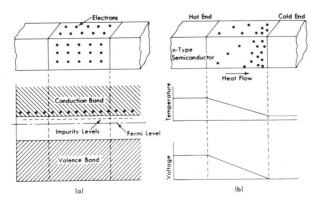

Fig. 19.58 Representation of Thermoelectric Effect.

peratures and is also the chemical potential of the electrons in the solid. If one side of the material is heated as in Fig. 19.58(b), the electrons in the bottom of the conduction band become thermally excited and tend to drift toward the cold end of the material. As a result, there will be a separation of charge between the hot and cold ends of the material and a potential gradient developed. The same effect will occur in a metallic conductor, but because of the degenerate nature of the electron gas, the effect will be very much smaller. This is a simple explanation of the *Seebeck effect*, in which a small temperature difference ΔT across a material results in a voltage difference ΔV. The *Seebeck coefficient* or *thermoelectric power*

$$S = \lim_{\Delta T \to 0} \frac{\Delta V}{\Delta T}$$

is defined for the case where there is no net electrical current flowing. For a *p*-type semiconductor, holes (positive charges) tend to drift from the hot to the cold end of the material. Here, the Seebeck coefficient is of a sign opposite to that of an *n*-type semiconductor. Thus, *n*- and *p*-type semiconductors containing temperature gradients can be connected singly as in Fig. 19.59(a) or in series as shown in Fig. 19.59(b), so that voltages produced within each are additive. When one junction is heated and the other is cooled, a flow of carriers is created by which electrons in the *n*-type leg and holes in the *p*-type leg flow away from the hot junction. Consequently an electric current is established, and should an external load be connected in the circuit, useful work would be performed. If, on the other hand, current is supplied to the installation from an external source, the action is reversed, and one junction heats up while the other cools down. This is the Peltier effect and it is used for refrigeration purposes.

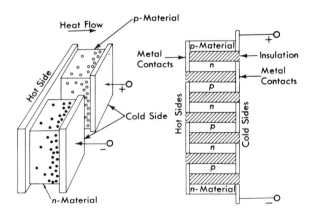

Fig. 19.59 Thermoelectric Generator.

The amount of power generated depends upon the Seebeck coefficient of the materials and upon the amount of heat which is being carried by the electrical charge carriers. A quantitative analysis by Ioffe and others has led to the use of a *figure of merit* defined as

$$Z = \frac{S^2}{\rho K} \tag{19.58}$$

to evaluate the efficiency of a thermoelectric device. The higher the value of Z, the better is the performance. Here, S is the Seebeck coefficient, ρ is the electrical resistivity, and K is the thermal conductivity.

Another quantity which is often used to rate thermoelectric devices is the *efficiency index* represented by

$$M_w = \frac{TS^2}{4\rho K} \tag{19.59}$$

where T is the average absolute temperature at which the materials' properties are measured. Since the thermoelectric generator is analogous to a heat engine, the Carnot efficiency $(T_h - T_c)T_h$ enters into the picture so that the overall efficiency of the thermoelectric device as a heat engine is given by

$$\eta = \left(\frac{T_h - T_c}{T_h}\right) M_w \tag{19.60}$$

where T_h and T_c are the hot and cold junction temperatures respectively. If the thermoelectric device is used as a refrigerator, the evaluation is in terms of a *coefficient of performance* given by

$$\epsilon = \left(\frac{T_c}{T_h - T_c}\right) M_w - \frac{1}{2} \tag{19.61}$$

From the above discussion, it is apparent that the design of an efficient thermoelectric generator involves not only the use of a high hot-junction temperature, but also the use of materials having the desirable properties of (1) high Seebeck coefficient, (2) low electrical resistivity, (3) low thermal conductivity, and (4) good physical and chemical stability at high temperatures. Since this combination of properties is difficult to achieve, the aim of any development work is to obtain a compromise. On the basis of solid state theory, the Seebeck coefficient is predominantly proportional to the log of the reciprocal of the carrier concentration. In other words, the coefficient approaches infinity as the concentration approaches zero. Thus, insulators should do very well from the standpoint of having a high Seebeck coefficient, but this is of no avail since the resistivity is too high.

Figure 19.60 shows the variation of S, ρ, and K with carrier concentration (electrons). It is seen that the optimum value for Z occurs at a concentration of around 10^{19} charge carriers per cubic centimeter. With lower concentrations (insulators), the resistivity is too high, while at higher concentrations (metals), the Seebeck coefficient is too low.

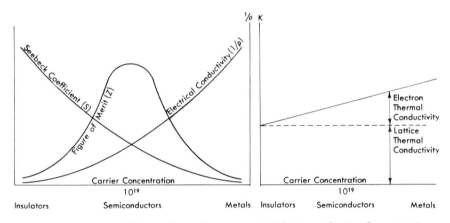

Fig. 19.60 Variation of Thermoelectric Parameters in Relation to Carrier Concentrations.

The figure also illustrates the primary advantage of semiconductors over metals for use in thermoelectric devices. A great deal of work has been done in recent years to develop semiconductors, so that materials are now available which over a reasonable temperature range can produce electricity with an efficiency of 17 per cent. Small thermoelectric generators have actually been constructed having efficiencies in the order of 6 per cent. Unfortunately, other effects occur which reduce the efficiency of heat-to-electricity conversion. Chief among these is the energy loss due to heat flowing directly from the hot to the cold junction by means of thermal conduction and the loss due to resistive heating within the material. These heat effects virtually bypass the mechanism of interconversion of heat and electrical energy.

19.33 Thermionic Generator

In its simplest form, the thermionic converter or generator consists of two metal plates separated by either a vapor or a vacuum. The arrangement, as shown in Fig. 19.61(a), can be likened to a vacuum tube with a heated cathode and an anode at a lower temperature. At sufficiently high temperatures, large numbers of electrons are driven off the surface of the cathode, and these electrons would flow to the anode with little hindrance if the elec-rons themselves did not set up a counteracting space charge between the electrodes. Even so, however, the more energetic electrons overcome the retarding space charge to reach the anode. The process of electron emission by the application of heat is called *thermionic emission*.

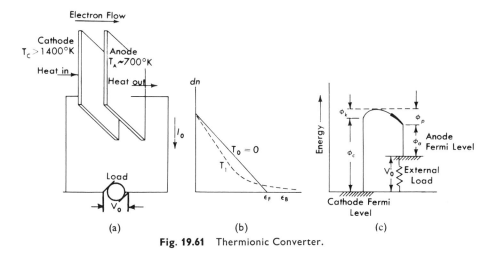

Fig. 19.61 Thermionic Converter.

For an electron to be emitted from a metal surface, its velocity must be mainly directed toward the surface. When only electrons having outward-directed velocities are considered, the electron energy distribution is as shown in Fig. 19.61(b), where the curve labeled T_0 is for absolute zero temperature, and the curve labeled T is for a higher temperature. It is seen that the curve T approaches the abscissa asymptotically so that there are some electrons with high enough energies to break through the barrier energy ϵ_B to be emitted. The current represented by these electrons per unit area of surface may be obtained by integrating the equation of the distribu-tion from ϵ_B to infinity (this gives the number of electrons passing through the surface) and multiplying by the average velocity of the electrons and the charge carried per electron. The result is the *Richardson–Dushman equation*.

$$J = A T^2 e^{-\phi_c/kT} \qquad (19.62)$$

where J is the current density (amp/cm²), A is a constant (120 amp/cm²-°K²), T is the cathode temperature (°K), k is the Boltzmann constant (1.38×10^{-23} watt-sec °K⁻¹), and ϕ_c is the cathode *work function* (ev). The latter is the work per unit charge required to free an electron from the influence of neighboring charges in order to escape from the surface of a metal. It is equal to $\epsilon_B - \epsilon_F$ since even at absolute zero temperature many electrons in a metal possess an energy near ϵ_F so that it is only necessary to supply the difference between the barrier energy ϵ_B and ϵ_F to secure the emission of an electron. A relation similar to Eq. (19.62) exists for the anode current. This, however, is usually negligible because of the smaller temperature at the anode and the exponential dependence of the current on the reciprocal temperature. The potential energy diagram of Fig. 19.61(c) shows the relationship between the work functions, the kinetic energy of the electrons, the space charge potential, and the output voltage. In general,

$$V_0 = \phi_c + \phi_k - \phi_p - \phi_a \tag{19.63}$$

where V_0 is the output voltage, ϕ_c is the cathode work function, ϕ_k is the kinetic energy of the electrons, ϕ_p is the plasma drop, and ϕ_a is the anode work function. Neglecting the kinetic energy of the electrons and effects of space charge, the maximum voltage obtainable is simply the difference in the work functions.

Thermodynamically speaking, the thermionic converter is a kind of heat engine with electrons as the working fluid. Electrons are boiled off the cathode by means of heat addition to boost them over the potential-energy hill [Fig. 19.61(c)], and when they flow to the anode and pass through the load, useful work is done. One difficulty to be overcome, however, is the cloud of electrons that tends to form in the space between the cathode and the anode and this space charge tends to limit the current output of the device. To reduce this effect, the electrodes can be moved closer together or an ionized gas may be introduced between the electrodes. The two types of converters receiving the most attention today are classified by the manner in which they overcome the space charge problem. In the *close-spaced diode* or *vacuum-type* of thermionic converter, the two electrodes are placed within 0.001 cm or less of one another. With such a spacing, the retarding potential on the emission current due to the space charge does not build up to a significant value. Diodes of this type operate between temperatures of 1200 to 1700 °K on the cathode and 900 °K on the anode. Depending on the cathode temperature, power densities of 2 to 11 watts/cm² with efficiencies of 3 to 12 per cent are obtainable. From a mechanical design standpoint, however, the maintenance of an extremely small clearance between surfaces represents a burden to be avoided. In the *plasma diode*, positive ions are introduced between the electrodes to neutralize the space charge; the resulting mixture of ions and electrons being called a plasma. The positive ions are obtained by the ionization of cesium vapor (of pressure 1 mm Hg or less) between the electrodes. Cathode temperatures of 1600 to 2600 °K are used. These higher temperatures are required at the cathode than in the close-spaced diode in order to obtain enough ions to neutralize the space charge. However, it is possible to use larger spacings (0.1 cm) between the electrodes and efficiencies of around 15 per cent are attainable.

A possible scheme for using a thermionic converter as a topping device in conjunction with a Rankine cycle is shown in Fig. 19.62. This is a good

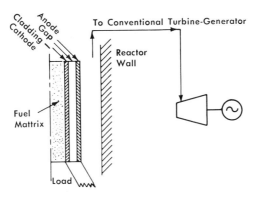

Fig. 19.62 Thermionic Converter as Topping Device for Rankine Cycle.

illustration of how thermionic converters may be incorporated in a power supply. They may be used directly in a nuclear reactor, in contact with a radioisotope fuel, or with any high-temperature heat source. Here, the thermionic converter is attached to a reactor fuel element. The heat sink may be the surrounding space itself, (through radiation), or a heat transfer fluid which is used to drive some electromechanical conversion equipment.

19.34 MHD Generator

If the steam of a conventional power cycle is replaced with a working fluid that is an electrical conductor, a magnetic field can be applied to generate a voltage gradient in the moving fluid in accordance with Faraday's law of induction. When connections are made to this generated voltage, power is delivered to an external load. Such a device is known as a *magnetohydrodynamic (MHD) generator*, and is shown in Fig. 19.63.

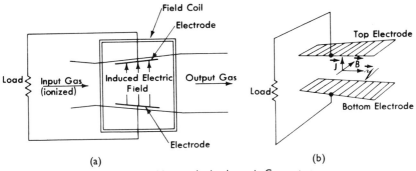

Fig. 19.63 Magnetohydrodynamic Generator.

The working fluid is an ionized gas or plasma. A *plasma* is a macroscopically neutral mixture of ions, electrons, and neutral particles. It is obtained by heating a gas to a high temperature at high pressure by a primary heat source, which could be the burning of a fossil fuel, or a high-temperature nuclear reaction. The high-temperature, high-pressure gas is exhausted through a nozzle and passed through a magnetic field at velocities of the order of 10^3 meters/sec. Since the gas has electrical conductivity and moves across a magnetic field, an electric field perpendicular to both the fluid motion and the magnetic field is produced within the gas. This is the same principle used in producing electricity in a dynamo except that no rotating machinery is required for an MHD generator. The gas expands and cools adiabatically with enthalpy being removed from it by the flow of electric current. Electrodes, placed in the fluid, collect the current resulting from the induced electric field and deliver the power to an external load. The gas leaves the generator at a reduced but still high enough temperature that it can be further utilized in a conventional heat engine. In fact, a primary application proposed for an MHD generator is its use as a topping device for a Rankine steam cycle. Figure 19.63(b) is a vector diagram depicting the interaction of the magnetic field with the field of an electrically conducting fluid such as mercury or an ionized gas. The gas travels in the x-direction and its velocity is represented by the vector $\mathscr{V}$. At right angles to this, a magnetic field is applied, its field strength being represented by the vector **B**. Due to the interaction of the two fields, an electric field at right angles to both $\mathscr{V}$ and **B** is induced. This induced electric field is given by the vector equation

$$\mathbf{E} = \mathscr{V} \times \mathbf{B} \tag{19.64}$$

and is as shown in Fig. 19.63(b). If σ (a scalar quantity) denotes the electrical conductivity of the fluid, then by Ohm's law, the density of the current induced in the conducting fluid is

$$\mathbf{J} = \sigma\mathbf{E} = \sigma(\mathscr{V} \times \mathbf{B}) \tag{19.65}$$

Simultaneously occurring with the induced current is the induced body force in the gas given by

$$\mathbf{F} = \mathbf{J} \times \mathbf{B} \tag{19.66}$$

This force, called the *ponderomotive* force, occurs because the conducting fluid cuts the magnetic field lines. It is perpendicular to both **J** and **B** and is parallel, but in opposite direction, to $\mathscr{V}$. The above equations serve to describe the various phenomena occurring in an MHD generator. They need no further elaboration here for an understanding of the workings of the generator.

An MHD generator of the type described above can be made of any size. Typical design parameters for a 100 megawatt installation with a conductivity of 1 mho per meter are a magnetic field of 10,000 gauss and a temperature of 3,000 °F. One of the largest single factors influencing the performance is the gas conductivity. If the gas is seeded by a small amount (1 per cent) of an easily ionized impurity such as an alkali metal, conductivity can be obtained down to 2,000 °K. It is important that the temperature of the gas immediately adjacent to the electrodes is not cooled to too great an extent, otherwise the gas will lose its ionization and the generator will be open-circuited. For this reason the electrodes in an MHD generator must be operated at high temperatures. In fact, the generator rejects its waste heat at temperatures close to those required for ionization. This is the reason for having most MHD power plants use the MHD duct as a topping device for a conventional turbine-generator cycle. Although relatively little is known about the life of possible materials required for the construction of an MHD duct, and only a few of the many possible plasma compositions have been studied, power production by means of small MHD units have been demonstrated in the laboratory, utilizing an electric arc as a source of high-temperature plasma. Aluminum oxide and other ceramics have been tried for these small ducts.

19.35 Photovoltaic Cell

There are several ways in which light or electromagnetic radiation may be converted directly into electrical energy. A familiar example is the photoelectric cell which has an efficiency of 1 to 2 per cent. A more attractive device, however, is the *photovoltaic converter* or *solar cell* which is an outgrowth of semiconductor development. Photon energy (light) impinging on the device is directly converted into electrical energy. This conversion process is illustrated in Fig. 19.64.

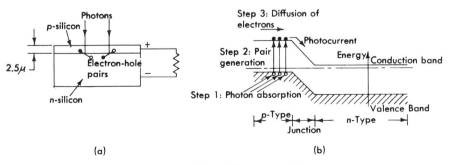

Fig. 19.64 Solar Cell and Photovoltaic Conversion.

At a junction between p- and n-type semiconductors the Fermi level is the same in both materials. As a result of this condition, there is a transfer of charge across the junction, and a potential appears across the barrier or transition layer between the two materials, usually of the order of 10^{-4} cm thick. When photons are absorbed near the junction, they generate electron-hole pairs, and the positive and negative charges move under the influence of the field to give rise to a current in the external circuit. A practical solar cell is comprised of a thin section of p silicon about 2.5 μ thick overlaying a thicker section of n silicon. The positive terminal is on the p side and the negative terminal on the n side. Sunlight is admitted through the thin p layer. Such cells have power densities of around 200 watts/m². This corresponds to an over-all efficiency of between 10 to 14 per cent. Actually, only about half of the photons in sunlight are energetic enough to create an electron-hole pair. This is because to produce emission, a photon ($h\nu$) must contribute the work function $e\phi$ before emission occurs. Since $e\phi$ is constant for a particular surface, it is obvious that at some frequency ν_0 given by

$$\nu_0 = \frac{e\phi}{h} \qquad (19.67)$$

emission will cease. This is called the *threshold frequency*. Any lower frequency does not have sufficient energy per photon to overcome the work function and cause emission.

19.36 Fuel Cell

A fuel cell is basically an electric battery using inexpensive fuels which are fed continuously to it. Ordinary batteries are not considered as fuel cells, though they convert chemical energy directly into electricity, because they use expensive fuels such as zinc, lead, mercury, etc. Furthermore, the operation of a fuel cell is just the opposite to that of a battery since the latter splits an electrolyte into its components, whereas the fuel cell combines hydrogen and oxygen to form water and release electrons in the process. Theoretically, a fuel cell could operate at 100 per cent efficiency, although in practice they operate with efficiencies of from 60 to 80 per cent. These efficiencies compare well with the best efficiencies of 40 to 45 per cent of present-day steam power plants. This is because unlike heat power plants, conventional or unconventional, the fuel cell is not limited by the restrictions of the Carnot cycle.

Figure 19.65 illustrates the basic principle of the fuel cell. It is like a storage battery in that it has positive and negative electrodes immersed in an electrolyte. However, instead of having to be recharged periodically, the fuel cell generates electricity as long as the fuel (hydrogen, propane, etc.)

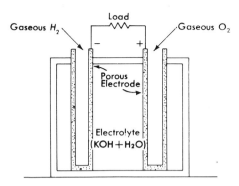

Fig. 19.65 Hydrogen-Oxygen Fuel Cell.

and air are fed into it. Consider, for example, the reaction between hydrogen and oxygen to form water. Hydrogen and oxygen, under pressures between 40 and 50 atm, are introduced into porous nickel electrodes immersed in a 180 °C potassium hydroxide. At the anode, H_2 molecules diffuse through the porous structure and are absorbed on the surface in the form of H atoms. The H atoms react with OH^- hydroxyl ions in the electrolyte to form water and free electrons. At the cathode, oxygen diffuses through the electrode and is absorbed on the surface. Here, the absorbed oxygen, the water in the electrolyte, and the electrons react to form hydroxyl ions. The latter then migrate through the electrolyte to the cathode. The following are the reactions taking place at the electrodes:

$$\text{Anode:} \quad 2H_2 + 4OH^- \rightarrow 4H_2O + 4e^-$$

$$\text{Cathode:} \; O_2 + 2H_2O + 4e^- \rightarrow 4OH^-$$

The cell reaction is $2H_2 + O_2 \rightarrow 2H_2O$ or $H_2 + (1/2)O_2 \rightarrow H_2O$, with $\Delta H = 286{,}000$ joules/mole. Part of the heat released, ΔH, is available for conversion into electrical energy. This part is the free energy change, ΔG, which is 237,000 joules/mole. The maximum voltage available is $V = (\Delta G/Q_e) = 1.23$ volts, where Q_e is the total charge transfer between the electrodes while forming one mole of water. The essential step in the operation of the fuel cell is the transfer of electrons from the negative terminal to the positive terminal through the external circuit. This flow of electrons constitutes the electric current or useful output of the cell.

PROBLEMS

19.1. A Rankine cycle operates with throttle conditions of 950 psia, 800 °F, and a condenser pressure of 1 psia. Determine: (a) the thermal efficiency, (b) the ratio of pump work to turbine work, (c) the fraction of the heat added which is unavailable energy if the lowest existing sink temperature is 70 °F.

19.2. What would be the efficiency of a steam power plant operating on a Carnot cycle having an isothermal heat addition at 250 psia and an isothermal heat rejection at 10 psia? The fluid states at the beginning of the isothermal expansion are saturated liquid and saturated (dry) vapor respectively.

19.3. Isentropic expansion in a Rankine cycle occurs from 590 psia and 650 °F to a condensing temperature of 100 °F. For a flow of 1 lbm/sec of steam, determine the heat added, the heat rejected, the work, and the thermal efficiency. What is the thermal efficiency of the Rankine engine operating between the given end states?

19.4. Steam is first supplied to a turbine at 400 psia and 550 °F. To what pressure must it be throttled to reduce its work to two thirds of that obtainable without throttling? Assume the exhaust pressure to remain unchanged at 1 psia.

19.5. A certain turbo-generator has a combined steam rate of 11.5 lbm/kw-hr. at its rated output of 30,000 kw. The steam supply is at 260 psia and 530 °F. The exhaust is at 1.8 psia. Determine: (a) the combined heat rate, (b) the combined thermal efficiency, and (c) the combined engine efficiency.

19.6. A certain steam engine with a mechanical efficiency of 90 per cent has a brake steam rate of 28.1 lbm/bhp-hr. At the throttle, the steam has an enthalpy of 1,210 Btu/lbm. What is the quality of the steam at exhaust if the exhaust pressure is 15 psia?

19.7. A certain turbine has a brake steam rate of 6.2 lbm/bhp-hr. The specific enthalpy of the entering steam is 1,416 Btu. What is the quality of the exhaust steam if the pressure in the condenser is 4.75 in.Hg abs?

19.8. An ideal incomplete-expansion engine is supplied with saturated steam at 180 psia. Release occurs at 30 psia, and the exhaust is at 14.7 psia. For a flow of 1 lbm/sec of steam, determine: (a) the work, (b) the steam rate, (c) the thermal efficiency, (d) the mean effective pressure.

19.9. A certain locomotive engine has a steam consumption of 24.6 lbm/ihp-hr. It is supplied with steam at 220 psia and 480 °F. Release is at 40 psia, and exhaust is at 15 psia. Determine: (a) the indicated engine efficiency, (b) the enthalpy of the exhaust steam, (c) the indicated thermal efficiency. What is the thermal efficiency of the Rankine cycle through the same end states?

19.10. A certain steam turbine operates on a throttle temperature not to exceed 1,200 °F and an exhaust pressure of 1 psia. The moisture in the exhaust is not to exceed 10 per cent. What is the maximum throttle pressure which can be used if the turbine efficiency is (a) 100 per cent, (b) 80 per cent? Consider the turbine efficiency as the ratio of the actual work of expansion to the isentropic work of expansion.

19.11. Steam enters a turbine at 4,500 psia, 1,150 °F, and expands to 0.5 psia. Suppose that at a section where the quality reaches 85 per cent, the liquid is mechanically separated from the steam and removed from the turbine. By what amount will the ideal turbine work be changed?

19.1 2. A certain turbo-generator receives steam at 175 psia and 480 °F while exhausting at a temperature of 95 °F. The combined steam rate is 11.6 lbm/kw-hr, and the generator efficiency is 95 per cent. Determine: (a) the quality of the exhaust steam, (b) the loss of Rankine work due to irreversibilities.

19.13. A steam generator delivers steam at 560 psia and 500 °F. Because of frictional losses in the line and the throttling at the turbine, the steam enters the turbine nozzle at 460 psia. The condenser temperature is 100 °F. The turbine has a brake engine efficiency of 72 per cent and the generator has an efficiency of 94 per cent. For the turbine using the throttled steam, find: (a) the brake work, (b) the combined thermal efficiency. Also, determine the loss of Rankine work caused by the reduced load and friction in the line.

19.14. An 11×13 in. double-acting steam engine receives steam at 130 psia and 60 degrees of superheat. The pressure in the condenser is 1 psia and the speed of the engine is 250 rpm. The piston rod has a 2 in. diameter. The indicator cards for the head end and crank end have areas of 1.6 sq. in. and 1.61 sq. in. respectively. Both cards have a length of 3 in. The scale of the indicator spring is 80 lb. The net load on the prony brake is 230 lb and the length of the arm is 63 in. The steam rate, as measured, averages 21 lbm/bhp-hr. Find: (a) the ihp, (b) the bhp, (c) the mechanical efficiency, (d) the heat rate in Btu/bhp-hr.

19.15. An ideal reheat cycle operates from throttle conditions of 1,800 psia, 900 °F, and reheats at 560 psia to 900 °F. The exhaust pressure is 1 psia. Determine: (a) the thermal efficiency of the cycle, (b) the unavailable energy per pound of throttle steam referred to a sink temperature of 70 °F.

19.16. Steam is supplied to a turbine at 4,800 psia, 1,100 °F, and exhausted to a condenser at 1 psia. It is required to have a double reheat arrangement, with no moisture entering a reheat and not more than 10 per cent moisture entering the condenser. Furthermore, reheat temperatures are not to exceed 1,000 °F and equal enthalpy drops are to occur across each portion of the turbine. Determine the reheat pressures to be used. Consider the expansion in the turbine to be isentropic.

19.17. A regenerative steam power cycle operates with throttle conditions of 1,000 psia, 850 °F, and condenser pressure of 1 psia. There is one open feedwater heater, at 90 psia. Determine: (a) the amount of steam bled per pound of throttle steam, (b) the total work per pound of steam entering the turbine, (c) the thermal efficiency and compare this with the efficiency of a Rankine cycle having the same throttle conditions and exhaust pressure, but no regenerative feedwater heating.

19.18. Steam enters a turbine at 920 psia, 1,000 °F, and exhausts at 15 psia. There is one extraction, at 200 psia. The efficiency of the turbine is 80 per cent up to the point of extraction and 76 per cent after the point of extraction. Assuming ideal conditions, determine the flow of throttle steam for a turbine output of 4,000 hp.

19.19. A 35,000-kw turbo-generator receives steam at 600 psia, 700 °F, and exhausts at 2 in. Hg abs. Part of the steam is withdrawn at 100 psia, 400 °F, to be used for feedwater heating, while the remainder passes through a reheater.

The reheated steam enters the turbine at 110 psia, 700 °F, and a second extraction for feedwater heating occurs at 20 psia, 400 °F. A third extraction occurs at 6 psia, 200 °F. The exhaust steam from the turbine contains 6 per cent moisture, and the temperatures of the feedwater leaving the heaters are 160 °F, 225 °F, and 330 °F respectively. Determine: (a) the percentage of steam extracted at each point, (b) the hourly flow of throttle steam, (c) the thermal efficiency of the cycle.

19.20. An ideal reheat-regenerative cycle is to produce 150,000 kw from throttle conditions of 2,300 psia and 1,100 °F. Reheat is at 300 psia to 1,100 °F. There are closed feedwater heaters at 800 psia, 300 psia, 120 psia, and 8 psia. The condensed steam leaving each heater is saturated liquid, whereas the feedwater leaving each heater is considered to be at a temperature infinitesimally lower than that of the condensed steam. Determine the thermal efficiency of the cycle and the required flow rate from the steam generator.

19.21. A mercury-steam binary cycle consists of two superimposed Rankine cycles. The mercury turbine is supplied with saturated vapor at 180 psia, 1,000 °F, with condensation taking place at 500 °F. The heat rejected by the mercury cycle is used to supply saturated steam at 500 °F to the steam turbine, the exhaust vapor condensing at 100 °F. The latent heat of vaporization of mercury at 180 psia is 124.3 Btu/lbm, and its heat capacity at constant pressure is 0.0315 Btu/lbm–°F. The specific volume of the liquid is 0.0015 ft³/lbm. Assuming reversible adiabatic processes in the turbines and pumps, determine: (a) the thermal efficiency of the cycle, (b) the thermodynamic effectiveness of the cycle. Consider the isothermal source and sink to be at 1,000 °F and 100 °F respectively.

19.22. The Hartford, Conn. plant has a 10,000-kw mercury cycle topping a 12,400-kw steam cycle. Mercury vapor is generated at 70 psia, 883 °F, and is condensed at 500 °F. The condenser-boiler receives feedwater at 150 °F. Steam leaves the superheater elements at 400 psia, 700 °F, and after expansion in the steam turbine, is condensed at 1 psig. The mercury cycle has a combined consumption rate of 108 lbm/kw-hr. The mercury boiler, which uses fuel oil having a heating value of 19,200 Btu/lbm, has an efficiency of 86 per cent. The following properties of Hg are given:

$$t_{70 \text{ psia sat}} = 856.4 \,^{\circ}F, \; h_{g, \, 70 \text{ psia}} = 151.2 \text{ Btu/lbm},$$

$$s_{g, \, 70 \text{ psia}} = 0.12668 \text{ Btu/lbm–}^{\circ}R, \; h_{f, \, 500 \,^{\circ}F} = 15.32 \text{ Btu/lbm},$$

$$hf_{g, \, 500 \,^{\circ}F} = 126.53 \text{ Btu/lbm}, \; s_{f, \, 500 \,^{\circ}F} = 0.02189 \text{ Btu/lbm–}^{\circ}R$$

$$s_{fg, \, 500 \,^{\circ}F} = 0.13185 \text{ Btu/lbm–}^{\circ}R; \; c_{p} = 0.0247 \text{ Btu/lbm–}^{\circ}R$$

Determine: (a) the combined thermal efficiency of the binary cycle, (b) the lbm/hr of fuel oil used, (c) the ideal steam rate for the steam turbine.

19.23. In a certain nuclear power plant, the flow of liquid sodium in the primary circuit is 97,000 lbm/hr. The liquid sodium leaves the reactor at 20 psia, 700 °F, and goes to a heat exchanger where it is cooled to 580 °F before returning to the reactor. In the heat exchanger, heat is transferred to liquid sodium in the intermediate circuit, which in turn transfers heat to a steam generator producing saturated steam at 950 psia. The steam then expands adiabatically through a turbine having an efficiency of 65 per cent to an exhaust pressure of 1.5 psia. Assuming a specific heat of sodium to be constant at 0.30 Btu/lbm–°F, and neglecting the work of the sodium pumps, determine: (a) the power available from the plant, (b) the irreversibility (Btu/hr) resulting from the transfer of heat from the sodium in the primary circuit to the steam in the turbine circuit.

19.24. A certain manufacturing plant requires steam at 22 psia for heating purposes. The supply is to be obtained by drawing steam through a pressure-reducing valve from a line where the steam is dry and saturated at 110 psia. The heating load is 22,000,000 Btu/hr, and the condensate leaves the heating system at 180 °F (with negligible pressure loss). It is proposed to install a turbine in place of the pressure-reducing valve so as to obtain some by-product power while still carrying the heating load. Assuming a turbine efficiency of 65 per cent, what is the amount of power obtainable and what is the new steam rate (lbm/hr) compared to the original steam flow rate?

19.25. In a cold air-standard Otto cycle (constant specific heats) the working medium at the beginning of the compression is 14.7 psia, 85 °F, and has a volume of 1.05 cu ft. At the end of compression, the pressure is 145 psia, and during constant-volume combustion, 10 Btu are added in the process. Determine: (a) the thermal efficiency, (b) the fraction of heat added which is available energy. Consider the sink temperature to be the same as the lowest temperature of the cycle.

19.26. A cold air-standard Diesel cycle (constant specific heats) has a compression ratio of 16 and a cut-off ratio of 2. At the beginning of compression, the air is at 14.7 psia, 45 °F. If the cylinder volume is 0.5 cu ft and the temperature in the surroundings is 45 °F, what is the fraction of heat added which is available energy?

19.27. Show that the mean effective pressure of a Diesel cycle using an ideal gas with constant specific heats is

$$p_m = p_1 \left[\frac{\gamma \eta_v{}^\gamma (\eta_c - 1) - \eta_v (\eta_c{}^\gamma - 1)}{(\gamma - 1)(\eta_v - 1)} \right]$$

where p_1 is the pressure at the beginning of the compression stroke, η_v is the compression ratio, and η_c is the cutoff ratio.

19.28. A cold air-standard dual cycle (constant specific heats) has a compression ratio of 7. The cylinder diameter is 10 in., and the stroke is 12 in. At the start of compression, the air is at 14.7 psia, 75 °F. At the end of compression, the pressure is 800 psia. Heat is added at constant pressure during 3 per cent of the stroke. Determine: (a) the heat added, (b) the thermal efficiency, (c) the fraction of heat rejected which is available energy.

19.29. Discuss the derivation of Eq. (19.5). To what degree does the efficiency of a dual cycle approach that of an Otto cycle?

19.30. A gas-turbine operates at a pressure ratio of 5. The inlet conditions to the compressor are 14.7 psia, 70 °F; the turbine inlet temperature is 1,600 °F. Determine the compressor work, the turbine work, and the thermal efficiency of the cycle based on (a) cold air-standard analysis using constant specific heats at room temperature values, (b) air-standard analysis using the gas tables. Will the compressor work turn out to be the same in both analyses? Why? If a constant c_p ($=0.24$ Btu/lbm–°R) is used, does the cold air-standard analysis give a work output in the turbine which is too low in comparison with the more accurate result obtained from an analysis using the gas tables? Why?

19.31. For equal pressure and temperature limits, rank in order of increasing efficiency, a gas-turbine cycle using as working medium: (a) air, (b) helium, (c) carbon dioxide.

19.32. A power plant is to be operated by combining a Brayton cycle and a Rankine cycle in such a way that heat transferred from the gas leaving the turbine of the Brayton cycle is used to generate steam for the Rankine cycle. The maximum pressure of the Brayton cycle is 75 psia, and the minimum pressure is 14.7 psia. Its maximum temperature is 1,540 °F, and its minimum temperature is 70 °F. The Rankine cycle, utilizing steam has a maximum pressure of 400 psia, a maximum temperature of 600 °F, and a minimum pressure of 2 psia. Determine the efficiency of the combined cycle.

19.33. Compressed air is supplied by a gas-turbine plant by having the output of the turbine used solely to drive the compressor. The airstream from the compressor is divided into two parts: that which is delivered by the plant, and that which goes to the combustion chamber. The inlet conditions to the compressor are 14.7 psia, 70 °F, and the discharge pressure is 100 psia. The turbine inlet temperature is 1,600 °F. Assuming reversible adiabatic compression and expansion, estimate the mass ratio of compressed air delivered to air drawn in.

19.34. As an emergency power supply, it is proposed to use an arrangement in which a turbine is driven by compressed air from a storage tank. The air in the tank is initially at 100 psia, 70 °F, and the turbine is to operate between the decreasing pressure in the tank and atmospheric pressure (14.7 psia). Assuming a turbine efficiency of 60 per cent, estimate the size of tank needed in order for the turbine to deliver 6 hp for 15 minutes.

19.35. Steam and gas turbines have similar mechanical design limitations such as strength of metal at high temperatures, etc. Yet steam power plants are built in much larger capacities than gas turbine power plants. Why is this?

19.36. It was shown in Sec. 19.13 that for a Brayton cycle operating between temperature limits of T_3 (high) and T_1 (low) the pressure ratio η_p for maximum work is given by

$$(\eta_p)_{\text{optimum}} = \left(\frac{T_3}{T_1}\right)^{\gamma/[2(\gamma-1)]}$$

What is the pressure ratio in terms of T_3 and T_1 for the Brayton cycle to have an efficiency equal to that of a Carnot cycle? Determine the pressure ratio for maximum work between temperature limits of 1,540 °F and 80 °F, and compare the Brayton cycle efficiency to that of a Carnot cycle operating between the same temperature limits.

19.37. In the case of a Brayton-cycle gas-turbine power plant, a large proportion of the turbine output is used to drive the compressor. This compressor work is known as the *back work*. Discuss how the back work can be reduced by intercooling. Can the proportion of back work be also reduced by reheating the gas after expanding over a fraction of its over-all pressure ratio in the turbine to the original inlet temperature? Why? Sketch a gas turbine installation combining intercooling, reheating, and regeneration.

19.38. Prove that for a turbine using an ideal gas with constant specific heats, the work output for a given pressure ratio is proportional to the inlet absolute temperature.

19.39. A cold air-standard regenerative gas-turbine cycle operates between pressures of 14.7 psia and 100 psia. The compressor inlet temperature is 70 °F and the turbine inlet temperature is 1,250 °F. Both turbine and compressor have an efficiency of 80 per cent. The regenerator has an effectiveness of 75 per cent. Determine the thermal efficiency of the cycle and the effectiveness (the latter being defined as the ratio of actual work output to the available energy). Consider the temperature in the surroundings to be 70 °F.

19.40. Air enters the compressor of a regenerative gas-turbine cycle at 14.7 psia, 80 °F, and leaves at 74 psia, 500 °F. After passing through the regenerator, it enters the combustion chamber at 800 °F and leaves at 1,650 °F. It then enters the turbine and leaves at 1,060 °F. The temperature in the surroundings is 80 °F. Based on an air-standard analysis using the gas tables, determine: (a) the thermal efficiency of the cycle, (b) the irreversibility of the compression process, (c) the irreversibility of the expansion process, (d) the irreversibility of the heat transfer process in the regenerator and, (e) the fraction of the heat added which is available energy.

19.41. From momentum considerations, show that the internal thrust for a jet propulsion engine is given by

$$F_i = (p_2 A_2 + \dot{m} \mathscr{V}_2) - (p_1 A_1 + \dot{m} \mathscr{V}_1)$$

where F_i is the resultant (in the direction of flow) of all the internal forces exerted by the duct upon the fluid passing through it, and p_1, p_2, A_1, A_2 are the pressure and areas at inlet and outlet respectively. In actual flight, there is an additional force: the product of atmospheric pressure p_a times the area difference $A_2 - A_1$ which acts opposite to the internal thrust. The net or external thrust is thus

$$F = F_i - p_a(A_2 - A_1)$$
$$= (p_2 A_2 + \dot{m} \mathscr{V}_2) - (p_1 A_1 + \dot{m} \mathscr{V}_1) - p_a(A_2 - A_1)$$

Show that for a rocket engine, this becomes

$$F = \dot{m} \mathscr{V}_2 + A_2(p_2 - p_a)$$

which for the case of the pressure in the exit plane of the nozzle being equal to the atmosphere pressure, reduces to

$$F = \dot{m} \mathscr{V}_2$$

19.42. A ramjet engine takes in air at 11 psia, 45 °F. The air enters the diffuser at 1,500 fps (craft speed) through a cross-sectional area of 0.8 sq. ft. and is decelerated to 260 fps relative to the engine. Fuel at the rate of 0.02 times the air flow rate is burned to bring the temperature to 1,650 °F, and the combustion products (which can be treated as air) are expanded through a nozzle to the ambient pressure to leave at 2,600 fps. Calculate the thrust developed.

19.43. A turbojet travels at 610 miles per hour at an altitude where the ambient pressure is 10 psia and the temperature is −10 °F. Air entering the diffuser (of 90 per cent efficiency) is reduced to negligible velocity, after which it is compressed through a pressure ratio of 10 to 1 in a compressor of 84 per cent efficiency. Octane, with a lower heating value of 19,200 Btu/lbm is burned to yield a temperature of 1,750 °F at the turbine inlet. After expanding through the turbine (of 84 per cent efficiency), the products expand further in the nozzle (of 90 per cent efficiency), to ambient pressure (10 psia). Determine: (a) the fuel to air ratio, (b) the total thrust if the effective cross-sectional area of the inlet air is 1.2 sq. ft., (c) the propulsive efficiency.

19.44. Eight tons of refrigeration are to be supplied by a refrigerating machine operating on the reversed Carnot cycle. The evaporator temperature is −5 °F and the condenser temperature is 85 °F. Determine the power required and the coefficient of performance.

19.45. An ammonia compression refrigerating installation has a capacity of 20 tons. Saturated liquid leaves the condenser at 140 psia and saturated vapor leaves the evaporator at 20 psia. The liquid and the vapor pass through a heat exchanger in which the vapor is superheated 20 °F and the liquid is subcooled. The liquid then enters the expansion valve and the vapor enters the compressor, from which it is discharged at a temperature of 315 °F. Assuming compression to be adiabatic, determine the power input and the coefficient of performance.

19.46. An ideal vapor-compression refrigerating cycle operates between temperature limits of 35 °F and 85 °F. Saturated liquid and dry saturated vapor enter the expansion valve and the compressor respectively. For a refrigerating capacity of 10 tons, calculate the required power input and the refrigerant flow rate (lbm/min) if the refrigerant is (a) ammonia, (b) Freon 12, (c) propane, (d) water.

19.47. Saturated ammonia vapor at 40 psia enters a 6 ×6 in., twin-cylinder, single acting compressor having a volumetric efficiency of 85 per cent and running at 300 rpm. The head pressure is 140 psia, and liquid ammonia at 70 °F enters the expansion valve. Assuming an ideal cycle, find: (a) the pounds of ammonia circulated per minute, (b) the tons of refrigeration, (c) the coefficient of performance, (d) the volume of atmospheric air (cfm) at 14.7 psia, 40 °F, which may be heated to 75 °F if the installation is used for reversed-cycle heating, (e) the coefficient of performance of the heating cycle.

19.48. The average rate of heat flow from a kitchen into the low temperature region of a domestic refrigerator is 1,000 Btu/hr. The refrigerator uses a sealed 0.25 hp motor for the compressor operation and a 0.10 hp motor for circulating air over the condenser elements. The motors each have an efficiency of 80 per cent and operate 30 per cent of the time. Determine: (a) the average coefficient of performance, (b) the net heat added to the kitchen per hour.

19.49. A vapor-compression refrigerating installation circulates 19.8 lbm/min of Freon 12. The refrigerant enters the suction side of the compressor at 0 °F and 100 per cent quality, and is discharged at 120 psia. Liquid refrigerant at 80 °F enters the expansion valve. For an ideal cycle, determine the horsepower input and the compressor cylinder size if there are twin cylinders with a stroke to bore ratio of 1 (called square design), a volumetric efficiency of 80 per cent, and a shaft speed of 450 rpm.

19.50. A vapor compression cycle uses SO_2 as refrigerant. Saturated vapor at 10 °F enters the compressor, while discharge is at 80 psia, 235 °F. Liquid SO_2 enters the expansion valve at 90 °F. Determine (a) the required horsepower per ton, (b) the coefficient of performance, (c) the compression efficiency, (d) the flow of SO_2(lbm/min) for a refrigerating capacity of 20 tons.

19.51. A reversed vapor-compression cycle using Freon 12 is to be used for heating. The maximum demand is 1000 cfm of 40 °F outside air to be heated to 85 °F. The evaporator temperature is 20 °F, and the condenser pressure is 140 psia. Saturated vapor enters the compressor and saturated liquid enters the expansion valve. Determine: (a) the flow of refrigerant in pounds per minute, (b) the coefficient of performance of the heating cycle, (c) the cost of heating at 2 cents/kw-hr, (d) the cost of heating if fuel oil at 13 cents/gal is used. The fuel oil has a heating value of 135,000 Btu/gal and the efficiency of the heater is 80 per cent.

19.52. Show that in a compressor the net work of compressing m pounds of fluid between intake pressure p_1 and receiver pressure p_2 is given by

$$W = mc_pT_1\left[1 - \left(\frac{p_2}{p_1}\right)^{(\gamma-1)/\gamma}\right]$$

Does clearance volume affect the work of compression per pound of fluid? Does clearance volume affect the volumetric efficiency? Explain.

19.53. A two-stage compressor draws in 350 cfm of air at 14.7 psia, 80 °F and compresses it polytropically ($n = 1.3$) to 147 psia. An intercooler cools the air to its initial temperature before it enters the second stage. Determine the amount of work saved in comparison with a single-stage compression with the same value of n.

19.54. Consider a two-stage compression with intercooling between pressure limits p_1 and p_2 (Fig. 19.66). The gas enters the low pressure stage at p_1, T_1, is

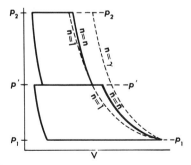

Fig. 19.66 Combined Indicator Cards for Two-Stage Compressor.

compressed to an intermediate pressure p', and then compressed in the high-pressure stage to the pressure p_2. For perfect intercooling (when the temperature of the gas entering the high-pressure stage is equal to that entering the low pressure stage and when the exponent of compression n is the same in the two stages), show that the work required is

$$W = \frac{n}{n-1} p_1 (V_1 - V_4) \left[\left(\frac{p'}{p_1} \right)^{(n-1)/n} + \left(\frac{p_2}{p'} \right)^{(n-1)/n} - 2 \right]$$

and that this is a minimum when

$$p' = \sqrt{p_1 p_2}$$

19.55. Consider again Prob. 19.54, except that it is for a three-stage compressor with two intercoolers. Show that the intermediate pressures p' and p'' are given by

$$p' = \sqrt[3]{p_1^2 p_2} \; ; \; p'' = \sqrt[3]{p_1 p_2^2}$$

and that the total work required is

$$W = \frac{3n}{n-1} p_1 (V_1 - V_4) \left[\left(\frac{p_2}{p_1} \right)^{(n-1)/3n} - 1 \right]$$

19.56. A 10-ton vacuum refrigerating installation operates with an evaporator temperature of 44 °F. Warm water at 55 °F enters the evaporator and the steam consumption of the ejector is 34.9 lbm/hr-ton of saturated steam at 100 psia. Determine (a) the volume of vapor to be removed from the evaporator, (b) the input per Btu of refrigeration.

19.57. An ammonia-absorption refrigeration cycle operates with an evaporator temperature of 10 °F and a condenser temperature of 120 °F. The generator temperature is 302 °F, and for each Btu transferred to the ammonia solution in the generator, 0.42 Btu are transferred to the ammonia in the evaporator. It is desirable to compare the performance of this cycle with that of a vapor-compression cycle. To this end, assume that a heat reservoir is available at 302 °F, and that heat is transferred from this reservoir to a reversible engine which rejects heat to the surroundings at 75 °F. The work from the heat engine is then used to drive the vapor-compression installation. Assuming the vapor-compression cycle to be ideal, compare the amount of refrigeration thus obtained with the 0.42 Btu obtained in the absorption cycle.

19.58. An absorption refrigeration installation operates between pressure limits of 215 psia and 55 psia. The generator temperature is 200 °F and the absorber temperature is 80 °F. Determine (a) the amount of liquid (strong solution) to be pumped for each pound of ammonia entering the condenser, (b) the amount of heat added for each pound of ammonia entering the condenser, (c) the coefficient of performance if the temperature of the evaporator is 30 °F.

19.59. A dense air refrigerating machine (one that uses high pressures in order to limit the physical size of the equipment) has a capacity of 10 tons. It operates between 50 psia and 200 psia. The temperatures of the air entering the compressor and the expander are 30 °F and 95 °F respectively. Assuming the compression to be polytropic with $n = 1.35$ and the expansion to be isentropic, determine (a) the power required, (b) the coefficient of performance, (c) the displacement (cfm) of both compressor and expander. Neglect clearance.

19.60. An aircraft refrigerating installation uses 11 lbm/min of air at 105 in. Hg abs and 526 °F which is bled from the air compressor serving the jet engine of the plane. The air passes through a heat exchanger, leaving at 102 in. Hg abs and 166 °F, at which point it is expanded through a turbine to 22 in. Hg abs and 18 °F. Finally, the air leaves the plane at 90 °F. (a) What is the amount of refrigeration (tons) with respect to 90 °F? (b) If the inlet stagnation condition to the jet engine compressor is 31 in. Hg abs and 210 °F, and if the turbine is to drive a centrifugal fan for passing coolant air through the heat exchanger, what is the total input?

CHAPTER 20

Dynamics and Thermodynamics of One-Dimensional Steady Flow

20.1 Introduction

This chapter deals with certain aspects of fluid flow related to thermo-dynamics. With the advent of high-speed flight, jet engines, rockets, and space flight, the science of fluid dynamics, particularly the branch dealing with compressible flow known as *gas dynamics*, has assumed increasingly greater importance in engineering. Because of this, and because the mechanical and thermodynamic properties of a fluid at the inlet and outlet of a control volume are related to the heat and work transfers across its boundary by the first law of thermodynamics, it is advisable that some attention be given to fluid dynamics in a thermodynamics text.

628

Traditionally, fluid dynamics has been regarded as a science separate from thermodynamics. There is justification for such a point of view, inasmuch as thermodynamics deals essentially with equilibrium states and grows out of the first and second laws, whereas fluid dynamics evolves from Newton's laws of motion and is not necessarily restricted to equilibrium states. Nevertheless, it is desirable to introduce some of the basic aspects of fluid flow from the standpoint of both the laws of thermodynamics and Newton's laws. In this chapter, the first law, the second law, and the principles of mechanics will all be used to give a deeper understanding of fluid flow than was obtained in Chap. 6.

20.2 Fundamental Equations of Fluid Flow

When dealing with fluid flow it is necessary to satisfy four equations, namely, the equations of conservation of mass, energy, and momentum, and the equation of state of the particular fluid. In three-dimensional flow, the manipulation of these equations is cumbersome at best; consequently, it is standard procedure to make simplifying assumptions. One such assumption is that the flow is one-dimensional, meaning that the flow properties change only in the direction of flow. This does not necessarily imply constant-area flow, for one-dimensional analysis can be successfully applied to variable-area devices such as nozzles and diffusers. All that is required is that the flow properties remain the same in any one plane perpendicular to the direction of flow. Thus, one-dimensional flow is not as restrictive as it would first seem; it has many useful applications. The following are the basic equations of fluid flow, written for one-dimensional motion.

Continuity Equation. Consider the flow in an element of stream tube as shown in Fig. 20.1. The mass contained between Sections 1 and 2 is $\rho A dx$. According to the law of conservation of mass, the rate of increase, $\partial(\rho A dx)/\partial t$, is equal to the mass flow entering through Section 1 minus

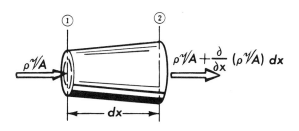

Fig. 20.1 Flow through Element of Stream Tube.

the mass flow leaving through Section 2. Thus,

$$\frac{\partial}{\partial t}(\rho A dx) = \rho \mathscr{V} A - \left[\rho \mathscr{V} A + \frac{\partial}{\partial x}(\rho \mathscr{V} A) dx \right]$$

or, upon simplification

$$\frac{\partial}{\partial x}(\rho \mathscr{V} A) + \frac{\partial}{\partial t}(\rho A) = 0 \qquad (20.1)$$

Equation (20.1) is the continuity equation for one-dimensional flow. In the case of steady-flow ($\partial/\partial t = 0$) it reduces to

$$\frac{d}{dx}(\rho \mathscr{V} A) = 0 \qquad (20.2)$$

or

$$\rho \mathscr{V} A = \text{constant} \qquad (20.3)$$

Sometimes, it is convenient to separate the respective effects of variations in density, velocity and area. To do this, Eq. (20.3) is differentiated logarithmically to give

$$\frac{d\rho}{\rho} + \frac{d\mathscr{V}}{\mathscr{V}} + \frac{dA}{A} = 0 \qquad (20.4)$$

If, furthermore, an equation of state $p = \rho R T$ is assumed for the flowing fluid, this becomes

$$\frac{dp}{p} + \frac{d\mathscr{V}}{\mathscr{V}} + \frac{dA}{A} - \frac{dT}{T} = 0 \qquad (20.5)$$

Momentum Equation. In thermodynamics, it is customary to deal with a *system*, which is an arbitrarily fixed mass. In gas dynamics, a similar but slightly different concept is used: the so-called *control volume*. This is an arbitrary volume, fixed in space, which is bounded by a closed surface and which allows fluid to enter and leave. The basic characteristic of a control volume, namely that it is fixed in space, leads to the Eulerian[†] equations of flow. In Fig. 20.2, let an element of stream tube be chosen as the control volume. The rate of momentum flow[‡] into the control volume

---

[†] In contrast to the Lagrangian equations, which are obtained by using a *moving* frame of reference.

[‡] The quantity $(\dot{m}/g_c)\mathscr{V} = (\rho A \mathscr{V}/g_c)\mathscr{V}$ is often called the *momentum flux*. Note that in the usual system of units with mass expressed in pounds and density expressed in pounds per cubic foot, g_c must be inserted when writing the expression for the momentum flux.

across the left face is

$$\left(\frac{\rho A \mathscr{V}}{g_c}\right)\mathscr{V} = \frac{\rho A \mathscr{V}^2}{g_c}$$

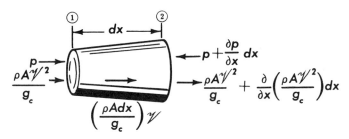

Fig. 20.2 Momentum Flux through a Control Volume.

Similarly, the rate of momentum flow out of the control volume across the right face is

$$\frac{\rho A \mathscr{V}^2}{g_c} + \frac{\partial}{\partial x}\left(\frac{\rho A \mathscr{V}^2}{g_c}\right)dx$$

The rate of momentum change across the boundary of the control volume is then

$$\left[\frac{\rho A \mathscr{V}^2}{g_c} + \frac{\partial}{\partial x}\left(\frac{\rho A \mathscr{V}^2}{g_c}\right)dx\right] - \frac{\rho A \mathscr{V}^2}{g_c} = \frac{\partial}{\partial x}\left(\frac{\rho A \mathscr{V}^2}{g_c}\right)dx$$

The rate of momentum change for the fluid in the control volume is

$$\frac{\partial}{\partial t}\int_1^2 \left(\frac{\rho A dx}{g_c}\right)\mathscr{V} = \frac{\partial}{\partial t}\int_1^2\left(\frac{\rho A \mathscr{V}}{g_c}\right)dx$$

where the integration, with respect to x, is between sections 1 and 2. The total rate of momentum change for the control volume is thus

$$\frac{\partial}{\partial x}\left(\frac{\rho A \mathscr{V}^2}{g_c}\right)dx + \frac{\partial}{\partial t}\int_1^2\left(\frac{\rho A \mathscr{V}}{g_c}\right)dx$$

According to Newton's second law, this rate of momentum change must be equal to the resultant force:

$$\frac{\partial}{\partial x}\left(\frac{\rho A \mathscr{V}^2}{g_c}\right)dx + \frac{\partial}{\partial t}\left(\frac{\rho A \mathscr{V}}{g_c}\right)dx = \sum F \qquad (20.6)$$

Equation (20.6) is the *momentum equation* in its general one-dimensional form. It is valid for steady or unsteady, compressible or incompressible, and reversible or irreversible flow (since no restriction has yet been placed upon ΣF).

For the case of steady-flow involving only pressure forces, $\partial/\partial t = 0$, while the resultant force in the direction of motion is (see Fig. 20.2):

$$\sum F = pA - \left[pA + \left(\frac{\partial p}{\partial x}dx\right)A\right] = -A\frac{\partial p}{\partial x}dx$$

Consequently, Eq. (20.6) becomes

$$d\left(\frac{\rho A \mathcal{V}^2}{g_c}\right) = -Adp \qquad (20.7)$$

Equation (20.7), which is valid when viscous forces are negligible, leads to some well-known results, for it may be written as

$$\left(\frac{\rho A \mathcal{V}}{g_c}\right)d\mathcal{V} + \mathcal{V}d\left(\frac{\rho A \mathcal{V}}{g_c}\right) = -Adp$$

Now, $d(\rho A \mathcal{V}) = 0$ from the continuity equation, and therefore

$$\frac{\rho A \mathcal{V}}{g_c}d\mathcal{V} = -Adp$$

This simplifies to

$$\frac{\mathcal{V}d\mathcal{V}}{g_c} + \frac{dp}{\rho} = 0 \qquad (20.8)$$

Equation (20.8) is *Euler's equation;* it can be integrated if the relation between p and ρ is known. For the case of an incompressible fluid it takes on the simple form of

$$\frac{\mathcal{V}^2}{2g_c} + \frac{p}{\rho} = \text{constant} \qquad (20.9)$$

which is *Bernoulli's equation.*

Energy Equation. Consider again a control volume as in the preceding discussion. The energy flux (i.e., rate of energy flow) is the product of the mass flow rate, $\rho A \mathcal{V}$, and the energy per unit mass, e. Thus the rate of energy flow into the control volume (across its left face) is $\rho A \mathcal{V} e$ and the rate of energy flow out of the control volume (across its right face) is $\rho A \mathcal{V} e + \partial/\partial x(\rho A \mathcal{V} e)dx$. The net rate of energy flow is then

$$\rho A \mathcal{V} e - \left[\rho A \mathcal{V} e + \frac{\partial}{\partial x}(\rho A \mathcal{V} e)dx\right] = -\frac{\partial}{dx}(\rho A \mathcal{V} e)dx$$

But this is not the only energy interaction across the boundary of the control volume. In addition, work at the rate of $pA\mathcal{V}$ is transferred into the control volume at the left face and work at the rate of $pA\mathscr{V} + \partial/\partial x(pA\mathscr{V})dx$ is transferred out of the control volume at the right face. The net rate of work transfer is thus

$$pA\mathscr{V} - \left[pA\mathscr{V} + \frac{\partial}{\partial x}(pA\mathscr{V})dx\right] = -\frac{\partial}{\partial x}(pA\mathscr{V})dx$$

The total rate of energy flux for the control volume is

$$-\frac{\partial}{\partial x}(\rho A\mathscr{V}e)dx - \frac{\partial}{\partial x}(pA\mathscr{V})dx$$

and this must, according to the principle of conservation of energy, be equal to the time rate of energy change in the control volume,

$$\frac{\partial}{\partial t}\int_1^2 (\rho A dx)e$$

In other words,

$$-\frac{\partial}{\partial x}(\rho A\mathscr{V}e)dx - \frac{\partial}{\partial x}(pA\mathscr{V})dx = \frac{\partial}{\partial t}\int_1^2 (\rho Ae)dx$$

Now, e, the energy per unit mass, is (neglecting potential-energy changes),

$$e = u + \frac{\mathscr{V}^2}{2g_c}$$

Replacing this in the preceding equation gives

$$-\frac{\partial}{\partial x}\left[\rho A\mathscr{V}\left(u + \frac{\mathscr{V}^2}{2g_c}\right)\right]dx - \frac{\partial}{\partial x}(pA\mathscr{V})dx$$

$$= \frac{\partial}{\partial t}\int_1^2 \left[\rho A\left(u + \frac{\mathscr{V}^2}{2g_c}\right)\right]dx$$

or

$$\frac{\partial}{\partial t}\int_1^2 \left[\rho A\left(u + \frac{\mathscr{V}^2}{2g_c}\right)\right]dx + \frac{\partial}{\partial x}\left[\rho A\mathscr{V}\left(u + \frac{p}{\rho} + \frac{\mathscr{V}^2}{2g_c}\right)\right]dx = 0$$

Since $\mu + p/\rho$ is equal to h, the specific enthalpy, the above relation becomes

$$\frac{\partial}{\partial t}\int_1^2 \left[\rho A\left(u + \frac{\mathscr{V}^2}{2g_c}\right)\right]dx + \frac{\partial}{\partial x}\left[\rho A\mathscr{V}\left(h + \frac{\mathscr{V}^2}{2g_c}\right)\right]dx = 0 \qquad (20.10)$$

Equation (20.10) is the energy equation for adiabatic flow in the absence of shaft work. Note that it is essentially the same as the energy equation developed in Chap. 5 with heat transfer Q and shaft work W absent. For steady-state adiabatic flow, Eq. (20.10) becomes

$$d\left[\rho A \mathscr{V}\left(h + \frac{\mathscr{V}^2}{2g_c}\right)\right] = 0$$

which may be written as

$$(\rho A \mathscr{V})d\left(h + \frac{\mathscr{V}^2}{2g_c}\right) + \left(h + \frac{\mathscr{V}^2}{2g_c}\right)d(\rho A \mathscr{V}) = 0$$

But $d(\rho A \mathscr{V}) = 0$ from the continuity equation, so that the above reduces to

$$d\left(h + \frac{\mathscr{V}^2}{2g_c}\right) = 0 \tag{20.11}$$

This is the familiar conservation of energy relation (in the absence of potential energy changes).

Equation of state. The final equation in the list is the equation of state. In fact, a relation between pressure and density must be known before Euler's equation can be integrated. For most cases, a perfect gas is assumed, so that the equation of state $p = \rho R T$ applies. Thus, for the case of a perfect gas undergoing an adiabatic and reversible process, the relation between p and ρ becomes

$$\frac{p}{\rho^\gamma} = \text{const} = c_1$$

or

$$dp = c_1 \gamma \rho^{\gamma-1} d\rho$$

With this, Eq. (20.8) can be integrated to give

$$\frac{\mathscr{V}^2}{2g_c} + c_1 \gamma \int \frac{\rho^{\gamma-1} d\rho}{\rho} = \text{const} = c_2$$

$$\frac{\mathscr{V}^2}{2g_c} + c_1 \gamma \frac{\rho^{\gamma-1}}{\gamma - 1} = c_2$$

Replacing c_1 by p/ρ^γ, this becomes

$$\frac{\mathscr{V}^2}{2g_c} + \frac{\gamma}{\gamma - 1} \cdot \frac{p}{\rho} = \text{const} = c_2 \tag{20.12}$$

Example 20.1. Derive an expression for the thrust developed in a jet propulsion engine. Assume steady-flow conditions.

Solution. Consider a jet propulsion engine as shown in Fig. 20.3. Newton's second law of motion states that the force is equal to the rate of change of momentum. For steady-flow conditions, this gives

$$\Sigma F = \dot{m}(\mathscr{V}_2 - \mathscr{V}_1) \qquad (20.13)$$

Now ΣF is comprised of the resultant F_i (in the direction of flow) of all the internal forces exerted by the duct (and whatever inner obstructions) upon the fluid passing through, and the net pressure force $(p_1 A_1 - p_2 A_2)$ acting on the fluid at the end sections. Thus, Eq. (20.13) may be written as

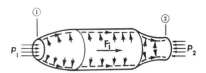

Fig. 20.3 Jet Propulsion System.

$$F_i + p_1 A_1 - p_2 A_2 = \dot{m}(\mathscr{V}_2 - \mathscr{V}_1) \qquad (20.14)$$

Note that F_i represents the action on the fluid of the duct and any inner object such as a rod, strut, compressor or turbine blade. It is the internal thrust. Equation (20.14) applies whether the process occurring within the duct is reversible or not; it may be solved for F_i:

$$F_i = (p_2 A_2 + \dot{m}\mathscr{V}_2) - (p_1 A_1 + \dot{m}\mathscr{V}_1) \qquad (20.15)$$

where the quantity $(pA + m\mathscr{V})$ is known in gas dynamics as the **thrust function**.† Equation (20.15) gives the static thrust (such as that of a jet engine mounted on a test stand and supplied with air). In flight, there is an additional force, exclusive of forces due to external friction which are normally included in the drag of the aircraft; this is the product of the atmospheric pressure p_a times the area difference $(A_2 - A_1)$. It is in the nature of an ambient pressure times a projected area, and it opposes the internal thrust. The net or external thrust is therefore

$$\begin{aligned} F &= F_i - p_a(A_2 - A_1) \\ &= (p_2 A_2 + \dot{m}\mathscr{V}_2) - (p_1 A_1 + \dot{m}\mathscr{V}_1) - p_a(A_2 - A_1) \end{aligned} \qquad (20.16)$$

Equation (20.16) is the general expression for the net thrust, based on the assumption that the mass flow is constant between inlet and outlet of the engine (this assumption is quite valid for engines having a large air/fuel ratio). In many instances, it can be reduced to simpler form. For a rocket, the working fluid has no initial velocity relative to the rocket, and $\mathscr{V}_1$, p_2 and A_1 are zero. Equation (20.16) then becomes

$$F = (p_2 A_2 + \dot{m}\mathscr{V}_2) - p_2 A_2 = \dot{m}\mathscr{V}_2 + A_2(p_2 - p_a) \qquad (20.17)$$

If furthermore, the nozzle is designed for complete expansion from the combustion pressure to atmospheric pressure, $p_2 = p_a$, and the net thrust is simply

$$F = \dot{m}\mathscr{V}_2 \qquad (20.18)$$

where $\mathscr{V}_2$ is the exit velocity relative to the engine. Recall that this is the ex-

---

† The thrust function $F = pA + \dot{m}\mathscr{V} = pA + (\rho A \mathscr{V}^2)/g_c = pA + (1 + \gamma M^2)$ is tabulated in the gas tables against values of the Mach number M.

pression used in part (b). of Ex. 19.10. If $\mathcal{V}$ is the velocity at which the rocket is moving through the air, the propulsive horsepower is

$$hp = \frac{\dot{m}\mathcal{V}_2\mathcal{V}}{550}$$
(20.19)

where $\dot{m}$ is the mass rate of flow per second.

For subsonic aircraft, the entering pressure, exit pressure, and atmospheric pressure are essentially equal (this is not true for supersonic aircraft because of the effect of shock waves at the inlet); Eq. (20.16) then becomes

$$F = \dot{m}(\mathcal{V}_2 - \mathcal{V}_1)$$
(20.20)

and the horsepower is

$$hp = \frac{\dot{m}(\mathcal{V}_2 - \mathcal{V}_1)\mathcal{V}_1}{550}$$
(20.21)

where $\mathcal{V}_1$, the inlet velocity, is also the velocity of the aircraft, and $\mathcal{V}_2$ is the velocity of the exhaust gas relative to the engine. It is interesting to note from Eq. (20.21) that the same thrust may be achieved by using either an engine producing a high-velocity jet of low mass flow rate (case of the turbo-jet) or an engine which produces a low-velocity jet of high mass flow rate (case of propeller-driven aircraft).

20.3   Energy Transfer in Turbomachinery

The principles just developed may be applied to turbomachinery such as turbines, axial-flow compressors, blowers and torque converters. In all these devices, work exchanges are effected by means of velocity (momentum) changes rather than by means of a boundary displacement such as with piston devices.

Consider, as in Fig. 20.4, the flow of a fluid through a moving blade or a rotor. The velocity of the fluid at any point has three mutually perpendicular components, namely, the radial component, the axial component, and the tangential component. The torque on the fluid (equal and opposite in sign to the torque of the fluid on the rotor) is given by the time rate of change of angular momentum:

$$T = \frac{\dot{m}}{g_c}(r_2\mathcal{V}_{\tan2} - r_1\mathcal{V}_{\tan1})$$
(20.22)

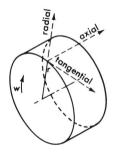

Fig. 20.4
Turbo-Machinery System.

where $\dot{m}$ is the mass flow rate, r_1 and r_2 the radii at the inlet and outlet of the rotor, and $\mathcal{V}_{\tan1}$ and $\mathcal{V}_{\tan2}$ the tangential velocities at the inlet and outlet. Equation (20.22) is the basic dynamic equation for one-dimensional steady flow through a rotor. If ω is the angular velocity of the rotor, the power delivered to the fluid is the product $T\omega$:

$$T\omega = \frac{\dot{m}}{g_c}\omega(r_2\mathscr{V}_{\tan2} - r_1\mathscr{V}_{\tan1}) \tag{20.23}$$

and the work done per pound of fluid is

$$w = \frac{\omega}{g_c}(r_2\mathscr{V}_{\tan2} - r_1\mathscr{V}_{\tan1})$$

$$= \frac{1}{g_c}(\mathscr{V}_{b2}\mathscr{V}_{\tan2} - \mathscr{V}_{b1}\mathscr{V}_{\tan1}) \tag{20.24}$$

where $\mathscr{V}_{b1}$ and $\mathscr{V}_{b2}$ are the linear velocities at the entrance and exit of a blade or rotor. If the fluid enters and leaves the blade or rotor at the same radius, then $\mathscr{V}_{b1} = \mathscr{V}_{b2} = \mathscr{V}_b$. Note that no matter what the path inside the rotor is, the torque depends only on the flow rate, the inlet and outlet radii, and the tangential velocities at the inlet and outlet of the rotor. The following sections discuss in some detail the relationship between the fluid velocity and the blade velocity for an impulse turbine, a reaction turbine, and an axial flow compressor.

20.4   Turbine Impulse Stage

Consider a stage of the simple De Laval† turbine shown in Fig. 20.5. This is the case of a single-stage impulse turbine, wherein expansion takes place in fixed nozzles or stator blades and the kinetic energy of the high-velocity jets is absorbed by moving blades (rotor) to produce shaft work.

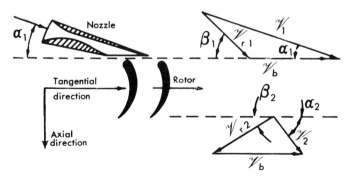

Fig. 20.5 Turbine-Impulse Stage.

---

† Carl Juster De Laval (1845–1913) was a Swedish engineer who invented this type of turbine in connection with the development of his cream separator.

From the principle of impulse and momentum, the force exerted on the blade in the tangential direction is

$$F = \frac{\dot{m}}{g_c}(\mathscr{V}_1 \cos \alpha_1 - \mathscr{V}_2 \cos \alpha_2)$$

where $\dot{m}$ is the mass flow rate, α_1 and α_2 (chosen to be $< 90°$) are the angles between the tangential direction and the absolute velocities $\mathscr{V}_1$ and $\mathscr{V}_2$ at entrance and exit of the blade respectively. The above equation is written from the point of view of a stationary observer. A similar equation may, however, be obtained from the point of view of a moving observer (traveling with the blade):

$$F = \frac{\dot{m}}{g_c}(\mathscr{V}_{r1} \cos \beta_1 + \mathscr{V}_{r2} \cos \beta_2)$$

where β_1 and β_2 are the angles (chosen to be $< 90°$) between the tangential direction and the relative velocities $\mathscr{V}_{r1}$ and $\mathscr{V}_{r2}$ at the entrance and exit of the blade. The power or rate at which work is done on the blade is

$$\dot{w} = \frac{\dot{m}}{g_c}(\mathscr{V}_1 \cos \alpha_1 - \mathscr{V}_2 \cos \alpha_2)\mathscr{V}_b \qquad (20.25)$$

or, alternatively,

$$\dot{w} = \frac{\dot{m}}{g_c}(\mathscr{V}_{r1} \cos \beta_1 + \mathscr{V}_{r2} \cos \beta_2)\mathscr{V}_b \qquad (20.26)$$

where $\mathscr{V}_b$ is the blade velocity. The same result may be obtained from thermodynamic considerations, for the energy equation (per pound of fluid) relative to a stationary observer is

$$h_1 + \frac{\mathscr{V}_1^2}{2g_c} = h_2 + \frac{\mathscr{V}_2^2}{2g_c} + w$$

Relative to a moving observer, however, no work is done on the blade, and the energy equation is,

$$h_1 + \frac{\mathscr{V}_{r1}^2}{2g_c} = h_2 + \frac{\mathscr{V}_{r2}^2}{2g_c}$$

These two equations combine to give

$$w = \frac{(\mathscr{V}_1^2 - \mathscr{V}_{r1}^2) - (\mathscr{V}_2^2 - \mathscr{V}_{r2}^2)}{2g_c} \qquad (20.27)$$

The reader can verify that this result is equivalent to either Eq. (20.25) or Eq. (20.26) divided by $\dot{m}$.

Example 20.2. In a certain impulse stage, the designed isentropic drop in enthalpy of the steam in the nozzle is 25 Btu/lbm. Steam flowing through the nozzle at the rate of 0.70 lbm/sec enters the blade passage at an angle of 15° and leaves the blade with a relative velocity $\mathscr{V}_{r2} = 0.95\,\mathscr{V}_{r1}$. The blade speed is 570 fps and the nozzle velocity coefficient is 0.98. Determine the tangential thrust, the horsepower developed, and the stage efficiency.

Solution. A nozzle velocity coefficient of 0.98 means that 98 per cent of the isentropic enthalpy drop is converted into kinetic energy. The nozzle discharge velocity is thus

$$\mathscr{V}_1 = 0.98\sqrt{2(32.2)(778)(25)} = 1096\ \text{fps}$$

With $\mathscr{V}_1 = 1096$, $\alpha_1 = 15°$, and $\mathscr{V}_b = 570$, the velocity diagram (Fig. 20.5) for the blade inlet may be constructed to give $\mathscr{V}_{r1} = 565$ fps and $\beta_1 = 30°$. At the blade exit, $\mathscr{V}_{r2} = 0.95(565) = 537$ fps, $\mathscr{V}_b = 570$, and $\beta_2 = 30°$ (the blade is assumed to be symmetrical), so that construction of a velocity diagram gives $\mathscr{V}_2 = 290$ fps. Choosing the point of view of an observer traveling with the blade, the tangential thrust is

$$F = \frac{\dot{m}}{g_c}(\mathscr{V}_{r1}\cos\beta_1 + \mathscr{V}_{r2}\cos\beta_2)$$

$$= \frac{0.7}{32.2}(565\cos 30° + 537\cos 30°) = 20.6\ \text{lbf}$$

The work rate is, according to Eq. (20.26):

$$\dot{w} = \frac{\dot{m}}{g_c}(\mathscr{V}_{r1}\cos\beta_1 + \mathscr{V}_{r2}\cos\beta_2)\mathscr{V}_b$$

$$= F\mathscr{V}_b = (20.6)(570) = 11,700\ \text{ft lbf/sec}$$

$$= 21.3\ \text{hp}$$

The stage efficiency is the efficiency of the combination of nozzle *and* blade. It is the ratio of the work actually obtained per pound of steam to the isentropic enthalpy drop for the stage. Since the work per pound of steam is

$$\frac{11,700}{0.70} = 16,750\ \text{ft lbf}$$

the stage efficiency is thus

$$\eta_{\text{nozzle and blade}} = \frac{16,750}{(778)(25)} = 0.862\ \text{or } 86.2\ \text{per cent}$$

20.5 Reaction Stage

In the design of turbines, reaction stages may be used as well as impulse stages. In an impulse stage or turbine, there is no pressure change in the moving blades (the expansion of the steam occurs mainly in the nozzles and to a small extent in the stationary blades which are shaped like converging nozzles). In a reaction stage or turbine, however, a large expansion of the fluid occurs in the moving blades (rotor) as well as in the fixed nozzle or stator blades. In other words, the moving blades are so shaped as to act as convergent nozzles, thus inducing an enthalpy drop. (In contrast, the cross-sectional area of the blade passages in an impulse turbine is almost constant.)

Referring to Fig. 20.6, the steam at pressure p_0 and temperature T_0 is first accelerated through the stator blades to a pressure p_1, thus attaining

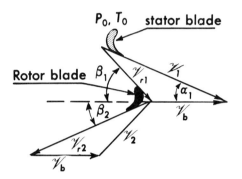

Fig. 20.6   Turbine-Reaction Stage.

a velocity $\mathscr{V}_1$. With the rotor blades moving at a velocity $\mathscr{V}_b$, the relative velocity of the fluid entering the rotor is $\mathscr{V}_{r1}$. In going through the rotor, the fluid is further expanded to a velocity $\mathscr{V}_{r2}$. Note that in the case of a reaction state, $\mathscr{V}_{r2}$ is greater than $\mathscr{V}_{r1}$. The work for the reaction stage is given by

$$\dot{W} = \frac{\dot{m}}{g_c}(\mathscr{V}_{r1}\cos\beta_1 + \mathscr{V}_{r2}\cos\beta_2)\mathscr{V}_b$$

Note that in a pure reaction stage, the entire pressure drop occurs in the moving blades. The pure reaction stage, however, is used infrequently. Rather, most reaction turbines have a pressure drop in both the fixed and the moving blades; the degree of reaction being defined as

$$\text{percentage reaction} = \frac{\text{enthalpy drop in the rotor}}{\text{enthalpy drop in the stage}}$$

The first reaction turbine of practical importance was designed by Charles A. Parsons (1854–1931) so that a reaction stage is often known as a Parsons stage.

20.6   Axial Flow Compressor Stage

From the point of view of the exchange of energy between the fluid and the rotor, a compressor can be regarded as a reversed turbine. A compressor is basically comprised of two parts: a rotor which does work on the fluid, increasing its kinetic energy and pressure, and a stator which serves as a diffuser to reduce the velocity of the fluid and further increase its pressure. Figure 20.7 shows an axial-flow compressor stage which

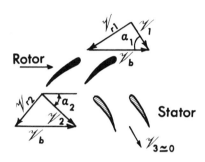

Fig. 20.7   Compressor Stage.

consists of a row of rotor blades followed by a row of stator blades. The fluid approaches the rotor blades with an absolute velocity $\mathscr{V}_1$ at an angle α_1. The inlet relative velocity $\mathscr{V}_{r1}$ is obtained by vectorial subtraction of the blade speed $\mathscr{V}_b$. The rotor blade passages are divergent passages so that the flow is diffused and the fluid leaves with a reduced velocity $\mathscr{V}_{r2}$. Vectorial addition of the blade speed with $\mathscr{V}_{r2}$ gives the absolute velocity $\mathscr{V}_2$ at the outlet of the rotor. In the stator blade passage, the velocity is reduced to $\mathscr{V}_3 \approx 0$ or to $\mathscr{V}_3 \approx \mathscr{V}_1$ if the fluid is to enter another stage. The rate of work done per stage is

$$\dot{W} = \frac{\dot{m}}{g_c}(\mathscr{V}_1 \cos \alpha_1 - \mathscr{V}_2 \cos \alpha_2)\mathscr{V}_b$$

It is of interest to note the essential difference between a turbine blade passage and a compressor blade passage. The flow in the former is accelerating, whereas the flow in the latter is diffusing. Although an axial-flow compressor has been described as a turbine driven in reverse and absorbing work, its design limitations are far more severe than those of a turbine. This is because it is more difficult to arrange for an efficient deceleration of flow than for an acceleration. In a diffusion process there is a tendency for the fluid to break away from the wall of the diverging passage (i.e., the boundary layer tends to grow). This will occur if the passage diverges at too great a rate or if the passage is considerably curved. Turbine blade profiles can be constructed satisfactorily of circular arcs and straight lines, but compressor blades must be of aerodynamic shape (airfoil section).

20.7   Acoustic Velocity; Mach Number

A parameter of great importance in the study of fluid flow, especially compressible flow, is the sonic or acoustic velocity. This is the speed with which a small disturbance is propagated through a medium. In Fig. 20.8(a) consider the disturbance created by the movement of a piston at the end of a long tube filled with gas.

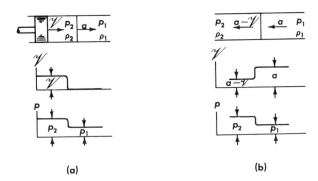

(a)   (b)

Fig. 20.8   Pressure Wave on a Gas.

Let the piston be moved with a velocity $\mathscr{V}$. This sets up a wave which travels down the tube with a velocity a, which is greater than or equal to the velocity $\mathscr{V}$ of the gas immediately next to the piston. Ahead of the wave, the gas is not affected by the motion of the piston or the approaching wave, but behind the wave, the velocity, pressure and density increase. To find the wave velocity in terms of the properties of the fluid ahead of the wave, it is convenient to use a different frame of reference. Figure 20.8(a) shows how things look to an observer traveling with the wave front at velocity a. The wave front is now stationary, and fluid flows from right to left. It approaches the wave front with a velocity a and leaves the wave front with a velocity $a - \mathscr{V}$. Similarly, the pressure rises from p_1 to p_2 across the wave, and the density from ρ_1 to ρ_2. The continuity and momentum equations across the wave front thus become

$$\rho_1 A a = \rho_2 A(a - \mathscr{V}) \tag{20.28}$$

$$p_1 A_1 - p_2 A_2 = \frac{m(\Delta \mathscr{V})}{g_c} = \frac{\rho_1 A a(a - \mathscr{V} - a)}{g_c} \tag{20.29}$$

Eliminating $\mathscr{V}$ between Eqs. (20.28) and (20.29) and solving for a gives

$$a = \sqrt{\frac{\rho_2}{\rho_1} \cdot \frac{(p_1 - p_2)}{(\rho_1 - \rho_2)} \cdot g_c} \tag{20.30}$$

This is the velocity of a pressure wave of finite amplitude. To obtain the sonic or acoustic velocity, which is the velocity of a pressure wave of infinitesimal amplitude, p_2 is made to approach p_1 and ρ_2 to approach ρ_1. Thus, Eq. (20.30) becomes

$$a = \sqrt{\left(\frac{dp}{d\rho}\right) g_c}$$

Furthermore, for an infinitesimally small disturbance, the process may be assumed to take place adiabatically and reversibly, so that the *sonic velocity* is

$$a = \sqrt{\left(\frac{\partial p}{\partial \rho}\right)_s g_c} \tag{20.31}$$

Equation (20.31) was first derived by Laplace. For a perfect gas undergoing a reversible adiabatic process, $p/\rho^\gamma = \text{constant}$, so that

$$\left(\frac{\partial p}{\partial \rho}\right)_s = \frac{\gamma p}{\rho}$$

and Eq. (20.31) yields

$$a = \sqrt{\frac{\gamma p}{\rho} \cdot g_c} = \sqrt{g_c \gamma R T} \tag{20.32}$$

Equation (20.32) shows that for an ideal gas, the sonic velocity is function of temperature only. The sonic velocity is thus a property of the gas. To simplify calculations, the factor $\sqrt{g_c \gamma R}$ is often calculated as a single constant for a given gas. Thus, for the case of air,

$$a = 49.1\sqrt{T} \tag{20.33}$$

As a matter of interest, the NASA standard velocity for air at 59 °F is 1,117 fps.

Important as is the velocity of sound, it takes on significance only when it is compared to the speed of flow. This introduces a dimensionless parameter, called the *Mach number*, which is defined as the ratio of the local flow velocity to the acoustic velocity of the medium at the same location. Thus,

$$M = \frac{\mathscr{V}}{a} = \frac{\mathscr{V}}{\sqrt{g_c \gamma R T}} \qquad (20.34)$$

It is evident that M will vary from point to point in the flow field, not only because $\mathscr{V}$ varies from point to point, but also because T depends on the local conditions. For adiabatic flow, an increase in M always corresponds to an increase in $\mathscr{V}$. A flow is often classified according to the value of the local Mach number. Thus, if M is less than 1, the flow is called *subsonic*; if greater than 1, it is called *supersonic*. If M is much greater than 1, the flow is called *hypersonic*.

The variation of the Mach number in terms of velocity and temperature changes may be obtained by squaring Eq. (20.34) and differentiating logarithmically, i.e.,

$$M^2 = \frac{\mathscr{V}^2}{g_c \gamma R T}$$

Taking the logarithm and differentiating gives

$$2 \ln M = 2 \ln \mathscr{V} - \ln \gamma - \ln g_c - \ln R - \ln T$$

$$2\frac{dM}{M} = 2\frac{d\mathscr{V}}{\mathscr{V}} - \frac{dT}{T}$$

or

$$\frac{dM}{M} = \frac{d\mathscr{V}}{\mathscr{V}} - \frac{1}{2}\frac{dT}{T} \qquad (20.35)$$

Equation (20.35) is particularly useful in isothermal flow, in which case the variation of the local Mach number may be obtained in terms of the variation of the local velocity alone.

20.8   Compressible and Incompressible Flow; Pressure Field Due to a Moving Point Disturbance

The effect of compressibility serves to classify a flow either as incompressible flow (usually known as incompressible fluid mechanics) or as compressible flow (often called gas dynamics). In incompressible flow, the fluid velocities are small compared with the velocity of sound, and the fractional variation in density is small. The fractional variations in pressure and temperature, however, may be large. Although no fluid is truly incompressible, for many applications, the flow may be treated as incompressible with very little error. This is a distinct advantage, since incompressible flow is not only mathematically simpler than compressible flow, but is also well established. In gas dynamics or compressible flow, the fluid velocities are appreciable compared with the local velocity of sound, and the fractional variations in pressure, temperature, and density are sizable.

To further illustrate the effect of compressibility, consider, in Fig. 20.9, the disturbance created by a body moving through a fluid. The pressure pulse thus created propagates throughout the fluid with the speed of sound. At each instant of time, the spreading of the wave and the position of the body is noted. There are four cases of interest, each corresponding to a different ratio of the speed of the body in relation to the speed of sound in the fluid.

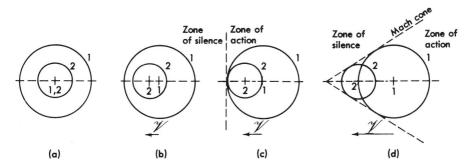

Fig. 20.9 Propagation of Disturbance in a Fluid.

Figure 20.9(a) corresponds to the case of a stationary source. The ratio $\mathscr{V}/a$ is zero, and the circles 1, 2, . . . representing the propagation of the pulse at time $t = 1, 2, . . .$ are concentric. This is also the case of incompressible flow, since the speed of sound, a is infinite for an incompressible fluid. In fact, a pulse emitted anywhere in an incompressible fluid is felt simultaneously at all points within the fluid.

Figure 20.9(b) is for the case of compressible subsonic flow ($0 < \mathscr{V}/a < 1$). Here, the body is moving at a subsonic speed through the fluid, and the disturbance is felt in all directions and at all points within the fluid, but the pressure pattern is no longer symmetrical.

Figure 20.9(c) represents the case of a body traveling at sonic speed in a compressible fluid ($\mathscr{V}/a = 1$). The flow field is now divided by a vertical line into a zone of silence and a zone of action. The pressure change produced by the body no longer spreads throughout the fluid ahead of the body.

Figure 20.9(d) shows compressible supersonic flow. The spreading of the pressure change produced by the body now lags the body, and the zone of action is confined to a cone extending downstream from the body. Also, the intensity of the disturbance is concentrated in the neighbourhood of the boundary of the Mach cone. This explains why an object moving at supersonic speed cannot be heard until the object has passed overhead.

20.9 Stagnation Properties

Essentially, the flow of a compressible fluid may be visualized as taking place from an infinite reservoir as shown in Fig. 20.10. The velocity in the reservoir is zero, and the properties of the fluid are denoted by the subscript 0. The flow section itself may be of any shape. To define the flow, the local (static) properties of the fluid must be known. However, remember that the measured properties are stagnation properties (since measuring devices are stationary and do not move with the flow). By definition, the *stagnation state* is that state of the fluid which is brought to rest reversibly and adiabatically. For example, the *stagnation enthalpy*† is obtained from the energy equation

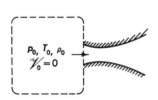

Fig. 20.10
Flow from Stagnation Reservoir.

$$h + \frac{\mathscr{V}^2}{2g_c} = \text{constant} = h_0 \qquad (20.36)$$

For a perfect gas, this becomes

$$c_p T + \frac{\mathscr{V}^2}{2g_c} = c_p T_0 \qquad (20.37)$$

or, with $c_p = \gamma R / (\gamma - 1)$

$$\frac{\gamma R}{\gamma - 1}(T_0 - T) = \frac{\mathscr{V}^2}{2g_c}$$

---

† Strictly speaking, it is only necessary, in the definition for the stagnation enthalpy, to stipulate that the fluid be brought to rest adiabatically. However, in the case of other stagnation properties such as pressure, the stipulation of reversibility must be included.

Solving for T_0/T gives

$$\frac{T_0}{T} = 1 + \frac{\gamma-1}{2}\frac{\mathscr{V}^2}{g_c \gamma R T} = 1 + \frac{\gamma-1}{2}\frac{\mathscr{V}^2}{a^2}$$

$$= 1 + \frac{\gamma-1}{2}M^2 \tag{20.38}$$

Equation (20.38) is the relation between the stagnation temperature and the static temperature in terms of the Mach number. Other relations (between p_0 and p and ρ_0 and ρ, and a_0 and a) are obtained from the isentropic relations for a perfect gas:

$$\frac{p_0}{p} = \left(\frac{\rho_0}{\rho}\right)^\gamma = \left(\frac{T_0}{T}\right)^{\gamma/(\gamma-1)}$$

The result is

$$\frac{p_0}{p} = \left[1 + \frac{\gamma-1}{2}M^2\right]^{\gamma/(\gamma-1)} \tag{20.39}$$

$$\frac{p_0}{\rho} = \left[1 + \frac{\gamma-1}{2}M^2\right]^{1/(\gamma-1)} \tag{20.40}$$

$$\frac{a_0}{a} = \left(\frac{T_0}{T}\right)^{1/2} = \left[1 + \frac{\gamma-1}{2}M^2\right]^{1/2} \tag{20.41}$$

The relationship between stagnation and local properties is given physical meaning in Fig. 20.11. Note that T_0 and a_0 are constant throughout the flow; they are those of the initial reservoir. The values of p_0 and ρ_0 are "local" reservoir values; they are constant only if the flow is isentropic throughout. Note also that the ratios T_0/T, p_0/p, and ρ_0/ρ from Eqs. (20.38), (20.39), and (20.40) have been tabulated for a wide range of Mach numbers in the gas tables.

Example 20.3. Air ($c_p = 0.25$) at a temperature of 400 °F and a pressure of 15 psia is flowing at a velocity of 1000 fps. Assuming it to be a perfect gas, find the stagnation temperature and the stagnation pressure.

Solution. From Eq. (20.37), the energy equation,

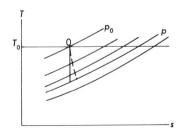

Fig. 20.11 Relation between Stagnation and Local Properties.

$$T_0 = T + \frac{\mathscr{V}^2}{2g_c c_p} = 860 + \frac{1000^2}{2(32.2)(778)(0.25)}$$
$$= 941 \text{ °R or } 481 \text{ °F}$$

From the isentropic relation for a perfect gas,

$$p_0 = p\left(\frac{T_0}{T}\right)^{\gamma/(\gamma-1)} = 15\left(\frac{941}{860}\right)^{1.4/(1.4-1)} = 20.7 \text{ psia}$$

The reader may check these answers by means of the gas tables.

20.10   Flow in Area-Varying Channel

The converging-diverging channel is the basic element used in obtaining prescribed flows. It is widely used in wind tunnels and other aerodynamic installations. The simplest configuration is that shown in Fig. 20.12. The channel is supplied with fluid at high pressure p_0; it exhausts into a region of lower pressure p_e. The nozzle may either be attached at the inlet to a high-pressure reservoir and allowed to discharge into the atmosphere, or it may be connected at the outlet to a vacuum tank and allowed to draw from the atmosphere.

A first item of interest concerning nozzles or diffusers is whether the shape should be convergent or divergent. To investigate the variation of flow parameters in relation to the sectional area of the channel, the assumption is made that the flow is one-dimensional, i.e., conditions across a given section are considered uniform. This is quite justifiable in long, slender nozzles or diffusers if viscous effects are neglected. Equation (20.4), the continuity equation, gives

$$\frac{d\rho}{\rho} + \frac{d\mathcal{V}}{\mathcal{V}} + \frac{dA}{A} = 0$$

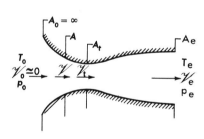

For incompressible flow, $d\rho = 0$, and the above relation shows that the increase in velocity is simply proportional to the decrease in area.

For compressible flow, Euler's equation, Eq. (20.8), gives

Fig. 20.12

One-Dimensional Flow through Nozzle.

$$\frac{\mathcal{V}d\mathcal{V}}{g_c} = -\frac{dp}{\rho} = -\frac{dp}{d\rho}\frac{d\rho}{\rho}$$

Assuming isentropic conditions, $dp/d\rho \equiv (\partial p/\partial \rho)_s = a^2/g_c$ (cf. definition of acoustic velocity), so that

$$\mathcal{V}d\mathcal{V} = -a^2\frac{d\rho}{\rho}$$

Dividing by $\mathcal{V}^2$ and introducing the definition of the Mach number

[Eq. (20.34)], this becomes

$$\frac{d\rho}{\rho} = -M^2 \frac{d\mathscr{V}}{\mathscr{V}} \tag{20.42}$$

Equation (20.42) clearly shows the influence of the Mach number: For flow at very small Mach numbers, it gives $d\rho/\rho \approx 0$; this means that density changes are very small compared to velocity changes and therefore may be neglected in calculating the flow field.

To further investigate the role of the Mach number, Eq. (20.42) is combined with the continuity equation to give

$$-M^2 \frac{d\mathscr{V}}{\mathscr{V}} + \frac{d\mathscr{V}}{\mathscr{V}} + \frac{dA}{A} = 0$$

or

$$\frac{d\mathscr{V}}{\mathscr{V}} = -\left(\frac{1}{1-M^2}\right)\frac{dA}{A} \tag{20.43}$$

This is a significant equation; from it may be drawn the following conclusions regarding the shape of nozzles or diffusers. For $M \approx 0$, the velocity increases with a decrease in area (the flow behaves like incompressible flow). For $0 < M < 1$, i.e., for subsonic speeds, the relation between velocity and area is qualitatively the same as for incompressible flow, namely, an increase in velocity requires a decrease in area. This means that a subsonic nozzle is convergent and a subsonic diffuser is divergent. The effect of area decrease on the velocity, however, is more pronounced, since the denominator is less than unity. For $M > 1$, the denominator on the right hand side of Eq. (20.43) is negative, and an increase in velocity requires an increase in area. This means that a supersonic nozzle is divergent and a supersonic diffuser is convergent. The conclusion, startling to ordinary experience, is due to the fact that, at supersonic speeds, the density decreases faster than the velocity increases, so that the area must increase (as required by the equation of continuity). The above results are represented graphically in Fig. 20.13.

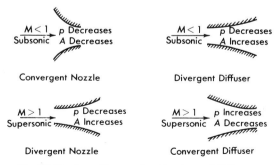

Fig. 20.13 Area Changes for Nozzles and Diffusers.

So far, $M = 1$ has not been discussed. For this case, Eq. (20.43) shows that $d\mathcal{V}/\mathcal{V}$ can be finite only if dA/A is zero. Now, consider a channel in which the velocity increases continuously from zero to eventually supersonic speed. The preceding discussion shows that the channel must converge in the subsonic portion and diverge in the supersonic portion. This means that at $M = 1$ there must be a throat. Similarly, for a channel in which the velocity decreases continuously from supersonic to subsonic, there must be a throat at $M = 1$. In other words, sonic velocity can be attained only at the throat of a channel or tube. The inverse, however, does not hold; i.e., M is not always equal to 1 at the throat. This is a subtle point. The channel shapes for the whole continuous spectrum of velocities is summarized in Fig. (20.14).

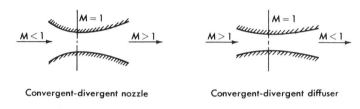

Convergent-divergent nozzle   Convergent-divergent diffuser

Fig. 20.14   Summary of Channel Area Change.

20.11 Reference Speeds

Before continuing with the discussion of the flow in a nozzle, it is desirable to introduce the definitions of three reference speeds. Consider first the definition of the stagnation enthalpy for a perfect gas [Eq. (20.37)]:

$$c_p T + \frac{\mathcal{V}^2}{2g_c} = c_p T_0$$

Replacing c_p with $\gamma R/(\gamma - 1)$ and solving for the velocity gives

$$\mathcal{V} = \sqrt{\frac{2g_c \gamma R}{\gamma - 1}(T_0 - T)} \tag{20.44}$$

It is evident from Eq. (20.44) that the *maximum velocity* corresponding to a given stagnation temperature is when the local temperature at some point in the expansion reaches zero. Thus,

$$\mathcal{V}_{\max} = \sqrt{\frac{2g_c \gamma R T_0}{\gamma - 1}} \tag{20.45}$$

This is the first of several reference speeds used in gas dynamics. In practice, $\mathscr{V}_{max}$ is never reached, since absolute temperature is never reached. However, Eq. (20.45) shows why the air entering a supersonic wind tunnel must be heated if very high velocities are to be achieved. Another reference speed is the *speed of sound at the stagnation temperature,*

$$a_0 = \sqrt{g_c \gamma R T_0} \tag{20.46}$$

The local speed of sound, a, is related to the speed of sound at the stagnation temperature, a_0, as follows. The steady-flow energy equation, Eq. (20.11), gives

$$d\left(h + \frac{\mathscr{V}^2}{2g_c}\right) = d\left(c_p T + \frac{\mathscr{V}^2}{2g_c}\right) = 0$$

Replacing c_v by $\gamma R/(\gamma - 1)$ and integrating gives

$$\frac{\gamma R}{\gamma - 1} \int_{T_0}^{T} dT + \int_0^{\mathscr{V}} \frac{\mathscr{V}d\mathscr{V}}{g_c} = 0$$

or

$$\frac{\gamma R T}{\gamma - 1} + \frac{\mathscr{V}^2}{2g_c} = \frac{\gamma R T_0}{\gamma - 1}$$

and, upon introduction of the velocity of sound

$$\frac{a^2}{\gamma - 1} + \frac{\mathscr{V}^2}{2} = \frac{a_0^2}{\gamma - 1} \tag{20.47}$$

Equation (20.47) shows that the speed of sound at reservoir conditions, a_0 is greater than the local speed of sound, a at any point in the flow.

A third reference speed used in gas dynamics is the *critical speed,* i.e., the velocity at a Mach number of unity. Consider a flow starting from subsonic speed and imagine a gradual increase of the local velocity $\mathscr{V}$ until the acoustic velocity a is reached. At this point, the velocity is said to be critical. Using an asterisk to denote this condition, it follows that $\mathscr{V}^* = a^*$ and consequently, $M = 1$. Since

$$\mathscr{V}^* = \sqrt{\frac{2g_c \gamma R}{\gamma - 1}(T_0 - T^*)},$$

from Eq. (20.44), and

$$a^* = \sqrt{g_c \gamma R T}$$

from the definition for the speed of sound, it follows that

$$\sqrt{\frac{2g_c\gamma R}{\gamma - 1}(T_0 - T^*)} = \sqrt{g_c\gamma RT^*}$$

This may be written as

$$\frac{T^*}{T_0} = \frac{2}{\gamma + 1} \qquad (20.48)$$

Solving for T^* and substituting back in the expression for the velocity of sound $\sqrt{g_c\gamma RT^*}$ yields

$$a^* = \mathcal{V}^* = \sqrt{\frac{2g_c\gamma RT_0}{\gamma + 1}} = \sqrt{\frac{2a_0^2}{\gamma + 1}} \qquad (20.49)$$

The condition of $M = 1$ is particularly important; it enables some other point in the flow to be used for reference instead of the reservoir. In addition to the ratio of sonic temperature to reservoir temperature given by Eq. (20.48), other ratios (p^*/p_0 and ρ^*/ρ_0) are easily obtained by setting M equal to 1 in Eqs. (20.39) and (20.40). The result is

$$\frac{p^*}{p_0} = \left(\frac{2}{\gamma + 1}\right)^{\gamma/(\gamma-1)} \qquad (20.50)$$

$$\frac{\rho^*}{\rho_0} = \left(\frac{2}{\gamma + 1}\right)^{1/(\gamma-1)} \qquad (20.51)$$

Note that a throat actually existing in the flow is not necessary for sonic values to be used as a reference.

In many flow problems, especially transonic ones, the Mach number is not a convenient parameter to use. Instead, it is more convenient to work with a dimensionless number, M^*, defined as

$$M^* = \frac{\mathcal{V}}{a^*} = \frac{\mathcal{V}}{\mathcal{V}^*} \qquad (20.52)$$

There are several advantages for using M^* instead of M. First, M^* is a parameter which at any location is a function of velocity alone. Second, at very high speeds M tends toward infinity, because while the velocity increases, the local acoustic velocity decreases (due to decrease in temperature). Defining a parameter based on a^* removes these difficulties. The relation between M^* and M for a perfect gas can be obtained by means of the definition for stagnation temperature, Eq. (20.37):

$$c_p T + \frac{\mathcal{V}^2}{2g_c} = c_p T_0$$

Noting that $c_p = \gamma R/(\gamma - 1)$, and $a^2 = g_c \gamma RT$, this becomes

$$\frac{2a^2}{\gamma - 1} + \mathcal{V}^2 = \frac{2a_0{}^2}{\gamma - 1}$$

Applying this to any two states, one of which is sonic, gives

$$\frac{2a^2}{\gamma - 1} + \mathcal{V}^2 = \frac{2a^{*2}}{\gamma - 1} + \mathcal{V}^{*2} = \frac{\gamma + 1}{\gamma - 1} a^{*2}$$

Dividing through by a^{*2} yields

$$\frac{2}{\gamma - 1} \frac{a^2}{a^{*2}} + \frac{\mathcal{V}^2}{a^{*2}} = \frac{\gamma + 1}{\gamma - 1}$$

But $\mathcal{V}^2/a^{*2} = M^{*2}$, and

$$\frac{a^2}{a^{*2}} = \frac{a^2/\mathcal{V}^2}{a^{*2}/\mathcal{V}^2} = \frac{M^{*2}}{M^2}$$

Thus,

$$\frac{2}{\gamma - 1} \cdot \frac{M^{*2}}{M^2} + M^{*2} = \frac{\gamma + 1}{\gamma - 1} \qquad (20.53)$$

Equation (20.53) is the relation between M^* and M. It may be solved for either M^{*2} or M^2 to give

$$M^{*2} = \frac{[(\gamma + 1)/2]M^2}{1 + [(\gamma - 1)/2]M^2}; \quad M^2 = \frac{[2/(\gamma + 1)]M^{*2}}{1 - [(\gamma - 1)/(\gamma + 1)]M^{*2}}$$

These equations show that when $M < 1$, $M^* < 1$, when $M > 1$, $M^* > 1$, and when $M = \infty$, $M^* = \sqrt{(\gamma + 1)/(\gamma - 1)}$

20.12 Relations for Nozzle Flow

Having established the preceding background, the relations pertaining to nozzle flow will now be further developed. A relation of particular importance is the expression for the velocity, derived below. Equation (20.37), the energy equation, may be written as

$$c_p dT + \frac{\mathcal{V} d\mathcal{V}}{g_c} = \frac{\gamma R}{\gamma - 1} dT + \frac{\mathcal{V} d\mathcal{V}}{g_c} = 0$$

Integrating between limits T_1 and T_2, and $\mathscr{V}_1$ and $\mathscr{V}_2$ gives

$$\frac{\gamma R}{\gamma - 1}(T_2 - T_1) + \frac{\mathscr{V}_2{}^2 - \mathscr{V}_1{}^2}{2g_c} = 0$$

This becomes, upon replacement of RT by p/ρ,

$$\frac{\gamma}{\gamma - 1}\left(\frac{p_2}{\rho_2} - \frac{p_1}{\rho_1}\right) + \frac{\mathscr{V}_2{}^2 - \mathscr{V}_1{}^2}{2g_c} = 0$$

Replacing $\mathscr{V}_1$ by $A_2\rho_2\mathscr{V}_2/A_1\rho_1$ from the continuity equation ($\rho_1 A_1 \mathscr{V}_1 = \rho_2 A_2 \mathscr{V}_2$) gives

$$\frac{\gamma}{\gamma - 1}\frac{p_1}{\rho_1}\left(\frac{p_2}{p_1}\frac{\rho_1}{\rho_2} - 1\right) + \frac{\mathscr{V}_2{}^2}{2g_c}\left[1 - \left(\frac{A_2}{A_1}\right)^2\left(\frac{\rho_2}{\rho_1}\right)^2\right] = 0$$

Eliminating ρ_2 by use of the isentropic relation

$$\frac{\rho_2}{\rho_1} = \left(\frac{p_2}{p_1}\right)^{1/\gamma}$$

and solving for $\mathscr{V}_2$ yields

$$\mathscr{V}_2 = \sqrt{\left(\frac{2g_c\gamma}{\gamma - 1}\right)\left(\frac{p_1}{\rho_1}\right)\frac{[1 - (p_2/p_1)^{(\gamma-1)/\gamma}]}{[1 - (A_2/A_1)^2(p_2/p_1)^{2/\gamma}]}} \qquad (20.54)$$

Now, let state 1 be selected as the reservoir condition (denoted by subscript 0) and state 2 be the condition at any point along the flow. Then $A/A_0 = 0$ (equivalent to saying that $\mathscr{V}_0 = 0$), and Eq. (20.54) becomes

$$\mathscr{V} = \sqrt{\left(\frac{2g_c\gamma}{\gamma - 1}\right)\left(\frac{p_0}{\rho_0}\right)\left[1 - \left(\frac{p}{p_0}\right)^{(\gamma-1)/\gamma}\right]}$$

$$= \sqrt{\frac{2g_c\gamma R T_0}{\gamma - 1}\left[1 - \left(\frac{p}{p_0}\right)^{(\gamma-1)/\gamma}\right]} \qquad (20.55)$$

Equation (20.55) is the desired result. It gives the velocity at any point in terms of the reservoir conditions.

The mass rate of flow is given by

$$\dot{m} = \rho A \mathscr{V} = \rho A \sqrt{\frac{2g_c\gamma R T_0}{\gamma - 1}\left[1 - \left(\frac{p}{p_0}\right)^{(\gamma-1)/\gamma}\right]} \qquad (20.56)$$

In most cases of nozzle design, however, it is not the mass flow rate which is of interest, but the mass flow rate per unit area, $\dot{m}/A$. Thus, Eq. (20.56) becomes

$$\frac{\dot{m}}{A} = \rho\sqrt{\frac{2g_c\gamma RT_0}{\gamma-1}\left[1-\left(\frac{p}{p_0}\right)^{(\gamma-1)/\gamma}\right]}$$

which may be written, with the aid of the isentropic relation $\rho/\rho_0 = (p/p_0)^{1/\gamma}$, as

$$\frac{\dot{m}}{A} = \rho_0\sqrt{\frac{2g_c\gamma RT_0}{\gamma-1}\left[\left(\frac{p}{p_0}\right)^{2/\gamma}-\left(\frac{p}{p_0}\right)^{(\gamma+1)/\gamma}\right]} \qquad (20.57)$$

Eq. (20.57) enables the *critical pressure ratio* p_c/p_0 to be calculated. This is the pressure ratio for which the mass flow rate per unit area is a maximum. Thus differentiating with respect to p/p_0, setting to zero, and solving for p/p_0 gives:

$$\frac{2}{\gamma}\left(\frac{p_c}{p_0}\right)^{(2-\gamma)/\gamma} - \frac{\gamma+1}{\gamma}\left(\frac{p_c}{p_0}\right)^{1/\gamma} = 0$$

or

$$\frac{p_c}{p_0} = \left(\frac{2}{\gamma+1}\right)^{\gamma/(\gamma-1)} \qquad (20.58)$$

For air ($\gamma = 1.4$), $p_c/p_0 = 0.528$.

Several important results may be deduced from the above relations. By substitution of known fixed values of p_0, T_0, ρ_0, and $\dot{m}$, the area, the velocity and the density may be found for successive values of p/p_0 along the nozzle. A typical result is shown in Fig. 20.15. It is seen that as the velocity increases, the area first decreases, reaching a minimum or throat section at the sonic speed. This minimum area corresponds to the maximum mass flow rate per unit area. The area then increases as the velocity increases in the supersonic region. In other words, if the ratio of discharge pressure to admission pressure is low ($< p_c/p_0$), the nozzle is a convergent–divergent passage. If the ratio of discharge pressure to admission pressure is high ($> p_c/p_0$), the nozzle consists only of a convergent portion. That the velocity at the throat is equal to the local acoustic velocity may be seen by substituting the critical pressure ratio [Eq. (20.58)] into Eq. (20.55).

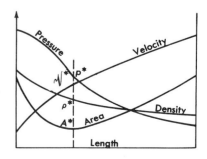

Fig. 20.15 Variation of Area, Velocity, and Specific Volume for Nozzle Flow.

The result is

$$\mathscr{V}_{\text{throat}} = \sqrt{\frac{2g_c\gamma R T_0}{\gamma+1}}$$

Since $g_c\gamma R T_0 = a_0^2$ by definition of the velocity of sound, this may be written as

$$\mathscr{V}_{\text{throat}} = \sqrt{\frac{2a_0^2}{\gamma+1}}$$

But the right-hand side of this equation is a^*, according to Eq. (20.49). Thus the velocity at the throat is equal to the local velocity of sound, and

$$\mathscr{V}_t = a^* = \sqrt{g_c\gamma R T_t} \qquad (20.59)$$

where the subscript refers to throat conditions.

Essentially the same results as above may also be obtained by considering the Mach number as the principal variable. Equation (20.37), the energy equation, gives

$$c_p dT + \frac{\mathscr{V} d\mathscr{V}}{g_c} = 0$$

or

$$\frac{\gamma R}{\gamma-1} dT + \frac{\mathscr{V} d\mathscr{V}}{g_c} = 0$$

This may be written in terms of the Mach number as

$$\frac{d\mathscr{V}}{\mathscr{V}} = -\frac{1}{(\gamma-1)M^2}\frac{dT}{T} \qquad (20.60)$$

Now the definition for the Mach number is $M = \mathscr{V}/\sqrt{g_c\gamma R T}$. Logarithmic differentiation then gives

$$\frac{d\mathscr{V}}{\mathscr{V}} = \frac{1}{2}\frac{dT}{T} + \frac{dM}{M}$$

Equation (20.60) thus becomes, upon replacement of $d\mathscr{V}/\mathscr{V}$,

$$\frac{dT}{T} = -\frac{2(\gamma-1)M dM}{(\gamma-1)M^2+2}$$

This is integrated between the reference section where $M = 1$ and $T = T^*$, and a section where $M = M$ and $T = T$:

$$\int_{T*}^{T} \frac{dT}{T} = -2 \int_{1}^{M} \frac{M dM}{M^2 + [2/(\gamma-1)]}$$

$$\ln \frac{T}{T*} = -\left[\ln\left(M^2 + \frac{2}{\gamma-1}\right)\right]_{1}^{M} = -\ln\left[\frac{[(\gamma-1)M^2+2]/(\gamma-1)}{[(\gamma-1)+2]/(\gamma-1)}\right]$$

$$= -\ln \frac{(\gamma-1)M^2+2}{\gamma+1}$$

or

$$\frac{T}{T*} = \frac{\gamma-1}{(\gamma-1)M^2+2} \tag{20.61}$$

In a similar manner, relations for $\mathscr{V}/\mathscr{V}^*$, p/p^*, ρ/ρ^* and A/A^* are obtained

$$\frac{\mathscr{V}}{\mathscr{V}*} = M\left[\frac{\gamma+1}{(\gamma-1)M^2+2}\right]^{1/2} \tag{20.62}$$

$$\frac{p}{p*} = \left(\frac{T}{T*}\right)^{\gamma/(\gamma-1)} = \left[\frac{\gamma+1}{(\gamma-1)M^2+2}\right]^{\gamma/(\gamma-1)} \tag{20.63}$$

$$\frac{\rho}{\rho*} = \left(\frac{p}{p*}\right)^{1/\gamma} = \left[\frac{\gamma+1}{(\gamma-1)M^2+2}\right]^{1/(\gamma-1)}$$

$$\frac{A}{A*} = \left(\frac{\rho*}{\rho}\right)\left(\frac{\mathscr{V}*}{\mathscr{V}}\right) = \frac{1}{M}\left[\frac{(\gamma-1)M^2+2}{\gamma+1}\right]^{(\gamma+1)/2(\gamma-1)}$$

These results are plotted in Fig. 20.16. Note how A/A^* varies, starting as ∞ at the entrance, reaching a minimum of 1 at $M = 1$, and increasing again. The curve is double-valued, with a subsonic and a supersonic branch. If the flow is subsonic throughout, the nozzle is convergent, and the maximum velocity occurs at the section of minimum area. If the flow becomes supersonic, the sonic condition is at the throat. The study of nozzles will now be illustrated by means of the following examples. The first example deals with a convergent nozzle, the second example with a convergent-divergent nozzle.

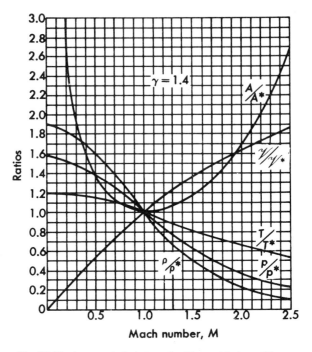

Fig. 20.16   Isentropic Relations for Flow with Area Change.

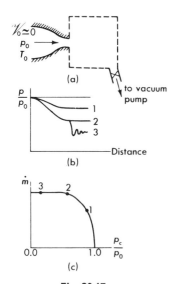

Fig. 20.17

Flow in Convergent Nozzle.

Example 20.3. A convergent nozzle has an exit area of 2 sq. in. Air enters the nozzle with a stagnation pressure of 100 psia and a stagnation temperature of 200 °F. Determine the respective mass flow rates for exit pressures of 80 psia, 52.8 psia and 30 psia.

Solution. For an exit pressure of $p_e = 80$, the flow follows curve 1 [Fig. 20.17(b)]. Table 30 of the Keenan and Kaye tables gives (corresponding to $p/p_0 = 80/100$) an exit Mach number of $M_e = 0.573$ and a temperature ratio $T_e/T_0 = 0.938$. The temperature at the exit is thus

$$T_e = (0.938)(660) = 619 \text{ °R}$$

and the local velocity of sound is

$$a_e = \sqrt{g_c \gamma R T_e} = \sqrt{(32.2)(1.4)(53.3)(619)}$$
$$= 1220 \text{ fps}$$

Knowing the local Mach number and the local sound speed, the exit velocity is calculated as

$$\mathscr{V}_e = (a_e)(M_e) = (1220)(0.573) = 700 \text{ fps}$$

The exit density is

$$\rho_e = \frac{p_e}{RT_e} = \frac{(80)(144)}{(53.3)(619)} = 0.35 \text{ lbm/cu ft}$$

The mass flow rate is then

$$\dot{m} = \rho_e A_e \mathscr{V}_e = (0.35)\left(\frac{2}{144}\right)(700) = 3.4 \text{ lbm/sec}$$

This is plotted as point 1 in Fig. 20.17(c).

For an exit pressure of $p_c = 52.8$, the pressure ratio becomes

$$\frac{p_e}{p_0} = \frac{52.8}{100} = 0.528$$

which is precisely equal to the critical pressure ratio as listed in the gas tables. Thus, $M = 1$, and calculations similar to above give a mass flow rate of

$$\dot{m} = \rho^* A \mathscr{V}^* = (0.260)\left(\frac{2}{144}\right)(1150) = 4.15 \text{ lbm/sec}$$

This is plotted as point 2 [Fig. 20.17(c)]; the corresponding flow is along curve 2 [Fig. 20.17(b)].

When the exit pressure is decreased below the critical pressure (52.8 psia in this case), there is no further increase in the mass rate of flow. Thus, for an exit pressure of 30 psia, the flow rate remains 4.15 lbm/sec [point 3, Fig. 20.17(c)]. The nozzle is said to be *choked*. The flow, however, follows curve 3 [Fig. 20.17(b)], with the drop in pressure from 52.8 psia to 30 psia taking place *outside* the nozzle.

Example 20.4. A convergent-divergent nozzle having a throat area of 2 sq. in. and an exit area of 4 sq. in. expands air from the same inlet conditions as Ex. 20.3. Determine: (a) the maximum flow rate, (b) the exit velocity, pressure and temperature corresponding to design conditions, i.e., when sonic velocity is attained at the throat and the divergent portion of the nozzle acts as a supersonic nozzle, (c) the exit velocity, pressure and temperature when sonic velocity is attained at the throat, but the divergent portion of the nozzle acts as a subsonic diffuser.

Solution. A convergent-divergent nozzle, when operating at the design pressure ratio corresponding to the throat and exit areas, accelerates the flow continuously from subsonic to supersonic velocity. The pressure and velocity distributions are then represented by the curves (labeled 1) in Figs. 20.18(b) and 20.18(c). Starting with an exit pressure $p_e = p_0$, consider what happens in such a nozzle as p_e is gradually reduced. At first, the device acts as a subsonic nozzle followed by a subsonic diffuser, i.e., as a venturi, with pressure and velocity distributions shown by curves 2. As p_e is progressively lowered, the mass flow increases until conditions are such that sonic speed is attained in the throat. At that stage, $M = 1$, and $p = 52.8$ psia, at the throat.

(a) The calculation for mass flow rate is identical to that of Ex. 20.3, and since the throat area is of the same size as that used in the preceding example, the answer is the same, namely, 4.15 lbm/sec. This is the maximum flow rate. Further reduction of p_e will not alter the conditions at the throat or upstream. Nor will it increase the mass flow rate, but will result in choking.

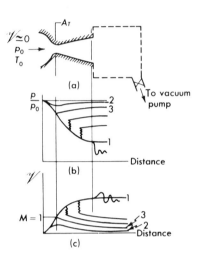

Fig. 20.18

Flow in Convergent-Divergent Nozzle.

(b) Proceeding with the solution of the problem, the ratio of exit area to throat area in the present case is 2. Now in Table 30 of the gas tables, it will be noticed that there are two Mach numbers listed for the ratio $A/A^* = 2$. One of these ($M = 2.197$) is greater than unity, and the other ($M = 0.306$) is less than unity. The Mach number of 2.197 corresponds to the condition of the divergent section acting as a supersonic nozzle. Along with it, Table 30 gives $p_e/p_0 = 0.0939$, $T_e/T_0 = 0.5089$. The exit pressure and temperature are thus

$$p_e = 0.0939(100) = 9.39 \text{ psia}$$
$$T_e = 0.5089(660) = 336 \, °\text{R}$$

The local speed of sound being

$$a_e = \sqrt{g_c\gamma R T_e} = \sqrt{(32.2)(1.4)(53.3)(336)}$$
$$= 900 \text{ fps}$$

the exit velocity is

$$\mathscr{V}_e = M_e a_e = 2.197(900) = 1977 \text{ fps}$$

(c) The Mach number of $M = 0.306$ corresponds to the divergent portion acting as a subsonic diffuser. The flow then follows curve 3. For this condition, Table 30 gives $p_e/p_0 = 0.9371$, $T_e/T_0 = 0.9816$, so that the exit pressure and temperature are

$$p_e = 0.9371(100) = 93.71 \text{ psia}$$
$$T_e = 0.9816(660) = 649 \, °\text{R}$$

The local sonic speed is

$$a_e = \sqrt{(32.2)(1.4)(53.3)(649)} = 1250 \text{ fps}$$

The critical-pressure ratio [Eq. (20.58)] for steam is therefore

$$\frac{p^*}{p_0} = \left(\frac{2}{\gamma+1}\right)^{\gamma/(\gamma-1)} = \left(\frac{2}{2.3}\right)^{1.3/3} = 0.545$$

so that the exit velocity is

$$\mathscr{V}_e = .306\,(1250) = 383 \text{ fps}$$

The above example explains a great deal about nozzles: First, for exit pressures above 93.71 psia, the flow is entirely subsonic and is represented by a curve such as curve 2. In this range of exhaust pressures the convergent-divergent nozzle performs like a venturi; the flow, in the absence of friction, is isentropic. For the condition of sonic speed at the throat, there are two possible exit pressures, namely, 93.71 psia and 9.39 psia; for both of these pressures, the flow is isentropic. The two isentropic solutions, one subsonic, the other supersonic, are represented by curves 3 and 1. The latter curve represents the performance for which the nozzle was designed. The question may be asked: what about exit pressures between 93.71 psia and 9.39 psia? The answer is that, for them, there are *no* isentropic solutions. Instead, the flow proceeds along the intermediate lines between curves 1 and 3, with the occurrence of a shock and a resultant entropy increase. Across the shock, the velocity changes from supersonic to subsonic. (The subject of shock is discussed in Sec. 20.18.)

20.13   Flow of Steam Through a Nozzle

The results that have been developed for the isentropic flow of an ideal gas also apply to the isentropic flow of a vapor. However, because vapors do not follow closely perfect gas relations, appropriate tables or charts must be available if problems involving vapors are to be solved.

Consider the isentropic expansion of steam in a nozzle as shown in Fig. 20.19. The value of the specific-heat ratio varies, but $\gamma = 1.3$ is a good approximation for steam over a considerable range. The critical pressure ratio for steam is therefore

$$\frac{p^*}{p_0} = \left(\frac{2}{\gamma+1}\right)^{\gamma/(\gamma-1)}$$

$$= \left(\frac{2}{1.3+1}\right)^{1.3/(1.3-1)} = 0.545$$

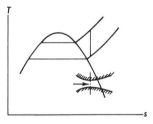

Fig. 20.19
Flow of Steam through Nozzle.

Knowing the value of the critical-pressure ratio, the throat conditions, exit conditions and flow rate can be calculated in a manner similar to that for air. The following example illustrates this.

Example 20.5. Steam at stagnation conditions of 150 psia and 450 °F expands in a nozzle to an exit pressure of 30 psia. Determine the throat area and the exit area for a flow of 1.0 lbm/sec.

Solution. Since the exit-to-inlet pressure ratio, 30/150, is well below the critical-pressure ratio of 0.545, sonic conditions will be attained at the throat.

Thus,

$$p_t = p^* = 0.545(150) = 82 \text{ psia}$$

The specific entropy at the throat is $s_t = s^* = s_0 = 1.6312$ Btu/lbm-°R. By interpolation, the enthalpy and specific volume at the throat are (from steam tables):

$$h_t = h^* = 1194 \text{ Btu/lbm}$$
$$v_t = v^* = 5.510 \text{ cu ft/lbm}$$

The velocity at the throat is

$$\mathscr{V}_t = \mathscr{V}^* = \sqrt{2g_c(h_0 - h^*)}$$
$$= \sqrt{(2)(32.2)(778)(1248 - 1194)} = 1640 \text{ fps}$$

Note that the velocity has been calculated from the correct relation of $\mathscr{V} = \sqrt{2g_c \Delta h}$ rather than from Eq. (20.55) which applies only to perfect gases. The throat area is

$$A_t = A^* = \frac{mv^*}{\mathscr{V}^*} = \frac{(1.0)(5.510)}{1640}$$

In other words, between points a and b the vapor is not in a state of equilibrium, but is in a supersaturated or metastable state. Between a and b, the temperature of the vapor is less than the saturation temperature corresponding to that pressure, and the path of the process is shown dotted because the corresponding states are not equilibrium states. Any finite disturbance, such as the introduction of a measuring instrument, brings about condensation (with increase in entropy and pressure). When supersaturation occurs in a nozzle, the flow may be slightly greater than that obtained for isentropic flow without supersaturation. In practice, a coefficient or efficiency number is introduced in the design of nozzles to allow for the entropy increase due to friction, supersaturation, and other factors. These coefficients are discussed in the next section.

20.14   Nozzle and Diffuser Coefficients

As pointed out previously a coefficient or efficiency number is introduced to allow for irreversibilities occurring in nozzle or diffuser flow. Selecting isentropic flow as the standard of comparison, the various coefficients are defined as follows:

Nozzle efficiency. The nozzle efficiency, η_N, is defined as the ratio of the actual enthalpy drop to the isentropic enthalpy drop

$$\eta_N = \frac{h_0 - h_e}{h_0 - h_{ei}} \tag{20.64}$$

In Fig. 20.20, state 0 represents the stagnation state of the fluid entering the nozzle; state e represents the actual state at the exit of the nozzle, and state ei represents the state that would have been obtained if the flow had been ideal (i.e., isentropic). Nozzle efficiencies vary from 90 to 99 per cent, with large nozzles usually having a higher efficiency than small nozzles.

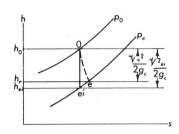

Fig. 20.20
Ideal and Actual Flow in Nozzle.

Velocity Coefficient. The velocity coefficient is defined as the ratio of the actual exit velocity to the isentropic velocity obtained for the same pressure drop

$$C_{\mathscr{V}} = \frac{\mathscr{V}_e}{\mathscr{V}_{ei}} \tag{20.65}$$

Referring to Fig. 20.20, the relation between nozzle efficiency and velocity coefficient may be obtained as follows

$$C_{\mathscr{V}}^2 = \frac{\mathscr{V}_e^2}{\mathscr{V}_{ei}^2} = \frac{h_0 - h_e}{h_0 - h_{ei}} = \eta_N$$

or

$$C_{\mathscr{V}} = \sqrt{\eta_N} \tag{20.66}$$

Coefficient of Discharge. The coefficient of discharge is defined as the ratio of the actual mass rate of flow to the isentropic mass rate of flow:

$$C_D = \frac{m}{m_{\text{isen.}}} \tag{20.67}$$

where $m_{\text{isen.}}$ is determined by using the actual back pressure if the nozzle is not choked. If the nozzle is choked, $m_{\text{isen.}}$ is obtained by using sonic velocity at the minimum section.

Diffuser Efficiency. While nozzles are flow channels whose purpose is to accelerate a fluid with a corresponding reduction in pressure, diffusers are channels whose purpose is to decelerate a fluid with a corresponding increase in pressure. In Fig. 20.21, point 1 represents the state of the fluid entering the diffuser. If decelerated isentropically to rest, it

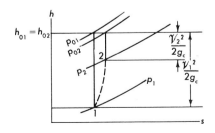

Fig. 20.21 Flow in a Diffuser.

would attain a stagnation pressure of p_{01} and a stagnation enthalpy of h_{01}. The actual flow through the diffuser, however, is non-isentropic (dotted line) and the fluid leaves the diffuser at state 2, with a corresponding stagnation enthalpy p_{02} lower than p_{01}. The stagnation enthalpy h_{02}, however, is equal to h_{01} because of the principle of conservation of energy. The diffuser efficiency is defined as the ratio of the outlet stagnation pressure to the inlet stagnation pressure, i.e.

$$\eta_D = \frac{p_{02}}{p_{01}} \tag{20.68}$$

Diffusers are inherently not as efficient as nozzles. This is because a decreasing pressure in the direction of flow tends to reduce the boundary layer thickness in a nozzle, whereas an increasing pressure in the direction of flow results in boundary layer growth and excessive turbulence in a diffuser (Fig. 20.22). The efficiency of a diffuser whose inlet velocity is subsonic can be fairly high, but the efficiency of a diffuser whose inlet velocity is supersonic is rather low.

Nozzle   Diffuser

Fig. 20.22 Boundary Layer in Nozzle and Diffuser.

When the efficiency of a diffuser is known, the stagnation pressure at the exit may be calculated for a given inlet condition as follows: From Eq. (20.39),

$$p_{01} = p_1 \left[1 + \frac{\gamma - 1}{2} M_1^2 \right]^{\gamma/(\gamma-1)}$$

Whereupon, from Eq. (20.68),

$$p_{02} = \eta_D p_{01} = \eta_D p_1 \left[1 + \frac{\gamma - 1}{2} M_1^2 \right]^{\gamma/(\gamma-1)}$$

$$= \eta_D p_1 \left[1 + \frac{(\gamma - 1)\mathscr{V}_1^2}{2 g_c \gamma R T_1} \right]^{\gamma/(\gamma-1)} \tag{20.69}$$

Example 20.6. Air enters a diffuser with a velocity of 700 fps, a static pressure of 14.7 psia, and a static temperature of 60 °F. The diffuser efficiency is 83 per cent. What is the exit stagnation pressure and temperature?

Solution. From Eq. (20.69), the exit stagnation pressure is

$$p_{02} = 0.83(14.7)\left[1 + \frac{(1.4-1)(700)^2}{2(32.2)(1.4)(53.3)(520)}\right]^{1.4/0.4}$$

$$= 15.9 \text{ psia}$$

From Eq. (20.38):

$$T_{01} = T_1\left[1 + \frac{\gamma-1}{2}M_1^2\right] = T_1\left[1 + \frac{\gamma-1}{2}\cdot\frac{V_1^2}{g_c\gamma RT_1}\right]$$

$$= 520\left[1 + \frac{(1.4-1)(700)^2}{2(32.2)(1.4)(53.3)(520)}\right]$$

$$= 561 °R$$

Since $h_{02} = h_{01}$, it follows that, for a perfect gas, $T_{02} = T_{01} = 561°R$.

20.15 Flow with Friction in Constant Area Duct; Fanno Line

So far, the inclusion of friction in the flow equations has not been made. In this section, a friction term will be introduced in the differential equation of motion. Such an equation, often called the *friction equation* for steady flow, is derived below.

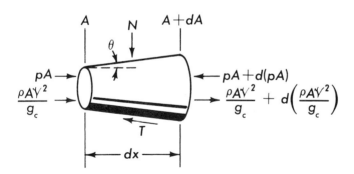

Fig. 20.23 Forces Acting on a Stream Tube.

Consider an element of stream tube as shown in Fig. 20.23. Let N denote the normal force on the fluid at the peripheral surface dA_s due to pressure. Let $T = \tau A_s$ denote the tangential surface force due to the shear stress τ at the wall. For steady-flow conditions, the momentum equation (see Sec. 20.2) in the x direction becomes

$$d\left(\frac{\rho A \mathscr{V}^2}{g_c}\right) = pA - [pA + d(pA)] + N \sin \theta - T \cos \theta$$

But $N \sin \theta = p\,dA$, and $T \cos \theta = \tau A_s \cos \theta = \tau \mathscr{P} dx$ where $\mathscr{P}$ is the wetted perimeter. Furthermore, if a hydraulic diameter (defined as the ratio $D = 4A/\mathscr{P}$) is introduced, $T \cos \theta$ may be written as $\tau[(4A)/(D)]dx$, and the above equation becomes

$$d\left(\frac{\rho A \mathscr{V}^2}{g_c}\right) = pA - [pA + d(pA)] + p\,dA - \tau\frac{4A}{D}dx$$

$$= -A\,dp - \tau\frac{4A}{D}dx$$

or

$$d\left(\frac{\rho A \mathscr{V}^2}{g_c}\right) + A\,dp + \tau\frac{4A}{D}dx = 0 \qquad (20.70)$$

Now,

$$d\left(\frac{\rho A \mathscr{V}^2}{g_c}\right) = \frac{\rho A \mathscr{V}}{g_c}d\mathscr{V} + \mathscr{V}d\left(\frac{\rho A \mathscr{V}}{g_c}\right) = \frac{\rho A \mathscr{V}}{g_c}d\mathscr{V},$$

since $\rho A \mathscr{V}/g_c$ is a constant. Thus, Eq. (20.70) reduces to

$$\frac{\rho A \mathscr{V}}{g_c}d\mathscr{V} + A\,dp + \tau\frac{4A}{D}dx = 0$$

whereupon

$$\frac{\mathscr{V}d\mathscr{V}}{g_c} + \frac{dp}{\rho} + \tau\frac{4}{\rho D}dx = 0$$

Introducing the *friction factor*[†], f, defined by $\tau = f\rho\mathscr{V}^2/2g_c$ enables the above equation to be written as

$$\frac{\mathscr{V}d\mathscr{V}}{g_c} + \frac{dp}{\rho} + 4f\frac{\mathscr{V}^2}{2g_c D}dx = 0 \qquad (20.71)$$

Equation (20.71) is the desired result. For a constant-area duct, it may be re-written in terms of the mass flow rate per unit area, $G \equiv \dot{m}/A = \rho\mathscr{V} = \mathscr{V}/v$ as

$$\frac{G^2}{g_c} \cdot \frac{dv}{v} + \frac{dp}{v} + 4f\frac{G^2}{2g_c D}dx = 0 \qquad (20.72)$$

[†] The definition given for f follows that of Shapiro and Keenan. It may differ from that of other texts by a factor of 4.

This may be integrated, using an average value $\bar{f}$ for the friction factor, as

$$\frac{G^2}{g_c}\ln\frac{v_2}{v_1}+\int_1^2\frac{dp}{v}+4\bar{f}\frac{G^2}{2g_cD}(x_2-x_1)=0 \qquad (20.73)$$

The value of f, for subsonic flow, has been found experimentally to be a function of the *Reynolds number, $R_e \equiv \rho \mathcal{V}D/\mu$* and of the *roughness factor, ϵ/D*. It has been plotted by Moody as shown in Fig 20.24. The data may be summarized by stating that:

(a) For laminar flow in pipes,

$$4f=\frac{64}{R_e} \qquad (20.74)$$

(b) For turbulent flow in smooth pipes,

$$\frac{1}{\sqrt{4f}}=2\log_{10}R_e\sqrt{4f}-0.8 \qquad (20.75)$$

(c) For turbulent flow in rough pipes,

$$\frac{1}{\sqrt{4f}}=2\log_{10}\frac{D}{\epsilon}+1.14 \qquad (20.76)$$

Equations (20.75) and (20.76) are the well-known *Karman-Nikuradse-Prandtl resistance equations.*

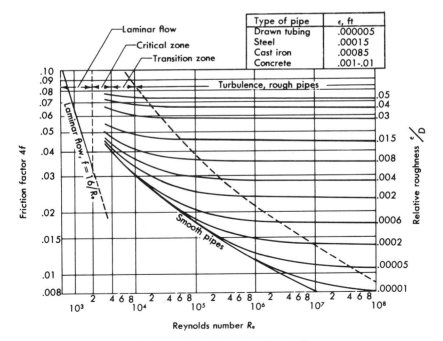

Fig. 20.24 Friction Factor for Flow in Pipes.

Having established the notion of viscous flow in a pipe, consider now the adiabatic steady flow of a fluid in a constant-area passage with no work done. The energy equation, in terms of the stagnation enthalpy is

$$h + \frac{\mathscr{V}^2}{2g_c} = h_0$$

This may be written, with the aid of the continuity equation

$$\frac{\dot{m}}{A} = \rho \mathscr{V} = \frac{\mathscr{V}}{v} = \text{constant} = G,$$

as

$$h + \frac{G^2 v^2}{2g_c} = h_0 \tag{20.77}$$

Equation (20.77) represents a relationship between h and v, and consequently between any two properties, since a fluid is a pure substance† from the thermodynamics standpoint. The states which satisfy Equation (20.77), when plotted on an h-s diagram as in Fig. 20.25, yield a series of lines called *Fanno lines*. Each line, corresponding to a different value of G, has a different amount of friction arbitrarily assigned to it, and is the locus of states through which a fluid passes in adiabatic pipe flow for given entrance conditions. A limiting case is the isenthalpic line, $G = 0$, which is a Fanno line of zero flow (infinite friction). Each curve shows that at some pressure, the entropy reaches a maximum value, then decreases with any change in pressure. Since an entropy decrease in adiabatic flow would violate the second law of thermodynamics, an expansion or compression at constant area cannot proceed beyond the point of maximum entropy. Thus, each path can only be traveled in the directions indicated by the arrows.

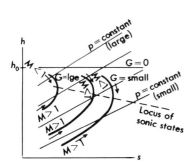

Fig. 20.25   Fanno Lines.

To investigate conditions at the point of maximum entropy on a Fanno line, let the energy equation be written in differential form:

$$dh + \frac{\mathscr{V} d\mathscr{V}}{g_c} = 0$$

---

† Recall that the state of a pure substance is fully established by specifying two independent properties.

From the continuity equation for constant-area flow, $\rho\mathscr{V} = $ constant, it follows that $\rho d\mathscr{V} + \mathscr{V}d\rho = 0$, or $d\mathscr{V} = -\mathscr{V}d\rho/\rho$, and consequently

$$dh - \frac{\mathscr{V}^2}{g_c} \cdot \frac{d\rho}{\rho} = 0$$

Also, from the Tds equation $Tds = dh - vdp$, dh may be replaced by $Tds + vdp$, so that

$$Tds + vdp - \frac{\mathscr{V}^2}{g_c} \cdot \frac{d\rho}{\rho} = 0$$

Now, at the point of maximum entropy, $ds = 0$; therefore,

$$vdp - \frac{\mathscr{V}^2}{g_c} \cdot \frac{d\rho}{\rho} = 0$$

or

$$\mathscr{V} = \sqrt{g_c\left(\frac{dp}{d\rho}\right)} = \sqrt{g_c\left(\frac{\partial p}{\partial \rho}\right)_s} \qquad (20.78)$$

Equation (20.78) shows that the velocity is sonic for the state of maximum entropy on a Fanno curve. Now, the upper part of each Fanno line represents states of subsonic flow, while the lower part represents states of supersonic flow. Thus, for subsonic adiabatic flow in a pipe, the velocity increases as the pressure and enthalpy decrease until, in the limit, sonic speed is attained. Similarly, for supersonic adiabatic flow in a pipe, the velocity decreases as the pressure and enthalpy increase until, in the limit, the sonic speed is reached. In neither case, can the flow proceed past the point of maximum entropy, for this would violate the second law. If an insulated pipe carrying fluid at subsonic velocities discharges into a region of pressure lower than that corresponding to the maximum-entropy point on the Fanno curve, the additional expansion must occur outside of the pipe. Likewise, if an insulated pipe carrying fluid at supersonic velocities discharges into a receiver at a pressure higher than that of the maximum-entropy point on the Fanno line, the additional increase in pressure must occur beyond the end of the pipe.

Example 20.6. Air, from a supply reservoir at a stagnation enthalpy of 240 °F, is expanded adiabatically and reversibly in an entrance nozzle to a state of one atmosphere and a Mach number of 1.8. It enters and flows steadily through a rough 2-inch I.D. insulated pipe having a friction factor $f = 0.0025$. Determine: (a) the properties of the flow at $M = 1.8$ and $M = 1.5$, (b) the pipe length between $M = 1.8$ and $M = 1.5$. (c) the maximum allowable length of the pipe before a shock occurs in the passage.

Solution. (a) The properties of the stream at $M = 1.8$ are first determined: From Eq. (20.38):

$$T = T_0\left(1+\frac{\gamma-1}{2}M^2\right)^{-1} = 700\left(1+\frac{1.4-1}{2}\overline{1.8^2}\right)^{-1} = 424\,°R$$

From Eq. (20.33):

$$a = 49.1\sqrt{T} = 49.1\sqrt{424} = 1010\ \text{ft/sec}$$

From Eq. (20.34):

$$\mathcal{V} = aM = (1010)(1.8) = 1820\ \text{ft/sec}$$

These answers could also have been obtained by means of Table 30 of the gas tables. In fact, these tables will be used for the remainder of the problem.

The properties of the stream at $M = 1.5$ are obtained as follows: From Eq. (20.38):

$$T = T_0\left(1+\frac{\gamma-1}{2}M^2\right)^{-1}$$

Applying this to the state at which $M = 1$ gives

$$T^* = \frac{2T_0}{\gamma+1}$$

Thus,

$$\frac{T}{T^*} = \frac{(\gamma+1)/2}{1+[(\gamma-1)/2]M^2}$$

Similar relations may be obtained for p/p^*, p_0/p_0^*, $\mathcal{V}/\mathcal{V}^*$, F/F^*, and $4f(L_{max}/D)$ along a Fanno line (cf. Table 20.1). These ratios are also listed in Table 42 of the gas tables. In the present problem, $T/T^* = 0.728$, $p/p^* = 0.474$, $\mathcal{V}/\mathcal{V}^* = 1.54$, $F/F^* = 1.09$, and $4f(L_{max}/D) = 0.242$. At $M = 1.5$, the values of these ratios are $T/T^* = 0.828$, $p/p^* = 0.606$, $\mathcal{V}/\mathcal{V}^* = 1.37$, $F/F^* = 1.05$, and $4f(L_{max}/D) = 0.136$. The properties of the stream at $M = 1.5$ are then obtained by writing

$$\frac{T_2}{T_1} = \frac{(T/T^*)_2}{(T/T^*)_2} = \frac{0.828}{0.728}$$

or

$$T_2 = 424\left(\frac{0.828}{0.728}\right) = 482\,°R$$

Similarly,

$$p_2 = p_1\frac{(p/p^*)_2}{(p/p^*)_2} = 14.7\left(\frac{0.606}{0.474}\right) = 18.8\ \text{psia}$$

$$\mathcal{V}_2 = \mathcal{V}_1\frac{(\mathcal{V}/\mathcal{V}^*)_2}{(\mathcal{V}/\mathcal{V}^*)_1} = 1820\left(\frac{1.37}{1.54}\right) = 1620\ \text{ft/sec}$$

(b) In Table 42 of the gas tables, L_{max} refers to the pipe length between a given Mach number M and the Mach number unity. The pipe length between $M = 1.8$ and $M = 1.5$ is therefore obtained by writing

$$4f\frac{L}{D} = \left(4f\frac{L_{max}}{D}\right)_{M=1.8} - \left(4f\frac{L_{max}}{D}\right)_{M=1.5}$$

or

$$L = \frac{2}{12} \cdot \frac{1}{4(0.0025)} \cdot (0.242 - 0.136) = 1.76 \text{ ft}$$

(c) The effect of varying the pipe length is seen from the following calculation based on a friction factor $f = 0.0025$:

M	0	.25	.50	.75	1	1.5	2	3	∞
$\dfrac{L_{max}}{D}$		850	100	12	0	14	31	52	82

Consider first subsonic flow: for a given M_1, the pipe has a maximum length (corresponding to $M_2 = 1$). What happens when the pipe length is increased beyond this maximum? Since the flow cannot exceed sonic speed, an increase in length will act to decrease M_1 until M_2 becomes unity. This results in a reduction of the flow rate and a consequent shift to a Fanno line with a smaller value of $G(\equiv \dot{m}/A)$. In other words, the increase friction in the duct acts to "choke" the flow.

For the case of supersonic flow, frictional effects are even more significant. For one thing, the length of pipe is limited to 82 diameters for a friction coefficient of 0.0025 if supersonic flow is to be maintained throughout. In the present case, this would mean a pipe length of 13.7 ft. An increase in the length over its maximum value produces a shock which moves upstream as the pipe length is increased. Figure 20.26 shows the course of events in a pipe of varying

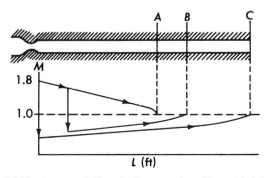

Fig. 20.26 Supersonic Flow in Constant Area Pipe with Friction.

length with an initial Mach number of 1.8. Length A represents the maximum length for flow without shock. When the length is increased to B, a shock stands in the passage. Finally, if the length is increased to C, the shock stands at the inlet of the pipe and the flow becomes subsonic throughout the entire pipe.

20.16   Flow in Constant-Area Duct with Heat Transfer; Rayleigh Line

Consider a frictionless flow in a constant area passage with no work done, but with possible heat transfer. Equation (20.71), with $f = 0$, or Eq. (20.8), the frictionless momentum equation, gives

$$\frac{\mathscr{V} d\mathscr{V}}{g_c} + \frac{dp}{\rho} = 0$$

or

$$dp + \rho \frac{\mathscr{V} d\mathscr{V}}{g_c} = 0$$

Since $\rho v = \dot{m}/A = \text{constant} = G$, from the continuity equation, the above expression integrates into

$$p + \frac{\rho \mathscr{V}^2}{g_c} = \text{constant}$$

which may be written, with the definition for the thrust function

$$F \equiv pA + \frac{\rho A \mathscr{V}^2}{g_c},$$

as

$$p + \frac{\rho \mathscr{V}^2}{g_c} = \frac{F}{A}$$

or

$$p + \frac{G^2 v}{g_c} = \frac{F}{A} \tag{20.79}$$

For a fixed value of the mass flow per unit area and of the impulse function per unit area, Eq. (20.79) defines a unique relation between the pressure and the density, and consequently between other properties. This relationship is called the *Rayleigh line*, and is plotted on h–s co-ordinates as shown in Fig. 20.27. For comparison, a Fanno line has been shown as a dotted line. Since a Fanno line is a line of constant stagnation enthalpy, it is seen that the stagnation enthalpy must vary along a Rayleigh line. This means that a fluid can proceed along a Rayleigh line only if there is heat transfer.

As in the case of the Fanno line, the velocity at the point of maximum entropy is sonic. This is shown by writing Eq. (20.79) in differential form:

$$dp + \frac{G^2}{g_c}d\left(\frac{1}{\rho}\right) = 0 = dp - \frac{G^2}{g_c}\frac{dp}{\rho^2}$$

$$= dp - \frac{\mathscr{V}^2}{g_c}d\rho$$

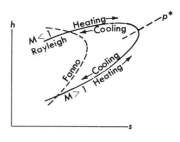

Fig. 20.27 Rayleigh Line.

or

$$\mathscr{V} = \sqrt{g_c\left(\frac{dp}{d\rho}\right)}$$

This becomes, with $ds = 0$ at the point of maximum entropy,

$$\mathscr{V} = \sqrt{g_c\left(\frac{\partial p}{\partial \rho}\right)_s}$$

which is the velocity of sound. The upper branch of the Rayleigh curve corresponds to subsonic flow, whereas the lower branch corresponds to supersonic flow. Since heat addition corresponds to an entropy increase and heat rejection to an entropy decrease, it is seen that, in subsonic flow the Mach number is increased by heating and decreased by cooling, whereas in supersonic flow, the Mach number is decreased by heating and increased by cooling. In neither subsonic nor supersonic flow, however, can the amount of heat input be greater than that for which the leaving Mach number is unity. If this occurs, the flow becomes *choked*, and the initial Mach number is reduced to a value consistent with the amount of heat added.

The change of stream properties along a Rayleigh line is a function of the change in stagnation temperature. The latter depends on the amount of heat transferred, and is obtained from the energy equation

$$q = c_p(T_{02} - T_{01}) \tag{20.80}$$

Since

$$c_p T_0 = c_p T + \frac{\mathscr{V}^2}{2g_c} = c_p T\left(1 + \frac{\gamma-1}{2}M^2\right)$$

it follows that the ratio of stagnation temperatures is

$$\frac{T_{02}}{T_{01}} = \frac{T_2}{T_1} \cdot \frac{1 + [(\gamma-1)/2]M_2^2}{1 + [(\gamma-1)/2]M_1^2} \tag{20.81}$$

Now, as earlier stated, the momentum equation in the absence of frictional forces is

$$\rho \frac{\mathscr{V} d\mathscr{V}}{g_c} + dp = 0$$

and, since $\rho\mathscr{V}$ is constant for a constant-area flow,

$$\frac{\rho\mathscr{V}(\mathscr{V}_2 - \mathscr{V}_1)}{g_c} + p_2 - p_1 = 0$$

Moreover, from the perfect gas law,

$$\rho \frac{\mathscr{V}^2}{g_c} = \frac{p}{RT} \cdot \frac{\mathscr{V}^2}{g_c} = \gamma p M^2$$

so that the above equations combine to give

$$\gamma p_2 M_2{}^2 - \gamma p_1 M_1{}^2 + p_2 - p_1 = 0$$

$$\frac{p_2}{p_1} = \frac{1 + \gamma M_1{}^2}{1 + \gamma M_2{}^2}$$

But $p_2/p_1 = \rho_2 T_2/\rho_1 T_1$, and since $\rho_2/\rho_1 = \mathscr{V}_1/\mathscr{V}_2$ from the continuity equation, it follows that

$$\frac{p_2}{p_1} = \frac{\mathscr{V}_1}{\mathscr{V}_2} \cdot \frac{T_2}{T_1} = \frac{1 + \gamma M_1{}^2}{1 + \gamma M_2{}^2}$$

or

$$\frac{T_2}{T_1} = \frac{1 + \gamma M_1{}^2}{1 + \gamma M_2{}^2} \cdot \frac{\mathscr{V}_2}{\mathscr{V}_1}$$

Since $\mathscr{V}_2\mathscr{V}_1 = M_2 a_2 / M_1 a_1 = (M_2/M_1) \cdot (T_2/T_1)^{1/2}$,

this becomes

$$\frac{T_2}{T_1} = \frac{(1 + \gamma M_1{}^2)^2}{(1 + \gamma M_2)^2} \cdot \frac{M_2{}^2}{M_1{}^2}$$

Replacing T_2/T_1 by this value in Eq. (20.81) gives

$$\frac{T_{02}}{T_{01}} = \frac{(1 + \gamma M_1{}^2)^2 M_2{}^2}{(1 + \gamma M_2{}^2)^2 M_1{}^2} \cdot \frac{1 + [(\gamma - 1)/2] M_2{}^2}{1 + [(\gamma - 1)/2] M_1{}^2}$$

If this is applied to Sec. 1 where $M_1 = 1$, $p_1 = p^*$, $T_1 = T^*$, $\rho_1 = \rho^*$, $T_{01} = T_0{}^*$, etc., and Sec. 2 where $M_2 = M$, $p_2 = p$, $T_2 = T$, $\rho_2 = \rho$, $T_{02} = T_0$, etc., the result is

$$\frac{T_0}{T_0^*} = \frac{2(\gamma+1)M^2\{1+[(\gamma-1)/2]M^2\}}{(1+\gamma M^2)^2} \qquad (20.82)$$

Other ratios, namely, T/T^*, p/p^*, p_0/p^*_0, and $\mathscr{V}/\mathscr{V}^*$ are obtained in similar fashion and are listed in Table 20.1. They are also given in Table 36 of the gas tables.

20.17 Simple Types of Flow

From a one-dimensional point of view, the three most important factors tending to alter the state of a flowing stream are: (a) changes in area, (b) wall friction, and (c) heat addition or rejection. In Sec. 20.10, the effect of area change without friction and heat transfer was studied. In Sec. 20.15, the effect of friction without area change and heat transfer was studied, and, in the preceding section, the effect of heat transfer without area change and friction was discussed.

These flows are known as *simple area change, simple friction,* and *simple T_0 change* respectively. They are represented on a *T–s* diagram in Fig. 20.28. Their working formulas are summarized in Table 20.1. Although

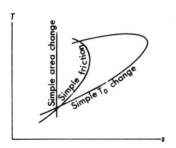

Fig. 20.28 Simple Types of Flow.

such idealized conditions are not easily achieved in practice, the slight inaccuracies introduced are in most cases well compensated by the resulting simplicity. For example, in a stagnation temperature change due to combustion, there will be a change in chemical composition as well as some frictional effects being present. However, for the combustion of a hydrocarbon with air, the fuel-air ratio is rather small; consequently, effects due to composition change are negligible. Furthermore, if the temperature

TABLE 20.1 RELATIONS FOR ONE-DIMENSIONAL SIMPLE FLOW

	Simple Area Change T_0 constant, No Friction	Simple Friction T_0 constant, A constant	Simple T_0 Change A constant, No friction
$\dfrac{A}{A^*}$	$\dfrac{1}{M}\sqrt{\left[\dfrac{2\{2+[(\gamma-1)/2]M^2\}}{\gamma+1}\right]^{(\gamma+1)/(\gamma-1)}}$	1	1
$\dfrac{T_0}{T_0^*}$	1		$\dfrac{2(\gamma-1)M^2\{1+[(\gamma-1)/2]M^2\}}{(1+\gamma M^2)^2}$
$\dfrac{p_0}{p_0^*}$	1	$\dfrac{1}{M}\sqrt{\left[\dfrac{2\{1+[(\gamma-1)/2]M^2\}}{\gamma+1}\right]^{(\gamma+1)/(\gamma-1)}}$	$\dfrac{\gamma+1}{1+\gamma M^2}\left[\dfrac{2\{1+[(\gamma-1)/2]M^2\}}{\gamma+1}\right]^{\gamma/(\gamma-1)}$
$4f\dfrac{L_{\max}}{D}$	0	$\dfrac{1-M^2}{\gamma M^2}+\dfrac{\gamma+1}{2\gamma}\ln\dfrac{(\gamma+1)M^2}{2\{1+[(\gamma-1)/2]M^2\}}$	0
$\dfrac{\mathscr{V}}{\mathscr{V}^*}$	$M\sqrt{\dfrac{\gamma+1}{2\{1+[(\gamma-1)/2]M^2\}}}$	$M\sqrt{\dfrac{\gamma+1}{2\{1+[(\gamma-1)/2]M^2\}}}$	$\dfrac{(\gamma+1)M^2}{1+\gamma M^2}$
$\dfrac{T}{T^*}$	$\dfrac{\gamma+1}{2\{1+[(\gamma-1)/2]M^2\}}$	$\dfrac{\gamma+1}{2\{1+[(\gamma-1)/2]M^2\}}$	$\dfrac{(\gamma+1)^2 M^2}{(1+\gamma M^2)^2}$
$\dfrac{p}{p^*}$	$\left[\dfrac{\gamma+1}{2\{1+[(\gamma-1)/2]M^2\}}\right]^{\gamma/(\gamma-1)}$	$\dfrac{1}{M}\sqrt{\dfrac{\gamma+1}{2\{1+[(\gamma-1)/2]M^2\}}}$	$\dfrac{\gamma+1}{1+\gamma M^2}$
$\dfrac{\rho}{\rho^*}$	$\left[\dfrac{\gamma+1}{2\{1+[(\gamma-1)/2]M^2\}}\right]^{1/(\gamma-1)}$	$\dfrac{1}{M}\sqrt{\dfrac{\gamma+1}{2\{1+[(\gamma-1)/2]M^2\}}}$	$\dfrac{1+\gamma M^2}{(\gamma+1)M^2}$
$\dfrac{F}{F^*}$	$\dfrac{1+\gamma M^2}{M\sqrt{2(\gamma+1)\{1+[(\gamma-1)/2]M^2\}}}$	$\dfrac{1+\gamma M^2}{M\sqrt{2(\gamma+1)\{1+[(\gamma-1)/2]M^2\}}}$	1
$\dfrac{s-s^*}{c_p}$	0	$\ln M^2\left[\dfrac{\gamma+1}{2\{1+[(\gamma-1)/2]M^2\}}\right]^{(\gamma+1)/\gamma}$	$\ln M^2\left(\dfrac{\gamma+1}{1+\gamma M^2}\right)^{(\gamma+1)/\gamma}$

difference between the wall and the flowing stream is large, frictional effects per unit length of duct will be relatively unimportant compared to heating effects.

Example 20.7. Air and fuel enter the combustion chamber of a ram-jet with a velocity of 250 fps, a temperature 580 °R, and a pressure of 10 psia. The enthalpy of reaction Δh for the particular air-fuel ratio employed is 500 Btu per pound of mixture. Considering the cross-sectional area of the combustion chamber to be constant, and assuming frictional effects to be negligible, deter- mine the properties of the flow at the exit of the combustion chamber and the maximum enthalpy of reaction without choking.

Solution. This is a case of flow with simple T_0 change. The properties at the inlet of the combustion chamber are first calculated:

$$a_1 = 49.1 \sqrt{T} = 49.1 \sqrt{580} = 1180 \text{ ft/sec}$$

$$M_1 = \frac{V_1}{a_1} = \frac{250}{1180} = 0.21$$

Corresponding to this Mach number, the stagnation temperature and pressure are determined from the ratios $T/T_0 = 0.991$ and $p/p_0 = 0.970$ as read from Table 30 for isentropic flow. Thus, at entrance to the combustion chamber,

$$T_{01} = \frac{580}{0.991} = 584 \text{ °R}$$

$$p_{01} = \frac{10}{0.970} = 10.3 \text{ psia}$$

At entrance to the combustion chamber $M_1 = 0.21$, and the ratio of stream properties at this Mach number on a Rayleigh line to the corresponding properties at the point of maximum entropy, $M = 1$, are read from Table 36:

$$\left(\frac{T_0}{T_0{}^*}\right) = 0.189; \quad \left(\frac{T}{T^*}\right)_1 = 0.225; \quad \left(\frac{p}{p^*}\right)_1 = 2.260;$$

$$\left(\frac{p_0}{p_0{}^*}\right)_1 = 1.231; \quad \left(\frac{V}{V^*}\right)_1 = 0.100$$

Now, the stagnation temperature at exit is computed from

$$\Delta h = 500 = c_p(T_{02} - T_{01}) = 0.24(T_{02} - 584)$$

whence

$$T_{02} = 2660 \text{ °R}$$

and

$$\frac{T_{02}}{T_{01}} = \frac{2660}{584} = 4.56$$

The properties at exit are found with the help of this ratio, because

$$\frac{T_{02}}{T_{01}} = 4.56 = \frac{(T_0/T_0^*)_2}{(T_0/T_0^*)_1} = \frac{(T_0/T_0^*)_2}{0.189}$$

or

$$\left(\frac{T_0}{T_0^*}\right)_2 = 0.189(4.56) = 0.866$$

Corresponding to this value of the ratio T_0/T_0^*, it is read from Table 36 that

$$M_2 = 0.65; \quad \left(\frac{T}{T^*}\right)_2 = 0.961; \quad \left(\frac{p}{p^*}\right)_2 = 1.508$$

$$\left(\frac{p_0}{p_0^*}\right)_2 = 1.058; \quad \left(\frac{\mathscr{V}}{\mathscr{V}^*}\right)_2 = 0.637$$

The properties at exit of the combustion chamber are thus

$$T_2 = T_1\frac{(T/T^*)_2}{(T/T^*)_1} = (580)\left(\frac{0.961}{0.225}\right) = 2480 \text{ °R}$$

$$p_2 = p_1\frac{(p/p^*)_2}{(p/p^*)_1} = (10)\left(\frac{1.508}{2.260}\right) = 6.67 \text{ psia}$$

$$p_{02} = p_{01}\frac{(p_0/p_0^*)_2}{(p_0/p_0^*)_1} = (10.3)\left(\frac{1.058}{1.231}\right) = 8.84 \text{ psia}$$

$$\mathscr{V}_2 = \mathscr{V}_1\frac{(\mathscr{V}/\mathscr{V}^*)_2}{(\mathscr{V}/\mathscr{V}^*)_1} = (250)\left(\frac{0.637}{0.100}\right) = 1590 \text{ fps}$$

To find the maximum enthalpy of reaction $(\Delta h)_{max}$ for which flow with the specified initial conditions may be maintained, the Mach number at exit of the combustion chamber is set equal to unity. Denoting choking conditions by subscript 3, this gives $(T_0/T_0^*)_3 = 1.000$ from Table 36, and consequently

$$T_{03} = T_{01}\frac{(T_0/T_0^*)_3}{(T_0/T_0^*)_1} = 584\left(\frac{1.000}{0.189}\right) = 3090 \text{ °R}$$

or

$$(\Delta h)_{max} = c_p(T_{03} - T_{01}) = 0.24(3090-584) = 600 \text{ Btu/lbm}$$

Further enrichment of the combustible mixture beyond an enthalpy of reaction corresponding to this value will produce a reduction in the mass flow rate and a reduction of the initial Mach number.

20.18 Normal Shock

Consider the adiabatic flow through a thin and dissipative region as shown in Fig. 20.29. Let the subscripts x and y denote the conditions upstream and downstream respectively. (The choice of this particular set of subscripts is purely to conform with the notation employed in the gas tables.) The continuity, energy, and momentum equations are respectively:

$$\rho_x \mathcal{V}_x = \rho_y \mathcal{V}_y \tag{20.83}$$

$$h_x + \frac{\mathcal{V}_x^2}{2g_c} = h_{0x} = h_y + \frac{\mathcal{V}_y^2}{2g_c} = h_{0y} \tag{20.84}$$

$$p_x + \frac{\rho_x \mathcal{V}_x^2}{2g_c} = p_y + \frac{\rho_y \mathcal{V}_y^2}{2g_c} \tag{20.85}$$

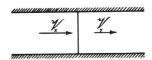

Fig. 20.29 Normal Shock in Flow Field.

There is no restriction on the size or details of the dissipative region, except that x and y are chosen just outside of the region. In particular, let the region be made vanishingly thin, so that the fluid properties are said to "jump" across the region. Such a discontinuity or abrupt change in the flow field is called a *shock wave*. Of course, this is a highly idealized description of the large gradients which actually occur in shock waves, but such a description is nevertheless sufficient for the purposes here. These severe gradients are accompanied by non-equilibrium or dissipative conditions inside the shock.

The continuity equation and the energy equation combine to give an equation which, when plotted on h–s co-ordinates, is the Fanno line. Similarly, the continuity equation and the momentum equation combine to give an equation which, on h–s co-ordinates, is the Rayleigh line. Figure 20.30 shows a Fanno line and a Rayleigh line passing through the same point x. Since a shock must satisfy the continuity, the energy and the momentum equations, the end state of a normal shock for a given upstream condition x, must lie at the intersection y of both the Fanno line and the Rayleigh line. The shock proceeds from x, in the supersonic region, to y in the subsonic region. It cannot proceed from y to x, since this would violate the second law of thermodynamics which requires that, in an adiabatic process, the entropy increase.

For a given fluid and a given upstream condition x, Eqs. 20.83, 20.84, and 20.85 must, in general, be solved numerically. However, for the case of a perfect gas, it is possible to obtain explicit solutions in terms of the Mach number M_x ahead of the shock. This will now be done. The first goal, however, is to develop a relation between M_x and M_y. From the definition of stagnation enthalpy, $h_0 = h + (\mathscr{V}^2/2g_c)$ or $c_p T_0 = c_p T + (\mathscr{V}^2/2g_c)$, it follows that

$$\mathscr{V}^2 = 2g_c c_p (T_0 - T) = 2g_c \frac{\gamma R T}{\gamma - 1}\left(\frac{T_0}{T} - 1\right)$$

Dividing by $a^2 = \gamma g_c R T$ and introducing the definition for Mach number, this becomes

$$\frac{\mathscr{V}^2}{a^2} = M^2 = \frac{2}{\gamma - 1}\left(\frac{T_0}{T} - 1\right)$$

or

$$\frac{T_0}{T} = 1 + \frac{\gamma - 1}{2} M^2$$

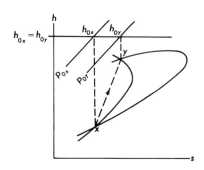

Fig. 20.30   End States for Normal Shock.

Applying this relation to conditions upstream and downstream gives

$$\frac{T_{0x}}{T_x} = 1 + \frac{\gamma - 1}{2} M_x{}^2; \quad \frac{T_{0y}}{T_y} = 1 + \frac{\gamma - 1}{2} M_y{}^2$$

But $T_{0x} = T_{0y}$, from Eq. (20.84), so that

$$\left[1 + \frac{\gamma - 1}{2} M_x{}^2\right] T_x = \left[1 + \frac{\gamma - 1}{2} M_y{}^2\right] T_y$$

or

$$\frac{T_y}{T_x} = \frac{1 + [(\gamma - 1)/2] M_x{}^2}{1 + [(\gamma - 1)/2] M_y{}^2} \tag{20.86}$$

Now, making use of the equation of state, $p = \rho R T$, the continuity equation, $\rho_x \mathscr{V}_x = \rho_y \mathscr{V}_y$, and the definition for the velocity of sound, the ratio T_y/T_x can be written as

$$\frac{T_y}{T_x} = \frac{p_y/\rho_y}{p_x/\rho_x} = \frac{p_y}{p_x} \cdot \frac{\rho_x}{\rho_y} = \frac{p_y}{p_x} \cdot \frac{\mathscr{V}_y}{\mathscr{V}_x} = \frac{p_y}{p_x} \cdot \frac{M_y a_y}{M_x a_x} = \frac{p_y}{p_x} \cdot \frac{M_y \sqrt{T_y}}{M_x \sqrt{T_x}}$$

or

$$\frac{T_y}{T_x} = \left(\frac{p_y}{p_x}\right)^2\left(\frac{M_y}{M_x}\right)^2 \tag{20.87}$$

Equations (20.86) and (20.87), involving the energy equation and the continuity equation, combine to give the equation of the Fanno line,

$$\frac{p_y}{p_x} = \frac{M_x}{M_y} \cdot \frac{\{1+[(\gamma-1)/2]M_x^2\}^{1/2}}{\{1+[(\gamma-1)/2]M_y^2\}^{1/2}} \tag{20.88}$$

Similarly, the combined momentum and continuity equation, $p_x + \rho_x \mathcal{V}_x^2 = p_y + \rho_y \mathcal{V}_y^2$, yields with the aid of the perfect gas relation, $\rho \mathcal{V}^2 = \gamma p M^2$, the equation of the Rayleigh line:

$$\frac{p_y}{p_x} = \frac{1+\gamma M_x^2}{1+\gamma M_y^2} \tag{20.89}$$

Equations (20.88) and (20.89) give the relationship between M_x and M_y as

$$\frac{M_x}{M_y} \cdot \frac{\{1+[(\gamma-1)/2]M_x^2\}^{1/2}}{\{1+[(\gamma-1)/2]M_y^2\}^{1/2}} = \frac{1+\gamma M_x^2}{1+\gamma M_y^2}$$

or

$$M_y^2 = \frac{M_x^2 + [2/(\gamma-1)]}{[2\gamma/(\gamma-1)]M_y^2 - 1} \tag{20.90}$$

20.19   Prandtl Relation and Rankine–Hugoniot Relation for Normal Shock

Equation (20.90) relates the conditions between the upstream and downstream side of a normal shock. It may be written more simply in terms of M_x^* and M_y^* by employing the relation developed in Sec. 20.11:

$$M^2 = \frac{[2/(\gamma+1)]M^{*2}}{1 - [(\gamma-1)/(\gamma+1)]M^{*2}}$$

The result is

$$M_x^* M_y^* = 1 \tag{20.91}$$

Equation (20.91) is known as *Prandtl's relation*. It confirms the fact that the velocity change across a shock is from supersonic to subsonic, or vice versa. The latter possibility, however, is eliminated by the second law.

It is of interest to mention a few of the many useful formulas pertaining to shocks. For example, to find the ratio of pressures across a shock, substitute Eq. (20.90) into Eq. (20.89) and obtain

$$\frac{p_y}{p_x} = \frac{2\gamma}{\gamma+1} M_x^2 - \frac{\gamma-1}{\gamma+1} \tag{20.92}$$

Similarly, substitution of Eq. (20.90) into Eq. (20.86) gives

$$\frac{T_y}{T_x} = \frac{\{1+[(\gamma-1)/2\,|M_x^2\}\{[2\gamma/(\gamma-1)M_x^2-1]\}}{[(\gamma+1)^2/2(\gamma-1)]M_x^2} \qquad (20.93)$$

The ratios

$$\frac{p_x}{p_x}, \quad \frac{\rho_y}{\rho_x}, \quad \frac{T_y}{T_x}, \quad \frac{p_{0y}}{p_{0x}}, \quad \frac{p_{0y}}{p_x}$$

and the value of M_y are all listed in Table 48 of the gas tables in terms of M_x. Note that the stagnation pressure decreases across a shock, whereas the entropy increases across a shock.

Another equation of importance is the relation between the pressure ratio and the density ratio. Substituting the values of $M_y{}^2$ from Eq. (20.90) into Eq. (20.86) gives

$$\frac{T_y}{T_x} = \frac{(p_y/p_x)+[(\gamma-1)/(\gamma+1)](p_y/p_x)^2}{(p_y/p_x)+[(\gamma-1)/(\gamma+1)]}$$

Introducing $\rho_y/\rho_x = (p_y/p_x) \cdot (T_x/T_y)$, this becomes

$$\frac{\rho_y}{\rho_x} = \frac{1+[(\gamma+1)/(\gamma-1)] \cdot (p_y/p_x)}{[(\gamma+1)/(\gamma-1)]+(p_y/p_x)}$$

and, solving for ρ_y/ρ_x,

$$\frac{p_y}{p_x} = \frac{[(\gamma+1)/(\gamma-1)] \cdot (\rho_y/\rho_x)-1}{[(\gamma+1)/(\gamma-1)]-(\rho_y/\rho_x)} \qquad (20.94)$$

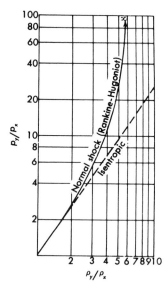

P_y/P_x

ρ_y/ρ_x

Fig. 20.31

Comparisons of Rankine-Hugoniot Curve with Isentropic Curve.

Equation (20.94) is the *Rankine–Hugoniot relation* in one of its several forms. It is plotted in Fig. (20.31) as a pressure rise across a normal shock against the density rise across the shock. On the same diagram, the pressure ratio for isentropic flow is plotted. It is seen that, as the pressure ratio increases, the deviation between the Rankine–Hugoniot curve and the isentropic curve increases. It is also noted, however, that weak shocks (in which the pressure rise is small) are very nearly isentropic. The *shock strength* is defined as the ratio of the pressure increase to the initial pressure. It is expressed by means of Eq. (20.92) as

$$\frac{p_y - p_x}{p_x} = \frac{2\gamma}{\gamma+1}(M_x^2 - 1) \tag{20.95}$$

Equation (20.95) shows that if the shock strength approaches zero, M_x approaches unity. This in turn makes M_y approach unity because of Eq. (20.90). Thus, a shock of infinitesimal strength is identical to a sound wave; in other words, a very weak pressure disturbance propagates with the speed of sound throughout a fluid.

Example 20.8. Consider a pitot tube being used in both subsonic and supersonic flow. For subsonic flow, the Mach number M, the static pressure p, and the stagnation pressure p_0 are related by the usual isentropic-flow relation [Eq. (20.39)]:

$$\frac{p_0}{p} = \left(1 + \frac{\gamma-1}{2}M^2\right)^{\gamma/(\gamma-1)}$$

For supersonic flow, photographs reveal that a shock wave is formed ahead of the tube as shown in Fig. 20.32. Since the shock wave gives rise to an entropy increase, the preceding relation cannot be used in conjunction with supersonic flow. Referring to Fig. 20.32, develop the following relation between Mach number, static pressure, and stagnation pressure:

$$\frac{p_{0y}}{p_x} = \left[\frac{\{[(\gamma+1)/2]M_x^2\}^\gamma}{[2\gamma/(\gamma+1)]M_x^2 - [(\gamma-1)/(\gamma+1)]}\right]^{1/(\gamma-1)}$$

Fig. 20.32
Pitot Tube in
Supersonic
Flow.

Solution. The ratio p_{0y}/p_x may be written as

$$\frac{p_{0y}}{p_x} = \frac{p_{0y}}{p_y} \cdot \frac{p_y}{p_x} \tag{20.96}$$

Now, the flow before the shock wave is isentropic. Across the shock wave, the flow undergoes an increase in entropy and a deceleration. After the shock wave, the flow is further decelerated isentropically to a stagnation pressure p_{0y}. Thus, p_{0y}/p_y may be expressed in terms of M_y by using the isentropic relation, Eq. (20.39):

$$\frac{p_{0y}}{p_y} = \left(1 + \frac{\gamma-1}{2}M_y^2\right)^{\gamma/(\gamma-1)}$$

M_y in turn, is related to M_x by means of Eq. (20.90):

$$M_y^2 = \frac{M_x^2 + [2/(\gamma-1)]}{[2\gamma/(\gamma-1)]M_x^2 - 1}$$

As for p_y/p_x, it is related to M_x through Eq. (20.92):

$$\frac{p_y}{p_x} = \frac{2\gamma}{\gamma+1}M_x^2 - \frac{\gamma-1}{\gamma+1}$$

Making use of the last three relations, Eq. (20.96) becomes

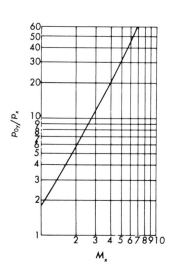

Fig. 20.33
Rayleigh Supersonic Pitot
Equation.

$$\frac{p_{0y}}{p_x} = \left[\frac{\{[(\gamma+1)/2]M_x^2\}^\gamma}{[2\gamma/(\gamma+1)]M_x^2 - [(\gamma-1)/(\gamma+1)]} \right]^{1/(\gamma-1)}$$

(20.97)

Equation (20.97) is called the *Rayleigh supersonic pitot-tube equation*. It is plotted for $\gamma = 1.4$ in Fig. 20.33. Note that p_x must be measured upstream of the shock. In a wind tunnel, this may be done with a static pressure tap in the wall of the tunnel. In the case of a flow not confined in a wind tunnel, the static tap may be incorporated into the side wall of the probe itself.

Experimental evidence indicates that if the tap is placed ten tube diameters aft of the tip of the probe, the static pressure reading becomes a close approximation to the static pressure upstream of the shock.

PROBLEMS

20.1. A body of liquid moving in a straight line with a uniform acceleration is said to be in relative equilibrium, since there is no relative motion between the fluid particles. The free surface of the liquid is still a plane surface, as shown in Fig. 20.34, but it need not be horizontal.

(a) Consider a vertical element of fluid of height h, and show that the pressure at this height is

$$p = \rho \frac{g}{g_c} h$$

where ρ is the density in lbm/cu ft. (b) Consider a horizontal element of fluid of length x, and from Newton's second law of motion $(p_2 A - p_1 A = a\rho x A/g_c)$ show that

$$\rho \frac{g}{g_c}(h_2 - h_1) = \frac{a\rho x}{g_c}$$

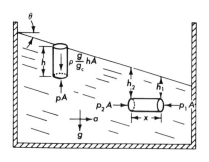

Fig. 20.34 Body of Fluid
in Uniform Linear Acceleration.

or

$$\frac{h_2 - h_1}{x} = \frac{a}{g_c} = \tan\theta$$

20.2. An open tank car 30 ft long, 3 ft wide, and 7 ft high contains water to a depth of 6 ft. The tank is part of a train which is traveling at 65 mph. What is the minimum length of time at constant deceleration in which the train can come to a stop without spilling the water?

20.3. A cylindrical tank of liquid placed on a turntable and rotated at a uniform angular velocity represents a fluid in relative equilibrium, because there is no relative motion between the fluid particles. (a) Referring to Fig. 20.35, consider

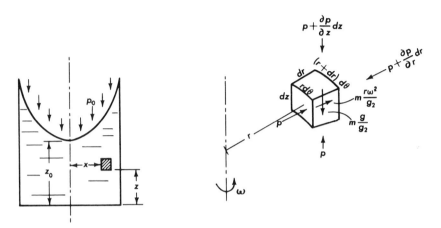

Fig. 20.35 Body of Fluid under Uniform Angular Spin.

an element of fluid, and show by means of a balance of forces in the vertical direction that

$$\frac{\partial p}{\partial z} = -\rho \frac{g}{g_c}$$

(b) Show that a balance of forces in the radial direction gives

$$\frac{\partial p}{\partial r} = \frac{\rho r \omega^2}{g_c}$$

(c) From

$$dp = \frac{\partial p}{\partial z} dz + \frac{\partial p}{\partial r} dr = -\rho \frac{g}{g_c} dz + \frac{\rho r \omega^2}{g_c} dr$$

obtain

$$p = -\frac{\rho g}{g_c}(z - z_0) + \frac{\rho r^2 \omega^2}{2g_c} + p_0$$

where p_0 is the pressure at the free surface. Show also that the free surface is a paraboloid of revolution

$$z = z_0 + \frac{r^2 \omega^2}{2g}$$

20.4. It is known that, under ordinary circumstances, the amount of heat received by an element of the atmosphere from the ground is

$$Q = 0.119(T_g - T) \text{ Btu/lbm}$$

where T_g is the temperature of the ground and T is the temperature of the element at elevation z. From the first law of thermodynamics, show that the variation of the temperature with the elevation is given by

$$T = T_g - 3.566 \times 10^{-3}z$$

20.5. (a) Develop the following hydrostatic equation for a compressible fluid such as the atmosphere:

$$dp + \rho \frac{g}{g_c} dz = 0$$

(b) It is known that in the first 35,600 ft, the temperature of the atmosphere decreases linearly with altitude at the rate of $dT/dz = -\lambda = -0.003566R/\text{ft}$. This is known as the *lapse rate* (cf. Prob. 20.4). Show that

$$dp - \frac{\rho g \, dT}{\lambda g_c} = dp - \frac{p}{R\lambda} \cdot \frac{g}{g_c} \cdot \frac{dT}{T} = 0$$

and that this leads to

$$\frac{p}{\rho^n} = \text{constant}$$

where $n = 1/[1 - (g_c/g)R\lambda]$. (c) Show that the relationship between pressure and altitude (up to 35,600 ft) is given by

$$z - z_0 = \frac{T_0}{\lambda} \left[1 - \left(\frac{p}{p_0} \right)^{R\lambda g_c / g} \right]$$

where p_0 and T_0 are the values of p and T at the sea level z_0.

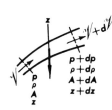

Fig. 20.36

20.6. Consider a frictionless steady-flow in an infinitesimal streamtube as shown in Fig. 20.36. Show from the momentum theorem, that

$$dp + \frac{\rho}{g_c} \mathscr{V} d\mathscr{V} + \rho \frac{g}{g_c} dz = 0$$

Integrate this equation for an incompressible fluid.

20.7. A turbomachine is a device which utilizes the forces resulting from the interaction of a fluid with a moving vane. If work is done by the fluid on the vane, the device is a turbine. If, on the other hand, work is done by the vane on the fluid, the device is known as a pump or compressor. Consider a vane with a turning angle θ as shown in Fig. 20.37. The jet leaves the nozzle with a velocity $\mathscr{V}$. The velocity of the vane is u, so that the mass rate of flow striking the vane is

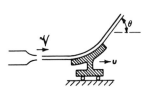

Fig. 20.37 Velocity Diagram for Moving Vane.

$pA(\mathscr{V} - u)$, where A is the area of the fluid stream. Determine the change in momentum based either on the absolute entering and leaving velocities or on the relative entering and leaving velocities, and obtain in both cases,

$$F = \frac{\rho A}{g_c}(\mathscr{V}-u)^2(1-\cos\theta)$$

Show that the work done is a maximum when $u/\mathscr{V} = 1/3$.

In an actual turbomachine, vanes are mounted all around the periphery of a wheel, so that the fluid deflected by the entire vane system is $\rho\mathscr{V}A$. For such a case, show that the work done is a maximum when $u/\mathscr{V} = 1/2$.

20.8. An ideal, incompressible fluid has velocity components in the x and y directions given by

$$u = x^2-y^2+2xy$$

$$v = xy+yz+z^2$$

Find the velocity in the z direction which satisfies the continuity equation. Is the solution unique?

20.9. Calculate the velocity of sound at 60 °F for the following media: (a) air, (b) hydrogen, (c) liquid water having a bulk modulus $\beta = \rho(dp/d\rho) = 300,000$ psi.

20.10. (a) The atmospheric temperature is 10 °F at the altitude where a turbojet aircraft is flying at 660 mph. Find the stagnation temperature. (b) The area of the intake scoop on a turbojet is 4.2 ft², and the area of the tail pipe is 6 ft². The aircraft is travelling at 500 mph and the combustion products leave the tail pipe with $M = 1.20$. The atmospheric pressure is 12 psia and the temperature is 0 °F. Find the net thrust which may be used to overcome friction and drag forces.

20.11. Photographs taken of a bullet in flight show that at a distance from the bullet, the total included angle of the shock cone is 50°. The pressure and temperature of the undisturbed air are 14.7 psia and 70 °F respectively. Determine the velocity and Mach number of the bullet relative to the undisturbed air.

20.12. Calculate the highest possible velocity which can result from the expansion of air at standard temperature of 60 °F and compare this with the velocity of sound propagation at the same temperature. Does the limitation of maximum possible velocity from a given reservoir also limit the speed of an aircraft?

20.13. (a) The stagnation properties are related to the entropy change by the fundamental equation of thermodynamics:

$$T_0ds = dh_0-v_0dp$$

From this, show that for a perfect gas,

$$\frac{p_{02}}{p_{01}} = e^{(s_1-s_2)/R}$$

(b) Show that the stagnation pressure is given by

$$p_0 = p\left[1 + \frac{\gamma-1}{2}M^2\right]^{\gamma/(\gamma-1)}$$

and therefore

$$\frac{p_2}{p_1} = \left[\frac{1 + [(\gamma-1)/2]M_1^2}{1 + [(\gamma-1)/2]M_2^2}\right]^{\gamma/(\gamma-1)} e^{(s_1-s_2)/R}$$

20.14. A certain missile travels with a Mach number of 7.0 at an altitude of 150,000 ft where the temperature is 537 °R. Determine the temperature at the nose of the missile. What is the ratio of stagnation pressure to static pressure?

20.15. Show that, for compressible flow,

$$p_0 = p + \tfrac{1}{2}\rho\frac{\mathscr{V}^2}{g_c}\left(1 + \frac{M^2}{4} + \frac{2-\gamma}{24}M^4 + \ldots\right)$$

and compare this with Bernouilli's equation for incompressible flow,

$$p_0 = p + \frac{1}{2}\frac{\rho\mathscr{V}^2}{g_c}$$

by plotting $p_0 - p$ versus Mach number for both equations. What relation does this problem have with an aircraft speed indicator?

20.16. In the vicinity of a wall, shear stresses reduce the fluid velocity to zero right at the wall. The deceleration of the fluid layers near the wall causes an increase in enthalpy, and therefore in temperature. The fluid temperature at the wall T_w is called the *adiabatic wall temperature*. Since the pressure is considered to be constant along a line normal to the wall, T_w is located at the intersection of the constant enthalpy line drawn from h_0 and the isobaric line passing through point *a*, representing the state of the flowing fluid. For the case of a perfect gas the adiabatic wall temperature and the stagnation temperature are equal as shown in Fig. 20.38. For the general case of any fluid, this is not so. Why? Discuss the answer by means of a *h–s* diagram.

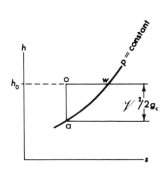

Fig. 20.38 Concept of Adiabatic Wall Temperature.

20.17. Air is supplied at 80 psia and 340 °F to a nozzle with an exit area of 10 sq in. The discharge pressure is 50 psia. Assuming no loss, determine the discharge temperature, the discharge velocity and Mach number, and the mass flow.

20.18. (a) Steam expands adiabatically in a nozzle under steady-flow conditions from a stagnation pressure and stagnation temperature of 290 psia and 700 °F to a static pressure and temperature of 145 psia and 560 °F. Determine the exit velocity and the change in specific entropy. (b) Water, under steady-flow conditions, has its pressure increased at constant volume from a stagnation pressure of 15 psia to a stagnation pressure of 30 psia. What power is required for a flow of 10 gpm?

20.19. For a given inlet condition, the isentropic flow through a convergent-divergent nozzle has two possible solutions. (Fig. 20.39.) For the exit pressure p_a, the divergent portion of the nozzle acts as a subsonic diffuser to compress the gas isentropically. For the exit pressure p_b, the divergent portion acts as a supersonic nozzle to further expand the gas isentropically. Show, by combining the energy equation, the ideal-gas equation of state, the continuity equation, and the definition of the Mach number, that this is so, and obtain

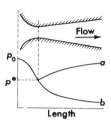

Fig. 20.39 The Two Possible Solutions of Isentropic Flow.

$$\frac{A}{A^*} = \frac{1}{M}\left[\left(\frac{2}{\gamma+1}\right)\left(1 - \frac{\gamma-1}{2}M^2\right)\right]^{(\gamma+1)/2(\gamma-1)}$$

Note that two different values of M, one greater than unity and the other less than unity, satisfy this equation for any A/A^*.

20.20. A nozzle is to be designed for expanding steam from 250 psia and 600 °F at the rate of 2.2 lbm/sec. The exit pressure is 40 psia. Assuming the initial velocity to be negligible and the flow to be isentropic, compute the velocity and the area at sections where the pressure is 150, 100, 80, and 40 psia respectively. (Make use of the Mollier chart.)

20.21. Steam enters a nozzle at 760 psia and 900 °F. The velocity leaving the nozzle is 2400 fps and the nozzle efficiency η is 90 per cent. Assuming inlet velocity is negligible and that

$$\eta = \frac{(\Delta h)_{\text{actual}}}{(\Delta h)_{\text{ideal}}},$$

find the entropy increase between the inlet and discharge states.

20.22. Air is supplied at 80 psia and 340 °F to a nozzle with an exit area of 10 sq in. Assuming a velocity coefficient of 0.9, find the discharge temperature, the discharge velocity and Mach number, the mass flow, and the entropy increase. The discharge pressure is 50 psia. (Compare the results of this problem with those of Prob. 20.17.)

20.23. Show that for a nozzle having an efficiency η between the inlet and any station downstream, the relation between pressure and Mach number is given by

$$\frac{p}{p_0} = \left[1 - \frac{1}{\eta}\cdot\frac{[(\gamma-1)/2]M^2}{1+[(\gamma-1)/2]M^2}\right]^{\gamma/(\gamma-1)}$$

20.24. Air flows through a duct of area 0.8 sq. ft at a velocity of 750 feet per second. If the temperature is 140 °F, and the pressure is 50 psia, what is the area of the minimum section downstream which will assure that this flow is "choked"?

20.25. A diffuser having an area ratio of 0.5 has an inlet Mach number of 0.65 and an exit Mach number of 0.30. Find (a) the ratio of the inlet stagnation pressure to the exit stagnation pressure, (b) the entropy increase.

20.26. A certain diffuser has an area ratio of 1.5 to 1. The initial Mach number is 0.7. Determine the ratio of the final pressure to the initial pressure if (a) the diffuser is 100 per cent efficient, (b) the diffuser is 90 per cent efficient.

20.27. (a) In laminar flow, the viscous shear stress, τ, is found to be proportional to the velocity gradient, du/dy, so that

$$\tau \sim \frac{du}{dy} = \mu\frac{du}{dy}$$

The constant of proportionality, μ is called the *absolute viscosity*. Its units are lbf-sec/ft². In mass units, this becomes

$$\mu\left[\frac{\text{lbf-sec}}{\text{ft}^2}\right] \times \left[32.2\frac{\text{lbm ft}}{\text{lbf sec}^2}\right] = \mu\left[\frac{\text{lbm}}{\text{ft-sec}}\right]$$

In the metric system, viscosity is expressed in units of the poise or centipoise (1/100 poise), where 1 poise = 1gm(mass)/cm-sec. At atmospheric pressure and 80 °F, the absolute viscosity of water is 0.0005778 lbm/ft-sec. Express this in centipoises. (b) It is often convenient to define a property referred to as the *kinematic viscosity*. This is the ratio of the absolute viscosity to the fluid density:

$$\nu = \frac{\mu}{\rho}$$

Its units are ft²/sec. In the metric system, the units of kinematic viscosity is the stoke or centistoke (1/100 stoke), where 1 stoke = 1 cm²/sec.

At atmospheric pressure and 80 °F, the density of water is 62.2 lbm/ft². What is the kinematic viscosity in centistokes?

20.28. Two parallel plates are 0.04 in. apart. One plate is moving relative to the other at a rate of 2.6 ft/sec. The shear stress on one plate is 0.72 psi. Determine (a) the rate of angular deformation of the fluid between the plates, (b) the viscosity.

20.29. (a) Consider an element of incompressible viscous fluid flowing in a pipe as shown in Fig. 20.40. From a balance of forces in the x-direction obtain

$$\tau dx = -\frac{r}{2}dp \tag{1}$$

For fully developed flow, τ is independent of x; furthermore if r is equal to the

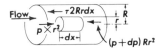

Fig. 20.40 Element of Fluid in Viscous Flow.

pipe radius R, the shear stress becomes the wall shear stress τ_w, and Eq. (1) may be integrated between O and L to give the pressure drop

$$\Delta p = \frac{2\tau_w L}{R} \tag{2}$$

From dimensional analysis, the wall shear stress is given in terms of the friction factor f as

$$\tau_w = f\frac{\rho \mathscr{V}^2}{2g_c} \tag{3}$$

so that Eqs. (2) and (3) combine to yield the well-known Darcy–Fanning equation

$$\Delta p = 4f\frac{L}{D}\frac{\rho \mathscr{V}^2}{2g_c} \tag{4}$$

(b) Water at 70°F flows through a 2 in. pipe having a roughness ratio of 0.02. The average velocity of the water is 10 ft/sec. Determine: (a) the Reynolds number, (b) the pressure loss due to friction in the pipe.

20.30. Consider an incompressible fluid flowing through a circular pipe. For fully developed laminar flow, shown that the velocity distribution is given by

$$\mathscr{V} = \mathscr{V}_{\max}\left(1 - \frac{r^2}{a^2}\right) = 2\mathscr{V}_{\mathrm{av}}\left(1 - \frac{r^2}{a^2}\right)$$

where $\mathscr{V}$ is the velocity at any radius r, $\mathscr{V}_{\max}$ is the velocity at the pipe axis, $\mathscr{V}_{\mathrm{av}}$ is the average velocity at the cross-section, and a is the radius of the pipe. Show that the kinetic energy for a flow rate of m pounds per second is

$$\frac{m}{g_c}\mathscr{V}_{\mathrm{av}}^2$$

20.31. Show that for the incompressible flow of a perfect gas in an insulated pipe, the fractional pressure drop due to frictional effects is given by

$$\frac{p_1 - p_2}{p_1} = \frac{\gamma M_1^2}{2}4f\frac{L}{D}$$

20.32. For most supersonic flow, the coefficient of friction f is between 0.002 and 0.003. This is in contrast to incompressible flow for which the friction factor is between 0.003 and 0.0065. Consider an air stream being decelerated from $M = 3$ to $M = 1$ in a 2 in. I.D. pipe having a friction factor of 0.002. Find the length of pipe.

20.33. In the study of fluid-flow problems, the following dimensionless groups have been found to be useful:

Reynolds number: $\dfrac{\rho \mathscr{V} l}{\mu}$ Froude number: $\dfrac{\rho \mathscr{V}^2}{(\rho g L)/g_c}$

Mach number: $\dfrac{\mathscr{V}}{a}$ Weber number: $\dfrac{\rho \mathscr{V}^2 L}{\sigma}$

$$\text{Euler number:} \quad \frac{\Delta p}{(\rho \mathscr{V}^2)/g_c} \qquad \text{Cauchy number:} \quad \frac{\rho \mathscr{V}^2}{E}$$

where σ is the surface tension, E is the elastic modulus, and the other quantities are as previously defined. The Reynolds number is the ratio of inertia forces to viscous forces; the Mach number is the ratio of the local velocity to the velocity of sound propagation; the Euler number is the ratio of pressure to inertia forces; the Froude number is the ratio of inertia forces to gravity forces; the Weber number is the ratio of inertia forces to surface tension forces; the Cauchy number the square of the Mach number. To these dimensionless numbers, should be added the geometric ratio, which is merely an expression of the shape or geometry of an object.

An important application of dimensional analysis is the study of models instead of full-scale mock-ups of a proposed design. Thus, the airplane designer tests small-scale models in a wind tunnel; the naval architect tests boat models in a towing basin; and the civil engineer studies rivers, harbors, and dams by using a scale of say, 1 ft of model to 1000 ft of prototype. To obtain complete dynamic similarity between geometrically similar model and prototype, the ratio of all forces: pressure, gravity, inertia, viscous, elastic, and surface tension must be the same for the model and the prototype. This means that all the above mentioned parameters must be the same for the model and the prototype; a realization that is impossible to achieve. Fortunately, in any one problem, some of the parameters do not play an important part and they may be neglected. For example, in low-speed flow problems, only the Reynolds number need be made the same for model and prototype. In high-speed flow problems, the Cauchy or Mach number must be the same for model and prototype. In the study of ship hulls, on the other hand, inertia, gravity, and viscous forces all play an important role, so that the Reynolds number and the Froude number must be the same for model and prototype.

A 1:10 scale model of an ICBM is to be tested in a supersonic wind tunnel using nitrogen as the atmosphere; the nitrogen is being contained in a large tank at a pressure of 2100 psia and a temperature of 120 °F. To what pressure must the nitrogen be expanded if the missile prototype is to travel at a Mach number of 2.2 at 60,000 ft?

20.34. In Sec. 20.12, the following equation was derived:

$$\frac{\mathscr{V} d\mathscr{V}}{g_c} + \frac{dp}{\rho} + 4f \frac{\mathscr{V}^2}{2g_c D} dx = \frac{\rho \mathscr{V} d\mathscr{V}}{p} + \frac{dp}{p} + 4f \frac{\rho \mathscr{V}^2}{2g_c p D} dx = 0$$

Show that for a perfect gas flowing in a constant area duct, this becomes

$$4f \frac{dx}{D} = \frac{2(1-M^2)dM}{\gamma M^3 \{[(\gamma-1)/2]M^2 + 1\}}$$

which integrates into

$$\int_{x=0}^{x=L_{\max}} 4f \frac{dx}{D} = 4f \frac{L_{\max}}{D} = \int_M^1 \frac{2(1-M^2)dM}{\gamma M^3 \{[(\gamma-1)/2]M^2+1\}}$$

20.35. Determine the pressure loss due to friction in a 12 inch diameter galvanized iron duct, 100 ft long, carrying 1000 cfm of air at 76 °F, and 14.7 psia.

20.36. Air is flowing in an insulated duct with a Mach number of 0.26. At a section down stream the entropy is greater (as a result of friction) by an amount of 0.032 Btu/lbm-°R. What is the Mach number, velocity, and pressure at this section? Initially the air is at 100 psia and 140 °F.

20.37. Air at 190 psia and 540 °F is flowing in an insulated duct with a velocity of 600 ft/sec. (a) Find the temperature in this duct where the pressure has dropped to 150 psia as a result of friction. (b) If the duct has a diameter of 6 in. and if the friction factor is 0.02, find the distance between the two points.

20.38. A perfect gas flows in an insulated pipe. Show that when "choking" due to friction takes place, the pressure at the choking condition is given by

$$p^* = \rho v \sqrt{\frac{R}{\gamma} \cdot \frac{2T_0}{\gamma+1}}$$

20.39. Air enters the combustion chamber of a jet with a velocity of 360 ft/sec, a temperature of 140 °F and a pressure of 50 psia. If 200 Btu per pound of air are added through the combustion process, find, (a) The stagnation temperature after combustion (assume constant specific heats, with $c_p = 0.24$ Btu/lbm-°R and $\gamma = 1.4$), (b) The Mach number, the temperature, the pressure, and the velocity after combustion.

20.40. Air is flowing in a constant area frictionless duct with a Mach number of 1.5. The stagnation temperature and stagnation pressure are 1060 °R and 100 psia respectively. By means of a cooling process the stagnation temperature is brought to 850 °R. Find the Mach number, the pressure, and temperature after cooling.

20.41. The amount of heat which may be added to a flow system is given by

$$q = c_p(T_{02} - T_{01})$$

From this is obtained the heat ratio

$$\frac{q}{c_p T_1} = \frac{T_{01}}{T_1}\left(\frac{T_{02}}{T_{01}} - 1\right) \tag{1}$$

Equation (1) is known as Damköhler's second ratio. Substituting for T_{01}/T_1, its equivalent in terms of M_1, and letting $M_2 = 1$, show that the maximum heat transfer ratio is

$$\frac{q_{max}}{c_p T_1} = \frac{(M^2 - 1)^2}{2M^2(\gamma+1)}$$

Plot $q_{max}/c_p T_1$ against M and show that

$$\frac{q_{max}}{c_p T_1} \to \infty$$

as $M \to 0$. How much heat is required to accelerate a very slow flow?

20.42. (a) Derive the asymptotic forms of the simple T_0 change formulas for low Mach numbers. (b) Show that at Mach numbers less than 0.2, changes in density are due almost exclusively to changes in temperature.

20.43. An athodyd is dropped from the belly of a mother plane and starts in standard air (60 °F) with a Mach number of 0.5. The combustion chamber of the athodyd is of the constant-area can type, with an allowable exit stagnation temperature of 2600 °R after combustion. Assuming friction to be negligible, determine: (a) whether or not there will be initial choking, (b) the new entrance Mach number after the flow has readjusted itself in the athodyd. Hint: First find T_0^* corresponding to a Mach number of 0.5. If 2600 °R is greater than T_0^*, choking will occur. To find the new entrance Mach number after the flow readjusts itself, find the static temperature T_2 at exit, then from

$$\frac{(T/T^*)_2}{(T/T^*)_1} = \frac{T_2}{T_1}$$

find the new $(T/T^*)_1$. Of course, $(T/T^*)_2 = 1 = M_2$. The new entrance Mach number is the Mach number corresponding to $(T/T^*)_1$.

20.44. A certain nozzle is designed for an isentropic-flow exit Mach number of 2.0. When this nozzle exhausts to a pressure above the design value a shock appears. Find the pressure ratio (exit pressure to inlet pressure) which locates the shock at a point halfway down the diverging section of the nozzle. Also, find the entropy increase and the nozzle efficiency.

20.45. An air nozzle is designed for a Mach number of 2.5. The inlet stagnation pressure is 100 psia. What must be the change in exhaust pressure to move the shock wave from the throat to the exit section?

20.46. A diffuser having an inlet Mach number of 1.6 diverges uniformly to an area 1.5 times the inlet area. The exit Mach number under actual operating conditions is 0.4. Determine (a) the shock location, (b) the entropy increase, (c) the diffuser efficiency.

20.47. The total or stagnation pressure may be measured by means of a Pitot tube with the open end facing the flowstream. Consider a Pitot tube to be used in air streams of $M = 0.4$ and $M = 1.5$ respectively, and atmospheric pressure. What is the stagnation pressure obtained in the two cases?

20.48. From the well-known Tds equation of thermodynamics:

$$s_2 - s_1 = c_p \ln \frac{T_2}{T_1} - R \ln \frac{p_2}{p_1}$$

which may be written as

$$\frac{s_2 - s_1}{R} = \ln \left[\left(\frac{p_2}{p_1}\right)^{1/(\gamma-1)} \left(\frac{p_2}{p_1}\right)^{-\gamma/(\gamma-1)} \right]$$

show that the entropy change in terms of the Mach number is given by

$$\frac{s_2-s_1}{R} = \ln\left[1+\frac{2\gamma}{\gamma+1}(M_1{}^2-1)\right]^{1/(\gamma-1)}\left[\frac{(\gamma+1)M_1{}^2}{(\gamma-1)M_1{}^2+2}\right]^{-[\gamma/(\gamma-1)]}$$

Letting $M_1{}^2-1 = m$, this becomes

$$\frac{s_2-s_1}{R} = \ln\left\{\left[\left(1+\frac{2\gamma}{\gamma+1}m\right)\right]^{1/(\gamma-1)}(1+m)^{-[\gamma/(\gamma-1)]}\left(\frac{\gamma-1}{\gamma+1}m+1\right)^{\gamma/(\gamma-1)}\right\}$$

For $M_1 \to 1$, m is very small, so that each term in parenthesis is like $1+\epsilon$, with $\epsilon \ll 1$. Thus, the logarithmic product rule yields three terms of the type $\ln(1+\epsilon)$ which has the series expansion $\epsilon-(\epsilon^2/2)+(\epsilon^3/3)- \ldots$ This gives

$$\frac{s_2-s_1}{R} = \frac{2\gamma}{(\gamma+1)^2}\frac{m^3}{3}+ \ldots \approx \frac{2\gamma}{3(\gamma+1)^2}(M_1{}^2-1)^3$$

Verify the statement made in Sec. 20.15 that a shock occurs only from supersonic ($M_1 \geq 1$) to subsonic flow. (The entropy can only increase in an adiabatic process.)

20.49. In Prob. 20.48, it was shown that, for weak shocks, the entropy increase is given by

$$\frac{s_y-s_x}{R} = \frac{2\gamma}{3(\gamma+1)^2}(M_x{}^2-1)^3 \tag{1}$$

The relation between entropy increase and stagnation pressure ratio, on the other hand, was established in Prob. 20.13 as

$$\exp\left(\frac{s_y-s_x}{R}\right) = \frac{p_{0x}}{p_{0y}} \tag{2}$$

Using the expansion $e^x = 1+x+x^2/2!+x^3/3!+ \ldots$, show that Eqs. (1) and (2) combine to give, for the case of a weak shock in air,

$$\frac{p_{0x}-p_{0y}}{p_{0x}} \cong 1.3(M_x-1)^3$$

CHAPTER 21

Thermodynamics of Special Systems: Elastic, Electric, Magnetic, Surface, and Radiating Systems

21.1 Other Coordinates

In the present study of thermodynamics, attention until now has been focused mainly on systems whose equilibrium states can be described in terms of the coordinates p, V, and T. For such systems, the forces taken into account in calculating the work done are usually those arising from the pressure, so that during an infinitesimal process the work is given by $dW = pdV$. In other words, p is the intensive coordinate, V the extensive co-ordinate, and p is the force conjugate to the displacement dV.

The laws of thermodynamics, however, are of sufficient generality to include force fields other than pressure, such as electric, magnetic, gravitational, and radiation fields. It may be pointed out that only for certain class of problems are the pressure and the volume the most convenient variables to use. Other variables, such as the linear extension of a string, or the magnetization per unit volume of a substance, may be more convenient to adopt. Moreover, two variables chosen from p, V, and T no longer completely determine the state of a system when electric, magnetic, and gravitational effects are present. It is the objective in this chapter to introduce some variables other than pressure, and to develop a number of useful relations (such as Maxwell equations and Tds equations) for several specialized systems.

21.2 Generalized Work

As previously pointed out, for systems whose states are describable in terms of p, V, and T, the work done during an infinitesimal process is given by $dW = pdV$. (Such systems are often called chemical systems.) Recall that the concept of work can be generalized by means of the following statement: Work $F_r dx_r$ is done by a system if, during a displacement of the coordinate x_r, the product $F_r dx_r$ can be reflected solely in the rise of a weight. Here are the expressions for the work associated with various systems:

TABLE 21.1 APPROPRIATE COORDINATES FOR DIFFERENT SYSTEMS

System	Generalized force	Generalized displacement	Work done
Chemical	Pressure, p	Volume change, dv	pdv
Elastic bar	Stress, σ	Strain, $d\epsilon$	$-\sigma d\epsilon$
Stretched wire	Tension, τ	Extension, dL	$-\tau dL$
Reversible cell	Electromotive force, $\mathscr{E}$	Charge, dQ_e	$-\mathscr{E}dQ_e$
Capacitor	Voltage, V	Charge, dQ_e	$-VdQ_e$
Dielectric	Applied field, E	Polarization, $d\mathscr{P}$	$-Ed\mathscr{P}$
Magnetic	Magnetic field, $\mathscr{H}$	Magnetization, $d\mathscr{M}$	$-\mathscr{H}d\mathscr{M}$

For the general case of a system which cannot be completely described by two variables chosen from p, v, T, but in addition requires electric, magnetic, etc. effects to be taken into account, the first law of thermodynamics takes on the form

$$dq = de + (pdv - \mathscr{E}dQ_e - \mathscr{H}d\mathscr{M} - \ldots)$$

$$= de + \sum_{r=1}^{n} F_r dx_r \tag{21.1}$$

where e is now a function of $x_1, x_2, \ldots x_n$, and T. Equation (21.1) may be written in the form of

$$dq = \left(\frac{\partial e}{\partial T}\right)_{x_1, x_2, \ldots x_n} dT + \sum_{r=1}^{n}\left[F_r + \left(\frac{\partial e}{\partial x_r}\right)_{T, x_1 \ldots x_{j \neq r}, \ldots x_n}\right]dx_r$$

This in turn, enables the entropy to be written as

$$ds = \frac{1}{T}\left(\frac{\partial e}{\partial T}\right)_{x_1, x_2, \ldots x_n} dT + \frac{1}{T}\sum_{r=1}^{n}\left[F_r + \left(\frac{\partial e}{\partial x_r}\right)_{T, x_1, \ldots x_{j \neq r}, \ldots x_n}\right]dx_r \qquad (21.2)$$

The condition that ds should be an exact differential can now be applied to the various terms of Eq. (21.2), taking two at a time. There is obtained two sets of equations, those including the first term and those excluding it:

$$\frac{1}{T}\frac{\partial}{\partial x_r}\left(\frac{\partial e}{\partial T}\right)_{x_1, \ldots x_n} = \frac{\partial}{\partial T}\left[\frac{F_r}{T} + \frac{1}{T}\left(\frac{\partial e}{\partial x_r}\right)_{T, x_1, \ldots x_{j \neq r}, \ldots x_n}\right] \qquad (21.3)$$

$$\frac{\partial}{\partial x_s}\left[F_r + \left(\frac{\partial e}{\partial x_r}\right)_{T, x_1, \ldots x_{j \neq r}, \ldots x_n}\right] = \frac{\partial}{\partial x_r}\left[F_s + \left(\frac{\partial e}{\partial x_s}\right)_{T, x_1, \ldots x_{j \neq s}, \ldots x_n}\right] \qquad (21.4)$$

Since $\dfrac{\partial^2 e}{\partial x_s \partial x_r} = \dfrac{\partial^2 e}{\partial x_r \partial x_s}$, the latter set of equations reduce to

$$\frac{\partial F_r}{\partial x_s} = \frac{\partial F_s}{\partial x_r} \qquad (21.5)$$

Equation (21.5) implies that the forces F_r are *conservative*, for it is recalled that for a conservative system,

$$\oint \sum_{r=1}^{n} F_r dx_r = 0$$

and this is equivalent to saying that $x_1, x_2, \ldots x_n$ are all derivable from a potential ϕ $(x_1, x_2, \ldots x_n, T)$ such that

$$F_r = -\left(\frac{\partial \phi}{\partial x_r}\right)_{T, x_1, \ldots x_{j \neq r}, \ldots x_n}$$

But this equation leads to

$$\frac{\partial F_r}{\partial x_s} = \frac{\partial F_s}{\partial x_r}$$

for any pair of values r and s. This is precisely the condition represented by Eq. (21.5). In other words, for a process to be reversible, the forces involved must be conservative.

As for the set of equations (21.3), they are expanded and reduced to

$$\frac{1}{T}\left(\frac{\partial^2 e}{\partial x_r \partial T}\right) = -\frac{F_r}{T^2} + \frac{1}{T}\left(\frac{\partial F_r}{\partial T}\right) - \frac{1}{T^2}\left(\frac{\partial e}{\partial x_r}\right) + \frac{1}{T}\left(\frac{\partial^2 e}{\partial T \partial x_r}\right)$$

or

$$\frac{\partial e}{\partial x_r} = T\left(\frac{\partial F_r}{\partial T}\right) - F_r \tag{21.6}$$

Equation (21.6) is of great interest and generality in thermodynamics. It enables the energy e of a system to be determined from a single thermal measurement if the variation of the generalized forces F_r with respect to T is known (equivalent to knowing the equation of state). For a particular $x_r = v$, it gives

$$\left(\frac{\partial e}{\partial v}\right) = T\left(\frac{\partial p}{\partial T}\right) - p \tag{21.7}$$

This is recognized to be one of the well-known relations previously obtained in Chap. 11.

The above illustrates the power and general applicability of thermodynamic principles. In many cases, even when forces other than hydrostatic pressure are present, the number of coordinates F_r and x_r need not be very large, so that the mathematical manipulation can be kept fairly short. The analysis of a number of special systems in the following sections will bear this out.

21.3 Elastic System

Having developed specific expressions for the work, the thermodynamics of various special systems will now be discussed. Consider first the thermodynamics of an elastic bar. The description of the system will be in terms of the following coordinates:†

$$\text{stress: } \sigma = F/A$$
$$\text{strain: } \epsilon = \delta/L_0$$
$$\text{temperature: } T$$

The bar is acted upon by a force F as shown in Fig. (21.1). The initial length and elongation are L_0 and δ respectively. A is the cross-sectional area.

Fig. 21.1 Bar under Tension.

---

† The analysis given here is based on the work of Dr. P. Chenea, Purdue University.

When the bar undergoes an infinitesimal change from one state of equilibrium to another, such as a change in length, the change may be written as

$$de = \left(\frac{\partial \epsilon}{\partial T}\right)_\sigma dT + \left(\frac{\partial \epsilon}{\partial \sigma}\right)_T d\sigma \qquad (21.8)$$

It is convenient to introduce the following coefficients:

$$\text{Linear expansivity: } \alpha = \frac{\partial \epsilon}{\partial T} \qquad (21.9)$$

$$\text{Young's isothermal modulus: } Y = \left(\frac{\partial \sigma}{\partial \epsilon}\right)_T \qquad (21.10)$$

$$\text{Specific heat at constant stress: } c_\sigma = \left(\frac{dq}{\partial T}\right)_\sigma \qquad (21.11)$$

$$\text{Specific heat at constant strain: } c_\epsilon = \left(\frac{dq}{dT}\right)_\epsilon \qquad (21.12)$$

For an infinitesimal change in length, the elemental work per unit volume is given by

$$dw = -\sigma d\epsilon$$

The minus sign is used because a positive value of $d\epsilon$ means an extension of the bar, for which work must be done *on* the system. The first law of thermodynamics based on a unit volume of the bar is thus

$$dq = du - \sigma d\epsilon \qquad (21.13)$$

The second law ($Tds = dq$), which defines the entropy change for a reversible process, then becomes

$$Tds = du - \sigma d\epsilon \qquad (21.14)$$

This is the fundamental equation for an elastic system as based on the first and second laws. From it, a number of useful relations may be developed.

First, the specific heat at constant strain may be obtained in terms of several variables:

$$c_\epsilon = \left(\frac{dq}{dT}\right)_\epsilon = T\left(\frac{\partial s}{\partial T}\right)_\epsilon = \left(\frac{\partial u}{\partial T}\right)_\epsilon \qquad (21.15)$$

To obtain a relation for the specific heat at constant stress, let the enthalpy function for an elastic bar to be introduced:

$$h = u - \sigma \epsilon \qquad (21.16)$$

Differentiating:

$$dh = du - \sigma d\epsilon - \epsilon d\sigma$$

Replacing $du - \sigma d\epsilon$ by Tds from Eq. (21.14), this becomes

$$dh = Tds - \epsilon d\sigma$$

or

$$Tds = dh + \epsilon d\sigma \tag{21.17}$$

The specific heat at constant stress thus becomes

$$c_\sigma = \left(\frac{dq}{dT}\right)_\sigma = T\left(\frac{\partial s}{\partial T}\right)_\sigma = \left(\frac{\partial h}{\partial T}\right)_\sigma \tag{21.18}$$

The Maxwell equations for an elastic bar are developed by introducing the Helmholtz and Gibbs functions

$$a = u - Ts \tag{21.19}$$

$$g = h - Ts = u - \sigma\epsilon - Ts \tag{21.20}$$

Differentiating and rearranging with the aid of Eq. (21.14) gives

$$da = du - Tds - sdT = du - (du - \sigma d\epsilon) - sdT$$

$$= \sigma d\epsilon - sdT \tag{21.21}$$

$$dg = du - \sigma d\epsilon - \epsilon d\sigma - Tds - sdT$$

$$= Tds - \epsilon d\sigma - Tds - sdT$$

$$= -\epsilon d\sigma - sdT \tag{21.22}$$

Equations (21.14), (21.17), (21.21), and (21.22) give the differential of the quantities u, h, a, and g. Since all these quantities are state functions, the condition for a perfect differential gives the *Maxwell relations* for an *elastic bar*:

$$\left(\frac{\partial T}{\partial \epsilon}\right)_s = \left(\frac{\partial \sigma}{\partial s}\right)_\epsilon \tag{21.23}$$

$$\left(\frac{\partial T}{\partial \sigma}\right)_s = -\left(\frac{\partial \epsilon}{\partial s}\right)_\sigma \tag{21.24}$$

$$\left(\frac{\partial \sigma}{\partial T}\right)_\epsilon = -\left(\frac{\partial s}{\partial \epsilon}\right)_T \tag{21.25}$$

$$\left(\frac{\partial \epsilon}{\partial T}\right)_\sigma = \left(\frac{\partial s}{\partial \sigma}\right)_T \tag{21.26}$$

To develop Tds equations for a thermoelastic system, consider s as a function of T and ϵ, and write

$$ds = \left(\frac{\partial s}{\partial T}\right)_\epsilon dT + \left(\frac{\partial s}{\partial \epsilon}\right)_T d\epsilon$$

or

$$Tds = T\left(\frac{\partial s}{\partial T}\right)_\epsilon dT + T\left(\frac{\partial s}{\partial \epsilon}\right)_T d\epsilon$$

But $T(\partial s/\partial T)_\epsilon = c_\epsilon$ by Eq. (21.15), and $(\partial s/\partial \epsilon)_T = -(\partial \sigma/\partial T)_\epsilon$ by Eq. (21.25), so that

$$Tds = c_\epsilon dT - T\left(\frac{\partial \sigma}{\partial T}\right)_\epsilon d\epsilon \qquad (21.27)$$

This is the Tds equation corresponding to T and ϵ as independent variables. Similarly if T and σ are chosen independent,

$$ds = \left(\frac{\partial s}{\partial T}\right)_\sigma dT + \left(\frac{\partial s}{\partial \sigma}\right)_T d\sigma$$

or

$$Tds = T\left(\frac{\partial s}{\partial T}\right)_\sigma dT + T\left(\frac{\partial s}{\partial \sigma}\right)_T d\sigma$$

But $T(\partial s/\partial T)_\sigma = c_\sigma$ by Eq. (21.18), and $(\partial s/\partial \sigma)_T = (\partial \epsilon/\partial T)_\sigma = \alpha$ by Eq. (21.9), so that

$$Tds = c_\sigma dT + \alpha T d\sigma \qquad (21.28)$$

Finally, to develop a relation for du in terms of the state variables σ, ϵ, T, their partial derivatives, and the specific heats, rewrite Eq. (21.14) as

$$du = Tds + \sigma d\epsilon$$

Making use of Eq. (21.27), this becomes

$$du = c_\epsilon dT + \left[\sigma - T\left(\frac{\partial \sigma}{\partial T}\right)_\epsilon\right] d\epsilon \qquad (21.29)$$

Example 21.1. An elastic bar undergoes a reversible adiabatic process from (T_0, ϵ_0) to (T, ϵ). Determine the relation between T, ϵ, T_0, and ϵ_0.

Solution. From Eq. (21.27)

$$Tds = 0 = c_\epsilon dT - T\left(\frac{\partial \sigma}{\partial T}\right)_\epsilon d\epsilon$$

or

$$c_\epsilon \frac{dT}{T} = \left(\frac{\partial \sigma}{\partial T}\right)_\epsilon d\epsilon$$

Letting $\beta = (\partial \sigma/\partial T)_\epsilon$, this becomes

$$c_\epsilon \frac{dT}{T} = \beta d\epsilon$$

Integration gives

$$c_\epsilon \ln \frac{T}{T_0} = \beta(\epsilon - \epsilon_0)$$

whence

$$\frac{T}{T_0} = e^{\beta(\epsilon - \epsilon_0)/c_\epsilon}$$

Example 21.2. A large class of elastometers (polymeric material of the rubber-like type) have a positive coefficient $(\partial\sigma/\partial T)_\epsilon$. Determine whether an elastic string heats up or cools when suddenly stretched.

Solution. Consider the stretching to be reversible adiabatic. From Eq. (21.27),

$$T ds = 0 = c_\epsilon dT - T\left(\frac{\partial\sigma}{\partial T}\right)_\epsilon d\epsilon$$

or

$$\left(\frac{\partial T}{\partial \epsilon}\right)_s = \frac{T}{c_\epsilon}\left(\frac{\partial\sigma}{\partial T}\right)_\epsilon$$

Now, T and c_ϵ are positive, so that $(\partial T/\partial\epsilon)_s$ and $(\partial\sigma/\partial T)_\epsilon$ have the same sign. Thus, if $(\partial\sigma/\partial T)_\epsilon$ is positive, the elastic string will heat up if suddenly stretched. Rubber behaves this way.

21.4 Surface Film

Let a wire frame equipped with a sliding cross-piece be dipped into a soap solution and a film be formed (Fig. 21.2). The surface tends, like a stretched membrane, to assume a shape of minimum area (corresponding to stable equilibrium). The film exerts an inward force on the frame and it is therefore necessary to apply a force F to the right to keep the cross piece in place. If the slider has length L, and the surface tension is $\mathscr{S}$, the total force is $2\mathscr{S}L$ (the film has two surfaces). For an infinitesimal displacement dx, the elemental work is

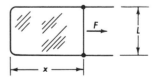

Fig. 21.2 Surface Film.

$$dW = -2\mathscr{S}L dx = \mathscr{S}dA \quad (21.30)$$

where $2\,Lds = dA$ is the total area. It is of interest to note that although the film area increases, the force F remains constant as long as the temperature is constant. The surface tension $\mathscr{S}$ depends only on the temperature, and in this respect a surface film *does not* act like a rubber membrane, for which the force increases with increasing area.

To obtain thermodynamic equations for a surface film, it is necessary merely to replace in the corresponding equation for a chemical system (described by p, V, and T), p by $-\mathscr{S}$, and V by A. For example, the following TdS equation for a chemical system:

$$TdS = C_V dT + T\left(\frac{\partial p}{\partial T}\right)_V dV$$

becomes, for a surface film,

$$TdS = C_A dT - T\left(\frac{\partial \mathscr{S}}{\partial T}\right)_A dA \qquad (21.31)$$

For an isothermal expansion, this simplifies to

$$TdS = dQ = -T\left(\frac{\partial \mathscr{S}}{\partial T}\right)_A dA$$

Let the surface film be expanded from a small initial area to a relatively large final area. Since $\mathscr{S}$ is function of T only, the above equation gives

$$Q = -T(A-0)\frac{d\mathscr{S}}{dT}$$

As for the work done, it is obtained from Eq. (21.30),

$$W = -\int_0^A \mathscr{S}\,dA = -\mathscr{S}(A-0)$$

Replacing Q and W by these values, the first law of thermodynamics ($Q = \Delta U + W$) becomes

$$-TA\frac{d\mathscr{S}}{dT} = (U-U_0) - \mathscr{S}A$$

or

$$\frac{U-U_0}{A} = \mathscr{S} - T\frac{d\mathscr{S}}{dT} \qquad (21.32)$$

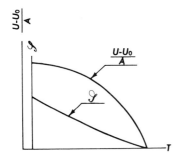

Fig. 21.3 Surface-energy per Unit Area and Surface-tension versus Temperature.

The left-hand side of Eq. (21.32) represents the surface energy per unit area. It has the same dimensions as $\mathscr{S}$, namely force per unit length. The surface energy may be obtained once the surface tension $\mathscr{S}$ has been measured as a function of temperature. The upper curve of Fig. 21.3 shows the surface energy for water as a function of T. The lower curve shows the surface tension.

Surface energy plays an important part in the kinetic theory of liquids. Vaporization is presumed to take place when a molecule of liquid acquires sufficient energy to break through the film at the surface of the liquid. The heat of vaporization and the surface energy are therefore related to each other. They vary with temperature in the same manner, both approaching zero at the critical temperature.

21.5 Dielectric System

Consider first a parallel plate capacitor with a vacuum between the plates [Fig. 21.4(a)], and let a charge Q_e be placed on the plates. The electrical field thus created is, according to electrostatics,

$$E = \frac{Q_e}{A\epsilon_0} \qquad (21.33)$$

where A is the area of the plates and ϵ_0 is the permittivity of free space. If L is the distance between the plates, the potential difference is

$$V = EL = \frac{Q_e}{A\epsilon_0}L \qquad (21.34)$$

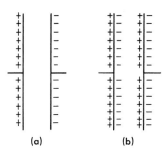

(a)　　　　(b)

Fig. 21.4

Polarization of a Dielectric.

and the capacity is

$$C = \frac{Q_e}{V} = \frac{A\epsilon_0}{L} \qquad (21.35)$$

For an increase of charge dQ_e, the work required is

$$dW = VdQ_e = \frac{L}{A\epsilon_0}Q_e dQ_e$$

or, by Eq. (21.34),

$$dW = (AL)\epsilon_0 EdE \qquad (21.36)$$

where the quantity AL represents the volume of the capacitor.

Now, let a dielectric material be placed between the plates. Under the influence of the applied field, the molecules of the dielectric orient themselves, their $+$ ends attracted towards the $-$ plate and their $-$ ends attracted toward the $+$ plate. There is no net charge in the interior of the material, but due to the rotation of the molecules, there is an excess charge at the edges [Fig. 21.4(b)]. The dielectric is said to be *polarized*. The electric intensity and the difference of potential between plates are reduced to

$$E = \frac{Q_e}{A\epsilon_0 K} \tag{21.37}$$

$$V = \frac{Q_e}{A\epsilon_0 K}L \tag{21.38}$$

and the capacity is increased to

$$C = \frac{Q_e}{V} = \frac{A\epsilon_0 K}{L} \tag{21.39}$$

where $K (= \epsilon/\epsilon_0)$ is the ratio of the permittivity of the material to that of free space. The work done in charging the capacitor is then

$$dW = VdQ_e = \frac{LQ_e}{A\epsilon_0 K}dQ_e = (AL)\epsilon_0 KEdE \tag{21.40}$$

Subtracting from this the work done on the free space [Eq. (21.36)] gives the work done in polarizing the material:

$$dW_{\text{polarization}} = (AL)\epsilon_0 KEdE - (AL)\epsilon_0 EdE$$

$$= (AL)(K-1)\epsilon_0 EdE = (AL)Ed\mathscr{P} \tag{21.41}$$

where $\mathscr{P} \equiv (K-1)\epsilon_0 E$ is the polarization or dipole moment per unit volume of material. Equation (21.41) represents the amount of work required to increase the polarization of the dielectric by $d\mathscr{P}$. In keeping with the conventional rule in thermodynamics that work required is negative, it would be written as

$$dW_{\text{polarization}} = -(AL)Ed\mathscr{P} \tag{21.42}$$

This shows, by comparison with a chemical system, that $-E$ corresponds to the pressure p and $(AL)d\mathscr{P}$ corresponds to volume change dV. Consequently, thermodynamic relations for a dielectric system may be easily obtained from those of a chemical system by replacing p by $-E$, and V by $Al\mathscr{P}$ (or v by $\mathscr{P}$). For example, the Tds equation

$$Tds = c_p dT - T\left(\frac{\partial v}{\partial T}\right)_p dp \tag{21.43}$$

becomes

$$Tds = c_E dT + T\left(\frac{\partial \mathscr{P}}{\partial T}\right)_E dE \tag{21.44}$$

Equation (21.44) may be applied for instance to a reversible adiabatic change of field, in which case $ds = 0$, and the temperature change accompanying the field change can be calculated. It may also be applied to an isothermal process for which the entropy change in relation to the polarization change may be found. Such effects are known as *pyroelectric* effects.

21.6 Piezoelectric System

The preceding section showed that a dielectric whose coordinates are E, $\mathscr{P}$, and T undergoes adiabatic temperature changes or isothermal entropy changes when the electric field or the polarization is changed. If, in addition the substance undergoes adiabatic temperature changes or isothermal entropy changes when the tension or the length is changed, then five coordinates are necessary to describe the system. A possible choice would be the stress σ, the strain ϵ, the electric field E, the polarization $\mathscr{P}$, and the temperature T. The work term then becomes $-\sigma d\epsilon - Ed\mathscr{P}$, and the combined first and second laws written as

$$Tds = du - \sigma d\epsilon - Ed\mathscr{P} \qquad (21.45)$$

A system described by Eq. (21.45) is often called a *piezoelectric* system. Its entropy is function of three variables, which may be any one of the following sets: (σ, E, T), $(\sigma, \mathscr{P}, T)$, (ϵ, E, T), or $(\epsilon, \mathscr{P}, T)$. Selecting the first set yields

$$ds = \left(\frac{\partial s}{\partial \sigma}\right)_{E,T} d\sigma + \left(\frac{\partial s}{\partial E}\right)_{\sigma,T} dE + \left(\frac{\partial s}{\partial T}\right)_{\sigma,E} dT$$

or

$$Tds = T\left(\frac{\partial s}{\partial \sigma}\right)_{E,T} d\sigma + T\left(\frac{\partial s}{\partial E}\right)_{\sigma,T} dE + T\left(\frac{\partial s}{\partial T}\right)_{\sigma,E} dT \qquad (21.46)$$

The last term on the right-hand side of Eq. (21.46) is recognized as the heat capacity at constant stress and constant field, i.e.,

$$T\left(\frac{\partial s}{\partial T}\right)_{\sigma,E} = c_{\sigma,E} \qquad (21.47)$$

Maxwell relations for a piezoelectric system may be obtained by means of the piezoelectric enthalpy and the piezoelectric Gibbs function:

$$h = u - \sigma\epsilon - Ed\mathscr{P} \qquad (21.48)$$

$$g = h - Ts = u - \sigma\epsilon - E\mathscr{P} - Ts \qquad (21.49)$$

The latter equation gives, upon differentiation,

$$dg = du - \sigma d\epsilon - \epsilon d\sigma - Ed\mathscr{P} - \mathscr{P}dE - Tds - sdT$$

Since $Tds = du - \sigma d\epsilon - E d\mathscr{P}$ by Eq. (21.45), this simplifies to

$$dg = -\epsilon d\sigma - \mathscr{P}dE - sdT \qquad (21.50)$$

Equation (21.50) yields the following relations:

At constant σ: $(dg)_\sigma = \mathscr{P}(dE)_\sigma - s(dT)_\sigma$

$$\left(\frac{\partial \mathscr{P}}{\partial T}\right)_{E,\sigma} = \left(\frac{\partial s}{\partial E}\right)_{T,\sigma} \qquad (21.51)$$

At constant E: $(dg)_E = -\epsilon(d\sigma)_E - s(dT)_E$

$$\left(\frac{\partial \epsilon}{\partial T}\right)_{\sigma,E} = \left(\frac{\partial s}{\partial \sigma}\right)_{T,E} \qquad (21.52)$$

At constant T: $(dg)_T = -\epsilon(d\sigma)_T - \mathscr{P}(dE)_T$

$$\left(\frac{\partial \epsilon}{\partial E}\right)_{\sigma,T} = \left(\frac{\partial \mathscr{P}}{\partial \sigma}\right)_{E,T} \qquad (21.53)$$

Equations (21.47), (21.51), and (21.52) allows Eq. (21.46) to be written as

$$Tds = c_{\sigma,\epsilon}dT + T\left(\frac{\partial \epsilon}{\partial T}\right)_{\sigma,E} d\sigma + T\left(\frac{\partial \mathscr{P}}{\partial T}\right)_{E,\sigma} dE \qquad (21.54)$$

This result may be used to calculate isothermal entropy changes or adiabatic temperature changes where σ or E are changed. Similarly, other Tds equations and Maxwell relations may be obtained by choosing different sets of variables.

The above development is a good illustration of the general case when several types of work are present and the Tds equation is written as

$$Tds = du + \sum_r F_r dx_r \qquad (21.55)$$

where

$$\sum_r F_r dx_r$$

represents all types of work, not just pdv work. In fact, there is no reason why the combined first and second laws could not have been written in the form of Eq. (21.55) from the very beginning of the study of thermodynamics, except that in the absence of motion, gravity, capillarity, electricity, magnetism, etc., the simpler expression $Tds = du + pdv$ is more convenient to work with.

21.7 Reversible Cell

Consider a reversible cell in which a chemical reaction is taking place. If dV is the change in volume and dQ_e is the charge generated, then the total work is $pdV - dQ_e$, and the TdS equation is

$$TdS = dU + pdV - \mathscr{E}dQ_e$$

where $\mathscr{E}$ is the emf. However, the change in volume is negligible in many cases, so that the above equation reduces to

$$TdS = dU - \mathscr{E}dQ_e$$

Thus, relations for a cell may be obtained quite simply from corresponding relations for a chemical system by replacing p by $-\mathscr{E}$ and V by Q_e.

For example, the TdS equation with T and V as independent variables:

$$TdS = T\left(\frac{\partial S}{\partial T}\right)_V dT + T\left(\frac{\partial S}{\partial T}\right)_V dV$$

$$= C_V dT + T\left(\frac{\partial p}{\partial T}\right)_V dV$$

is transformed into

$$TdS = C_{Q_e} dT - T\left(\frac{\partial \mathscr{E}}{\partial T}\right)_{Q_e} dQ_e$$

Furthermore, if the emf depends on the temperature only, as in the case of a saturated reversible cell, this becomes

$$TdS = C_{Q_e} dT - T\frac{d\mathscr{E}}{dT}dQ_e \tag{21.56}$$

Other TdS relations may be treated in the same manner.

An important relation, the Gibbs–Helmholtz equation for a reversible cell, will now be developed. Consider the reversible isothermal operation of a cell; Eq. (21.56) gives

$$T\Delta S = Q = -T\frac{d\mathscr{E}}{dT}(Q_{e2} - Q_{e1}) \tag{21.57}$$

Now, according to *Faraday's law*,[†]

$$Q_{e1} - Q_{e2} = n\mathscr{F} \tag{21.58}$$

---

† Faraday's law of electrolysis states that to deposit (or dissolve) one gram equivalent of any material at an electrode requires the passage of $\mathscr{F}$ ($= 96{,}500$) coulombs of electricity. The equivalent weight or gram equivalent n is the atomic weight of the element divided by its volume.

where n is the equivalent weight and $\mathscr{F}$ is the *Faraday constant*. Equation (21.57) thus becomes

$$Q = n\mathscr{F} T \frac{d\mathscr{E}}{dT} \tag{21.59}$$

During the process of transferring the quantity of electricity, the work done is

$$W = - \int_{Q_{e1}}^{Q_{e2}} \mathscr{E} dQ_e = -\mathscr{E}(Q_{e2} - Q_{e1})$$

or

$$W = n\mathscr{E}\mathscr{F} \tag{21.60}$$

With the aid of Eqs. (21.59) and (21.60), the first law of thermodynamics $Q = \Delta U + W$, becomes

$$n\mathscr{F} T \frac{d\mathscr{E}}{dT} = \Delta U + n\mathscr{E}\mathscr{F}$$

For a process taking place at constant pressure with negligible volume change, ΔU can be replaced by ΔH, since $\Delta H = \Delta U + p\Delta V + V\Delta p = \Delta U$. Thus,

$$n\mathscr{F} T \frac{d\mathscr{E}}{dT} = \Delta H + n\mathscr{E}\mathscr{F}$$

or

$$\Delta H = -n\mathscr{F}\left(\mathscr{E} - T \frac{d\mathscr{E}}{dT}\right) \tag{21.61}$$

Equation (21.61) is the *Gibbs–Helmholtz equation* pertaining to a *reversible cell*. One of its chief applications in thermodynamics is that it provides a method for determining thermodynamic properties from the measurement of electromotive force (which can be made with great accuracy). For example, in the case of the Daniell cell, the flow of current is accompanied by the reaction

$$Zn + CuSO_4 \rightarrow Cu + ZnSO_4$$

When $n\mathscr{F}$ coulombs of electricity are transferred, 1 mole of each of the initial constituents disappears, and 1 mole of each of the final constituents is formed. The enthalpy change (equal to the enthalpy of the final constituents minus the enthalpy of the initial constituents at the same temperature and pressure) is, by definition, the *heat of reaction*. If the reaction can be made to proceed in an electric cell, all that is necessary to determine the heat of reaction is to measure the cell potential and the temperature coefficient of the cell potential.

Reactions occurring in electrochemical cells with the production of electricity are of great interest in thermodynamics, because they can be carried out under conditions which are close to reversible. These conditions are achieved by balancing the electromotive force of the cell by an opposing emf which is just less than that of the cell. (This is done, for example, with the laboratory potentiometer, in which an external source of emf, such as a battery, is balanced against the standard cell.) Under these conditions, the current flow is very small, and irreversibilities such as voltage drop through the cell, changes in concentration due to passage of electricity, etc. are minimized.

Example 21.3. The heat of reaction, ΔH, for the reaction

$$Zn + CuSO_4 \rightarrow Cu + ZnSO_4$$

is $-55,200$ calories/mole at 273 °K as determined by calorimetric methods. Compare this with the result obtained from the emf of a Daniell cell at 273 °K, which is 1.0934 volts. The temperature coefficient of the emf is -4.53×10^{-4} volt/degree, and the valence is 2.

Solution. It is first recalled that 1 joule = (1 coulomb) (1 volt), and that 4.186 joules = 1 calorie. Hence, Eq. (21.61) becomes, if ΔH is to be expressed in calories and $\mathscr{E}$ in volts,

$$\Delta H = -n\mathscr{F}\left(\mathscr{E} - T\frac{d\mathscr{E}}{dT}\right)$$

$$= -n\left(\frac{96,500}{4.186}\right)\left(\mathscr{E} - T\frac{d\mathscr{E}}{dT}\right)$$

$$= -23,070(n)\left(\mathscr{E} - T\frac{d\mathscr{E}}{dT}\right)$$

With $n = 2$, $\mathscr{E} = 1.0934$, and $d\mathscr{E}/dT = -0.000453$, this gives

$$\Delta H = -(23,070)(2)[1.0934 - (273)(-0.000453)]$$

$$= -56,150$$

The minus sign indicates an exothermic reaction, i.e., a reaction in which heat is released.

Example 21.4. Strictly speaking, the work done in a reversible cell consists of pdV and $-\mathscr{E}dQ_e$ work as shown in Fig. 21.5. Using the 5 coordinates: p, V, T, $\mathscr{E}$, and Q_e for a more rigorous description of the cell, obtain

$$\Delta H = -n\mathscr{F}\left[\mathscr{E} - T\left(\frac{\partial \mathscr{E}}{\partial T}\right)_{p,Q_e}\right]$$

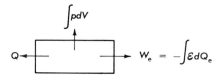

Fig. 21.5 Energy Quantities in a Reversible Cell.

Solution. Since $dW = pdV - \mathscr{E}dQ_e$, the first and second laws combine to give

$$dQ = TdS = dU + dW = dU + pdV - \mathscr{E}dQ_e$$

or

$$dU = TdS - pdV + \mathscr{E}dQ_e$$

From the definition of enthalpy: $H = U + pV$,

$$
\begin{aligned}
dH &= dU + pdV + Vdp \\
&= (TdS - pdV + \mathscr{E}dQ_e) + pdV + Vdp \\
&= TdS + \mathscr{E}dQ_e + Vdp
\end{aligned}
\tag{21.62}
$$

For a process at constant temperature and pressure, this becomes

$$\left(\frac{\partial H}{\partial Q_e}\right)_{T,p} = T\left(\frac{\partial S}{\partial Q_e}\right)_{T,p} + \mathscr{E} \tag{21.63}$$

To eliminate $(\partial S/\partial Q_e)_{T,p}$ in favor of a partial derivative of the coordinate variables p, V, T, $\mathscr{E}$, or Q_e, use the Gibbs function for a reversible cell, $G = H - TS$, to get

$$dG = dH - TdS - SdT$$

and, by Eq. (21.62),

$$
\begin{aligned}
dG &= (TdS + \mathscr{E}dQ_e + Vdp) - TdS - SdT \\
&= dQ_e + Vdp - SdT
\end{aligned}
$$

At constant p, this becomes

$$(dG)_p = \mathscr{E}(dQ_e)_p - S(dT)_p$$

whence

$$\left(\frac{\partial \mathscr{E}}{\partial T}\right)_{p,Q} = -\left(\frac{\partial S}{\partial Q_e}\right)_{p,T} \tag{21.64}$$

This is a Maxwell relation for a reversible cell. Replacing $(\partial S/\partial Q_e)_{p,T}$ by its value from Eq. (21.64), Eq. (21.63) can now be written as

$$\left(\frac{\partial H}{\partial Q_e}\right)_{T,p} = \mathscr{E} - T\left(\frac{\partial \epsilon}{\partial T}\right)_{p,Q_e} \tag{21.65}$$

Finally, to obtain the Gibbs-Helmholtz equation, consider H as a function of T, p, and Q_e. Then

$$dH = \left(\frac{\partial H}{\partial T}\right)_{p,Q_e} dT + \left(\frac{\partial H}{\partial p}\right)_{T,Q_c} dp + \left(\frac{\partial H}{\partial Z}\right)_{T,p} dQ_e$$

For a constant temperature, constant pressure process, this becomes

$$dH = \left(\frac{\partial H}{\partial Q_e}\right)_{T,p} dQ_e$$

or, by Eq. (21.65),

$$dH = \left[\mathcal{E} - T\left(\frac{\partial \mathcal{E}}{\partial T}\right)_{p,Q_e}\right] dQ_e = \mathcal{E}dQ_e - T\left(\frac{\partial \mathcal{E}}{\partial T}\right)_{p,Q_e} dQ_e \qquad (21.66)$$

For a saturated reversible cell, $\mathcal{E}$ is function of temperature only, so that at constant temperature and pressure, Eq. (21.66) integrates into

$$\Delta H = \int_0^{Q_e} \mathcal{E}dQ_e - T\left(\frac{\partial \mathcal{E}}{\partial T}\right)_{p,Q_e} \int_0^{Q_e} dQ_e$$

or

$$\Delta H = \mathcal{E}Q_e - T\left(\frac{\partial \mathcal{E}}{\partial T}\right)_{p,Q_e} Q_e$$

and, replacing Q_e by $-n\mathcal{F}$ from Faraday's law,

$$\Delta H = -\mathcal{E}n\mathcal{F} + T\left(\frac{\partial \mathcal{E}}{\partial T}\right)_{p,Q_e} n\mathcal{F} = -n\mathcal{F}\left[\mathcal{E} - T\left(\frac{\partial \mathcal{E}}{\partial T}\right)_{p,Q_e}\right] \qquad (21.67)$$

The above example is a good illustration of problems which involve *generalized forces*. In this case, the generalized forces are composed of mechanical force (due to pressure) and electrical force (due to electric potential).

21.8 Magnetic System

It was previously pointed out that one way of magnetizing a material is to place it inside the field created by a current-carrying coil or solenoid. The magnetic induction inside a toroid or infinite solenoid in vacuum is given by

$$\mathcal{B} = \mu_0 \mathcal{H} = \mu_0 ni \qquad (21.68)$$

where $\mathcal{B}$ is the flux density, $\mathcal{H}$ is the field of the external current i, n is the number of turns per unit length, and μ_0 is the permeability of free space. If the space within the solenoid is filled with say, iron, it is found that the flux is several thousandfold higher. With nickel and cobalt, there is an increase of several hundredfold. Materials which produce a large increase in flux are classified as *ferromagnetic*, those which increase the flux moderately are called *paramagnetic*, and those which reduce the flux are labeled *diamagnetic*.

The action of a magnetic field on a substance is to produce a magnetization, so that the magnetic induction becomes

$$\mathcal{B} = \mu_0(\mathcal{H} + \mathcal{M}) \qquad (21.69)$$

where $\mathcal{M}$ is the magnetization per unit volume of the substance. If the current i is changed, then in time dt the magnetic induction is changed by $d\mathscr{B}$, and according to Faraday's law of electromagnetic induction, there is induced in the winding a back emf

$$\mathscr{E} = -NA\frac{d\mathscr{B}}{dt} \tag{21.70}$$

where N is the number of turns composing the solenoid and A is the cross-sectional area of the solenoid. During the time interval dt, a quantity of electricity dQ_e is transferred in the circuit, so that the work done is

$$dW = \mathscr{E}\,dQ_e = -NA\frac{d\mathscr{B}}{dt}dQ_e = -NA\frac{dQ_e}{dt}d\mathscr{B}$$
$$= -NAi\,d\mathscr{B} \tag{21.71}$$

Since from Eq. (21.68), $\mathscr{H} = ni = Ni/L$ where L is the mean circumference of the toroid formed by the solenoid, Eq. (21.71) becomes

$$dW = -AL\mathscr{H}\,d\mathscr{B} = -V\mathscr{H}\,d\mathscr{B} \tag{21.72}$$

where $V = AL$ is the volume. Equation (21.72) may also be written with the aid of Eq. (21.69) as

$$dW = -\mu_0 V\mathscr{H}\,d\mathscr{H} - \mu_0 V\mathscr{H}\,d\mathscr{M} \tag{21.73}$$

The first term on the right-hand side of Eq. (21.73) represents the work done in increasing the magnetic field in a volume V of free space, the second term represents the work done in increasing the magnetization of the material by an amount $d\mathscr{M}$. Neglecting the first term, the work done is thus

$$dW = -\mu_0 V\mathscr{H}\,d\mathscr{M} \tag{21.74}$$

where the minus sign indicates that work input is required to increase the magnetization of a substance. Equation (21.74) enables the thermodynamic analysis of a magnetic system to be carried out very easily, for it is noticed that $\mathscr{H}$ corresponds to p and $-\mu_0 V\,d\mathscr{M}$ corresponds to dV of a chemical system. Therefore, to obtain thermodynamic relations for a magnetic system, it is merely necessary to replace, in the corresponding relations of a chemical system, p and V by their appropriate equivalents. For example, the following equations

$$C_p = \left(\frac{\partial U}{\partial T}\right)_p + p\left(\frac{\partial V}{\partial T}\right)_p$$

$$T\,dS = C_p\,dT - T\left(\frac{\partial V}{\partial T}\right)_p dp$$

$$\left(\frac{\partial U}{\partial p}\right)_T = -T\left(\frac{\partial V}{\partial T}\right)_p - p\left(\frac{\partial V}{\partial p}\right)_T$$

become, for a magnetic system,

$$c_{\mathscr{H}} = \left(\frac{\partial U}{\partial T}\right)_{\mathscr{H}} - \mu_0 V \mathscr{H} \left(\frac{\partial \mathscr{M}}{\partial T}\right)_{\mathscr{H}} \tag{21.75}$$

$$T dS = c_{\mathscr{H}} dT + \mu_0 V T \left(\frac{\partial \mathscr{M}}{\partial T}\right)_{\mathscr{H}} d\mathscr{H} \tag{21.76}$$

$$\left(\frac{\partial U}{\partial \mathscr{H}}\right)_T = \mu_0 V T \left(\frac{\partial \mathscr{M}}{\partial T}\right)_{\mathscr{H}} + \mu_0 V \mathscr{H} \left(\frac{\partial \mathscr{M}}{\partial \mathscr{H}}\right)_T \tag{21.77}$$

where $C_{\mathscr{H}}$ is the specific heat at constant field intensity. Numerical values of $C_{\mathscr{H}}$ and of the partial derivatives of $\mathscr{M}$ can be obtained by experiment or by calculation based on the molecular theory of magnetization. For many paramagnetic substances, it is found that the magnetization is directly proportional to the magnetic field intensity and inversely proportional to the Kelvin temperature. In other words,

$$\mathscr{M} = C \frac{\mathscr{H}}{T} \tag{21.78}$$

where C is a constant called the *Curie constant*. Equation (21.78) is an equation of state for a magnetic system in the same sense that $p = \rho RT$ is an equation of state for a chemical system.

Example 21.5. A common technique in the production of very low temperatures (of the order of 1 °K or less) is cyclic magnetization and demagnetization. A paramagnetic salt is first cooled in liquid helium and magnetized isothermally while removing heat from it (process 1–2, Fig. 21.6). It is then demagnetized adiabatically (process 2–3) with a resultant temperature drop (in the same manner that a gas cools when expanded adiabatically). This provides material at temperature T_3 to serve as heat reservoir for the next isothermal magnetization 3–4, which in turn is followed by another adiabatic demagnetization 4–5, and so on.

A sample of paramagnetic salt having a total heat capacity $C_{\mathscr{H}}$ is cooled to a temperature T_1 in liquid helium. At this point, it is magnetized isothermally, with Q amount of heat removed. This is followed by an adiabatic demagnetization to a lower temperature T_2. Assuming the sample to obey Curie's law, determine the temperature T_2 at the end of adiabatic demagnetization.

Solution. For a reversible isothermal process, Eq. (21.76) gives

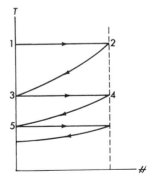

Fig. 21.6 Production of Low Temperatures by Cyclic Magnetization and Demagnetization.

$$TdS = dQ = \mu_0 VT\left(\frac{\partial \mathscr{M}}{\partial T}\right)_{\mathscr{H}} d\mathscr{H}$$

or

$$Q = \int_0^{\mathscr{H}} \mu_0 VT\left(\frac{\partial \mathscr{M}}{\partial T}\right)_{\mathscr{H}} d\mathscr{H}$$

Now,

$$\left(\frac{\partial \mathscr{M}}{\partial T}\right)_{\mathscr{H}} = -\frac{C\mathscr{H}}{T^2}$$

from Curie's law, so that at T_1,

$$Q = -\int_0^{\mathscr{H}} \frac{\mu_0 VC}{T_1} \mathscr{H} d\mathscr{H} = -\frac{\mu_0 VC\mathscr{H}^2}{2T_1}$$

The temperature change when the magnetic field is changed adiabatically and reversibly is again obtained from Eq. (21.76). Setting $dS = 0$ gives

$$dT = -\frac{\mu_0 VT}{C_{\mathscr{H}}}\left(\frac{\partial \mathscr{M}}{\partial T}\right)_{\mathscr{H}} d\mathscr{H} = \frac{\mu_0 VC\mathscr{H}}{C_{\mathscr{H}} T} d\mathscr{H}$$

and, upon integration,

$$\int_{T_1}^{T_2} TdT = \int_{\mathscr{H}}^0 \frac{\mu_0 VC\mathscr{H}}{C_{\mathscr{H}}} d\mathscr{H}$$

$$T_2^2 = T_1^2 - \frac{\mu_0 VC\mathscr{H}^2}{C_{\mathscr{H}}}$$

This may be written, in terms of the amount of heat removed, as

$$T_2^2 = T_1^2 - \frac{2QT_1}{C_{\mathscr{H}}}$$

21.9 Thermal Radiation

Consider the thermodynamics of radiation. This is a process by which energy is transmitted through space without the necessary presence of matter. Let a certain body at a given temperature be surrounded in one case by colder bodies, and in another case by hotter ones. In the first case the body will transfer heat by radiation to its surroundings and thus be cooled; in the second case, it will receive heat by radiation and its temperature will rise. Since the original condition of the body is the same, it must radiate energy in both cases, but the difference is that in one case the body radiates more energy than it receives, while in the other case it receives more than it radiates. The equilibrium condition, one in which all bodies remain at the same temperature, does not imply absence of radiation, but only equality of the amounts of radiation exchanged between each pair of bodies. In other words, there is a continuous interchange of energy among bodies as a result of radiation and absorption, this interchange of energy continuing even after thermal equilibrium has been reached. This concept, according to which a body would cease to emit thermal radiation only when its temperature has been reduced to absolute zero, was first enunciated in 1792 by Prevost, and is known as the *theory of exchanges*.

A general way of characterizing radiant energy is to say that it is the energy of *electromagnetic* waves. These waves can travel through empty space without the aid of a material medium, and their speed of propagation in vacuum is the speed of light. Electromagnetic radiant energy includes such forms of energy as radio waves, heat radiation, infra-red light, visible light, ultraviolet light, x-rays, and gamma-rays, arranged in order of frequency. The starting of waves of radiant energy is called *emission*. Being electromagnetic in nature, these waves are generated by moving particles which are electrically charged. In the case of heat radiation, this is due to the random distribution of kinetic energy among the atoms and molecules of the emitting body rather than to any specific electrical action such as in the case of a radio antenna. The energy emitted in heat radiation is at the expense of the energy of motion of the molecules and atoms, and is thus equivalent to a removal of heat from the emitting body.

When radiation strikes a body, it is partially absorbed, partially reflected, and partially transmitted. The relation between the fraction of energy absorbed, reflected, and transmitted is

$$\alpha + \rho + \tau = 1 \qquad (21.79)$$

where α is the *absorptivity* (fraction of the incident radiation absorbed by the body), ρ is the *reflectivity* (fraction of the incident radiation reflected from the body), and τ is the *transmissivity* (fraction of the incident radiation transmitted through the body). A large number of bodies, however, are *opaque*, i.e., they do not transmit radiation. The incident radiation penetrates only very slightly into these bodies, all of the radiation being practically absorbed in a thin surface layer less than 0.05 inch in depth. For opaque bodies, Eq. (21.79) reduces to

$$\alpha + \rho = 1 \qquad (21.80)$$

With the exception of glass and rock salt, Eq. (21.80) describes the behavior of solid and liquid materials. Gases, on the other hand, reflect very little of incident radiation, but instead transmit an appreciable portion. For gases, therefore, ρ is negligible, and Eq. (21.79) reduces to

$$\alpha + \tau = 1 \qquad (21.81)$$

The laws governing the thermal radiation emitted by a body are especially simple if the body absorbs all the incident radiation, and reflects none from its surface ($\alpha = 1$, $\rho = 0$). Such a body is called a *black body*.

(The name comes from the fact that a surface which absorbs all light rays appears black to the eye. A surface can, however, absorb practically all thermal radiation without absorbing all light rays and therefore without appearing black to the eye. Such a surface is snow, which has an absorptivity of 0.98 for thermal radiation from a body whose temperature is not too high). The total rate of energy emission per unit area of a black surface to the hemispherical region above it is given by the *Stefan–Boltzmann* law:

$$e_b = \sigma T^4 \tag{21.82}$$

where e_b is the emissive power of the black body, σ is a constant which, in English units, has the value of 0.173×10^{-8} Btu/hr ft^2 °R, and T is the absolute temperature in degrees Rankine. Equation (21.82) will be derived first from thermodynamic considerations alone, and then from quantum theory using Planck's law.

Although totally black surfaces do not exist in nature, the concept of a black body is a useful standard of comparison for other surfaces which reflect part of the incident radiation. Thus, the emissive power, e, of a body is given by

$$e = \alpha e_b \tag{21.83}$$

and the ratio of the emissive power of a body to that of a black body at the same temperature is called the emissivity ϵ. Dividing both sides of Eq. (21.83) by e_b gives

$$\epsilon = \alpha \tag{21.84}$$

This is known as *Kirchhoff's law.*

21.10 Thermodynamics of Radiation; Stefan–Boltzmann Law

Stefan–Boltzmann's law may be derived quite simply from thermodynamic considerations alone if we make use of some well-known facts concerning radiation. First, consider a hollow space in which there is a small opening (Fig. 21.7). This is called a *hohlraum*, and represents an approximation to a black body. The walls of the space are kept at uniform temperature. Any incident radiation is reflected repeatedly before it leaves the space again, so that if the surface of the space has absorptivity, then, after several reflections, most of the radiation is absorbed. The opening of the cavity therefore acts as a black body, and the cavity, if heated, emits black body radiation. Provided the walls of the cavity are opaque, the quality of the radiation in equilibrium inside is dependent on the temperature only. This means that all the extensive thermodynamic variables of the radiation in the cavity are proportional to the volume, i.e., $U = uV$, $S = sV$, etc., where u, s, (etc.) are functions of temperature only. Note that u is known as the *density of radiation*, i.e., the total radiation contained per unit volume.

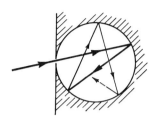

Fig. 21.7 Hohlraum.

Now, the cavity containing the radiation may be treated as if it were a vessel containing a gas, and the fundamental thermodynamic equation may be applied to it. For this purpose, use is made of the information that radiation impinging on a surface exerts a pressure on that surface, and that the magnitude of that pressure is

$$p = \frac{u}{3} \tag{21.85}$$

where u is the radiation density. Equation (21.85) may be derived from electromagnetic theory. A simpler alternative, however, is to consider the radiation as a photon gas whose particles all move with the velocity of light, c, and write for the pressure

$$p = \frac{\rho c^2}{3} \tag{21.86}$$

where ρ is the density (mass per unit volume) of the photons. But according to Einstein's mass-energy relation, ρc^2 is simply the energy in the gas, so that Eq. (21.86) gives

$$p = \frac{u}{3}$$

Having established that the radiation density and therefore the radiation pressure† is a function of temperature only, the fundamental equation of thermodynamics, $dU = TdS - pdV$, may be written, with $U = uV$, and $p = u/3$, as

$$u\,dV + V\,du = T(s\,dV + V\,ds) - \frac{u}{3}\,dV$$

---

† The radiation pressure is usually quite small. For example, solar radiation exerts at the surface of the earth a pressure of 0.4 mg/m².

or

$$du = Tds + \frac{1}{V}\left(Ts - \frac{4}{3}u\right)dV \qquad (21.87)$$

Since u and s are functions of temperature only, Eq. (21.87) gives

$$du = Tds \qquad (21.88)$$

$$Ts = \frac{4}{3}u \qquad (21.89)$$

Eliminating T between these equations gives $du/ds = (4/3) \cdot (u/s)$ or $u \propto s^{(4/3)}$. Replacing this in Eq. (21.89) gives

$$u = aT^4 \qquad (21.90)$$

$$s = \frac{4}{3}aT^4 \qquad (21.91)$$

where a is a constant. Equation (21.90) is the *Stefan–Boltzmann fourth-power law* for black-body radiation. It may be written in terms of the emissive power (rate of energy emission per unit area) as follows: Consider a small element of surface dA with a sphere of unit radius surrounding it (Fig. 21.8). The energy travels in all directions with the velocity of light, c. Since there are 4π solid angles in a sphere, the energy density in any solid angle $d\omega$ is $u(cd\omega/4\pi)$, and the amount of radiation crossing dA at the angle θ from the normal is

$$u \cdot \frac{cd\omega}{4\pi} \cdot dA \cdot \cos\theta \qquad (21.92)$$

This is known as *Lambert's cosine law*. Now, at the angle θ, the solid angle swept by the increment of angle $d\theta$ is $d\omega = 2\pi \sin\theta \, d\theta$, so that the radiation crossing dA is

$$u \cdot \frac{c \sin\theta \, d\theta}{2} \cdot dA \cdot \cos\theta$$

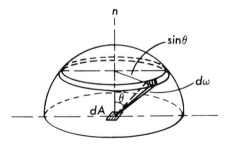

Fig. 21.8 Radiation from a Surface Element.

The emissive power of the black body, e_b, being the rate of energy emission per unit area, is the above quantity divided by dA and integrated from 0 to 2π:

$$e_b = \int_0^{2\pi} \frac{uc \sin\theta \cos\theta d\theta dA}{2dA} = \frac{uc}{4} \tag{21.93}$$

With this result, Eq. (21.90) becomes

$$e_b = \frac{ac T^4}{4} = \sigma T^4 \tag{21.94}$$

where $\sigma = (ac)/4$. This is precisely the same as Eq. (21.82).

21.11 Planck's Distribution Law

The quantity e_b in Eq. (21.94) is the total amount of radiant energy of a black body per unit area and unit time for all wavelengths. In other words,

$$e_b = \sigma T^4 = \int_0^\infty (e_{b,\lambda}) d\lambda \tag{21.95}$$

where λ is the wavelength, and $e_{b,\lambda}$ denotes the monochromatic emissive power at wavelength λ. The value of $e_{b,\lambda}$ depends on the wavelength and the temperature, and when plotted against λ for various fixed values of T is as shown in Fig. 21.9. It can be seen that at any temperature, a black

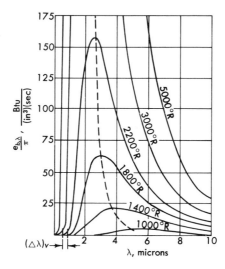

Fig. 21.9 Black-body Radiation Distribution for Different Temperatures.

body radiates heat in a wide range of wavelengths; the visible range of wavelengths being indicated by $(\Delta\lambda)_v$. As the temperature increases, an increasingly greater part of the radiation falls into the visible range. However, even at high temperatures, the visible part is comparatively small and the radiant energy is almost entirely in the infrared range. Only at 10,000 °R (the approximate temperature of the sun) does the maximum value of the radiation lie within the visible range. The wavelength corresponding to the peak in the radiation spectrum can be found from thermodynamic considerations to be inversely proportional to the absolute temperature, i.e.,

$$\lambda_m T = \text{constant} \tag{21.96}$$

where λ_m is the wavelength at which the curves of Fig. (21.9) have their maxima. Equation (21.96) is known as *Wien's displacement law*.

Toward the end of the nineteenth century, many attempts were made to deduce the radiation curves from classical theory, but these attempts failed, and it was not until Planck introduced quantum concepts that agreement with experiment was achieved. One of the unsuccessful attempts was that of Rayleigh and Jeans, who derived the following expression for the radiation energy per unit volume within the frequency range dv:

$$u(v)dv = \frac{8\pi v^2 k T}{c^3} dv \tag{21.97}$$

where $v(=c/\lambda)$ is the frequency, k is the Boltzmann constant ($= 1.38 \times 10^{-23}$ joule/molecule $-$ °K), and c is the velocity of light ($= 2.99 \times 10^8$ m/sec). Equation (21.97) is known as the *Rayleigh-Jeans law*. It agrees with experimental results at long wavelengths, but fails at shorter ones. Instead of passing through a maximum and then falling off as λ is further decreased, curves plotted from Eq. (21.97) rise even more rapidly for smaller and smaller values of λ. This complete disagreement with experimental data is known as the *ultraviolet catastrophe*.

Without going into the details of the Rayleigh–Jeans law, it may be pointed out that this law was based on classical mechanics and the principle of equipartion of energy, according to which an oscillator† in thermal equilibrium with its environment has an average energy equal to kT, $\frac{1}{2}kT$ for its kinetic energy, and $\frac{1}{2}kT$ for its potential energy, where k is the Boltzmann constant. Classical theory also states that the average energy depends in no way on the frequency of the oscillator. The radiation within a hohlraum is considered to be made up of standing waves of various

---

† The simplest way by which electromagnetic waves can be generated is to have an arrangement of two atoms using a plus and minus electric charge and interconnected by elastic forces so that they perform oscillations. A large number of such oscillations with different frequencies may be arranged along the walls of the enclosure to produce black body radiation.

frequencies, and the problem of the energy distribution over the various frequencies is one of determining the number of allowed vibrations in any range of frequencies. Statistical mechanics gives, for the number of oscillations per unit volume between v and $v + dv$,

$$dn = 8\pi \frac{v^2}{c^3} dv \tag{21.98}$$

Now, the number of allowed vibrations increases rapidly as the frequency increases, so that possible high frequency vibrations greatly outnumber low-frequency ones. Since, by the principle of equipartition of energy, all frequencies have the same average energy, it follows that the radiation of a black body should rise continuously with increasing frequency. This conclusion follows inescapably from classical mechanics, yet it is in complete disagreement with experimental findings!

These circumstances led Planck to formulate the quantum theory. He discarded the notion that an oscillator could take up energy continuously in arbitrarily small increments,* and suggested instead that an oscillator could acquire energy only in discrete units. In other words, the apparently continuous electromagnetic waves are quantized and consist of discrete quanta, called *photons*, each photon having an energy ϵ which depends only on the frequency accorded to the relation

$$\epsilon = hv \tag{21.99}$$

where h is a constant called Planck's constant, having a value 6.625×10^{-34} joule-sec. Thus, a beam of light of frequency v consists of particle-like photons, each having an energy hv. With the introduction of quantization, it becomes immediately clear why the intensity of black body radiation falls off at high frequencies (short wavelengths). At these frequencies, $hv \gg kT$, and the size of the quantum is much larger than the mean kinetic energy of the atoms comprising the radiator. Since the chance of an oscillator having an energy ϵ depends on the Boltzmann factor $e^{-\epsilon/kT}$ (see Chap. 13), it follows that the larger the quantum becomes, the smaller is the chance of the oscillator attaining this energy.

Consider now a collection of N oscillators having a vibration frequency v. These can have energy only in increments of hv. The allowed energies are therefore 0, hv, $2hv$, etc., as shown in Fig. 21.10. It was shown in Chap. 13 that if N_0 is the number of molecules in a given energy state, the number N_i in a state whose energy is ϵ_i above that of the given state is

$$N_i = N_0 e^{-\epsilon_i/kT}$$

---

* Classical Newtonian mechanics is based on the assumption that matter is atomic in its constitution, but that energy is continuous.

Thus, in the collection of oscillators,

$$N_0 = N_0 e^{-0/kT}$$
$$N_1 = N_0 e^{-h\nu/kT}$$
$$N_2 = N_0 e^{-2h\nu/kT}$$
$$\vdots$$

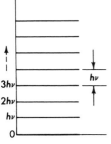

Fig. 21.10

Allowed Energies of Monochromatic Electromagnetic Radiation.†

so that

$$N = N_0 + N_0 e^{-h\nu/kT} + N_0 e^{-2h\nu/kT} + \cdots$$

$$= N_0 \sum_{i=0}^{\infty} e^{-ih\nu/kT} \qquad (21.100)$$

The total energy of all the oscillators is the energy of each level times the number in that level:

$$E = 0 \cdot N_0 + h\nu N_0 e^{-h\nu/kT} + 2h\nu N_0 e^{-2h\nu/kT} + \cdots$$

$$= N_0 h\nu \sum_{i=0}^{\infty} i e^{-ih\nu/kT} \qquad (21.101)$$

The average energy of an oscillator is the total energy divided by the total number of oscillators, or

$$\bar{\epsilon} = \frac{E}{N} = \frac{N_0 h\nu \sum_{i=0}^{\infty} i e^{-ih\nu/kT}}{N_0 \sum_{i=0}^{\infty} e^{-ih\nu/kT}} = h\nu \frac{\sum_{i=0}^{\infty} i e^{-ih\nu/kT}}{\sum_{i=0}^{\infty} e^{-ih\nu/kT}}$$

Letting $x = (h\nu/kT)$, this simplifies to

$$\bar{\epsilon} = h\nu \frac{\sum_{i=0}^{\infty} i e^{-ix}}{\sum_{i=0}^{\infty} e^{-ix}} = \frac{h\nu}{e^x - 1} = \frac{h\nu}{e^{h\nu/kT} - 1} \qquad (21.102)$$

Equation (21.102) gives the average energy which an oscillator assumes at the temperature T. Using this result in place of the classical value of kT given by the equipartition law, Planck obtained an equation for the

---

† The total energy of a beam of monochromatic electromagnetic radiation is precisely an integral multiple of the energy $h\nu$ of a single photon. The atomicity of electromagnetic radiation, however, is not conspicuous in ordinary observations because of the exceedingly small energy of an individual photon and because of the enormous number of photons in a beam of electromagnetic radiation.

energy density which is in full agreement with the experimental data for black-body radiation. The energy density $u(\nu)d\nu$ within the frequency range $d\nu$ is simply the number of oscillations per unit volume [Eq. (21.98)] times the average energy of an oscillation [Eq. (21.102)]. Thus

$$u(\nu)d\nu = \frac{8\pi h\nu^3}{c^3} \cdot \frac{d\nu}{e^{h\nu/kT} - 1} \tag{21.103}$$

Equation (21.103) is the famous *Planck equation* for the black-body radiation spectrum. For low frequencies, i.e., $(h\nu)/(kT) \ll 1$, it reduces to the classical Rayleigh–Jeans equation:

$$u(\nu)d\nu = \frac{8\pi h\nu^3}{c^3}d\nu \tag{21.104}$$

This equation fails in the high-frequency region. For high frequencies, i.e., $h\nu/kT \gg 1$, Planck's equation reduces to Wein's equation:

$$u(\nu)d\nu = \frac{8\pi h\nu^3}{c^3}e^{-h\nu/kT}d\nu \tag{21.105}$$

This equation fails in the low-frequency region.

For a given temperature, the distribution given by Eq. (21.103) has a maximum. The value ν for which this maximum occurs is found by setting $(d/d\nu)[u(\nu)] = 0$ and solving for ν. The result is

$$\frac{kT}{h\nu_{max}} = \text{constant} \tag{21.106}$$

This is Wien's displacement law.

The total energy radiated from a black body in the whole range of emitted frequencies is obtained from Planck's equation by integration:

$$u(T) = \int_0^\infty u(\nu)d\nu = \int_0^\infty \frac{8\pi h\nu^3}{c^3} \cdot \frac{d\nu}{e^{h\nu/kT} - 1}$$

The integration may be performed by letting $h\nu/kT = x$, in which case

$$u(T) = \frac{8\pi k^4 T^4}{h^3 c^3} \int_0^\infty \frac{x^3}{e^x - 1}dx$$

The value of

$$\int_0^\infty \frac{x^3 dx}{e^x - 1}$$

is found in Jahnke and Emde's tables to be

$$\frac{(3!)\pi^4}{90}$$

Thus,

$$u(T) = \frac{8\pi^5 k^4 T^4}{15 h^3 c^3} = a T^4 \qquad (21.107)$$

This is seen to be Stefan–Boltzmann's law, Eq. (21.90). Planck's equation is indeed a great achievement; it not only gave birth to the quantum theory, but also became the basis for the development of modern physics!

PROBLEMS

21.1. Consider an elastic string of length l whose elastic modulus is λ. Then the work done is given by

$$dw = -\frac{\lambda(l-l_0)}{l_0} dl$$

where l_0 is the length of the string when unstretched. In general, both l and λ will be functions of the temperature T. Show that the change in free energy or Helmholtz function is given by

$$a = a_0 + \frac{\lambda(l-l_0)^2}{2l_0}$$

Hint: The work done during a non-flow isothermal process is, according to Sec. 10.4, equal to the decrease in the Helmholtz function. Thus,

$$a - a_0 = \int_{l_0}^{l} \frac{\lambda(l-l_0)}{l_0} dl$$

21.2. (a) The elastic modulus λ of a spherical container is related to the surface tension by means of the equation

$$\mathcal{S} = \lambda \frac{\Delta A}{A_0}$$

where ΔA is the increase in area, and A_0 is the area under no excess pressure. Show that the change in Helmholtz function of a container when filled with gas at pressure p greater than the external pressure p_0 is equal to

$$\frac{A_0}{8\lambda}(\beta - p_0)^2 r^2$$

where r is the radius of the container. (b) What is the energy available for work stored in a container having a radius of 15 cm when filled with air at 60 atm, the value of λ being such that the container increases its radius by 0.01 per cent when the gas is introduced?

21.3. An elastic wire can be described by the following co-ordinates: T (temperature), $\mathscr{F}$ (tension), and L (length). To obtain a desired thermodynamic relation, it is merely necessary to replace p by $-\mathscr{F}$ and V by L in the corresponding equation for a chemical system. A certain elastic wire has the following equation of state:

$$\mathscr{F} = KT\left(\frac{L}{L_0} - \frac{L_0^2}{L^2}\right)$$

where K is a constant, and L is the length at zero tension. Show that if the wire is stretched reversibly and isothermally from an original length L_0 to twice its length, the heat transferred is

$$Q = -KTL_0\left(1 + \frac{5}{2}\alpha_0 T\right)$$

where $\alpha_0 = (1/L_0)(dL_0/dT)$ is the linear expansivity at zero tension.

21.4. A steel wire has its tension increased reversibly and isothermally from zero to 10^7 dynes. The length of the wire is 1.5 m, its diameter is 1.2 mm, and its temperature is 300 °K. Determine (a) the heat transferred in Joules, (b) the work done, (c) the change in internal energy.

21.5. Show that for an elastic bar, the change of internal energy between two states $(T_0,\ \epsilon_0)$, $(T,\ \epsilon)$ is given by

$$u - u_0 = c_\epsilon(T - T_0) + \tfrac{1}{2} Y(\epsilon^2 - \epsilon_0^2)$$

where Y is Young's isothermal modulus.

21.6. It is known that surface tension causes the pressure inside a liquid drop to exceed the pressure outside the drop. For a spherical drop of radius r in equilibrium with its vapor (Fig. 21.11), show that that difference between internal and external pressure is

$$p_i - p_e = \frac{2\sigma}{r}$$

where p_i = internal pressure, p_e = external pressure, and σ = surface tension. Hint: Surface tension forces on a half drop result in a force of $2\pi\sigma r$; pressure forces on a half drop result in $(p_i - p_e)\pi r^2$.

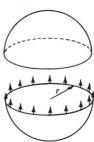

Fig. 21.11

21.7. Show that for a liquid or solid under hydrostatic pressure, the volume change $v - v_0$ corresponding to a temperature change $T - T_0$ and a pressure change $p - p_0$ is given by

$$v - v_0 = v_0\beta(T - T_0) - v_0\kappa(\beta - p_0)$$

21.8. Show that, for a solid or liquid, the heat absorbed, the change in internal energy, the change in entropy, and the work done in an isothermal process are respectively

$$q = v_0 T\beta(p-p_0)$$

$$u-u_0 = -v_0 T\beta(p-p_0)+\frac{v_0}{2}\kappa(p^2-p_0^2)$$

$$s-s_0 = -v_0\beta(p-p_0)$$

$$w = -\frac{v_0}{2}\kappa(p^2-p_0^2)$$

21.9. The pressure on a block of copper is increased at a constant temperature of 60 °F from 1 atm to 100 atm. If $\beta = 2.8 \times 10^{-5}/°R$, $\kappa = 5.9 \times 10^{-8}$ in²/lbf, and $v_{60\ °F,\ 1\ atm} = 1.82 \times 10^{-3}$ cu ft/lbm, what is the heat transferred and the work done per unit mass?

21.10. Water, at a temperature of 50 °F, has a coefficient β of approximately $9 \times 10^{-6}/°F$. What is the final temperature if water in a hydraulic press is compressed adiabatically and reversibly from 1 atm to 900 atm?

21.11. It is known that near the absolute zero, the value of c_p for a solid is given by an expression of the form $c(T/T_1)^3$. Consider a solid having its specific heat given by $c(T/T_1)$ for $T<T_1$ and equal to c for $T >T_1$, c being a constant. Show that the changes in the entropy, enthalpy, and Gibbs function on warming up at constant pressure from $T = 0$ to $T >T_1$ are respectively given by

$$\Delta s = \frac{c}{3} +c \ln\frac{T}{T_1}$$

$$\Delta h = c\left(T-\frac{3}{4}T_1\right)$$

$$\Delta g = CT\left(\frac{2}{3} - \ln\frac{T}{T_1}\right)-\frac{3CT_1}{4}$$

21.12. The heat transfer during the reversible charging of a condenser is given by

$$dQ = dU - VdQ_e$$

where U is a function of the temperature and the charge Q_e. Show that the entropy change may be expressed as

$$dS = \frac{1}{T}\left(\frac{\partial U}{\partial T}\right)_{Q_e} dT+\frac{Q_e}{C^2}\frac{dC}{dT}dQ_e$$

where C is the capacity of the condenser, which is a function of T only.

21.13. Show that the increase of entropy on charging isothermally a condenser is given by

$$\frac{1}{2}\left(\frac{Q_e}{C}\right)^2\frac{dC}{dT}$$

and that the increase in free energy or Helmholtz function is given by

$$\frac{1}{2}\frac{Q_e^2}{C}$$

21.14. (a) Show that for a dielectric system describable by the co-ordinates E, $\mathscr{P}$, and T, the following relation holds:

$$\left(\frac{\partial u}{\partial E}\right)_T = E\left(\frac{\partial \mathscr{P}}{\partial E}\right)_T + T\left(\frac{\partial \mathscr{P}}{\partial T}\right)_E$$

(b) Assume the polarization per unit volume of a material to obey the following equation of state:

$$\mathscr{P} = \chi E$$

where χ (called the susceptibility) is a function of T only, and the volume is constant. Show that the energy per unit volume is equal to

$$u = \frac{E^2}{2}\left(\chi + \frac{\partial \chi}{dT}\right) + \varphi(T)$$

where $\varphi(T)$ is a function of temperature.

21.15. Consider a cell in which a chemical relation is taking place. If all changes take place reversibly at constant temperature and pressure, the total work is

$$p\,dV - \mathscr{E}\,dQ_e$$

where V is the volume, $\mathscr{E}$ is the emf, and Q_e is the charge. For small changes in volume, write the Tds equation with T and Q_e as independent variables:

$$T\,dS = \left(\frac{\partial U}{\partial T}\right)_{Q_e} dT + \left(\frac{\partial U}{\partial Q_e}\right) dQ_e - \mathscr{E}\,dQ_e$$

and obtain the following relationship between the variation of internal energy with charge passing and the rate of change of emf with temperature:

$$\left(\frac{\partial U}{\partial Q_e}\right)_T = \mathscr{E} - T\left(\frac{\partial \mathscr{E}}{\partial T}\right)_{Q_e}$$

Compare this with Eq. (21.77) of the text.

21.16. For a thermodynamic system described with the aid of five co-ordinates such as p, V, T, S, and A, show that

$$dQ = -S\,dT + V\,dp + S\,dA$$

$$\left(\frac{\partial S}{\partial p}\right)_{T,A} = \left(\frac{\partial V}{\partial A}\right)_{T,p}$$

21.17. Show that the Gibbs–Helmholtz equation for a reversible cell may be written as

$$\frac{d(\mathscr{E}/T)}{dT} = \frac{\Delta H}{n\mathscr{F}T^2}$$

where n is the equivalent weight and $\mathscr{F}$ is the Faraday constant.

21.18. By means of Eq. (21.72), calculate the heat of reaction for a reversible cell whose emf varies with temperature according to the equation

$$\mathscr{E} = a + bT + cT^2 + dT^3$$

where a, b, c, and d are constants.

21.19. The electromotive force of a reversible cell is found to be

$$\mathscr{E} = 1.25 + 2.0 \times 10^{-4}t + 5.41 \times 10^{-6}t^2$$

where $\mathscr{E}$ = volts, and t = °C. (a) If the cell is discharged reversibly at the rate of 1.2 ampere, at what rate (calories per hour) must heat be supplied to maintain it at constant temperature of 18 °C? (b) What would the rate of heat supply be if the cell has an internal resistance of 0.005 ohm?

21.20. Develop a relation for the increase in Helmholtz function when a substance obeying Curie's law is taken isothermally from a state $(T_1, \mathscr{H}_1)$ to a state $(T_1, \mathscr{H}_2)$. Hint: The work done is equal to the decrease in the Helmholtz function, i.e., $(dW)_{T_1} = A_1 - A_2$.

21.21. Determine the ratio β/κ for a magnetic system and verify the following Tds equation:

$$Tds = C_{\mathscr{M}}dT - \mu_0 VT\left(\frac{\partial \mathscr{H}}{\partial T}\right)_{\mathscr{M}} d\mathscr{M}$$

21.22. Show that

$$\left(\frac{\partial S}{\partial \mathscr{H}}\right)_T = \mu_0\left(\frac{\partial \mathscr{M} V}{\partial T}\right)_{\mathscr{H}}$$

$$\left(\frac{\partial T}{\partial \mathscr{H}}\right)_S = -\frac{\mu_0 T}{C_{\mathscr{H}}}\left(\frac{\partial \mathscr{M} V}{\partial T}\right)_{\mathscr{H}}$$

21.23. (a) Assuming Curie's law to be valid, evaluate the following integral for the entropy change of a paramagnetic solid during an isothermal increase of magnetic field from zero to $\mathscr{H}$:

$$\Delta S = \mu_0 VT \int_0^{\mathscr{H}} \left(\frac{\partial \mathscr{M}}{\partial T}\right)_{\mathscr{H}} d\mathscr{H}$$

(b) Show that as T approaches zero, ΔS does not approach zero, in violation of the third law of thermodynamics. Curie's law therefore is not valid at very low temperatures. (An equation of state valid for all values of $\mathscr{H}/T$ was proposed by Brillouin. It can be shown that if Brillouin's equation is used instead of Curie's equation, ΔS approaches zero as T approaches zero, in agreement with the third law.)

21.24. A sample paramagnetic salt obeying Curie's law is cooled to 3 °K in liquid helium and magnetized isothermally while 5.4×10^{-3} Joule of heat is removed. It is then demagnetized adiabatically. If the total heat capacity is $C_{\mathscr{H}} = 10^{-3}T^3$ Joule/deg, what is the temperature attained at the end of the demagnetization process?

21.25. From $p = u/3$ and $u = aT^4$, it is seen that the equation of state for black-body radiation takes on the form

$$p = \frac{a}{3}T^4$$

(a) Show that

$$\left(\frac{\partial p}{\partial T}\right)_V = \frac{4}{3}aT^3$$

$$C_V = \left(\frac{\partial U}{\partial T}\right)_V = 4VaT^3$$

and therefore the Tds equation

$$TdS = C_V dT + T\left(\frac{\partial p}{\partial T}\right)_V dV$$

becomes

$$TdS = 4aVT^3dT + \frac{4}{3}aT^4dV$$

(b) Show that if black-body radiation, in equilibrium with the walls of a cavity at a temperature T is caused to expand isothermally from V_1 to V_2, the heat supplied to the walls to keep the temperature constant is

$$Q = \frac{4}{3}aT^4(V_2 - V_1)$$

(c) Show that for black-body radiation,

$$pV^{4/3} = \text{constant}$$

for an isentropic process.

21.26. It is known theoretically and experimentally that all electromagnetic radiation exerts pressure and therefore carries momentum and mass. Let Φ be the flux (radiant energy crossing a unit surface in unit time) and c be the speed of light. Making use of Einstein's relation for the energy, mc^2, show that: (a) the momentum (mc) carried across a unit area in unit time is

$$\frac{\Phi}{c}$$

(b) the pressure exerted on a surface which absorbs all the incident radiation is

$$p_{\text{rad}} = \left(\frac{\Phi}{c}\right)_{\text{absorption}}$$

(c) the pressure exerted on a surface which reflects all the incident radiation is

$$p_{\text{rad}} = \left(\frac{2\Phi}{c}\right)_{\text{reflection}}$$

21.27. The energy flux (Φ) from the sun has been measured to be 1.37 kw/m^2 = 1.37×10^6 ergs/cm^2-sec. Determine the pressure and the acceleration on an aluminized plastic sail of 10^{-4} gm/cm^2 in the vicinity of the Earth's orbit. (Fig. 21.12.) Neglect gravitational effects.

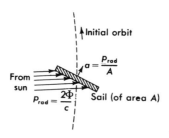

Fig. 21.12 Solar Sail for Voyage to Superior Planet.

21.28. The rate of energy absorption for an object is given by

$$Q_a = \alpha \Phi A$$

where α is the coefficient of absorption of the surface material, Φ is the energy flux, and A is the cross-sectional area presented to the flux. The rate of energy-radiation into space for an object is given by

$$Q_r = \epsilon \sigma S T^4$$

where ϵ is the emissivity, σ is the Stefan–Boltzmann constant, $5.67(10^{-5})$ erg/cm^2-sec-$(K)^4$, S is the surface area of the body, and T is the absolute temperature in degrees Kelvin. At equilibrium, the rate of energy absorption is equal to the rate of energy radiation, so that

$$\alpha \Phi A = \epsilon \sigma S T^4$$

A spherical black body is placed in orbit at the Earth's orbital distance from the sun, yet sufficiently distant from the Earth so that heat transfer effects from the Earth to the body can be neglected. If the energy flux Φ from the sun is 1.37×10^6 ergs/cm^2-sec, what is the equilibrium temperature of the object?

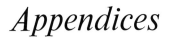

Appendices

APPENDIX A

Some Useful Definitions, Constants and Conversion Factors

Length:

1 in = 2.5400 cm
1 cm = 0.01 m = 0.3933 in = 10^4 μ = 10^8 Å
1 ft = 12 in = 30.4801 cm
1 yd = 3 ft = 0.9144 m
1 mile = 5280 ft = 1.609 km
1 nautical mile = 6080.27 ft
1 mph = 88 fpm = 44.70 cm/sec
1 knot = 1 nautical mile/hr

Mass:

1 lbm = 453.5924 gm = 16 oz = 7000 grains
1 ton (short) = 2000 lbm

735

Mass:
$$1 \text{ gm} = 15.432 \text{ grains}$$
$$1 \text{ kgm} = 2.2005 \text{ lbm}$$
$$1 \text{ slug} = 32.1739 \text{ lbm}$$

Pressure:
$$1 \text{ atm} = 14.6960 \text{ lbf/in}^2 = 760 \text{ mm Hg (at } 32°\text{F)} = 29.9212 \text{ in. Hg (at } 32°\text{F)} = 1.0332 \text{ kgf/cm}^2 = 101.3250 \times 10^4 \text{ dynes/cm}^2 = 33.9340 \text{ ft } H_2O \text{ (at } 60°\text{F)}$$
$$1 \text{ bar} = 10^6 \text{ dynes/cm}^2 = 0.9869 \text{ atm}$$

Energy:
1 international calorie (IT cal) $= \frac{1}{860}$ international watt-hour
$$1 \text{ Btu} = 251.996 \text{ IT cal}$$
$$1 \text{ joule} = 10^7 \text{ dyne-centimeters} = 10^7 \text{ ergs}$$
$$= 1 \text{ watt-sec}$$
$$1 \text{ int. joule} = 1.000165 \text{ joules}$$
$$1 \text{ int. watt} = 1.000165 \text{ watts}$$
$$1 \text{ Btu} = 778.16 \text{ ft-lbf}$$
$$1 \text{ int. cal} = 1.000654 \text{ cal}$$
$$1 \text{ hp-sec} = 550 \text{ ft-lbf}$$
$$1 \text{ hp-min} = 33,000 \text{ ft-lbf} = 42.408 \text{ Btu}$$
$$1 \text{ hp-hr} = 2544.48 \text{ Btu}$$
$$1 \text{ kwhr} = 3412.19 \text{ Btu} = 1.341 \text{ hp-hr}$$
$$1 \text{ watt-hr} = 3600 \text{ joules}$$
$$1 \frac{\text{Btu}}{\text{lbm}-°\text{R}} = 1 \frac{\text{IT cal}}{\text{gm}-°\text{K}}$$

Avogadro's number:
$$N = 6.025 \times 10^{23}/\text{gm mole}$$

Boltzmann's constant:
$$k = 1.380 \times 10^{-23} \text{ joule/molecule}-°\text{K}$$
$$= 1.380 \times 10^{-16} \text{ erg/molecule}-°\text{K}$$

Electronic charge:
$$e = 1.6021 \times 10^{-19} \text{ coulomb}$$

Electron volt:
$$1 \text{ ev} = 1.602 \times 10^{-19} \text{ joule}$$

Mass-energy conversion factor: $1 \text{ amu} = 931.16 \text{ Mev}$

Gas constant:
$$\bar{R} = 1545.33 \frac{\text{ft-lbf}}{\text{mole}-°\text{R}} = 1.9859 \frac{\text{IT Btu}}{\text{mole}-°\text{R}}$$
$$= 1.9859 \frac{\text{IT cal}}{(\text{g mole})-°\text{K}}$$
$$= 0.08205 \frac{\text{atm-liter}}{(\text{g mole})-°\text{K}}$$

Planck's constant:
$$h = 6.625 \times 10^{-34} \text{ joule-sec} = 6.625 \times 10^{-27} \text{ erg-sec}$$

Speed of light:
$$c = 2.998 \times 10^8 \text{ m/sec}$$

TABLE A.1
Conversion Factors For Length

		m	cm	μ	$\overset{\circ}{A}$	in.	ft	yd
1 Meter (m)	=	1	100	10^6	10^{10}	39.37	3.280	1.0936
1 Centimeter (cm)	=	0.01	1	10^4	10^8	0.3937	0.0328	0.0109
1 Micron (μ)	=	10^{-6}	10^{-4}	1	10^4	0.3937×10^{-4}	0.0328×10^{-4}	0.0109×10^{-4}
1 Angstrom (Å)	=	10^{-10}	10^{-8}	10^{-4}	1	0.3937×10^{-8}	0.0328×10^{-8}	0.0109×10^{-8}
1 Inch (in.)	=	0.0254	2.540	25.4×10^4	2.540×10^8	1	0.0833	0.0277
1 Foot (ft)	=	0.3048	30.48	30.48×10^4	30.43×10^8	12	1	0.3333
1 Yard (yd)	=	0.9144	91.440	91.440×10^4	91.440×10^8	36	3	1

TABLE A.2
Conversion Factors For Area

		cm^2	m^2	sq in.	sq ft	sq yd
1 cm²	=	1	10^{-4}	0.1550	1.07639	1.1960×10^{-4}
1 m²	=	10^4	1	1550	10.7639	1.1960
1 sq in.	=	6.4516	6.4516×10^{-4}	1	6.9444	7.7160×10^{-4}
1 sq ft	=	929.034	929.034×10^{-4}	144	1	0.11111
1 sq yd	=	8361.307	8361.307×10^{-4}	1296	9	1

TABLE A.3

CONVERSION FACTORS FOR VOLUME

		cm^3	$cu\ in.$	$cu\ ft$	ml	$liter$	gal
1 cm³	=	1	610.23×10^{-4}	35.3145×10^{-4}	999.972×10^{-6}	999.972×10^{-6}	264.170×10^{-6}
1 cu in.	=	16.3872	1	5.7870×10^{-4}	16.3867	16.3867×10^{-3}	432.900×10^{-5}
1 cu ft	=	283.170×10^2	1728	1	28.3162×10^3	28.3162	7.4805
1 ml	=	1.000028	610.251×10^{-4}	353.154×10^{-7}	1	0.001	264.178×10^{-6}
1 liter	=	1000.028	61.0251	353.154×10^{-4}	1000	1	264.178×10^{-3}
1 gal	=	3785.434	231	133.680×10^{-3}	3785.329	3.785329	1

TABLE A.4

CONVERSION FACTORS FOR MASS

		lbm	$slugs$	gm	kg	ton
1 lbm	=	1	0.03108	453.59	0.45359	0.0005
1 slug	=	32.174	1	1.4594×10^4	14.594	0.016087
1 gm	=	2.2046×10^{-3}	6.8521×10^{-5}	1	10^{-3}	1.1023×10^{-6}
1 kg	=	2.2046	6.8521×10^{-3}	10^3	1	1.1023×10^{-3}
1 ton	=	2000	62.162	9.0718×10^5	907.18	1

TABLE A.5

VALUE OF g_c FOR DIFFERENT SYSTEMS OF UNITS

System of Units				Value of Dimensional Constant g_c
Force (F)	Mass (M)	Length (L)	Time (t)	
lbf	lbm	foot	second	$32.174 \dfrac{\text{lbm-ft}}{\text{lbf-sec}^2}$
lbf	slug	foot	second	$1 \dfrac{\text{slug-ft}}{\text{lbf-sec}^2}$
poundal	lbm	foot	second	$1 \dfrac{\text{lbm-ft}}{\text{pdl-sec}^2}$
dyne	gram	cm	second	$1 \dfrac{\text{gm-cm}}{\text{dyne-sec}^2}$
newton	kilogram	meter	second	$1 \dfrac{\text{kg-m}}{\text{newt-sec}^2}$

TABLE A.6

CONVERSION FACTORS FOR DENSITY

	lbm/cu ft	slug/cu ft	lbm/cu in.	lbm/gal	gm/cc
1 lbm/cu ft =	1	0.03108	5.787×10^{-4}	0.13386	0.01602
1 slug/cu ft =	32.174	1	0.01862	4.3010	0.51543
1 lbm/cu in. =	1728	53.706	1	231	27.680
1 lbm/gal =	7.4805	0.2325	4.329×10^{-3}	1	0.11983
1 gm/cc =	62.428	1.9403	0.03613	8.345	1

TABLE A.7
CONVERSION FACTORS FOR PRESSURE

		lbf/in^2	$dyne/cm^2$	kgf/cm^2	in. Hg	mm Hg	in. H_2O	atm	bar
1 lbf/in^2	=	1	689.473×10^2	0.07031	2.0360	51.715	27.71	0.06805	0.06895
1 $dyne/cm^2$	=	145.0383×10^{-7}	1	101.972×10^{-8}	295.299×10^{-7}	750.062×10^{-6}	4.0188×10^{-4}	986.923×10^{-9}	10^{-6}
1 kgf/cm^2	=	14.2234	980.665×10^3	1	28.959	735.559	394.0918	967.841×10^{-3}	980.665×10^{-3}
1 in. Hg	=	0.4912	338.64×10^2	0.03453	1	25.40	13.608	0.03342	0.03386
1 mm Hg	=	0.01934	1333.223	1.3595×10^{-3}	0.03937	1	0.5358	1.315×10^{-3}	1.333×10^{-3}
1 in. H_2O	=	0.03609	24.883×10^2	2.537×10^{-3}	0.0735	1.8665	1	2.458×10^{-3}	2.488×10^{-3}
1 atm	=	14.6960	101.325×10^4	1.03323	29.9212	760	460.80	1	1.01325
1 bar	=	14.5038	10^6	1.01972	29.5299	750.0617	401.969	986.923×10^{-3}	1

TABLE A.8

CONVERSION FACTORS FOR ENERGY

	ft lbf	abs joule	int joule	cal	I.T. cal
1 ft lbf =	1	1.35582	1.355597	0.32405	0.32384
1 abs joule =	0.73756	1	0.999835	0.23885	0.238849
1 int joule =	0.737682	1.000165	1	0.239045	0.238889
1 cal =	3.08596	4.18401	4.1833	1	0.99934
1 I.T. cal =	3.08799	4.18676	4.18605	1.000657	1
1 Btu =	778.16	1055.045	1054.866	252.161	251.996
1 int kilowatt-hr =	265.567×10^4	360.0612×10^4	360.000×10^4	860.565×10^3	860.000×10^3
1 hp-hr =	198.0000×10^4	268.4525×10^4	268.082×10^4	641.615×10^3	641.194×10^3
1 liter-atm =	74.7354	101.3278	101.3111	24.2179	24.2020

	Btu	int kilowatt-hr	hp-hr	liter-atm
1 ft lbf =	128.5083×10^{-5}	376.553×10^{-9}	505.051×10^{-9}	133.8054×10^{-4}
1 abs joule =	947.827×10^{-6}	277.731×10^{-9}	372.505×10^{-9}	986.896×10^{-5}
1 int joule =	0.947988×10^{-3}	2.777778×10^{-7}	3.7256×10^{-7}	9.87058×10^{-3}
1 cal =	396.572×10^{-5}	116.2028×10^{-8}	155.8566×10^{-8}	412.918×10^{-4}
1 I.T. cal =	396.832×10^{-5}	116.2791×10^{-8}	155.9590×10^{-8}	413.189×10^{-4}
1 Btu =	1	293.018×10^{-6}	293.010×10^{-6}	10.4122
1 int kilowatt-hr =	3412.76	1	1.3412	255.343×10^2
1 hp-hr =	2544.46	0.74558	1	264.935×10^2
1 liter-atm =	0.09604	281.718×10^{-7}	377.452×10^{-7}	1

TABLE A.9

CONVERSION FACTORS FOR VISCOSITY

	1 poise $\frac{\text{1-dyne-sec}}{cm^2}$	$\frac{gf\text{-}sec}{cm^2}$	$\frac{gm}{cm\text{-}sec}$	$\frac{kgf\text{-}sec}{m^2}$	$\frac{kgm}{m\text{-}sec}$	$\frac{poundal\text{-}sec}{ft^2}$	$\frac{lbf\text{-}sec}{ft^2}$	$\frac{lbm}{ft\text{-}sec}$	$\frac{slugs}{ft\text{-}sec}$
1 poise =	1	101.97×10^{-5}	1	1.0197×10^{-2}	0.1	0.0672	0.00209	0.0672	0.00209
1 $\frac{gf\text{-}sec}{cm^2}$ =	980.67	1	980.67	10	98.067	65.898	2.0482	65.898	2.0482
1 $\frac{gm}{cm\text{-}sec}$ =	1	101.97×10^{-5}	1	1.0197×10^{-2}	0.1	0.0672	0.00209	0.0672	0.00209
1 $\frac{kgf\text{-}sec}{m^2}$ =	98.067	0.1	98.067	1	9.8067	6.5898	0.20482	6.5898	0.20482
1 $\frac{kgm}{m\text{-}sec}$ =	10	101.97×10^{-4}	10	0.10197	1	0.672	0.0209	0.672	0.0209
1 $\frac{poundal\text{-}sec}{ft^2}$ =	14.8816	0.015175	14.8816	0.15175	1.48816	1	0.03108	1	0.03018
1 $\frac{lbf\text{-}sec}{ft^2}$ =	477.9	0.4882	477.9	4.8820	47.79	32.176	1	32.174	1
1 $\frac{lbm}{ft\text{-}sec}$ =	14.8816	0.015175	14.8816	0.15175	1.48816	1	0.03108	1	1.03108
1 $\frac{slug}{ft\text{-}sec}$ =	477.9	0.4882	477.9	4.8820	47.79	32.174	1	32.174	1

APPENDIX B

Properties of Substances

TABLE B.1
Characteristic Constants For Gases

	Formula	Molecular Weight	c_p (Btu/lbm–°R)	c_v (Btu/lbm–°R)	$\gamma = \dfrac{c_p}{c_v}$	R (ft-lbf/lbm–°R)
Air		28.97	0.240	0.171	1.40	53.34
Argon	A	39.94	1.23	0.074	1.67	38.65
Helium	He	4.003	1.25	0.75	1.66	386.3
Carbon monoxide	CO	28.01	0.249	0.178	1.40	55.13
Hydrogen	H_2	2.016	3.42	2.43	1.41	767.0
Nitrogen	N_2	28.02	0.248	0.177	1.40	55.13
Oxygen	O_2	32.00	0.219	0.156	1.40	48.24
Carbon dioxide	CO_2	44.01	0.202	0.156	1.30	34.88
Sulfur dioxide	SO_2	64.07	0.154	0.122	1.26	23.55
Water vapor	H_2O	18.016	0.446	0.336	1.33	85.58
Acetylene	C_2H_2	26.04	0.409	0.333	1.23	58.77
Ethane	C_2H_6	30.07	0.422	0.357	1.18	50.82
Ethylene	C_2H_4	28.05	0.374	0.304	1.23	54.7
Isobutane	C_4H_{10}	58.12	0.420	0.387	1.09	25.8
Methane	CH_4	16.04	0.532	0.408	1.30	96.4
Propane	C_3H_8	44.09	0.404	0.360	1.12	34.1

TABLE B.2
CONSTANT-PRESSURE SPECIFIC HEATS AT ZERO PRESSURE*

Substance	c_p (Btu/lbm-°R)	$\bar{c}_p$ (Btu/mole-°R)
Air	$c_p = 0.219 + \dfrac{0.342\,T}{10^4} - \dfrac{0.293\,T^2}{10^8}$	$\bar{c}_p = 6.36 + \dfrac{9.92\,T}{10^4} - \dfrac{8.52\,T^2}{10^8}$
Carbon monoxide, CO	$c_p = 0.338 - \dfrac{117.5}{T} + \dfrac{3.82 \times 10^4}{T^2}$	$\bar{c}_p = 9.46 - \dfrac{3290}{T} + \dfrac{107 \times 10^4}{T^2}$
Hydrogen, H_2	$c_p = 2.857 + \dfrac{2.867\,T}{10^4} + \dfrac{9.92}{\sqrt{T}}$	$\bar{c}_p = 5.76 + \dfrac{5.78\,T}{10^4} + \dfrac{20}{\sqrt{T}}$
Nitrogen, N_2	$c_p = 0.338 - \dfrac{123.8}{T} + \dfrac{4.14 \times 10^4}{T^2}$	$\bar{c}_p = 9.47 - \dfrac{3470}{T} + \dfrac{116 \times 10^4}{T^2}$
Oxygen, O_2	$c_p = 0.36 - \dfrac{5.375}{\sqrt{T}} + \dfrac{47.8}{T}$	$\bar{c}_p = 11.515 - \dfrac{173}{\sqrt{T}} + \dfrac{1530}{T}$
Carbon dioxide, CO_2	$c_p = 0.368 - \dfrac{148.4}{T} + \dfrac{3.2 \times 10^4}{T^2}$	$\bar{c}_p = 16.2 - \dfrac{6530}{T} + \dfrac{141 \times 10^4}{T^2}$
Sulfur dioxide, SO_2	$c_p = 0.1875 + \dfrac{0.0944\,T}{10^4} - \dfrac{1.336 \times 10^4}{T^2}$	$\bar{c}_p = 11.89 + \dfrac{6.05\,T}{10^4} - \dfrac{85.6 \times 10^4}{T^2}$
Water vapor, H_2O	$c_p = 1.102 - \dfrac{33.1}{\sqrt{T}} + \dfrac{416}{T}$	$\bar{c}_p = 19.86 - \dfrac{597}{\sqrt{T}} + \dfrac{7500}{T}$
Acetylene, C_2H_2	$c_p = 0.459 + \dfrac{0.937\,T}{10^4} - \dfrac{2.89 \times 10^4}{T^2}$	$\bar{c}_p = 11.94 + \dfrac{24.37\,T}{10^4} - \dfrac{75.2 \times 10^4}{T^2}$
Ethane, C_2H_6	$c_p = 0.0731 + \dfrac{7.08\,T}{10^4} - \dfrac{11.3\,T^2}{10^8}$	$\bar{c}_p = 2.195 + \dfrac{212.7\,T}{10^4} - \dfrac{340\,T^2}{10^8}$
Ethylene, C_2H_4	$c_p = 0.0965 + \dfrac{5.78\,T}{10^4} - \dfrac{9.97\,T^2}{10^8}$	$\bar{c}_p = 2.706 + \dfrac{162\,T}{10^4} - \dfrac{279.6\,T^2}{10^8}$
Isobutane, C_4H_{10}	$c_p = 0.075 + \dfrac{6.94\,T}{10^4} - \dfrac{11.77\,T^2}{10^8}$	$\bar{c}_p = 4.36 + \dfrac{403\,T}{10^4} - \dfrac{683\,T^2}{10^8}$
Methane, CH_4	$c_p = 0.211 + \dfrac{6.25\,T}{10^4} - \dfrac{8.28\,T^2}{10^8}$	$\bar{c}_p = 3.38 + \dfrac{100.2\,T}{10^4} - \dfrac{132.7\,T^2}{10^8}$
Propane, C_3H_8	$c_p = 0.0152 + \dfrac{7.27\,T}{10^4} - \dfrac{12.32\,T^2}{10^8}$	$\bar{c}_p = 2.258 + \dfrac{320\,T}{10^4} - \dfrac{543\,T^2}{10^8}$

* Values derived from Spencer, Justice, Flanagan, Chipman, and Fontana, *Jour. Am. Chem. Soc.*, Vols. 56, 57, 64, 67, and Sweigert and Beardsley, *Ga. Inst. of Tech. Eng. Exp. Sta. Bull.* No. 2.

TABLE B.3
CRITICAL CONSTANTS

Substance	T_c (°K)	p_c (atm)	v_c (cm³/g mole)	v_c (ft³/mole)	$z_c = \dfrac{p_c v_c}{RT_c}$
Air	132.41	37.25	92.35		
Argon, A	150.72	47.99	75	1.20	0.291
Helium, He	5.19	2.26	58	0.929	0.308
Carbon monoxide, CO	132.91	34.529	93	1.49	0.294
Hydrogen, H$_2$	33.24	12.797	65	1.04	0.304
Nitrogen, N$_2$	126.2	33.54	90	0.144	0.291
Oxygen, O$_2$	154.78	50.14	74	1.19	0.292
Carbon dioxide, CO$_2$	304.20	72.90	94	1.51	0.275
Sulfur dioxide, SO$_2$	430.7	77.8	122		0.269
Water vapor, H$_2$O	647.27	218.167	56	0.897	0.230
Acetylene, C$_2$H$_2$	309.5	61.6	113		0.274
Ethane, C$_2$H$_6$	305.48	48.20	148	2.37	0.285
Ethylene, C$_2$H$_4$	283.06	50.50	124	1.99	0.270
n-Butane, C$_4$H$_{10}$	425.17	37.47	255	4.08	0.274
Methane, CH$_4$	190.7	45.8	99	1.59	0.290
Propane, C$_3$H$_8$	370.01	42.1	200	3.20	0.277

TABLE B.4
CONSTANTS FOR EQUATIONS OF STATE*

Substance	Van Der Waals Gas		Beattie-Bridgeman Gas				
	a $\dfrac{atm\text{-}ft^6}{mole^2}$	b $\dfrac{ft^3}{mole}$	A_0 $\dfrac{atm\text{-}ft^6}{mole^2}$	a $\dfrac{ft^3}{mole}$	B_0 $\dfrac{ft^3}{mole}$	b $\dfrac{ft^3}{mole}$	c $\dfrac{ft^3\text{-}{}^\circ R^3}{mole}$
Air	343.8	0.585	334.1	0.309	0.739	−0.716	4.05×10^6
Hydrogen, H_2	63.02	0.427	50.57	−0.0811	0.336	−0.698	0.0471×10^6
Nitrogen, N_2	346.0	0.618	344.92	0.419	0.808	−0.111	3.92×10^6
Oxygen, O_2	349.5	0.510	382.53	0.410	0.741	0.0674	4.48×10^6
Carbon monoxide, CO	374.7	0.630	344.9	0.419	0.808	−0.111	3.92×10^6
Carbon dioxide, CO_2	924.2	0.685	1284.9	1.143	1.678	1.159	61.65×10^6
Methane, CH_4	578.9	0.684	584.6	0.297	0.895	−0.254	11.98×10^6
Propane, C_3H_8	2374.0	1.446	305.8	1.173	2.90	0.688	112.2×10^6
n-Butane, C_4H_{10}	3675.0	1.944	456.5	1.948	3.944	1.51	327.02×10^6

* Evaluated from critical data and from Beattie and Bridgeman, *Proc. Am. Acad. Arts, Sci.*, **63**: 229–308 (1928); *J.A.C.S.*, **50**: 3133 (1928).

TABLE B.5
Air Tables*
(For 1 pound)

T °F abs	t °F	h Btu/lb	p_r	u Btu/lb	v_r	ϕ Btu/lb-°F	T °F abs	t °F	h Btu/lb	p_r	u Btu/lb	v_r	ϕ Btu/lb-°F
100	−360	23.7	.00384	16.9	9640	.1971	500	40	119.5	1.059	85.2	174.9	.5823
120	−340	28.5	.00726	20.3	6120	.2408	520	60	124.3	1.215	88.6	158.6	.5917
140	−320	33.3	.01244	23.7	4170	.2777	540	80	129.1	1.386	92.0	144.3	.6008
160	−300	38.1	.01982	27.1	2990	.3096	560	100	133.9	1.574	95.5	131.8	.6095
180	−280	42.9	.0299	30.6	2230	.3378	580	120	138.7	1.780	98.9	120.7	.6179
200	−260	47.7	.0432	34.0	1715	.3630	600	140	143.5	2.00	102.3	110.9	.6261
220	−240	52.5	.0603	37.4	1352	.3858	620	160	148.3	2.25	105.8	102.1	.6340
240	−220	57.2	.0816	40.8	1089	.4067	640	180	153.1	2.51	109.2	94.3	.6416
260	−200	62.0	.1080	44.2	892	.4258	660	200	157.9	2.80	112.7	87.3	.6490
280	−180	66.8	.1399	47.6	742	.4436	680	220	162.7	3.11	116.1	81.0	.6562
300	−160	71.6	.1780	51.0	624	.4601	700	240	167.6	3.45	119.6	75.2	.6632
320	−140	76.4	.2229	54.5	532	.4755	720	260	172.4	3.81	123.0	70.1	.6700
340	−120	81.2	.2754	57.9	457	.4900	740	280	177.2	4.19	126.5	65.4	.6766
360	−100	86.0	.336	61.3	397	.5037	760	300	182.1	4.61	130.0	61.1	.6831
380	−80	90.8	.406	64.7	347	.5166	780	320	186.9	5.05	133.5	57.2	.6894
400	−60	95.5	.486	68.1	305	.5289	800	340	191.8	5.53	137.0	53.6	.6956
420	−40	100.3	.576	71.5	270	.5406	820	360	196.7	6.03	140.5	50.4	.7016
440	−20	105.1	.678	74.9	241	.5517	840	380	201.6	6.67	144.0	47.3	.7075
460	0	109.9	.791	78.4	215.3	.5624	860	400	206.5	7.15	147.5	44.6	.7132
480	20	114.7	.918	81.8	193.6	.5726	880	420	211.4	7.76	151.0	42.0	.7189

T (°R)	T (°F)	h	p_r	u	v_r	φ
900	440	216.3	8.41	154.6	39.6	.7244
920	460	221.2	9.10	158.1	37.4	.7298
940	480	226.1	9.83	161.7	35.4	.7351
960	500	231.1	10.61	165.3	33.5	.7403
980	520	236.0	11.43	168.8	31.8	.7454
1000	540	241.0	12.30	172.4	30.1	.7504
1020	560	246.0	13.22	176.0	28.6	.7554
1040	580	251.0	14.18	179.7	27.2	.7602
1060	600	256.0	15.20	183.3	25.8	.7650
1080	620	261.0	16.28	186.9	24.6	.7696
1100	640	266.0	17.41	190.6	23.4	.7743
1120	660	271.0	18.60	194.2	22.3	.7788
1140	680	276.1	19.86	197.9	21.3	.7833
1160	700	281.1	21.2	201.6	20.29	.7877
1180	720	286.2	22.6	205.3	19.38	.7920
1200	740	291.3	24.0	209.0	18.51	.7963
1220	760	296.4	25.2	212.8	17.70	.8005
1240	780	301.5	27.1	216.5	16.93	.8047
1260	800	306.6	28.8	220.3	16.20	.8088
1280	820	311.8	30.6	224.0	15.52	.8128
1300	840	316.9	32.4	227.8	14.87	.8168
1320	860	322.1	34.3	231.6	14.25	.8208
1340	880	327.3	36.3	235.4	13.67	.8246
1360	900	332.5	38.4	239.2	13.12	.8285
1380	920	337.7	40.6	243.1	12.59	.8323
1400	940	342.9	42.9	246.9	12.10	.8360
1420	960	348.1	45.3	250.8	11.62	.8398
1440	980	353.4	47.8	254.7	11.17	.8434
1460	1000	358.6	50.3	258.5	10.74	.8470
1480	1020	363.9	53.0	262.4	10.34	.8506
1500	1040	369.2	55.9	266.3	9.95	.8542
1520	1060	374.5	58.8	270.3	9.58	.8568
1540	1080	379.8	61.8	274.2	9.23	.8611
1560	1100	385.1	65.0	278.1	8.89	.8646
1580	1120	390.4	68.3	282.1	8.57	.8679
1600	1140	395.7	71.7	286.1	8.26	.8713
1620	1160	401.1	75.3	290.0	7.97	.8746
1640	1180	406.4	79.0	294.0	7.69	.8779
1660	1200	411.8	82.8	298.0	7.42	.8812
1680	1220	417.2	86.8	302.0	7.17	.8844
1700	1240	422.6	91.0	306.1	6.92	.8876
1720	1260	428.0	95.2	310.1	6.69	.8907
1740	1280	433.4	99.7	314.1	6.46	.8939
1760	1300	438.8	104.3	318.2	6.25	.8970
1780	1320	444.3	109.1	322.2	6.04	.9000
1800	1340	449.7	114.0	326.3	5.85	.9031
1820	1360	455.2	119.2	330.4	5.66	.9061
1840	1380	460.6	124.5	334.5	5.48	.9091
1860	1400	466.1	130.0	338.6	5.30	.9120
1880	1420	471.6	135.6	342.7	5.13	.9150

* Abridged from *Gas Tables* by J. H. Keenan and J. Kaye, John Wiley & Sons, Inc., New York, 1948, by permission of the publisher.

TABLE B.5
Air Tables*—cont.
(For 1 pound)

T °F abs	t °F	h Btu/lb	p_r	u Btu/lb	v_r	φ Btu/lb-°F
1900	1440	477.1	141.5	346.8	4.97	.9179
1920	1460	482.6	147.6	351.0	4.82	.9208
1940	1480	488.1	153.9	355.1	4.67	.9236
1960	1500	493.6	160.4	359.3	4.53	.9264
1980	1520	499.1	167.1	363.4	4.39	.9293
2000	1540	504.7	174.0	367.6	4.26	.9320
2020	1560	510.3	181.2	371.8	4.13	.9348
2040	1580	515.8	188.5	376.0	4.01	.9376
2060	1600	521.4	196.2	380.2	3.89	.9403
2080	1620	527.0	204.0	384.4	3.78	.9430
2100	1640	532.6	212	388.6	3.67	.9456
2120	1660	538.2	220	392.8	3.56	.9483
2140	1680	543.7	229	397.0	3.46	.9509
2160	1700	549.4	238	401.3	3.36	.9535
2180	1720	555.0	247	405.5	3.27	.9561
2200	1740	560.6	257	409.8	3.18	.9587
2220	1760	566.2	266	414.0	3.09	.9612
2240	1780	571.9	276	418.3	3.00	.9638
2260	1800	577.5	287	422.6	2.92	.9663
2280	1820	583.2	297	426.9	2.84	.9688
2300	1840	588.8	308	431.2	2.76	.9712
2320	1860	594.5	319	435.5	2.69	.9737
2340	1880	600.2	331	439.8	2.62	.9761
2360	1900	605.8	343	444.1	2.55	.9785
2380	1920	611.5	355	448.4	2.48	.9809
2400	1940	617.2	368	452.7	2.42	.9833
2420	1960	622.9	380	457.0	2.36	.9857
2440	1980	628.6	394	461.4	2.30	.9880
2460	2000	634.3	407	465.7	2.24	.9904
2480	2020	640.0	421	470.0	2.18	.9927
2500	2040	645.8	436	474.4	2.12	.9950
2520	2060	651.5	450	478.8	2.07	.9972
2540	2080	657.2	466	483.1	2.02	.9995
2560	2100	663.0	481	487.5	1.971	1.0018
2580	2120	668.7	497	491.9	1.922	1.0040
2600	2140	674.5	514	496.3	1.876	1.0062
2620	2160	680.2	530	500.6	1.830	1.0084
2640	2180	686.0	548	505.0	1.786	1.0106
2660	2200	691.8	565	509.4	1.743	1.0128
2680	2220	697.6	583	513.8	1.702	1.0150

2700	2240	703.4	602	518.3	1.662	1.0171	3200	2740	849.5	1242	630.1	.955	1.0668
2720	2260	709.1	621	522.7	1.623	1.0193	3220	2760	855.4	1276	634.6	.935	1.0686
2740	2280	714.9	640	527.1	1.585	1.0214	3240	2780	861.3	1310	639.2	.916	1.0704
2760	2300	720.7	660	531.5	1.548	1.0235	3260	2800	867.2	1345	643.7	.898	1.0722
2780	2320	726.5	681	536.0	1.512	1.0256	3280	2820	873.1	1381	648.3	.880	1.0740
2800	2340	732.3	702	540.4	1.478	1.0277	3300	2840	879.0	1418	652.8	.862	1.0758
2820	2360	738.2	724	544.8	1.444	1.0297	3320	2860	884.9	1455	657.4	.845	1.0776
2840	2380	744.0	746	549.3	1.411	1.0318	3340	2880	890.9	1494	661.9	.828	1.0794
2860	2400	749.8	768	553.7	1.379	1.0338	3360	2900	896.8	1533	666.5	.812	1.0812
2880	2420	755.6	791	558.2	1.348	1.0359	3380	2920	902.7	1573	671.0	.796	1.0830
2900	2440	761.4	815	562.7	1.318	1.0379	3400	2940	908.7	1613	675.6	.781	1.0847
2920	2460	767.3	839	567.1	1.289	1.0399	3420	2960	914.6	1655	680.2	.766	1.0864
2940	2480	773.1	864	571.6	1.261	1.0419	3440	2980	920.6	1697	684.8	.751	1.0882
2960	2500	779.0	889	576.1	1.233	1.0439	3460	3000	926.5	1740	689.3	.736	1.0899
2980	2520	784.8	915	580.6	1.206	1.0458	3480	3020	932.4	1784	693.9	.722	1.0916
3000	2540	790.7	941	585.0	1.180	1.0478	3500	3040	938.4	1829	698.5	.709	1.0933
3020	2560	796.5	969	589.5	1.155	1.0497	3520	3060	944.4	1875	703.1	.695	1.0950
3040	2580	802.4	996	594.0	1.130	1.0517	3540	3080	950.3	1922	707.6	.682	1.0967
3060	2600	808.3	1025	598.5	1.106	1.0536	3560	3100	956.3	1970	712.2	.670	1.0984
3080	2620	814.2	1054	603.0	1.083	1.0555	3580	3120	962.2	2018	716.8	.657	1.1000
3100	2640	820.0	1083	607.5	1.060	1.0574	3600	3140	968.2	2068	721.4	.645	1.1017
3120	2660	825.9	1114	612.0	1.038	1.0593	3620	3160	974.2	2118	726.0	.633	1.1034
3140	2680	831.8	1145	616.6	1.016	1.0612	3640	3180	980.2	2170	730.6	.621	1.1050
3160	2700	837.7	1176	621.1	.995	1.0630	3660	3200	986.1	2222	735.3	.610	1.1066
3180	2720	843.6	1209	625.6	.975	1.0649	3680	3220	992.1	2276	739.9	.599	1.1083

TABLE B.6
Dry Saturated Steam, Temperature Table*

Temp, °F, t	Abs press., psi, p	Specific volume			Enthalpy			Entropy			Temp, °F, t
		Sat. liquid v_f	Evap. v_{fg}	Sat. vapor v_g	Sat. liquid h_f	Evap. h_{fg}	Sat. vapor h_g	Sat. liquid s_f	Evap. s_{fg}	Sat. vapor s_g	
32	0.08854	0.01602	3306	3306	0.00	1075.8	1075.8	0.0000	2.1877	2.1877	32
35	0.099995	0.01602	2947	2947	3.02	1074.1	1077.1	0.0061	2.1709	2.1770	35
40	0.12170	0.01602	2444	2444	8.05	1071.3	1079.3	0.0162	2.1435	2.1597	40
45	0.14752	0.01602	2036.4	2036.4	13.06	1068.4	1081.5	0.0262	2.1167	2.1429	45
50	0.17811	0.01603	1703.2	1703.2	18.07	1065.6	1083.7	0.0361	2.0903	2.1264	50
60	0.2563	0.01604	1206.6	1206.7	28.06	1059.9	1088.0	0.0555	2.0393	2.0948	60
70	0.3631	0.01606	867.8	867.9	38.04	1054.3	1092.3	0.0745	1.9902	2.0647	70
80	0.5069	0.01608	633.1	633.1	48.02	1048.6	1096.6	0.0932	1.9428	2.0360	80
90	0.6982	0.01610	468.0	468.0	57.99	1042.9	1100.9	0.1115	1.8972	2.0087	90
100	0.9492	0.01613	350.3	350.4	67.97	1037.2	1105.2	0.1295	1.8531	1.9826	100
110	1.2748	0.01617	265.3	265.4	77.94	1031.6	1109.5	0.1471	1.8106	1.9577	110
120	1.6924	0.01620	203.25	203.27	87.92	1025.8	1113.7	0.1645	1.7694	1.9339	120
130	2.2225	0.01625	157.32	157.34	97.90	1020.0	1117.9	0.1816	1.7296	1.9112	130
140	2.8886	0.01629	122.99	123.01	107.89	1014.1	1122.0	0.1984	1.6910	1.8894	140
150	3.718	0.01634	97.06	97.07	117.89	1008.2	1126.1	0.2149	1.6537	1.8685	150
160	4.741	0.01639	77.27	77.29	127.89	1002.3	1130.2	0.2311	1.6174	1.8485	160
170	5.992	0.01645	62.04	62.06	137.90	996.3	1134.2	0.2472	1.5822	1.8293	170
180	7.510	0.01651	50.21	50.23	147.92	990.2	1138.1	0.2630	1.5480	1.8109	180
190	9.339	0.01657	40.94	40.96	157.95	984.1	1142.0	0.2785	1.5147	1.7932	190
200	11.526	0.01663	33.62	33.64	167.99	977.9	1145.9	0.2938	1.4824	1.7762	200

Temp	Abs Press	v_f	v_{fg}	v_g	h_f	h_{fg}	h_g	s_f	s_{fg}	s_g	Temp
210	14.123	0.01670	27.80	27.82	178.05	971.6	1149.7	0.3090	1.4508	1.7598	210
212	14.696	0.01672	26.78	26.80	180.07	970.3	1150.4	0.3120	1.4446	1.7566	212
220	17.186	0.01677	23.13	23.15	188.13	965.2	1153.4	0.3239	1.4201	1.7440	220
230	20.780	0.01684	19.365	19.382	198.23	958.8	1157.0	0.3387	1.3901	1.7288	230
240	24.969	0.01692	16.306	16.323	208.34	952.2	1160.5	0.3531	1.3609	1.7140	240
250	29.825	0.01700	13.804	13.821	216.48	945.6	1164.0	0.3675	1.3323	1.6998	250
260	35.429	0.01709	11.746	11.763	228.64	938.7	1167.3	0.3817	1.3043	1.6860	260
270	41.858	0.01717	10.044	10.061	238.84	931.8	1170.6	0.3958	1.2769	1.6727	270
280	49.203	0.01726	8.628	8.645	249.06	924.7	1173.8	0.4096	1.2501	1.6597	280
290	57.556	0.01735	7.444	7.461	259.31	917.5	1176.8	0.4234	1.2238	1.6472	290
300	67.013	0.01745	6.449	6.466	269.59	910.1	1179.7	0.4369	1.1980	1.6350	300
310	77.68	0.01755	5.609	5.626	279.92	902.6	1182.5	0.4504	1.1727	1.6231	310
320	89.66	0.01765	4.896	4.914	290.28	894.9	1185.2	0.4637	1.1478	1.6115	320
330	103.06	0.01776	4.289	4.307	300.68	887.0	1187.7	0.4769	1.1233	1.6002	330
340	118.01	0.01787	3.770	3.788	311.13	879.0	1190.1	0.4900	1.0992	1.5891	340
350	134.63	0.01799	3.324	3.342	321.63	870.7	1192.3	0.5029	1.0754	1.5783	350
360	153.04	0.01811	2.939	2.957	332.18	862.2	1194.4	0.5158	1.0519	1.5677	360
370	173.37	0.01823	2.606	2.625	342.79	853.5	1196.3	0.5286	1.0287	1.5573	370
380	195.77	0.01836	2.317	2.335	353.45	844.6	1198.1	0.5413	1.0059	1.5471	380
390	220.37	0.01850	2.0651	2.0836	364.17	835.4	1199.6	0.5539	0.9832	1.5371	390
400	247.31	0.01864	1.8447	1.8633	374.97	826.0	1201.0	0.5664	0.9608	1.5272	400
410	276.75	0.01878	1.6512	1.6700	385.83	816.3	1202.1	0.5788	0.9386	1.5174	410
420	308.83	0.01894	1.4811	1.5000	396.77	806.3	1203.1	0.5912	0.9166	1.5078	420
430	343.72	0.01910	1.3308	1.3499	407.79	796.0	1203.8	0.6035	0.6035	0.8947	430
440	381.59	0.01926	1.1979	1.2171	418.90	785.4	1204.3	0.6158	0.8730	1.4887	440

* Abridged from *Thermodynamic Properties of Steam* by Joseph H. Keenan and Frederick G. Keyes, John Wiley & Sons, Inc., New York, 1937, by permission of the publisher.

TABLE B.6
Dry Saturated Steam, Temperature Table—cont.

Temp, °F, t	Abs press., psi, p	Specific volume			Enthalpy			Entropy			Temp, °F, t
		Sat. liquid v_f	Evap. v_{fg}	Sat. vapor v_g	Sat. liquid h_f	Evap. h_{fg}	Sat. vapor h_g	Sat. liquid s_f	Evap. s_{fg}	Sat. vapor s_g	
450	422.6	0.0194	1.0799	1.0993	430.1	774.5	1204.6	0.6280	0.8513	1.4793	450
460	466.9	0.0196	0.9748	0.9944	441.4	763.2	1204.6	0.6402	0.8298	1.4700	460
470	514.7	0.0198	0.8811	0.9009	452.8	751.5	1204.3	0.6523	0.8083	1.4606	470
480	566.1	0.0200	0.7972	0.8172	464.4	739.4	1203.7	0.6645	0.7868	1.4513	480
490	621.4	0.0202	0.7221	0.7423	476.0	726.8	1202.8	0.6766	0.7653	1.4419	490
500	680.8	0.0204	0.6545	0.6749	487.8	713.9	1201.7	0.6887	0.7438	1.4325	500
520	812.4	0.0209	0.5385	0.5594	511.9	686.4	1198.2	0.7130	0.7006	1.4136	520
540	962.5	0.0215	0.4434	0.4649	536.6	656.6	1193.2	0.7374	0.6568	1.3942	540
560	1133.1	0.0221	0.3647	0.3868	562.2	624.2	1186.4	0.7621	0.6121	1.3742	560
580	1325.8	0.0228	0.2980	0.3217	577.9	588.4	1177.3	0.7872	0.5659	1.3532	580
600	1342.9	0.0236	0.2432	0.2668	617.0	548.5	1165.5	0.8131	0.5176	1.3307	600
620	1786.6	0.0247	0.1955	0.2201	646.7	503.6	1150.3	0.8398	0.4664	1.3062	620
640	2059.7	0.0260	0.1538	0.1798	678.6	452.0	1130.5	0.8679	0.4110	1.2789	640
660	2365.4	0.0278	0.1165	0.1442	714.2	390.2	1104.4	0.8987	0.3485	1.2472	660
680	2708.1	0.0305	0.0819	0.1115	757.3	309.9	1067.2	0.9351	0.2719	1.2071	680
700	3093.7	0.0369	0.0392	0.0761	823.3	172.1	995.4	0.9905	0.1484	1.1389	700
705.4	3206.2	0.0503	0	0.0503	902.7	0	902.7	1.0580	0	1.0580	705.4

TABLE B.7
DRY SATURATED STEAM, PRESSURE TABLE*

Abs press., psi, p	Temp, °F, t	Sat. liquid v_f	Sat. vapor v_g	Sat. liquid h_f	Evap. h_{fg}	Sat. vapor h_g	Sat. liquid s_f	Evap. s_{fg}	Sat. vapor s_g	Sat. liquid u_f	Sat. vapor u_g	Abs press., psi, p
1.0	101.74	0.01614	333.6	69.70	1036.3	1106.0	0.1326	1.8456	1.9782	69.70	1044.3	1.0
2.0	126.08	0.01623	173.73	93.99	1022.2	1116.2	0.1749	1.7451	1.9200	93.98	1051.9	2.0
3.0	141.48	0.01630	118.71	109.37	1013.2	1122.6	0.2008	1.6855	1.8863	109.36	1056.7	3.0
4.0	152.97	0.01636	90.63	120.86	1006.4	1127.3	0.2198	1.6427	1.8625	120.85	1060.2	4.0
5.0	162.24	0.01640	73.52	130.13	1001.0	1131.0	0.2347	1.6094	1.8441	130.12	1063.1	5.0
6.0	170.06	0.01645	61.98	137.96	996.2	1134.2	0.2472	1.5820	1.8292	137.94	1065.4	6.0
7.0	176.85	0.01649	53.64	144.76	992.1	1136.9	0.2581	1.5586	1.8167	144.74	1067.4	7.0
8.0	182.86	0.01653	47.34	150.79	988.5	1139.3	0.2674	1.5383	1.8057	150.77	1069.2	8.0
9.0	188.28	0.01656	42.40	156.22	985.2	1141.4	0.2759	1.5203	1.7962	156.19	1070.8	9.0
10	193.21	0.01659	38.42	161.17	982.1	1143.3	0.2835	1.5041	1.7876	161.14	1072.2	10
14.696	212.00	0.01672	26.80	180.07	970.3	1150.4	0.3120	1.4446	1.7566	180.02	1077.5	14.696
15	213.03	0.01672	26.29	181.11	969.7	1150.8	0.3135	1.4415	1.7549	181.06	1077.8	15
20	227.96	0.01683	20.089	196.16	960.1	1156.3	0.3356	1.3962	1.7319	196.10	1081.9	20
25	240.07	0.01692	16.303	208.42	952.1	1160.6	0.3533	1.3606	1.7139	208.34	1085.1	25
30	250.33	0.01701	13.746	218.82	945.3	1164.1	0.3680	1.3313	1.6993	218.73	1087.8	30
35	259.28	0.01708	11.898	227.91	939.2	1167.1	0.3807	1.3063	1.6870	227.80	1090.1	35
40	267.25	0.01715	10.498	236.03	933.7	1169.7	0.3919	1.2844	1.6763	235.90	1092.0	40
45	274.44	0.01721	9.401	243.36	928.6	1172.0	0.4019	1.2650	1.6669	243.22	1093.7	45
50	281.01	0.01727	8.515	250.09	924.0	1174.1	0.4110	1.2474	1.6585	249.93	1095.3	50
55	287.07	0.01732	7.787	256.30	919.6	1175.9	0.4193	1.2316	1.6509	256.12	1096.7	55

* Abridged from *Thermodynamic Properties of Steam* by Joseph H. Keenan and Frederick G. Keyes, John Wiley & Sons, Inc., New York, 1937, by permission of the publisher.

TABLE B.7

DRY SATURATED STEAM, PRESSURE TABLE—cont.

Abs press., psi, p	Temp, °F, t	Sat. liquid v_f	Sat. vapor v_g	Sat. liquid h_f	Evap. h_{fg}	Sat. vapor h_g	Sat. liquid s_f	Evap. s_{fg}	Sat. vapor s_g	Sat. liquid u_f	Sat. vapor u_g	Abs press., psi, p
60	292.71	0.01738	7.175	262.09	915.5	1177.6	0.4270	1.2168	1.6438	261.90	1097.9	60
65	297.97	0.01743	6.655	267.50	911.6	1179.1	0.4342	1.2032	1.6374	267.29	1099.1	65
70	302.92	0.01748	6.206	272.61	907.9	1180.6	0.3309	1.1906	1.6315	272.38	1100.2	70
75	307.60	0.01753	5.816	277.43	904.5	1181.9	0.4472	1.1787	1.6259	277.19	1101.2	75
80	312.03	0.01757	5.472	282.02	901.1	1183.1	0.4531	1.1676	1.6207	281.76	1102.1	80
85	316.25	0.01761	5.168	286.39	897.8	1184.2	0.4587	1.1571	1.6158	286.11	1102.9	85
90	320.27	0.01766	4.896	290.56	894.7	1185.3	0.4641	1.1471	1.6112	290.27	1103.7	90
95	324.12	0.01770	4.652	294.56	891.7	1186.2	0.4692	1.1376	1.6068	294.25	1104.5	95
100	327.81	0.01774	4.432	298.40	888.8	1187.2	0.4740	1.1286	1.6026	298.08	1105.2	100
120	341.25	0.01789	3.728	312.44	877.9	1190.4	0.4916	1.0062	1.5878	312.05	1107.6	120
130	347.32	0.01796	3.455	318.81	872.9	1191.7	0.4995	1.0817	1.5812	318.38	1108.6	130
140	353.02	0.01802	3.220	324.82	868.2	1193.0	0.5069	1.0682	1.5751	324.35	1109.6	140
150	358.42	0.01809	3.015	330.51	863.6	1194.1	0.5138	1.0556	1.5694	330.01	1110.5	150
160	363.53	0.01815	2.834	335.93	859.2	1195.1	0.5204	1.0436	1.5640	335.39	1111.2	160
170	368.41	0.01822	2.675	341.09	854.9	1196.0	0.5266	1.0324	1.5590	340.52	1111.9	170
180	373.06	0.01827	2.532	346.03	850.8	1196.9	0.5325	1.0217	1.5542	345.42	1112.5	180
190	377.51	0.01833	2.404	350.79	846.8	1197.6	0.5381	1.0116	1.5497	350.15	1113.1	190
200	381.79	0.01839	2.288	355.36	843.0	1198.4	0.5435	1.0018	1.5453	354.68	1113.7	200
250	400.95	0.01865	1.8438	376.00	825.1	1201.1	0.5675	0.9588	1.5263	375.14	1115.8	250
300	417.33	0.01890	1.5433	393.84	809.0	1202.8	0.5879	0.9225	1.5104	392.79	1117.1	300

350	1118.0	408.45	1.4966	0.8910	0.6056	1203.9	794.2	409.69	1.3260	0.01913	431.72	350
400	1118.5	422.6	1.4844	0.8630	0.6214	1204.5	780.5	424.0	1.1613	0.0193	444.59	400
450	1118.7	435.5	1.4734	0.8378	0.6356	1204.6	767.4	437.2	1.0320	0.0195	456.28	450
500	1118.7	447.6	1.4634	0.8147	0.6487	1204.4	755.0	449.4	0.9278	0.0197	467.01	500
550	1118.2	458.8	1.4542	0.7934	0.6608	1203.9	743.1	460.8	0.8424	0.0199	476.94	550
600	1117.7	469.4	1.4454	0.7734	0.6720	1203.2	731.6	471.6	0.7698	0.0201	486.21	600
650	1117.1	479.4	1.4374	0.7548	0.6826	1202.3	720.5	481.8	0.7083	0.0203	494.90	650
700	1116.3	488.8	1.4296	0.7371	0.6925	1201.2	709.7	491.5	0.6554	0.0205	503.10	700
750	1115.4	598.0	1.4223	0.7204	0.7019	1200.0	699.2	500.8	0.6092	0.0207	510.86	750
800	1114.4	506.6	1.4153	0.7045	0.7108	1198.6	688.9	509.7	0.5687	0.0209	518.23	800
850	1113.3	515.0	1.4085	0.6891	0.7194	1197.1	678.8	518.3	0.5327	0.0210	525.26	850
900	1112.1	523.1	1.4020	0.6744	0.7275	1195.4	668.8	526.6	0.5006	0.0212	531.98	900
950	1110.8	530.9	1.3957	0.6602	0.7355	1193.7	659.1	534.6	0.4717	0.0214	538.43	950
1000	1109.4	538.4	1.3897	0.6467	0.7430	1191.8	649.4	542.4	0.4456	0.0216	544.61	1000
1100	1106.4	552.9	1.3780	0.6205	0.7575	1187.8	630.4	557.4	0.4001	0.0220	556.31	1100
1200	1103.0	566.7	1.3667	0.5956	0.7711	1183.4	611.7	571.7	0.3619	0.0223	567.22	1200
1300	1099.4	580.0	1.3559	0.5719	0.7840	1178.6	593.2	585.4	0.3293	0.0227	577.46	1300
1400	1095.4	592.7	1.3454	0.5491	0.7963	1173.4	575.7	598.7	0.3012	0.0231	587.10	1400
1500	1091.2	605.1	1.3351	0.5269	0.8082	1167.9	556.3	611.6	0.2765	0.0235	596.23	1500
2000	1065.6	662.2	1.2849	0.4230	0.8619	1135.1	463.4	671.7	0.1878	0.0257	635.82	2000
2500	1030.6	717.3	1.2322	0.3197	0.9126	1091.1	360.5	730.6	0.1307	0.0287	668.13	2500
3000	972.7	783.4	1.1615	0.1885	0.9731	1020.3	217.8	802.5	0.0858	0.0346	695.36	3000
3206.2	872.9	872.9	1.0580	0	1.0580	902.7	0	902.7	0.0503	0.0503	705.40	3206.2

TABLE B.8
PROPERTIES OF SUPERHEATED STEAM*

Abs press., psi (Sat. temp)		Temperature, degrees Fahrenheit												
		200	300	400	500	600	700	800	900	1000	1100	1200	1400	1600
1 (101.74)	v..	392.6	452.3	512.0	571.6	631.2	690.8	750.4	809.9	869.5	929.1	988.7	1107.8	1227.0
	h..	1150.4	1195.8	1241.7	1288.3	1335.7	1383.8	1432.8	1482.7	1533.5	1585.2	1637.7	1745.7	1857.5
	s..	2.0512	2.1153	2.1720	2.2233	2.2702	2.3137	2.3542	2.3923	2.4283	2.4625	2.4952	2.5566	2.6137
5 (162.24)	v..	78.16	90.25	102.26	114.22	126.16	138.10	150.03	161.95	173.87	185.79	197.71	221.6	245.4
	h..	1148.8	1195.0	1241.2	1288.0	1335.4	1383.6	1432.7	1482.6	1533.4	1585.1	1637.7	1745.7	1857.4
	s..	1.8718	1.9370	1.9942	2.0456	2.0927	2.1361	2.1767	2.2148	2.2509	2.2851	2.3178	2.3792	2.4363
10 (193.21)	v..	38.85	45.00	51.04	57.05	63.03	69.01	74.98	80.95	86.92	92.88	98.84	110.77	122.69
	h..	1146.6	1193.9	1240.6	1287.5	1335.1	1383.4	1432.5	1432.4	1533.2	1585.0	1637.6	1745.6	1857.3
	s..	1.7927	1.8595	1.9172	1.9689	2.0160	2.0596	2.1002	2.1383	2.1744	2.2086	2.2413	2.3028	2.3598
14.696 (212.00)	v..	......	30.53	34.68	38.78	42.86	46.94	51.00	55.07	59.13	63.19	67.25	75.37	83.48
	h..	......	1192.8	1239.9	1287.1	1334.8	1383.2	1432.3	1482.3	1533.1	1584.8	1637.5	1747.5	1857.3
	s..	......	1.8160	1.8743	1.9261	1.9734	2.0170	2.0576	2.0958	2.1319	2.1662	2.1989	2.2603	2.3174
20 (227.96)	v..	......	22.36	25.43	28.46	31.47	34.47	37.46	40.45	43.44	46.42	49.41	55.37	61.34
	h..	......	1191.6	1239.2	1286.6	1334.4	1382.9	1432.1	1482.1	1533.0	1584.7	1637.4	1745.4	1857.2
	s..	......	1.7808	1.8396	1.8918	1.9392	1.9829	2.0235	2.0618	2.0978	2.1321	2.1648	2.2263	2.2834
40 (267.25)	v..	......	11.040	12.628	14.168	15.688	17.198	18.702	20.20	21.70	23.20	24.69	27.68	30.66
	h..	......	1186.8	1236.5	1284.8	1333.1	1381.9	1431.3	1481.4	1532.4	1584.3	1637.0	1745.1	1857.0
	s..	......	1.6994	1.7608	1.8140	1.8619	1.9058	1.9467	1.9850	2.0212	2.0555	2.0883	2.1498	2.2069
60 (292.71)	v..	......	7.259	8.357	9.403	10.427	11.441	12.449	13.452	14.454	15.453	16.451	18.446	20.44
	h..	......	1181.6	1233.6	1283.0	1331.8	1380.9	1430.5	1480.8	1531.9	1583.8	1636.6	1744.8	1856.7
	s..	......	1.6492	1.7135	1.7678	1.8162	1.8605	1.9015	1.9400	1.9762	2.0106	2.0434	2.1049	2.1621

80 (312.03)	v..	6.220	7.020	7.797	8.562	9.322	10.077	10.830	11.582	12.332	13.830	15.325
	h..	1230.7	1281.1	1330.5	1379.9	1429.7	1480.1	1531.3	1583.4	1636.2	1744.5	1856.5
	s..	1.6791	1.7346	1.7836	1.8281	1.8694	1.9079	1.9442	1.9787	2.0115	2.0731	2.1303
100 (327.81)	v..	4.937	5.589	6.218	6.835	7.446	8.052	8.656	9.259	9.860	11.060	12.258
	h..	1227.6	1279.1	1329.1	1378.9	1428.9	1479.5	1530.8	1582.9	1635.7	1744.2	1856.2
	s..	1.6518	1.7085	1.7581	1.8029	1.8443	1.8829	1.9193	1.9538	1.9867	2.0484	2.1056
120 (341.25)	v..	4.081	4.636	5.165	5.683	6.195	6.702	7.207	7.710	8.212	9.214	10.213
	h..	1224.4	1277.2	1327.7	1377.8	1428.1	1478.8	1530.2	1582.4	1635.3	1743.9	1856.0
	s..	1.6287	1.6869	1.7370	1.7822	1.8237	1.8625	1.8990	1.9335	1.9664	2.0281	2.0854
140 (353.02)	v..	3.468	3.954	4.413	4.861	5.301	5.738	6.172	6.604	7.035	7.895	8.752
	h..	1221.1	1275.2	1326.4	1376.8	1427.3	1478.2	1529.7	1581.9	1634.9	1743.5	1855.7
	s..	1.6087	1.6683	1.7190	1.7645	1.8063	1.8451	1.8817	1.9163	1.9493	2.0110	2.0683
160 (363.53)	v..	3.008	3.443	3.849	4.244	4.631	5.015	5.396	5.775	6.152	6.906	7.656
	h..	1217.6	1273.1	1325.0	1375.7	1426.4	1477.5	1529.1	1581.4	1634.5	1743.2	1855.5
	s..	1.5908	1.6519	1.7033	1.7491	1.7911	1.8301	1.8667	1.9014	1.9344	1.9962	2.0535
180 (373.06)	v..	2.649	3.044	3.411	3.764	4.110	4.452	4.792	5.129	5.466	6.136	6.804
	h..	1214.0	1271.0	1323.5	1374.7	1425.6	1476.8	1528.6	1581.0	1634.1	1742.9	1855.2
	s..	1.5745	1.6373	1.6894	1.7355	1.7776	1.8167	1.8534	1.8882	1.9212	1.9831	2.0404
200 (381.79)	v..	2.361	2.726	3.060	3.380	3.693	4.002	4.309	4.613	4.917	5.521	6.123
	h..	1210.3	1268.9	1322.1	1373.6	1424.8	1476.2	1528.0	1580.5	1633.7	1742.6	1855.0
	s..	1.5594	1.6240	1.6767	1.7232	1.7655	1.8048	1.8415	1.8763	1.9094	1.9713	2.0287
220 (389.86)	v..	2.125	2.465	2.772	3.066	3.352	3.634	3.913	4.191	4.467	5.017	5.565
	h..	1206.5	1266.7	1320.7	1372.6	1424.0	1475.5	1527.5	1580.0	1633.3	1742.3	1854.7
	s..	1.5453	1.6117	1.6652	1.7120	1.7545	1.7939	1.8308	1.8656	1.8987	1.9607	2.0181

* Abridged from *Thermodynamic Properties of Steam* by Joseph H. Keenan and Frederick G. Keyes, John Wiley & Sons, Inc., New York, 1937, by permission of the publisher.

TABLE B.8
PROPERTIES OF SUPERHEATED STEAM—cont.

Abs press., psi (Sat. temp)		Temperature, degrees Fahrenheit												
		200	300	400	500	600	700	800	900	1000	1100	1200	1400	1600
240 (397.37)	v..	.....	.....	1.9276	2.247	2.533	2.804	3.068	3.327	3.584	3.839	4.093	4.597	5.100
	h..	.....	.....	1202.5	1264.5	1319.2	1371.5	1423.2	1474.8	1526.9	1579.6	1632.9	1742.0	1854.5
	s..	.....	.....	1.5319	1.6003	1.6546	1.7017	1.7444	1.7839	1.8209	1.8558	1.8889	1.9510	2.0084
260 (404.42)	v..	.....	.....	.....	2.063	2.330	2.582	2.827	3.067	3.305	3.541	3.776	4.242	4.707
	h..	.....	.....	.....	1262.3	1317.7	1370.4	1422.3	1474.2	1526.3	1579.1	1632.5	1741.7	1854.2
	s..	.....	.....	.....	1.5897	1.6447	1.6922	1.7352	1.7748	1.8118	1.8467	1.8799	1.9420	1.9995
280 (411.05)	v..	.....	.....	.....	1.9047	2.156	2.392	2.621	2.845	3.066	3.286	3.504	3.938	4.370
	h..	.....	.....	.....	1260.0	1316.2	1369.4	1421.5	1473.5	1525.8	1578.6	1632.1	1741.4	1854.0
	s..	.....	.....	.....	1.5796	1.6354	1.6834	1.7265	1.7662	1.8033	1.8383	1.8716	1.9337	1.9912
300 (417.33)	v..	.....	.....	.....	1.7675	2.005	2.227	2.442	2.652	2.859	3.065	3.269	3.674	4.078
	h..	.....	.....	.....	1257.6	1314.7	1368.3	1420.6	1472.8	1525.2	1578.1	1631.7	1741.0	1853.7
	s..	.....	.....	.....	1.5701	1.6268	1.6751	1.7184	1.7582	1.7954	1.8305	1.8638	1.9260	1.9835
350 (431.72)	v..	.....	.....	.....	1.4923	1.7036	1.8980	2.084	2.266	2.445	2.622	2.798	3.147	3.493
	h..	.....	.....	.....	1251.5	1310.9	1365.5	1418.5	1471.1	1523.8	1577.0	1630.7	1740.3	1853.1
	s..	.....	.....	.....	1.5481	1.6070	1.6563	1.7002	1.7403	1.7777	1.8130	1.8463	1.9086	1.9663
400 (444.59)	v..	.....	.....	.....	1.2851	1.4770	1.6508	1.8161	1.9767	2.134	2.290	2.445	2.751	3.055
	h..	.....	.....	.....	1245.1	1306.9	1362.7	1416.4	1469.4	1522.4	1575.8	1629.6	1739.5	1852.5
	s..	.....	.....	.....	1.5281	1.5894	1.6398	1.6842	1.7247	1.7623	1.7977	1.8311	1.8936	1.9513

TABLE B.8
PROPERTIES OF SUPERHEATED STEAM—cont.

Abs press., psi (Sat. temp)		Temperature, degrees Fahrenheit													
		500	550	600	620	640	660	680	700	800	900	1000	1200	1400	1600
450 (456.28)	v	1.1231	1.2155	1.3005	1.3332	1.3652	1.3967	1.4278	1.4584	1.6074	1.7516	1.8928	2.170	2.443	2.714
	h	1238.4	1272.0	1302.8	1314.6	1326.2	1337.5	1348.8	1359.9	1414.3	1467.8	1521.0	1628.6	1738.7	1851.9
	s	1.5095	1.5437	1.5735	1.5845	1.5951	1.6054	1.6153	1.6250	1.6699	1.7108	1.7486	1.8177	1.8803	1.9381
500 (467.01)	v	0.9927	1.0800	1.1591	1.1893	1.2188	1.2478	1.2763	1.3044	1.4405	1.5715	1.6996	1.9504	2.197	2.442
	h	1231.3	1266.8	1298.6	1310.7	1322.6	1334.2	1345.7	1357.0	1412.1	1466.0	1519.6	1627.6	1737.9	1851.3
	s	1.4919	1.5280	1.5588	1.5701	1.5810	1.5915	1.6016	1.6115	1.6571	1.6982	1.7363	1.8056	1.8683	1.9262
550 (476.94)	v	0.8852	0.9686	1.0431	1.0714	1.0989	1.1259	1.1523	1.1783	1.3038	1.4241	1.5414	1.7706	1.9957	2.219
	h	1223.7	1261.2	1294.3	1306.6	1318.9	1330.8	1342.5	1354.0	1409.9	1464.3	1518.2	1626.6	1737.1	1850.6
	s	1.4751	1.5131	1.5451	1.5568	1.5680	1.5787	1.5890	1.5991	1.6452	1.6868	1.7250	1.7946	1.8575	1.9155
600 (486.21)	v	0.7947	0.8753	0.9463	0.9729	0.9988	1.0241	1.0489	1.0732	1.1899	1.3013	1.4096	1.6208	1.8279	2.033
	h	1215.7	1255.5	1289.9	1302.7	1315.2	1327.4	1339.3	1351.1	1407.7	1462.5	1516.7	1625.5	1736.3	1850.0
	s	1.4586	1.4990	1.5323	1.5443	1.5558	1.5667	1.5773	1.5875	1.6343	1.6762	1.7147	1.7846	1.8476	1.9056
700 (503.10)	v	.....	0.7277	0.7934	0.8177	0.8411	0.8639	0.8860	0.9088	1.0108	1.1082	1.2024	1.3853	1.5641	1.7405
	h	.....	1243.2	1280.6	1294.3	1307.5	1320.3	1332.8	1345.0	1403.2	1459.0	1513.9	1623.5	1734.8	1848.8
	s	.....	1.4722	1.5084	1.5212	1.5333	1.5449	1.5559	1.5665	1.6147	1.6573	1.6963	1.7666	1.8299	1.8881
800 (518.23)	v	.....	0.6154	0.6779	0.7006	0.7223	0.7433	0.7635	0.7833	0.8763	0.9633	1.0470	1.2088	1.3662	1.5214
	h	.....	1229.8	1270.7	1285.4	1299.4	1312.9	1325.9	1338.6	1398.6	1455.4	1511.0	1621.4	1733.2	1847.5
	s	.....	1.4467	1.4863	1.5000	1.5129	1.5250	1.5366	1.5476	1.5972	1.6407	1.6801	1.7510	1.8146	1.8729
900 (531.98)	v	.....	0.5264	0.5873	0.6089	0.6294	0.6491	0.6680	0.6863	0.7716	0.8506	0.9262	1.0714	1.2124	1.3509
	h	.....	1215.0	1260.1	1275.9	1290.9	1305.1	1318.8	1332.1	1393.9	1451.8	1508.1	1619.3	1731.6	1846.3
	s	.....	1.4216	1.4653	1.4800	1.4938	1.5066	1.5187	1.5303	1.5814	1.6257	1.6656	1.7371	1.8009	1.8595

TABLE B.8
Properties of Superheated Steam—cont.

Abs press., psi (Sat. temp)		\multicolumn{14}{c}{Temperature, degrees Fahrenheit}												
		500	550	600	620	640	660	680	700	800	900	1000	1200	1400	1600
1000 (544.64)	v..	0.4533	....	0.5140	0.5350	0.5546	0.5733	0.5912	0.6084	0.6878	0.7604	0.8294	0.9615	1.0893	1.2146
	h..	1198.3	....	1248.8	1265.9	1281.9	1297.0	1311.4	1325.3	1389.2	1448.2	1505.1	1617.3	1730.0	1845.0
	s..	1.3961	....	1.4450	1.4610	1.4757	1.4893	1.5021	1.5141	1.5670	1.6121	1.6525	1.7245	1.7886	1.8474
1100 (556.31)	v..	....	....	0.4532	0.4738	0.4929	0.5110	0.5281	0.5445	0.6191	0.6866	0.7503	0.8716	0.9885	1.1031
	h..	....	....	1236.7	1255.3	1272.4	1288.5	1303.7	1318.3	1384.3	1444.5	1502.2	1615.2	1728.4	1843.8
	s..	....	....	1.4251	1.4425	1.4583	1.4728	1.4862	1.4989	1.5535	1.5995	1.6405	1.7130	1.7775	1.8363
1200 (567.22)	v..	....	....	0.4016	0.4222	0.4410	0.4586	0.4752	0.4909	0.5617	0.6250	0.6843	0.7967	0.9046	1.0101
	h..	....	....	1223.5	1243.9	1262.4	1279.6	1295.7	1311.0	1379.3	1440.7	1499.2	1613.1	1726.9	1842.5
	s..	....	....	1.4052	1.4243	1.4413	1.4568	1.4710	1.4843	1.5409	1.5879	1.6293	1.7025	1.7672	1.8263
1400 (587.10)	v..	....	....	0.3174	0.3390	0.3580	0.3753	0.3912	0.4062	0.4714	0.5281	0.5805	0.6789	0.7727	0.8640
	h..	....	....	1193.0	1218.4	1240.4	1260.3	1278.5	1295.5	1369.1	1433.1	1493.2	1608.9	1723.7	1840.0
	s..	....	....	1.3639	1.3877	1.4079	1.4258	1.4419	1.4567	1.5177	1.5666	1.6093	1.6836	1.7489	1.8083
1600 (602.90)	v..	....	....	....	0.2733	0.2936	0.3112	0.3271	0.3417	0.4034	0.4553	0.5027	0.5906	0.6738	0.7545
	h..	....	....	....	1187.8	1215.2	1238.7	1259.6	1278.7	1358.4	1425.3	1487.0	1604.6	1720.5	1837.5
	s..	....	....	....	1.3489	1.3741	1.3952	1.4137	1.4303	1.4964	1.5476	1.5914	1.6669	1.7328	1.7926
1800 (621.03)	v..	....	....	....	....	0.2407	0.2597	0.2760	0.2907	0.3502	0.3986	0.4421	0.5218	0.5968	0.6693
	h..	....	....	....	....	1185.1	1214.0	1238.5	1260.3	1347.2	1417.4	1480.8	1600.4	1717.3	1835.0
	s..	....	....	....	....	1.3377	1.3638	1.3855	1.4044	1.4765	1.5301	1.5752	1.6520	1.7185	1.7786
2000 (635.82)	v..	....	....	....	....	0.1936	0.2161	0.2337	0.2489	0.3074	0.3532	0.3935	0.4668	0.5352	0.6011
	h..	....	....	....	....	1145.6	1184.9	1214.8	1240.0	1335.5	1409.2	1474.5	1596.1	1714.1	1832.5
	s..	....	....	....	....	1.2945	1.3300	1.3564	1.3783	1.4576	1.5139	1.5603	1.6384	1.7055	1.7660

Press.									
2500 (668.13)	v..	0.1484	0.1686	0.2294	0.2710	0.3061	0.3678	0.4244	0.4784
	h..	1132.3	1176.8	1303.6	1387.8	1458.4	1585.3	1706.1	1826.2
	s..	1.2687	1.3073	1.4127	1.4772	1.5273	1.6088	1.6775	1.7389
3000 (695.36)	v..	.....	0.0984	0.1760	0.2159	0.2476	0.3018	0.3505	0.3966
	h..	.....	1060.7	1267.2	1365.0	1441.8	1574.3	1698.0	1819.9
	s..	.....	1.1966	1.3690	1.4439	1.4984	1.5837	1.6540	1.7163
3206.2 (705.40)	v..	.....	.....	0.1583	0.1981	0.2288	0.2806	0.3267	0.3703
	h..	.....	.....	1250.5	1355.2	1434.7	1569.8	1694.6	1817.2
	s..	.....	.....	1.3508	1.4309	1.4874	1.5742	1.6452	1.7080
3500	v..	.....	0.0306	0.1364	0.1762	0.2058	0.2546	0.2977	0.3381
	h..	.....	780.5	1224.9	1340.7	1424.5	1563.3	1689.8	1813.6
	s..	.....	0.9515	1.3241	1.4127	1.4723	1.5615	1.6336	1.6968
4000	v..	.....	0.0287	0.1052	0.1462	0.1743	0.2192	0.2581	0.2943
	h..	.....	763.8	1174.8	1314.4	1406.8	1552.1	1681.7	1807.2
	s..	.....	0.9347	1.2757	1.3827	1.4482	1.5417	1.6154	1.6795
4500	v..	.....	0.0276	0.0798	0.1226	0.1500	0.1917	0.2273	0.2602
	h..	.....	753.5	1113.9	1286.5	1388.4	1540.8	1673.5	1800.9
	s..	.....	0.9235	1.2204	1.3529	1.4253	1.5235	1.5990	1.6640
5000	v..	.....	0.0268	0.0593	0.1036	0.1303	0.1696	0.2027	0.2329
	h..	.....	746.4	1047.1	1256.5	1369.5	1529.5	1665.3	1794.5
	s..	.....	0.9152	1.1622	1.3231	1.4034	1.5066	1.5839	1.6499
5500	v..	.....	0.0262	0.0463	0.0880	0.1143	0.1516	0.1825	0.2106
	h..	.....	741.3	985.0	1224.1	1349.3	1518.2	1657.0	1788.1
	s..	.....	0.9090	1.1093	1.2930	1.3821	1.4908	1.5699	1.6369

PROPERTIES OF SUBSTANCES

TABLE B.9
COMPRESSED LIQUID*

Abs press. lbf/in² (Sat. temp.)	Saturated Liquid		Temperature F							
			32	100	200	300	400	500	600	700
	P		0.08854	0.9492	11.526	67.013	247.31	680.8	1542.9	3093.7
	v_f		0.016022	0.016132	0.016634	0.017449	0.018639	0.020432	0.023629	0.03692
	h_f		0	67.97	167.99	269.59	374.97	487.82	617.0	823.3
	s_f		0	0.12948	0.29382	0.43694	0.56638	0.68871	0.8131	0.9905
200 (381.79)	$(v - v_f) \cdot 10^5$		−1.1	−1.1	−1.1	−1.1				
	$(h - h_f)$		+0.61	+0.54	+0.41	+0.23				
	$(s - s_f) \cdot 10^3$		+0.03	−0.05	−0.21	−0.21				
400 (444.59)	$(v - v_f) \cdot 10^5$		−2.3	−2.1	−2.2	−2.8	−2.1			
	$(h - h_f)$		+1.21	+1.09	+0.88	+0.61	+0.16			
	$(s - s_f) \cdot 10^3$		+0.04	−0.16	−0.47	−0.56	−0.40			
800 (518.23)	$(v - v_f) \cdot 10^5$		−4.6	−4.0	−4.4	−5.6	−6.5	−1.7		
	$(h - h_f)$		+2.39	+2.17	+1.78	+1.35	+0.61	−0.05		
	$(s - s_f) \cdot 10^3$		+0.10	−0.40	−0.97	−1.27	−1.48	−0.53		
1000 (544.61)	$(v - v_f) \cdot 10^5$		−5.7	−5.1	−5.4	−6.9	−8.7	−6.4		
	$(h - h_f)$		+2.99	+2.70	+2.21	+1.75	+0.84	−0.14		
	$(s - s_f) \cdot 10^3$		+0.15	−0.53	−1.20	−1.64	−2.00	−1.41		

* Abridged from *Thermodynamic Properties of Steam*, by Joseph H. Keenan and Frederick G. Keyes. Copyright 1936, by Joseph H. Keenan and Frederick G. Keyes. Published by John Wiley & Sons, Inc., New York.

TABLE B.9

COMPRESSED LIQUID*—cont.

Abs press. lbf/in² (Sat. temp.)	Saturated Liquid	32	100	200	300	400	500	600	700
	P	0.08854	0.9492	11.526	67.013	247.31	680.8	1542.9	3093.7
	v_f	0.016022	0.016132	0.016634	0.017449	0.018639	0.020432	0.023629	0.03692
	h_f	0	67.97	167.99	269.59	374.97	487.82	617.0	823.3
	s_f	0	0.12948	0.29382	0.43694	0.56638	0.68871	0.8131	0.9905
1500 (596.23)	$(v - v_f) \cdot 10^5$	−8.4	−7.5	−8.1	−10.4	−14.1	−17.3	−32.6	−821.0
	$(h - h_f)$	+4.48	+3.99	+3.36	+2.70	+1.44	−0.29	−2.5	−59.5
	$(s - s_f) \cdot 10^3$	+0.20	−0.86	−1.79	−2.53	−3.32	−3.56	−4.3	−55.8
2000 (635.82)	$(v - v_f) \cdot 10^5$	−11.0	−9.9	−10.8	−13.8	−19.5	−27.8	−87.9	−1017.0
	$(h - h_f)$	+5.97	+5.31	+4.51	+3.64	+2.03	−0.38	−6.9	−76.9
	$(s - s_f) \cdot 10^3$	+0.22	−1.18	+2.39	−3.42	−4.57	−5.58	−12.4	−75.3
3000 (695.36)	$(v - v_f) \cdot 10^5$	−16.3	−14.7	−16.0	−20.7	−30.0	−47.1	−132.2	
	$(h - h_f)$	+9.00	+7.88	+6.77	+5.49	+3.33	−0.41	−10.0	
	$(s - s_f) \cdot 10^3$	+0.28	−1.79	−3.56	−5.12	−7.03	−9.42	−19.3	
4000	$(v - v_f) \cdot 10^5$	−21.5	−19.2	−21.0	−27.5	−40.0	−64.5	−169.3	
	$(h - h_f)$	+11.88	+10.49	+9.03	+7.41	+4.71	−0.16	−12.1	
	$(s - s_f) \cdot 10^3$	+0.29	−2.42	−4.74	−6.77	−9.40	−13.03	−25.3	
5000	$(v - v_f) \cdot 10^5$	−26.7	−23.6	−26.0	−34.0	−49.6	−80.5		
	$(h - h_f)$	+14.75	+13.08	+11.30	+9.36	+6.08	+0.25		
	$(s - s_f) \cdot 10^3$	+0.22	−3.07	−5.92	−8.40	−11.74	−16.47		

Temperature F

TABLE B.10

Steam Tables (continued)

SATURATION: SOLID-VAPOR*

Temp., F, t	Abs press., lbf/in², P	Specific Volume ft³/lbm		Enthalpy Btu/lbm			Entropy, Btu/lbm R		
		Sat. Solid v_i	Sat. Vapor $v_g \times 10^{-3}$	Sat. Solid h_i	Subl. h_{ig}	Sat. Vapor h_g	Sat. Solid s_i	Subl. s_{ig}	Sat. Vapor s_g
32	0.0885	0.01747	3.306	−143.35	1218.1	1075.8	−0.2916	2.4793	2.1877
30	0.0808	0.01747	3.609	−144.35	1219.3	1074.9	−0.2936	2.4897	2.1961
20	0.0505	0.01745	5.658	−149.31	1219.9	1070.6	−0.3038	2.5425	2.2387
10	0.0309	0.01744	9.05	−154.17	1220.4	1066.2	−0.3141	2.5977	2.2836
0	0.0185	0.01742	14.77	−158.93	1220.7	1061.8	−0.3241	2.6546	2.3305
−10	0.0108	0.01741	24.67	−163.59	1221.0	1057.4	−0.3346	2.7143	2.3797
−20	0.0062	0.01739	42.2	−168.16	1221.2	1053.0	−0.3448	2.7764	2.4316
−30	0.0035	0.01738	74.1	−172.63	1221.2	1048.6	−0.3551	2.8411	2.4860
−40	0.0019	0.01737	133.9	−177.00	1221.2	1044.2	−0.3654	2.9087	2.5433

* Abridged from *Thermodynamic Properties of Steam*, by Joseph H. Keenan and Frederick G. Keyes. Copyright 1936, by Joseph H. Keenan and Frederick G. Keyes. Published by John Wiley & Sons, Inc., New York.

TABLE B.11

SATURATED AMMONIA*

Temp	Pressure		Vol-ume	Den-sity	Enthalpy from −40 °F			Entropy from −40 °F	
°F, t	Abs, psi, p	Gage, psi, p_d	Vapor, cu ft/lb, v_g	Vapor, lb/cu ft, $1/v_g$	Liquid, Btu/lb, h_f	Vapor, Btu/lb, h_g	Latent, Btu/lb, h_{fg}	Liquid, Btu/lb, °F, s_f	Vapor, Btu/lb, °F, s_g
− 60	5.55	18.6†	44.73	0.02235	− 21.2	589.6	610.8	− 0.0517	1.4769
− 55	6.54	16.6†	38.38	0.02605	− 15.9	591.6	607.5	− 0.0386	1.4631
− 50	7.67	14.3†	33.08	0.03023	− 10.6	593.7	604.3	− 0.0256	1.4497
− 45	8.95	11.7†	28.62	0.03494	− 5.3	595.6	600.9	− 0.0127	1.4368
− 40	10.41	8.7†	24.86	0.04022	0.0	597.6	597.6	0.0000	1.4242
− 38	11.04	7.4†	23.53	.04251	2.1	598.3	596.2	.0051	.4193
− 36	11.71	6.1†	22.27	.04489	4.3	599.1	594.8	.0101	.4144
− 34	12.41	4.7†	21.10	.04739	6.4	599.9	593.5	.0151	.4096
− 32	13.14	3.2†	20.00	.04999	8.5	600.6	592.1	.0201	.4048
− 30	13.90	1.6†	18.97	0.05271	10.7	601.4	590.7	0.0250	1.4001
− 28	14.71	0.0	18.00	.05555	12.8	602.1	589.3	.0300	.3955
− 26	15.55	0.8	17.09	.05850	14.9	602.8	587.9	.0350	.3909
− 24	16.42	1.7	16.24	.06158	17.1	603.6	586.5	.0399	.3863
− 22	17.34	2.6	15.43	.06479	19.2	603.4	585.1	.0448	.3818
− 20	18.30	3.6	14.68	0.06813	21.4	605.0	583.6	0.0498	1.3774
− 18	19.30	4.6	13.97	.07161	23.5	605.7	582.2	.0545	.3729
− 16	20.34	5.6	13.29	.07522	25.6	606.4	580.8	.0594	.3686
− 14	21.43	6.7	12.66	.07898	27.8	607.1	579.3	.0642	.3643
− 12	22.56	7.9	12.06	.08289	30.0	607.8	577.8	.0690	.3600
− 10	23.74	9.0	11.50	0.08695	32.1	608.5	576.4	0.0738	1.3558
− 8	24.97	10.3	10.97	.09117	34.3	609.2	574.9	.0786	.3516
− 6	26.26	11.6	10.47	.09555	36.4	609.8	573.4	.0833	.3474
− 4	27.59	12.9	9.991	.1001	38.6	610.5	571.9	.0880	.3433
− 2	28.98	14.3	9.541	.1048	40.7	611.1	570.4	.0928	.3393
0	30.42	15.7	9.116	0.1097	42.9	611.8	568.9	0.0975	1.3353
2	31.92	17.2	8.714	.1148	45.1	612.4	567.3	.1022	.3312
4	33.47	18.8	8.333	.1200	47.2	613.0	565.8	.1069	.3273
6	35.09	20.4	7.971	.1254	49.4	613.6	564.2	.1115	.3234
8	36.77	21.1	6.629	.1311	51.6	614.3	562.7	.1162	.3195

* Abridged, by permission, from "Tables of Thermodynamic Properties of Ammonia," U. S. Department of Commerce, Bureau of Standards, *Circular* 142, 1945.
† Inches of mercury below 1 atm.

TABLE B.11

SATURATED AMMONIA—cont.

Temp	Pressure		Vol-ume	Den-sity	Enthalpy from −40 °F			Entropy from −40 °F	
°F, t	Abs, psi, p	Gage, psi, p_d	Vapor, cu ft/lb, v_g	Vapor, lb/cu ft, $1/v_g$	Liquid, Btu/lb, h_f	Vapor, Btu/lb, h_g	Latent, Btu/lb, h_{fg}	Liquid, Btu/lb, °F, s_f	Vapor, Btu/lb °F, s_g
10	38.51	23.8	7.304	0.1369	53.8	614.9	561.1	0.1208	1.3157
12	40.31	25.6	6.996	.1429	56.0	615.5	559.5	.1254	.3118
14	42.18	27.5	6.703	.1492	58.2	616.1	557.9	.1300	.3081
16	44.12	29.4	6.425	.1556	60.3	616.6	556.3	.1346	.3043
18	46.13	31.4	6.161	.1623	62.5	617.2	554.7	.1392	.3006
20	48.21	33.5	5.910	0.1692	64.7	617.8	553.1	0.1437	1.2969
22	50.36	35.7	5.671	.1763	66.9	618.3	551.4	.1483	.2933
24	52.59	37.9	5.443	.1837	69.1	618.9	549.8	.1528	.2897
26	54.90	40.2	5.227	.1913	71.3	619.4	548.1	.1573	.2861
28	57.28	42.6	5.021	.1992	73.5	619.9	546.4	.1618	.2825
30	59.74	45.0	4.825	0.2073	75.7	620.5	544.8	0.1663	1.2790
32	62.29	47.6	4.637	.2156	77.9	621.0	543.1	.1708	.2755
34	64.91	50.2	4.459	.2243	80.1	621.5	541.4	.1753	.2721
36	67.63	52.9	4.289	.2332	82.3	622.0	539.7	.1797	.2686
38	70.43	55.7	4.126	.2423	84.6	622.5	537.9	.1841	.2652
40	73.32	58.6	3.971	0.2518	86.8	623.0	536.2	0.1885	1.2618
42	76.31	61.6	3.823	.2616	89.0	623.4	534.4	.1930	.2585
44	79.38	64.7	3.682	.2716	91.2	623.9	532.7	.1974	.2552
46	82.55	67.9	3.547	.2819	93.5	624.4	530.9	.2018	.2519
48	85.82	71.1	3.418	.2926	95.7	624.8	529.1	.2062	.2486
50	89.19	74.5	3.294	0.3036	97.9	625.2	527.3	0.2105	1.2453
52	92.66	78.0	3.176	.3149	100.2	625.7	525.5	.2149	.2421
54	96.23	81.5	3.063	.3265	102.4	626.1	523.7	.2192	.2389
56	99.91	85.2	2.954	.3385	104.7	626.5	521.8	.2236	.2357
58	103.7	89.0	2.851	.3508	106.9	626.9	520.0	.2279	.2325
60	107.6	92.9	2.751	0.3635	109.2	627.3	518.1	0.2322	1.2294
62	111.6	96.9	2.656	.3765	111.5	627.7	516.2	.2365	.2262
64	115.7	101.0	2.565	.3399	113.7	628.0	514.3	.2408	.2231
66	120.0	105.3	2.477	.4037	116.0	628.4	512.4	.2451	.2201
68	124.3	109.6	2.393	.4179	118.3	628.8	510.5	.2494	.2170

TABLE B.11

SATURATED AMMONIA—cont.

Temp	Pressure		Vol-ume	Den-sity	Enthalpy from −40 °F			Entropy from −40 °F	
°F, t	Abs, psi, p	Gage, psi, p_d	Vapor, cu ft/lb, v_g	Vapor, lb/cu ft, $1/v_g$	Liquid, Btu/lb, h_f	Vapor, Btu/lb, h_g	Latent, Btu/lb, h_{fg}	Liquid, Btu/lb, °F, s_f	Vapor, Btu/lb, °F, s_g
70	128.8	114.1	2.312	0.4325	120.5	629.1	508.6	0.2537	1.2140
72	133.4	118.7	2.235	.4474	122.8	629.4	506.6	.2579	.2110
74	138.1	123.4	2.161	.4628	125.1	629.8	504.7	.2622	.2080
76	143.0	128.3	2.089	.4786	127.4	630.1	502.7	.2664	.2050
78	147.9	133.2	2.021	.4949	129.7	630.4	500.7	.2706	.2020
80	153.0	138.3	1.955	0.5115	132.0	630.7	498.7	0.2749	1.1991
82	158.3	143.6	1.892	.5287	134.3	631.0	496.7	.2791	.1962
84	163.7	149.0	1.831	.5462	136.6	631.3	494.7	.2833	.1933
86	169.2	154.5	1.772	.5643	138.9	631.5	492.6	.2875	.1904
88	174.8	160.1	1.716	.5828	141.2	631.8	490.6	.2917	.1875
90	180.6	165.9	1.661	0.6019	143.5	632.0	488.5	0.2958	1.1846
92	186.6	171.9	1.609	.6214	145.8	632.2	486.4	.3000	.1818
94	192.7	178.0	1.559	.6415	148.2	632.5	484.3	.3041	.1789
96	198.9	184.2	1.510	.6620	150.5	632.6	482.1	.3083	.1861
98	205.3	190.6	1.464	.6832	152.9	632.9	480.0	.3125	.1733
100	211.9	197.2	1.419	0.7048	155.2	633.0	477.8	0.3166	1.1705
102	218.6	203.9	1.375	.7270	157.6	633.2	475.6	.3207	.1677
104	225.4	210.7	1.334	.7498	159.9	633.4	473.5	.3248	.1649
106	232.5	217.8	1.293	.7732	162.3	633.5	471.2	.3289	.1621
108	239.7	225.0	1.254	.7972	164.6	633.6	469.0	.3330	.1593
110	247.0	232.3	1.217	0.8219	167.0	633.7	466.7	0.3372	1.1566
112	254.5	239.8	1.180	.8471	169.4	633.8	464.4	.3413	.1538
114	262.2	247.5	1.145	.8730	171.8	633.9	462.1	.3453	.1510
116	270.1	255.4	1.112	.8996	174.2	634.0	459.8	.3495	.1455
118	278.2	263.5	1.079	.9269	176.6	634.0	457.4	.3535	.1455
120	286.4	271.7	1.047	0.9549	179.0	634.0	455.0	0.3576	1.1427
122	294.8	280.1	1.017	.9837	181.4	634.0	452.6	.3618	.1400
124	303.4	288.7	0.987	1.0132	183.9	634.0	450.1	.3659	.1372

TABLE B.12

SUPERHEATED AMMONIA*

	[Absolute pressure, psi (saturation temperature in italics)]											
Temp, °F	50 *21.67*			60 *30.21*			70 *37.70*			80 *44.40*		
t	v	h	s	v	h	s	v	h	s	v	h	s
Sat.	5.710	618.2	1.2939	4.805	620.5	1.2787	4.151	622.4	1.2658	3.655	624.0	1.2545
30	5.838	623.4	1.3046									
40	5.988	629.5	.3169	4.933	626.8	1.2913	4.177	623.9	1.2688			
50	6.135	635.4	1.3286	5.060	632.9	1.3035	4.290	630.4	1.2816	3.712	627.7	1.2619
60	6.280	641.2	.3399	5.184	639.0	.3152	4.401	636.6	.2937	3.812	634.3	.2745
70	6.423	646.9	.3508	5.307	644.9	.3265	4.509	642.7	.3054	3.909	640.6	.2866
80	6.564	652.6	.3613	5.428	650.7	.3373	4.615	648.7	.3166	4.005	646.7	.2981
90	6.704	658.2	.3716	5.547	656.4	.3479	4.719	654.6	.3274	4.098	652.8	.3092
100	6.843	663.7	1.3816	5.665	662.1	1.3581	4.822	660.4	1.3378	4.190	658.7	1.3199
110	6.980	669.2	.3914	5.781	667.7	.3681	4.924	666.1	.3480	4.281	664.6	.3303
120	7.117	674.7	.4009	5.897	673.3	.3778	5.025	671.8	.3579	4.371	670.4	.3404
130	7.252	680.2	.4103	6.012	678.9	.3873	5.125	677.5	.3676	4.460	676.1	.3502
140	7.387	685.7	.4195	6.126	684.4	.3966	5.224	683.1	.3770	4.548	681.8	.3508
150	7.521	691.1	1.4286	6.239	689.9	1.4058	5.323	688.7	1.3863	4.635	687.5	1.3692
160	7.655	696.6	.4374	6.352	695.5	.4148	5.420	694.3	.3954	4.722	693.2	.3784
170	7.788	702.1	.4462	6.464	701.0	.4236	5.518	699.9	.4043	4.808	698.8	.3874
180	7.921	707.5	.4548	6.576	706.5	.4323	5.615	705.5	.4131	4.893	704.4	.3963
190	8.053	713.0	.4633	6.687	712.0	.4409	5.611	711.0	.4217	4.978	710.0	.4050
200	8.185	718.5	1.4716	6.798	717.5	1.4493	5.807	716.6	1.4302	5.063	715.6	1.4136
210	8.317	724.0	.4799	6.909	723.1	.4576	5.902	722.2	.4386	5.147	721.3	.4220
220	8.448	729.4	.4880	7.019	728.6	.4658	5.998	727.7	.4469	5.231	726.9	.4304
240	8.710	740.5	.5040	7.238	739.7	.4819	6.187	738.9	.4631	5.398	738.1	.4467
260	8.970	751.6	.5197	7.457	750.9	.4976	6.376	750.1	.4789	5.565	749.4	.4626
280	9.230	762.7	1.5350	7.675	762.1	1.5130	6.563	761.4	1.4943	5.730	760.7	1.4781
300	9.489	774.0	.5500	7.892	773.3	.5281	6.750	772.7	.5095	5.894	772.1	.4933

* Abridged, by permission, from "Tables of Thermodynamic Properties of Ammonia," U.S. Department of Commerce, Bureau of Standards, Circular 142, 1945.

TABLE B.12

SUPERHEATED AMMONIA—cont.

Temp, °F	[Absolute pressure, psi (saturation temperature in italics)]											
	90 *50.47*			100 *56.05*			120 *66.02*			140 *74.79*		
t	v	h	s	v	h	s	v	h	s	v	h	s
Sat.	3.266	625.3	1.2443	2.952	626.5	1.2356	2.476	628.4	1.2201	2.132	629.9	1.2068
50												
60	3.353	631.8	1.2571	2.985	629.3	1.2409						
70	3.443	638.3	.2695	3.068	636.0	.2539	2.505	631.3	1.2255			
80	3.529	644.7	.2814	3.149	642.6	.2661	2.576	638.3	.2386	2.166	633.8	1.2140
90	3.614	650.9	.2928	3.227	649.0	.2778	2.645	645.0	.2510	2.228	640.9	.2272
100	3.698	657.0	1.3038	3.304	655.2	1.2891	2.712	651.6	1.2628	2.288	647.8	1.2396
110	3.780	663.0	.3144	3.380	661.3	.2999	2.778	658.0	.2741	2.347	654.5	.2515
120	3.862	668.9	.3247	3.454	667.3	.3104	2.842	664.2	.2850	2.404	661.1	.2628
130	3.942	674.7	.3347	3.527	673.3	.3206	2.905	670.4	.2956	2.460	667.4	.2738
140	4.021	680.5	.3444	3.600	679.2	.3305	2.967	676.5	.3058	2.515	673.7	.2843
150	4.100	686.3	1.3539	3.672	685.0	1.3401	3.029	682.5	1.3157	2.569	679.9	1.2945
160	4.178	692.0	.3633	3.743	690.8	.3495	3.089	688.4	.3254	2.622	686.0	.3045
170	4.255	697.7	.3724	3.813	696.6	.3588	3.149	694.3	.3348	2.675	692.0	.3141
180	4.332	703.4	.3813	3.883	702.3	.3678	3.209	700.2	.3441	2.727	698.0	.3236
190	4.408	709.0	.3901	3.952	708.0	.3767	3.268	706.0	.3531	2.779	704.0	.3328
200	4.484	714.7	1.3988	4.021	713.7	1.3854	3.326	711.8	1.3620	2.830	709.9	1.3418
210	4.560	720.4	.4073	4.090	719.4	.3940	3.385	717.6	.3707	2.880	715.8	.3507
220	4.635	726.0	.4157	4.158	725.1	.4024	3.443	723.4	.3793	2.931	721.6	.3594
230	4.710	731.7	.4239	4.226	730.8	.4108	3.500	729.2	.3877	2.981	727.5	.3679
240	4.785	737.3	.4321	4.294	736.5	.4190	3.557	734.9	.3960	3.030	733.3	.3763
250	4.859	743.0	1.4401	4.361	742.2	1.4271	3.614	740.7	1.4042	3.080	739.2	1.3846
260	4.933	748.7	.4481	4.428	747.9	.4350	3.671	746.5	.4123	3.129	745.0	.3928
280	5.081	760.0	.4637	4.562	759.4	.4507	3.783	748.0	.4281	3.227	756.7	.4088
300	5.228	771.5	.4789	4.695	770.8	.4660	3.895	769.6	.4435	3.323	768.3	.4243

TABLE B.12

Superheated Ammonia—cont.

	[Absolute pressure, psi (saturation temperature in italics)]											
Temp, °F	160 *82.64*			180 *89.78*			200 *96.34*			220 *102.42*		
t	v	h	s	v	h	s	v	h	s	v	h	s
Sat.	1.872	631.1	1.1952	1.667	632.0	1.1850	1.502	632.7	1.1756	1.367	633.2	1.1671
90	1.914	636.6	1.2055	1.668	632.2	1.1853						
100	1.969	643.9	1.2186	1.720	639.9	1.1922						
110	2.023	651.0	.2311	1.770	647.3	.2123	1.567	643.4	1.1947	1.400	639.4	1.1781
120	2.075	657.8	.2429	1.818	654.4	.2247	1.612	650.9	.2077	1.443	647.3	.1917
130	2.125	664.4	.2542	1.865	661.3	.2364	1.656	658.1	.2200	1.485	654.8	.2045
140	2.175	670.9	.2652	1.910	668.0	.2477	1.698	665.0	.2317	1.525	662.0	.2167
150	2.224	677.2	1.2757	1.955	674.6	1.2586	1.740	671.8	1.2429	1.564	669.0	1.2281
160	2.272	683.5	.2859	1.999	681.0	.2691	1.780	678.4	.2537	1.601	675.8	.2394
170	2.319	689.7	.2958	2.042	687.3	.2792	1.820	684.9	.2641	1.638	682.5	.2501
180	2.365	695.8	.3054	2.084	693.6	.2891	1.859	691.3	.2742	1.675	689.1	.2604
190	2.411	701.9	.3148	2.126	699.8	.2987	1.897	697.7	.2840	1.710	695.5	.2704
200	2.457	707.9	1.3240	2.167	705.9	1.3081	1.935	703.9	1.2935	1.745	701.9	1.2801
210	2.502	713.9	.3331	2.208	712.0	.3172	1.972	710.1	.3029	1.780	708.2	.2896
220	2.547	719.9	.3410	2.248	718.1	.3262	2.009	716.3	.3120	1.814	714.4	.2989
230	2.591	725.8	.3506	2.288	724.1	.3350	2.046	722.4	.3209	1.848	720.6	.3079
240	2.635	731.7	.3591	2.328	730.1	.3436	2.082	728.4	.3296	1.881	726.8	.3168
250	2.679	737.6	1.3675	2.367	736.1	1.3521	2.118	734.5	1.3382	1.914	732.9	1.3255
260	2.723	743.5	.3757	2.407	742.0	.3605	2.154	740.5	.3467	1.947	739.0	.3340
270	2.766	749.4	.3838	2.446	748.0	.3687	2.189	746.5	.3550	1.980	745.1	.3424
280	2.809	755.3	.3919	2.484	753.9	.3768	2.225	752.5	.3631	2.012	751.1	.3507
290	2.852	761.2	.3998	2.523	759.9	.3847	2.260	758.5	.3712	2.044	757.2	.3588
300	2.895	767.1	1.4076	1.561	765.8	1.3926	2.295	764.5	1.3791	2.076	763.2	1.3668
320	2.980	778.9	.4229	2.657	777.7	.4081	2.364	776.5	.3947	2.140	775.3	.3825
340	3.064	790.7	.4379	2.713	789.6	.4231	2.432	788.5	.4099	2.203	787.4	.3978
360	.....	.....	.....	.....	.....	.....	2.500	800.5	.4247	2.265	799.5	.4127
380	.....	.....	.....	.....	.....	.....	2.568	812.5	.4392	2.327	811.6	.4273

TABLE B.12

SUPERHEATED AMMONIA—cont.

[Absolute pressure, psi (saturation temperature in italics)]

Temp, °F	240 *108.09*			260 *113.42*			280 *118.45*			300 *123.21*		
t	v	h	s	v	h	s	v	h	s	v	h	s
Sat.	1.253	633.6	1.1592	1.155	633.9	1.1518	1.072	634.0	1.1449	0.999	684.0	1.1383
110	1.261	635.3	1.1621									
120	1.302	643.5	.1764	1.182	639.5	1.1617	1.078	635.4	1.1473			
130	1.342	651.3	.1898	1.220	647.8	.1757	1.115	644.0	.1621	1.023	640.1	1.1487
140	1.380	658.8	.2025	1.257	655.6	.1889	1.151	652.2	.1759	1.058	648.7	.1632
150	1.416	666.1	1.2145	1.292	663.1	1.2014	1.184	660.1	1.1888	1.091	656.9	1.1767
160	1.452	673.1	.2259	1.326	670.4	.2132	1.217	667.6	.2011	1.123	664.7	.1894
170	1.487	680.0	.2369	1.359	677.5	.2245	1.249	674.9	.2127	1.153	672.2	.2014
180	1.521	686.7	.2475	1.391	684.4	.2354	1.279	681.9	.2239	1.183	679.5	.2129
190	1.554	693.3	.2577	1.422	691.1	.2458	1.309	688.9	.2346	1.211	686.5	.2239
200	1.587	699.8	1.2677	1.453	697.7	1.2560	1.339	695.6	1.2449	1.239	693.5	1.2344
210	1.619	706.2	.2773	1.484	704.3	.2658	1.367	702.3	.2550	1.267	700.3	.2447
220	1.651	712.6	.2867	1.514	710.7	.2754	1.396	708.8	.2647	1.294	706.9	.2546
230	1.683	718.9	.2959	1.543	717.1	.2847	1.424	715.3	.2742	1.320	713.5	.2642
240	1.714	725.1	.3049	1.572	723.4	.2938	1.451	721.8	.2834	1.346	720.0	.2736
250	1.745	731.3	1.3137	1.601	729.7	1.3027	1.478	728.1	1.2924	1.372	726.5	1.2827
260	1.775	737.5	.3224	1.630	736.0	.3115	1.505	734.4	.3013	1.397	732.9	.2917
270	1.805	743.6	.3308	1.658	742.2	.3200	1.532	740.7	.3099	1.422	739.2	.3004
280	1.835	749.8	.3392	1.686	748.4	.3285	1.558	747.0	.3184	1.447	745.5	.3090
290	1.865	755.9	.3474	1.714	754.5	.3367	1.584	753.2	.3268	1.472	751.8	.3175
300	1.895	762.0	1.3554	1.741	760.7	1.3449	1.610	759.4	1.3350	1.496	758.1	1.3257
320	1.954	774.1	.3712	1.796	772.9	.3608	1.661	771.7	.3511	1.544	770.5	.3419
340	2.012	786.3	.3866	1.850	785.2	.3763	1.712	784.0	.3667	1.592	782.9	.3576
360	2.069	798.4	.4016	1.904	797.4	.3914	1.762	796.3	.3819	1.639	795.3	.3729
380	2.126	810.6	.4163	1.957	809.6	.4062	1.811	808.7	.3967	1.686	807.7	.3878
400	.....	.....	.....	2.009	821.9	1.4206	1.861	821.0	1.4112	1.732	820.1	1.4024

TABLE B.13
Mercury Table*

Press., psia	Temp, °F	Enthalpy, Btu/lb			Entropy, Btu/lb–°R			Sp. vol. sat. vapor, cu ft/lb
		Sat. liquid	Evap.	Sat. vapor	Sat. liquid	Evap.	Sat. vapor	
.010	233.57	6.668	127.732	134.400	.01137	.18428	.19565	3637
.020	259.88	7.532	127.614	135.146	.01259	.17735	.18994	1893
.030	276.22	8.068	127.540	135.608	.01332	.17332	.18664	1292
.040	288.32	8.463	127.486	135.949	.01386	.17044	.18430	986
.050	297.97	8.778	127.442	136.220	.01427	.16821	.18248	799
.075	316.19	9.373	127.361	136.734	.01504	.16415	.17919	545
.100	329.73	9.814	127.300	137.114	.01561	.16126	.17687	416
.200	364.25	10.936	127.144	138.080	.01699	.15432	.17131	217.3
.300	385.92	11.639	127.047	138.686	.01783	.15024	.16807	148.6
.400	401.98	12.159	126.975	139.134	.01844	.14736	.16580	113.7
.500	415.00	12.568	126.916	139.484	.01892	.14511	.16403	92.18
.600	425.82	12.929	126.868	139.797	.01932	.14328	.16260	77.84
.700	435.23	13.233	126.825	140.058	.01965	.14172	.16137	67.45
.800	443.50	13.500	126.788	140.288	.01994	.14038	.16032	59.58
.900	451.00	13.740	126.755	140.495	.02021	.13919	.15940	53.40
1.00	457.72	13.959	126.724	140.683	.02045	.13814	.15859	48.42
2.00	504.93	15.476	126.512	141.988	.02205	.13116	.15321	25.39
3.00	535.25	16.439	126.377	142.816	.02302	.12706	.15008	17.50
4.00	557.85	17.161	126.275	143.436	.02373	.12434	.14787	13.38
5.00	575.7	17.741	126.193	143.934	.02430	.12188	.14618	10.90
6.00	591.2	18.233	126.124	144.357	.02477	.12002	.14479	9.26
7.00	604.7	18.657	126.065	144.722	.02516	.11846	.14362	8.04
8.00	616.5	19.035	126.011	145.046	.02551	.11712	.14262	7.12
9.00	627.3	19.381	125.962	145.343	.02583	.11588	.14171	6.39
10	637.0	19.685	125.919	145.604	.02610	.11483	.14093	5.81
20	706.0	21.864	125.609	147.473	.02800	.10779	.13579	3.09
30	750.6	23.277	125.407	148.684	.02918	.10361	.13279	2.14
40	784.4	24.345	125.255	149.600	.03004	.10068	.13072	1.648
50	812.1	25.203	125.131	150.334	.03070	.09838	.12909	1.348
60	835.7	25.940	125.024	150.964	.03127	.09652	.12779	1.144
70	856.4	25.585	124.931	151.516	.03175	.09493	.12668	0.998
80	874.8	27.149	124.849	152.008	.03218	.09356	.12574	0.885
90	891.5	27.680	124.774	152.454	.03255	.09234	.12489	0.797

TABLE B.13

MERCURY TABLE*—cont.

Press., psia	Temp, °F	Enthalpy, Btu/lb			Entropy, Btu/lb-°R			Sp. vol. sat. vapor, cu ft/lb
		Sat. liquid	Evap.	Sat. vapor	Sat. liquid	Evap.	Sat. vapor	
100	906.8	28.152	124.706	152.858	.03290	.09127	.12417	0.725
110	921.0	28.596	124.641	153.237	.03321	.09027	.12348	0.667
120	934.3	29.005	124.582	153.587	.03350	.08938	.12288	0.617
130	946.6	29.390	124.526	153.916	.03377	.08855	.12232	0.575
140	958.3	29.748	124.474	154.222	.03401	.08778	.12179	0.538
150	969.4	30.000	124.424	154.514	.03425	.08707	.12132	0.507
160	979.9	30.415	124.376	154.791	.03447	.08640	.12087	0.478
170	989.9	30.724	124.331	155.055	.03468	.08577	.12045	0.453
180	999.5	31.018	124.288	155.306	.03488	.08518	.12006	0.431
190	1008.8	31.290	124.249	155.539	.03506	.08464	.11970	0.410
200	1017.2	31.560	124.209	155.769	.03523	.08411	.11934	0.392
225	1038.0	32.204	124.115	156.319	.03565	.08287	.11852	0.354
250	1057.2	32.784	124.029	156.813	.03603	.08178	.11781	0.322
275	1074.8	33.322	123.950	157.272	.03637	.08079	.11716	0.297
300	1091.2	33.824	123.876	157.700	.03669	.07989	.11658	0.276
350	1121.4	34.747	123.740	158.487	.03725	.07828	.11553	0.241
400	1148.4	35.565	123.620	159.185	.03775	.07688	.11463	0.215
450	1173.2	36.315	123.509	159.824	.03820	.07566	.11386	0.194
500	1196.0	37.006	123.406	160.412	.03861	.07455	.11316	0.177
600	1236.8	38.245	123.221	161.466	.03932	.07264	.11196	0.151
700	1173.3	39.339	123.058	162.397	.03993	.07102	.11095	0.132
800	1306.1	40.324	122.910	163.234	.04047	.06961	.11008	0.118
900	1336.2	41.226	122.775	164.001	.04095	.06837	.10932	0.106
1000	1364.0	42.056	122.649	164.705	.04139	.06726	.10865	0.098
1100	1390.0	42.828	122.533	165.361	.04179	.06625	.10804	0.090

* Data from Lucian A. Sheldon, "Thermodynamic Properties of Mercury Vapor." Reprinted by permission of the General Electric Co.

APPENDIX C

Chemical Thermodynamic Properties
of Substances

CHEMICAL THERMODYNAMIC PROPERTIES

TABLE C.1

Enthalpies of Combustion, Enthalpies of Formation, and Absolute Entropies at 77 °F (25 °C) and 1 atm*

Substance	Enthalpy of Combustion				Enthalpy of Formation Btu/mole	Absolute Entropy Btu/mole-°R
	H_2O (l)		H_2O (g)			
	Btu/lbm	Btu/mole	Btu/lbm	Btu/mole		
Hydrogen, H_2	−60,958	−122,891	−51,571	−103,968	0	31.191
Water, H_2O					−103,968	45.077
Carbon, C	−14,087	−169,183	−14,087	−169,183	0	1.360
Carbon monoxide, CO	−4,344	−121,665	−4,344	−121,665	−47,517	47.270
Carbon dioxide, CO_2					−169,183	51.028
Nitrogen, N_2					0	45.737
Oxygen, O_2					0	48.971
Methane, CH_4	−23,861	−382,786	−21,502	−344,940	−32,179	44.47
Ethane, C_2H_6	−22,304	−670,637	−20,416	−613,868	−36,401	54.81
Propane, C_3H_8	−21,646	−954,464	−11,429	−878,774	−44,647	64.47
n-Butane, C_4H_{10}	−21,293	−1,237,558	−19,665	−1,142,943	−53,627	74.05
n-Pentane, C_5H_{12}	−21,072	−1,520,293	−19,499	−1,406,752	−62,959	83.22
n-Hexane, C_6H_{14}	−20,928	−1,803,456	−19,391	−1,670,981	−71,881	92.39
n-Heptane, C_7H_{16}	−20,825	−2,086,653	−19,314	−1,935,204	−80,749	101.57
n-Octane, C_8H_{18}	−20,747	−2,369,859	−19,197	−2,199,547	−89,617	110.75
Ethane, C_2H_4	−21,625	−606,624	−20,276	−568,772	−22,478	52.42
Propane, C_3H_6	−21,032	−884,998	−19,683	−828,228	8,776	63.76
Acetylene, C_2H_2	−21,460	−558,741	−20,734	−539,820	97,495	47.966
Benzene, C_6H_6	−18,172	−1,419,415	−17,446	−1,362,644	35,653	64.30
Hydrazine, N_2H_4	−8,346	−267,457	−7,165	−229,611	−21,675	

* Values derived from National Bureau of Standards Circular C461 (1947), and Circular 500 (1952).

TABLE C.2

Logarithms to the Base 10 of the Equilibrium Constant K_p

For the reaction $aA + bB \rightleftarrows cC + dD$ the equilibrium constant K_p is defined as

$$K_p = \frac{p_C^c p_D^d}{p_A^a p_B^b}$$

where p is the partial pressure in atmospheres*

Temp., °K	$H_2 \rightleftarrows 2H$	$O_2 \rightleftarrows 2O$	$H_2O(g) \rightleftarrows H_2 + \frac{1}{2}O_2$	$H_2O(g) \rightleftarrows OH + \frac{1}{2}H_2$	$CO_2 \rightleftarrows CO + \frac{1}{2}O_2$	$CO_2 + H_2 \rightleftarrows CO + H_2O(g)$	$N_2 \rightleftarrows 2N$	$\frac{1}{2}O_2 + \frac{1}{2}N_2 \rightleftarrows NO$
298	− 71.210	− 80.620	− 40.047	− 46.593	− 45.043	− 4.996	− 119.434	− 15.187
400	− 51.742	− 58.513	− 29.241	− 33.910	− 32.41	− 3.169	− 87.473	− 11.156
600	− 32.667	− 36.859	− 18.633	− 21.470	− 20.07	− 1.432	− 56.206	− 7.219
800	− 23.074	− 25.985	− 13.288	− 15.214	− 13.90	− 0.617	− 40.521	− 5.250
1000	− 17.288	− 19.440	− 10.060	− 11.444	− 10.199	− 0.139	− 31.084	− 4.068
1200	− 13.410	− 15.062	− 7.896	− 8.922	− 7.742	+ 0.154	− 24.619	− 3.279
1400	− 10.627	− 11.932	− 6.344	− 7.116	− 5.992	+ 0.352	− 20.262	− 2.717
1600	− 8.530	− 9.575	− 5.175	− 5.758	− 4.684	+ 0.490	− 16.869	− 2.294
1800	− 6.893	− 7.740	− 4.263	− 4.700	− 3.672	+ 0.591	− 14.225	− 1.966
2000	− 5.579	− 6.269	− 3.531	− 3.852	− 2.863	+ 0.668	− 12.106	− 1.703
2200	− 4.500	− 5.064	− 2.931	− 3.158	− 2.206	+ 0.725	− 10.370	− 1.488
2400	− 3.598	− 4.055	− 2.429	− 2.578	− 1.662	+ 0.767	− 8.922	− 1.309
2600	− 2.833	− 3.206	− 2.003	− 2.087	− 1.203	+ 0.800	− 7.694	− 1.157
2800	− 2.176	− 2.475	− 1.638	− 1.670	− 0.807	+ 0.831	− 6.640	− 1.028
3000	− 1.604	− 1.840	− 1.322	− 1.302	− 0.469	+ 0.853	− 5.726	− 0.915
3200	− 1.104	− 1.285	− 1.046	− 0.983	− 0.175	+ 0.871	− 4.925	− 0.817
3500	− 0.458	− 0.571	− 0.693	− 0.577	+ 0.201	+ 0.894	− 3.893	− 0.692
4000	+ 0.406	+ 0.382	− 0.221	− 0.035	+ 0.699	+ 0.920	− 2.514	− 0.526
4500	+ 1.078	+ 1.125	+ 0.153	+ 0.392	+ 1.081	+ 0.928	− 1.437	− 0.345
5000	+ 1.619	+ 1.719	+ 0.450	+ 0.799	+ 1.387	+ 0.937	− 0.570	− 0.298

* Values derived from "Selected Values of Chemical Thermodynamic Properties," Series III. National Bureau of Standards, Washington, D.C.

APPENDIX D

Tables of Compressible-Flow Functions

TABLE D.1

ISENTROPIC FLOW*

Perfect Gas, $\gamma = 1.4$

M	M^*	p/p_0	ρ/ρ_0	T/T_0	A/A^*	F/F^*	$\dfrac{A}{A^*} \cdot \dfrac{p}{p_0}$
0	0	1.0000,0	1.0000,0	1.00000	∞	∞	∞
.05	.05476	.0082,5	.9987,5	.99950	11.5,915	9.,1584	11.,5712
.10	.10943	.9930,3	.9950,2	.99800	5.8,218	4.6,236	5.7,812
.15	.16395	.9844,1	.9888,4	.99552	3.91,03	3.13,17	3.84,93
.20	.21822	.9725,0	.9802,7	.99206	2.96,35	2.40,04	2.88,20
.25	.27216	.9574,5	.9694,2	.98765	2.40,27	1.97,32	2.30,05
.30	.32572	.9394,7	.9563,8	.98232	2.035,1	1.697,9	1.911,9
.35	.37879	.9187,7	.9412,8	.97608	1.778,0	1.509,4	1.633,6
.40	.43133	.8956,2	.9242,8	.96899	1.590,1	1.374,9	1.424,1
.45	.48326	.8702,7	.9055,2	.96108	1.448,7	1.276,3	1.260,7
.50	.53452	.8430,2	.8851,7	.95238	1.339,8	1.202,7	1.129,51
.55	.58506	.8141,6	.86342	.94295	1.255,0	1.147,2	1.021,74
.60	.63480	.78400	.84045	.93284	1.188,2	1.1050,4	.931,55
.65	.68374	.75283	.81644	.92208	1.1356	1.0731,4	.8549,3
.70	.73179	.72092	.79158	.91075	1.0943,7	1.0491,5	.7889,6
.75	.77893	.68857	.76603	.89888	1.0624,2	1.0313,7	.7315,5
.80	.82514	.65602	.74000	.88652	1.0382,3	1.0185,3	.6811,0
.85	.87037	.62351	.71361	.87374	1.0206,7	1.0096,6	.6364,0
.90	.91460	.59126	.68704	.86058	1.0088,6	1.0039,9	.5965,0
.95	.95781	.55946	.66044	.84710	1.0021,4	1.0009,3	.5606,6
1.00	1.00000	.52828	.63394	.83333	1.0000,0	1.0000,0	.5282,8

* Abridged from *Gas Tables*, by J. H. Keenan and J. Kaye, by permission of John Wiley & Sons, Inc., New York, 1948.

(1) For values of M from 0 to 5, all digits to the left of the comma are valid for linear interpolation. Where no comma is indicated, all digits are valid for interpolation.

(2) Notations such as $.0_3429$ and 5370_4 signify .000429 and 5,370,000, respectively.

TABLE D.1

Isentropic Flow—cont.

Perfect Gas, $\gamma = 1.4$

M	M^*	p/p_0	ρ/ρ_0	T/T_0	A/A^*	F/F^*	$\dfrac{A}{A^*} \cdot \dfrac{p}{p_0}$
1.05	1.04114	.49787	.60765	.81933	1.0020,2	1.0008,2	.4988,8
1.10	1.08124	.46835	.58169	.80515	1.0079,3	1.00305	.4720,6
1.15	1.1203	.43983	.55616	.79083	1.0174,6	1.00646	.4475,1
1.20	1.1583	.4123,8	.53114	.77640	1.0304,4	1.01082	.4249,3
1.25	1.1952	.3860,6	.50670	.76190	1.0467,6	1.01594	.4041,1
1.30	1.2311	.3609,2	.48291	.74738	1.0663,1	1.02170	.3848,4
1.35	1.2660	.3369,7	.45980	.73287	1.0890,4	1.02794	.3669,6
1.40	1.2999	.3124,4	.43742	.71839	1.1149	1.03458	.35036
1.45	1.3327	.2927,2	.41581	.70397	1.1440	1.04153	.33486
1.50	1.3646	.2724,0	.39498	.68965	1.1762	1.04870	.32039
1.55	1.3955	.2532,6	.37496	.67545	1.2115	1.05604	.30685
1.60	1.4254	.23527	.35573	.66138	1.2502	1.06348	.29414
1.65	1.4544	.21839	.33731	.64746	1.2922	1.07098	.28221
1.70	1.4825	.20259	.31969	.63372	1.3376	1.07851	.27099
1.75	1.5097	.18782	.30287	.62016	1.3865	1.08603	.26042
1.80	1.5360	.17404	.28682	.60680	1.4390	1.09352	.25044
1.85	1.5614	.16120	.27153	.59365	1.4952	1.1009	.24102
1.90	1.5861	.14924	.25699	.58072	1.5552	1.1083	.23211
1.95	1.6099	.13813	.24317	.56802	1.6193	1.1155	.22367
2.00	1.6330	.12780	.23005	.55556	1.6875	1.1227	.21567

TABLE D.1

ISENTROPIC FLOW—cont.

Perfect Gas, $\gamma = 1.4$

M	M^*	p/p_0	ρ/ρ_0	T/T_0	A/A^*	F/F^*	$\frac{A}{A^*} \cdot \frac{p}{p_0}$
2.05	1.6553	.11823	.21760	.54333	1.7600	1.1297	.20808
2.10	1.6769	.10935	.20580	.53135	1.8369	1.1366	.20087
2.15	1.6977	.10113	.19463	.51962	1.9185	1.1434	.19403
2.20	1.7179	.09352	.18405	.50813	2.0050	1.1500	.18751
2.25	1.7374	.08648	.17404	.49689	2.0964	1.1565	.18130
2.30	1.7563	.07997	.16458	.48591	2.1931	1.1629	.17539
2.35	1.7745	.07396	.15564	.47517	2.2953	1.1690	.16975
2.40	1.7922	.06840	.14720	.46468	2.4031	1.1751	.16437
2.45	1.8093	.06327	.13922	.45444	2.5168	1.1810	.15923
2.50	1.8258	.05853	.13169	.44444	2.6367	1.1867	.15432
2.55	1.8417	.05415	.12458	.43469	2.7630	1.1923	.14963
2.60	1.8572	.05012	.11787	.42517	2.8960	1.1978	.14513
2.65	1.8721	.04639	.11154	.41589	3.0359	1.2031	.14083
2.70	1.8865	.04295	.10557	.40684	3.1830	1.2083	.13671
2.75	1.9005	.03977	.09994	.39801	3.3376	1.2133	.13276
2.80	1.9140	.03685	.09462	.39841	3.5001	1.2182	.12897
2.85	1.9271	.03415	.08962	.38102	3.6707	1.2230	.12534
2.90	1.9389	.03165	.08489	.37286	3.8498	1.2277	.12185
2.95	1.9521	.02935	.08043	.36490	4.0376	1.2322	.11850
3.00	1.964,0	.027,22	.076,23	.357,14	4.23,46	1.2366	.115,28

TABLE D.1
Isentropic Flow—cont.
Perfect Gas, $\gamma = 1.4$

M	M^*	p/p_0	ρ/ρ_0	T/T_0	A/A^*	F/F^*	$\frac{A}{A^*} \cdot \frac{p}{p_0}$
3.50	2.064,2	.0131,1	.045,23	.289,86	6.7,896	1.2743	.0890,2
4.00	2.138,1	.0065,8	.0276,6	.238,10	10.7,19	1.3029	.0705,9
4.50	2.193,6	.0034,6	.0174,5	.1980,2	16.5,62	1.3247	.0572,3
5.00	2.2361	.00189	.01134	.16667	25.000	1.3416	.04725
6.00	2.2953	$.0_3633$	.00519	.12195	53.180	1.3655	.03368
7.00	2.3333	$.0_3242$	.00261	.09259	104.143	1.3810	.02516
8.00	2.3591	$.0_3102$	.00141	.07246	190.109	1.3915	.01947
9.00	2.3772	$.0_4474$	$.0_3815$	.05814	327.189	1.3989	.01550
10.00	2.3904	$.0_4236$	$.0_3495$	.04762	535.938	1.4044	.01263
∞	2.4495	0	0	0	∞	1.4289	0

TABLE D.2

FRICTIONAL, ADIABATIC, CONSTANT-AREA FLOW (FANNO LINE)*

Perfect Gas, $\gamma = 1.4$

M	T/T^*	p/p^*	p_0/p_0^*	V/V^* and ρ^*/ρ	F/F^*	$4fL_{max}/D$
0.00	1.2000	∞	∞	0.00000	∞	∞
.05	1.1994	21.903	11.5914	.05476	9.1584	280.02
.10	1.1976	10.9435	5.8218	.10943	4.6236	66.922
.15	1.1946	7.2866	3.9103	.16395	3.1317	27.932
.20	1.1905	5.4555	2.9635	.21822	2.4004	14.533
.25	1.1852	4.3546	2.4027	.27217	1.9732	8.4834
.30	1.1788	3.6190	2.0351	.32572	1.6979	5.2992
.35	1.1713	3.0922	1.7780	.37880	1.5094	3.4525
.40	1.1628	2.6958	1.5901	.43133	1.3749	2.3085
.45	1.1533	2.3865	1.4486	.48326	1.2763	1.5664
.50	1.1429	2.1381	1.3399	.53453	1.2027	1.06908
.55	1.1315	1.9341	1.2549	.58506	1.1472	.72805
.60	1.1194	1.7634	1.1882	.63481	1.10504	.49081
.65	1.10650	1.6183	1.1356	.68374	1.07314	.32460
.70	1.09290	1.4934	1.09436	.73179	1.04915	.20814
.75	1.07856	1.3848	1.06242	.77893	1.03137	.12728
.80	1.06383	1.2892	1.03823	.82514	1.01853	.07229
.85	1.04849	1.2047	1.02067	.87037	1.00966	.03632
.90	1.03270	1.12913	1.00887	.91459	1.00399	.014513
.95	1.01652	1.06129	1.00215	.95782	1.00093	.003280

* Abridged from *Gas Tables* by J. H. Keenan and J. Kaye, by permission of John Wiley & Sons, Inc., New York, 1948.

TABLE D.2

FRICTIONAL, ADIABATIC, CONSTANT-AREA FLOW (FANNO LINE)—cont.

Perfect Gas, $\gamma = 1.4$

M	T/T^*	p/p^*	p_0/p_0^*	V/V^* and ρ^*/ρ	F/F^*	$4fL_{max}/D$
1.00	1.00000	1.00000	1.00000	1.00000	1.00000	0
1.05	.98320	.94435	1.00203	1.04115	1.00082	.002712
1.10	.96618	.89359	1.00793	1.08124	1.00305	.009933
1.15	.94899	.84710	1.01746	1.1203	1.00646	.02053
1.20	.93168	.80436	1.03044	1.1583	1.01082	.03364
1.25	.91429	.76495	1.04676	1.1952	1.01594	.04858
1.30	.89686	.72848	1.06630	1.2311	1.02169	.06483
1.35	.87944	.69466	1.08904	1.2660	1.02794	.08199
1.40	.86207	.66320	1.1149	1.2999	1.03458	.09974
1.45	.84477	.63387	1.1440	1.3327	1.04153	.11782
1.50	.82759	.60648	1.1762	1.3646	1.04870	.13605
1.55	.81054	.58084	1.2116	1.3955	1.05604	.15427
1.60	.79365	.55679	1.2502	1.4254	1.06348	.17236
1.65	.77695	.53421	1.2922	1.4544	1.07098	.19022
1.70	.76046	.51297	1.3376	1.4825	1.07851	.20780
1.75	.74419	.49295	1.3865	1.5097	1.08603	.22504
1.80	.72816	.47407	1.4390	1.5360	1.09352	.24189
1.85	.71238	.45623	1.4952	1.5614	1.1009	.25832
1.90	.69686	.43936	1.5552	1.5861	1.1083	.27433
1.95	.68162	.42339	1.6193	1.6099	1.1155	.28989

TABLE D.2

FRICTIONAL, ADIABATIC, CONSTANT-AREA FLOW (FANNO LINE)—cont.

Perfect Gas, $\gamma = 1.4$

M	T/T^*	p/p^*	p_0/p^*	V/V^* and ρ^*/ρ	F/F^*	$4fL_{max}/D$
2.00	.66667	.40825	1.6875	1.6330	1.1227	.30499
2.05	.65200	.39389	1.7600	1.6553	1.1297	.31965
2.10	.63762	.38024	1.8369	1.6769	1.1366	.33385
2.15	.62354	.36828	1.9185	1.6977	1.1434	.34760
2.20	.60976	.35494	2.0050	1.7179	1.1500	.36091
2.25	.59627	.34319	2.0964	1.7374	1.1565	.37378
2.30	.58309	.33200	2.1931	1.7563	1.1629	.38623
2.35	.57021	.32133	2.2953	1.7745	1.1690	.39826
2.40	.55762	.31114	2.4031	1.7922	1.1751	.40989
2.45	.54533	.30141	2.5168	1.8092	1.1810	.42113
2.50	.53333	.29212	2.6367	1.8257	1.1867	.43197
2.55	.52163	.28323	2.7630	1.8417	1.1923	.44247
2.60	.51020	.27473	2.8960	1.8571	1.1978	.45259
2.65	.49906	.26658	3.0359	1.8721	1.2031	.46237
2.70	.48820	.25878	3.1830	1.8865	1.2083	.47182
2.75	.47761	.25131	3.3376	1.9005	1.2133	.48095
2.80	.46729	.24414	3.5001	1.9150	1.2182	.48976
2.85	.45723	.23726	3.6707	1.9271	1.2230	.49828
2.90	.44743	.23066	3.8498	1.9398	1.2277	.50651
2.95	.43788	.22431	4.0376	1.9521	1.2322	.51447

TABLE D.2

FRICTIONAL, ADIABATIC, CONSTANT-AREA FLOW (FANNO LINE)—cont.

Perfect Gas, $\gamma = 1.4$

M	T/T^*	p/p^*	p_0/p_0^*	V/V^* and ρ^*/ρ	F/F^*	$4fL_{max}/D$
3.00	.42857	.21822	4.2346	1.9640	1.2366	.52216
3.50	.34783	.16850	6.7896	2.0642	1.2743	.58643
4.00	.28571	.13363	10.719	2.1381	1.3029	.63306
4.50	.23762	.10833	16.562	2.1936	1.3247	.66764
5.00	.20000	.08944	25.000	2.2361	1.3416	.69381
6.00	.14634	.06376	53.180	2.2953	1.3655	.72987
7.00	.11111	.04762	104.14	2.3333	1.3810	.75281
8.00	.08696	.03686	190.11	2.3591	1.3915	.76820
9.00	.06977	.02935	327.19	2.3772	1.3989	.77898
10.00	.05714	.02390	535.94	2.3905	1.4044	.78683
∞	0	0	∞	2.4495	1.4289	.82153

TABLE D.3

FRICTIONLESS, CONSTANT-AREA FLOW, WITH CHANGE IN STAGNATION TEMPERATURE (RAYLEIGH LINE)*

Perfect Gas, $\gamma = 1.4$

M	T_0/T_0^*	T/T^*	p/p^*	p_0/p_0^*	ρ^*/ρ and V/V^*
0.00	0.00000	0.00000	2.4000	1.2679	0.00000
.05	.01192	.01430	2.3916	1.2657	.00598
.10	.04678	.05602	2.3669	1.2691	.02367
.15	.10196	.12181	2.3267	1.2486	.05235
.20	.17355	.20661	2.2727	1.2346	.09091
.25	.25684	.30440	2.2069	1.2177	.13793
.30	.34686	.40887	2.1314	1.1985	.19183
.35	.43894	.51413	2.0487	1.1779	.25096
.40	.52903	.61515	1.9608	1.1566	.31372
.45	.61393	.70803	1.8699	1.1351	.37865
.50	.69136	.79012	1.7778	1.1140	.44445
.55	.75991	.85987	1.6860	1.09397	.51001
.60	.81892	.91670	1.5957	1.07525	.57447
.65	.86833	.96081	1.5080	1.05820	.63713
.70	.90850	.99289	1.4235	1.04310	.69751
.75	.94009	1.01403	1.3427	1.03010	.75525
.80	.96394	1.02548	1.2658	1.01934	.81012
.85	.98097	1.02854	1.1931	1.01091	.86204
.90	.99207	1.02451	1.1246	1.00485	.91097
.95	.99814	1.01463	1.06030	1.00121	.95692

* Abridged from *Gas Tables* by J. H. Keenan and J. Kaye, by permission of John Wiley & Sons, Inc., New York, 1948.

TABLE D.3

FRICTIONLESS, CONSTANT-AREA FLOW, WITH CHANGE IN STAGNATION
TEMPERATURE (RAYLEIGH LINE)—cont.

Perfect Gas, $\gamma = 1.4$

M	T_0/T_0^*	T/T^*	p/p^*	p_0/p_0^*	ρ^*/ρ and V/V^*
1.00	1.00000	1.00000	1.00000	1.00000	1.00000
1.05	.99838	.98161	.94358	1.00121	1.04030
1.10	.99392	.96031	.89086	1.00486	1.07795
1.15	.98721	.93685	.84166	1.01092	1.1131
1.20	.97872	.91185	.79576	1.01941	1.1459
1.25	.96886	.88581	.75294	1.03032	1.1764
1.30	.95798	.85917	.71301	1.04365	1.2050
1.35	.94636	.83227	.67577	1.05943	1.2316
1.40	.93425	.80540	.64102	1.07765	1.2564
1.45	.92184	.77875	.60860	1.0983	1.2796
1.50	.90928	.75250	.57831	1.1215	1.3012
1.55	.89669	.72680	.55002	1.1473	1.3214
1.60	.88419	.70173	.52356	1.1756	1.3403
1.65	.87184	.67738	.49881	1.2066	1.3580
1.70	.85970	.65377	.47563	1.2402	1.3745
1.75	.84785	.63096	.45390	1.2767	1.3901
1.80	.83628	.60894	.43353	1.3159	1.4046
1.85	.82504	.58773	.41440	1.3581	1.4183
1.90	.81414	.56734	.39643	1.4033	1.4311
1.95	.80359	.54774	.37954	1.4516	1.4432

TABLE D.3

FRICTIONLESS, CONSTANT-AREA FLOW, WITH CHANGE IN STAGNATION
TEMPERATURE (RAYLEIGH LINE)—cont.

Perfect Gas, $\gamma = 1.4$

M	T_0/T_0^*	T/T^*	p/p^*	p_0/p_0^*	ρ^*/ρ and V/V^*
2.00	.79339	.52893	.36364	1.5031	1.4545
2.05	.78355	.51087	.34866	1.5579	1.4652
2.10	.77406	.49356	.33454	1.6161	1.4753
2.15	.76493	.47696	.32122	1.6780	1.4849
2.20	.75614	.46106	.30864	1.7434	1.4939
2.25	.74767	.44582	.29675	1.8128	1.5024
2.30	.73954	.43122	.28551	1.8860	1.5104
2.35	.73173	.41724	.27487	1.9634	1.5180
2.40	.72421	.40383	.26478	2.0450	1.5252
2.45	.71700	.39100	.25523	2.1311	1.5320
2.50	.71005	.37870	.24616	2.2218	1.5385
2.55	.70340	.36691	.23754	2.3173	1.5446
2.60	.69699	.35561	.22936	2.4177	1.5505
2.65	.69084	.34478	.22158	2.5233	1.5560
2.70	.68494	.33439	.21417	2.6342	1.5613
2.75	.67926	.32442	.20712	2.7508	1.5663
2.80	.67380	.31486	.20040	2.8731	1.5711
2.85	.66855	.30568	.19399	3.0013	1.5757
2.90	.66350	.29687	.18788	3.1358	1.5801
2.95	.65865	.28841	.18205	3.2768	1.5843

TABLE D.3

FRICTIONLESS, CONSTANT-AREA FLOW, WITH CHANGE IN STAGNATION TEMPERATURE (RAYLEIGH LINE)—cont.

Perfect Gas, $\gamma = 1.4$

M	T_0/T_0^*	T/T^*	p/p^*	p_0/p_0^*	ρ^*/ρ and V/V^*
3.00	.65398	.28028	.17647	3.4244	1.5882
3.50	.61580	.21419	.13223	5.3280	1.6198
4.00	.58909	.16831	.10256	8.2268	1.6410
4.50	.56983	.13540	.08177	12.502	1.6559
5.00	.55555	.11111	.06667	18.634	1.6667
6.00	.53633	.07849	.04669	38.946	1.6809
7.00	.52437	.05826	.03448	75.414	1.6896
8.00	.51646	.04491	.02649	136.62	1.6954
9.00	.51098	.03565	.02098	233.88	1.6993
10.00	.50702	.02897	.01702	381.62	1.7021
∞	.48980	0	0	∞	1.7143

TABLE D.4

NORMAL SHOCK

Perfect Gas, $\gamma = 1.4$

M_x	M_y	p_y/p_x	V_x/V_y and ρ_y/ρ_x	T_y/T_x	A_x^*/A_y^* and p_{0x}/p_{0y}	p_{0y}/p_x
1.00	1.0000,0	1.0000,0	1.0000,0	1.0000,0	1.00000	1.8929
1.05	.9531,2	1.1196	1.0839,8	1.03284	.99987	2.0083
1.10	.9117,7	1.2450	1.1691	1.06494	.9989,2	2.1328
1.15	.8750,2	1.3762	1.2550	1.09657	.9966,9	2.2661
1.20	.8421,7	1.5133	1.3416	1.1280	.9928,0	2.4075
1.25	.8126,4	1.6562	1.4286	1.1594	.9870,6	2.5568
1.30	.7859,6	1.8050	1.5157	1.1909	.9793,5	2.7135
1.35	.7617,5	1.9596	1.6028	1.2226	.9697,2	2.8778
1.40	.7397,1	2.1200	1.6896	1.2547	.9581,9	3.0493
1.45	.7195,6	2.2862	1.7761	1.2872	.9448,3	3.2278
1.50	.7010,9	2.4583	1.8621	1.3202	.9297,8	3.4133
1.55	.6841,0	2.6363	1.9473	1.3538	.9131,9	3.6058
1.60	.66844	2.8201	2.0317	1.3880	.8952,0	3.8049
1.65	.65396	3.0096	2.1152	1.4228	.87598	4.0111
1.70	.64055	3.2050	2.1977	1.4583	.85573	4.2238
1.75	.62908	3.4062	2.2791	1.4946	.83456	4.4433
1.80	.61650	3.6133	2.3592	1.5316	.81268	4.6695
1.85	.60570	3.8262	2.4381	1.5694	.79021	4.9022
1.90	.59562	4.0450	2.5157	1.6079	.76735	5.1417
1.95	.58618	4.2696	2.5919	1.6473	.74418	5.3878

TABLE D.4

NORMAL SHOCK—cont.

Perfect Gas, $\gamma = 1.4$

M_x	M_y	p_y/p_x	V_x/V_y and ρ_y/ρ_x	T_y/T_x	A_x^*/A_y^* and p_{0x}/p_{0y}	p_{0y}/p_x
2.00	.57735	4.5000	2.6666	1.6875	.72088	5.6405
2.05	.56907	4.7363	2.7400	1.7286	.69752	5.8997
2.10	.56128	4.9784	2.8119	1.7704	.67422	6.1655
2.15	.55395	5.2262	2.8823	1.8132	.65105	6.4377
2.20	.54706	5.4800	2.9512	1.8569	.62812	6.7163
2.25	.54055	5.7396	3.0186	1.9014	.60554	7.0018
2.30	.53441	6.0050	3.0846	1.9468	.58331	7.2937
2.35	.52861	6.2762	3.1490	1.9931	.56148	7.5920
2.40	.52312	6.5533	3.2119	2.0403	.54015	7.8969
2.45	.51792	6.8362	3.2733	2.0885	.51932	8.2083
2.50	.51299	7.1250	3.3333	2.1375	.49902	8.5262
2.55	.50831	7.4196	3.3918	2.1875	.47927	8.8505
2.60	.50387	7.7200	3.4489	2.2383	.46012	9.1813
2.65	.49965	8.0262	3.5047	2.2901	.44155	9.5187
2.70	.49563	8.3383	3.5590	2.3429	.42359	9.8625
2.75	.49181	8.6562	3.6119	2.3966	.40622	10.212
2.80	.48817	8.9800	3.6635	2.4512	.38946	10.569
2.85	.48470	9.3096	3.7139	2.5067	.37330	10.933
2.90	.48138	9.6450	3.7629	2.5632	.35773	11.302
2.95	.47821	9.9863	3.8106	2.6206	.34275	11.679

TABLE D.4

NORMAL SHOCK—cont.

Perfect Gas, $\gamma = 1.4$

M_x	M_y	p_y/p_x	V_x/V_y and ρ_y/ρ_x	T_y/T_x	A_x^*/A_y^* and p_{0x}/p_{0y}	p_{0y}/p_x
3.00	.47519	10.333	3.8571	2.6790	.32834	12.061
3.50	.45115	14.125	4.2608	3.3150	.21295	16.242
4.00	.43496	18.500	4.5714	4.0469	.13876	21.068
4.50	.42355	23.458	4.8119	4.8751	.09170	26.539
5.00	.41523	29.000	5.0000	5.8000	.06172	32.654
6.00	.40416	41.833	5.2683	7.9406	.02965	46.815
7.00	.39736	57.000	5.4444	10.469	.01535	63.552
8.00	.39289	74.500	5.5652	13.387	.00849	82.865
9.00	.38980	94.333	5.6512	16.693	.00496	104.753
10.00	.38757	116.500	5.7143	20.388	.00304	129.217
∞	.37796	∞	6.0000	∞	0	∞

APPENDIX E

Charts and Diagrams of Physical Properties

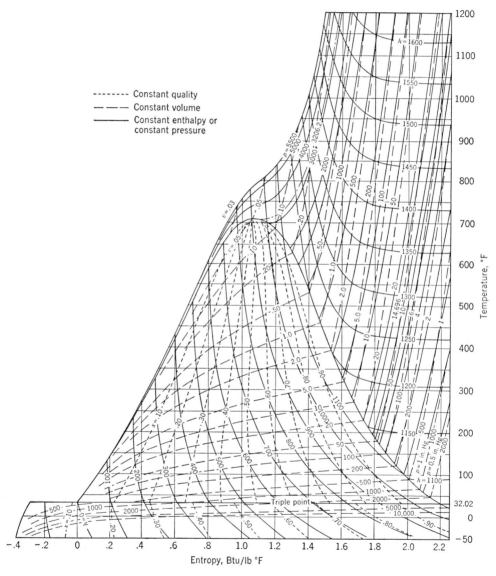

Redrawn by permission from data in *Thermodynamic Properties of Steam*, by J. H. Keenan and F. G. Keyes, published by John Wiley & Sons, Inc. Copyright, 1939.

Chart E.1 Temperature-Entropy Diagram for H_2O.

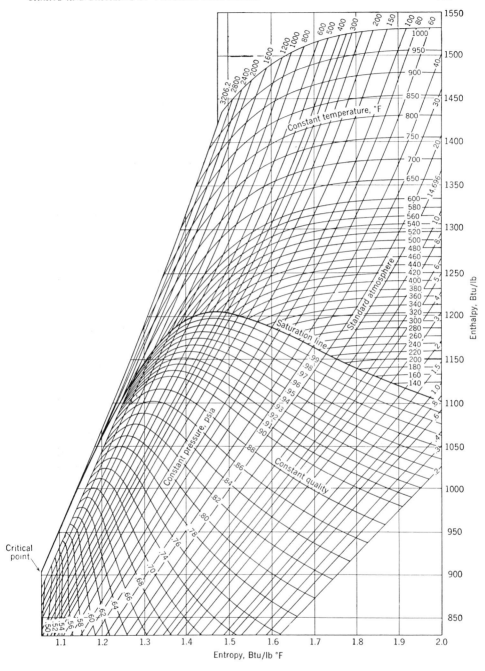

Redrawn by permission from data in *Thermodynamic Properties of Steams*, by J. H. Keenan and F. G. Keyes, published by John Wiley & Sons, Inc. Copyright 1939.

Chart E.2 Mollier Diagram.

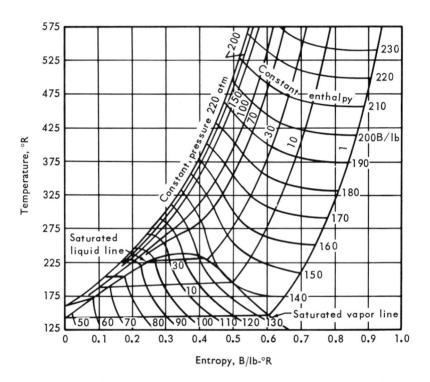

Chart E.3   Temperature-Entropy Diagram for Air.

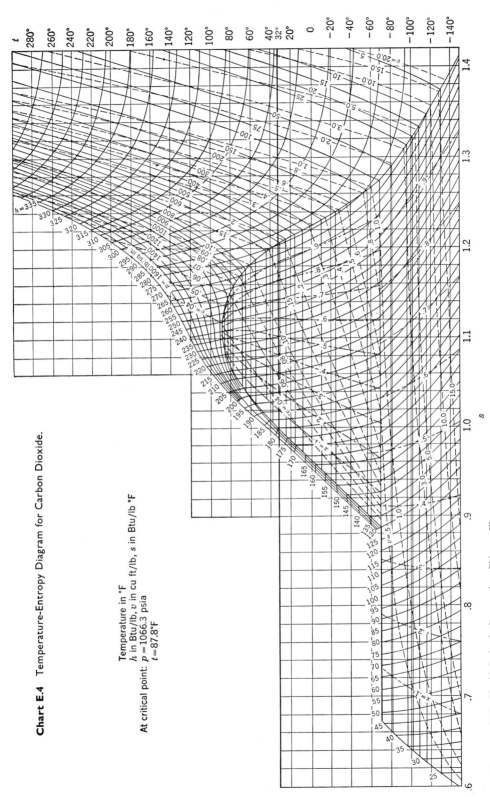

Chart E.4 Temperature-Entropy Diagram for Carbon Dioxide.

Temperature in °F
h in Btu/lb, v in cu ft/lb, s in Btu/lb °F
At critical point: $p = 1066.3$ psia
$t = 87.8$°F

Courtesy of The Liquid Carbonic Corporation, Chicago, Ill.

Temperature in °F; Volume in cu ft/lb; Entropy in Btu/lb/°F

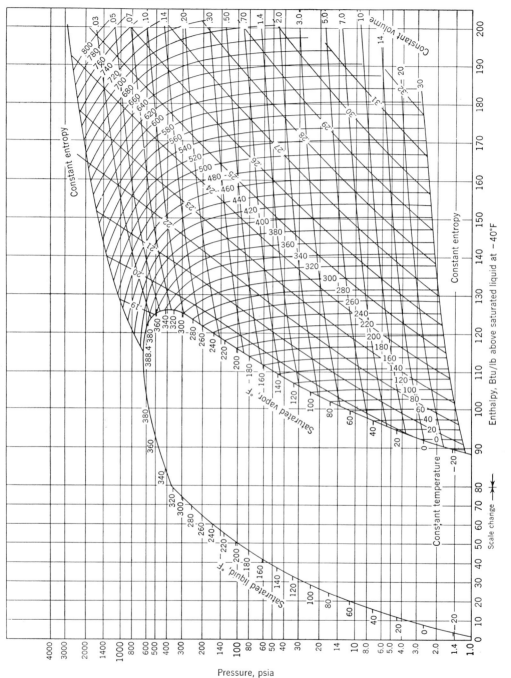

Chart E.5 Pressure-Enthalpy Diagram for Freon-11.
Courtesy "Freon" Products Division, E. I. du Pont de Nemours and Co., Inc.

Temperature in °F; Volume in cu ft/lb; Entropy in Btu/(lb)(°R); Quality in wt %

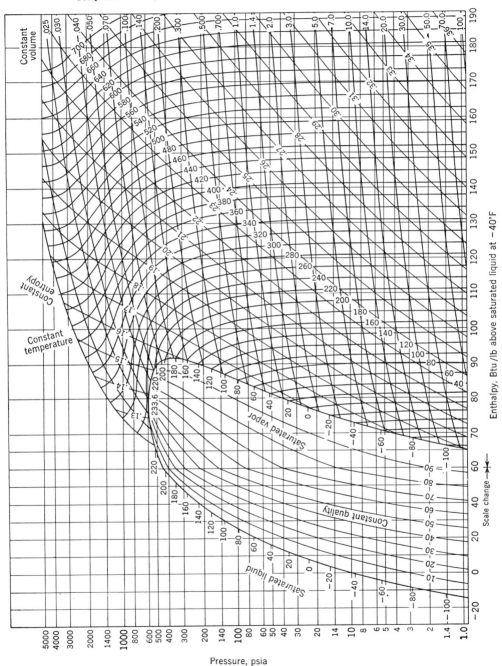

Chart E.6 Pressure-Enthalpy Diagram for Freon-12.
Courtesy "Freon" Products Division, E. I. du Pont de Nemours and Co., Inc.

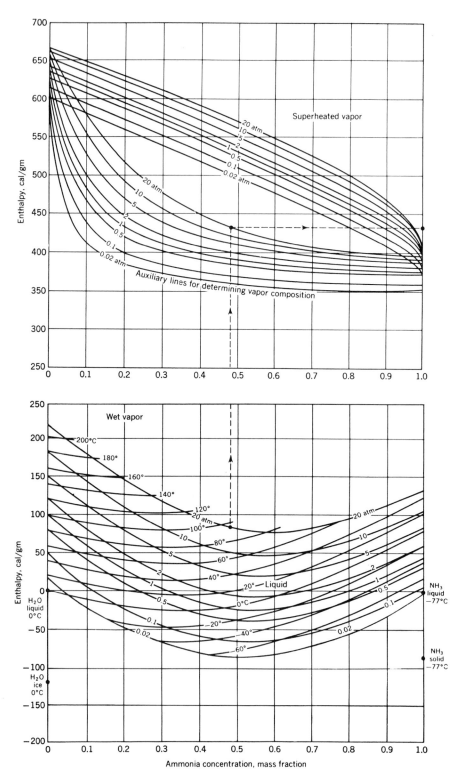

Chart E.7 Enthalpy-Concentration Diagram for Water-Ammonia Solutions.

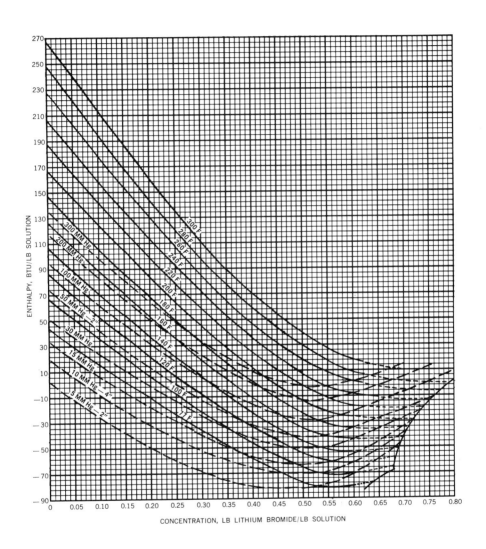

Chart E.8 Enthalpy-Concentration Diagram for Lithium Bromide-Water Solutions.

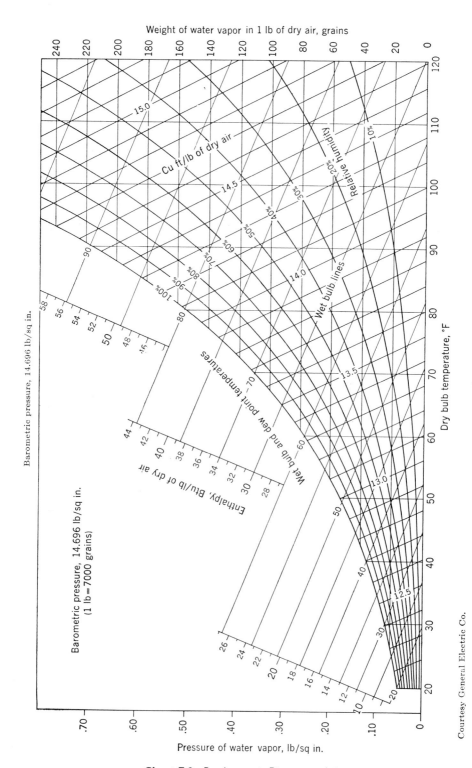

Chart E.9 Psychrometric Diagram at 1 Atm.

Weight of water vapor in 1 lb of dry air, grains

Barometric pressure, 14.696 lb/sq in.

Barometric pressure, 14.696 lb/sq in.
(1 lb = 7000 grains)

Cu ft/lb of dry air

Relative humidity

Wet bulb lines

Wet bulb and dew point temperatures

Enthalpy, Btu/lb of dry air

Dry bulb temperature, °F

Pressure of water vapor, lb/sq in.

Courtesy General Electric Co.

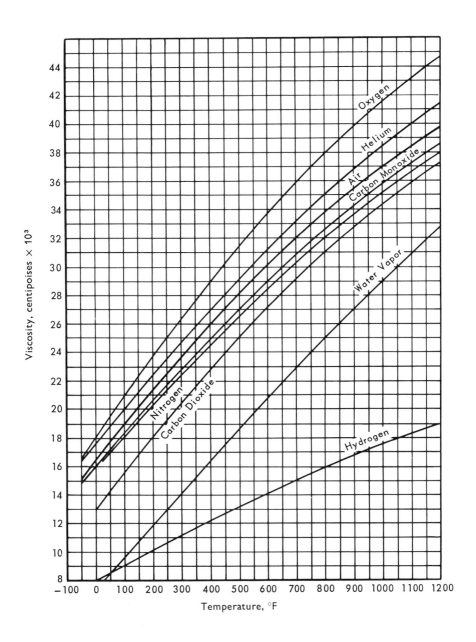

Chart E.10 Viscosity of Gases.

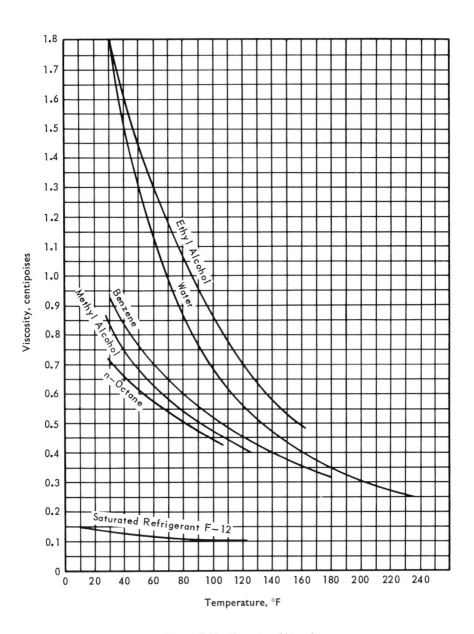

Chart E.11 Viscosity of Liquids.

APPENDIX F

Selected References

1. Allis, W. P., Herlin, M. A., *Thermodynamics and Statistical Mechanics*, New York: McGraw-Hill Book Company, Inc., 1952.
2. Brillouin, L., *Science and Information Theory*, New York: Academic Press, Inc., 1956.
3. Callen, H. B., *Thermodynamics*, New York: John Wiley & Sons, Inc., 1960.
4. Faires, V. M., *Thermodynamics*, New York: The Macmillan Company, 1962.
5. Fermi, E., *Thermodynamics*, Englewood Cliffs, New Jersey: Prentice-Hall, Inc., 1937.
6. Hall, N. A., Ibele, W. E., *Engineering Thermodynamics*, Englewood Cliffs, New Jersey: Prentice-Hall, Inc., 1960.
7. Howerton, M. T., *Engineering Thermodynamics,* Princeton, New Jersey, D. Van Nostrand Company, 1962.
8. Jones, J. B., Hawkins, G. A., *Engineering Thermodynamics*, New York: John Wiley & Sons, Inc., 1960.
9. Keenan, J. H., *Thermodynamics*, New York: John Wiley & Sons, Inc., 1941.
809

10. Kiefer, P. J., Kinney, G. F., Stuart, M. C., *Principles of Engineering Thermodynamics*, New York: John Wiley & Sons, Inc., 1954.

11. King, A. L., *Thermophysics*, San Francisco: W. H. Freeman and Company, 1962.

12. Lee, J. F., Sears, F. W., *Thermodynamics*, Reading, Massachusetts: Addison-Wesley Publishing Company, Inc., 1955.

13. Mackey, C. O., Barnard, W. N., Ellenwood, F. O., *Engineering Thermodynamics*, New York: John Wiley & Sons, Inc., 1957.

14. Mooney, D. A., *Mechanical Engineering Thermodynamics*, Englewood Cliffs, New Jersey: Prentice-Hall, Inc., 1953.

15. Obert, E. F., *Concepts of Thermodynamics*, New York: McGraw-Hill Book Company, Inc., 1960.

16. Reid, C. E., *Principles of Chemical Thermodynamics*, New York: Reinhold Publishing Company, 1960.

17. Rogers, G. F., Mayhew, Y. R., *Engineering Thermodynamics*, New York: Longmans, Green & Company, Inc., 1957.

18. Sabersky, R. H., *Elements of Engineering Thermodynamics*, New York: McGraw-Hill Book Company, Inc., 1957.

19. Schmidt, E., *Thermodynamics*, Third German Edition, Translation by Kestin, J., Oxford, England: Clarendon Press, 1949.

20. Sears, F. W., *Thermodynamics, The Kinetic Theory of Gases, and Statistical Mechanics*, Reading, Massachusetts: Addison-Wesley Publishing Company, Inc., 1955.

21. Smith, J. M., Van Ness, H. C., *Introduction to Chemical Engineering Thermodynamics*, New York: McGraw-Hill Book Company, Inc., 1959.

22. Smith, R. A., *The Physical Principles of Thermodynamics*, London: Chapman & Hall, Ltd., 1952.

23. Sommerfeld, A., *Thermodynamics and Statistical Mechanics*, New York: Academic Press, Inc., 1956.

24. Soo, S. L., *Thermodynamics of Engineering Science*, Englewood Cliffs, New Jersey: Prentice-Hall, Inc., 1958.

25. Spalding, D. B., Cole, E. H., *Engineering Thermodynamics*, New York: McGraw-Hill Book Company, Inc., 1959.

26. Tribus, M., *Thermostatics and Thermodynamics*, Princeton, New Jersey: D. Van Nostrand Company, 1961.

27. Van Wylen, G. J., *Thermodynamics*, New York: John Wiley & Sons, Inc., 1959.

28. Wall, F. T., *Chemical Thermodynamics,* San Francisco, W. H. Freeman & Company, 1958.

29. Weber, H. L., Meissner, H. P., *Thermodynamics For Chemical Engineers*, New York: John Wiley & Sons, Inc., 1957.

30. Zemansky, M. W., *Heat and Thermodynamics*, New York: McGraw-Hill Book Company, Inc., 1957.

INDEX

811